Basic Electronic Communications for the FCC General Radiotelephone Operator's License Exam

Basic Electronic Communications for the FCC General Radiotelephone Operator's License Exam

Victor F. C. Veley

TAB Books
Division of McGraw-Hill, Inc.
New York San Francisco Washington, D.C. Auckland Bogotá
Caracas Lisbon London Madrid Mexico City Milan
Montreal New Delhi San Juan Singapore
Sydney Tokyo Toronto

pbk 2 3 4 5 6 7 8 9 10 DOC/DOC 9 9 8 7 6 5
hc 1 2 3 4 5 6 7 8 9 DOC/DOC 9 9 8 7 6 5 4 3

Library of Congress Cataloging-in-Publication Data

Veley, Victor F.C.
Basic electronic communications for the FCC general radiotelephone operator's license exam / by Victor F.C. Veley.
p. cm.
Includes index.
ISBN 0-8306-2581-X. ISBN 0-8306-2580-1 (pbk.)
1. Radiotelephone—United States—Examinations—Study guides.
2. Radio operators—Licenses—United States. 3. Electronics.
I. Title.
TK6554.5.V425 1993
621.3845'076—dc20 92-30652
CIP

Acquisitions Editor: Roland S. Phelps
Editor: Andrew Yoder
Executive Editor: Bob Ostrander
Designer: Jaclyn J. Boone
Associate Designer: Brian K. Allison
Paperbound Cover Design and Illustration: Graphics Plus, Hanover, Pa. EL1

Dedication

To my beautiful wife, Joyce,
who has been my inspiration and strength for over 40 years,
and to those I hold dear:
Jackie, Gill, Phil, Ray, James, Nicola, Lisa, Kate, Peter, Paul, and Paula
also in memory of
Charles H. and Margaret A. Veley

Table of Contents

Introduction

The purpose of this book is to invite you to think and learn about electronic communications; only then can a technician hope to progress in this rapidly expanding field. To achieve these goals the following format is used:

1. Each section in a particular chapter contains a limited number of concepts that are explored in depth.
2. The order of the 14 chapters is a logical sequence so that there is a minimum amount of cross-referencing.
3. SI units are primarily used throughout the text.
4. The writing style is "active" and "friendly" so that you become involved in the discussion of basic principles. Nothing is assumed, except an everyday knowledge of such items as the light bulb and the car battery.

It is therefore emphasized that this book primarily stands on its merits as an introductory text on radio communications and as a reference manual for technicians. However, the format is also designed to prepare you to pass the FCC Element 3 examination, and thereby obtain your Commercial General Radiotelephone License (GROL). Each section in a particular chapter is followed by a number of related multiple-choice questions, which are similar to those in the actual FCC examinations. There are more than 950 such questions in the entire book; these provide a thorough preparation for obtaining your GROL and also act as a valuable self-review. To use these questions to their best advantage, you should read the introductory material on "How to apply for the Commercial General Radiotelephone License," "How to prepare for the Element 3 Examination," and "How to pass the FCC exam(s)."

To obtain the General Radiotelephone License, you must pass the FCC Element 3 examination, which contains 100 multiple-choice questions (each with five choices). The passing score is 75 or more correct and the grade is not recorded on your license. The holder of this license is entitled to operate, maintain, and repair transmitters in the Marine, Aviation, and International

Fixed Services. The possession of this license is also regarded as a valuable entry-level qualification for the electronic communications industry and as an asset for subsequent promotion.

In order to install, service, and maintain certain marine radar equipment, you must obtain the Ship Radar Endorsement to your General Radiotelephone Operator License. To acquire the endorsement, you must pass the FCC Element 8 examination, which contains 50 multiple-choice questions with a passing score of 38 or more correct.

To prepare yourself for the Element 3 examination, you need to study all 14 chapters and the appendix to this book. However, the material for the Element 8 examination is mainly contained in chapters 11 and 12 ("Microwave techniques" and "Principles of radar"). Note that you must have passed Element 3 before you are allowed to take Element 8.

I hope you will enjoy reading this book and it will be your first step toward a successful career in electronic communications.

I wish to acknowledge a considerable debt to my wife, Joyce, for typing the manuscript. Without her help and encouragement, this book would not have been possible.

How to apply for the Commercial General Radio Operator License

Prior to 1993, an applicant was required to complete FCC form 756 and pay a fee of $35.00 for taking the General Radiotelephone Examination. The application and payment were then forwarded to an FCC location in Pittsburgh. Subsequently, the applicant received an appointment letter indicating where and when he/she should appear for the examination to be administered. The examinations were held during the first full weeks of February and August.

In January 1993, the FCC decided to privatize the administration of all exams for the various commercial radio operator licenses; this decision was based on budgetary constraints. The February examination was cancelled, but in April and May the applicants were allowed to take the examination by using a one-time interim procedure. This involved the completion of the examination in the presence of a qualified licensee.

For years there have been a number of private organizations that have conducted their own examinations for the certification of technicians and engineers in the field of electronics and communications. At the time of publishing this book, the FCC is in the process of selecting those organizations who will set up a network of testing centers throughout the USA. Each of the centers will be controlled by an examination manager, who will be responsible for administering the various FCC examinations. This network is expected to be in operation by June/July 1993, and the first examinations should be given in August/September. It is anticipated that the content of the FCC exams will not be changed in the immediate future and that the exams themselves might be held more frequently than twice a year.

To apply to take the General Radiotelephone examination, you should:

1. Contact your local FCC office (a list of these offices with their addresses and telephone numbers appears on page xix). Ask for the name, address, and telephone number of the private organization who is conducting the examinations in your area.
2. Call the private organization and request an application form with its instructions. Make a note of the name of the person that you contact. Enquire when the next examination is to be held and ask about any deadline date for filing the application.

3. Complete and return the application form together with the payment of the required fee. As a precaution, you should use certified mail.

If you do not receive an acknowledgment from the private organization, determine whether your fee payment has been processed and then call the person that you originally contacted.

One last point. The FCC has normally allowed an applicant to take the General Radiotelephone Exam (Element 3) and the Ship Radar Endorsement (Element 8) on the same day without the payment of an additional fee. However, the candidate must first pass the Element 3 exam before being allowed to take Element 8. Remember that the Element 3 exam contains 100 multiple-choice questions with a passing score of 75 or more correct. By contrast, the Element 8 exam only has 50 questions with a passing score of 38 or more correct.

How to prepare for the Element 3 Examination

This book has 14 chapters and an appendix that cover the subject areas of direct current, alternating current, semiconductor diodes and power supplies, transistors and their applications, transmitters, amplitude modulation and AM transmitters, AM receivers, frequency modulation and FM transmitters, FM receivers, transmission lines and antennas, microwave techniques, principles of radar, number systems, digital principles, and FCC Rules and Regulations.

A particular chapter is divided into a sequence of sections, each of which cover a limited number of principles. Following each section is a group of FCC-type multiple-choice questions, which are similar to those in the actual Element 3 examinations. Each of these questions must be carefully studied in a step-by-step procedure.

1. After covering up the answer, read the question with each choice in turn. In other words, first read the question with Choice A; then read the question again with Choice B, and so on.
2. Look out for such words as "not" and "false" because these are vital to your understanding of the question.
3. Remember that you are required to select the *best* possible choice, which is not necessarily the only correct choice. For example, choice A and choice C might be correct answers; therefore, the best selection would be Choice E, which states "choices A and C are true." In a few questions, choices A, B, C, and D are all false answers, in which case the best selection would again be choice E, which states "none of the preceding choices is true."

The right choice is shown just below the question so that you have immediate feedback about your selection. If you made the correct choice, you should proceed to the next question, but if you were wrong, you should restudy the material of the section leading up to the question. This is the great advantage of including the questions within a complete reference text.

There are over 950 multiple-choice questions in the 14 chapters and the appendix. As your self-review, I recommend that you tape all of the questions and their answers, but leave a

10-second pause after each question so that you can make your choice before the actual answer is given. These tapes can then be played in your car or during periods that you have set aside for study.

In those questions that involve mathematical solutions, it is important to have a clear understanding of the steps involved in obtaining the answer. Sometimes the FCC answers are not precise and you must then select the choice that is closest in value to your result.

Notice that a few new questions were discovered in the Element 3 examinations held in August 1991 and February 1992. These questions have been included in Appendix A and are accompanied by answers and solutions where necessary. In addition, all those questions marked with an asterisk (*) are similar to those which have appeared in the more recent FCC examinations and therefore deserve particular attention.

As a final and important step in preparing for the Element 3 and Element 8 exams, I strongly recommend that you purchase a copy of "Practice Tests for the FCC General Radiotelephone Operator's License Examination(s)," #4504, also published by TAB Books. This supplement contains nine Element 3 and two Element 8 exams, whose answers and solutions are directly referenced to this text.

How to pass the FCC examination(s)

On the day before your appointment, avoid any last-minute cramming and go to bed early so that you can have a full night's sleep. Leave yourself plenty of time to get to the testing center so as to minimize any stress caused by traffic problems. Make sure that your nonprogrammable scientific calculator is in good shape and wear comfortable clothes because the examination will probably last more than three hours. This also means that you should visit the restroom before presenting yourself for the examination. Smoking is not allowed during the exam, so you might like to consider chewing gum as an alternative.

Before being allowed to take the examination, you are required to identify yourself so that you will need your driver's license or a similar document that shows your photograph. You are not allowed to bring any textbooks or notes into the examination room; however, some scratch paper will be provided. You will need some #2 pencils for the mark-sign answer sheet as well as a ballpoint pen (black ink) to fill out forms related to personal and background information.

When you have received your examination paper and have been told to start, do *not* begin with Question #1 and struggle through to Question #100. Read through the entire exam and answer all easy questions (primarily those concerning FCC rules and regulations, circuit recognition, units, and so on). Probably about 30 to 40 questions should fall into this category and successful answers to these questions will certainly boost your morale.

Repeat the process and gradually fill in the gaps. Unless you are quite certain of the solutions, it is probably wise to leave all math problems until the end. Here is one point to remember. A particular solution might require the transposition of a basic formula. If you find difficulty with the transposition, you can substitute each one of the choices in the basic formula and see which one works—one advantage of taking a multiple-choice exam.

After completing the exam, you must review the entire answer sheet and make certain that:

1. the answer to each question corresponds to the choice you have selected. For example, you might have marked choice A on the answer sheet, but you intended choice B. Choice A must therefore be erased and choice B must be marked instead.

2. no answer has been accidently marked with two or more choices. Such an answer will automatically be graded as incorrect.
3. every question has been answered; there is no penalty for an incorrect choice. It follows that a blind guess is better than nothing because you have a 20% chance of being right. However, there are two ways to find the correct answer to a multiple-choice question. Either you know the answer straight off or you can find the right answer by eliminating all of the false choices (decoys). Moreover, if you are only able to eliminate three decoys, there are only two choices left, so you have raised your odds of finding the right choice from 20% to 50%.

Finally, the moment of truth! You present your paper to the examiner who will use a grading mask to obtain your score. He/she then informs you of the result (pass or fail) and will probably indicate your actual score. Remember that the pass mark is only 75% and your grade is not recorded on your license.

If you are successful, you will be immediately issued with a temporary authorization permit; your permanent license (valid for life) will then be forwarded to you within three months.

It only remains to wish you good luck in the examination and a successful career in the field of electronic communications.

FCC office addresses

ALASKA, Anchorage Office
Federal Communications Commission
6721 West Raspberry Road
Anchorage, Alaska 99502
Phone: (907) 243–2153

*ARIZONA, Douglas Office
Federal Communications Commission
P.O. Box 6
Douglas, Arizona 85608
Phone: (602) 364–8414

CALIFORNIA, San Diego Office
Federal Communications Commission
4542 Ruffner Street
Room 370
San Diego, California 92111-2216
Phone: (619) 557–5478

*CALIFORNIA, Livermore Office
Federal Communications Commission
P.O. Box 311
Livermore, California 94551-0311
Phone: (415) 447–3614

CALIFORNIA, Los Angeles Office
Federal Communications Commission
Cerritos Corporate Tower
18000 Studebaker Road, Room 660
Cerritos, California 90701
Phone: (310) 809–2096

CALIFORNIA, San Francisco Office
Federal Communications Commission
424 Customhouse
555 Battery Street
San Francisco, California 94111
Phone: (415) 705–1101

COLORADO, Denver Office
Federal Communications Commission
165 South Union Blvd., Suite 860
Lakewood, Colorado 80228
Phone: (303) 969–6497

*FLORIDA, Vero Beach Office
Federal Communications Commission
P.O. Box 1730
Vero Beach, Florida 32961-1730
Phone: (407) 778–3755

FLORIDA, Miami Office
Federal Communications Commission
Rochester Building, Room 310
8390 N.W. 53rd Street
Miami, Florida 33166
Phone: (305) 526-7420

FLORIDA, Tampa Office
Federal Communications Commission
Room 1215
2203 N. Lois Avenue
Tampa, Florida 33607-2356
Phone: (813) 228-2872

GEORGIA, Atlanta Office
Federal Communications Commission
Massell Building, Room 440
1365 Peachtree Street, N.E.
Atlanta, Georgia 30309
Phone: (404) 347-2631

*GEORGIA, Powder Springs Office
Federal Communications Commission
P.O. Box 85
Powder Springs, Georgia 30073
Phone: (404) 943-5420

HAWAII, Honolulu Office
Federal Communications Commission
P.O. Box 1030
Waipahu, Hawaii 96797
Phone: (808) 677-3318

ILLINOIS, Chicago Office
Federal Communications Commission
Park Ridge Office Center, Rm. 306
1550 Northwest Highway
Park Ridge, Illinois 60068
Phone: (312) 353-0195

LOUISIANA, New Orleans Office
Federal Communications Commission
800 West Commerce Rd., Room 505
New Orleans, Louisiana 70123
Phone: (504) 589-2095

*MAINE, Belfast Office
Federal Communications Commission
P.O. Box 470
Belfast, Maine 04915
Phone: (207) 338-4088

MARYLAND, Baltimore Office
Federal Communications Commission
1017 Federal Building
31 Hopkins Plaza
Baltimore, Maryland 21201
Phone: (301) 962-2729

*MARYLAND, Laurel Office
Federal Communications Commission
P.O. Box 250
Columbia, Maryland 21045
Phone: (301) 725-3474

MASSACHUSETTS, Boston Office
Federal Communications Commission
NFPA Building
1 Batterymarch Park
Quincy, Massachusetts 02169
Phone: (617) 770-4023

*MICHIGAN, Allegan Office
Federal Communications Commission
P.O. Box 89
Allegan, Michigan 49010
Phone: (616) 673-2063

MICHIGAN, Detroit Office
Federal Communications Commission
24897 Hathaway Street
Farmington Hills, Michigan 48335-1552
Phone: (313) 226-6078

MINNESOTA, St. Paul Office
Federal Communications Commission
693 Federal Building & U.S. Courthouse
316 North Robert Street
St. Paul, Minnesota 55101
Phone: (612) 290-3819

MISSOURI, Kansas City Office
Federal Communications Commission
Brywood Office Tower, Room 320
8800 East 63rd Street
Kansas City, Missouri 64133
Phone: (816) 926-5111

*NEBRASKA, Grand Island Office
Federal Communications Commission
P.O. Box 1588
Grand Island, Nebraska 68802
Phone: (308) 382-4296

NEW YORK, Buffalo Office
Federal Communications Commission
1307 Federal Building
111 W. Huron Street
Buffalo, New York 14202
Phone: (716) 846-4511

NEW YORK, New York Office
Federal Communications Commission
201 Varick Street
New York, New York 10014-4870
Phone: (212) 620-3437

OREGON, Portland Office
Federal Communications Commission
1782 Federal Office Building
1220 S.W. 3rd Avenue
Portland, Oregon 97204
Phone: (503) 326-4114

PENNSYLVANIA, Philadelphia Office
Federal Communications Commission
One Oxford Valley Office Building
2300 East Lincoln Highway
Room 404
Langhorne, Pennsylvania 19047
Phone: (215) 752-1324

PUERTO RICO, San Juan Office
Federal Communications Commission
747 Federal Building
Hato Rey, Puerto Rico 00918-2251
Phone: (809) 766-5567

TEXAS, Dallas Office
Federal Communications Commission
9330 LBJ Expressway, Room 1170
Dallas, Texas 75243
Phone: (214) 767-4827

TEXAS, Houston Office
Federal Communications Commission
1225 North Loop West, Room 900
Houston, Texas 77008
Phone: (713) 229-2748

*TEXAS, Kingsville Office
Federal Communications Commission
P.O. Box 632
Kingsville, Texas 78363-0632
Phone: (512) 592-2531

VIRGINIA, Norfolk Office
Federal Communications Commission
1200 Communications Circle
Virginia Beach, Virginia 23455-3725
Phone: (804) 441-6472

*WASHINGTON, Ferndale Office
Federal Communications Commission
1330 Loomis Trail Rd.
Custer, Washington 98240
Phone: (206) 354-4892

WASHINGTON, Seattle Office
Federal Communications Commission
One Newport, Room 414
3605 132nd Avenue, S.E.
Bellevue, Washington 98006
Phone: (206) 764-3324

*Licenses not available at these locations.

1
Principles of direct current

In this chapter you will learn:

- about molecules, elements, and the structure of the atom.
- the definitions of the mechanical SI units for velocity, acceleration, force, work, torque, and power.
- the definitions of the electrical SI units for current, charge, and voltage, together with their prefixes.
- the meaning of Ohm's Law, which leads to the concepts of resistance and conductance.
- how to interpret the color coding of composition resistors.
- how to avoid exceeding the wattage ratings of resistors.
- the factors that control the resistance of cylindrical conductors.
- about the properties of a series arrangement of resistors, which are connected across a voltage source.
- how to use the voltage division rule for resistors in series.
- about the use of the voltage-dropping resistor.
- about the properties of a parallel arrangement of resistors, which are connected across a voltage source.
- how to analyze a series-parallel arrangement of resistors.
- how to obtain an accurate measurement of resistance through the use of the Wheatstone bridge.
- about the concept of the internal resistance and the conditions under which maximum power is transferred to a resistive load.
- the principles and units of magnetism, electromagnetism, and electromagnetic induction.
- about the property of inductance and its related physical factors.
- the results of connecting inductors in series, in parallel, and in series-parallel.
- to understand the meaning of the time constant, L/R seconds.
- the results of connecting capacitors in series, in parallel, and in series-parallel.
- to understand the meaning of the time constant, RC seconds.

- how to measure values of current, voltage, and resistance.
- about the principles of dc generators and motors.
- about soldering techniques.

1-1. Atomic structure

All matter is essentially electrical in nature. You might be surprised to learn that the page you are reading contains literally billions upon billions of electrically charged particles; the word *charge* means a quantity of electricity. Half of these particles have a charge with a negative polarity, and the other half carry an equal charge with a positive polarity. The result is that these charges with opposite polarities cancel out and the page is neutral in the sense that it is not electrified. Positive and negative polarities are fully explained later in this section; however, you are probably already familiar with the positive and negative terminals of a cell, such as a flashlight battery.

As you shall learn, one substance is distinguished from another by the number and arrangement of its particles. Therefore, start by examining a very common substance, water. However, tap water has a number of substances dissolved in it. Pure distilled water, which has all of these substances removed, boils at 100°C (Celsius or centigrade) and freezes at 0°C. Take a drop of this water and divide it into smaller and smaller amounts (FIG. 1-1). Ultimately, you would come to the smallest quantity that still retains the property of water; such a quantity is called a *molecule.* Although water is, of course, a liquid, it is in fact a compound of two gases, hydrogen and oxygen. A molecule is the least amount of a compound that still retains the properties of the compound. The chemical formula for the water molecule is H_2O; if you subdivide the molecule, you would obtain two parts of hydrogen gas to one part of oxygen. The gases would be separated and the water molecule would no longer exist.

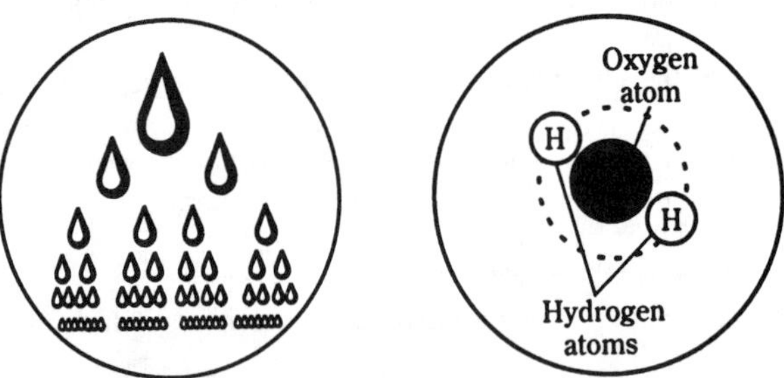

Fig. 1-1 The concept of the water molecule.

The particles of hydrogen and oxygen that combine to produce water are called *atoms.* Hydrogen and oxygen are themselves examples of *elements,* which are substances capable of a separate existence (they cannot be broken down further by chemical action). The atom of the element is therefore the smallest particle that still retains all the properties of the element. More than 100 different elements have been found; of these the first 92 occur naturally in the earth and the others have been created by humans.

Compounds can be divided into molecules, which in turn are made from the atoms of elements. But what is the composition of the atom? Because hydrogen is the lightest element, it might be assumed to have the simplest structure. In 1913, the Norwegian physicist Niels Bohr proposed that the hydrogen atom contained a core called the *nucleus,* where most of the atom's mass was concentrated. This nucleus of the hydrogen (H) atom is the *proton,* which is positively charged. Revolving around the nucleus in a circle is a much lighter particle, the *electron,* which carries an equal negative charge (FIG. 1-2). Hydrogen gas as a whole is electrically neutral. One law of electricity states that positive and negative charges attract. As a result, there would be tendency for the electron to merge with the proton. However, because the electron is revolving in a circular path, a *centrifugal* force acts outward to balance the inward force of attraction. An example of centrifugal force is produced by attaching a rock to a piece of string and then whirling the rock over your head. The faster the rock is whirled, the greater is the tension in the string; and if the string breaks, the rock will fly off as a result of the outward centrifugal force. A stable orbit for the electron requires that the radius of its circular path is approximately 5.3×10^{-11} m (now you can see why scientific notation is so necessary). The mass of the proton is 1.6726×10^{-27} kg and the mass of the electron is 9.1096×10^{-31} kg. Thus, the proton is more than 1800 times heavier than the electron.

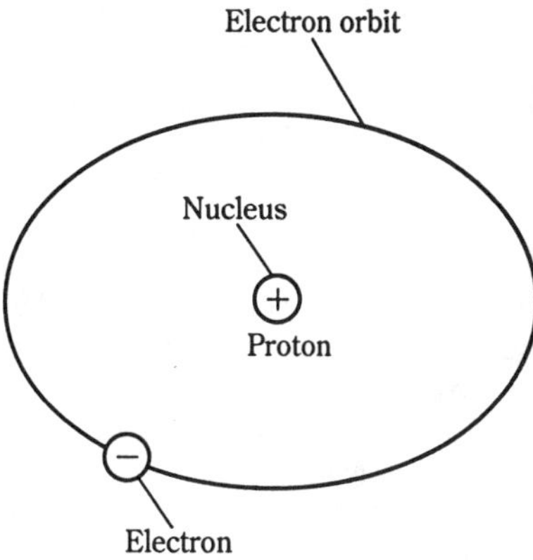

Fig. 1-2 The hydrogen atom.

Next to hydrogen, the lightest element is the gas helium (He), whose atom is about four times heavier than the atom of hydrogen. You would therefore assume that the helium nucleus contained four protons; however, there are only two orbiting electrons, and this would mean that all helium was positively charged. However, of course, helium is electrically neutral. This difficulty was solved in 1932 by the discovery of another particle, the *neutron,* which has about the same mass as the proton, but is uncharged. Consequently, the picture of the helium atom is that of a nucleus with two neutrons and two protons, which are prevented from flying apart by powerful short-range nuclear forces. Around the nucleus, there are the two orbiting electrons (FIG. 1-3). In fact, the atoms of all the elements are composed of the same three subatomic particles: electrons, protons, and neutrons.

Each of the elements has two associated numbers: the atomic number and the atomic weight. The *atomic number* distinguishes one element from another and is equal to the number of protons in the nucleus; this is also the same number of the orbiting electrons. The atomic numbers start at 1 (hydrogen) and proceed in sequence to over 100. By contrast, *atomic weight* compares the masses of the atoms and are not in sequence because they also account for the number of neutrons in the nucleus. To take a complex atom as an example, uranium (U) has an atomic number of 92 and an atomic weight of 238. Consequently, the uranium atom will have 92 protons, 92 orbiting electrons, and $238 - 92 = 146$ neutrons. This type of uranium is commonly mined from the earth. However, the uranium used in an atom bomb has an atomic weight of only 235. This uranium still has 92 protons and electrons, but only 143 neutrons; because of the different number of neutrons, this other form of uranium is known as an *isotope.*

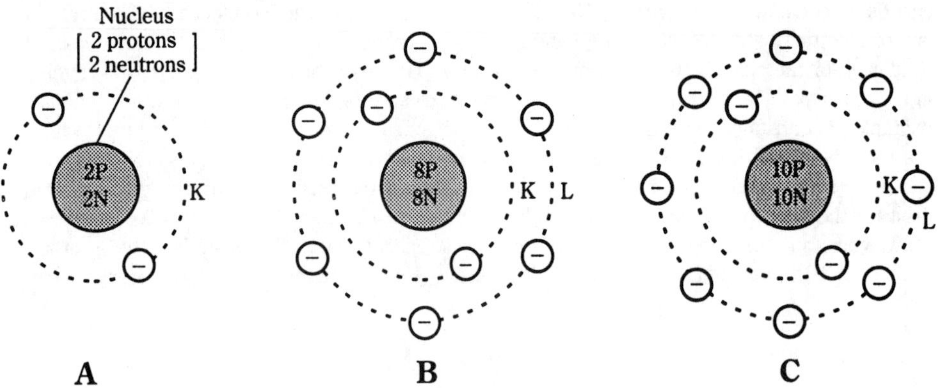

Fig. 1-3 The atomic structure of: A. helium B. oxygen and C. neon.

At this point, you know that compounds are made up of molecules that can be broken down chemically into the atoms of the elements. These atoms consist of protons and neutrons within the nucleus around which a number of electrons revolve (FIG. 1-4). The question arises: "Do the electrons move in random orbits or is their movement structured in some manner?" In general, the electrons are distributed between a number of *shells,* which are imaginary surfaces on which the electrons are considered to revolve. The shells are arranged in steps that correspond to certain fixed energy levels. The major shells are labeled K, L, M, N, O, P, and Q (FIG. 1-5), with the K shell representing the lowest energy level. For each shell: there is a maximum number of electrons that can be accommodated and the shells must be filled in the sequence K, L, and so on. The shells are considered to be filled when they contain the numbers shown in TABLE 1-1.

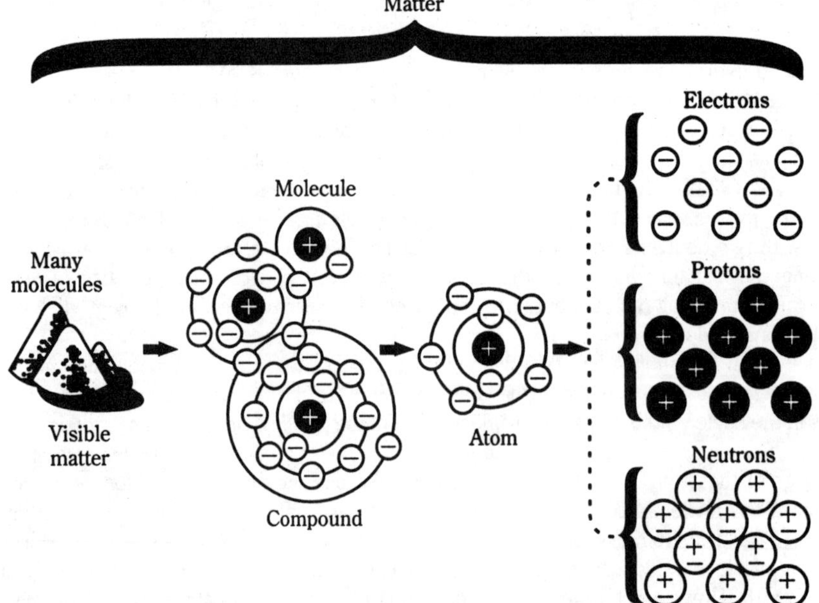

Fig. 1-4 Composition of matter; molecules, atoms and subatomic particles.

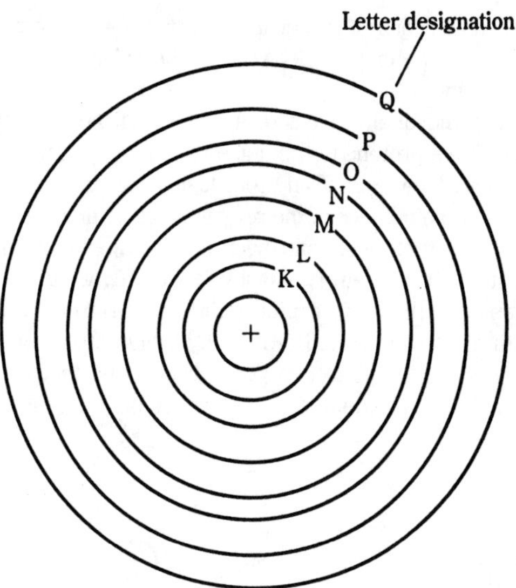

Fig. 1-5 The arrangement of shells in an atom.

Table 1-1. Maximum number of electrons in shells.

Shell designation	Maximum number of electrons
K	2
L	8
M	18
N	32
O	18
P	12
Q	2

The only elements with their major shells completely filled are the *inert gases:* helium (He), neon (Ne), argon (Ar), krypton (Kr), xenon (Xe), and radon (Rn). For example, neon has an atomic number of 10; two of the 10 orbiting electrons will reside in the *K* shell and the other eight in the *L* shell (FIG. 1-3). Because their shells are completely filled, the inert gases are stable in the sense that they are reluctant to combine with the other elements.

By contrast with the inert gases, copper (Cu) has an atomic number of 29. Consequently, the *K, L,* and *M* shells will be completely filled, for a total of 28 electrons, and there will be only one electron in the *N* shell. The number of the electrons in this last shell is called the *valence* of the atom; copper has a valence of 1. The outermost or valence shell therefore contains those electrons that are farthest away from the nucleus. A particular atom's valence governs its ability to either gain or lose an electron, which governs the element's chemical and electrical properties. When the valence shell is stable, it will contain a total of eight electrons. If only one or two electrons are lacking, the atom will easily gain these so that the shell is complete, but a large amount of energy will then be required to free any of the valence electrons from the shell. On the other hand, if there are only one or two electrons in the valence shell, these can be freed with only a small amount of energy.

When an atom gains one or more electrons, the total number of negative electrons will exceed the number of positive protons in the nucleus. The atom will then be negatively charged and is called a *negative* ion. However, if an atom loses one or more electrons, the number of protons will be greater than the number of the remaining electrons and the result will be a *positive ion.* To illustrate the formation of ions, refer back to the water molecule with its two hydrogen atoms and one oxygen atom. Hydrogen (H) has a valence of 1, while the valence of oxygen (O) is 6 (FIG. 1-3). The oxygen atom therefore captures the two electrons from the hydrogen atoms to fill its valence shell with eight electrons. Both the hydrogen atoms become positive ions, while the oxygen atom is a negative ion. The two positive ions and the single negative ion are then bonded together by their force of attraction to create a stable molecule of water (FIG. 1-6).

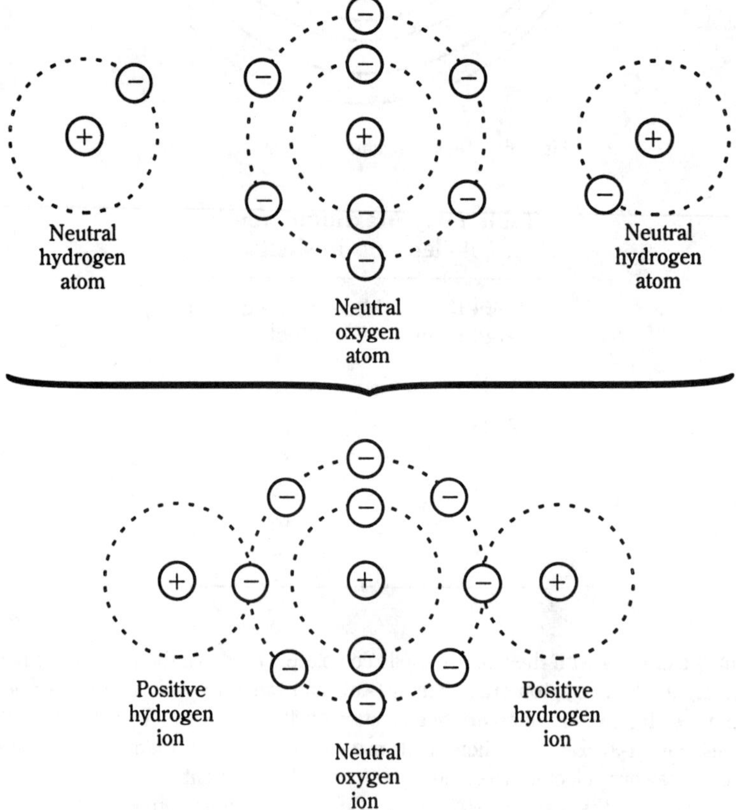

Fig. 1-6 The water molecule.

Conductors, insulators, and semiconductors

Conductors are materials that allow electricity to flow easily with minimum opposition. Such materials contain a large number of *free electrons,* which are loosely bound to their nuclei and are therefore able to move without difficulty from atom to atom. Generally speaking, all metals are good conductors and the three best (in descending order) are silver (Ag), copper (Cu), and gold (Au). It is no surprise to learn that each of these metals has a valence of 1. When an electric force is applied, this single valence electron is easily removed from its parent atom and becomes a free electron, capable of moving to another atom. Consequently, the concept of an electrical current is a flow of negative charges that are associated with the movement of the free electrons through a conductor. The next best conducting metal is aluminum, which has a valence of 3 and therefore offers more opposition to the flow of electricity than copper.

Insulators, such as rubber, paper, mica, and glass, are the opposite of conductors and are used to prevent the flow of electricity. These materials are normally compounds in which the valence electrons of certain atoms are used to fill the valence shells of other atoms. Consequently, no free electrons are naturally available and a large amount of energy must be added before any can be created. Pure water, which is a compound, is an insulator and does not conduct electricity easily. It is the dissolved salts and traces of acid that cause tap water to be a good conductor.

Halfway between conductors and insulators are the *semiconductors,* such as germanium (Ge) and silicon (Si). Each of these elements has a valance of 4; the number of free electrons available is limited. The semiconductors are therefore neither good conductors nor good insulators; however, silicon and germanium are extremely important in the manufacture of solid-state devices, such as diodes, transistors, and integrated circuits (ICs).

Question 1 When an atom gains an additional electron, the result is a :

A. positive ion B. negative molecule C. positive molecule D. negative ion E. negative neutron

Answer Choice D. The atom becomes negatively charged and is a negative ion.

Question 2 An electrical current in a copper wire is equivalent to a flow of:

A. negative ions B. positive ions C. valence electrons D. positive neutrons E. protons

Answer Choice C. The current is the result of an electron flow.

1-2. The International System (SI) of mechanical units

In 1901, Professor Giorgi of Italy proposed a new system founded on the meter (100 centimeters, slightly greater than 1 yard), the kilogram (1000 grams, about 2.2 pounds), and the second as the units of length, mass, and time. For electricity, it was necessary to define a fourth fundamental unit and then build on this foundation to establish other units. In 1948, the ampere, which measures electrical current, was internationally adopted as a fourth unit. This is the *MKSA* (meter, kilogram, second, ampere) system, which is also referred to as the *international system* or *SI* (Système Internationale d'Unités).

In any study of electricity and electronics, you often need to use mechanical units to measure such quantities as force and energy. Therefore, this chapter is used to establish the mechanical SI units. You will also see that some of these units are directly transferable to the electrical system. For example, electrical energy and mechanical energy are each measured by the same unit.

Unit of force

Isaac Newton stated that when a force is applied to an object or mass, the object or mass accelerates so that its speed or velocity increases. In the SI system, the velocity is measured in meters per second. We shall use the abbreviations of *m* for meter and *s* for second so that meters per second is written *m/s*. Acceleration will be expressed as meters per second per second (m/s^2). For example, if a mass starts from rest with zero velocity and is given an acceleration of 3 meters per second per second, its velocity after 1 second is 3 meters per second, after 2 s is 6 m/s, after 3 is 9 m/s and so on.

If the force applied to a particular mass is increased, the acceleration will be greater. However, if the force is kept the same, but the mass is greater, the acceleration will be less. The unit of force in the SI system is the *newton* (N), which will give a mass of 1 kg an acceleration of 1 m/s^2 in the direction of the force.

When a mass is falling under the force of the earth's gravity, its acceleration is 9.81 m/s^2. Therefore, the gravitational force on the mass of 1 kg is 9.81 N. This force is sometimes referred to as 1-kg weight. Of course, on the moon the force of gravity exerted on 1 kg would be less than 9.81 N. The equations related to these units are:

$$v = \frac{d}{t} \text{ m/s} \tag{1-1}$$

$$a = \frac{v}{t} = \frac{d}{t^2} \text{ m/s}^2 \tag{1-2}$$

$$F = m \times a \text{ newtons (N)} \tag{1-3}$$

where: d = distance (m)
a = acceleration (m/s^2)
t = time (s)
m = mass (kg)
F = force (N)
v = velocity (m/s)

Unit of energy or work

Energy is the capacity for doing work, and therefore both these quantities are measured by the same unit. When a force is applied through a certain distance in the direction of the force, the energy must be supplied so that work can be performed. A good example is lifting a mass at a constant speed against the force of gravity. When the mass has been raised through a given height or distance, you have expended some energy to perform a certain amount of work. The larger the force and the longer the distance through which the force is applied, the greater is the amount of work that must be done. The value of the work performed is then found by multiplying the force (in newtons) by the distance (in meters). The result of multiplying any two quantities together is called their *product.* You can therefore say that work is the product of force and distance. In the SI system, the unit of mechanical energy or work is the *joule (J)*. For example, if a force of 5 N is applied through a distance of 2 m, the work done in joules is 2 m × 5 N = 10 J. One joule can therefore be thought of as 1 meter-newton because it is the result of multiplying 1 meter by 1 newton.

The newton was defined in terms of the fundamental units of mass (kilogram), length (meter), and time (second). The joule is derived from the newton and the meter; in other words, each new unit is defined in terms of its predecessors. This is the logical manner in which a system of units is established.

The equation for the work is:

$$W = F \times d \text{ joules (J)} \tag{1-4}$$

where: F = force (N)
d = distance (m)
W = work (J)

Unit of torque

A *torque* produces a twisting effect, which you use every day when you open a door by either pushing or pulling its handle. The force that you apply is most effective when its direction is at right angles (90°) to the line that joins the handle to the door hinge (FIG. 1-7A). This is clearly so because if the force and the line were in the same direction, the door would not open at all. If the handle were positioned close to the hinge, it would be difficult to open the door. Therefore, the value of the torque must be equal to the result of multiplying the applied force, *F*, by the distance, *d*, which is at right angles (90°) to the force's direction. This distance is the length between the point, *P*, at which the force is applied and the pivot, *O*, about which the twisting effect or the rotation occurs (FIG. 1-7B). Torque is equal to the product of force and distance, but with one very important difference. In the case of work, the directions of the force and the distance are the same, but with torque, the directions are 90° apart. Consequently, torque is not measured in joules, but in *newton-meters* (N/m).

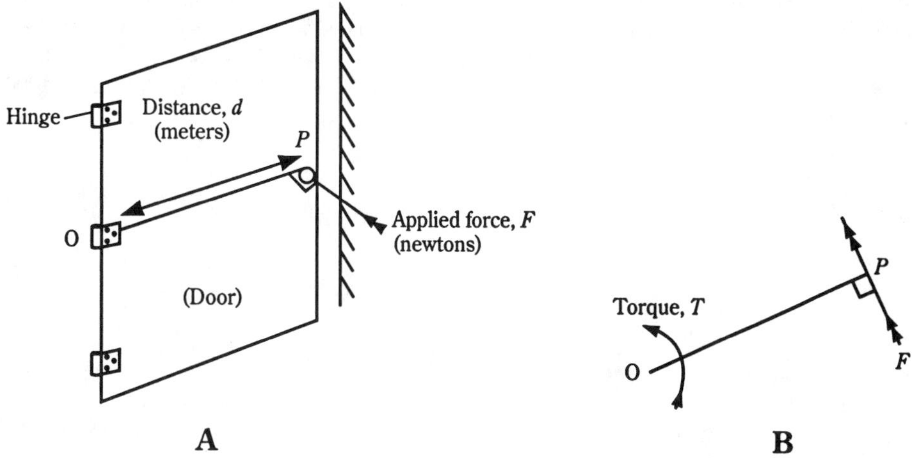

Fig. 1-7 The concept of torque.

The equation for torque is:

$$T = F \times d \text{ (N/m)} \tag{1-5}$$

where: F = force (N)
d = distance (m)
T = Torque (N/m)

Unit of power

There is often much confusion over the distinction between *work* and *power*. *Power* is the rate at which work is performed or energy is expended. As soon as you see the word *rate*, you must realize that time is involved. Here is a mechanical example. Suppose that you have a heavy weight and you ask a powerful adult to lift it up a certain height against the force of gravity. The adult will be able to perform this task quickly (in a short time) because of his or her power. However, you could have a complex pulley system attached to the weight and a wheel at the end of the system. A small child could turn the handle on the wheel and the weight would slowly rise to the same height that was achieved by the powerful adult. Neglecting the weight of the pulley system and its friction, the total work performed by the adult and the child is the same, but the child took a much longer time because he or she is much less powerful than the adult. An old British unit is the horsepower, which is equivalent to 550 foot-pounds per second. This means that a motor that has a mechanical output of 1 horsepower (hp) would be capable of lifting a mass of 550 pounds through a distance of 1 foot against the force of gravity in a time of 1 second.

The SI unit of power is the *watt,* whose unit symbol is W. The power is 1 watt if 1 joule of energy is created or used every second. For example, when you switch on a 60-W electric light bulb, 60 J of energy are released from the bulb every second, mostly in the form of heat, but a small amount as light. Therefore, watts are equivalent to joules per second, or joules are the same as watts × seconds, which can be written as *watts-seconds.* Because the horsepower and the watt both measure the same quantity, the two must be related. In fact, 1 hp is equivalent to 746 W.

If the 60-W light bulb is left on for 1 hr (3600 s), the energy consumed is 60 W × 3600 s = 21600 J, and this consumption would appear on the electricity bill. It is clear that, for everyday purposes, the joule is too small of a unit. In fact, about 8 J of energy is required to lift a 2-lb book through a distance of 1 yard and about half a million joules to boil a kettle of water. A larger unit would be the *watthour (Wh),* which is the energy consumed when a power of 1 watt is operated for a time of 1 hour. Because 1 h is the same as 3600 s, 1 Wh = 1 W × 3600 s = 3600 J. The unit on the electricity bill is still larger, it is the ***kilowatt-hour (kWh),*** which is equal to 1000 Wh or 3,600,000 J.

The equations for the power are:

$$P = \frac{W}{t} \tag{1-6}$$

$$= \frac{F \times d}{t} \tag{1-7}$$

$$= F \times v \text{ watts (W)} \tag{1-8}$$

where: W = work (J)
F = force (N)
v = velocity (m/s)
d = distance (m)
P = watts (W)

* **Question 1-3** A unit of electrical energy is the:

A. joule B. watt-second C. watt-hour D. kilowatt-hour E. all of the above are true

Answer Choice E. Because watts = joules per second, 1 joule = 1 watt-second. Larger units of energy or work are the watt-hour (1 Wh = 3600 J) and the kilowatt-hour (1 kWh = 1000 Wh = 3,600,000 J).

1-3. The International System (SI) of electrical units

Unit of charge

The word *charge* means a quantity of electricity and its letter symbol is Q. The SI unit is the *coulomb* (Charles A. Coulomb, 1736–1806), which was originally defined from a series of experiments that were performed in the 1830s by Michael Faraday (1791–1867). These experiments involved the flow of electron current through a chemical solution and demonstrated the phenomenon of electrolytic conduction.

In one experiment, a bar of silver and a nickel plate (referred to as the electrodes) are immersed in a silver nitrate solution (FIG. 1-8), which acts as the electrolyte. The silver bar is called the *anode* and is connected to one terminal of the battery while the nickel plate (*cathode*) is connected to the other terminal. As time passed, Faraday observed that silver was lost from the anode and an equal amount was deposited on the cathode. In addition, the silver was being transferred at a constant rate. At the time of this experiment, the existence of the electron was unknown and therefore Faraday (wrongly) considered that the movement of the electricity through the circuit was carrying the silver from the anode to the cathode. It was then assumed that the anode was connected to the battery's positive terminal, and the cathode was joined to the negative terminal so that the direction of the electrical flow or current was from positive to negative. In fact, there is a movement of positive silver ions from the anode to the cathode, while negative nitrate ions are traveling in the opposite direction through the electrolyte. The electron flow occurs in the external copper connecting wires; the electrons leave the battery's negative terminal and enter the positive terminal. Faraday's assumption is often referred to as the *conventional* or *mathematical current flow,* which is considered to flow from the battery's positive terminal to its negative terminal and is therefore in the opposite direction to the *actual* physical electron flow.

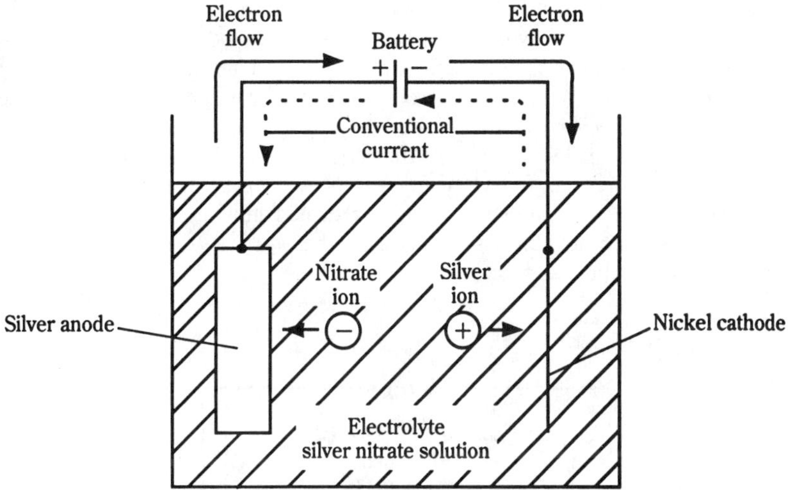

Fig. 1-8 Electrolytic conduction.

From this study of atomic structure, it follows that the practical charge of 1 coulomb must be equivalent to the negative charge that is associated with a certain number of electrons. The coulomb represents the charge carried by 6.24×10^{18} electrons so that the charge, e, possessed by a single electron is only $1/(6.24 \times 10^{18}) = 1.602 \times 10^{-19}$ coulomb (C).

The ampere is the fundamental SI unit for measuring the current. In 1948, the international ampere was defined as "that value of current which when flowing in each of two infinitely long parallel conductors whose centers are separated by 1 meter in a vacuum (free space), causes a force of 2×10^{-7} newton per meter length to be exerted on each conductor." For your needs, it is only necessary to quote this definition. The letter symbol for current is I, which is derived from the French word *intensité,* and the unit symbol for the ampere (sometimes abbreviated "amp") is A.

You can derive the coulomb from the ampere by including the unit of time, which is the second. When a current of one ampere flows for a time of one second, a charge of one coulomb passes a particular point in an electrical circuit. In other words amperes are equivalent to coulombs per second or coulombs are the same amperes × seconds.

The equations are:

$$I = \frac{Q}{t} \text{ amperes (A)} \tag{1-9}$$

$$Q = I \times t \text{ coulombs (C)} \tag{1-10}$$

where: t = time (s)

A larger unit of charge is the ampere-hour (Ah) which is the amount of charge moved passed a point when a current of one ampere flows for a time of one hour. Therefore, 1 Ah = 1 × 60 × 60 = 3600 C. The ampere-hour is normally used to measure a battery's capacity to store charge.

Unit of electromotive force

In establishing the International System of Electrical Units, the ampere is defined as the fourth fundamental unit of the MKSA or SI system. By combining the ampere with a unit of time (the second), the coulomb was derived as the unit of charge or quantity of electricity. Also, the joule was defined as the SI unit of energy or work. The same unit can be applied to electrical energy because the various forms of energy (mechanical, electrical, heat and so on) are interchangeable.

In obtaining the mechanical SI units, a force was necessary in order to accelerate the mass of an object and cause the object to move. In a similar way, the electrical equivalent of this force imparts a velocity to the free electrons so that the current is able to flow. This "electron moving force" is the *electromotive force (EMF)* whose letter symbol is E. The EMF is the force that gives electricity its motion (FIG. 1-9) and its unit is the *volt,* named after the Italian Count Alessandro Volta (1745–1827), who invented the first chemical cell that was able to generate electricity. The unit symbol for the volt is the letter V.

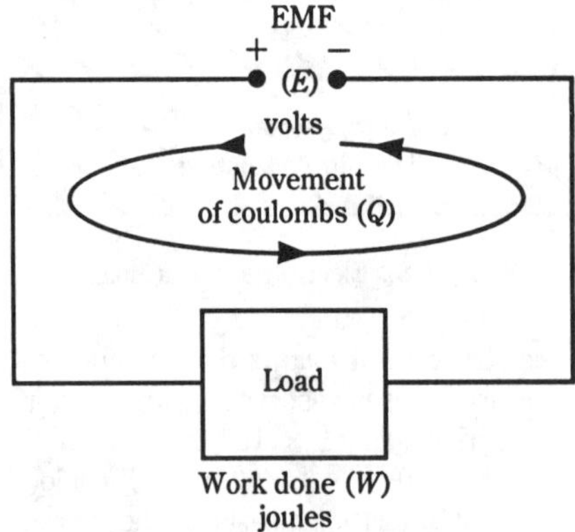

Fig. 1-9 The concept of electromotive force.

In order to drive the charge through a circuit, work must be done and it is the electrical source (for example, a battery) that must be capable of providing the necessary energy. The volt can therefore be defined in terms of the coulomb and the joule. The EMF is 1 V if, when 1 C is driven around an electrical circuit, the work done is 1 J. If you increase either the EMF and/or charge, the amount of work done will be greater.

A much smaller unit of work is the electron-volt (eV), which is the work done when the charge carried by an electron is driven around a circuit by an EMF of 1 V. Because 1 C is equivalent to the charge carried by 6.24×10^{18} electrons, one joule must be equal to 6.24×10^{18} electron-volts.

The equations that relate to voltage, work and charge, are:

$$W = Q \times E \text{ joules (J)} \tag{1-11}$$

$$Q = \frac{W}{E} \text{ coulombs (C)} \tag{1-12}$$

$$E = \frac{W}{Q} \text{ volts (V)} \tag{1-13}$$

where: W = work done or energy consumed (J)
Q = charge (C)
E = EMF (V)

Unit of power

Power is the rate at which work is performed or the rate at which energy is created. The letter symbol for power is P, and its unit is the watt (unit symbol, W). For example, a 100-W incandescent light bulb releases 100 joules of energy every second, mostly in the form of heat, but a small amount as light. Therefore, watts are equivalent to joules per second or joules are the same as watts × seconds (watt-seconds).

The energy consumed is the product of the power and the time. For example, if a 100-W bulb is left on for a time of 1 h, the energy consumed is 60 W × 3600 s = 216,000 joules. For every day use, the joule is obviously too small a unit. A larger unit is the Wh, which is the energy consumed when a power of 1 W is operated for a time of 1 h. Therefore, 1 Wh is the same as 1 W × 3600 s = 3600 J. However, the unit on the electricity bill is still larger. It is the kWh, which is equivalent to 1000 Wh or 3,600,000 J.

The power in watts is equal to the same number of joules per second, while the work in joules is the product of the EMF, E, in volts and the charge, Q, in coulombs (EQ. 1-11). The power is therefore the product of the EMF, E, and the current, I (FIG. 1-10) because the current in amperes is equivalent to the same number of coulombs per second (EQ. 1-3).

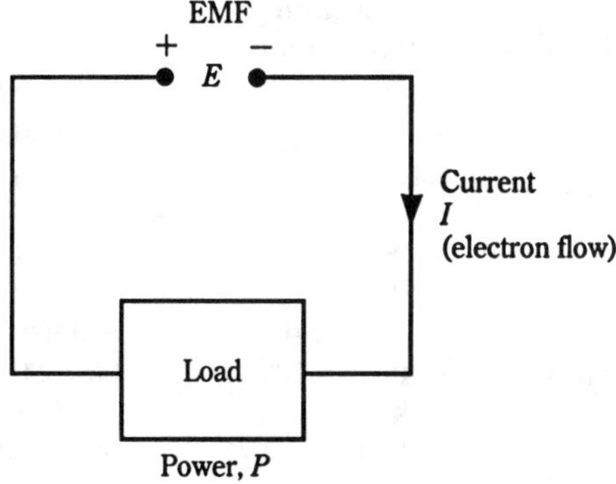

Fig. 1-10 The concept of electrical power.

The equations are:

$$P = \frac{W}{t} \tag{1-14}$$

$$= \frac{E \times Q}{t} \tag{1-11}$$

$$= E \times \frac{Q}{t} \tag{1-9}$$

$$= E \times I \text{ watts (W)} \tag{1-15}$$

It follows that:

$$I = \frac{P}{E} \text{ amperes (A)} \tag{1-16}$$

and:

$$E = \frac{P}{I} \text{ volts (V)} \tag{1-17}$$

where: P = power (W)
W = work (J)
E = EMF (V)
Q = charge (C)
I = current (A)
t = time (s)

Prefixes

As well as scientific notation, word prefixes are commonly used in electronics to represent both large and small quantities. The kilogram is equivalent to 1000 grams. The prefix "kilo" therefore means that the gram unit is multiplied by 1000. Such prefixes are based on the metric system, and the ones most commonly used in electronics are shown in TABLE 1-2. When substituting into formulas, it is important to express all values in basic units so that the answers will also appear in terms of their basic units.

Table 1-2. Prefixes commonly encountered in electronics.

Prefix	Symbol	Scientific notation equivalent	Meaning
tera-	T	$\times 10^{12}$	$\times$ 1,000,000,000,000
giga-	G	$\times 10^{9}$	$\times$ 1,000,000,000
mega-	M	$\times 10^{6}$	$\times$ 1,000,000
kilo-	k	$\times 10^{3}$	$\times$ 1000
centi-	c	$\div 10^{2}$ or $\times 10^{-2}$	$\div$ 100 or $\times$ 0.01
milli-	m	$\div 10^{3}$ or $\times 10^{-3}$	$\div$ 1000 or $\times$ 0.001
micro-	μ	$\div 10^{6}$ or $\times 10^{-6}$	$\div$ 1,000,000 or $\times$ 0.000001
nano-	n or ν	$\div 10^{9}$ or $\times 10^{-9}$	$\div$ 1,000,000,000 or $\times$ 0.000000001
pico- or micromicro	p or μμ	$\div 10^{12}$ or $\times 10^{-12}$	$\div$ 1,000,000,000,000 or $\times$ 0.000000000001

Question 1-4 A 60-W electric light bulb is rated at 120 V. What is the value of the current that flows through the filament of the light bulb?

A. 2 A
B. 0.5 A
C. 4 A
D. 1 A
E. 1.5 A

Answer Choice B.

Current:

$$I = \frac{P}{E} \tag{1-16}$$

$$= \frac{60\text{ W}}{120\text{ V}} = \frac{1}{2}\text{ A} = 0.5\text{ A}$$

Question 1-5 An electrical circuit operated with a power of 242 W for a time of 31 hs. The amount of energy consumed is:

A. 242 W B. 750 Wh C. 7.5 kWh D. 2.7×10^4 J E. Choices B and D are correct

Answer Choice C.

Energy consumed:

$$W = P \times t$$

$$= 242\text{ W} \times 31\text{ hr} \tag{1-6}$$

$$= 7502\text{ Wh}$$

$$= 7.5\text{ kWh, rounded off}$$

1-4. Ohm's Law: concepts of resistance and conductance

The electromotive force, E, is responsible for creating the current, I. Consequently, a relationship exists between E and I. It is only logical to assume that if the EMF that is applied to an electrical circuit, the current will also increase. However, in 1827 George Simon Ohm stated that the exact relationship between E and I was linear. Under the law that bears Ohm's name, the current flowing through a conductor (such as a very long length of thin wire made from silver, copper, aluminum, etc.) is *directly proportional* to the EMF that is applied across the conductor. This occurs under constant physical conditions of temperature, humidity, and pressure. This means that if you triple the voltage, the current will also be tripled; if you halve the voltage, the current will also be halved. Whatever you do to the voltage, the same will happen to the current. However, please do not think that Ohm's law is obviously true. Most electronic components *within their operating ranges* obey Ohm's law, but others do not. For example, if you double the forward voltage across a semiconductor diode, the current will increase, but will not double. In general, solid-state devices do not obey Ohm's law.

In FIG. 1-11, a voltage source whose EMF can be varied, is connected across a long length of copper wire, which acts as the conductor. An ammeter is placed in the path of the current, I, and will record the current value in amperes. A voltmeter is connected across the battery and will read the value of the EMF, E. To start with, it is obvious that if the applied voltage is 0, the current is also 0. When the initial EMF is 12 V, the recorded current is 2 A. If this EMF is now doubled to 24 V, the current will also double to 4 A. When the voltage is again doubled to 48 V, the new current is 8 A. If the EMF is multiplied by 10 to a value of $10 \times 12\text{ V} = 120\text{ V}$,

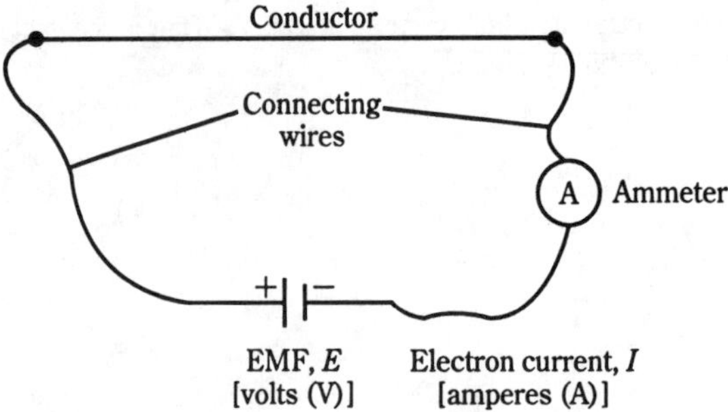

Fig. 1-11 Principle of Ohm's law.

Table 1-3. Example of the constant ratio of *E/I*.

EMF (*E*) volts	CURRENT (*I*) amperes	Ratio *E/I*
6 V	1 A	6
12 V	2 A	6
24 V	4 A	6
48 V	8 A	6
120 V	20 A	6

the accompanying current is 10 × 2 A = 20 A. Finally, if the initial EMF is halved to 12 V/2 = 6 V, the current drops to 2 A/2 = 1A. These corresponding values of *E* and *I* are illustrated in TABLE 1-3.

In TABLE 1-3, the ratio of *E:I* is calculated for each corresponding voltage and current. In every case, the answer is the same (6), which is a constant for the circuit of FIG. 1-11. Ohm's law can therefore be restated as: "Under constant physical conditions, the ratio of the voltage applied across a conductor to the current flowing through the conductor is a constant." This constant measures the conductor's opposition to current flow and is its resistance. The letter symbol for resistance is *R* and its unit is the ***ohm,*** which is denoted by the Greek capital letter, Ω. Therefore in FIG. 1-11, the conductor's resistance is 6 Ω.

Resistance is that property of an electrical circuit that opposes or limits the flow of current. The component possessing this property is called a resistor whose schematic symbol is ⏦.

If the graph of *E* versus *I* is plotted for the values of TABLE 1-2, the result is the straight line illustrated in FIG. 1-12. This means that there is a linear relationship between *E* and *I* and the straight line is the graphical way of showing that the current is directly proportional to the voltage. By contrast, when a component (such as a transistor) does not obey Ohm's law, its voltage/current relationship is some form of curve and not a straight line.

Potential difference across a resistor

In FIG. 1-13, a source whose EMF is 12 V is connected across a resistor and the measured (electron flow) current is 6 mA. Therefore, the value of the resistor is *E:I* = 12 V:6 mA = 2 kΩ. The electron flow from X to Y develops a voltage, V_R, across the resistor. This voltage is called the ***potential difference*** (*PD*) or ***difference of potential*** (*DP*) and exactly balances the EMF of the

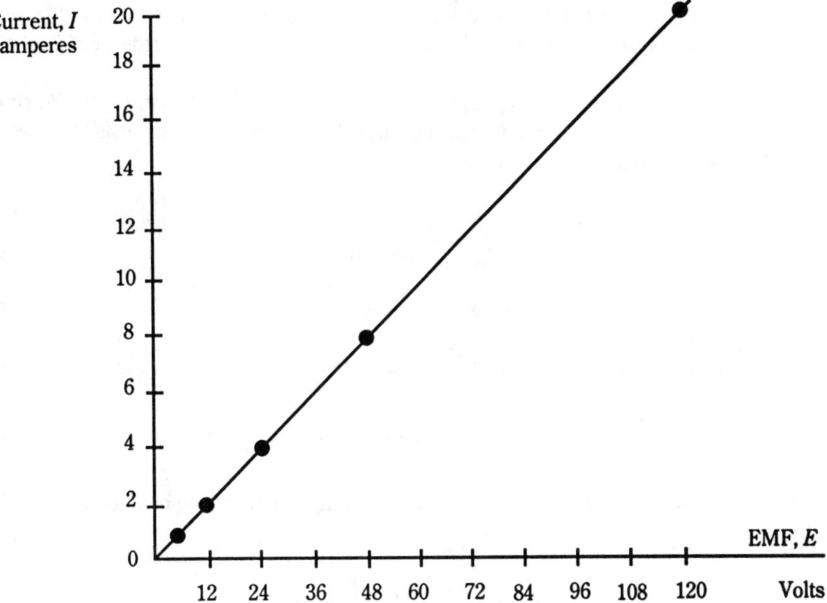

Fig. 1-12 Current versus voltage relationship for Ohm's law.

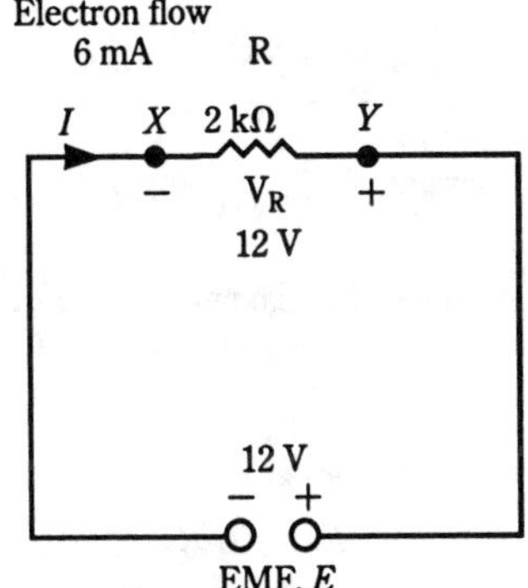

Fig. 1-13 Concept of potential difference.

source. Using a water analogy, the back pressure of a pipe always balances the forward pressure of the pump.

When the current flows through a resistor, the component becomes hot as the result of friction between the free electrons and the atoms of the material(s) from which the resistor is made. The heat represents an energy loss that must be supplied from the voltage source. The resistor dissipates (lost) power in the form of heat and has a power or wattage rating that should not be exceeded.

Conductance

Resistance is a measure of the opposition to current flow. However, it is just as valid to introduce an electrical property that measures the ease with which current is allowed to flow. Such a property is called the *conductance,* whose letter symbol is G and whose SI unit is the siemens (S). You might encounter an older unit, called the *mho* (ohm spelled backwards), but 1 mho is the same as 1 siemens.

Because a high resistance is obviously equivalent to a low conductance, G and R are reciprocals and are inversely related. It follows that because the ratio $E{:}I$ is the same as the resistance, the ratio $I{:}E$ must be equal to the conductance.

The equations are:

$$R = \frac{E}{I} \text{ ohms } (\Omega) \qquad (1\text{-}18)$$

$$E = I \times R \text{ volts (V)} \qquad (1\text{-}19)$$

$$I = \frac{E}{R} \text{ amperes (A)} \qquad (1\text{-}20)$$

$$G = \frac{I}{E} \text{ siemens (S)} \qquad (1\text{-}21)$$

provided that the resistance, R, is a constant over the range of operating conditions.

Power dissipated as heat:

$$P = E \times I \qquad (1\text{-}19)$$
$$= (I \times R) \times I$$
$$= I^2R \text{ watts (W)} \qquad (1\text{-}22)$$

Equation 1-22 yields:

$$\text{Current, } I = \sqrt{\frac{P}{R}} \text{ amperes (A)} \qquad (1\text{-}23)$$

Equation 1-23 enables you to determine the maximum value of current that can flow through a particular resistor without exceeding its power rating (see QUE. 1-6).

In addition, the power dissipated as heat:

$$P = E \times I \qquad (1\text{-}20)$$
$$= E \times (E/R)$$
$$= E^2/R \text{ watts (W)} \qquad (1\text{-}24)$$

Equation 1-24 yields:

$$\text{EMF, } E = \sqrt{P \times R} \text{ volts (V)} \qquad (1\text{-}25)$$

Equation 1-25 enables you to determine the maximum value of voltage which can be applied across a resistor without exceeding its power rating (see QUE. 1-7).

Question 1-6 Calculate the maximum value of current that can flow through a 10-kΩ 0.5-W resistor without exceeding its power rating.

A. 5 mA B. 7.1 mA C. 20 mA D. 50 mA E. 14.1 mA

Answer. Choice B.

Maximum current:

$$I = \sqrt{\frac{P}{R}}$$

$$= \sqrt{\frac{1/2\ \text{W}}{10000\ \Omega}}$$

$$= \sqrt{\frac{1}{20000}}\ \text{A}$$

$$= 7.1\ \text{mA, rounded off}$$

Question 1-7 Calculate the maximum voltage that can be applied across a 15-kΩ 2-W resistor without exceeding its power rating.

A. 150 V
B. 300 V
C. 122 V
D. 200 V
E. 173 V

Answer

Choice E. Maximum voltage:

$$E = \sqrt{P \times R}$$

$$= \sqrt{2\ \text{W} \times 15000\ \Omega} \qquad (1\text{-}25)$$

$$= \sqrt{30000}$$

$$= 173\ \text{V, rounded off}$$

Question 1-8 The conductance of a 2000-Ω 0.25-W resistor is:

A. 2 mS B. 5 mS C. 20 mS D. 50 μS E. 500 μS

Answer

Choice E. Conductance:

$$G = \frac{I}{E}$$

$$= \frac{1}{R} \qquad (1\text{-}21)$$

$$= \frac{1}{2000\ \Omega}$$

$$= 0.5 \times 10^{-3}\ \text{S}$$

$$= 500\ \mu\text{S}$$

* **Question 1-9** If a dc voltage across a resistance is doubled, by what factor must the resistance be multiplied if the dissipated power is unchanged?

A. 0.5 B. 4 C. 0.25 D. 2 E. None of the above choices is true

Answer Choice B. Choose some convenient numbers to solve the question:

Original conditions: $E = 10\text{ V}, R = 1\ \Omega$

Power dissipated: $P = \dfrac{(10\ V)^2}{1\ \Omega} = 100\text{ W}$

New conditions: $P = 100\text{ W}, E = 2 \times 10 = 20\text{ V}$

Resistance: $R = \dfrac{E^2}{P} = \dfrac{(20\text{ V})^2}{100\text{ W}} = 4\ \Omega$

The resistance must be quadrupled or multiplied by 4.

* **Question 1-10** A dc voltage is applied across a certain value of resistance. If the resistance value is halved, by what factor must the voltage be multiplied if the dissipated power is unchanged?

A. 0.5 B. 4 C. 0.25 D. 2 E. 0.707

Answer Choice E. Choose some convenient numbers to solve the question:

Original conditions: $E = 10\text{ V}, R = 2\ \Omega$

Power dissipated: $P = \dfrac{(10\ V)^2}{2\ \Omega} = 50\text{ W}$

New conditions: $P = 50\text{ W}, R = \dfrac{2\ \Omega}{2} = 1\ \Omega$

EMF: $E = \sqrt{50\text{ W} \times 1\ \Omega} = 7.07\text{ V}$

The voltage is multiplied by a factor of $\dfrac{7.07\text{ V}}{10\text{ V}} = 0.707$.

1-5. Composition resistors: color code

A *composition resistor* is the most common type of resistor used in electronics. These resistors are inexpensive and are manufactured in standard resistance values, which normally range from 2.7 Ω to 22 MΩ. The resistance values remain reasonably constant over a limited temperature range so that composition resistors are linear components and obey Ohm's law. However, such resistors can only dissipate a limited amount of power; the normal wattage ratings are only 1/8, 1/4, 1/2, 1 and 2 W. These ratings are judged from the resistor's physical size (FIG. 1-14A). Knowing the value of the power rating (P) and the resistance (R), the formulas $I = \sqrt{P/R}$ amperes and $E = \sqrt{P \times R}$ volts will enable you to calculate the maximum values of the voltage and the current that will not allow the resistor's power rating to be exceeded.

Composition resistors are normally manufactured from powdered carbon with its specific resistance of more than $3.325 \times 10^{-5}\ \Omega - m$. The carbon is mixed with an insulating substance, (such as talc) and a binding material, such as resin. The proportions of carbon and talc are then varied to produce a wide range of resistances. The resistor is finally coated with an insulating material that is baked to a hard finish. This coating provides protection against moisture and mechanical damage (FIG. 1-14B). At either end of the resistor, a tinned copper "pigtail" wire is deeply embedded and provides an adequate contact area for making a good connection with the carbon/talc mixture.

The main disadvantages of composition resistors is that they are not manufactured to precise values, but are normally sorted into three groups. The first group has a 5% tolerance, which means that their measured resistances are within ± 5% of their rated values. The second group

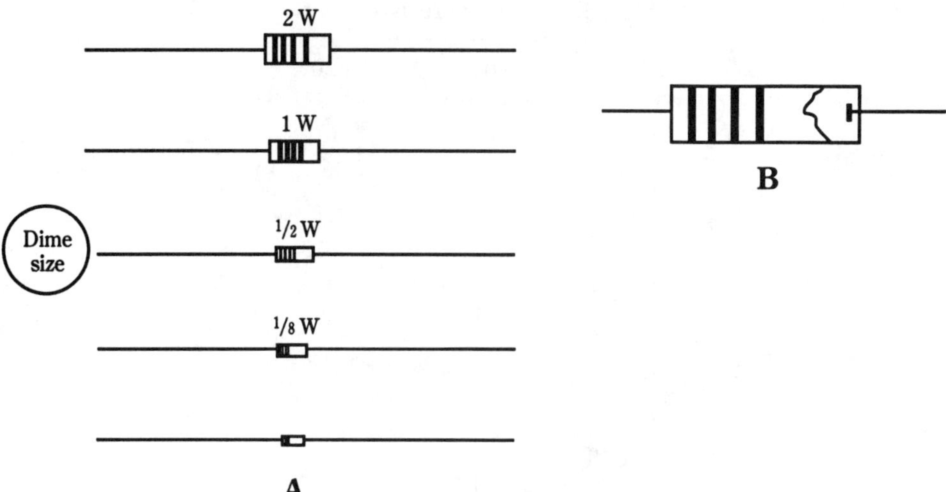

Fig. 1-14 Composition resistor.

has a tolerance between ± 5% and ± 10%, and the tolerance of the third and final group lies between ± 10% and ± 20%. Any resistor whose tolerance is greater than ± 20%, is discarded.

As an example, consider a 10% tolerance resistor that has a rated value of 10 kΩ. The actual resistance value must be between $10\ \text{k}\Omega + (10/100) \times 10\ \text{k}\Omega = 11\ \text{k}\Omega$ and $10\ \text{k}\Omega - (10/100) \times 10\ \text{k}\Omega = 9\ \text{k}\Omega$. Consequently, there would be no point in manufacturing 10.5- or 9.5-kΩ resistors because both these values lie within the tolerance of the rated 10-kΩ resistor. It follows that composition resistors are only made in certain standard values. Between 10 and 100 Ω in the 20% range, the only values manufactured are 10, 15, 22, 33, 47, 68, and 100 Ω. These values are chosen so that the upper tolerance limit of one resistor equals (or slightly overlaps) the lower limit of the next highest value of resistor. For example, the upper limit of a 22-Ω resistor is $22 + (20/100) \times 22 = 26.4\ \Omega$, while the lower limit of a 33-Ω resistor is $33 - (20/100) \times 33 = 26.4\ \Omega$. The ± 10% and ± 5% ranges are then formed by including additional standard values in the gaps of the 20% range (TABLE 1-4).

The higher resistances are formed by adding zeros to the values shown in TABLE 1-4. The least costly method of indicating the rated resistance value is to use a four-band color code. The first two bands represent the significant figures of the rated value, the third band is the *multiplier,* which indicates the number of zeros, and the fourth band (if present) shows the tolerance (FIG. 1-15). Sometimes a fifth band is used to indicate the fail-rate percentage for 1000 hours of operation.

Examples:

33 Ω-5%	Orange, orange, black (no zeros), gold
560 Ω-10%	Green, blue, brown, silver
2200 Ω-20%	Red, red, red (no fourth band for ± 20% tolerance)
39,000 Ω-10%	Orange, white, orange, silver
150,000 Ω-20%	Brown, green, yellow

Black is not allowed in the first band; if the rated value is less than 10 Ω, the four band system cannot be used. Gold and silver are then placed in the third band as multipliers of 0.1 and 0.01, respectively. For example, a 5.6-Ω resistor would be color-coded: green, blue, and gold.

Wirewound resistors are manufactured to more precise values than the composition type

Table 1-4. Standard resistor values.

5% tolerance	10% tolerance	20% tolerance
10	10	10
11		
12	12	
13		
15	15	15
16		
18	18	
20		
22	22	22
24		
27	27	
30		
33	33	33
36		
39	39	
43		
47	47	47
51		
56	56	
62		
68	68	68
75		
82	82	
91		

and are available in high wattage ratings (above 2 W). They are commonly made from constantan wire because of its low temperature coefficient.

* **Question 1-11** The color-coding of a resistor is: Brown, Black, Red, and Silver. What are the values of its nominal resistance and tolerance?

A. 1 kΩ, 10% B. 2000 Ω, 10% C. 100 Ω, 10% D. 10 Ω, 20% E. 100 kΩ, 10%

Answer Choice A. The nominal resistance value is 1 (Brown), 0 (Black), 00 (Red) = 1000 Ω = 1 kΩ. Silver indicates a 10% tolerance.

* **Question 1-12** The color-coding of a resistor is: Brown, Black, Black, and Gold. What is the value of its upper resistance limit?

A. 150 Ω B. 15 Ω C. 10.5 Ω D. 105 Ω E. 1.5 Ω

Answer Choice C. The nominal resistance value is: 1 (Brown), 0 (Black), with a zero multiplier (Black) = 10 Ω. Because gold indicates a 5% tolerance, the upper limit is $10\ (1 + 5/100) = 10.5\ \Omega$.

1-6. Resistance of a cylindrical conductor

Normally, a load is joined to its voltage by means of copper connecting wires. Ideally, these wires should have zero resistance, but in practice their resistance, although small, is not negligible.

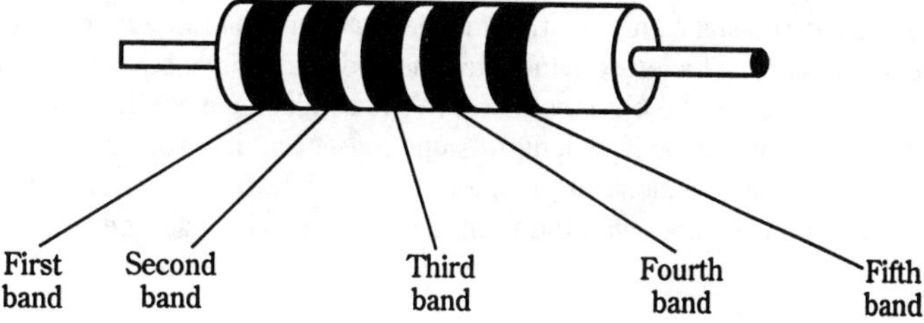

Color code	First significant figure	Second significant figure	Multiplier	Tolerance (%)	Fail-rate percent per 1000 hr
Black		0	$\times 1 = \times 10^0$		
Brown	1	1	$\times 10 = \times 10^1$		1.0
Red	2	2	$\times 100 = \times 10^2$		0.1
Orange	3	3	$\times 1000 = \times 10^3$		0.01
Yellow	4	4	$\times 10000 = \times 10^4$		0.001
Green	5	5	$\times 100000 = \times 10^5$		
Blue	6	6	$\times 1000000 = \times 10^6$		
Violet	7	7	$\times 10000000 = \times 10^7$		
Gray	8	8			
White	9	9			
Gold			$\times 0.1$	± 5	
Silver			$\times 0.01$	± 10	
No color				± 20	

Fig. 1-15 Resistor color coding.

Consequently, there will be some voltage drop across the connecting wires that will also dissipate power in the form of heat. To keep these effects to a minimum, the wires must have adequate thickness because the thickness determines the current-carrying capacity.

A length of a metal wire with a circular cross-section is an example of a cylindrical conductor. If two identical lengths are joined end to end in series, the resistance will be doubled. The conductor's resistance is therefore directly proportional to its length (FIG. 1-16). However, if the conductor is thickened by doubling its cross-sectional area, it is equivalent to connecting two identical lengths in parallel and the resistance is halved. To summarize, the resistance of a cylindrical conductor is directly proportional to its length, is inversely proportional to its cross-sectional area, and is dependent on the material from which the conductor is made.

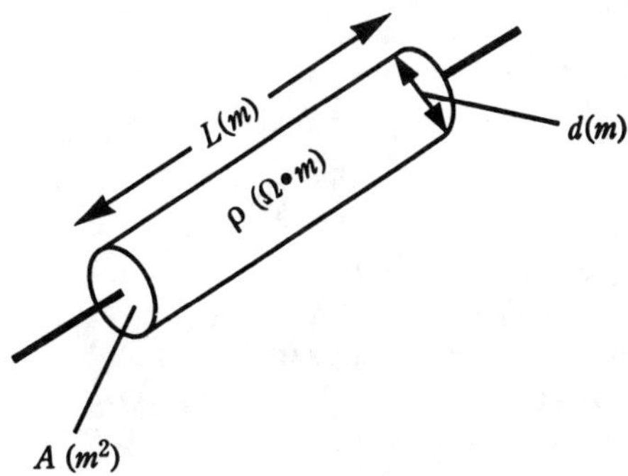

Fig. 1-16 Resistance of a cylindrical conductor.

The specific resistance or resistivity is the factor that allows you to compare the resistances of different materials. The letter symbol for the specific resistance is the Greek lowercase letter rho, ρ, and its SI unit is the ohm-meter (Ω-m). A conductor made from a particular material will have a resistance of ρ ohms if its length is one meter and its cross-sectional area is one square meter. The values of specific resistance for various materials are shown in TABLE 1-5. Because the specific resistance varies with the temperature, the values quoted in the table are for 20°C.

Table 1-5. Specific resistance (ρ) values for the various materials

Material	SI unit (specific resistance in Ω · m at 20° C)	British unit (specific resistance in Ω · cmil/ft at 20° C)
Silver	1.46×10^{-8}	9.86
Annealed copper	1.724×10^{-8}	10.37
Aluminum	2.83×10^{-8}	17.02
Tungsten	5.5×10^{-8}	33.08
Nickel	7.8×10^{-8}	46.9
Pure iron	1.2×10^{-7}	72.2
Constantan	4.9×10^{-7}	294.7
Nichrome	1.1×10^{-6}	660.0
Germanium (semiconductor)	0.55	3.3×10^{8}
Silicon (semiconductor)	550	3.3×10^{11}
Mica (insulator)	2×10^{10}	12.0×10^{18}

Although copper is excellent for connecting wires, it is far too good a conductor for a load such as a toaster. For example, the element of a 600-W/120-W toaster has a resistance of $E^2/P = (120\ \text{V})^2/600\ \text{W} = 24\ \Omega$, which could not be obtained from any practical length of copper wire with adequate current-carrying capacity. Consequently, the toaster element is made from nichrome (an alloy of nickel and chromium) wire, which has a much higher specific resistance than copper (see TABLE 1-5).

The equations are:

Resistance of a cylindrical conductor:

$$R = \frac{\rho L}{A} \qquad (1\text{-}26)$$

$$= \frac{\rho L}{\pi d^2/4}$$

$$= \frac{4\rho L}{\pi d^2}\ \Omega \qquad (1\text{-}27)$$

where: R = conductor's resistance in ohms (Ω)
L = conductor's length in meters (m)
A = cross-sectional area in square meters (m^2)
d = diameter in meters (m)
ρ = specific resistance or resistivity (Ω-m)
π = circular constant (3.1415926 . . .)

It is still more common to quote values in terms of the customary (British) system of units. Here, the chosen length is the foot, but the diameter is measured in mils (one linear mil is 0.001 inch). The cross-sectional area is given in circular mils, and one circular mil (cmil) is the area of a circle whose diameter is one mil. This simplifies the calculation of the cross-sectional area because, for example, if the diameter is 4 mils, the area is $4^2 = 16$ cmil. In this way, the complication of using π is avoided.

In customary units the resistance of a cylindrical conductor is:

$$R = \frac{\rho L}{A} = \frac{\rho L}{d^2}\ \Omega \tag{1-28}$$

where: R = conductor's resistance in ohms (Ω)
L = length in feet (ft)
A = cross-sectional area in circular mils (cmil)
d = diameter in linear mils (mil)
ρ = specific resistance (Ω-cmil/ft)

The conversion factor between the customary and SI unit systems is 1 Ω-m = 6.015×10^8 Ω-cmil/ft.

The American Wire Gage (AWG) number is based on the customary units. For example, household wiring is normally AWG #14, which has a diameter of 64 mils, a cross-sectional area of 4110 cmil, and a resistance of 2.58 Ω per 1000 ft at 25°C. The higher the gage number, the thinner the wire and the less is its current-carrying capacity.

Notice that in TABLE 1-5, the ρ values are quoted for a temperature of 20°C. This is necessary because when a conductor is heated, the rise in temperature causes the random motion of the valence (free) electrons to increase. If a voltage is then applied across the conductor, it is more difficult to move the electrons along the wire to create the flow of current; the resistance therefore increases. By contrast, certain alloys (such as manganin and constantan) have resistances that are practically independent of temperature changes.

Semiconductors (such as silicon, germanium and carbon) have very few electrons available at room temperature. However, if the temperature is increased, more electrons are moved from the valence band to a conduction band that represents a higher energy level; the resistance of the semiconductor then falls.

* **Question 1-13** A conductor is composed of copper wire with a circular cross-sectional area. If the diameter of the wire is doubled, but the length remains the same, the new resistance of the wire is:

A. doubled B. halved C. quadrupled D. quartered E. unchanged

Answer Choice D. Because the resistor is inversely proportional to the square of the diameter (EQ. 1-26), the resistance is multiplied by a factor of $\frac{1}{2^2}$ and is therefore quartered.

Question 1-14 A 36-ft length of wire has a resistance of 12 Ω/ft. If the wire's cross-sectional area is reduced to one third of its original value, the new resistance of the wire is:

A. 144 Ω B. 432 Ω C. 3888 Ω D. 1444 Ω E. 1296 Ω

Answer Choice E. Original resistance = 36 × 12 = 432 Ω.

New resistance $= \frac{432\ \Omega}{1/3} = 1296\ \Omega$.

* **Question 1-15** A 1-ft length of wire has a cross-sectional area of 5 circular mils and a resistance of 100 Ω. If the length is increased to 2 ft and the cross-sectional area is changed to 10 circular mils, the wire's new resistance is:

A. 100 Ω B. 200 Ω C. 50 Ω D. 400 Ω E. 25 Ω

Answer Choice A. Because: $R = \frac{\rho L}{A}$, the new resistance is: $\frac{100\ \Omega \times 2}{10/5} = 100\ \Omega$.

* **Question 1-16** Which of the following wire gages has the greatest current capacity with the smallest power loss?

A. #14 B. #10 C. #20 D. #12 E. #4

Answer Choice E. The lower the gage number, the thicker is the wire, and the lower is its resistance. The thickest, #4, wire will therefore have the greatest current capability and the smallest power loss.

* **Question 1-17** The gage number of a wire must be adequate for the current flowing through the wire, otherwise:

A. the insulation on the wire might melt
B. there might be too much power loss in the wire
C. the voltage drop across the wire might be excessive
D. if the wire is too thin, its resistance would be too high
E. all of the choices are true

Answer Choice E.

1-7. Resistors in series and voltage sources in series

Resistors in series are joined end to end so that there is only a single path for the current. Starting at the negative battery terminal (where a surplus of electrons exists), electrons flow through the connecting wires (which are assumed to possess zero resistance) and the three resistors. Finally, this flow reaches the positive terminal, where there is a deficit of electrons. The battery, through its chemical energy, is then responsible for maintaining the surplus of electrons at the negative terminal and the deficit at the positive terminal. It follows from this information that the current is the same throughout the circuit and that ammeters (FIG. 1-17A) A1, A2, A3, and A4 all have the same reading. Figure 1-17B shows the mounting of the resistors (top view) on a printed circuit board with the bottom view showing the conduction paths.

Across each resistor is developed a *difference of potential (DP),* which is sometimes referred to as *the potential difference (PD);* in this sense, *potential* is another word for *voltage.* For example, V_1 is the amount of voltage that is required to drive the current, I, through the resistor, R_1. Because $V_1 = IR_1$, the voltage is often called the "IR drop." The meaning of "drop" is illustrated in QUE. 1-20.

The sum of the voltages across the resistor must exactly balance the source voltage, E; this is an example of Kirchhoff's Voltage Law (KVL). Because the current through each resistor is the same, the highest value resistor will develop the greatest voltage drop and the lowest value resistor will have the smallest voltage drop. In the extreme case of the connecting wires, which theoretically have zero resistance, there will be no voltage drop. If, for example, a voltmeter is connected between points A and B (FIG. 1-17), its reading would be zero. The total equivalent resistance, R_T, is equal to the sum of the individual resistances.

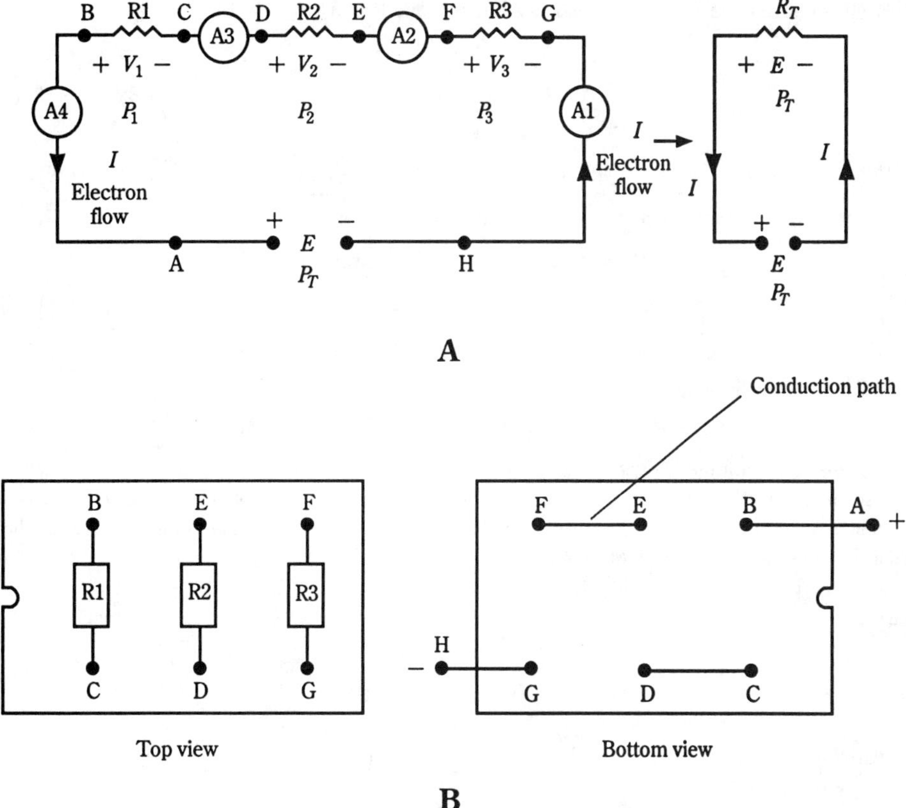

Fig. 1-17 Resistors in series.

Notice that other voltages exist in the circuit apart from V_1, V_2, V_3, and E. If a voltmeter is connected between points B and E, its reading will be the sum of the voltages V_1 and V_2; between points D and G, the voltage is equal to $V_2 + V_3$. It is often said that the order in which series resistors are connected is immaterial. This is true as far as current and the individual voltage drops are concerned, but not in terms of the other voltages that exist in the circuit.

In each resistor, a certain amount of power is dissipated in the form of heat (care must be taken that the amount of power dissipated does not exceed the resistor's wattage rating). The sum of the individual powers dissipated is equal to the total power that is derived from the source.

Finally, what is the purpose of connecting resistors in series? One obvious reason is to increase the total equivalent resistance, R_T, and thereby limit the current to a safe value; however, this could also be achieved by using a higher value of resistance with a single resistor. More importantly, adding resistors enables you to increase the overall wattage rating and to obtain nonstandard resistance values with standard components (SEC. 1-5). In addition, series resistors can be connected across a source voltage to provide a voltage-divider circuit.

The equations are:

Total resistance: $$R_T = R_1 + R_2 + R_3 \text{ ohms } (\Omega) \tag{1-29}$$

Current: $$I = \frac{E}{R_T} \text{ amperes (A)} \tag{1-30}$$

The voltage drop across the resistors R1, R2, and R3, are:

$$V_1 = IR_1 \text{ volts (V)}$$
$$V_2 = IR_2 \text{ volts (V)} \quad (1\text{-}31)$$
$$V_3 = IR_3 \text{ volts (V)}$$

EMF: $$E = V_1 + V_2 + V_3 \text{ volts (V)} \quad (1\text{-}32)$$

The powers dissipated in resistors R1, R2, and R3, are:

$$P_1 = I\,V_1 = I^2R_1 = V_1^2/R_1 \text{ watts (W)}$$
$$P_2 = I\,V_2 = I^2R_2 = V_2^2/R_2 \text{ watts (W)} \quad (1\text{-}33)$$
$$P_3 = I\,V_3 = I^2R_3 = V_3^2/R_3 \text{ watts (W)}$$

Total power dissipated:

$$P_T = P_1 + P_2 + P_3 = E\,I = I^2R_T = E^2/R_T \text{ watts (W)} \quad (1\text{-}34)$$

The source voltage is divided between the series resistors in a proportional manner, which is determined by the resistors' values. The fraction of the source voltage developed across a particular resistor is equal to the ratio of the resistor's value to the circuit's total resistance. This result is known as the *Voltage division rule (VDR).*

Current: $$I = \frac{E}{R_T} \text{ amperes (A)} \quad (1\text{-}30)$$

Voltage drop: $$V_1 = I \times R_1 = E \times \frac{R_1}{R_T} \text{ volts (V)}$$

Similarly: $$V_2 = E \times \frac{R_2}{R_T} \text{ volts (V)}$$

$$V_3 = E \times \frac{R_3}{R_T} \text{ volts (V)} \quad (1\text{-}35)$$

For two resistors in series: $$R_T = R_1 + R_2 \text{ ohms } (\Omega)$$

and: $$V_1 = E \times \frac{R_1}{R_T} = E \times \frac{R_1}{R_1 + R_2} \text{ volts (V)}$$

$$V_2 = E \times \frac{R_2}{R_1 + R_2} \text{ volts (V)} \quad (1\text{-}36)$$

Equations 1-35 and 1-36 represent the VDR.

Voltage sources in series

Two sources are in series-aiding when their polarities are such that they drive the current in the same direction around the circuit. This is illustrated in FIG. 1-18A, where the negative terminal of E_1 is directly connected to the positive terminal of E_2. Both voltages will then drive the electrons around the circuit in the counterclockwise direction. If both voltage sources are reversed, they will still be connected on series-aiding, but the electron flow will now be in the clockwise direction.

The normal purpose of connecting sources in series-aiding is to increase the amount of voltage applied to a circuit. A good example is the insertion of two 1.5-V "D" cells into a flashlight to create a total of 2 × 1.5 V = 3 V. In the case of the flashlight, the positive center terminal of one cell must be in contact with the negative casing of the other cell to provide the series-aiding connection.

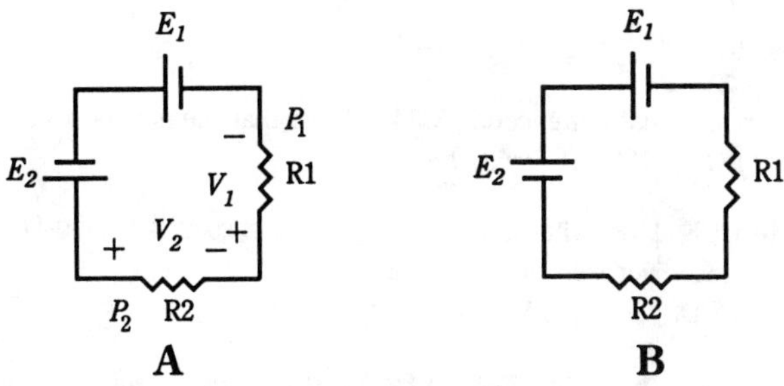

Fig. 1-18 Voltage sources in series.

If the E_1 cell is reversed (FIG. 1-18B), the polarities of the sources will drive currents in opposite directions around the circuit. The connection is therefore series-opposing and the total voltage available is the difference of the individual EMFs. The greater of the two EMFs will then determine the actual direction of the current flow. In the particular case when two identical voltage sources are connected in the series-opposing arrangement, the total voltage is zero. Consequently, the current is also zero, as are the individual voltage drops and the powers that are dissipated in the resistors.

In FIG. 1-18A:

Total source voltage: $$E_T = E_1 + E_2 \text{ volts (V)} \quad (1\text{-}37)$$

Total resistance: $$R_T = R_1 + R_2 \text{ ohms } (\Omega)$$

Current: $$I = \frac{E_T}{R_T} = \frac{E_1 + E_2}{R_1 + R_2} \text{ amperes (A)} \quad (1\text{-}38)$$

In FIG. 1-18B, assume that $E_1 > E_2$

Total source voltage: $$E_T = E_1 - E_2 \text{ volts (V)} \quad (1\text{-}39)$$

Current: $$I = \frac{E_T}{R_T} = \frac{E_1 - E_2}{R_1 + R_2} \text{ amperes (A)} \quad (1\text{-}40)$$

* **Question 1-18** In FIG. 1-19, what is the highest voltage that can be applied across the series combination without exceeding the power rating of either resistor?

A. 316 V B. 31.6 V C. 424 V D. 379 V E. 63 V

Answer Choice D. For each resistor, there is a certain maximum current above which the power rating of the resistor is exceeded.

Fig. 1-19 The circuit for questions 1-18 and 1-19.

For the 5000-Ω resistor:

$$I_{max} = \sqrt{\frac{P}{R}} = \sqrt{\frac{20 \text{ W}}{5000\ \Omega}} = 63.24 \text{ mA}$$

For the 1000-Ω resistor: $I_{max} = \sqrt{\dfrac{5\ \text{W}}{1000\ \Omega}} = 70.7\ \text{mA}$

It follows that the current must not exceed 63.24 mA and that the highest value of applied voltage is 63.24 mA × (5000 Ω + 1000 Ω) = 379 V.

* **Question 1-19** In QUE. 1-18, what is the voltage drop across the 5000-Ω resistor when the maximum voltage is applied across the combination?

A. 316 V B. 31.6 V C. 424 V D. 379 V E. 63 V

Answer Choice A. From the solution of QUE. 1-18, the maximum allowed current is 63.24 mA and therefore the voltage drop across the 5000-Ω resistor is 63.24 mA × 5 kΩ = 316 V.

Question 1-20 In FIG. 1-20, the reading of a voltmeter connected between the points B and D, is:

A. 500 V B. 250 V C. 200 V D. 100 V E. 20 V

Answer Choice D. The circuit represents a voltage divider. By the VDR:

Voltage between the points B and D: $V_{BD} = E \times \dfrac{R_{BD}}{R_T}$

$$= 500\ \text{V} \times \frac{40\ \text{k}\Omega + 10\ \text{k}\Omega}{200\ \text{k}\Omega + 40\ \text{k}\Omega + 10\ \text{k}\Omega} \qquad (1\text{-}35)$$

$$= 100\ \text{V}$$

Notice that if the black (negative) probe is permanently connected to point D and the red (positive) probe touches point A, the reading of the voltmeter is 500 V. If the red probe is now shifted to point B, the reading falls to 100 V so that the voltage drop across the 200-kΩ resistor is 400 V.

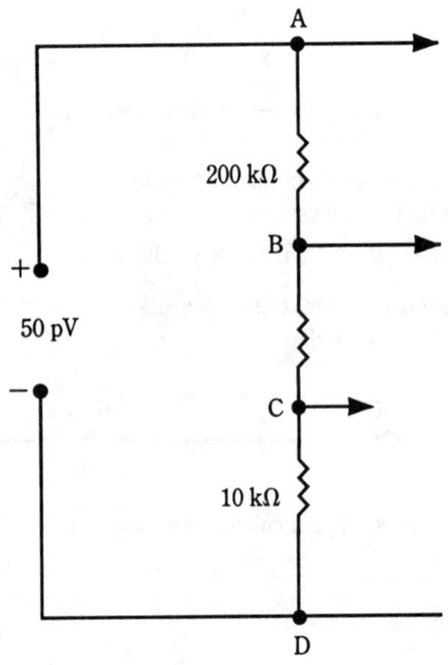

Fig. 1-20 The circuit for question 1-20.

Finally, if the red probe is moved to point C, the reading is only 20 V so that 80 V has been dropped across the 40-kΩ resistor.

Question 1-21 Which of the following enables 100 Vdc to be obtained from a 500 Vdc supply?

A. voltage inverter B. dc transformer C. voltage reducer D. voltage divider E. voltage converter

Answer Choice D. See solution to question 1-20.

1-8. Ground and the voltage reference level

Ground can be regarded as any large mass of conducting material in which there is essentially *zero* resistance between any two ground points. Examples of ground are the metal chassis of a transmitter, the aluminum chassis of a receiver, or a wide strip of copper plating on a printed circuit board.

The main reason for using a ground system is to simplify the circuitry by saving on the amount of wiring. This is done by using ground as the return path for many circuits; at any time, a number of currents are flowing through the ground system.

Figures 1-21A and B show two circuits that contain connecting wires. However, if a common ground (alternative symbols ▽ or ⏚, usually to signify earth ground, and ⏊ to signify chassis ground) is used for the return path (FIG. 1-21C), only two connecting wires are required; the schematic equivalent of FIG. 1-21C is shown in FIG. 1-21D. Here is where the concept of zero resistance is vital. If the ground resistance was not zero, the current flow in one circuit would develop a voltage between the ground points X and Y, and this would cause a current to flow in the other circuit. In other words, the two circuits would interfere with each other. It is therefore important to regard all ground points in a schematic as being electrically joined together as a single path. The zero resistance property of ground is essential to achieve isolation between all those circuits that use the same ground.

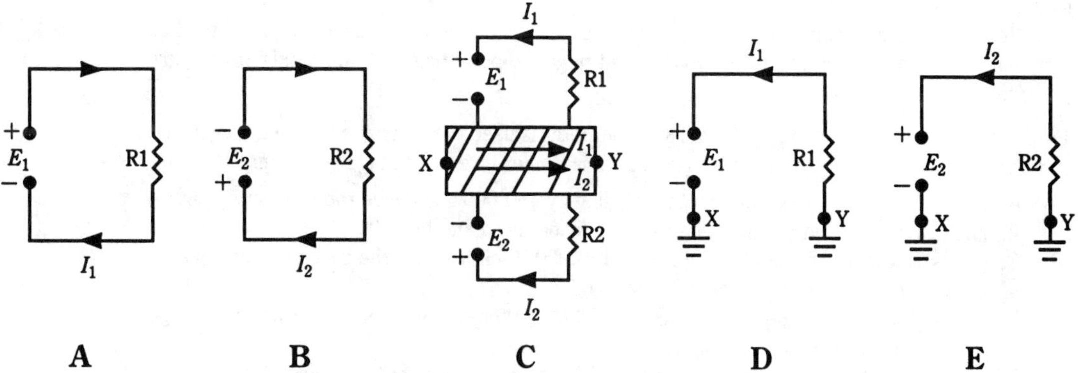

Fig. 1-21 The principle of a ground connection.

In the previous section, a voltage drop, potential difference, or difference of potential has been regarded as existing between two points; to have referred to the voltage at a single point would have been meaningless. However, if you create a common reference level to represent the voltage at one point, you can quote the voltages at other points in relation to the reference level. Ground is therefore chosen as a reference level of 0 V and the voltage (potential) at any point is then measured relative to ground. This is the manner in which the expected potentials at various points are indicated on a schematic.

In FIG. 1-22A, you could either say that the point X is 6 V positive, with respect to the point Y, or that the point Y is 6 V negative, with respect to the point X. However, if the negative battery terminal is grounded at 0 V (FIG. 1-22B), point X carries a potential of positive 6 V (+ 6 V), with respect to ground. By contrast, if the battery is reversed and its positive terminal is grounded (FIG. 1-22C), the potential at X is now negative 6 V (− 6 V), with respect to ground. When troubleshooting a circuit, it is normal practice to connect the black (common) probe of a voltmeter permanently to ground and to measure the potentials at various points using the red probe. The voltmeter's function switch has two positions marked "+ dc" and "− dc"; these enable either positive or negative potentials to be measured without removing the common probe from ground. Remember that a potential, with respect to ground, must always be indicated as either "+" or "−".

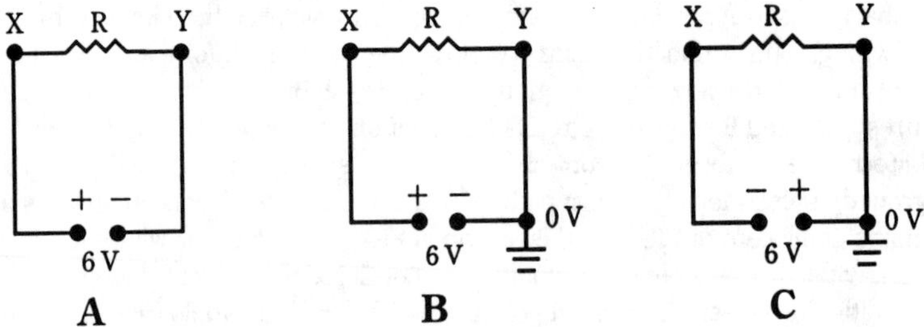

Fig. 1-22 Ground as a voltage reference level.

In any particular circuit, the potentials at the various points depend on which point is grounded. However, the potential differences between any two points must always remain the same.

Both positive and negative potentials are used in the operation of electronic circuits. For example, pnp transistor amplifiers normally need negative potentials and npn amplifiers require positive potentials.

* **Question 1-22** In the circuit of FIG. 1-23, a voltmeter is used to determine the total power that is delivered by the voltage source. One procedure is to measure the voltage between:

A. points W and Z. Then, multiply this reading by 150,000 and divide the product by 2000
B. points Y and Z. Square this voltage, then divide the result by 2000
C. points W and Y. Divide this voltage by 150,000, then multiply the result by the value of the voltage measured between points Y and Z
D. points W and X. Divide this voltage by 150,000, then multiply this result by the voltage measured between points W and Z
E. points W and X. Divide this voltage by 150,000, then multiply the result by the voltage that is measured between points W and Y

Answer Choice D. The power delivered by the source is the product of the source voltage and the source current. Because the ground points must be regarded as joined by a path of zero resistance, the source voltage, (*E*) is the same as the voltage measured between the points W and Z. The source current is:

$$\frac{V_{WX}}{150000} = \frac{V_{YZ}}{2000} = \frac{V_{WZ}}{150000 + 2000} = \frac{V_{WZ}}{152000} \text{ amps (A)}$$

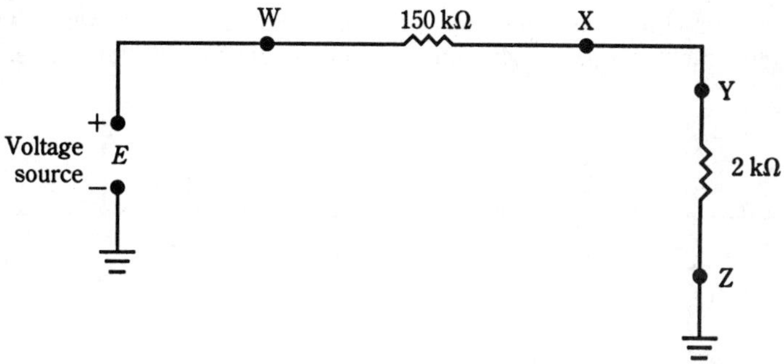

Fig. 1-23 The circuit for question 1-22.

Therefore, the power is: $V_{WZ} \times \frac{V_{WX}}{150000}$ watts (W)

* **Question 1-23** In the circuit of FIG. 1-24A, both indicated voltages are measured, with respect to ground. The value of the potential at the point A, with respect to ground is:

A. + 50 V B. + 35 V C. + 20 V D. − 20 V E. − 15 V

Answer Choice C. Insert the ground points so that the circuit can be redrawn as in FIG. 1-24B. The two voltage sources are in series-aiding so that the total voltage in the circuit is 35 + 15 = 50 V with the electron flow in the CCW direction. This current, I = 50 V/(30 kΩ + 70 kΩ) = 0.5 mA so that the voltage drop across the 70 kΩ resistor is 0.5 mA × 70 kΩ = 35 V with its polarity, as shown. Because this voltage drop and the 15-V source are in series-opposing, the potential at the point A, with respect to ground is + 35 − 15 V = + 20 V.

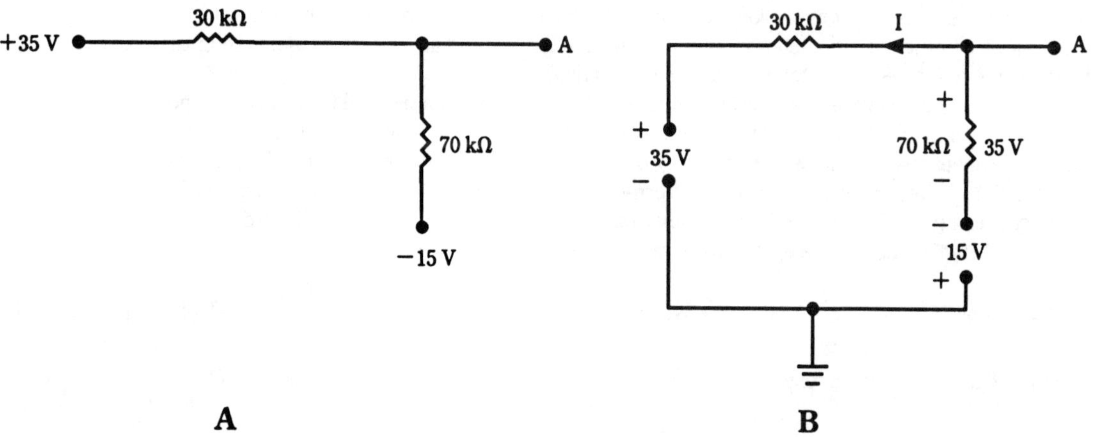

Fig. 1-24 The circuit for question 1-23.

1-9. The potentiometer and the rheostat

The potentiometer ("pot") is another practical application of the voltage-division rule. Essentially, it consists of a length of resistance wire (for example, nichrome wire) or a thin carbon track along which a moving contract or slider can be set at any point (FIG. 1-25A). The wire is wound on an insulating base that can either be straight or, more conveniently, formed into a circle.

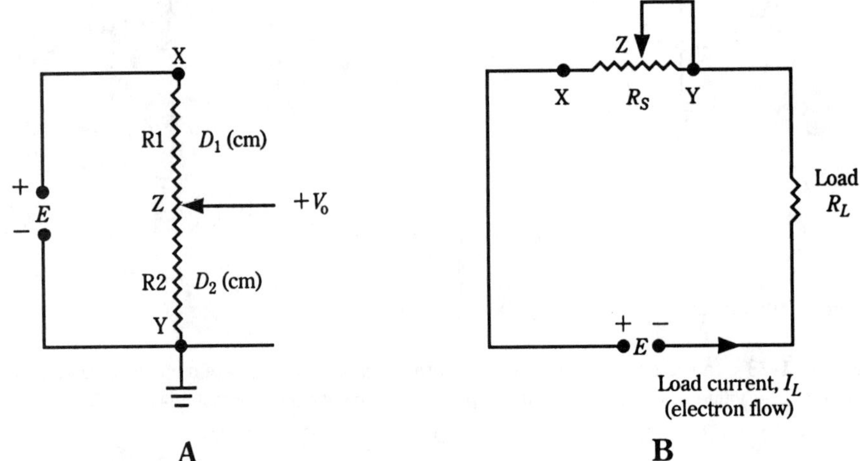

Fig. 1-25 The potentiometer and the rheostat.

The purpose of the potentiometer is to obtain an output voltage, V_o, which can be varied from 0 up to the full value of the source voltage, E. The two terminals, X and Y, are at the ends of the potentiometer, and the slider is connected to the third terminal, Z. The source voltage is then applied between the end terminals, X and Y, while the output voltage appears between the slider terminal, Z, and the end terminal, Y, which is commonly grounded. A practical example of the potentiometer is a receiver's volume control. In this case, the source is an audio signal, but the principles of the potentiometer apply equally well to both dc and ac. In either case, care must be taken not to exceed the potentiometer's power rating.

Although the potentiometer varies an output voltage, the rheostat is used for controlling the current in a series circuit (FIG. 1-25B). The construction of a rheostat is similar to that of a potentiometer, except that the rheostat needs only one end terminal, X, and the terminal, Z, which is connected to the moving contact. The third terminal, Y, is then directly joined to the terminal, Z. A practical example of a rheostat is the dimmer control for the lights on a car's dashboard.

In FIG. 1-25A, the voltage division rule yields:

Output voltage: $$V_o = E \times \frac{R_2}{R_1 + R_2} \text{ volts (V)} \tag{1-36}$$

In FIG. 1-25B, maximum current: $$I_{max} = \frac{E}{R_L} \text{ amperes (A)} \tag{1-37}$$

Minimum current: $$I_{min} = \frac{E}{R_S + R_L} \text{ amperes (A)} \tag{1-38}$$

* **Question 1-24** A variable resistor (such as a rheostat) and a fixed-value resistor are connected in series across a dc voltage source. If the value of the variable resistor is decreased:

A. the amount of power dissipated will decrease
B. the value of the source voltage will increase
C. the value of the current will increase

D. the voltage drop across the fixed value resistor will decrease
E. the voltage drop across the variable resistor will increase

Answer Choice C. Question 1-24 refers to a circuit, such as shown in FIG. 1-25B. If the value of R_S is decreased, then by EQ. 1-38, the current, I, increases.

1-10. Series voltage-dropping resistor

Every load normally has a voltage/current rating, as well as a wattage rating. For example, a 75-W bulb is also rated at 120 V. If the available source voltage is greater than the required load voltage, it is possible to insert a series-dropping resister so that the load is still operated correctly. Figure 1-26 illustrates a load, such as a transistor amplifier, which needs a supply voltage of 9 V with a corresponding current of 8 mA. If the available source voltage is 15 V, the series resistor is inserted to drop the voltage down to the 9 V that is required by the load. The voltage across R_D is therefore 15 V − 9 V = 6 V. This advantage of using a dropping resistor is achieved at the expense of cost and power dissipation.

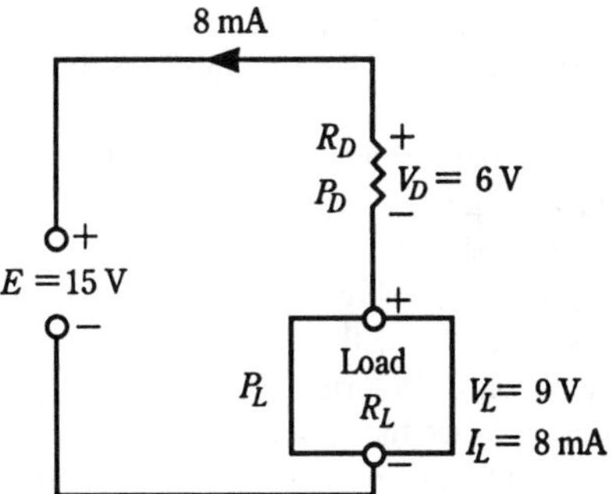

Fig. 1-26 The series voltage-dropping resistor.

Take care to calculate the required ohmic value of the dropping resistor, R_D, as well as its required power dissipation because the resistor will overheat if its power rating is too low.

In FIG. 1-26:

Voltage drop across R_D:
$$V_D = E - V_L = E - I_L R_L \text{ volts (V)} \quad (1\text{-}39)$$

Value of the dropping resistor:
$$R_D = \frac{V_D}{I_L} \text{ ohms } (\Omega) \quad (1\text{-}40)$$

Power dissipated in the dropping resistor:
$$P_D = I_L \times V_D \text{ watts (W)} \quad (1\text{-}41)$$

Question 1-25 A relay coil has a resistance of 600 Ω and operates with a current of 0.1 A. The relay coil is connected in series with a protection (dropping) resistor across a 100 Vdc source. The required resistance for the dropping resistor is:

A. 50 Ω B. 500 Ω C. 5 Ω D. 5 kΩ E. 0.5 Ω

Answer Choice B. The voltage, V_L, across the relay coil is 0.1 A × 600 Ω = 60 V. Voltage drop across the protection resistor is 110 V − 60 V = 50 V. Required resistance = 50 V/0.1 A = 500 Ω.

* **Question 1-26** In QUE. 1-25, the power dissipated in the protection resistor is:

A. 5 W B. 6 W C. 11 W D. 60 W E. 0.6 W

Answer Choice A. Power dissipated, $P_D = I_L V_D = 0.1\text{ A} \times 50\text{ W} = 5\text{ W}$. (1-41)

1-11. Resistors in parallel

All loads (lights, vacuum cleaner, toaster, etc.) in your home are normally stamped with a 120-V rating. It follows that all these loads must be connected directly across the household supply because although each load has its own power rating, its required voltage value in every case is the same. This is a parallel arrangement and is illustrated in FIGS. 1-27A B in which the three resistors are connected between two common points X, Y (FIG. 1-27A) or two common lines (FIG. 1-27B). These points or lines are then directly connected to the voltage source. It follows that the voltage drop across each parallel resistor is the same and is equal to the source voltage. This is in contrast with the series arrangement where voltage division occurred.

Each of the resistors in a parallel circuit is a path for current flow and each path is called a *branch.* Because the voltage across each branch is the same, each branch will carry its own current and the individual branch currents will be different (unless the branch resistances are the same, in which case their currents would also be equal). Notice that the branch currents are independent of one another. In other words, if one branch current is switched off, the other branch currents are unaffected. This would be equivalent to saying that, if you switch off the light in the kitchen, the TV set in the lounge continues to operate.

The total source current, I_T, splits at point X into individual branch currents. The current in a particular branch is inversely proportional to the value of the resistance in that branch. Consequently, the lowest-value resistor will carry the greatest current, while the smallest current will flow through the highest-value resistor. In terms of electron flow, the branch currents (I_1, I_2, I_3) are all leaving the junction point, X, while the total current (I_T) is entering the same junction point. Recombination of the branch currents then occurs at the junction point, Y. It follows that the total current is the *sum* of the individual branch currents; this is an example of *Kirchhoff's Current Law* (KCL).

In FIG. 1-27C, the total equivalent resistance, R_T, is defined as the ratio of the source voltage, E, to the source current, I_T. If an additional branch is added to a parallel arrangement of resistors, the total current must *increase* by the amount of the new branch current; therefore, the total equivalent resistance must *decrease.* For parallel resistors, the value of R_T must always be less than the lowest-value resistor in the arrangement. Figure 1-27D shows the top and bottom views of a pc board with the three resistors mounted in parallel.

Each parallel resistor dissipates its own power and the sum of the individual powers dissipated is equal to the total power delivered from the source. The greatest power is dissipated by the lowest-value resistor, which carries the greatest branch current. For example, the resistance of a nickel-iron 1000-W heater element is only one-tenth that of the tungsten filament for a 100-W electric light bulb.

Source voltage: $E = V_1 = V_2 = V_3$ volts (V) (1-42)

Branch currents

$$I_1 = \frac{V_1}{R_1} = \frac{E}{R_1} \text{ amperes (A)}$$

$$I_2 = \frac{V_2}{R_2} = \frac{E}{R_2} \text{ amperes (A)}$$

$$I_3 = \frac{V_3}{R_3} = \frac{E}{R_3} \text{ amperes (A)} \quad (1\text{-}43)$$

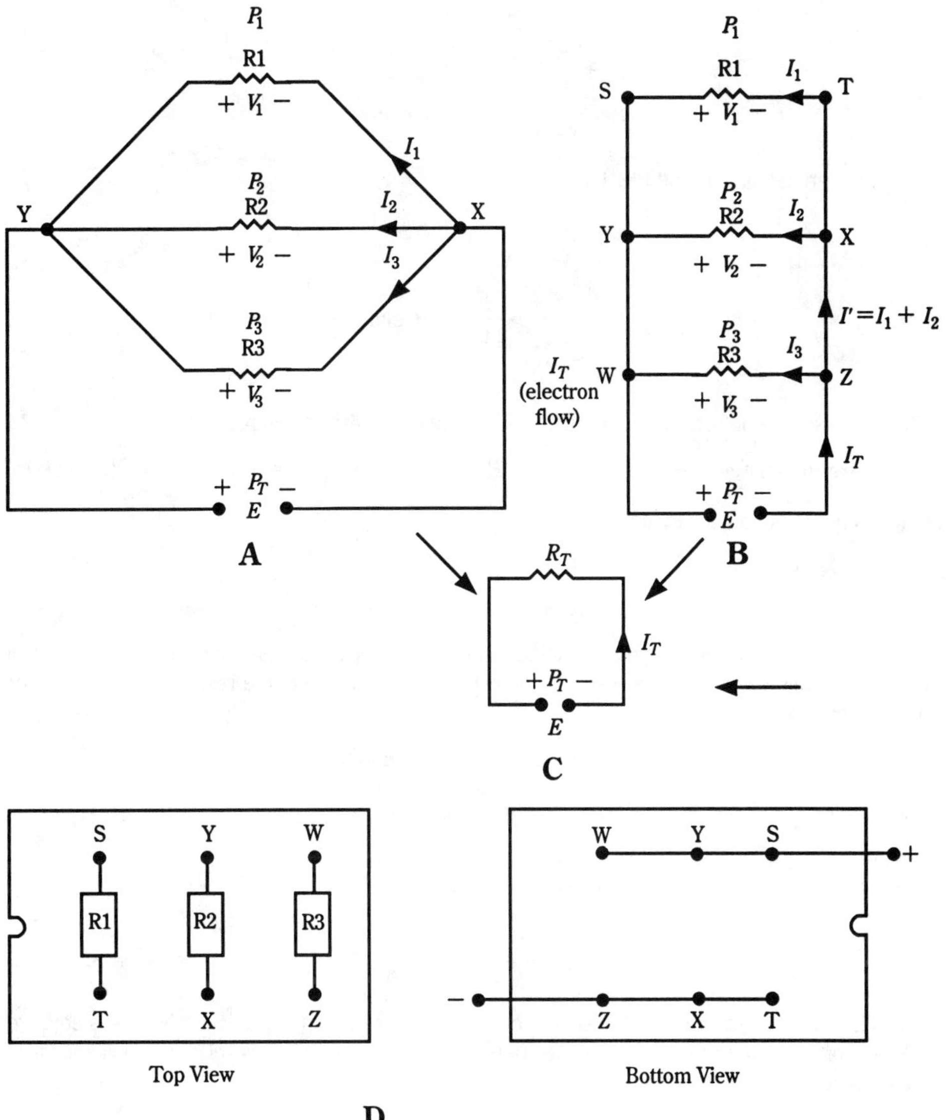

Fig. 1-27 Resistors in parallel.

$$I_3 = \frac{V_3}{R_3} = \frac{E}{R_3} \text{ amperes (A)} \tag{1-43}$$

Total source current:

$$I_T = I_1 + I_2 + I_3$$
$$= \frac{E}{R_1} + \frac{E}{R_2} + \frac{E}{R_3} \tag{1-44}$$

$$= E \times \left(\frac{1}{R_1} + \frac{1}{R_2} + \frac{1}{R_3}\right) \qquad (1\text{-}45)$$

$$= \frac{E}{R_T} = E \times \frac{1}{R_T} \text{ amperes (A)} \qquad (1\text{-}46)$$

Comparing EQ. 1-45 and EQ. 1-46:

$$\frac{1}{R_T} = \frac{1}{R_1} + \frac{1}{R_2} + \frac{1}{R_3}$$

or

$$R_T = \frac{1}{\frac{1}{R_1} + \frac{1}{R_2} + \frac{1}{R_3}} \text{ ohms } (\Omega) \qquad (1\text{-}47)$$

This is the so-called "reciprocal formula," which applies to resistors in parallel.

Power dissipated in the R1 resistor: $P_1 = I_1 \times E = I_1^2 R_1 = E^2/R_1$ watts (W) (1-48)

Similar equations hold for P_2 and P_3:

Total power dissipated: $P_T = P_1 + P_2 + P_3$ (1-49)

$$= I_T \times E = I_T^2 \times R_T = E^2/R_T \text{ watts (W)} \qquad (1\text{-}50)$$

Notice that a certain maximum voltage can safely be applied across a parallel arrangement of resistors. If this voltage is exceeded, the power dissipated in one of the resistors will be greater than its wattage rating.

Because: $I_1 = E/R_1$ and $I_T = E_T/R_T$

The current: $I_1 = I_T \times \frac{R_T}{R_1}$ amperes (A)

Similarly: $I_2 = I_T \times \frac{R_T}{R_2}$ amperes (A)

$$I_3 = I_T \times \frac{R_T}{R_3} \text{ amperes (A)} \qquad (1\text{-}51)$$

Therefore, the fraction of the source current flowing through a particular branch is equal to the ratio of the total equivalent resistance to the branch resistance. This relationship is known as the *current division rule (CDR)*.

For two resistors in parallel: $R_T = \frac{1}{R_1} + \frac{1}{R_2}$ ohms (Ω)

This yields: $R_T = \frac{R_1 R_2}{R_1 + R_2}$ ohms (Ω) (1-52)

Equation 1-52 is referred to as the *product-over-sum* formula.

Then: $I_1 = I_T \times \frac{R_2}{R_1 + R_2}$ amperes (A)

and: $I_2 = I_1 \times \frac{R_1}{R_1 + R_2}$ amperes (A) (1-53)

Voltage sources in parallel

Figure 1-28 illustrates three identical cells, each of EMF E, which are parallel-connected across a resistive load. All positive terminals are joined together so that any one of these terminals can be chosen as the positive output terminal; the negative terminals are likewise connected. If a voltmeter V is connected across any one of the cells, it must also be in parallel with all the other cells, so that the voltmeter reading is only E volts (the EMF of one cell). The purpose of connecting cells in parallel is therefore not to increase the total voltage. However, the current capability has been increased because the load current, I_L, will be shared between the batteries.

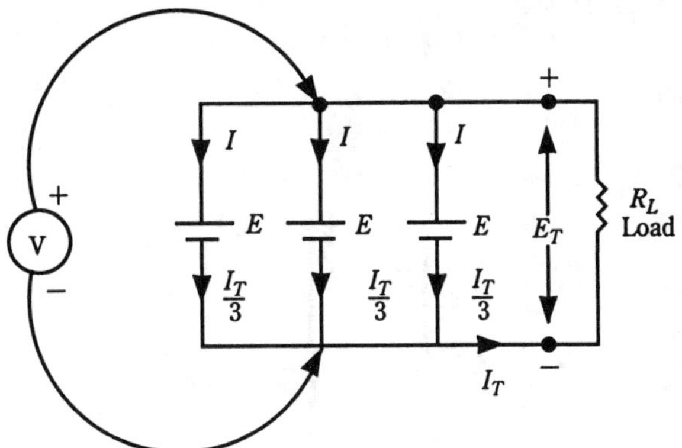

Fig. 1-28 Voltage sources in parallel.

An everyday example of parallel-connected batteries occurs when you give someone a "jump start" for his or her car. You use the cables to join the positive terminals of the two 12-V batteries together and make the same type of connection with the negative terminals. However, with this parallel arrangement, the total voltage available is still only equal to 12 V (the EMF of one battery).

Notice that in the loops containing the cells, the arrangement is series-opposing; there is no loading effect of one cell on another. With identical cells, no parallel-opposing arrangement is possible, with respect to the loads, because the cells would be in series-aiding around the loops. A very high circulating current would flow between the cells but no current would be supplied to the loads.

Total voltage of the parallel combination: $$E_T = E \text{ volts (V)} \qquad (1\text{-}54)$$

Total load current: $$I_L = \frac{E_T}{R_L} = \frac{E}{R_L} \text{ amperes (A)} \qquad (1\text{-}55)$$

Current supplied by each cell: $$\mathrm{I} = \frac{I_L}{3} \text{ amperes (A)} \qquad (1\text{-}56)$$

* **Question 1-27** A 100-Ω 10-W resistor and a 50-Ω 10-W resistor are connected in parallel across a dc source. Without exceeding the wattage rating of either resistor, what is the maximum power that this circuit can safely dissipate?

A. 20 W B. 10 W C. 13.3 W D. 15 W E. 12.5 W

Answer Choice D. The maximum voltage that can be safely applied across the 100-Ω resistor is $\sqrt{100\ \Omega \times 10\ \text{W}} = 31.6$ V. The maximum voltage which can be safely applied across the

50 Ω resistor is $\sqrt{50\ \Omega \times 10\ \text{W}} = 22.36$ V. Consequently the applied voltage must not exceed 22.36 V.

Total resistance: $$R_T = \frac{100 \times 50}{100 + 50} = 33.33\ \Omega \tag{1-52}$$

Maximum power: $$P_{max} = \frac{E^2}{R_T} = \frac{(22.36\ \text{V})^2}{33.33\ \Omega} = 15\ \text{W}$$

* **Question 1-28** In FIG. 1-29, the ratio of the power dissipated in the parallel circuit to the power dissipated in the series circuit is:

A. 2:1 B. 1:2 C. 4:1 D. 1:4 E. 3:1

Answer Choice C.

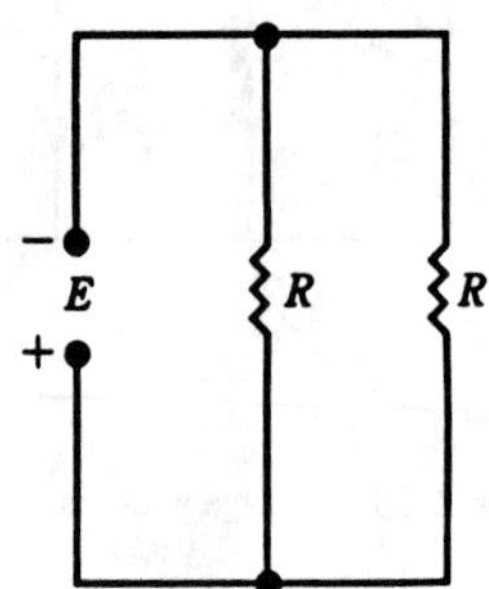

Fig. 1-29 The circuits for question 1-29.

Total resistance of the series circuit: $$R_S = R + R = 2R\,\Omega \tag{1-29}$$

Power dissipated in the series circuit: $$P_S = \frac{E^2}{R_S} = \frac{E^2}{2R}\ \text{W} \tag{1-24}$$

Total resistance of the parallel circuit: $$R_P = \frac{1}{\frac{1}{R} + \frac{1}{R}} = \frac{R}{2}\,\Omega \tag{1-47}$$

Power dissipated in the parallel circuit: $$P_P = \frac{E^2}{R_P} = \frac{E^2}{R/2} = \frac{2E^2}{R}\ \text{W} \tag{1-24}$$

Required ratio: $$\frac{P_P}{P_S} = \frac{2E^2/R}{E^2/2R} = 4{:}1$$

* **Question 1-29** In FIG. 1-30, the ratio of the power dissipated in the parallel circuit to the power dissipated in the series circuit is:

A. 2:1 B. 1:2 C. 4:1 D. 1:4 E. 4.5:1

Answer Choice E.

Total resistance in the series circuit: $R_S = 10 + 5 = 15\ \Omega$ (1-29)

Power dissipated in the series circuit: $P_S = \dfrac{(10\ \text{V})^2}{15\ \Omega} = 6\tfrac{2}{3}\ \text{W}$ (1-24)

Total resistance of the parallel circuit: $R_P = \dfrac{10 \times 5}{10 + 5} = \dfrac{50}{15} = 3\tfrac{1}{3}\ \Omega$ (1-52)

Power dissipated in the parallel circuit: $P_P = \dfrac{(10\ \text{V})^2}{3\tfrac{1}{3}\ \Omega} = 30\ \text{W}$ (1-24)

Required ratio: $\dfrac{P_P}{P_S} = \dfrac{30}{6\tfrac{2}{3}} = 4.5{:}1$

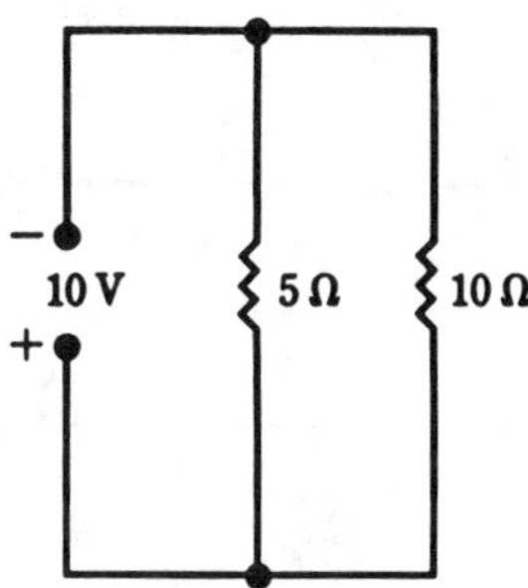

Fig. 1-30 The circuits for question 1-30.

* **Question 1-30** A 100-Ω 10-W resistor and a 10-Ω 10-W resistor are connected in parallel. If the wattage rating of either resistor is not to be exceeded, the maximum power dissipated in the circuit is:

A. 10 W B. 20 W C. 15 W D. 5 W E. 11 W

Answer Choice E. The maximum voltage that can be safely applied across a 100-Ω resistor is: $\sqrt{10\ \text{W} \times 100\ \Omega} = 31.6$ V. The maximum voltage that can be safely applied across the 10-Ω resistor is $\sqrt{10\ \text{W} \times 10\ \Omega} = 10$ V. Consequently, the applied voltage must not exceed 10 V. Power dissipated in the 100-Ω resistor equals $(10\ \text{V})^2/100\ \Omega = 1$ W; power dissipated in the 10-Ω resistor equals $(10\ \text{V})^2/10\ \Omega = 10$ W. Total maximum power dissipated is $1 + 10 = 11$ W.

1-12. Open and short circuits

The open circuit

An *open circuit* is regarded as a break that occurs in a circuit. For example, a resistor might burn out (FIG. 1-31A) as a result of excessive power dissipation or become disconnected from an adjacent resistor. In either case, the break would have theoretically infinite resistance so that no current can exist in an open circuit.

In the series string of FIG. 1-31A, resistor R2 has burned out so that the total equivalent resistance is theoretically infinite. There is zero current through the circuit and no voltage drops across resistors R1 and R3. Consequently, the source voltage appears across the open circuit and could be measured by a voltmeter connected between the points D and E.

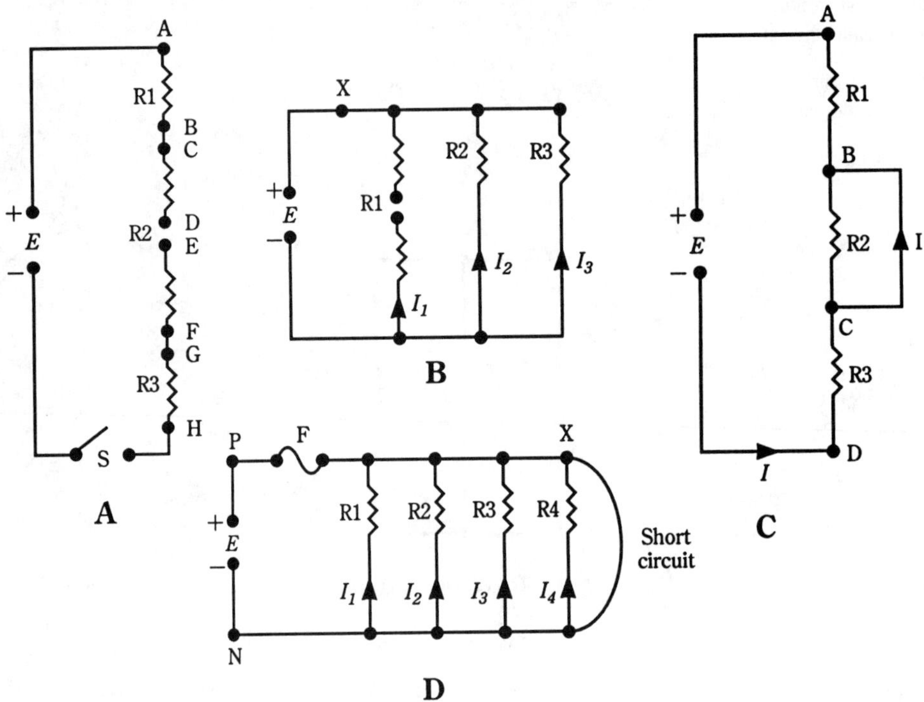

Fig. 1-31 Open and short circuits.

To locate the position of the break, the switch, S, is opened to remove power from the circuit. Using an ohmmeter on a high resistance range, the common probe is connected to the point H. With the red probe at point A, the ohmmeter reading is virtually infinite because the measured resistance contains the open circuit. The reading will not change when the red probe is moved in turn to points B, C, and D. However, as soon as the red probe is moved to the point E, the resistance falls to the relatively low value of R3. This change in the reading indicates that the open circuit exists between the points D and E. The ohmmeter has been used to conduct a *continuity test,* which has located a *discontinuity,* the open circuit.

If resistor R1 burns out in the parallel circuit of FIG. 1-31B, current I_1 is zero, but currents I_2 and I_3 remain the same. Total current I_T is reduced and the total equivalent resistance is greater. However, if a break occurs at point X, all current ceases and the total equivalent resistance is theoretically infinite.

The short circuit

A *short circuit* has theoretically zero resistance so that a current can flow through a short circuit without developing any voltage drop. Although resistors rarely short, a short circuit can occur as a result of the bare connecting wires contacting or being joined together by a stray drop of solder. The short circuit is therefore a zero-resistance path in parallel with (shunting across) the resistor.

An example of a short circuit is shown in the series circuit of FIG. 1-31C. No current will flow through resistor R2 and there will be no voltage drop between points B and C. The total equivalent resistance is given by: $R_T = R_1 + R_3$ and current, I, will increase as a result of the short circuit.

In the parallel circuit of FIG. 1-31D, a short circuit has developed across resistor R4. The same short circuit also exists in parallel with resistors R_1, R_2, R_3 so that currents I_1, I_2, I_3, I_4 are all zero. However, path NYXP has an extremely low resistance so that a high current would flow and the protection fuse, F, would melt. This would prevent possible damage to the connecting wires and the source.

Question 1-31 Which of the following meters is most frequently used to determine the presence of an open circuit or a short circuit?

A. ohmmeter B. voltmeter C. ammeter D. wattmeter E. electrometer

Answer Choice A. Ohmmeter.

1-13. Series-parallel networks of resistors

Briefly summarizing the series and parallel resistor sections, the single current was the same throughout the series circuit and the source voltage was divided among the resistors in proportion to their resistances. By contrast, the (same) source voltage was applied across each resistor in parallel and the (total) source current was divided between the various branches in inverse proportion to their resistances. However, series strings and parallel banks can be combined to create so-called *series-parallel circuits* of which the two simplest are shown in FIGS. 1-13A and B.

In FIG. 1-32A, resistors R2 and R3 are joined end-to-end so that the same current must flow through each of these resistors. Consequently, resistors R2 and R3 are in series. However, the (electron flow) current splits at point Y and combines at point X. Therefore, R1 is in parallel with the series combination of R2 and R3. The corresponding PC board is shown in FIG. 1-32C.

The (electron flow) current splits at point E, in FIG. 1-32B and recombines at point, F, so that R2 and R3 are in parallel. However, this parallel combination is joined to one end of R1 so that this resistor is in series with $R_{2,3}$ ($R_{2,3}$ is the equivalent resistance of the R2, R3 parallel combination; this combination can also be abbreviated to R2//R3). The corresponding PC board is shown in FIG. 1-32D.

It is important to realize that there is an infinite variety of complex series-parallel resistor networks. For example, you might be faced with the circuit of FIG. 1-33A and be asked to find the total equivalent resistance that is presented to the source. This problem is solved in a number of steps.

Step 1 Identify all points that are electrically different in the circuit. These points are P,N,X,Y, and Z. The circuit can then be redrawn in the more conventional manner of FIG. 1-33B.

Corresponding points are labeled in the two drawings and you must make certain that the same resistors are connected between any two such points.

Step 2 Combine all obvious series strings and parallel banks. Redraw the resulting simplified circuit. The general practice is to start furthest away from the source and then work your way toward the source.

In the example, R4 and R5 are in parallel and their equivalent resistance:

$$R_{4,5} = \frac{R_4 \times R_5}{R_4 + R_5} = \frac{4.7 \times 2.7}{4.7 + 2.7}$$

$$= 1.715 \text{ k}\Omega$$

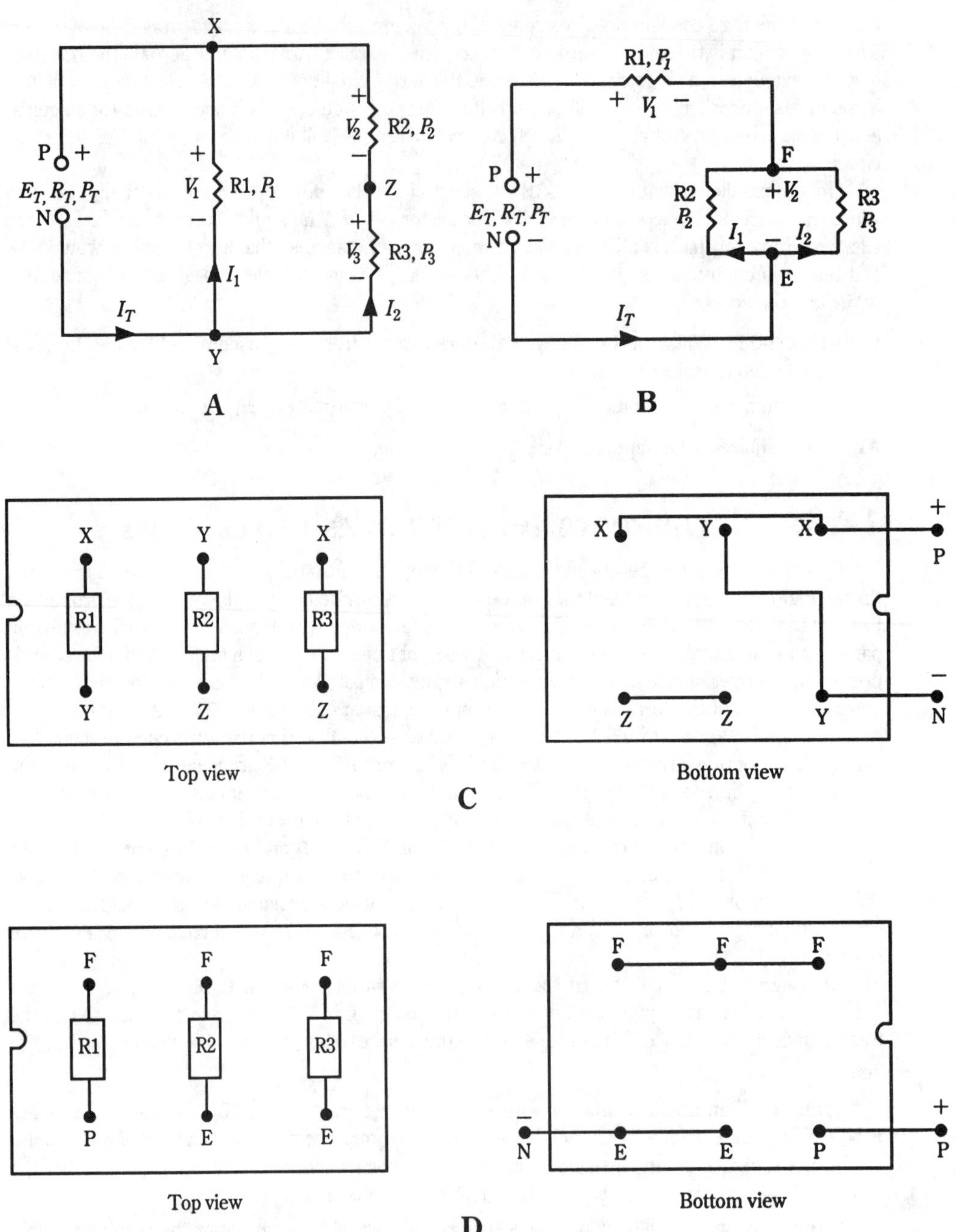

Fig. 1-32 Series—parallel arrangements of resistors.

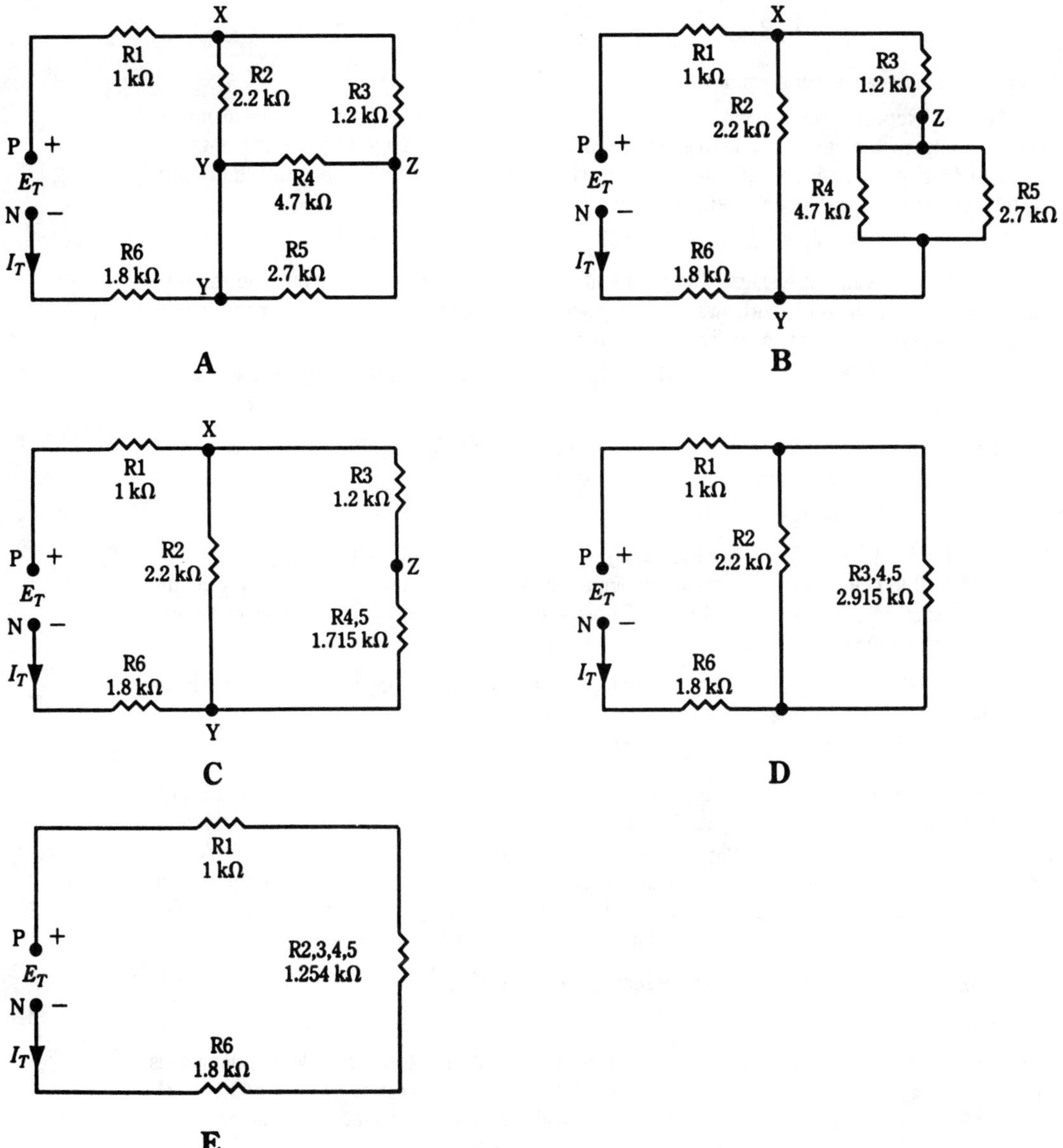

Fig. 1-33 Analysis of a series-parallel circuit.

The circuit can then be redrawn as shown in FIG. 1-33C.

Step 3 Add the series equivalent resistances and again draw the circuit. In FIG. 1-33C, R_3 is in series with $R_{4,5}$ so that the equivalent resistance of the combination is $R_{3,4,5} = 1.2 + 1.715 = 2.915$ kΩ. The circuit, redrawn, is shown in FIG. 1-33D.

Step 4 Use the product-over-sum or reciprocal formula to combine the equivalent parallel resistances. In the example, R_2 is in parallel with $R_{3,4,5}$ and the equivalent resistance of this combination is:

$$R_{2,3,4,5} = \frac{2.915 \times 2.2}{2.915 + 2.2} = 1.254 \text{ k}\Omega$$

When the circuit is again redrawn, its appearance is as in FIG. 1-33E.

Step 5 Repeat steps 3 and 4 alternatively and redraw the circuit as many times as necessary (with experience, it is possible to eliminate most, if not all, of the intermediate drawings).

The redrawn circuit of FIG. 1-33E is clearly a simple series arrangement; therefore, the total equivalent resistance presented to the source is:

$$R_T = R_1 + R_{2,3,4,5} + R_6 = 1 + 1.254 + 1.8 = 4.054 \text{ k}\Omega$$

Step 6 Knowing the value of the total equivalent resistance you can determine the total source current, I_T, and then work away from the source and calculate in turn the branch currents and the voltage drops across the individual resistors.

Step 7 Calculate the powers dissipated in the individual resistors and the total power drawn from the source.

* **Question 1-32** Figure 1-34A represents the top and bottom views of a PC board. Which of the schematics in FIG. 1-34B best corresponds to the circuit shown?

A. (a) B. (b) C. (c) D. (d) E. (e)

Answer Choice D. Identify all corresponding electrical points and label the different points as A, B, C. The 10-kΩ and 5-kΩ resistors are mounted in parallel between points A and B while the two 1-kΩ resistors are in series (A to C to B) between the same two points. These conditions are illustrated in the schematic (D).

* **Question 1-33** In the circuit of FIG. 1-35, determine the reading of the voltmeter, *V*, which has a very high value of resistance.

A. 90 V B. 100 V C. 80 V D. 10 V E. 0 V

Answer Choice E. Using Kirchhoff's Current Law at junction Z, the current flowing through the 9-Ω resistor is $12.5 - 2.5 = 10$ A. The voltage drop across the 9-Ω resistor is $10 \text{ A} \times 9\ \Omega = 90$ V. Therefore, the voltage at the point X, with respect to point Z, is $V_{XZ} = 90$ V.

The voltage drop across the 4-Ω resistor is $2.5 \text{ A} \times 4\ \Omega = 10$ V. It follows that the voltage at point Y, with respect to point Z, is $100 - 10 = 90$ V. Because points X and Y have the same voltage difference (90 V), with respect to point Z, the reading of *V* is $90 - 90 = 0$ V.

* **Question 1-34** In FIG. 1-36, what is the reading of meter *M*?

A. 5 A B. 4 A C. 3 A D. 2 A E. 1 A

Answer Choice D. Resistors R_2 and R_3 are in series so that their total equivalent resistance is $28 + 26 = 54\ \Omega$. Resistors R_5 and R_6 are in parallel and therefore $R_5//R_6 = 12 \times 24/(12 + 24) = 8\ \Omega$. R_4 is in series with $R_5//R_6$ and the total resistance of this branch is $10 + 8 = 18\ \Omega$. The equivalent resistance of $R_{2,3,4,5,6} = 18 \times 54/(18 + 54) = 13.5\ \Omega$. Resistance presented to the source: $R_T = 13.5 + 12 + 10 = 35.5\ \Omega$. Total current: $I_T = 142 \text{ V}/35.5\ \Omega = 4$ A. By the current division rule (CDR), $I_1 = 4 \text{ A} \times 54\ \Omega/(18\ \Omega + 54\ \Omega) = 3$ A. Repeating the current division rule, $I_3 = 3 \text{ A} \times 24\ \Omega/(12\ \Omega + 24\ \Omega) = 2$ A. Therefore, the reading of *M3* is 2 A.

1-14. The Wheatstone bridge circuit

The Wheatstone bridge circuit is used to obtain an accurate measurement of an unknown resistance, R_x. *Conventionally, the bridge circuit consists of four resistor arms R1, R2, R3, and* R_x (FIG. 1-37A) with a center link ("bridge") that contains a sensitive current-indicating device or

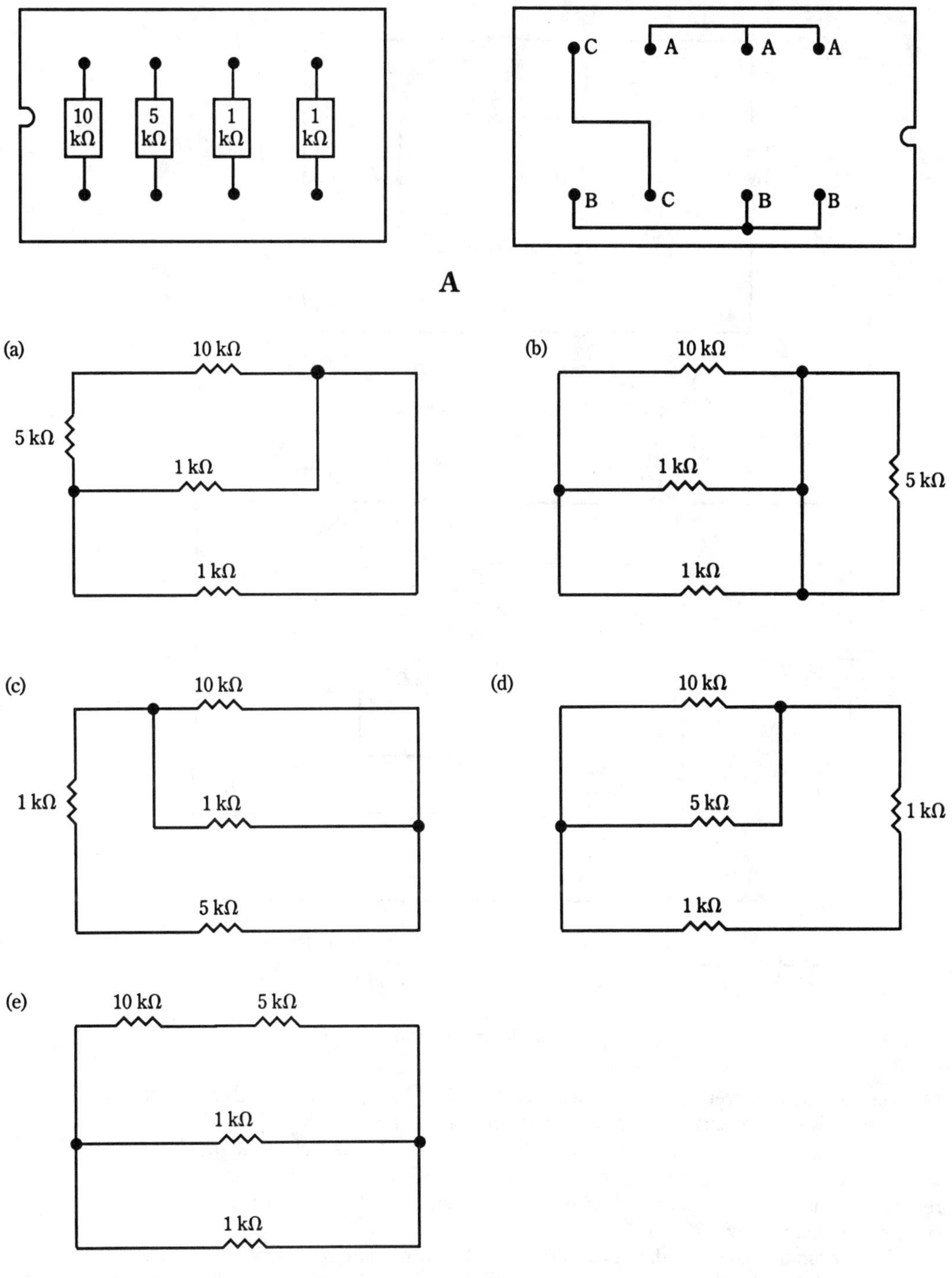

Fig. 1-34 The circuit for question 1-32.

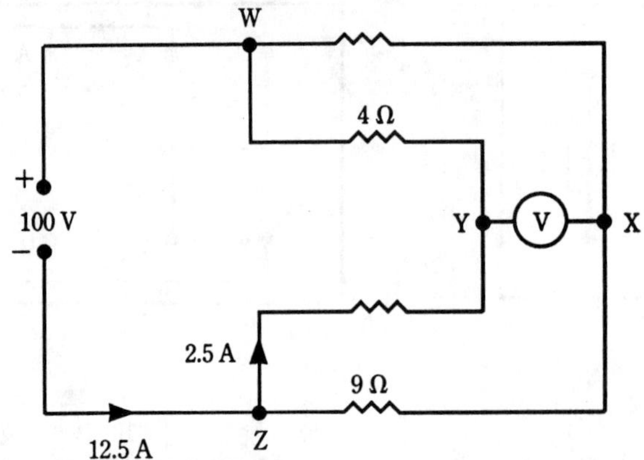

Fig. 1-35 The circuit for question 1-33.

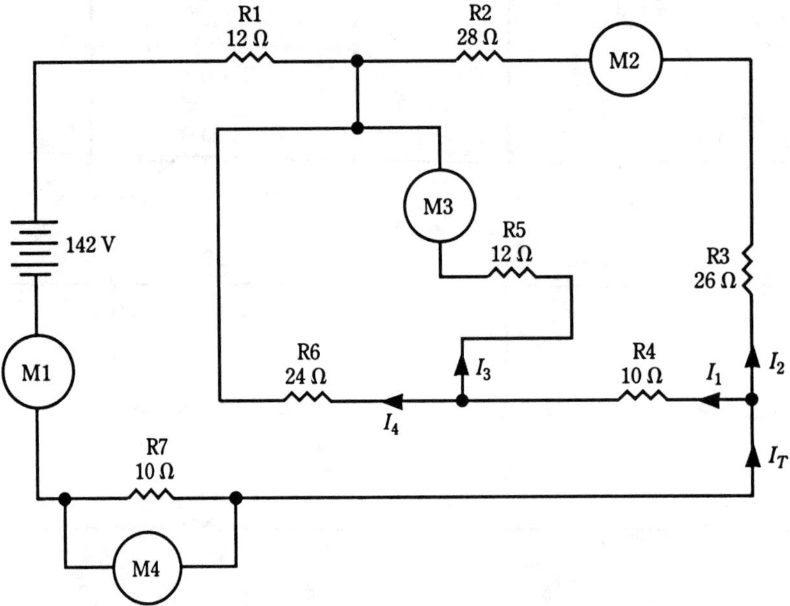

Fig. 1-36 The circuit for question 1-34.

galvanometer, *G*. However, the circuit can be redrawn (FIG. 1-37B) and you can then see that the bridge circuit is really an example of a series-parallel resistor arrangement.

The whole of the source voltage must be dropped across R1/R2, and also R3/R_x. However, unless there is a special relationship between the four resistance values, the current through resistor R1 will not be equal to the current through resistor R2 and the same applies to the currents through resistors R3 and R_x.

As an example, consider the circuit of FIG. 1-37B. If the low resistance of the sensitive galvanometer is neglected, resistor R1 is in parallel with resistor R_x, and resistor R3 is in parallel with resistor R2. The two parallel combinations are then in series. The total equivalent resistance presented to the source is 1 kΩ // 1 kΩ + 8 kΩ // 10 kΩ = 500 Ω + 4444 Ω = 4944 Ω. The

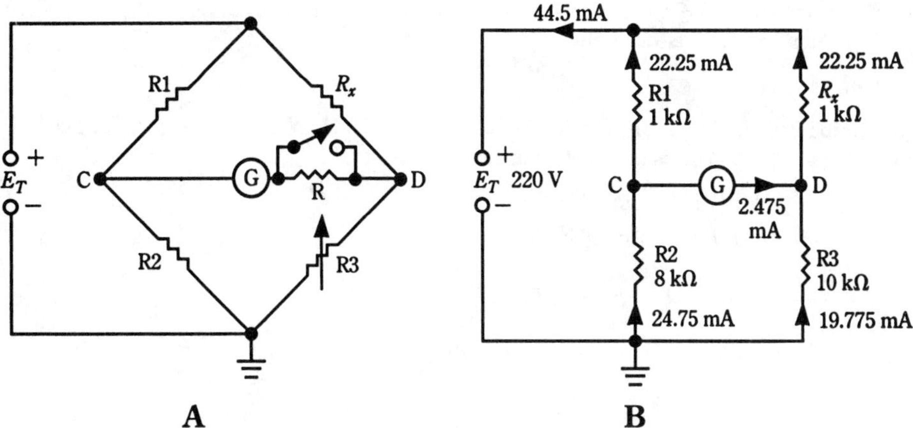

Fig. 1-37 The Wheatstone bridge circuit.

total current: I_T = 220 V/4944 Ω = 44.5 mA, which divides equally between the two 1-k Ω resistors. The voltage drop across each of these resistors is 44.5/2 mA × 1 kΩ = 22.25 V. The voltage drop across each of the 8-kΩ and 10-kΩ resistors is 220 V-22.25 V = 197.75 V. Consequently, the current in the 8-kΩ resistor is 197.75 V/8 kΩ = 24.72 mA, and the 10-kΩ resistor carries a current of 197.75 V/10 kΩ = 19.775 mA. The current in the link is then 22.25 − 19.775 (or 24.72 − 22.25) = 2.475 mA, with the electron flow in the direction from left to right (FIG. 1-37B). However, if the 8-kΩ resistor was replaced by a 10-kΩ resistor, the currents in the four resistors would be all the same and the current in the link (as recorded by the galvanometer) would be zero. Under such conditions, the bridge is said to be *balanced* though the situation in which $R_1 = R_x$ and $R_2 = R_3$ is a special case and is not the general condition for a balance to occur.

There will be no voltage difference between points C and D if the ratios R_1:R_2 and R_x:R_3 are equal. The reading of the galvanometer is zero and the bridge is balanced. The value of the unknown resistor, R_x, is then equal to $R_3 \times R_1/R_2$. Notice that in this condition, the products (R_2R_x and R_1R_3), of the opposing resistors are equal in the conventional bridge circuit of FIG. 1-37A.

To measure the value of R_x, R_3 is an accurately calibrated variable resistor, which is used to balance the bridge. A protection resistor, R, is commonly included to prevent the galvanometer from being subjected to excessive current. With R included, a rough balance is first obtained. Afterwards, the resistor is shorted out by the switch and R_3 is finally adjusted for an accurate balance.

Normally, the high-quality fixed resistors, R1 and R2, have possible values of 1 Ω, 10 Ω, 100 Ω, or 1000 Ω. By using switches to change the values of the resistors, the ratio R_1:R_2 can be set for 1000 Ω, 100 Ω, 10 Ω, 1 Ω, 0.1 Ω, and 0.001 Ω. The measured reading of R_x can therefore range from 1/1000 of the lowest value of R3 to 1000 times the highest value of R3. Consequently, the Wheatstone bridge is capable of providing accurate measurements over a wide range of resistance values.

The bridge is balanced when:

$$R_x \times R_2 = R_3 \times R_1 \qquad (1\text{-}57)$$

or:

$$R_x = R_3 \times \frac{R_1}{R_2} \text{ ohms } (\Omega) \qquad (1\text{-}58)$$

Question 1-35 Accurate measurements of resistance can be obtained by using a(n):

A. ohmmeter B. voltmeter C. ammeter D. combination of a voltmeter and an ammeter E. Wheatstone bridge

Answer Choice E.

Question 1-36 In FIG. 1-37A, $R_1 = 10\ \Omega$ and $R_2 = 1000\ \Omega$. When the bridge is balanced, R_3 is adjusted to $5.7\ \Omega$. What is the value of unknown resistor, R_x?

A. 5.7 Ω B. 5700 Ω C. 570 Ω D. 0.057 Ω E. 0.57 Ω

Answer Choice D. For a balanced bridge:

$$R_x = R_3 \times \frac{R_1}{R_2} \tag{1-58}$$

$$= 5.7 \times \frac{10}{1000} = 0.057\ \Omega$$

1-15. Internal resistance, voltage regulation, and maximum power transfer

The sources that were covered in previous sections, were in a certain sense, idealized because it was assumed that the source voltage remained constant and independent of the load current FIG. 1-38). This is not true in practice, as you know from the illustration with the car battery. When a large current is drawn from such a battery, the terminal voltage falls, with a "bad" battery, the terminal voltage is so low that the car will not start. The explanation for this effect lies within the voltage source itself and is caused by its internal resistance.

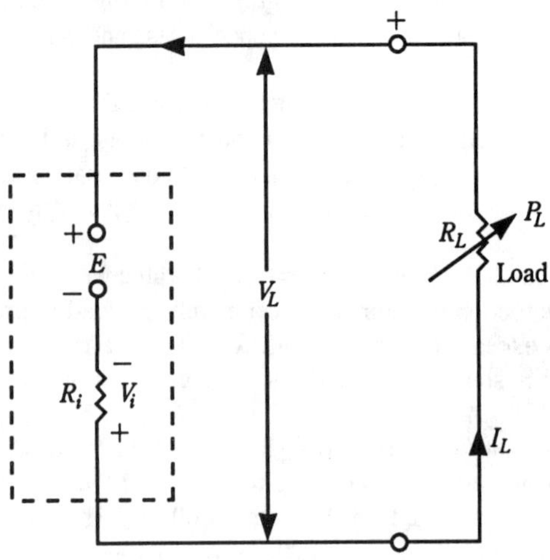

Fig. 1-38 The practical constant voltage source.

All sources possess internal resistance to some extent. For example, a primary (nonrechargeable) 1.5-V "D" cell has an internal resistance of the order of 1 Ω. This value of resistance depends on the size of the electrodes, their separation, and the nature of the electrolyte. By contrast, the basic lead-acid secondary (rechargeable) cell with an operating voltage slightly more than 2 V has a negative electrode of sponge lead, a positive electrode of lead peroxide, and an electrolyte of dilute sulfuric acid. During the cell's discharge, both the sponge lead and the lead peroxide are converted to lead sulphate while the specific gravity of the electrolyte falls; these conditions are reversed when the cell is recharged. If it is required to store the lead-acid battery for an appreciable time, the electrolyte is drained out and replaced by distilled water; this will prevent the lead sulphate from hardening on the electrodes. The large size of the electrodes results in a very low internal resistance, which is typically less than 10 mΩ. This is the major difference between a 12-V car battery and a 12-V cell for operating a transistor radio. The cell for the transistor radio has a much higher internal resistance and is therefore quite incapable of starting a car (whose initial current requirement is about 100 A or more!).

The capacity of a lead-acid battery is measured in ampere-hours (1 A.h = 3600 C). The product of the discharge current and the rating in hours over which the discharge occurs, is equal to the value of the capacity. For example, a battery with a capacity of 200 A.h and an 8-h rating permits a discharge current of 200 A.h/8 h = 25 A.

Another secondary cell is the nickel-cadmium type, which has a cadmium anode, a nickel hydroxide cathode, and a potassium hydroxide electrolyte. Such a cell has an operating voltage of approximately 1.25 V, which is accompanied by a very low internal resistance.

When a load current is drawn from a voltage source, the terminal voltage, V_L, falls as the load current, I_L, is increased. A model that explains this effect, is illustrated in FIG. 1-39. This model assumes that the source contains a constant voltage (EMF or E) that is in series with the internal resistance, R_i. Then, as the load resistance, R_L, is decreased, the load current, I_L, will rise. This will cause an increase in the voltage drop, V_i, across the internal resistance, R_i, and the terminal voltage, V_L, will drop.

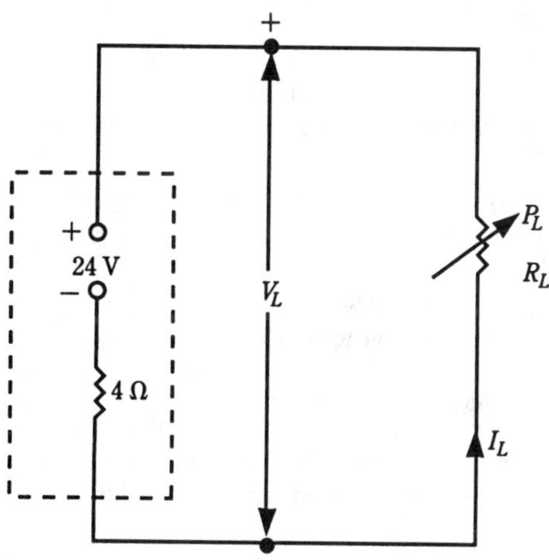

Fig. 1-39 A circuit to illustrate maximum power transfer.

Having established the model, you must have some means to find the values of E and R_i for any electrical source. The value of E is best measured by disconnecting the load, R_L, and then placing a voltmeter across the terminals. Assuming that the voltmeter draws virtually no current from the source, the voltage drop across the internal resistance is negligible. The voltmeter reading will then be equal to the value of E, which is often referred to as the *open-circuit* or *no-load terminal voltage.*

Having determined the value of E, then connect an ammeter of negligible resistance between the terminals so that only the internal resistance will now limit the current. The value of this current is therefore E/R_i amperes and because there is practically zero resistance between the terminals, this level is normally referred to as the *short-circuit terminal* current. The internal resistance can then be calculated from the ratio of the open-circuit terminal voltage to the short-circuit terminal current.

It might not be practical to measure the short-circuit current because such a large current might possibly damage the electrical source. A superior method of finding the internal resistance is to vary the value of the load resistance until the terminal load voltage, V_L, is equal to $E/2$. V_i will also be $E/2$ and the measured value of R_L will then equal the internal resistance, R_i.

The degree to which the load voltage, V_L, varies with changes in the load current is measured by the percentage voltage regulation. Ideal regulation means that the load voltage remains constant and independent of any changes in the load.

In FIG. 1-39:

$$\text{Open circuit or no load terminal voltage} = E \text{ volts (V)} \qquad (1\text{-}59)$$

Load current:

$$I_L = \frac{V_L}{R_L} = \frac{V_i}{R_i} = \frac{E}{R_L + R_i} \text{ amperes (A)} \qquad (1\text{-}60)$$

Terminal load voltage:

$$\begin{aligned} V_L &= I_L R_L \\ &= E - I_L R_i \\ &= E - \frac{ER_i}{R_i + R_L} \qquad (1\text{-}61) \\ &= E \times \frac{R_L}{R_i + R_L} \text{ volts (V)} \end{aligned}$$

Equation (1-61) is an example of the voltage division rule (VDR) because the source voltage, E, is divided between the load resistance, R_L, and the internal resistance, R_i. To obtain a high voltage across the load, R_L must be typically at least 5 to 10 times the value of R_L.

$$\text{Short-circuit terminal current} = \frac{E}{R_i} \text{ amperes (A)} \qquad (1\text{-}62)$$

Internal resistance:

$$R_i = \frac{\text{Open-circuit terminal voltage, } E}{\text{Short-circuit terminal current, } E/R_i} \text{ ohms } (\Omega) \qquad (1\text{-}63)$$

$$\text{Percentage voltage regulation} = \frac{V_{NL} - V_{FL}}{V_{FL}} \times 100\% \qquad (1\text{-}64)$$

where: V_{NL} = terminal voltage under no-load or minimum-load conditions.
V_{FL} = terminal voltage under full-load (current) conditions when the load resistance is R_{FL}.

For an ideal source, $V_{FL} = E$ and the percentage regulation is zero. If the no-load voltage is E volts:

$$\text{Percentage regulation} = \frac{R_i}{R_{FL}} \times 100\% \qquad (1\text{-}65)$$

Maximum power transfer and percentage efficiency

So far, you have explored the condition for a high voltage across the load. The load resistance, R_L, should be many times greater than the internal resistance, R_i; when the constant EMF, E, was divided between these two resistances, very little voltage was dropped across R_i and most appeared across the load.

Because there is both a load voltage, V_L, and a load current, I_L, it follows that a power, P_L, is developed in the load (FIG. 1-39). However, the condition for maximum power in the load cannot be the same as the condition for a high load voltage because for open- and short-circuit loads, the load power in both cases is zero. Consequently, the maximum load power must occur between these two extremes and this is well illustrated in the circuit of FIG. 1-40. Here, particular load resistances, R_L, are chosen and they calculate the corresponding values of I_L, V_L, and P_L. The results are shown in TABLE 1-6.

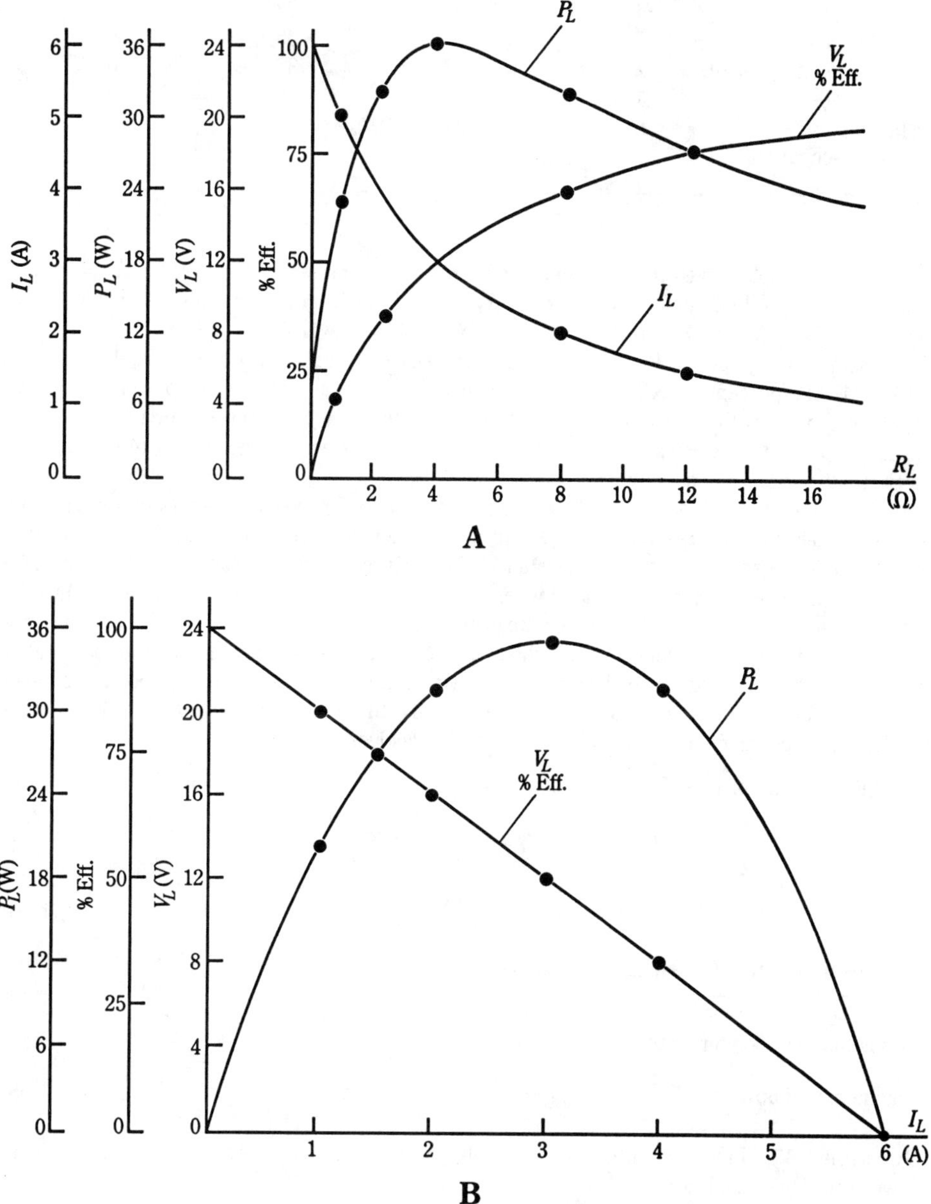

Fig. 1-40 Graphs of V_L, P_L, percentage efficiency versus R_L and I_L.

Table 1-6. Load resistance R_L vs. I_L, V_L, and P_L.

Load resistance (Ω) R_L	Load current (A) $I_L = E/(R_I + R_L)$	Load voltage (V) $V_L = I_L \times R_L$	Load power (W) $P_L = I_L \times V_L$	% Efficiency $P_L/P_T \times 100\%$
Zero (short-circuit)	6	0	0	0
2	4	8	32	33⅓
4	3	12	36	50
8	2	16	32	66⅔
20	1	20	20	83⅓
Infinite (open-circuit)	0	24	0	100

As an example, adjust the value of R_L to be 8 Ω. The total resistance is: $R_1 + R_L = 4\ \Omega + 8\ \Omega = 12\ \Omega$. The load current is: $E/(R_1 + R_L) = 24\ \text{V}/12\ \Omega = 2\ \text{A}$ and the load voltage is: $V_L = I_L \times R_L = 2\ \text{A} \times 8\ \Omega = 16\ \text{V}$. The corresponding load power is: $P_L = I_L \times V_L = 2\ \text{A} \times 16\ \text{V} = 32\ \text{W}$. The graphs of V_L, I_L, P_L, percentage efficiency versus R_L and I_L are illustrated in FIG. 1-41. The percentage efficiency is determined from the ratio of the *load* power to the *total* power drawn from the constant voltage EMF. When there is maximum power transfer to the load, the percentage efficiency is only 50% and it might therefore be necessary to compromise between the values of load power and percentage efficiency.

From the graph of P_L versus R_L, it is clear that the load power reaches its maximum value of 36 W when the load resistance is 4 Ω. It is no numerical coincidence that this value of load resistance is the same as the initial resistance of the source. In fact, it can be proven that there is maximum power transfer to the load when the load resistance is *matched* (made equal) to the internal resistance. This result is of more than academic significance. In the case of a radio transmitter, the antenna represents a load whose ohmic value must be matched to the load that is required by the final stage of the transmitter; only then can RF (radio frequency) power be effectively transferred from the transmitter to the antenna. In another example, the load of a loudspeaker must be matched to the load required by its receiver's output audio stage.

In the circuit of 1-39, Load power:

$$P_L = I_L \times V_L = \frac{E}{R_i + R_L} \times \frac{ER_L}{R_i + R_L}$$

$$= \frac{E^2 R_L}{(R_i + R_L)^2} \text{ watts (W)} \qquad (1\text{-}66)$$

It can be proved that P_L reaches its maximum value when:

$$R_i = R_L \qquad (1\text{-}67)$$

This is the condition for matching.

Maximum load power:

$$P_{L\max} = \frac{E^2}{4R_i} = \frac{E^2}{4R_L} \text{ watts} \qquad (1\text{-}68)$$

* **Question 1-37** In the circuit of FIG. 1-41, what is the value of R_L, which will allow maximum power transfer to the load?

A. 10 Ω B. 20 Ω C. 30 Ω D. 15 Ω E. 150 Ω

Answer Choice C. For maximum power transfer, the value of R_L must be matched (made equal) to the sum of all the resistance that is not associated with the load. Therefore, the required value of R_L is $10 + 20 = 30\ \Omega$. (This result is also true for an ac circuit, provided that the circuit contains resistance only.)

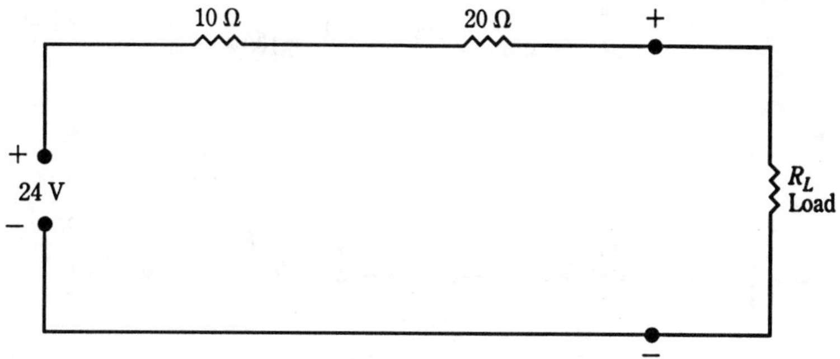

Fig. 1.41 The circuit for question 1-37.

Question 1-38 A 12.6-V 55-A.h battery continuously supplies 325 W to a transmitter and 50 W to a receiver. For how many hours can the battery supply full power to both the transmitter and the receiver?

A. 1.8 B. 375 C. 29.76 D. 55 E. 12.6

Answer Choice A.

Total power:

$$P_T = 325 + 50 = 375 \text{ W}$$

Total current:

$$I_T = \frac{375 \text{ W}}{12.6 \text{ V}} = 29.76 \text{ A}$$

Period of time:

$$t = \frac{55 \text{ A.h}}{29.76 \text{ A}} = 1.8 \text{ h}$$

Question 1-39 Two 3-W 6-V lamps are connected in parallel with a 6-V battery that has an internal resistance of 1.2 Ω. The amount of current drawn from the battery is:

A. 1 A B. 0.5 A C. 0.83 A D. 2 A E. 0.67 A

Answer Choice C.

Resistance of each lamp:

$$R = \frac{(6 \text{ V})^2}{3 \text{ W}} = 12\ \Omega$$

Total load:

$$R_L = \frac{12\ \Omega}{2} = 6\ \Omega$$

Current:

$$I_L = \frac{6 \text{ V}}{6\ \Omega + 1.2\ \Omega} = \frac{6}{7.2} = 0.83 \text{ A}$$

* **Question 1-40** A voltage source has a no-load terminal PD of 660 V and a full-load terminal PD of 600 V. The value of the percentage regulation is:

A. 9% B. 10% C. 11% D. 12% E. 15%

Answer Choice B.

$$\text{Percentage regulation} = \frac{660 - 600}{600} \times 100\% = 10\% \qquad (1\text{–}64)$$

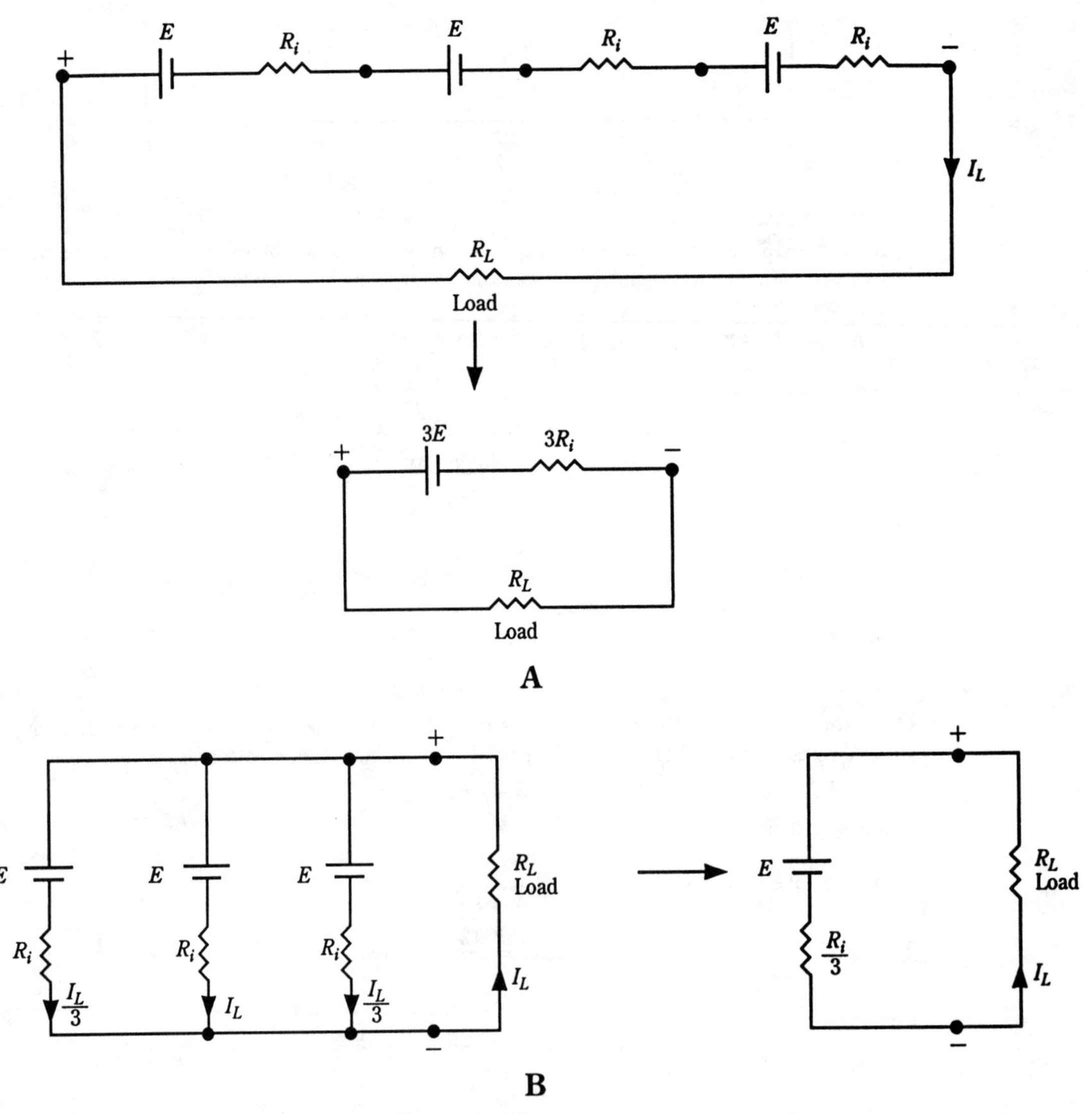

Fig. 1-42 Practical cells in series and parallel.

1-16. Practical sources in series and parallel

When the cells (in the section "Resistors in series and voltage sources in series") were connected in series-aiding, the total EMF available was the sum of the individual EMFs. However, these cells are idealized in the sense that the internal resistances were ignored.

Figure 1-42A illustrates three identical sources connecting in series-aiding. The total no-load terminal voltage will be the sum of the individual EMFs, but the internal resistances are also in series and must be added to obtain the total equivalent internal resistance. As a result, a series-aiding combination of sources will increase the total EMF available, but this advantage is only achieved at the expense of the higher total internal resistance.

Figure 1-42B shows three identical cells connected in parallel. The individual internal resistances are in parallel so that the total equivalent internal resistance is only one third of the internal resistance for the cell. However, the equivalent EMF is the same as that of one cell; the purpose of connecting practical cells in parallel is to reduce the effective internal resistance, as opposed to increasing the available voltage.

A series connection increases the available voltage at the expense of a greater internal resistance. By contrast, a parallel connection reduces the internal resistance, but does not raise the voltage. It is obviously possible to have the best of both worlds by using a series-parallel arrangement of identical cells. Suppose that 12 cells are available, each with an EMF of 6 V and an internal resistance of 0.9 Ω. Four of these cells are connected in series to form a single "bank" whose EMF is $4 \times 6 = 24$ V with an internal resistance of $4 \times 0.9 = 3.6$ Ω. If three such banks are connected in parallel for the total of 12 cells, the output EMF of this dc source remains at 24 V, but the internal resistance is reduced to $3.6/3 = 1.2$ Ω. However, the advantages of a series-parallel arrangement are achieved at the expense of a large, cumbersome, and costly power supply.

* **Question 1-41** Twelve nickel-cadmium cells are connected in series-aiding. What is the total available value of the EMF?

A. 1.25 V B. 2.05 V C. 12 V D. 24 V E. 15 V

Answer Choice E. Each nickel-cadmium cell has an operating voltage of 1.25 V. Total EMF available $= 12 \times 1.25 = 15$ V. (Note: the equivalent internal resistance of the series arrangement is still very low.)

1-17. Magnetism, electromagnetism, and magnetic SI units

Figure 1-43 shows a toroidal soft iron ring on which is wound a coil of N turns. A current of I amperes flows through the coil so that the ring is magnetized and a magnetic flux is established in the iron.

The flux is represented by magnetic lines of force. These are the directions in which isolated north poles would travel in a magnetic field. Such lines form closed loops, cannot intersect, and mutually repel one another. The degree of concentration of the lines of force indicates the strength of the magnetic field.

In a solid magnetized ring, the flux lines would be continuous and no magnetic poles would exist. However, if a radial cut is made in the ring to create an air gap (FIG. 1-43), a North pole exists on one side of the gap, and a South pole exists on the other side.

In a magnetic field, the total number of lines is referred to as the *magnetic flux*, represented by the Greek lowercase letter, phi (ϕ). In the SI system, the unit of magnetic flux is the *weber (Wb)*. This unit is defined through the phenomenon of electromagnetic induction. If a conductor

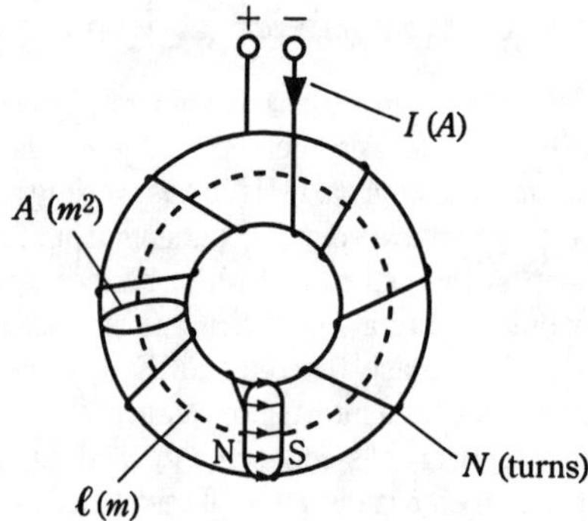

Fig. 1-43 The concepts of flux and flux density.

cuts a flux of 1 weber in one second, the voltage induced in the conductor is 1 volt. In practice, the weber is too large a unit for measuring a typical magnetic flux; the more common units are the microweber (μWb) and the milliweber (mWb).

To indicate the actual strength of a magnetic field, there must be a unit to measure the concentration of the lines of force. Referring to FIG. 1-43, the concentration in the air gap will be directly proportional to the magnetic flux, ϕ, but inversely proportional to the circular cross-sectional area, A, of the radial cut. The ratio of ϕ (Wb) to A (m^2) is called the ***flux density*** (B) and the unit is the tesla (T); it follows that 1 T = 1 Wb/m^2.

The equations are:

$$\text{Flux, } \phi = \text{BA webers (Wb)} \qquad (1\text{–}69)$$

$$\text{Flux density, B} = \frac{\phi}{\text{A}} \text{ teslas (T)} \qquad (1\text{–}70)$$

Consider a toroidal soft-iron ring that is wound with an exciting coil of N turns (FIG. 1-44). The ring is being magnetized by the flow of the current through the coil and the strength of the mag-

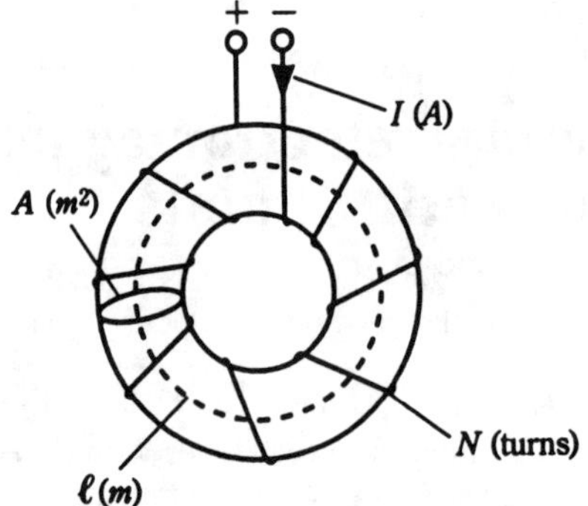

Fig. 1-44 The concepts of magnetomotive force and magnetic field intensity.

netic field will therefore depend on the number of turns and the value of the current. Their product, IN ampere-turns (amperes), is called the ***magnetomotive force (MMF)***, and the letter symbol is $\mathfrak{F}$. The magnetomotive force is the magnetic equivalent of the electromotive force (EMF). The EMF creates a current, I, the MMF establishes a flux, ϕ. Flux in magnetism is therefore the equivalent of current in electricity, but with one important difference. A current flows around an electrical network, but a flux is merely established in a magnetic circuit and does not flow.

Assume that the same values are kept for the current (I), the number of turns (N), and the cross-sectional area (A), but the ring is enlarged by increasing its circumference (the average of the inner and outer circumferences). Clearly, the turns will be spread further apart and the flux density, B teslas, in the iron ring will be reduced. Consequently, the value of the flux density depends not only on the current, I, and the number of turns, N, but also on the length, l, of the magnetic path, over which the flux is established. These three factors are contained in the *magnetic field intensity, H* (sometimes called the *magnetizing force*), which is equivalent to the MMF per unit length and is therefore measured in ampere-turns per meter or amperes per meter.

It follows that the magnetic field intensity is directly responsible for producing the flux density and that some relationship must exist between H and B.

The equations are:

Magnetomotive force (MMF):

$$\mathfrak{F} = IN = H \times l \text{ ampere-turns (AT) or amperes (A)} \qquad (1\text{–}71)$$

Magnetizing force:

$$H = \frac{IN}{l} = \frac{\mathfrak{F}}{l} \text{ ampere-turns per meter (AT/m) or amperes per meter (A/m)} \qquad (1\text{–}72)$$

In a vacuum the ratio of B and H is called the permeability of free space whose letter symbol is μ_o and whose value is $4\pi \times 10^{-7} = 12.57 \times 10^{-7}$ SI units. The term *permeability* measures the ability of a medium to allow the establishment of a flux density, B, by applying a magnetic field intensity, H.

For free space only:
$$\mu_o = \frac{B}{H} = 12.57 \times 10^{-7} \text{ SI units} \qquad (1\text{–}73)$$

Flux density:
$$B = \mu_0 H \text{ teslas (T)} \qquad (1\text{-}74)$$

Magnetic field intensity:
$$H = \frac{B}{\mu_0} \text{ ampere-turns per meter (AT/m)} \qquad (1\text{-}75)$$

Let a circular coil that consists of N turns and carries a current of I amperes, be placed in a vacuum (free space). As the result of the magnetic field intensity, H, a certain flux density $B(B = \mu_o H$ teslas) will be established. If the same coil is now wound on a ferromagnetic toroidal ring (FIG. 1-44), the flux density for the same magnetic field intensity will be greatly increased. The factor by which the flux density is increased is called the *relative permeability,* μ_r, which has no units and is just a number. However, the value of μ_r is not a constant, but depends on the magnetic field intensity (FIG. 1-45). This is a result of the ferromagnetic material's atomic structure. Notice that if the magnetic field intensity is reduced to zero, there is a small amount of residual or remanent magnetism so that the flux density is not zero. The phenomenon by which the effect (B) lags behind the cause (H) is called *hysteresis,* which is further covered in chapter 2.

Because the MMF of a magnetic circuit can be compared with the EMF of an electrical circuit, while the flux is regarded as similar to the current, it follows that the ratio of MMF:flux must be the magnetic equivalent of the resistance. This ratio is equal to a factor that is called the *reluctance* so that MMF, $\mathfrak{F}$/Flux, ϕ = Reluctance, $\mathfrak{R}$; this equation is sometimes referred to as *Rowland's law.* The reluctance is measured in ampere-turns per weber and is directly proportional to the length of the magnetic circuit, but is inversely proportional to the relative permeability and the cross-sectional area. This relationship recalls the equation for the resistance, R, of a cylindrical conductor, namely:

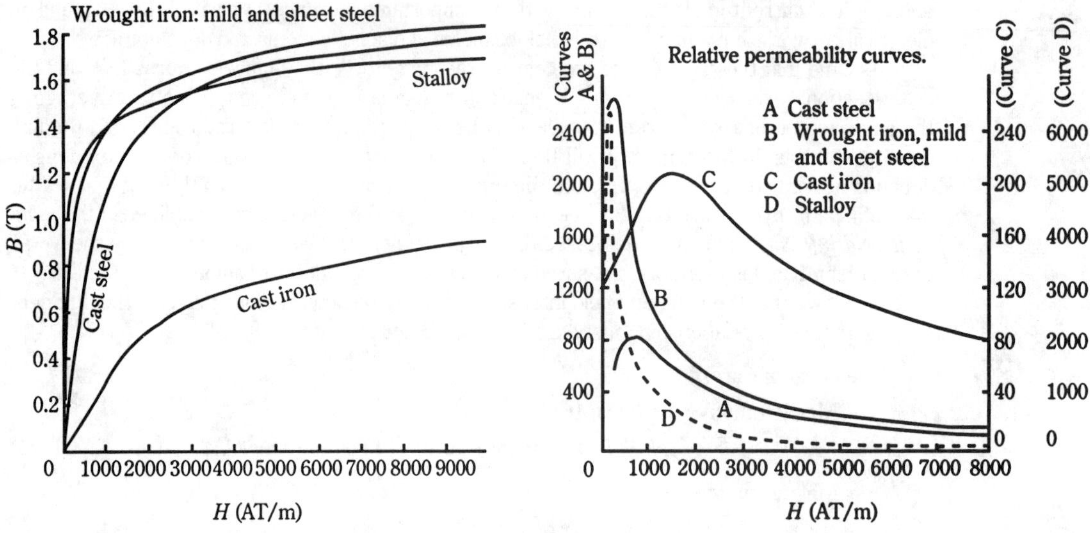

Fig. 1-45 Graphs of flux density and relative permeability versus magnetic field intensity.

$$R = \frac{\text{length, } l}{\text{conductivity, } \sigma \times \text{cross-sectional area, } A} \text{ ohms}(\Omega)$$

The principles outlined in the analyses of series and parallel resistor circuits can also be applied to magnetic circuits. For example, if a radial cut is made in the iron ring and we assume that the same flux is established in both the air gap and the iron, this is equivalent to saying that the current is the same throughout a series circuit. A certain number of ampere-turns would be necessary to establish the flux in the air gap and a different number would create the same flux in the iron. The total required MMF would then be obtained by adding together the individual numbers of ampere-turns. This is the same as finding the source voltage by adding together the individual voltage drops across two resistors in series.

Finally, the concept of power is another important difference between magnetic circuits and electrical circuits. For an electrical circuit that contains resistors, energy must be continuously supplied from the source, but when a flux is established in a magnetic circuit, no further energy is required.

Relative permeability: $$\mu_r = \frac{\textit{Flux density with a magnetic core}}{\textit{Flux density with a free space core}} \quad (1\text{-}76)$$

Flux density with a magnetic core: $$B = \mu_o \mu_r H = \mu H \text{ teslas (T)} \quad (1\text{-}77)$$

Absolute permeability: $$\mu = \mu_o \mu_r = \mu_r \times 12.57 \times 10^{-7} \text{ SI units} \quad (1\text{-}78)$$

Remembering that the total flux: $\phi = B \times A$ Wb and the magnetomotive force, $\mathfrak{F} = H \times 1$ ampere-turns:

$$\frac{\text{MMF } \mathfrak{F}}{\text{Flux, } \phi} = \frac{H \times l}{B \times A} = \frac{H \times l}{\mu_0 \mu_r H \times a} = \frac{l}{\mu_0 \mu_r A}$$

$$= \frac{l}{\mu A}$$

Therefore, Rowland's law is:

$$\text{Reluctance, } \mathfrak{R} = \frac{\mathcal{F}}{\phi}$$

$$= \frac{l}{\mu A} \text{ ampere-turns per weber} \tag{1-79}$$

Question 1-42 The term *residual magnetism* refers to:

A. the flux density that exists in the iron core when the magnetic field intensity is at its maximum value.
B. the flux density that exists in the iron core when the magnetic field intensity is reduced to zero.
C. the external magnetic field when the current is flowing through the exciting coil.
D. the flux density that exists in a nonmagnetic core when the magnetic field intensity is at its maximum value.
E. the flux density when the magnetic core is saturated.

Answer Choice B.

1-18. Electromagnetic induction, Faraday's law, and Lenz's law

Electromagnetic induction is the link between mechanical energy, magnetism, and electrical energy. In other words, these are the principles behind the electrical generator. In 1831, Faraday discovered that when a conductor cuts or is cut by (mechanical energy) a magnetic field (magnetism), an EMF (electricity) is *induced* in the conductor. Notice that is only necessary for there to be relative motion between the conductor and the flux lines of the magnetic field.

Faraday's law is illustrated in FIG. 1-41. This shows a conductor that is mechanically moved to cut the flux lines of a magnetic field at right angles (90°). The ends of the conductor are connected to a sensitive voltmeter that records the value of the EMF. When the conductor is stationary, the free electrons are moving in random directions. However, when the conductor cuts the magnetic flux, the electrons are given a movement in a particular direction. Through the motor effect, forces are then exerted on the moving charges so that the electrons are driven along the conductor. One end becomes negatively charged and the other end is positively charged so that an EMF is induced in the conductor. The magnitude of this EMF is directly proportional to the flux density, the length of the conductor, and its velocity at right angles to the lines of force. These are the results of Faraday's law, which states that the magnitude of the EMF depends on the rate of the cutting of the magnetic flux.

The directions of the current (electron flow), the magnetic flux, and the conductor's motion are mutually perpendicular. This can be found by the *left-hand "generator" rule;* the first finger indicates the direction of the flux, the second finger is the direction of the electron flow through the conductor, and the thumb shows the direction of the conductor's movement (FIG. 1-46A).

The output electrical energy is created from the work done in moving the conductor. The conductor itself carries a current and is therefore surrounded by its own flux, which reacts with the uniform magnetic field. Consequently, the conductor experiences a force whose direction opposes the motion of the conductor. Mechanical work must therefore be done in order to move the conductor against the opposing force (FIG. 1-46B). This is all summarized in Lenz's law, which

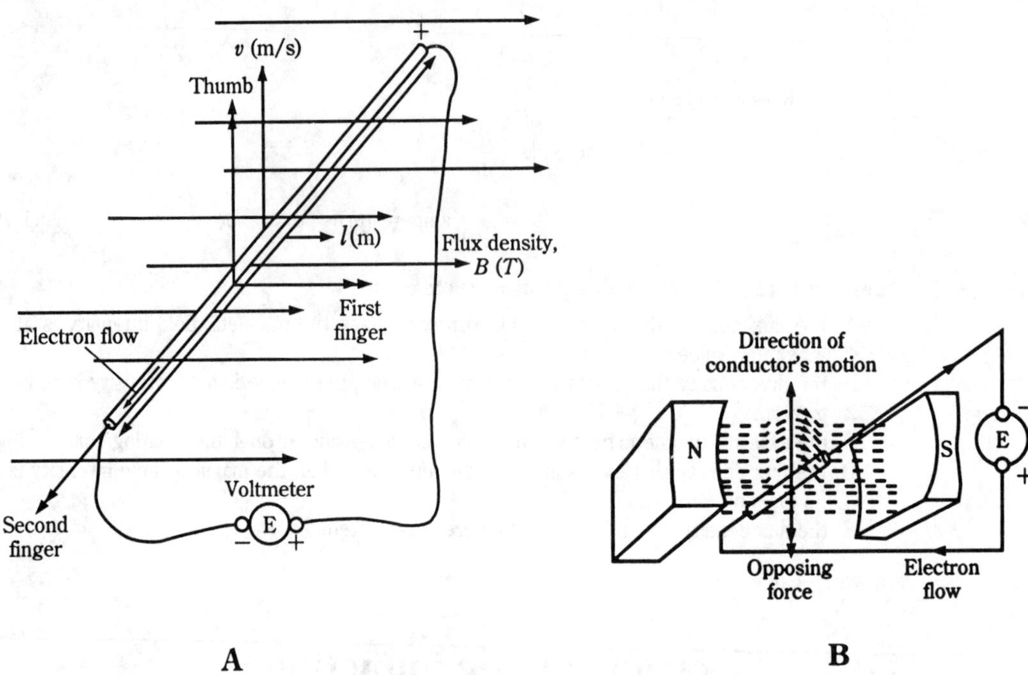

Fig. 1-46 Faraday's law and Lenz's law.

states that *the direction of the induced EMF is such as to oppose the change that originally created the EMF.* Such a law sounds more like a riddle. The "original change" is the conductor's motion that creates the induced EMF by cutting the uniform flux. This EMF produces a current flow in a particular direction so that a second magnetic field appears around the conductor. The reaction between the two fields causes a force to be exerted on the conductor and the direction of this force opposes the conductor's original motion. Lenz's law is really saying that you cannot obtain the electrical energy without supplying the mechanical work.

The value of the induced EMF: $E = Blv$ volts (V) (1-80)

where: B = flux density (T)
l = length of conductor (m)
v = velocity of conductor (m/s)

* **Question 1-43** A conductor is cutting a magnetic field. The value of the voltage induced in the inductor depends on the:

A. length of the conductor
B. velocity of the conductor
C. angle at which the conductor is cutting the flux lines
D. flux density
E. All of the above are true

Answer Choice E.

1-19. Self-inductance and the *L/R* time constant

An electrical circuit can only possess three passive quantities: resistance, inductance, and capacitance. Previous sections have already covered that resistance opposes and therefore limits the current. By contrast, inductance is defined as the electrical property that prevents any sudden or abrupt change of current and also limits the rate of the change in the current. Thus, if an electrical circuit contains inductance, the current in the circuit can neither rise nor fall instantaneously.

Although a straight length of wire possesses some inductance, the property is most marked in a coil which is called an *inductor* and whose circuit symbol is ⌇⌇⌇. When a current increases or decreases in a coil, the surrounding magnetic field will expand or collapse, and cut the turns of the coil itself. On the principle of electromagnetic induction, a voltage or counter EMF will be induced into the coil, but this voltage will depend on the rate at which the current is *changing*, rather than on the value of the current itself. As a result of the change in the current, the coil creates its own moving flux that cuts its own turns and induces the voltage across the coil. For these reasons, the property of the coil is referred to as its *self-inductance* (*L*).

Figure 1-47A compares the properties of resistance and inductance. When the switch is closed in position 1, the current in the resistor rises immediately from zero to a constant value of 10 V/5 Ω = 2 A (FIG. 1-47B). The voltage drop across the resistor (10 V) then exactly balances (or opposes) the source voltage (10 V).

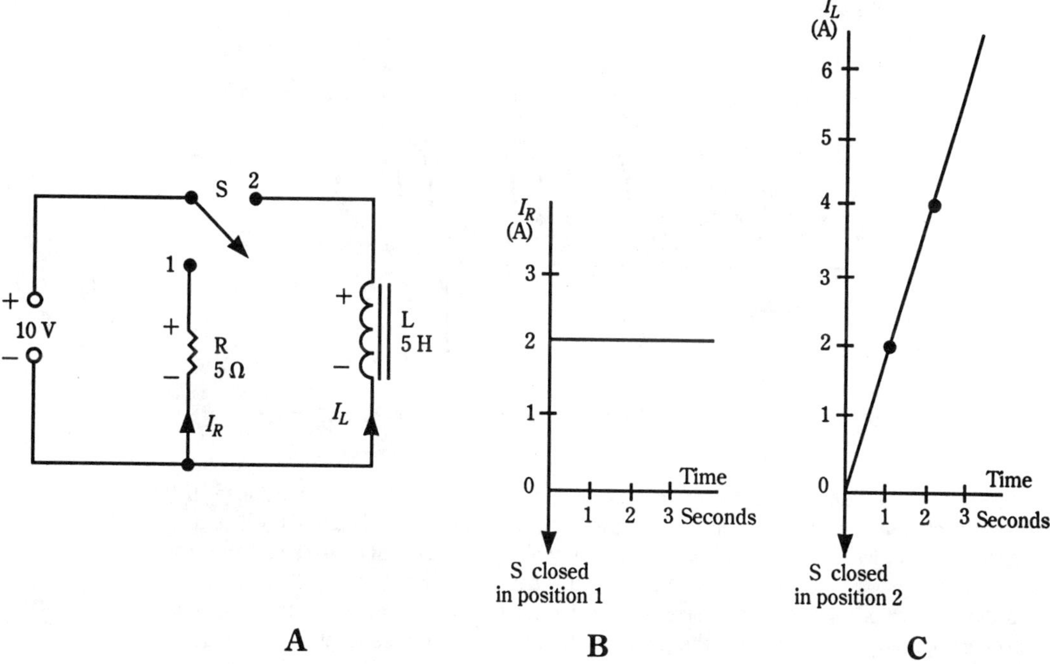

Fig. 1-47 A comparison between the properties of resistance and self-inductance.

If the switch is now moved to position 2, the resistor current immediately drops to zero, but the inductor current grows in the coil. This creates a magnetic flux which, as it expands outward, cuts the turns of the coil and induces the counter EMF, which must exactly balance the source voltage (assuming that the coil only possesses inductance and has zero resistance). Because the source voltage is fixed, it follows that the current must start at zero and must then grow at a constant rate measured in amperes per second (FIG. 1-47C).

Although the counter EMF is proportional to the rate of the change of the current, its value must also depend on some factor of the coil. This factor is called the self-inductance, L, which is determined by such physical quantities as the number of turns, the length, the cross-sectional area, and the nature of the core on which the coil is wound. The unit of inductance is the henry (H). The inductance is one henry if, when the current is changing at the rate of one ampere per second, the induced EMF is one volt. Consequently, in FIG. 1-47A, where the source voltage is 10 V and the inductance is 5 H, the rate of the growth of the current is 10 V/5 H = 2 A/s.

Thus, source voltage: $$E = L \times \text{rate of change of current (V)} \qquad (1\text{-}81)$$

$$\text{Rate of change of current} = \frac{E}{L} \text{ amperes per second (A/s)} \qquad (1\text{-}82)$$

Physical factors that determine a coil's inductance

For a coil, a high value of inductance requires that a large counter EMF is induced for a given rate of change in the current. Clearly, the number of turns is one of the factors involved because each turn can be regarded as a conductor and the magnetic field intensity is directly proportional to the number of turns (FIG. 1-48). In fact, the value of the inductance is directly proportional to the square of the number of turns.

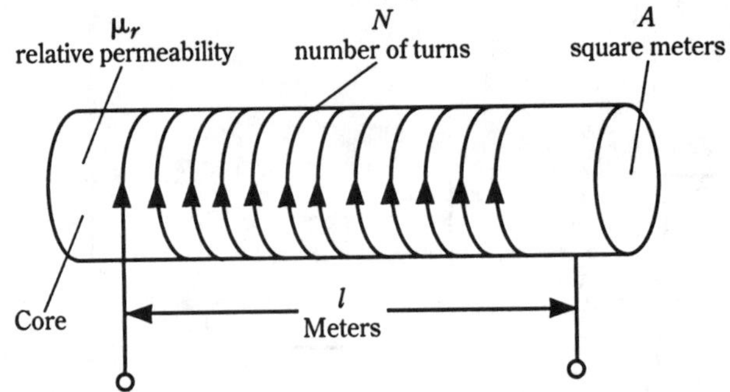

Fig. 1-48 Physical factors that determine a coil's self-inductance.

The size of each turn is another factor that determines the value of the inductance. If the cross-sectional area of each turn is increased, the coil's reluctance $\Re = l/(\mu_o \mu_r A)$ will be lesser and the flux density will be greater. Looking at it another way, if you continue to reduce the cross-sectional area, the coil would ultimately vanish and the inductance would obviously be zero.

If the number of turns and their sizes are kept constant, but the coil's length is increased, the turns are spread farther apart and there is a greater reluctance. Consequently, the flux density and the inductance are reduced.

Finally, you can replace a nonmagnetic core with one that is made from ferromagnetic material with a high relative permeability. This greatly lowers the amount of the reluctance and therefore increases the flux density. The result is a much higher inductance value.

Summarizing, the inductance value is directly proportional to the square of the number of turns, their cross-sectional area and the coil's permeability, but is inversely proportional to the coil's length.

The values of practical inductors range from henrys to microhenrys. Those with the value of several henrys are referred to as *chokes* (circuit symbol), which are a large number of copper turns wound on an iron core. The presence of the core is indicated by the two lines drawn to one side of the circuit symbol. Such a core is laminated (cut into slices that are insulated from each other) to reduce the loss from eddy currents. Because the relative permeability varies with the amount of the direct current flowing through the coil, the inductance value is normally quoted for a particular dc current level.

A coil with a value of a few microhenrys only consists of a few copper turns that are wound on a nonmagnetic core (circuit symbol). Between these two extremes are millihenry inductors with cores of either iron dust (circuit symbol) or a ferrite material. *Ferrite* is a ceramic substance with magnetic properties similar to those of iron; a ferrite core will increase the value of the self-inductance. However, ferrite is also an insulator that will not suffer from losses caused by eddy currents.

The value of the self-inductance: $$L = \frac{\mu_o \mu_r N^2 A}{l} \qquad (1\text{-}83)$$

where: μ_o = permeability of free space (12.57×10^{-7} SI units)
μ_r = relative permeability of the core
N = number of turns
A = cross-sectional area (m^2)
l = length (m)

Inductors in series

It is assumed that all three inductors of FIG. 1-49 are ideal in the sense that they have no losses and they only possess the property of inductance. Because these components are joined end-to-end, the same *rate of change* in the current will be associated with all of the inductors. In each inductor, the expanding magnetic field will induce a counter EMF (V_{L1}, V_{L2}, and V_{L3}) and the sum of these EMFs must exactly balance the source voltage.

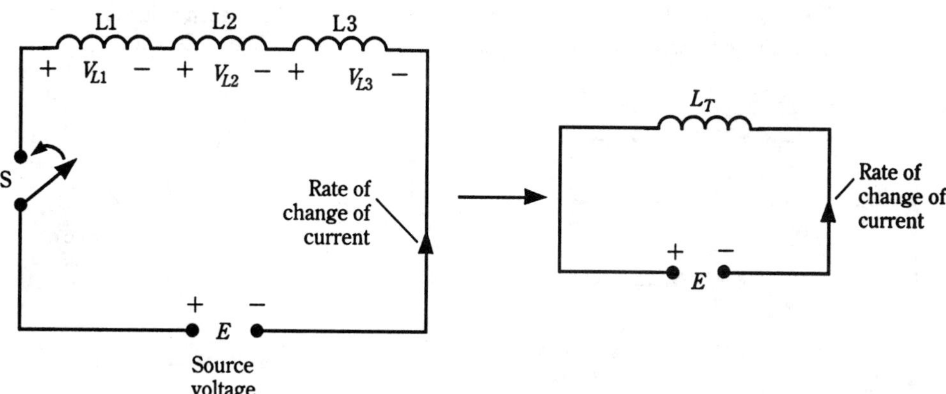

Fig. 1-49 Inductors in series.

When switch S is closed, there will be a constant rate of growth in the current, and the magnetic field surrounding each inductor will expand. After a period of time, a certain amount of energy will be stored in each of the magnetic fields, and the sum of these energies will equal the total energy derived from the source voltage. Because the inductors are regarded as ideal components, no power is dissipated in the circuit as heat.

Like the equation for resistors in series, the total inductance is the sum of the individual inductances. Consequently, one use of connecting inductors in series is to create a nonstandard total inductance value from standard components; in the same way, a series arrangement of small inductors can avoid the use of a physically larger inductor. However, in such an arrangement, it is essential for the current ratings of the series inductors to be compatible.

Total equivalent self-inductance:

$$L_T = L_1 + L_2 + L_3 \text{ henrys (H)} \tag{1-84}$$

Source voltage:

$$E = V_{L1} + V_{L2} + V_{L3} \text{ volts (V)} \tag{1-85}$$

$$\text{Rate of growth of current} = \frac{V_{L1}}{L_1} = \frac{V_{L2}}{L_2} = \frac{V_{L3}}{L_3} = \frac{E}{L_T} \text{ amperes per second (A/s)} \tag{1-86}$$

Inductors in parallel

It is assumed that all three inductors in FIG. 1-50 are ideal, in the sense that they have no losses and they only possess the property of inductance. Because these components are joined between two common points (A and B), the source voltage will be across every inductor. Then, each inductor will carry a different rate of growth of current so that its magnetic field will induce the same counter EMF, which exactly balances the source voltage. The sum of the individual rates of current growth will equal the total rate of growth that is associated with the source voltage.

When switch S is closed, a constant rate of current growth will be in each inductor and the associated magnetic fields will continue to expand. After a period of time, a certain amount of

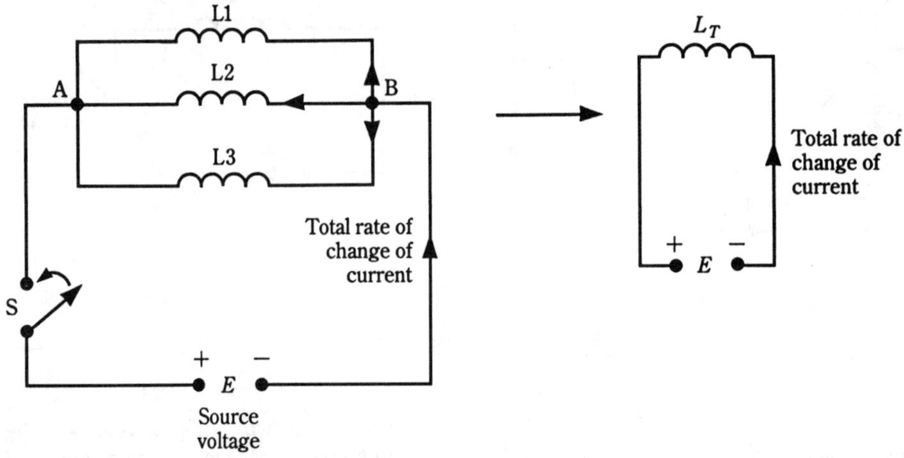

Fig. 1-50 Inductors in parallel.

energy will be stored in each of the three magnetic fields and the sum of these energies will equal the total energy derived from the source voltage. Because the inductors are regarded as ideal components, no power is dissipated in the circuit as heat.

Like resistors in parallel, the parallel arrangement of inductors reduces the value of the total inductance. The reasons for connecting inductors in parallel are to increase the current capability and to obtain nonstandard values from standard components.

The principles of inductors in series and parallel may be extended to series-parallel arrangements.

For parallel inductors, total equivalent self-inductance:

$$L_T = \frac{1}{\dfrac{1}{L_1} + \dfrac{1}{L_2} + \dfrac{1}{L_3}} \text{ henrys (H)} \qquad (1\text{-}87)$$

$$\text{Total rate of growth of current} = \frac{E}{L_T} \text{ amperes per second (A/s)} \qquad (1\text{-}88)$$

Question 1-44 A coil consists of 1600 turns of AWG #30 copper wire and has a self-inductance of 0.4 H. If the number of turns is increased to 2000, the new value of the self-inductance is:

A. 0.3 H B. 0.125 H C. 0.4 H D. greater than 0.4 H E. 3.5 H

Answer Choice D. Because the value of the self-inductance is directly proportional to the square of the number of turns, the self-inductance is increased.

Question 1-45 A coil consists of 2500 turns of AWG #26 copper wire and has a self-inductance of 0.3 H. If the air core is replaced by a soft iron core, the new value of the self-inductance is:

A. less than 0.3 H B. 0.25 H C. 0.3 H D. greater than 0.3 H E. Choices A and B are true

Answer Choice D. Because the relative permeability of soft iron is much greater than that of air, the self-inductance is increased.

Question 1-46 In the circuit of FIG. 1-51, the total self-inductance between points P and Q is:

A. 20 H B. 30 H C. 2.5 H D. 5 H E. 3.3 H

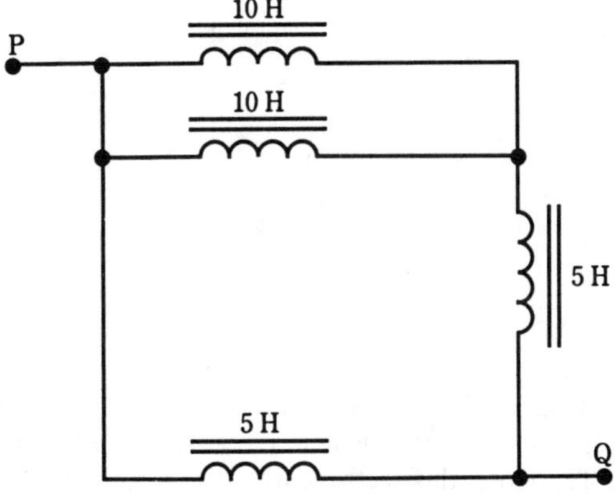

Fig. 1-51 The circuit for question 1-46.

Answer Choice E. The two 10-H inductors are in parallel so that their equivalent inductance is 10/2 = 5 H. This equivalent inductance is in series with the right-hand 5-H inductor so that one branch between points P and Q has a total inductance of 5 + 5 = 10 H. The other branch contains only the bottom 5-H inductor so that the total equivalent inductance of this series-parallel circuit is:

$$\frac{5 \times 10}{5 + 10} = \frac{50}{15} = 3.3 \text{ H, rounded off}$$

Question 1-47 The inductance of a coil with an air core is directly proportional to the:

A. number of turns
B. cross-sectional area of the wire
C. square of the number of turns
D. length of the core
E. Choices A and B are true

Answer Choice C. Because $L = N^2 A\mu / l$ H, L is directly proportional to N^2.

* **Question 1-48** A coil contains 500 turns of AWG #26 copper wire and has an air core. If a ferrite core is inserted into the coil, the value of the self-inductance is:

A. decreased
B. unchanged
C. multiplied by the relative permittivity of the ferrite material
D. increased
E. Choices C and D are true

Answer Choice D.

* **Question 1-49** In the circuit of FIG. 1-52, the value of the total equivalent self-inductance between the points X and Y is:

A. 2.5 H B. 5 H C. 10 H D. 25 H E. 4 H

Answer Choice A. The three inductors are in parallel. Therefore, the total self-inductance:

$$L_T = \frac{1}{\frac{1}{10} + \frac{1}{10} + \frac{1}{5}}$$

$$= \frac{1}{\frac{1 + 1 + 2}{10}}$$

$$= \frac{1}{4/10}$$

$$= \frac{10}{4} = 2.5 \text{ H}$$

L/R time constant

The property of self-inductance prevents any sudden change of the current and also limits the rate at which the current can change. Consequently, when switch S is closed in position 1 (FIG. 1-53A), the current must take a certain time before reaching a final steady level, which is determined by resistance R. Therefore, this section covers the factors that control the duration of the so-called *transient* or *changing* state. This is the interval between the time at which switch S is closed in position 1, and the time when the final or steady-state conditions are reached.

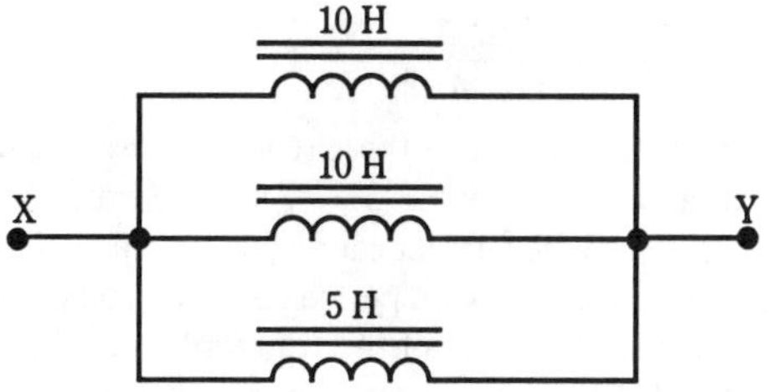

Fig. 1-52 The circuit for question 1-49.

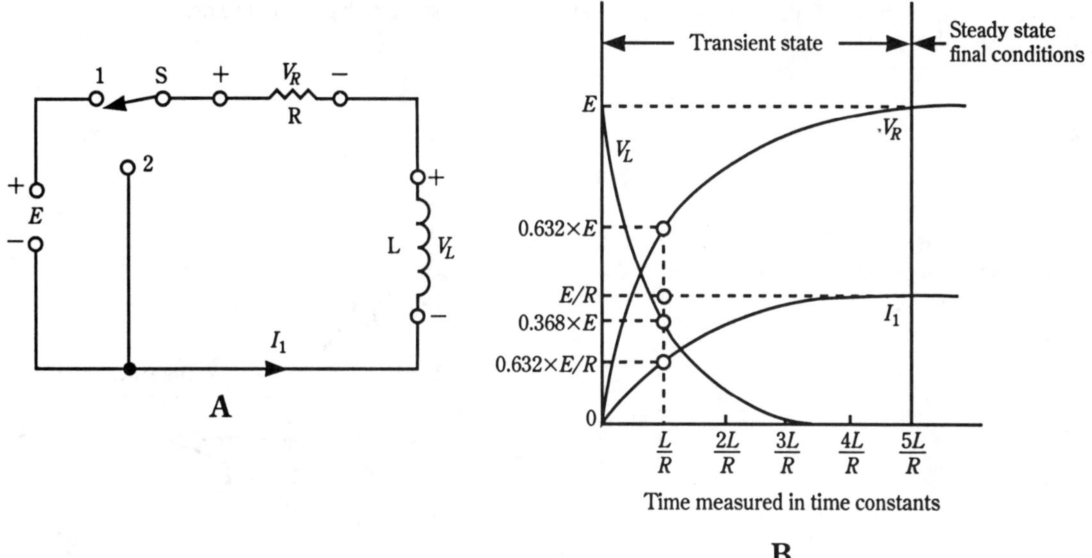

Fig. 1-53 The growth of current through an inductor and a resistor in series.

Immediately after the switch is closed in position 1, the current must initially be zero so that the voltage drop across resistor R must also be zero. Consequently, to satisfy Kirchhoff's voltage law, the counter EMF created in the inductor, L, must equal the source voltage, E. The initial rate of the current growth is therefore at its maximum value of E/L amperes per second.

As the current increases and the magnetic field expands outward, the voltage drop across the resistor rises and the counter EMF in the inductor falls because at all times the sum of these two voltages must exactly balance the source voltage, E. When the counter EMF falls, the rate of the current's growth is correspondingly less, so there is a situation in which the greater the value of the current, the less is its rate of growth. Theoretically, it would take infinite time for the current to reach its final steady value of E/R amperes; however, the current reaches its final value to within 1% after a finite time interval that is determined by the values of the inductance and the resistance.

Remember that the initial rate of current growth is E/L amperes per second and the final current value is E/R amperes. Consequently, if the initial rate of current growth was maintained, the current would reach its final value after an interval of:

$$\frac{E/R\ A}{E/L\ A/s} = \frac{L}{R} \text{ seconds}$$

which is referred to as the *time constant* of the circuit. However, because the rate of current growth falls off, the current only reaches 63.2% of its final value after one time constant. It requires five time constants before the current can rise to within 1% of E/R amperes (FIG. 1-53B) and you can assume that the transient growth period has been completed.

Notice that the conditions at the start of the transient state can be predicted by regarding the inductor as an open circuit. The final steady-state values can be obtained by considering the inductor to be a short circuit.

Assuming that the steady-state conditions have been reached, now move switch S to position 2. The current cannot change instantaneously; I_2 must still be E/R amperes and the voltage across the resistor must remain at E volts. By the KVL rule, the inductor's counter EMF will also be E volts, but its polarity is reversed because the magnetic field is starting to collapse rather than expand (FIG. 1-54A).

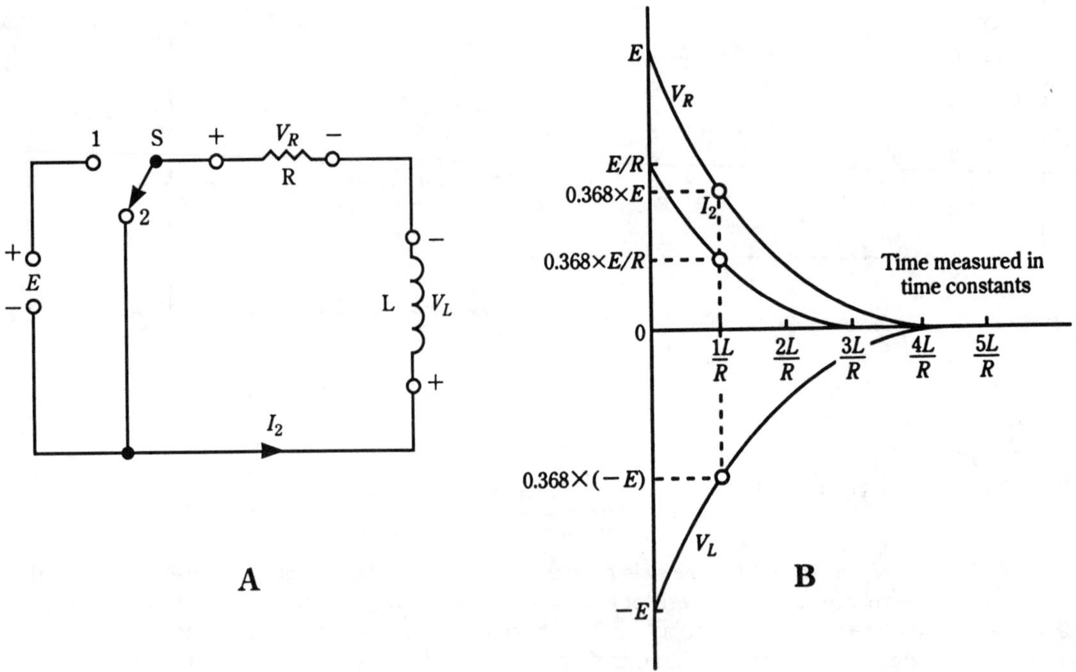

Fig. 1-54 The decay of current through an inductor and a resistor in series.

As the current decays, V_R and V_L must fall together in order to maintain the voltage balance around the closed loop. When V_L decreases, the rate of current decay is less; theoretically, it would take infinite time for the current to reach zero. However, after one time constant the current has lost 63.2% of its initial value and has dropped to 36.8% of E/R amperes. After five time constants, it is assumed the transient decay period has been concluded in the sense that I_2, V_R, and V_L have all fallen to less than 1% of their original values (FIG. 1-54B). The growth and decay percentages are contained in TABLE 1-7.

* **Question 1-50** An inductor and a resistor are connected in series. Their time constant is obtained by:

A. multiplying the inductance value by the resistance value
B. dividing the resistance value by the inductance value
C. dividing the inductance value by the conductance value
D. dividing the inductance value by the resistance value
E. None of the above choices is true

Answer Choice D. Time constant $= L/R$ seconds.

1-20. Electrostatics and capacitance

When two neutral insulators, such as a rubber rod and a piece of fur, are rubbed together, electrons will literally be wiped off from one insulator to the other. This is referred to as the *triboelectric effect* or *friction effect.* Electrons are transferred from the fur to the rod so that the fur has a deficit of electrons and is positively charged, and the rod has a surplus of electrons and carries an equal negative charge. If the two charged insulators are positioned near to one another, there is no electron flow, and the charges cannot move. This phenomenon is called *static electricity* or *electrostatics.* If the two insulators are then brought into contact, equalizing currents flow in the form of sparks, which produce a crackling sound and continue to discharge until the insulators are again electrically neutral.

In magnetism, similar poles repel and dissimilar poles attract. A similar law applies to electrostatics because charges with the same polarity (for example, two negative charges) repel each other, but charges with the opposite polarity (a positive charge and a negative charge) are subjected to a force of attraction. The force of attraction or repulsion is caused by the influence that a charged body exerts on its surroundings. This influence is called the *electric* or *electrostatic field,* which terminates on a charged body and extends between positive and negative charges. Such a field can exist in a vacuum (free space) or in insulators of air, waxed paper, etc.

As with a magnetic field, an electric field is represented by lines of force that show the direction and strength of the field so that a strong field is shown as a large number of lines, drawn close together. The total number of force lines is called the *electric flux* (ψ). In the SI system, a single flux line is assumed to emanate from a positive charge of one coulomb and to terminate on an equal negative charge. The number of flux lines is the same as the number of coulombs; therefore, an electric flux can be measured directly in coulombs.

Figures 1-55A and B show the electric flux patterns for the forces of attraction and repulsion. Coulomb discovered that the magnitude of the force between two charged bodies is directly proportional to the product of the charges, but is inversely proportional to the square of their separation.

Figure 1-56 illustrates two identical rectangular plates, which are made from a conducting material (such as silver, copper, aluminum, etc.). The area of one side of one plate is A square meters, and the two plates are separated by a distance of d meters in free space. These plates are charged to a potential difference of V_C volts so that one plate carries a negative charge of Q coulombs and the other plate has an equal positive charge. The total electric flux, ψ, is therefore Q coulombs and consists of Q lines of force, which are spread over an area of A square meters. The flux density, D, is found by dividing ψ by A and is measured in coulombs per square meter.

The flux density, D, is the result of the electric field intensity, $\mathcal{E}$ which exists between the two plates. Increasing the value of V_C and/or reducing the separation, d, between the plates, causes a stronger electric field so that the electric field intensity, $\mathcal{E}$ is expressed in terms of the voltage gradient, V_C/d, which is measured in volts per meter. The ratio of D: $\mathcal{E}$ is termed the

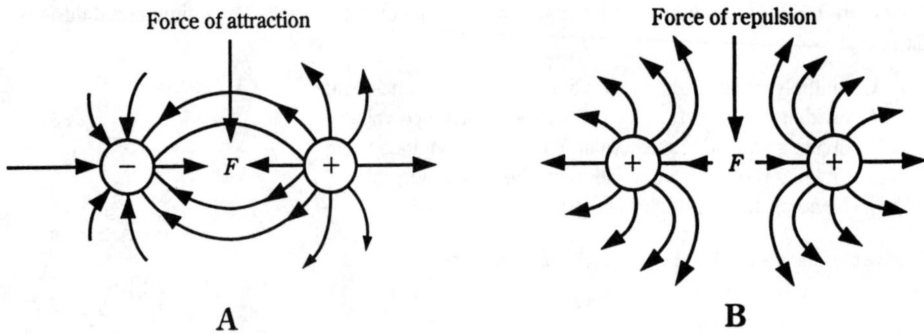

Fig. 1-55 Electric flux patterns.

permittivity of free space, ε_o (also known as the absolute permittivity of a vacuum), and whose value is 8.85×10^{-12} farad per meter in SI units.

If a negative charge (coulombs) is placed in a vacuum, it will be repelled from the negative plate and will be accelerated toward the positive plate. The accelerating force (in newtons) is directly proportional to the magnitude of the charge and the value of the electric field intensity.

If the free space between the plates is replaced by an insulating material (such as mica, waxed paper, etc.), the flux density for a given value of electric field intensity, is increased by a factor, called the *relative permittivity*, ε_r. This factor has no units and is defined by:

$$\text{Relative permittivity, } \varepsilon_r = \frac{\textit{electric flux density in the insulating material for a given field intensity}}{\textit{electric flux density in free space for the same field intensity}} \quad (1\text{-}89)$$

Values for ε_r are 1.0006 for air, 3 to 6 for mica, and 3.5 for waxed paper.

It follows that, for an insulating material, the ratio of D: $\mathcal{E}$ is $\varepsilon_o \varepsilon_r = \varepsilon$, which is the insulator's absolute permittivity, measured in farads per meter.

In FIG. 1-56:

Flux density: $$D = \frac{\psi}{A} \text{ coulombs per meter (C/m}^2\text{)} \quad (1\text{-}90)$$

Electric flux: $$\psi = D \times A \text{ coulombs (C)} \quad (1\text{-}91)$$

Electric field intensity: $$\mathcal{E} = \frac{V}{d} \text{ volts per meter (V/m)} \quad (1\text{-}92)$$

Absolute permittivity: $$\varepsilon = \frac{D}{\mathcal{E}} \text{ farads per meter (F/m)} \quad (1\text{-}93)$$

Capacitance and the capacitor

Capacitance is that property of an electrical circuit that prevents any sudden change in voltage and limits the rate of change in the voltage. In other words, the voltage across the capacitance, C, cannot change instantaneously.

The property of capacitance is possessed by a capacitor—a device for storing charge that consists of two conducting surfaces (copper, silver, aluminum, tin foil, etc.), which are separated by an insulator or dielectric (air, mica, ceramic, etc.).

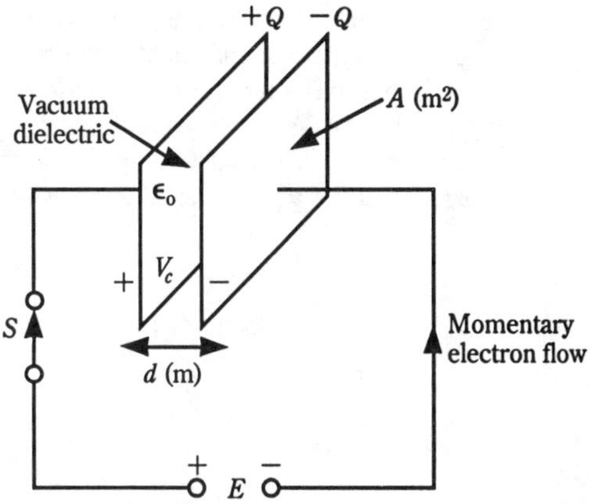

Fig. 1-56 Electric flux density and field intensity.

When a dc voltage, E, is switched across the capacitor, C (FIG. 1-57), electrons are drawn off the right-hand plate, flow through the voltage source, and are then deposited on the left-hand plate. The electron flow is only momentary and ceases when the voltage, V_C, between the plates exactly balances the source voltage, E. The charge then stored by the capacitor directly depends on the value of the applied voltage and also on some constant of the capacitor, called the *capacitance,* which is determined by the component's physical construction. The unit for the capacitance is the *farad,* F. The capacitance is one farad, if the voltage applied across the capacitor's plates is one volt and the charge stored is one coulomb. Unfortunately, the farad is far too large a unit for practical purposes, so capacitances are normally either measured in microfarads (μF) or picofarads (pF). Notice that a picofarad can alternatively be referred to as a micromicrofarad (μμF).

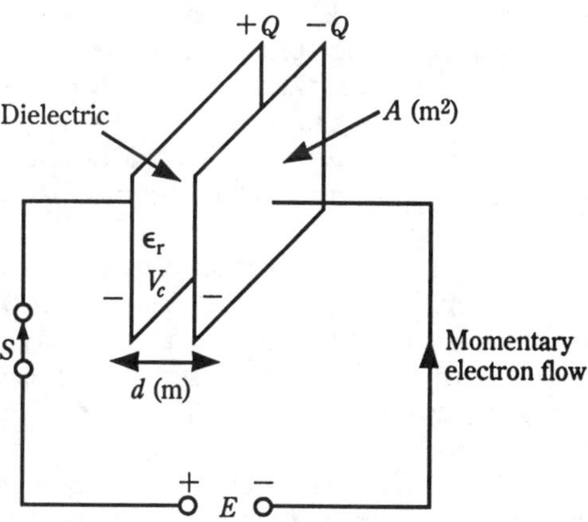

Fig. 1-57 The charging of a capacitor.

You already know that a particular electric field intensity (which is inversely proportional to the separation between the plates) produces a certain flux (which is directly proportional to the area of one of the plates). Thus, a capacitor's capacitance is directly proportional to the area of the plates, but is inversely proportional to their distance apart. It is true that the capacitance is increased if the conductor plates are brought closer together. However, if the dielectric is made too thin, the voltage between the plates might arc and damage the capacitor. Each type of insulator has a certain dielectric strength, which is a measure of the insulator's ability to withstand a high electric field intensity. For example, the dielectric strength of mica is typically 50 kV/mm; in order to avoid breakdown, no more than 50 kV should be applied across a 1-mm thickness of mica. It follows that each capacitor is rated for a particular *dc working voltage (WVdc)*.

In FIG. 1-57: Charge stored:

$$Q = CE \text{ coulombs (C)} \qquad (1\text{-}94)$$

Capacitance with a free space dielectric:

$$C = \frac{\varepsilon_o A}{d} \text{ farads (F)} \qquad (1\text{-}95)$$

If the dielectric has a relative permittivity of ε_r:

$$C = \frac{\varepsilon_o \varepsilon_r A}{d} = \frac{\varepsilon A}{d} \text{ farads (F)} \qquad (1\text{-}96)$$

where: Q = charge stored (C)
C = capacitance (F)
E = dc voltage applied to the capacitor (V)
ε_o = permittivity of free space (8.85×10^{-12} SI units)
ε_r = relative permittivity
ε = absolute permittivity (F/m)

Paper, mica, and ceramic capacitors are commonly encountered in electronics, but these types are normally not capable of producing capacitances of the order of several microfarads. By contrast, the electrolytic capacitor is capable of producing very high capacitance values, but is much smaller in size than the paper, mica, and ceramic capacitors. For the higher voltage ratings that exceed 450 V, the range of capacitances available is typically from 4 to 200 μF, but with the lower voltage ratings, the range is extended to 600 μF. In some computer circuits, you can find capacitance values up to 0.2 F! Generally speaking, electrolytic capacitors are used in circuits (for example, power supplies), where it is not important if the actual value of capacitance differs appreciably from the rated value.

The common type of electrolytic capacitor contains two aluminum surfaces, one of which is usually the external can or housing. The other surface is aluminum foil, which is in contact with an electrolyte of ammonium borate. During manufacture, a current is passed through the capacitor and this forms a thin aluminum oxide film on the foil surface. This oxide film, which is approximately 0.00001 cm thick, is the capacitor's dielectric. The thin dielectric accounts for the very high capacitance values.

Unlike the other types of capacitor, you must observe polarity when connecting electrolytic capacitors into a circuit. For this reason, the terminals of electrolytic capacitors are clearly marked "+" and "−"; internally, the + terminal is connected to the foil and the − terminal to the can. Externally, the + and − terminals must be connected to the positive and negative sides, respectively, of the circuit's dc voltage source. If this is not done, there will be a flow of current through the capacitor in the opposite direction of the flow that originally formed the dielectric film. As a result, the chemical action will be reversed, the film will be destroyed, and the capacitor is short circuited; in addition, gas is released during the destruction of the film, so pressure builds up inside the unit.

Capacitors in series

Because the capacitors are joined end-to-end in FIG. 1-58, there is only one path for current flow. Consequently, when S is closed in position 1, the charging current for each capacitor is the same; therefore, each capacitor must store the same charge, Q (coulombs). One problem is worth considering. Because the electron flow cannot pass through the dielectrics, which are theoretically open circuits, how does the middle capacitor become charged? The explanation lies in electrostatic induction. When the electron flow causes the plate, Pl, to acquire a positive charge, an equal negative charge is induced on the plate, P2. This causes another positive charge of the same size to appear on the plate, P3, and so on. As the result of this process, the total charge stored between plates P1 and P6 is Q (not $3Q$).

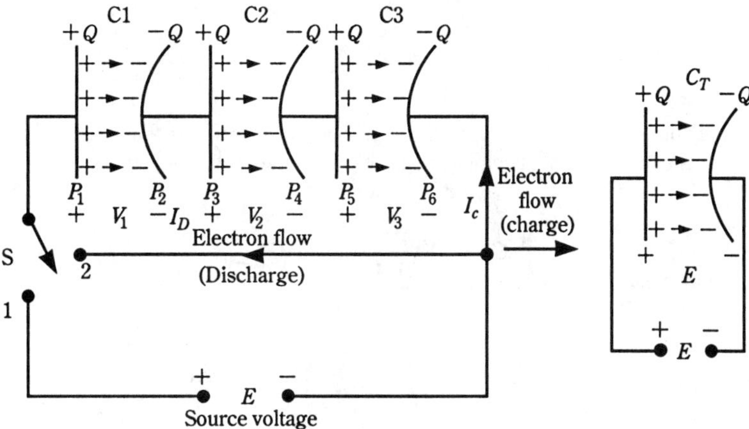

Fig. 1-58 Capacitors in series.

After the capacitors are charged, there is a voltage across each capacitor and the sum of these voltages must exactly balance the source voltage. Because $Q = VC$ (EQ. 94) and each capacitor carries the same charge, it follows that the highest voltage is across the lowest value of the capacitance and vice-versa.

Each capacitor stores a certain amount of energy in the form of the electric field between its plates. When the switch is moved to position 2, the capacitors discharge and the total energy stored is released in the form of a spark at the contacts of the switch. Incidentally, the spark creates an electromagnetic wave and this is the principle behind the early spark-gap transmitter.

Finally, what is the purpose of connecting capacitors in series? Connecting capacitors in series reduces the total capacitance so that the total capacitance is less than the value of the smallest capacitance in series. Basically, this is because the series arrangement effectively increases the distance between the end plates, P1 and P6, which are connected to the source voltage, and the capacitance is inversely proportional to this distance. Because the capacitor has a dc working voltage (WVdc), the series arrangement can be used to distribute the source voltage between the capacitors so that the voltage across an individual capacitor does not exceed its rating.

In FIG. 1-58, individual voltages across the capacitors:

$$V_1 = \frac{Q}{C_1},\ V_2 = \frac{Q}{C_2},\ V_3 = \frac{Q}{C_3} \text{ volts (V)} \qquad (1\text{-}97)$$

Source voltage:

$$E = V_1 + V_2 + V_3$$

$$= \frac{Q}{C_1} + \frac{Q}{C_2} + \frac{Q}{C_3} \tag{1-98}$$

$$= Q\left(\frac{1}{C_1} + \frac{1}{C_2} + \frac{1}{C_3}\right) \text{ volts (V)}$$

If C_T is the total equivalent capacitance:

$$E = \frac{Q}{C_T} = Q \times \frac{1}{C_T} \text{ volts (V)} \tag{1-99}$$

Comparing EQS. 1-98 and 1-99:

$$\frac{1}{C_T} = \frac{1}{C_1} + \frac{1}{C_2} + \frac{1}{C_3}$$

or

$$C_T = \frac{1}{\dfrac{1}{C_1} + \dfrac{1}{C_2} + \dfrac{1}{C_3}} \text{ farads (F)} \tag{1-100}$$

Therefore, the total equivalent capacitance for capacitors in series is found from the reciprocal formula, which is used for parallel combinations of either resistors or inductors.

For two capacitors in series, total equivalent capacitance:

$$C_T = \frac{C_1 \times C_2}{C_1 + C_2} \text{ farads (F)} \tag{1-101}$$

In FIG. 1-58, because $Q = EC_T$, the voltage across the capacitor C_1:

$$V_1 = \frac{Q}{C_1} = \frac{EC_T}{C_1} = E \times \frac{C_T}{C_1} \text{ volts (V)}$$

Similarly:

$$V_2 = E \times \frac{C_T}{C_2} \text{ volts (V)}$$

$$V_3 = E \times \frac{C_T}{C_2} \text{ volts (V)} \tag{1-102}$$

Capacitors in parallel

Capacitors in parallel are connected across two common points (A,B) or lines so that the source voltage is applied across each of the capacitors (FIG. 1-59). Because $Q = CV$, it follows that a different charge must be stored by each capacitor. This is because of the different momentary charging currents that exist at the instant that switch S is closed. The total charge is then equal to the sum of the individual charges that are stored by each capacitor.

The purpose of connecting capacitors in parallel is to increase the total capacitance. In FIG. 1-59, plates, P1, P3, and P5 have been connected together. On the other side, plates, P2, P4, and P6 have been connected together. The result is to increase the effective surface area to which the capacitance is directly proportional. The principles of capacitors in series and capacitors in parallel can be extended to series-parallel arrangements.

In FIG. 1-59, charges stored by the individual capacitors:

$$Q_1 = C_1E,\ Q_2 = C_2E,\ Q_3 = C_3E \text{ coulombs (C)} \tag{1-103}$$

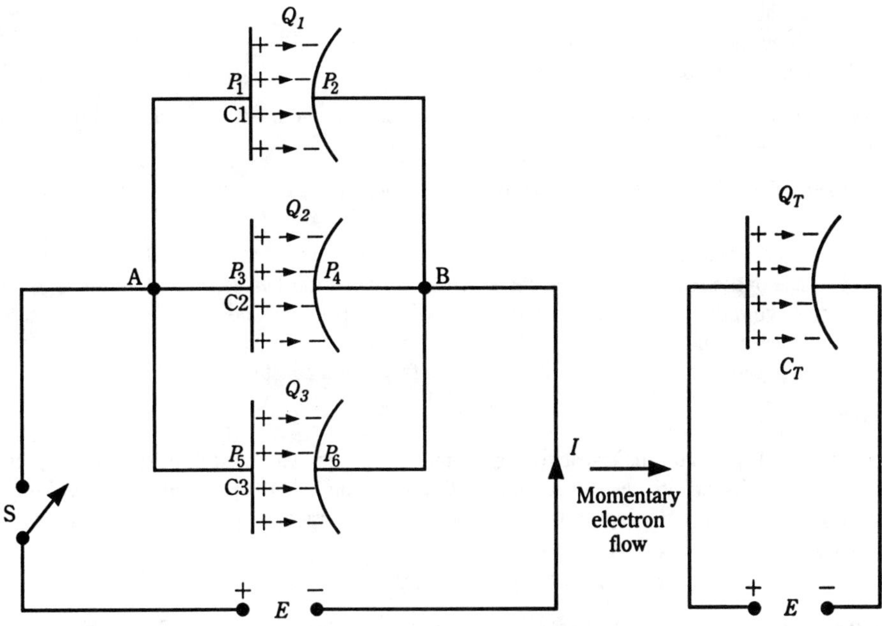

Fig. 1-59 Capacitors in parallel.

Total charge stored:

$$\begin{aligned} Q_T &= Q_1 + Q_2 + Q_3 \\ &= C_1E + C_2E + C_3E \\ &= E\,(C_1 + C_2 + C_3) \end{aligned} \tag{1-104}$$

If C_T is the total equivalent capacitance:

$$Q_T = E \times C_T \text{ coulombs (C)} \tag{1-105}$$

Comparing EQS. 1-104 and 1-105, total capacitance:

$$C_T = C_1 + C_2 + C_3 \text{ farads (F)} \tag{1-106}$$

Therefore, the total equivalent capacitance for capacitors in parallel is found by adding the individual capacitances; the same procedure is used for series combinations of either resistors or inductors.

Question 1-51 The charge on a capacitor:

A. can be disregarded while carrying out maintenance procedures
B. will only remain for a short while after the capacitor is charged from a dc source
C. is equal to the source voltage divided by the value of the capacitance
D. lasts indefinitely, unless it is deliberately bled off
E. is measured in coulombs per square meter

Answer Choice D.

Question 1-52 The capacitance of a capacitor is increased by:

A. reducing the value of the dielectric's relative permittivity
B. raising the spacing between the plates

C. increasing the size of the plates
D. raising the voltage across the plates
E. None of the above choices is true

Answer Choice C. Because $C = \varepsilon A/d$ F, the capacitance is directly proportional to the area of one side of one plate.

Question 1-53 When installing electrolytic capacitors, precautions should be taken to ensure that the:

A. correct polarity is observed
B. value of the capacitance does not exceed a certain critical value
C. voltage rating is not more than the value of the applied voltage
D. capacitor is not used in dc circuits
E. temperature of the surrounding air is maintained at a constant level

Answer Choice A.

Question 1-54 Two 0.1-μF capacitors are connected in series across a 120-Vdc source. These capacitors are subsequently disconnected from the source and are then carefully joined in parallel. If a third uncharged 0.1-μF capacitor is now connected in parallel with the other two capacitors, the voltage across the third capacitor is:

A. 60 V B. 40 V C. 120 V D. 0 V E. 80 V

Answer Choice B. When the two capacitors are connected across the 120-Vdc source, the voltage across each capacitor is 60 V and its charge stored is: 0.1 μF × 60 V = 6 μC. After the capacitors are disconnected and paralleled, the total charge stored is: 2 × 6 = 12 μC. With all three capacitors in parallel, the total capacitance is: 3 × 0.1 = 0.3 μF. The common voltage across each of the capacitors is: 12 μC/0.3 μF = 40 V.

Question 1-55 If a voltage difference exists between two points, but there is no current flowing:

A. there is no electric field intensity between the points
B. an electrostatic field exists between the points
C. an arc will ultimately occur
D. a magnetic field exists between the points
E. the voltage cannot exist without a current flowing

Answer Choice B.

Question 1-56 Two 0.1-μF capacitors are connected in series across a 120-Vdc source. The source is then removed and a third uncharged 0.1-μF capacitor is subsequently connected across the two series capacitors. What is the voltage across the third capacitor?

A. 120 V B. 60 V C. 80 V D. 40 V E. 0 V

Answer Choice D. The two capacitors in series have a total equivalent capacitance of 0.1/2 = 0.05 μF; the total charge stored is therefore 0.05 μF × 120 V = 6 μC. When the third capacitor is connected in parallel, the total capacitance is 0.05 + 0.1 = 0.15 μF. The voltage across the third capacitor is 6 μC/0.15 μF = 40 V.

Question 1-57 The circuit component that has the highest failure rate (is the most unstable) under normal conditions, is the:

A. air-core inductor B. choke C. transformer D. capacitor E. resistor

Answer Choice D. A capacitor can open circuit, short circuit or partially short circuit.

Question 1-58 Two 0.1-μF capacitors are connected in parallel across a 120-Vdc source. The voltage source is then removed and a third uncharged 0.1-μF capacitor is connected across the parallel combination. The voltage across the third capacitor is:

A. 80 V B. 120 V C. 60 V D. 0 V E. 40 V

Answer Choice A. The two capacitors in parallel have a total equivalent capacitance of: 2 × 0.1 = 0.2 μF. The total charge stored is: 0.2 μF × 120 V = 24 μC. When the third capacitor is connected, the total capacitance is: 3 × 0.1 = 0.3 μF. The voltage across the third capacitor is: 24 μC/0.3 μF = 80 V.

* **Question 1-59** In the circuit of FIG. 1-60, the total equivalent capacitance between the points X and Y is:

A. 1.2 μF B. 0.8 μF C. 1.5 μF D. 1.8 μF E. 8 μF

Answer Choice A. The capacitance of C_3 and C_4 in series is: $C_{3,4}$ = 2/2 = 1 μF. Capacitance C_2 is in parallel with $C_{3,4}$ for an equivalent capacitance of: 2 + 1 = 3 μF, which is in series with C_1. The total equivalent capacitance between the points X and Y is: 2 × 3/(2 + 3) = 1.2 μF.

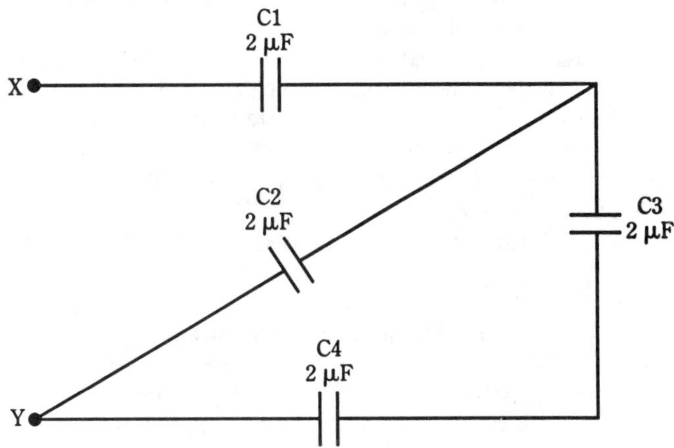

Fig. 1-60 The circuit for question 1-59.

1-21. *RC* time constant

The property of capacitance prevents any sudden change of voltage and also limits the rate at which the voltage can change. Consequently, when the switch, S, is closed in position 1 (FIG. 1-63A), the capacitor requires a certain time before it acquires its full change. This section covers the factors that determine the duration of the so-called *transient* or *changing state.* This is the interval between the time at which the switch, S, is closed in position 1 and the time when the final or steady-state conditions are reached.

Immediately after the switch is closed in position 1, the capacitor cannot charge instantaneously, so the initial value of V_C must be zero. Consequently, to satisfy KVL, the voltage drop across resistor V_R must balance the source voltage, E. The initial current must therefore be at its maximum level of E/R amperes.

As the capacitor charges, its voltage, V_C, rises and therefore the resistor's voltage, V_R, falls because at all times the sum of these voltages exactly balances the source voltage, E. When the voltage drop, V_R, falls, the current is correspondingly less and there is a decrease in the rate at which the capacitor charges. Consequently, this is a situation in which the more the capacitor is charged, the less is its rate of charging. Theoretically, it would take infinite time for the capacitor to charge fully; however, the capacitor acquires its ultimate charge of CE coulombs to within 1% after a finite time interval, which is determined by the capacitance and the resistance.

Remember that the initial current is E/R amperes (coulombs per second), and the capacitor's final charge is CE coulombs. If the initial current has been maintained, the capacitor would have been fully charged after a time of: CE coulombs/(E/R) coulombs per second = RC seconds, which is the *time constant* of the circuit. However, because the rate at which the capacitor charges falls off, the capacitor only acquires 63.2% of its final charge after 1 time constant and it requires 5 time constants before the capacitor is charged to within 1% of CE coulombs (FIG. 1-63B). Only then can you assume that the transient charging period has been concluded.

Notice that the conditions at the start of the transient interval can be predicted by regarding the capacitor as a short circuit, and the final steady-state values can be obtained by considering the capacitor to be an open circuit. Assuming that the steady-state conditions have been reached, now move the switch, S, to position 2 (FIG. 1-64B). The capacitor cannot discharge instantaneously, so V_C must still be equal to E volts. By the KVL rule, the voltage drop across the resistor must abruptly rise to E volts, but its polarity is reversed because the discharge current, I_D, is in the opposite direction to the original charging current, I_C.

As the capacitor discharges, V_C and V_R fall together in order to maintain the voltage balance around the closed loop. When V_R decreases, the current is reduced so that the capacitor discharges more slowly. Theoretically, it would take infinite time for the capacitor to discharge fully, but after one time constant the capacitor has *lost* 63.2% of its initial charge and its charge has therefore dropped to 36.8% of CE coulombs. After five time constants we assume that the transient discharge has been concluded in a sense that I_D, V_C, V_R have all fallen to less than 1% of their original values (FIG. 1-64B). The growth and decay percentages are shown in TABLE 1-7.

Table 1-7.
Growth and decay percentages.

Number of time constants	Growth percentage	Decay percentage
0.5	39.3	60.7
0.7	50.3	49.7
1.0	63.2	36.8
2.0	86.5	13.5
3.0	95.0	5.0
4.0	98.2	1.8
5.0	99.3	0.7

* **Question 1-60** In the circuit of FIG. 1-61, R_1 = 20 Ω, C = 40 μF, L = 0.1 H; the reading of V is 40 V and the reading of A is 3 A. The power can be calculated from:

A. the product of the readings of V and A
B. $V^2/(R_1 + R_2)$ watts
C. (Reading of A)^2 × $(R_1 + R_2)$ watts
D. the product of the readings of V and A multiplied by the power factor
E. the power cannot be calculated, but must be measured by a wattmeter

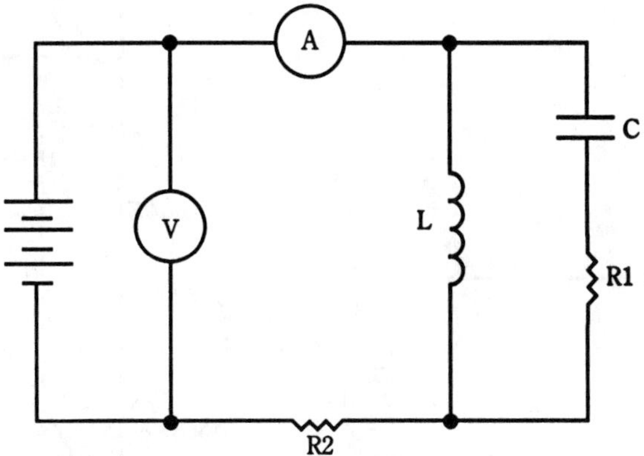

Fig. 1-61 The circuit for question 1-60.

Answer Choice A. Under steady-state conditions in this dc circuit, the inductor behaves as a short circuit and the capacitor as an open circuit. Power $= V \times A = V^2/R_2 = A^2 \times RW.$

Question 1-61 The conductance of the circuit in FIG. 1-62 is:

A. 30 Ω B. 0.05 S C. 0.1 S D. 0.033 S E. 20 S

Answer Choice D. Under steady-state conditions in a dc circuit, the inductor behaves as a short circuit and the capacitor as an open circuit. Total resistance = 20 + 10 = 30 Ω. Total conductance = 1/30 Ω = 0.033 S.

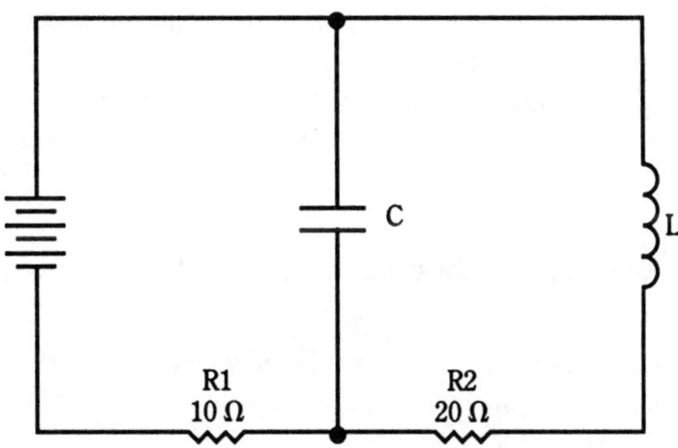

Fig. 1-62 The circuit for question 1-61.

Question 1-62 The time constant of a series RC circuit is found by:

A. dividing the value of the capacitance by the value of the resistance
B. dividing the value of the resistance by the value of the capacitance
C. multiplying the value of the capacitance by the value of the resistance
D. multiplying the value of the capacitance by the square of the value of the resistance
E. multiplying the square of the value of the capacitance by the value of the resistance

Answer Choice C. Time constant $= R \times C$ seconds.

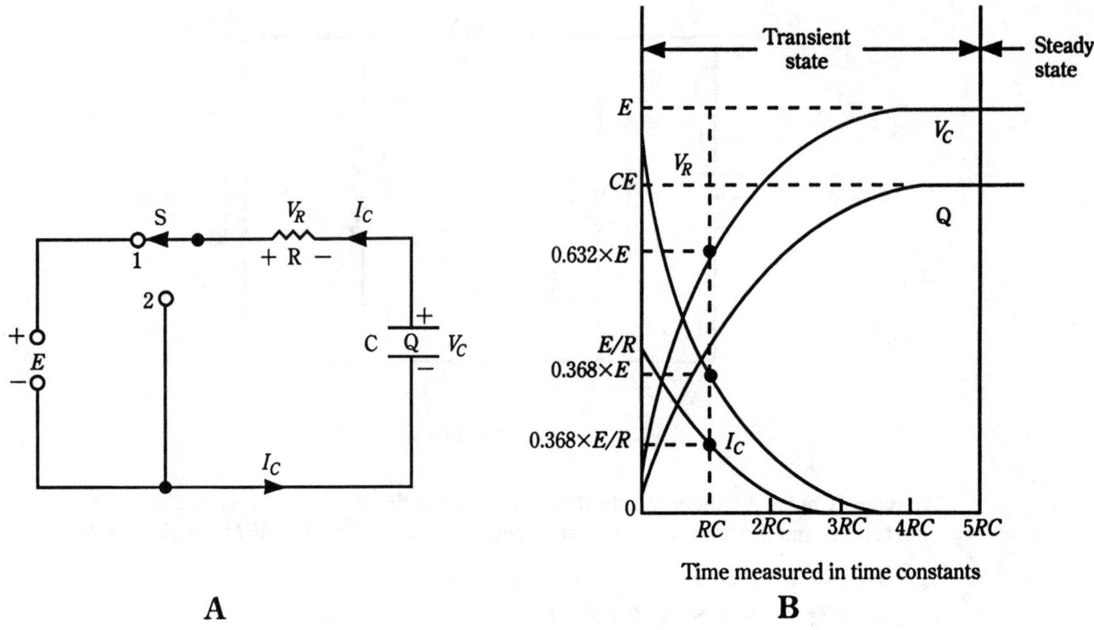

Fig. 1-63 Charging a capacitor through a resistor.

* **Question 1-63** A charged capacitor is connected across a resistor. The time constant of this circuit is:

A. the half-life of the capacitor when shunted by the resistor
B. equal to the natural period of the circuit's oscillation
C. equal to the value of the capacitance divided by the resistance
D. the time required for the capacitor to discharge to a certain percentage of its initial voltage
E. the time required for the capacitor to discharge completely

Answer Choice D. After one time constant, the capacitor has discharged to 36.8% of its initial voltage.

* **Question 1-64** In the circuit of FIG. 1-65, what is the voltage across the capacitor, C, after the switch, S, has been closed for a time interval of 500 ms?

A. 0 V B. 7.56 V C. 3.78 V D. 5 V E. 12 V

Answer Choice E. The time constant of the circuit is $RC = 20 \times 10^3 \times 5 \times 10^{-6}$ s = 100 ms. Because 500 ms is equivalent to five time constants, the capacitor is assumed to be fully charged to 12 V.

* **Question 1-65** In the circuit of FIG. 1-66, what is the voltage across the capacitor, C, after the switch, S, has been closed for a time interval of 0.5 s?

A. 3.93 V B. 6.32 V C. 5 V D. 10 V E. 0 V

Answer Choice A. The time constant of the circuit is: $RC = 10 \times 10^6 \times 0.1 \times 10^{-6}$s = 1 s. After the 0.5 time constant, the capacitor is charged to: $0.393 \times 10 = 3.93$ V (TABLE 1-7).

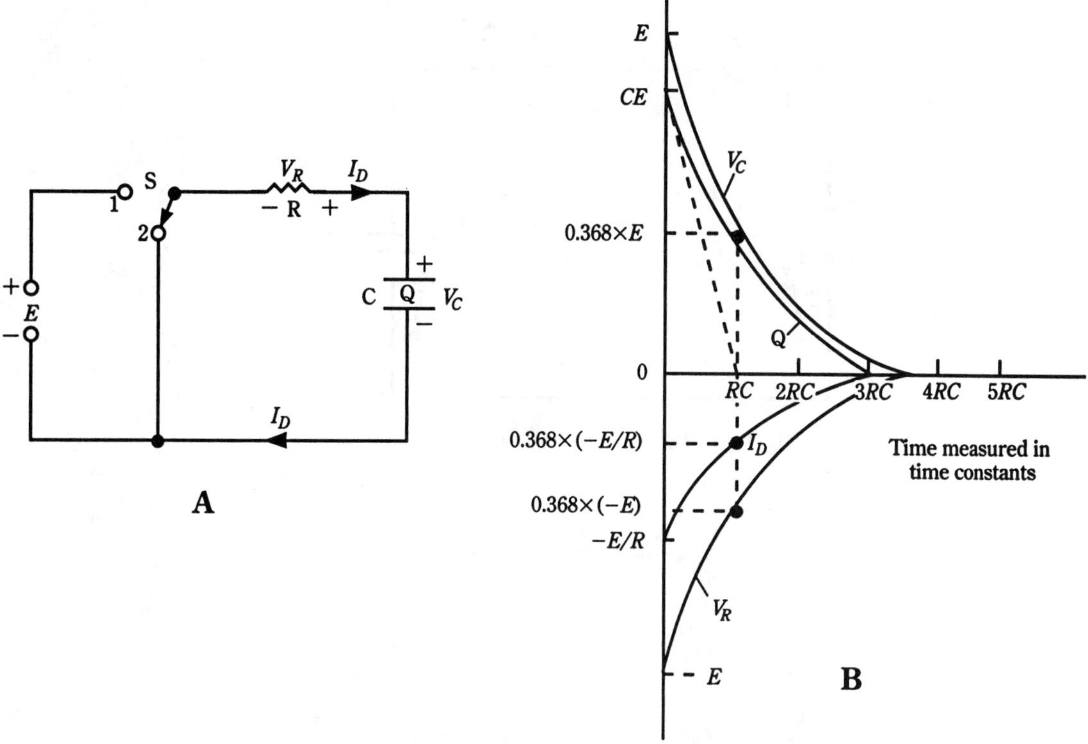

Fig. 1-64 Discharging of a capacitor through a resistor.

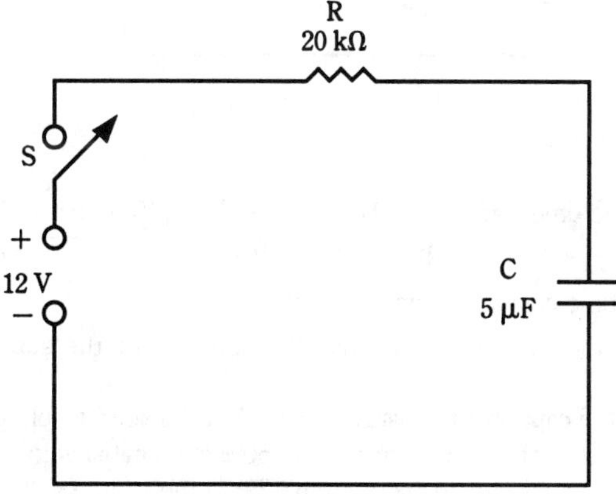

Fig. 1-65 The circuit for question 1-64.

* **Question 1-66** In the circuit of FIG. 1-67, what is the voltage across the capacitor, C, after the switch, S, has been closed for a time interval of 50 ms?

A. 7.56 V B. 3.78 V C. 5 V D. 10 V E. 0 V

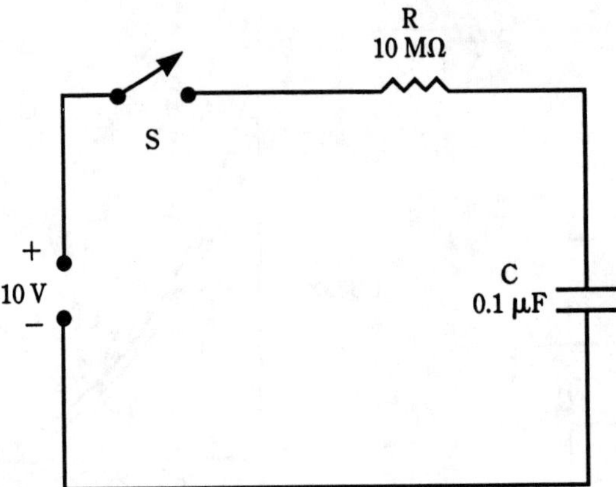

Fig. 1-66 The circuit for question 1-65.

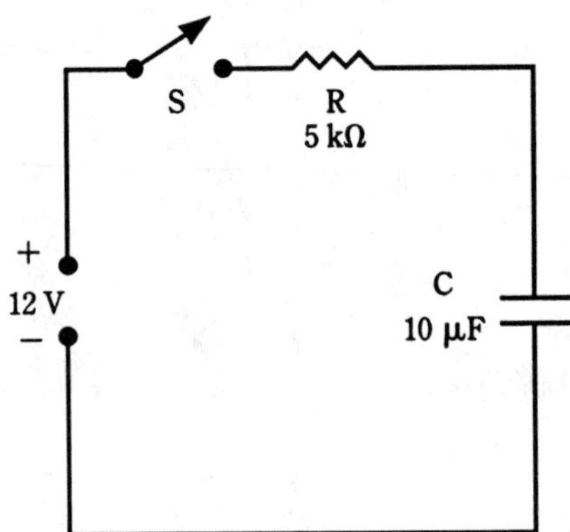

Fig. 1-67 The circuit for question 1-66.

Answer Choice A. The time constant of the circuit is: $RC = 5 \times 10^3 \times 10 \times 10^{-6}\text{s} = 50$ ms. After one time constant, the capacitor is charged to: $0.632 \times 12 = 7.56$ V.

* **Question 1-67** The time constant of an RC circuit is the:

A. time taken by the capacitor to charge completely after the source voltage is initially applied
B. time taken by the capacitor to charge to 39.3% of the source voltage
C. time taken for the capacitor to discharge to 50% of its initial voltage
D. time taken by the capacitor to charge to 63.2% of the source voltage
E. time taken for the capacitor to discharge to 63.2% of its initial voltage

Answer Choice D. Refer to TABLE 1-7.

1-22. Dc measurements of current, voltage, and resistance

The moving-coil meter movement

The *moving-coil meter movement* is an electromechanical device whose action depends on the motor effect. One of its main applications is the voltmeter/ohmmeter/milliammeter (VOM), which is a multimeter that is capable of measuring voltage, current, and resistance. Such an instrument does not require an external power supply for its operation.

The meter movement itself essentially consists of a rectangular coil that is made from fine insulated copper wire wound on a light aluminum frame (FIG. 1-68A). This frame is carried by a spindle that pivots in jeweled bearings. The current that creates the deflection is lead into and out of the coil by the spiral hair springs, HH′, which behave as the controlling device and provide the restoring torque. The whole assembly is mounted between the poles of a permanent magnet so that the amount of current flowing through the coil, creates the deflecting torque. The coil is then free to move in the gaps between the permanent magnetic pole pieces, P, and the soft-iron cylinder, A, which is normally carried by a nonmagnetic bridge attached to P (FIG. 1-68A). The purpose of the soft-iron cylinder is to concentrate the magnetic flux and to produce a radial magnetic field with a uniform flux density. For a given current, the deflecting torque will then be constant over a wide arc (FIG. 1-68B).

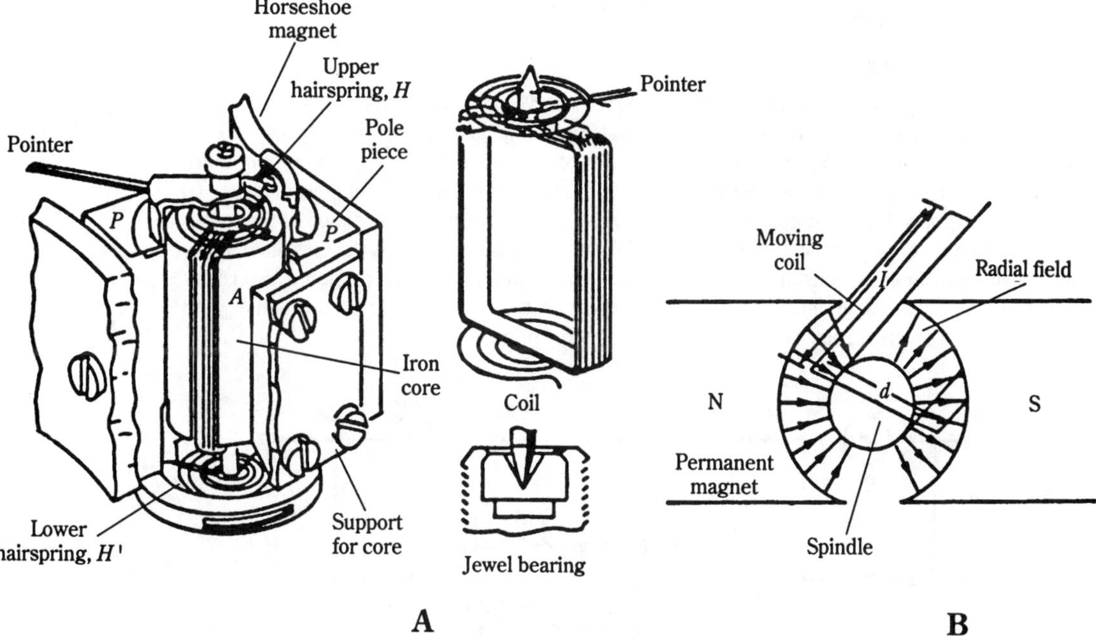

Fig. 1-68 The D'Arsonval meter movement.

The motor effect shows that the deflecting torque is directly proportional to the current so that the divisions on the scale of the VOM are equally spaced.

When the coil rotates toward the equilibrium position, where the deflecting and restoring torques are balanced, there could be an overswing and the coil could oscillate before finally coming to rest. This unwanted oscillation is prevented by eddy current damping of the aluminum frame (Lenz's law).

The sensitivity of the moving-coil meter movement is inversely related to the amount of the current required to provide full-scale deflection. A high sensitivity will require many turns of fine copper wire to be mounted on a light aluminum frame and then be attached to delicate hair springs. In particular, the sensitivity will depend on the strength of the meter's permanent magnet because with a high flux density, even a weak current passing through the coil will be able to produce an appreciable deflection torque.

Any flow of current through the deflecting copper coil will raise its temperature and increase its resistance. A swamping resistor with a negative temperature coefficient is therefore added in series with the coil to provide a suitable total resistance (for example, 50 Ω), which is virtually independent of temperature.

The accuracy of the meter is given as the percentage error related to the full-scale current. For example, if the error of a 0.1-mA meter movement is ± 2%, the accuracy for the reading of 1 mA is ± 2/100 × 1 mA = ± 0.02 mA, but if the reading is only 0.1 mA, the accuracy is still ±0.02 mA and the percentage error rises to (± 0.02/0.1) × 100 = ±20%.

$$Sensitivity = \frac{1}{Full\text{-}scale\ deflection\ current} \text{ ohms per volt } (\Omega/\text{V}) \qquad (1\text{-}107)$$

$$Full\ scale\ deflection\ current = \frac{1}{Sensitivity} \text{ amperes (A)} \qquad (1\text{-}108)$$

The milliammeter

Assume that you have a basic moving-coil meter movement whose total resistance (coil resistance and swamping resistance) is 50 Ω and whose full-scale deflection is 50 μA (sensitivity = 1/50 μA = 20,000 Ω/V). Clearly, such an instrument would not be capable of measuring a current of more than 50 μA, whereas you might be required to measure currents of hundreds of milliamperes. To solve this problem, a shunt resistor, R_{sh}, is connected across the series combination of the meter movement and the swamp resistor (FIG. 1-69A). This shunt resistor is a low-value precision type, which is usually made from constantan wire with its negligible temperature coefficient. As a result of the shunt's low resistance, most of the current to be measured will be diverted through R_{sh} and only a small part of the current will pass through the meter movement.

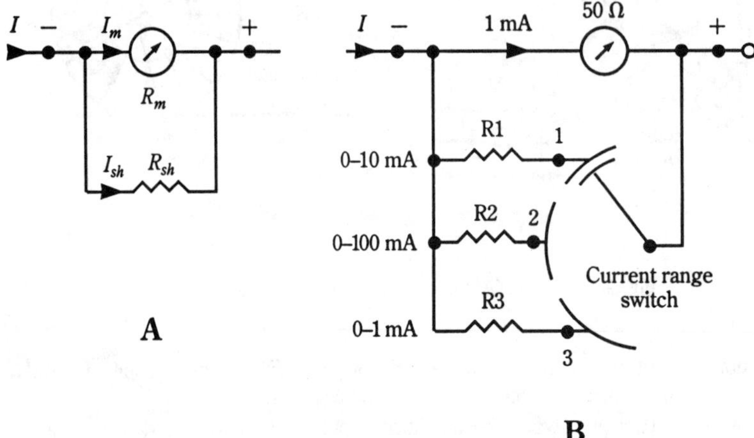

Fig. 1-69 The milliammeter.

Figure 1-69B, shows an arrangement that has a number of shunts for different current ranges. However, in order to take a current reading, the circuit must first be broken. The instrument is then inserted in the break so that it is directly in the path of the current to be measured. When switching from one current range to another, the meter movement could momentarily be placed in the circuit without the protection of the shunt; as a result, the meter movement might be damaged. This could be avoided by using a make-before-break switch.

Because of its very low resistance, a current meter must never be placed directly across a voltage source. After your current measurements have been completed, you should, for safety's sake, switch to a high-voltage range. Moreover, if you have no idea of the value of the current to be measured, you should start with the highest current range and then, if necessary, move to lower ranges until you obtain an appropriate deflection.

In FIG. 1-69A, measured current: $I = I_m + I_{sh}$ amperes (A) (1-109)

Because the shunt resistance and the total resistance of the meter movement are in parallel:

$$I_{sh} \times R_{sh} = I_m \times R_m \text{ volts (V)} \quad (1\text{-}110)$$

Combining EQS. 1-109 and 1-110, the value of the shunt resistance:

$$R_{sh} = \frac{I_m \times R_m}{I_{sh}} = \frac{I_m \times R_m}{I - I_m} \text{ ohms } (\Omega) \quad (1\text{-}111)$$

where: I = current to be measured (A or mA)
I_m = current flow through the meter movement (mA or µA)
R_{sh} = shunt resistance (Ω)
R_m = total resistance of the meter movement (Ω)

The voltmeter and the loading effect

A voltmeter is placed in parallel with (shunting across) the component whose potential difference is to be measured. This means that the voltmeter must possess as high a resistance as possible so that it has a minimum loading effect on the circuit being monitored. The moving-coil meter movement by itself is basically a millivoltmeter or microvoltmeter so that, in order to adapt the movement for higher voltages, it is necessary to connect a series "multiplier" resistor, R_S (FIG. 1-70A). Most of the voltage to be measured is then dropped across this high-value series resistor and only a small amount appears across the meter movement to provide the necessary deflection. For a multirange voltmeter, a separate multiplier resistor can be used for each range.

On a particular range, the total resistance of VOM (including the multiplier resistor) can be found from the product of the sensitivity and the range's full-scale deflection voltage. For example, if the sensitivity is 20,000 Ω/V and the full-scale deflection voltage is 10 V, the voltmeter's resistance is: 20,000 Ω/V × 10 V = 200,000 Ω = 200 kΩ. On the 100-V range, the voltmeter's resistance would be: 20,000 Ω/V × 100 V = 2,000,000 Ω = 2 MΩ.

Loading effect

An ideal voltmeter would have infinite resistance so that the instrument does not load the circuit being monitored. However, the resistance of a moving-coil voltmeter is far from infinite; moreover, its resistance changes with the particular voltage range that you select. The worst loading effect occurs with a low-voltage, high-resistance circuit (such as shown in FIG. 1-70B).

With no voltmeter present, the voltage existing between points A and B is 6 V, so you would switch to the 0- to 10-V range. Assuming that the voltmeter's sensitivity is 20,000 Ω/V, the voltmeter's resistance is 200 kΩ. To read the voltage between points A and B, the voltmeter is connected across the lower 200-kΩ resistor. However, the parallel combination of this resistor

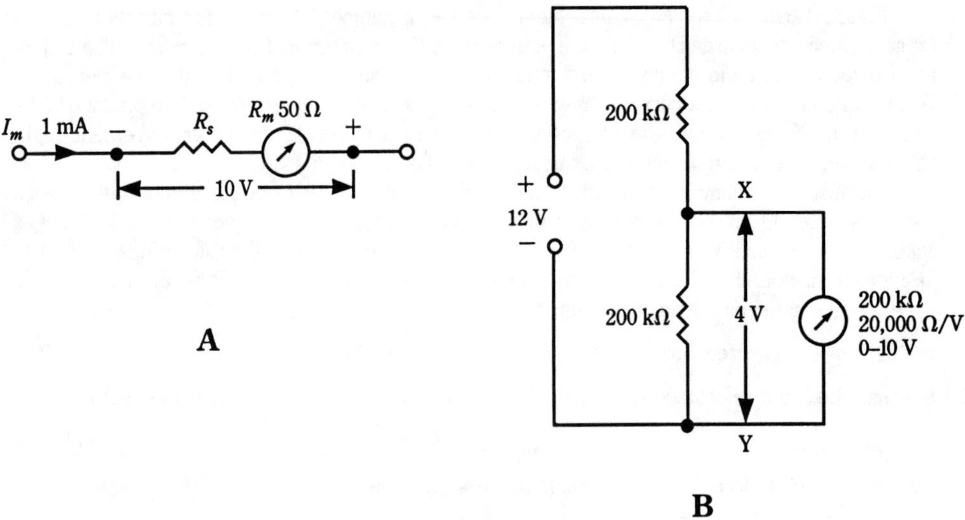

Fig. 1-70 The voltmeter and its loading effect.

and the voltmeter only has a total resistance of: 200 kΩ/2 = 100 kΩ. Therefore, by using the VDR, the voltmeter reading will be 12 V × 100 kΩ/(100 kΩ + 200 kΩ) = 4 V. The loading effect of the voltmeter has therefore reduced the voltage between A and B from 6 V down to 4 V.

Most solid-state voltmeters have very high resistances (several MΩ), which are independent of the voltage range chosen; such voltmeters have a minimum loading effect on the circuit being monitored.

In FIG. 1-70A, total resistance of the voltmeter:

$$R_v = \frac{V}{I_m} \text{ ohms } (\Omega) = V \times (\text{sensitivity in } \Omega/\text{V}) \tag{1-112}$$

Resistance of series multiplier resistor:

$$R_s = \frac{V}{I_m} - R_m = V \times (\text{sensitivity in } \Omega/\text{V}) - R_m \text{ ohms } (\Omega) \tag{1-113}$$

where: R_s = resistance of series multiplier resistor (Ω)
V = full-scale deflection voltage (V)
I_m = full-scale deflection current (A)
R_m = total resistance of the meter movement (Ω)
R_v = total resistance of the voltmeter (Ω)

The ohmmeter

Because all resistance measurements must be made with power removed from the circuit, it is necessary to provide one or more primary cells to create the necessary deflection. The cells are normally included within the instrument itself.

In its simplest form (FIG. 1-71A), an ohmmeter would consist of a 1.5-V primary cell, a rheostat and a 0- to 1-mA moving-coil meter movement with its 50-Ω total resistance. The unknown resistance, R_x, is then connected between the probes of the ohmmeter.

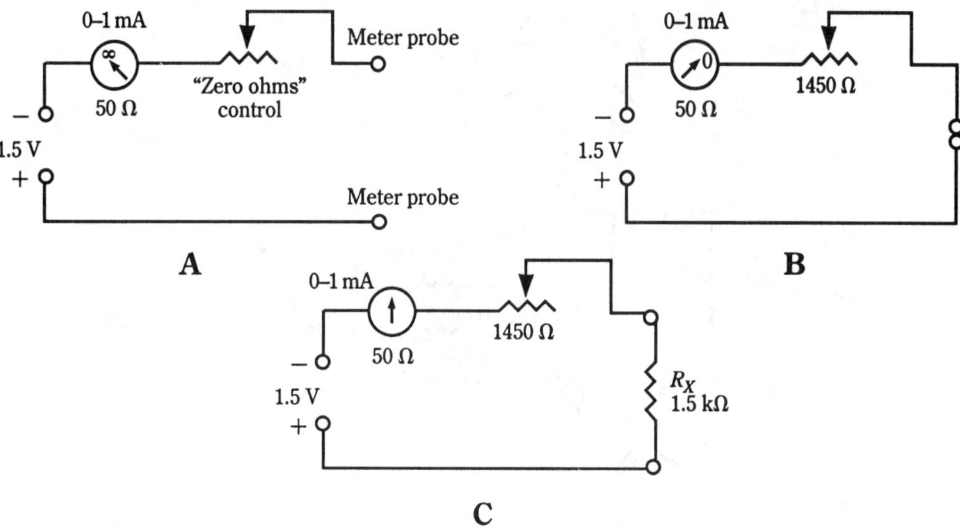

Fig. 1-71 The basic ohmmeter.

The steps involved with taking a resistance reading are:

1. Place the probes apart so that an open circuit (infinite resistance) exists and there is zero current. The needle will then be on the far left-hand side of the scale (FIG. 1-71A) so that the reading is zero current, but infinite ohms. The symbol for infinity is ∞, which is normally marked on the ohms scale. If the needle is not correctly on the zero current mark, the torque provided by the hairsprings can be mechanically adjusted.
2. Short the probes together (FIG. 1-71B) to create zero resistance, then adjust the rheostat until the full-scale deflection current of 1 mA flows and the needle is on the far right of the scale. The circuit's total resistance is now 1.5V/1 mA = 1500 Ω and the value of the rheostat, R_{rh}, is then 1550 Ω − 50 Ω = 1450 Ω. As the cell ages, its terminal voltage decreases and the rheostat can be adjusted to bring the current back up to 1 mA.
3. Assume that a 1500-Ω resistor, R_x, is now connected between the probes (FIG. 1-71C). The current would then be 1.5 V/(1450 Ω + 50 Ω + 1500 Ω) = 0.5 mA and the needle would be in the center of the scale. Consequently, we have ∞ on the left of the scale, 0 Ω on the right, and 1500 Ω in the center. The scale is therefore nonlinear because the deflection current is inversely dependent on the value of the unknown resistance. The deflection marks are expanded on the low-resistance side, but are crowded on the high-resistance end. Clearly, such a scale could not be used for accurate measurements of high resistances (greater than 10 kΩ).

With the VOM, it is common practice to have three resistance ranges: $R \times 1$, $R \times 100$, $R \times 10{,}000$. This is achieved by including the multiplier resistors, R_S, as shown in FIG. 1-72. On the $R \times 1$ range, the multiplier resistor, R_{S1}, has a high resistance so that if R_x has a value of 150 kΩ (for example), the needle would be close to the infinite mark and an accurate reading would be impossible. However, if you now switch to the $R \times 100$ range, with its lower multiplier resistor, R_{S2}, the needle is deflected to the middle of the scale and the reading would be 1500 Ω × 100 = 150,000 Ω = 150 kΩ.

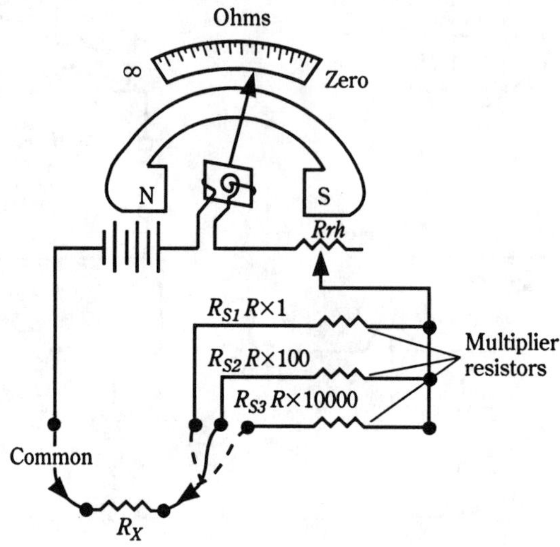

Fig. 1-72 Resistance ranges of the ohmmeter.

Notice that because the multiplier resistors have different values, you must always readjust the "zero ohms" rheostat when switching from one resistance range to another.

* **Question 1-68** A voltmeter on its 0- to 50-V range has a total resistance of 50 kΩ. The value of the instrument's sensitivity is:

A. 1000 Ω/V B. 1000 V/Ω C. 5000 Ω/V D. 5000 V/Ω E. 10,000 Ω/V

Answer Choice A. The sensitivity is 50 kΩ/50 V = 1 kΩ/V = 1000 Ω/V.

* **Question 1-69** An ammeter with a resistance of 3750 Ω has a scale with 12 divisions. When 120 V is applied to the meter, the reading shows full-scale deflection. When another resistor is added in series with the meter, the reading is 7.5 divisions if the applied voltage is increased to 135 V. The value of the additional resistor is:

A. 1500 Ω B. 7500 Ω C. 6750 Ω D. 3750 Ω E. 3000 Ω

Answer Choice E. Full-scale deflection current $= \dfrac{120\text{ V}}{3750\ \Omega} = 0.032$ A. When 135 V is applied, the current is 0.032 A × 7.5/12 = 0.02 A. Total resistance is: 135 V/0.02 A = 6750 Ω. The value of the additional resistor is: 6750 − 3750 = 3000 Ω.

* **Question 1-70** A high-value resistor is added in series with a moving-coil meter movement. The purpose of this resistor is to:

A. swamp out variations in the moving coil's resistance as a result of temperature changes
B. prevent the needle from overswinging
C. increase the current range of the meter
D. decrease the current range of the meter
E. extend the voltage range of the meter

Answer Choice E. The high resistor acts as a "multiplier" to extend the voltage range.

1-23 Dc machines

Principles of the dc electrical generator

The *dc generator* or *dynamo* is a practical application of electromagnetic induction. In its simplest form, the generator consists of a single turn or loop, which is mounted on a shaft; this shaft is then turned by some external form of mechanical energy. The loop is rotated at constant speed in a uniform magnetic field, which is normally produced by electromagnets, rather than by permanent poles; these electromagnets are excited by the flow of current through a field coil. The flux is then cut by the loop's conductors T and T′ (FIG. 1-73) so that electromagnetic induction will cause a voltage to appear at the ends of the loop. In position B, one conductor (T) is moving vertically upward while the other conductor (T′) is moving downward. Using the left-hand rule for the generator effect, one end of the loop (point X) is negative, with respect to the other end (point Y). However, after one-half revolution of the loop (position D), the movements of the two conductors are reversed so that the polarities at X and Y are changed. Thus, a loop that rotates in a magnetic field naturally generates an alternating voltage.

As a means of delivering this ac voltage to a load, the ends of the loop are taken to two brass slip rings, which rotate with the shaft and make contact with two stationary carbon brushes.

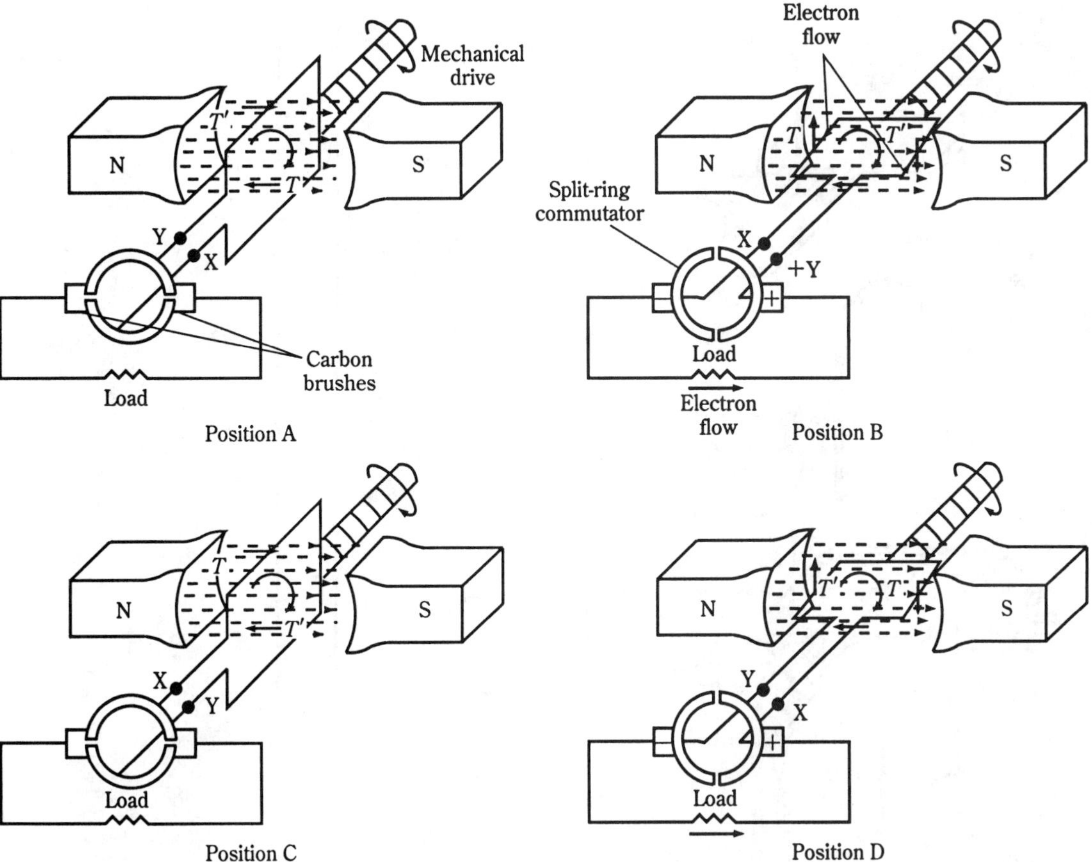

Fig. 1-73 Principles of the dc generator.

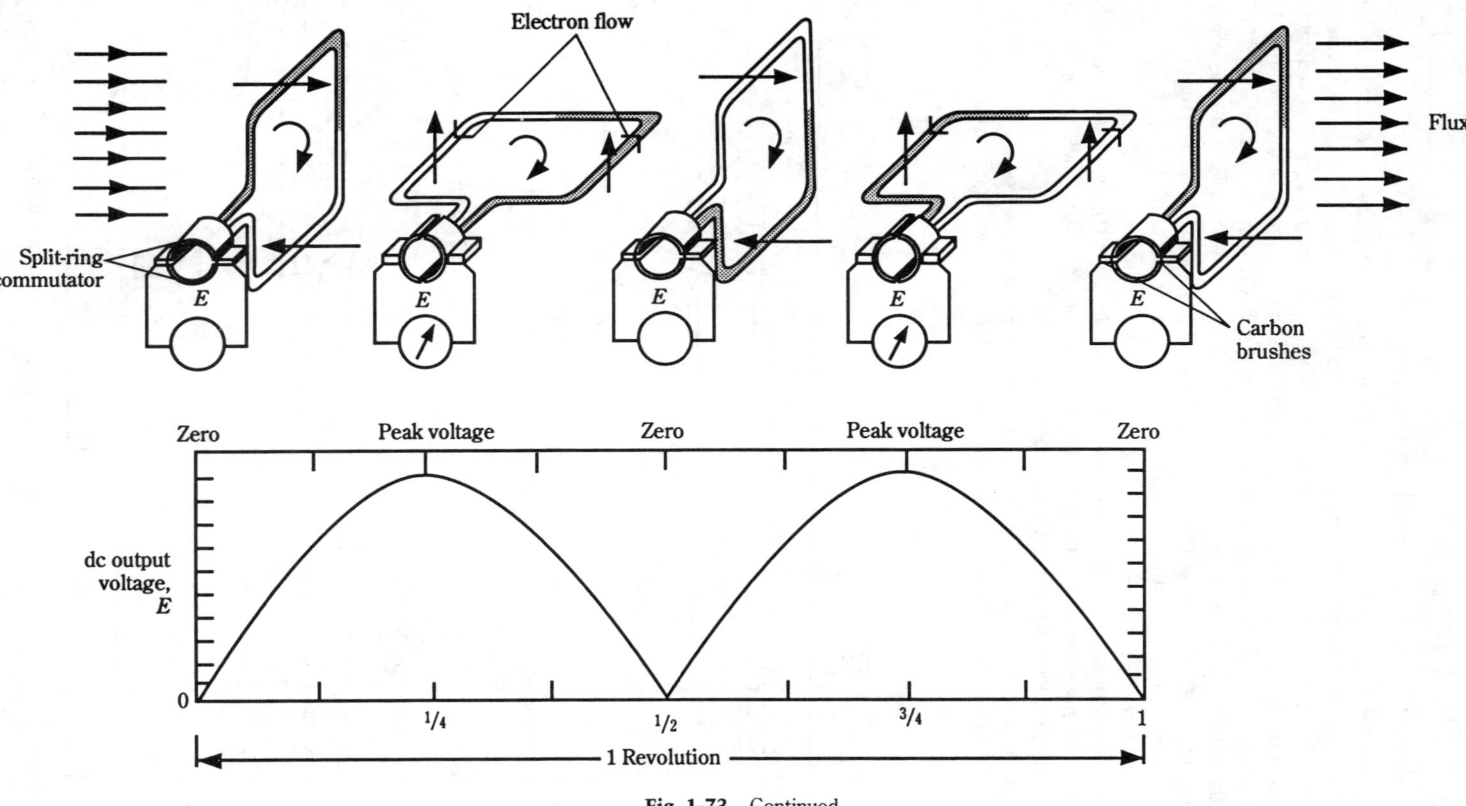

Fig. 1-73 Continued

These brushes are then joined to the generator's external terminals, across which the load is connected.

In order to produce a dc output voltage, the two separate slip rings are replaced by a single ring, and split into two segments, which are insulated from each other. This split ring is called a *commutator,* which mechanically reverses the coil connections to the load at the same instant that the polarity of the generated voltage reverses in the loop. By this means, the alternating voltage, which is naturally generated by the loop, is converted into a form of dc voltage to be applied to the load. A device that converts ac to dc is called a *rectifier,* so the commutator is behaving as a type of mechanical rectifier.

As the loop is rotated clockwise from position A to position B, the loop is cutting the flux at an increasing angle, so the EMF is rising and driving an electron flow from left to right through the load. When you reach position B, the conductors of the loop are instantaneously cutting the flux at right angles, so the generated EMF reaches its maximum value. As the rotation is continued from position B to position C, the angle at which the loop's conductors are cutting the flux is decreasing, so the output voltage across the load falls. In position C, the conductors are momentarily moving parallel with the flux, so no lines are cut and the generated EMF is zero. At this same instant, each of the carbon brushes makes contact with both segments of the split ring, so the loop is temporarily short-circuited. As you move from position C to position D, the output voltage again rises from zero to a maximum, but the polarities of the voltages induced in the loop's conductors are reversed. However, because the segments of the commutator have rotated with the loop and are now connected to opposite carbon brushes, the direction of the electron flow through the load remains unchanged. The output voltage across the load is described as being fluctuating, but it is unidirectional because its polarity never reverses.

Figure 1-73 shows the graph of the fluctuating dc output voltage for one complete rotation of the loop. This type of dc voltage could be used to charge a battery (such as a lead-acid secondary cell), but it is unsuitable for most applications. Practical dc generators create a steady dc voltage, which is accompanied by a small fluctuation or ripple. The ripple represents the variation in the output voltage as the conductors are rotated; it is, of course, undesirable and must be reduced to an acceptable level.

To increase the output voltage, the single loop can be replaced by a coil that consists of a number of turns. This coil is mounted on a slotted cylindrical armature, which is made of sheet steel laminations. To reduce the large ripple generated by a single coil, two separate coils can be connected to a commutator, which is split into four segments (FIG. 1-74). When the voltage generated by one coil falls to the level that is represented by E_1, the brushes break contact with the pair of opposite segments connected to this coil. At the same instant, the brushes contact the other pair of segments, which are connected to the coil whose generated EMF is rising toward the maximum level, E_2. The variation in the output voltage is now restricted to the difference between E_1 and E_2 levels. The ripple can obviously be further reduced by distributing more coils around the solid armature and splitting the commutator into a greater number of segments.

Practical dc generators

So far, the exciting field winding provides the magnetic flux and the armature winding is where the generated EMF is induced. Now consider the various methods of connecting the field winding and the armature winding.

Figure 1-75 shows the general arrangement of a four-pole machine, which has less ripple than the two-pole generator. The four-pole machine has four brushes, B, which contact the commutator. These brushes are alternatively positive and negative so that the two positive brushes are connected together and to the positive terminal, A. Similarly, the negative brushes are joined together and to the negative terminal, A′.

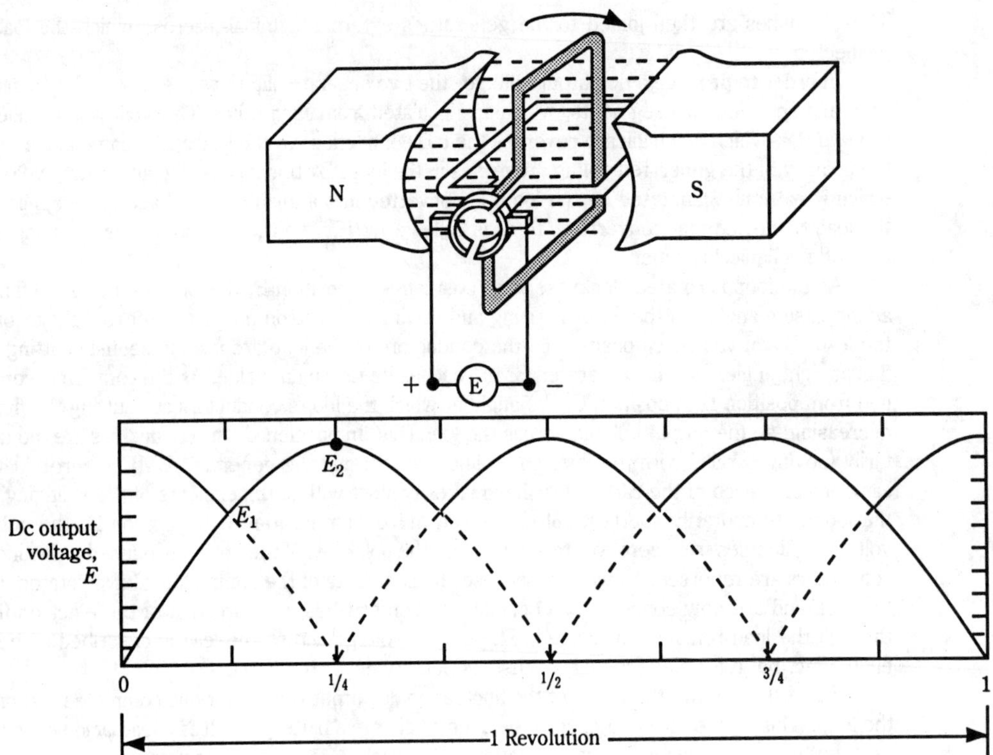

Fig. 1-74 A dc generator with two coils.

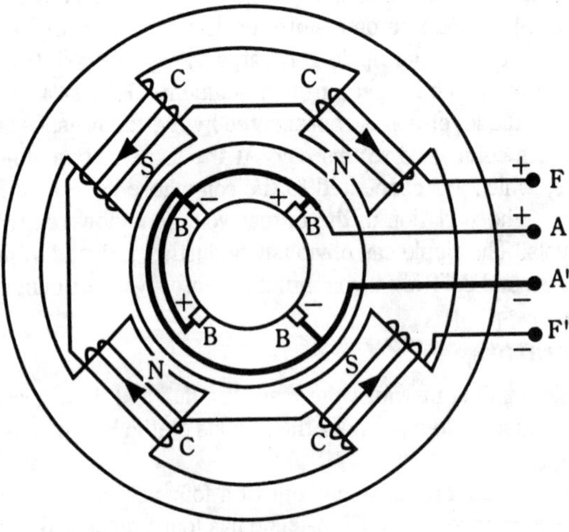

Fig. 1-75 Armature and field connections for a four-pole generator.

The four exciting or field coils, C, are usually joined in series and the ends are brought out to the terminals, F and F′. These coils must be connected to produce alternative N and S poles.

The following methods can be used to connect field and armature windings:

1. Separately excited dc generators. The field winding is connected to a separate voltage source and not to the armature.
2. Self-excited dc generators, which can be sub-divided into:
   a. Shunt-wound dc generator. The field winding is connected in parallel across the armature terminals.
   b. Series-wound dc generator. The field winding is connected in series with the armature winding.

Separately-excited dc generator

Figure 1-76 shows a simple way to represent the armature and field windings; A and A′ are the armature terminals, and F and F′ are the field terminals. The field winding is connected to a separate dc voltage source.

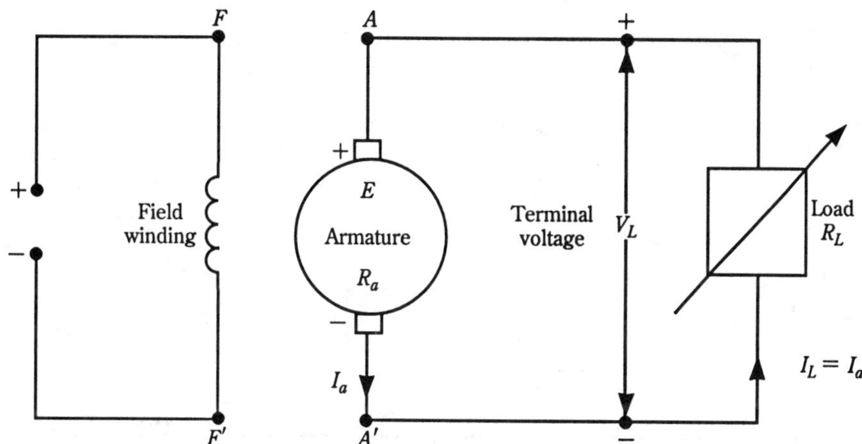

Fig. 1-76 A separately-excited dc generator.

Now consider how the terminal voltage, V_L, changes as the load current, I_L, is varied. If the load current increases, a greater voltage drop is across the armature winding so that the terminal voltage falls. For example, if the full-load current is 100 A and the resistance of the armature circuit is 0.08 Ω, the corresponding voltage drop is 100 A × 0.08 Ω = 8 V. If the generated EMF is 235 V, the terminal voltage: $V_L = 235 - 8 = 227$ V. Therefore:

$$V_L = E - I_a R_a \tag{1-114}$$

where: V_L = terminal voltage (V)
E = no-load EMF (V)
I_a = armature (load) current (A)
R_a = armature resistance (Ω)

The corresponding regulation curve is shown in FIG. 1-77. The percentage regulation is given by:

$$\text{Percentage regulation} = \frac{E_{NL} - V_{FL}}{V_{FL}} \times 100\%$$
$$= \frac{235 - 227}{227} \times 100 \qquad (1\text{-}115)$$
$$= 3.4\%$$

The separately excited generator has the disadvantage of requiring a dc voltage source for the field winding and is therefore only used in special cases.

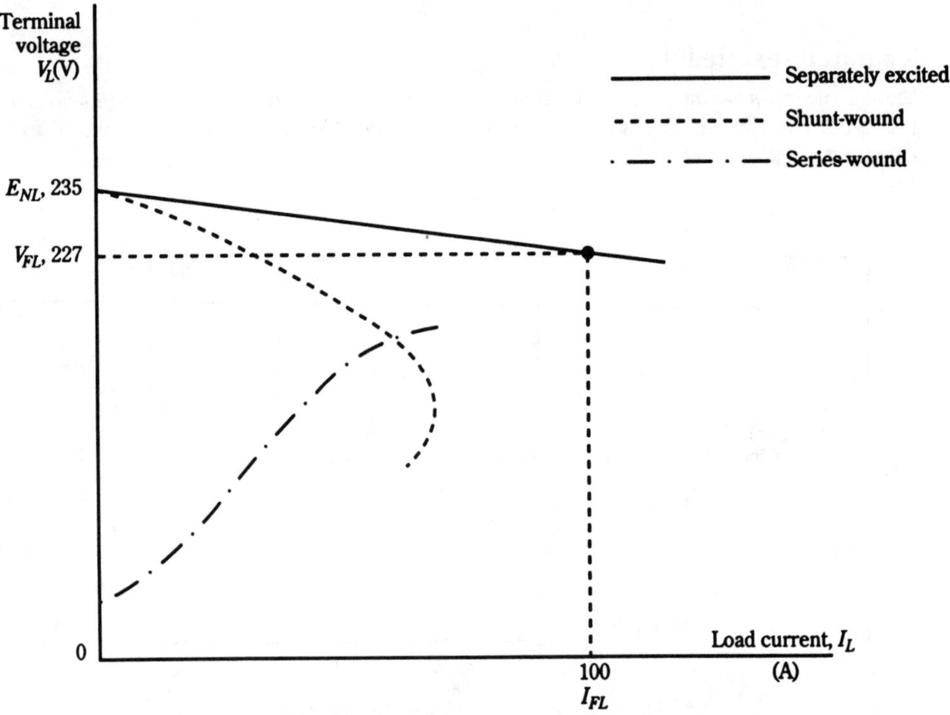

Fig. 1-77 Regulation curves of practical dc generator.

Shunt-wound dc generator

The field winding is connected in series with a rheostat and this combination is placed across the armature terminals (FIG. 1-78). The power absorbed by the circuit of the field winding is kept within reasonable limits by winding the field coils with many turns of comparatively thin wire.

The variation of the terminal voltage, V_L, with the load current, I_L, is greater than that for the corresponding separately excited generator (FIG. 1-77). When the load current increases, the terminal voltage falls; this causes a reduction in the field current so that the magnetic flux is less and the generated EMF, E, drops. If the load current is further increased, these variations become more marked. Ultimately, the load current reaches an unstable value, when the effect of reducing the load resistance still further causes the terminal voltage to fall so much that the load current decreases.

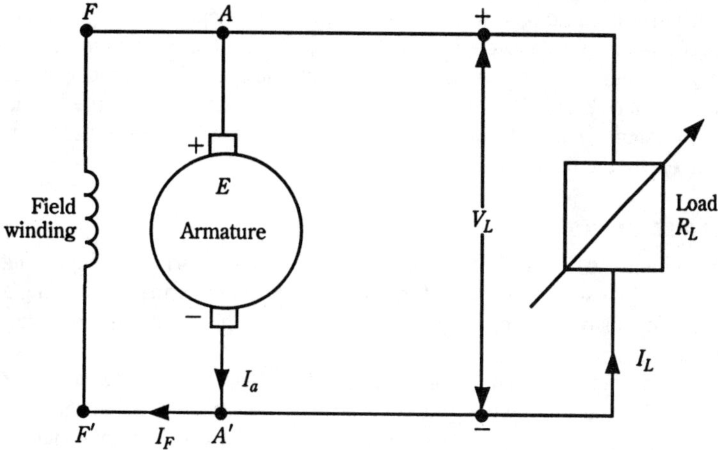

Fig. 1-78 The shunt-wound dc generator.

Series-wound dc generator

All of the armature current passes through the field winding (FIG. 1-79), which therefore consists of comparatively few turns of thick wire.

When the machine is on an open-circuit (the switch, S, is open), the terminal voltage, V_L, is very small and is only caused by the residual flux in the poles of the electromagnets. If S is closed when the load resistance, R_L, is large, the machine is virtually unexcited. However, as R_L is reduced, a value is reached when a slight reduction in R_L is accompanied by a relatively large increase in V_L. From the regulation curve shown in FIG. 1-77, it is obvious that the series-wound dc generator is unsuitable when the terminal voltage must remain approximately constant over a wide range of load current.

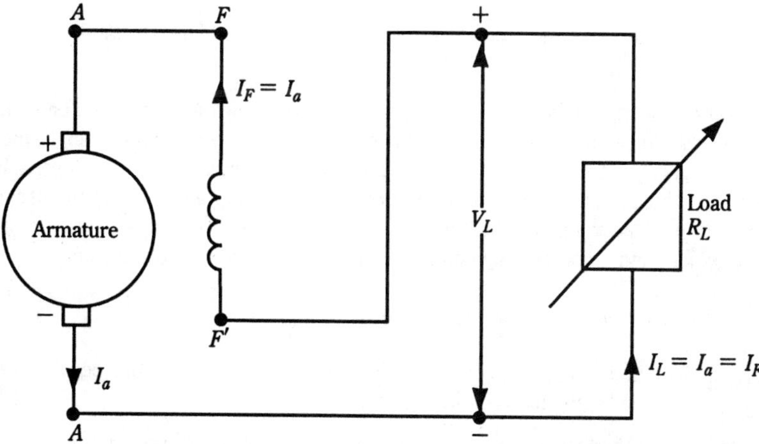

Fig. 1-79 The series-wound dc generator.

Practical dc motors

There is no difference in construction between a dc generator and a dc motor. In its basic form, a dc motor converts electrical energy into mechanical energy and consists of current-carrying conductors that are mounted on a armature and are then positioned in a magnetic field. One end of the armature shaft is then connected to the mechanical load. A permanent magnet could provide the necessary flux, but it is more usual to use an electromagnet whose winding is referred to as the *field coil.* Such a coil could be operated separately from another dc source, but it is far more common for the same voltage to drive a current through the low resistance of the armature winding and to excite the field coil.

The series dc motor

Two basic arrangements have different relationships between the armature speed and a changing mechanical load. In the series-wound motor, the field coil and the armature winding are joined in series with the dc supply voltage. In the shunt version, the field coil and the armature winding are in parallel across the supply.

The circuit of a series-wound motor appears in FIG. 1-80. When switching on, there is little resistance to limit the current so that there is a strong magnetic field and a high starting torque. As the armature speeds up, its counter EMF increases until an equilibrium condition is reached for a particular load. The rheostat, R, normally is included with high-power motors to reduce the initial current and to control the speed to a limited extent.

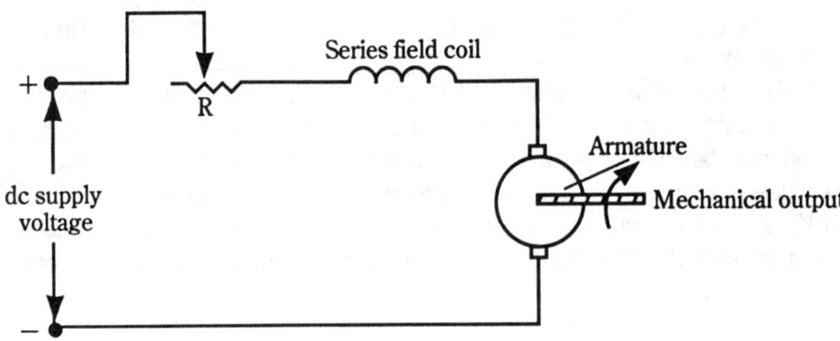

Fig. 1-80 The series-wound dc motor.

If the load on the motor increases, the armature slows down and the counter EMF is reduced. The current through the armature is greater and therefore the field strength increases; the speed is then reduced to a low level. However, the armature current is not excessive because the torque is directly proportional to the product of the flux density and to the armature current. Consequently, the torque varies as the square of the current. The speed regulation of a series-wound motor is poor and its percentage speed regulation, as defined below, is high:

$$\text{Percentage speed regulation} = \frac{N_{NL} - N_{FL}}{N_{FL}} \times 100\% \qquad (1\text{-}116)$$

where: N_{NL} = speed under no-load or minimum load conditions in revolutions per minute (rpm)
N_{FL} = speed under full-load conditions (rpm)

Disaster occurs if the load is removed abruptly from the series-wound motor; the armature speeds up and a higher counter EMF is induced into the armature winding. This reduces the armature current that also flows through the field coil. The weakened field causes the armature to turn still faster. The effect is therefore cumulative, and the motor ultimately will be destroyed. For this reason, series motors are connected directly to their loads and never by a belt. Summarizing, the series-wound motor has an excellent starting torque, but poor speed regulation.

The shunt dc motor

The basic current of a *shunt-wound motor* appears in FIG. 1-81. Initially, the rheostat (in series with the field coil) is adjusted for zero resistance so that the magnetic flux is at its highest level. The rheostat (in series with the armature) is a starter box whose resistance is set initially at the maximum value so that the armature current is limited to a safe level. As the armature speeds up to create the counter EMF, the resistance of the starter box is cut out in a series of steps. When this resistance finally reaches zero, the armature runs at its full speed corresponding to the load; the sum of the counter EMF and the IR drop across the armature is then equal to the source voltage. Subsequently, the speed can be controlled by setting the field rheostat. For example, if the rheostat's resistance increases, the field is reduced and the armature speed increases to restore the counter EMF.

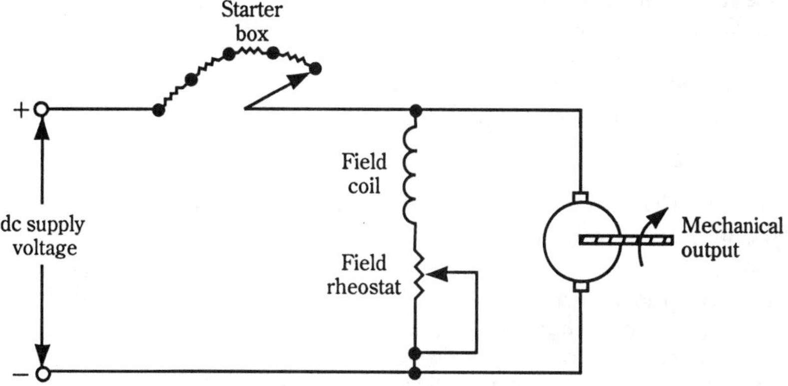

Fig. 1-81 The shunt-wound dc motor.

When no load is applied to the shunt motor, the only torque necessary is that which is required to overcome bearing friction and wind resistance. The counter EMF then limits the armature current to the low level, which provides the necessary torque to run the motor without a load. However, if the field coil then opens or burns out, the counter EMF nearly drops to zero; the armature then races at an ever increasing speed until the motor is destroyed.

When the external load is applied, the shunt motor slows down only slightly. The small decrease in speed causes a corresponding fall in the counter EMF. However, because the armature resistance is low, the increases in the armature current and the torque are relatively large. The torque rises until it provides the value that is required by the load. The speed then stabilizes at a new value that is determined by the load. Because wide variations in the load cause only small changes in the shunt motor's speed, its speed regulation is good.

The mechanical output of a dc motor is rated in horsepower (1 horsepower (hp) = 746 watts). This equation is:

$$\text{output power} = \frac{E \times I \times F}{746 \times 100}\ \text{hp} \qquad (1\text{-}117)$$

where: E = dc voltage source (V)
I = dc source current (A)
F = percentage efficiency (%)

* **Question 1-71** What values are required to calculate the percentage regulation for a dc generator?

A. the values of the output terminal voltage under no-load and full-load conditions
B. the values of the armature speed under no-load and full-load conditions
C. the values of the field current under no-load and full-load conditions
D. a knowledge of the resistance for both the armature and field windings
E. the number of poles and the number of commutator segments

Answer Choice A. The percentage of regulation for a dc generator is equal to:

$$\frac{E_{NL} - E_{FL}}{E_{FL}} \times 100\%$$

* **Question 1-72** The speed of a series-wound dc motor is primarily controlled by the:

A. the value of the applied dc voltage
B. the value of the armature current
C. the value of the field current
D. mechanical load
E. mechanical torque

Answer Choice D.

* **Question 1-73** The load on a shunt-wound motor is temporarily removed. What occurs if the field winding then open circuits?

A. the motor stops
B. there is a sharp decrease in the speed
C. there is virtually no change in the speed
D. the direction of the armature rotation reverses
E. the armature speeds up and may ultimately be destroyed

Answer. Choice E.

* **Question 1-74** A series-wound dc motor is operating under normal conditions. If the mechanical load is suddenly removed:

A. the motor stops
B. there is virtually no change in the speed
C. the motor is ultimately destroyed
D. there is a sharp decrease in the speed
E. the direction of the armature's rotation is reversed

Answer Choice C.

1-24. Soldering techniques

Soldering is a manual skill that can and must be learned by all personnel who work in the field of electronics. To develop proficient soldering techniques requires practice, which should be accompanied by a thorough understanding of the basic principles involved.

The main tools that you will use include:

- The *soldering iron* operates in the approximate temperature range of 250° to 300° Celsius. When leads are soldered to terminals, it is common practice to use a 100-W iron, but for working on a pc board the 25-W midget iron or soldering pencil is preferred because it is lighter, easier to handle, and has a miniature tip that can operate in difficult places. Both the standard iron and the pencil work at the same temperature, but the pencil does not have the capacity to transfer large quantities of heat.

- *Dykes* or *diagonal pliers* are made for cutting copper or aluminum wires as well as component leads. Some dykes can also be used for stripping #22 copper wire, which is commonly used in the electronics circuitry.
- *Needlenose pliers* hold the wire ends that have been stripped of insulation. These wires can then be steered and pushed through a terminal eye or partially wrapped around a terminal post. The long, thin jaws allow you to reach into difficult positions, where there is little room to maneuver.
- The *wire stripper* bares the ends of connecting wires by removing the insulation. The simplest type of stripper operates effectively only on one particular diameter, such as #22 wire, but the more sophisticated versions can be used with wires of differing diameters.
- The *soldering aid* has one pointed end to clear away unwanted solder from terminal lugs, eyes, and forks. The other end is slotted and can grip wire as it is being unwrapped and disconnected from terminals during the desoldering process.
- The *"solder sucker" syringe* (FIG. 1-82) sucks up excess solder from a joint or a pc board and its tip withstands the temperature of molten solder. Apart from these five tools, other aids, such as brushes, probes, scrapers, and knives, are frequently used in the soldering process.

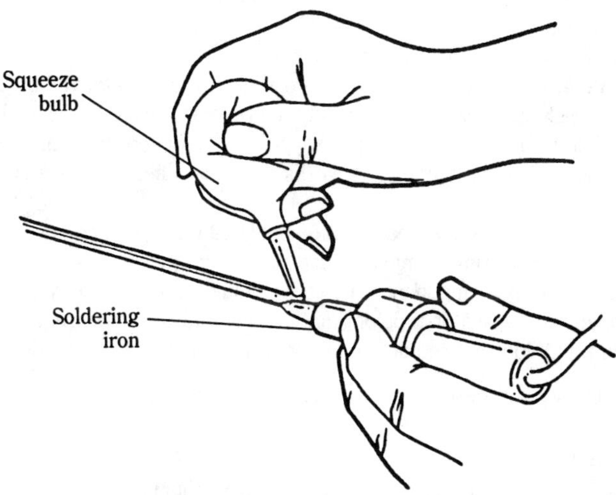

Fig. 1-82 The "solder-sucker" syringe.

Solder and the soldering process

The three grades of solder generally used for electronics work are 40-60, 50-50, and 60-40. The first figure is the percentage of tin; the second is the percentage of lead. The higher the percentage of tin, the lower is the temperature required for melting. Also, the higher the tin content, the easier the flow, the less time required to harden, and generally the easier it is to do a good soldering job. Consequently, the most commonly used grade for electronics work is 60-40 (60% tin, 40% lead).

In addition to the solder, there must be flux to remove any oxide film on the metals being joined; otherwise, they cannot fuse. The flux enables the molten solder to set the metals so that the solder can stick. Rosin flux (never acid flux) is always used for the light soldering work involved in making wire connections. Generally, the rosin is in the hollow core of solder intended for electronics work, so that separate flux is unnecessary. However, flux is not a substitute for cleaning the metals to be soldered. The metal must be shiny clean for the solder to stick.

Cleanliness is a prime prerequisite for efficient, effective soldering. Solder will not adhere to dirty, greasy, or oxidized surfaces. Heated metals tend to oxidize rapidly, and the oxide must be removed before soldering. Oxides, scale, and dirt can be removed by mechanical means (such as scraping or cutting with an abrasive) or by chemical means. Grease or oil films can be removed by a suitable solvent. You should clean immediately before soldering.

Items to be soldered should normally be tinned before making a mechanical connection. *Tinning* is the coating of the material to be soldered with a light coat of solder. When the surface has been properly cleaned, a thin, even coating of flux can be placed over the surface to be tinned to prevent oxidation while the part is being heated to soldering temperature.

The tinning on a wire should extend only far enough to take advantage of the depth of the terminal or receptacle. Tinning or soldering on wires subject to flexing causes stiffness, which might result in breakage.

The tinned surfaces to be joined should, if necessary, be shaped and fitted, then mechanically joined to make good mechanical and electrical contact. They must be held still with no relative movement of the parts. Any motion between parts will probably result in a poor connection.

Some type of thermal shunt is essential in all soldering operations that involve a heat-sensitive component, such as a microchip. Pliers or tweezers can be used for some applications, but their effectiveness is limited. A superior heat shunt or sink (FIG. 1-83) permits soldering the leads of component parts without overheating the part itself.

For maximum effectiveness, any protective coating should be removed before applying the heat shunt. The shunt should be attached carefully to prevent damage to the leads, terminals, or component parts. The shunt should be clipped to the lead between the joint and the part to be protected. As the joint is heated, the shunt absorbs the excess heat before it can reach the part and cause damage.

At the end of the operation, the heat source should be removed immediately, but the shunt should be left in place. Premature removal of the heat shunt permits unrestricted flow of heat from the metal solder into the component. The shunt should be allowed to remain in place until it cools to room temperature. A slip-on type of shunt is preferred because it requires positive action to remove the shunt, but does not require you to hold it in place.

* **Question 1-75** During the desoldering of a microchip, the necessary heat shunt should be clipped:

A. to the pin of the microchip
B. to the underside of the pc board on which the microchip is mounted
C. to the tip of the soldering iron
D. between the tip of the soldering iron and the terminal of the microchip
E. to all the pins on one side of the microchip

Answer Choice D.

* **Question 1-76** The solder grade primarily used for electronics work, is:

A. 60% tin, 40% lead B. 50% tin, 50% lead C. 70% tin, 30% lead D. 40% tin, 60% lead E. 30% tin, 70% lead

Answer Choice A.

* **Question 1-77** Excess solder is normally removed from the holes in a pc board with the aid of:

A. a soldering aid B. dykes C. a suction syringe D. needlenose pliers E. a soldering brush

Answer Choice C.

* **Question 1-78** Which of the following is *not* correct soldering practice for electronics work?

A. provide maximum mechanical support and strength to the parts to be joined
B. cleanliness is a prime requisite for efficient soldering
C. use 60-40 grade of solder
D. never use flux to eliminate oxidation
E. items to be soldered should normally be tinned

Answer Choice D.

* **Question 1-79** In the soldering process for electronics work, rosin flux is used to:

A. reduce the temperature of the soldering iron
B. remove any oxide film from the metals being joined
C. eliminate the need for tinning
D. prevent the molten solder from wetting the metals
E. acid flux, not rosin flux, should be used

Answer Choice B.

* **Question 1-80** Just before making a soldering connection, it is common to place a small amount of solder on the tip of a soldering iron. The purpose of this procedure is to:

A. decrease the amount of flux
B. reduce the temperature of the soldering iron's tip
C. allow the solder to wet the metals so that the solder can stick
D. remove any oxide film that might be present
E. none of the above is true

Answer Choice D.

* **Question 1-81** When carrying out a soldering procedure in electronics work, it is necessary to:

A. use acid flux
B. use the least possible amount of solder
C. use an adequate, but not excessive, amount of heat
D. clean all parts after soldering
E. use a thermal shunt in all soldering operations for components that are not heat-sensitive

Answer Choice C.

* **Question 1-82** During the soldering process, the leads of the components are normally tinned to:

A. prevent any movement of the parts being soldered
B. aid the connections between the metals and decrease the amount of time required for the heating process
C. wet the metals so that the solder can stick
D. prevent the leads from breaking
E. make the leads more flexible

Answer Choice B.

2
Principles of alternating current

In this chapter you will study:

- the waveforms of various alternating voltages and the concepts of cycle, frequency, angular frequency, period, harmonics, peak value, and peak-to-peak value.
- the meaning of the effective and average values of the sine-wave voltage or current, and the relationships between root-mean-square (rms) and peak values.
- how to represent an ac voltage or current by means of a phasor.
- the phase difference between two sinusoidal waveforms of the same frequency.
- how to add two sine-wave voltages (or currents) that differ in phase.
- what occurs when a sine-wave voltage is applied across a resistor.
- the concept of inductive reactance, which measures an inductor's opposition to the flow of alternating current.
- the concept of capacitive reactance, which measures a capacitor's opposition to the flow of alternating current.
- how to analyze ac circuits in which a sine-wave voltage is applied to series and parallel combinations of L, C, and R.
- the definition of resonance and the behavior of a series LCR resonant circuit.
- how to express power and voltage ratios in terms of decibels.
- the meanings of Q, selectivity, and bandwidth.
- the properties of parallel LCR and "tank" circuits at resonance.
- the phenomenon of mutual inductance and its application to power, AF, and RF transformers.
- the operation of constant-k and m-derived filters.
- how alternating voltage, current, and power are measured by various instruments, including the oscilloscope.
- the harmonic analysis of periodic, nonsinusoidal waveforms.
- the principles of the single-phase revolving field alternator.

2-1. Introduction to alternating current

Chapter 1 covered direct current, in which the electron flow is always in the same direction, although the magnitude of the flow is not necessarily constant.

With alternating current, the current reverses its direction periodically and has an average value of zero. If the average value of the waveform is not zero, it is regarded as a combination of a dc component and an ac component. The alternating current can assume a variety of waveforms, some of which are shown in FIGS. 2-1A, B, C, and D. In every case, a single complete waveform is known as a *cycle* and the number of cycles occurring in one second is the *frequency,* which is the rate at which the waveform repeats.

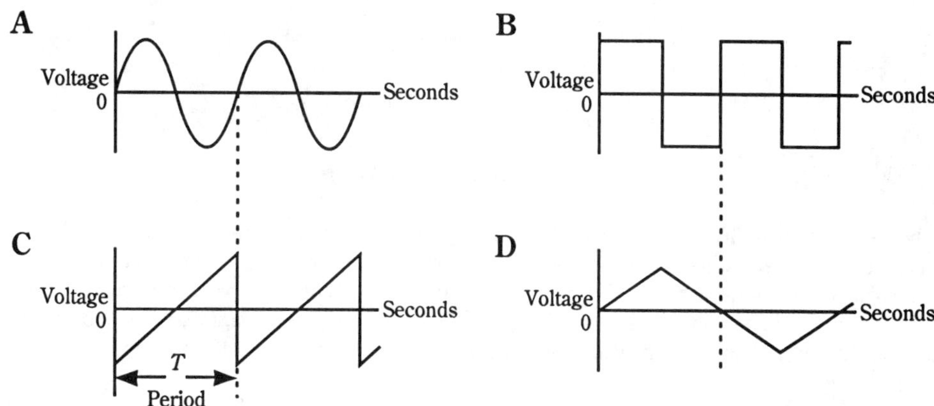

Fig. 2-1 Waveforms of various ac voltages.

The letter symbol for frequency is f and its SI unit in the hertz (Hz), which is equivalent to one cycle per second. The time interval taken by a complete cycle is the *period,* which is equal to the reciprocal of the frequency. The letter symbol for the period is T and its basic unit is the second (s). As an example, the commercial ac line voltage has a frequency of 60 Hz, and its period is $\frac{1}{60}$th of a second.

Frequency: $$f = \frac{1}{T} \text{ Hertz (Hz)} \quad (2\text{-}1)$$

Period: $$T = \frac{1}{f} \text{ seconds (s)} \quad (2\text{-}2)$$

The sine wave is not only associated with the commercial line voltage, but it is also widely used for communications. The curve itself is the result of plotting the mathematical sine function, Sin. θ. versus the angle θ, measured in either degrees or radians (FIG. 2-2).

One *radian* is the angle at the center of a circle, which subtends (is opposite to) an arc (l), which is equal in length to the radius (r).

Angle: $$\theta = \frac{l}{r} \text{ radians (rad)} \quad (2\text{-}3)$$

Because the total length of the circle's circumference is $2\pi r$ radians, the angle of 360° must be equivalent to $2\pi r/r = 2\pi$ radians. Therefore:

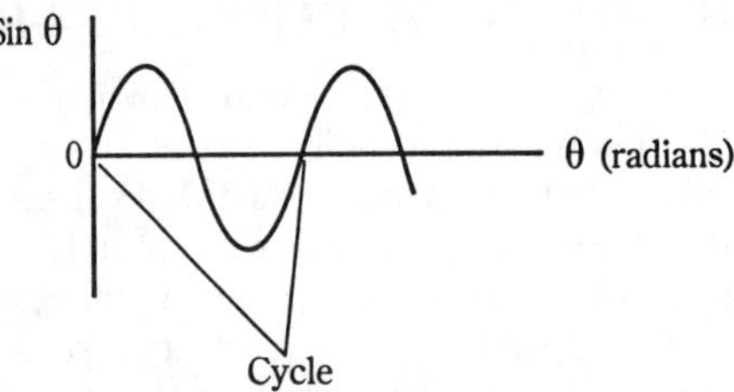

Fig. 2-2 The sine wave.

$$\theta \text{ (degrees)} = \frac{360}{2\pi} \times \theta \text{ radians} = \frac{180}{\pi} \times \theta \text{ radians} \quad (2\text{-}4)$$

$$\theta \text{ (radians)} = \frac{\pi}{180} \times \theta \text{ degrees} \quad (2\text{-}5)$$

It follows that:

$$1 \text{ radian} = \frac{180}{\pi} \text{ degrees} = 57.296° \approx 57.3°$$

The vertical axis in FIG. 2-2 measures one of a number of electrical parameters (such as voltage, current, and power), while the horizontal axis is a time scale. It follows that, for every sine wave, a certain number of radians on the horizontal scale must correspond to a particular time interval. The angular frequency whose letter symbol is the Greek lowercase omega, (ω), is found by dividing the number of radians by the equivalent time interval and is therefore measured in radians per second (rad/s).

Angular frequency:

$$\omega = \frac{\theta}{t} = \frac{2\pi}{T} = 2\pi f \text{ radians per second (rad/s)} \quad (2\text{-}6)$$

Angle:

$$\theta = 2\pi f t \text{ radians} \quad (2\text{-}7)$$

where t is the time in seconds.

Period:

$$T = \frac{2\pi}{\omega} \text{ seconds} \quad (2\text{-}8)$$

If the frequency is 1 Hz: $\omega = 2\pi \times 1 = 2\pi$ radians per second

Therefore, a frequency of 1 Hz corresponds to an angular frequency of 2π rad/s. One cycle occurs over an angle of 360° (2π radians) and over a time of $\frac{2\pi}{\omega}$ seconds.

One cycle of a sine wave consists of a "positive" alternation and a "negative" alternation (FIG. 2-3). The maximum excursion from its *average (zero) line* is called the *peak* or maximum (E_{max}) value while the distance between the wave's crest and trough is a measure of the peak-to-peak (E_{p-p}) value. The concepts of E_{RMS} and E_{av} are explained in the next section.

Peak-to-peak voltage:

$$E_{p-p} = 2 \times E_{max} \text{ volts (V)} \quad (2\text{-}9)$$

Sine waves are of particular importance because Fourier analysis allows the waveforms of FIGS. 2-1B, C, and D to be broken down into a series of sine waves that consist of a fundamental component, together with its harmonics (FIG. 2-4). The harmonic of a sine wave is another sine wave whose frequency is a whole number times the original or fundamental frequency. For example, if the fundamental frequency is 1 kHz (f), the second harmonic has a frequency of 2 kHz ($2f$), the third harmonic frequency is 3 kHz ($3f$), etc.

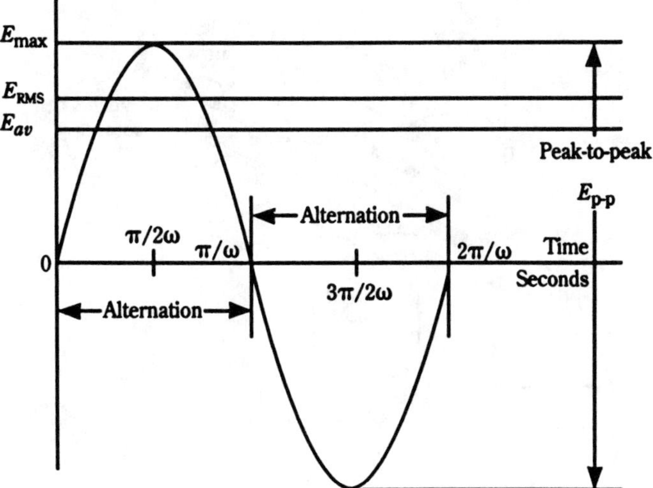

Fig. 2-3 Peak and peak-to-peak values of the sine-wave voltage.

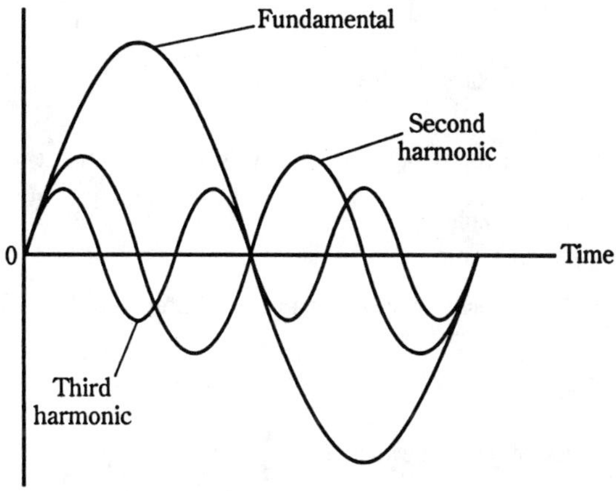

Fig. 2-4 Harmonics of a fundamental sine wave.

The simple ac generator (alternator)

The ac generator is a machine that is capable of converting mechanical energy into alternating electrical energy. In its simplest form (FIG. 2-5), shaft DD′ is driven around by mechanical energy. Attached to the shaft, but insulated from it, is a copper loop, AB, that rotates between the poles, PP′, of a permanent magnet or an electromagnet (energized by direct current).

The ends of the rotating loop are joined to two separate slip rings, SS′ that makes continuous contact with the stationary carbon brushes, CC′; these brushes are then connected to the electrical load.

The poles' pieces, PP′, are specially shaped to provide a constant flux density in which the loop rotates. One complete rotation of the loop will generate one cycle of alternating voltage, which is applied across the load. If the output frequency is 60 Hz, the loop's speed of rotation is

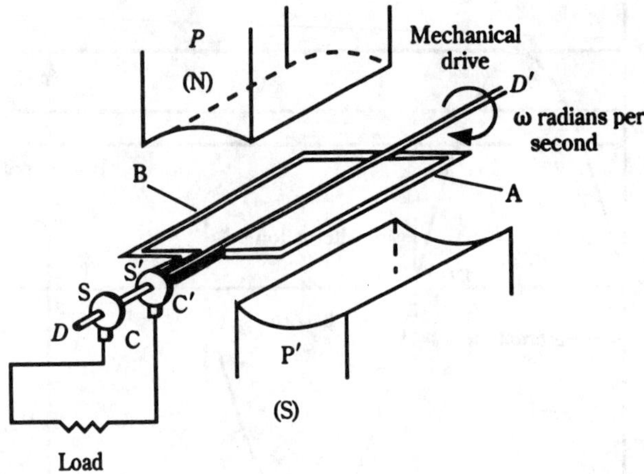

Fig. 2-5 The simple alternator.

60 × 60 = 3600 rotations per min. However, if the alternator has four poles, each complete rotation of the loop generates two cycles of alternating voltage and therefore the required speed for a 60-Hz output is only 1800 rpm.

$$\text{Generated frequency, } f = \frac{np}{60} \text{ hertz} \tag{2-10}$$

$$\text{Speed of rotation, } n = \frac{60f}{p} \text{ revolutions per minute} \tag{2-11}$$

where: p = number of pairs of poles
n = speed of rotation in rpm

Question 2-1 Five cycles of a sine wave occur in a time interval of 1⁄50 s. The frequency of the sine wave is:

A. 50 Hz B. 500 Hz C. 125 Hz D. 250 Hz E. 1000 Hz

Answer Choice D. Period of the sine wave: $T = \frac{1}{5} \times \frac{1}{50} = \frac{1}{250}$ s

Frequency:
$$f = \frac{1}{T} = \frac{1}{1/250} = 250 \text{ Hz} \tag{2-1}$$

* **Question 2-2** Three quarters of one cycle of a sine wave cover an angle of:

A. 2π radians B. π radians C. 90° D. 270° E. 450°

Answer Choice D. One cycle corresponds to an angle of 360° or 2π radians. The angle for three quarters of a cycle is:

$$\frac{3}{4} \times 2\pi = 3\pi/2 \text{ radians or } \frac{3}{4} \times 360° = 270°$$

* **Question 2-3** One hertz is equivalent to an angular frequency of:

A. π radians/second B. 2π cycles/second C. π cycles/second D. 2π radians/second E. π meters/second

Answer Choice D. Angular frequency, $\omega = 2\pi f$ radians/second (EQ. 2-6). If $f = 1$ Hz, $\omega = 2\pi$ radians/second.

* **Question 2-4** The frequency of the fifth harmonic of a 520-kHz signal is:

A. 2650 kHz B. 2600 Hz C. 2.6 MHz D. 104 kHz E. 2.6 kHz

Answer Choice C. The frequency of the fifth harmonic is 5 × 520 = 2600 kHz = 2.6 MHz.

* **Question 2-5** A six-pole alternator rotates at a speed of 1000 rpm. The value of the generated frequency is:

A. 50 Hz B. 40 Hz C. 60 Hz D. 25 Hz E. 120 Hz

Answer Choice A.

$$\text{Generated frequency} = \frac{np}{60} = \frac{1000 \times 6}{60 \times 2} = 50 \text{ Hz} \qquad (2\text{-}10)$$

2-2. Effective (RMS) and average values of an ac voltage or current

Effective value

The last section showed that the magnitude of a sine-wave voltage or current could be measured in terms of its peak or peak-to-peak value. In fact, it is common practice to use a cathode-ray oscilloscope (CRO) to obtain the peak-to-peak value of an alternating voltage. Because the peaks of a sine wave only occur twice instantaneously during a cycle, you would normally prefer to use a value that reflects the whole of the cycle. However, you cannot use the average over the complete cycle because this value is always zero. Instead, turn to the *root-mean-square* (RMS) or effective value. Nonmathematically, this is the ac value that will provide the same heating or power effect as its equivalent dc value. In other words, a 100-W 100-V bulb that is connected to a 100-V RMS, 60-Hz supply will appear to have the same brightness as an identical bulb that is joined to a 100-Vdc source.

The bulb's tungsten filament, which is operated from the dc source, will glow continuously at a constant brightness. However, when the identical bulb is connected to the ac supply, the filament, with its low thermal capacity, alternately glows very brightly and is extinguished at the rate of 120 times per second. Because of the persistence of vision, the eye cannot directly observe a flicker effect whose rate exceeds 30 times per second; consequently, the brightness is "averaged out" and appears to be the same as that of a bulb that operates from a dc source. The flicker effect can indirectly be perceived with the aid of a stroboscope.

In FIG. 2-6A, an ac sine-wave source with a peak value of 10 V is connected across a 1-Ω resistor, while in FIG. 2-6B another 1-Ω resistor is joined to a dc source with a terminal voltage, E. If the average power in the ac circuit over the complete cycle is the same as the constant power of the dc circuit, E must equal the RMS value of the ac voltage. When the ac voltage is instantaneously zero, the instantaneous power is also zero, but when the voltage is 10 V, the instantaneous power rises to its peak value of $(10 \text{ V})^2/1\ \Omega = 100$ W (this result is independent of the voltage's polarity, which changes with each alternation). The instantaneous power therefore fluctuates between 0 and 100 W and has an average value of 50 W. Notice that the frequency of the power curve is twice that of the ac voltage.

If the power in the dc circuit is 50 W, the terminal voltage: $E = \sqrt{P \times R} = \sqrt{50 \text{ W} \times 1\ \Omega} = 7.07$ V. Consequently, an ac voltage with a peak value of 10 V has an effective value of 7.07 V. Therefore, for a sine wave, the effective value = 0.707 × the peak value or the peak value = (1/0.707) × the effective value = 1.414 × the effective value

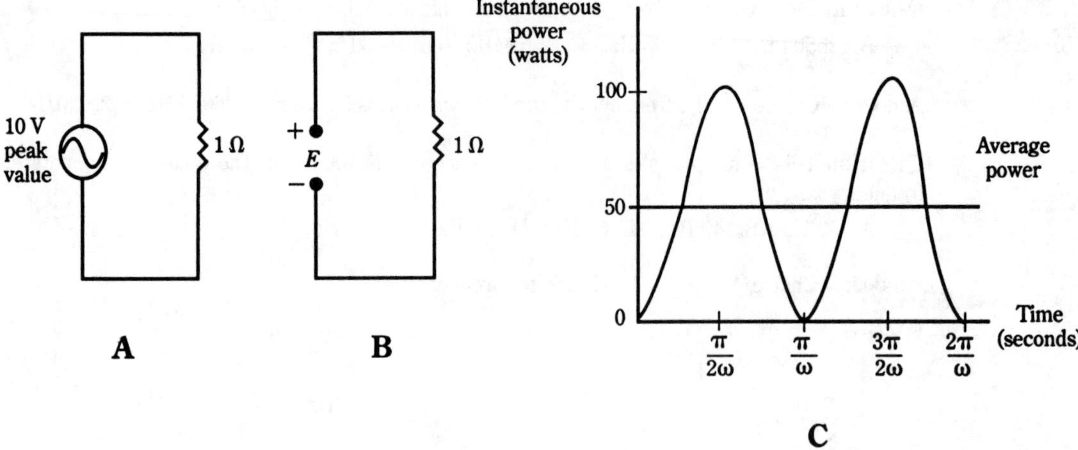

Fig. 2-6 Effective value of a sine-wave voltage.

(FIG. 2-3). These relationships are only true for the sine wave. For example, the effective value of the square wave in FIG. 1-1B must be the same as the peak value; for the triangular wave of FIG. 1-1D, the effective value is only 0.577 × the peak value.

Finally, what is the meaning of the term *root mean square* (RMS)? The value of 7.07 V is obtained from the expression:

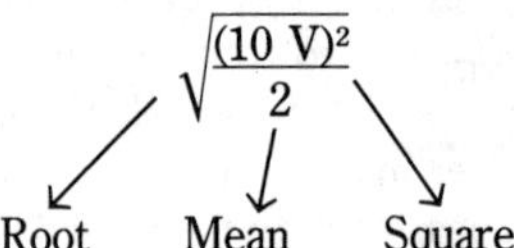

In other words, the peak value was squared to obtain a value that was proportional to the peak power. Then, the result is divided by 2 to obtain the average or mean power. Finally, the square root was taken to obtain the effective value.

Most alternating voltage and current measurements are in terms of effective values. However, the insulation in ac circuits must normally be able to withstand the peak voltage. For example, the commercial 110-V RMS, 60-Hz line voltage has a peak value of 110 V × 1.414 = 155.5 V and the peak-to-peak value of 2 × 155.5 V = 311 V.

The equation relating the peak and effective values are:

Effective value:

$$E_{\text{RMS}} = 0.707 \times E_{\text{peak}} = \frac{E_{\text{peak}}}{1.414} = \frac{E_{\text{peak}}}{\sqrt{2}} \text{ volts (V)} \tag{2-11}$$

Peak value:

$$E_{\text{peak}} = 1.414 \times E_{\text{RMS}} = \sqrt{2} \times E_{\text{RMS}} \text{ volts (V)} \tag{2-12}$$

The same equations apply to a sine-wave current.

Average value

The full cycle of a sine wave is composed to two alternations (FIG. 2-3). One "positive" alternation extends from 0° to 180° and the other "negative" alternation stretches from 180° to 360°. Although the average value of the sine wave over the complete cycle is zero, the average value over an alternation can be found by the use of calculus and is important in any discussion of half-wave and full-wave rectifier circuits.

Because the "positive" alternation is symmetrical about the 90° mark, it is possible to find the approximate relationship between the average and peak values by computing the mean of the sine values between 0° and 90°. Table 2-1 shows the values for 5° steps and the computation of the average value. In fact, the average value $= 0.63662 \times$ peak value $\approx 0.637 \times$ peak value.

The ratio of the effective value to the average value of an alternating current or voltage is the *form factor* of the waveform. For the sine wave:

$$Form\ factor = \frac{RMS\ value}{average\ value} = \frac{0.707 \times peak\ value}{0.637 \times peak\ value}$$
$$= 1.11$$

The square wave has a form factor of 1.0, and the form factor of a triangular wave is 0.557/0.5 = 1.12. Compared to other ac waveforms, the sine wave is relatively easy to generate and has a high RMS value with a good form factor.

Table 2-1. Average value over a sine-wave alternation.

Angle θ°	Sin θ
0°	0.000000
5°	0.087156
10°	0.173648
15°	0.258819
20°	0.342020
25°	0.422618
30°	0.500000
35°	0.573576
40°	0.642788
45°	0.707107
50°	0.766044
55°	0.819152
60°	0.866025
65°	0.906308
70°	0.939693
75°	0.965926
80°	0.984808
85°	0.996195
90°	1.000000
	11.951883

The 19 values total 11.951883. Average value = 11.951883/19 = 0.63 × Peak Value.

Question 2-6 If a sine-wave voltage has an effective value of 20 V, its peak value is:

A. 28.3 V B. 14.1 V C. 56.6 V D. 20 V E. 7.07 V

Answer Choice A.

Peak value:

$$
\begin{aligned}
E_{peak} &= E_{RMS} \times 1.414 \\
&= 20 \times 1.414 \qquad (2\text{-}12) \\
&= 28.3 \text{ V, rounded off}
\end{aligned}
$$

* **Question 2-7** The effective value of a sine-wave voltage is equal to the:

A. peak value $\times \sqrt{2}$ B. peak value $\times$ 1.414 C. average value $\div$ 1.11 D. peak value $\div$ 0.707 E. peak value $\div \sqrt{2}$

Answer Choice E. Refer to EQ. 2-11.

2-3. Phasor representation of an ac sine-wave voltage or current

If two components are in series across an ac source, an alternating voltage will be across each component. If these two voltages are then added, their resultant exactly balances the source voltage (Kirchhoff's voltage law). In the case of a parallel circuit, the individual branch currents must be added to obtain the total current that is drawn from the source. So far, a sine wave has been shown in terms of its waveform. When you need to add or subtract ac quantities, the combination of waveforms tends to be tedious.

A second method involves the representation of ac quantities by means of phasors. For a sine-wave voltage, its phasor is a line whose length is a measure of E_{max}. By convention, the line phasor is assumed to rotate in the positive or counterclockwise direction with an angular velocity of $\omega = 2\pi f$ radians per second, where f is the voltage's frequency in hertz. The vertical projection, PN, of the phasor on the horizontal reference line is then equal to the instantaneous value, e, of the ac voltage (FIG. 2-7). Therefore, as the phasor rotates, the extremity of the line can be said to *trace out* the voltage's sinusoidal waveform with a frequency that is equal to the phasor's speed of rotation in revolutions per second. One complete rotation of the phasor then traces out one cycle of the sine wave. The phasor diagram therefore contains the same information as the waveform presentation, but it is obviously easier to work with lines than sine waves.

Because there is a constant relationship between effective and peak values (effective value = 0.707 × peak value), the phasor's length can instead be used to indicate the RMS value.

Prior to about 1960, the word *vector* was used instead of a *phasor.* A vector is a quantity that possesses both magnitude and direction; a mechanical force is an example of a vector. By contrast, a scalar quantity (such as mass) possesses magnitude only. The rules for adding or subtracting mechanical vectors are the same as those for adding or subtracting ac phasors. However, the vector rules for multiplication and division are totally different from the corresponding phasor rules. For this reason, ***vectors*** are no longer used to represent ac quantities and the word ***phasor*** was introduced instead.

* **Question 2-8** The commercial line voltage has a frequency of 60 Hz. Its phasor rotates with an angular velocity of:

A. 60 rad./s B. 3600 rad./s C. 377 rad./s D. 189 rad./s E. 755 rad./s

Answer Choice C.

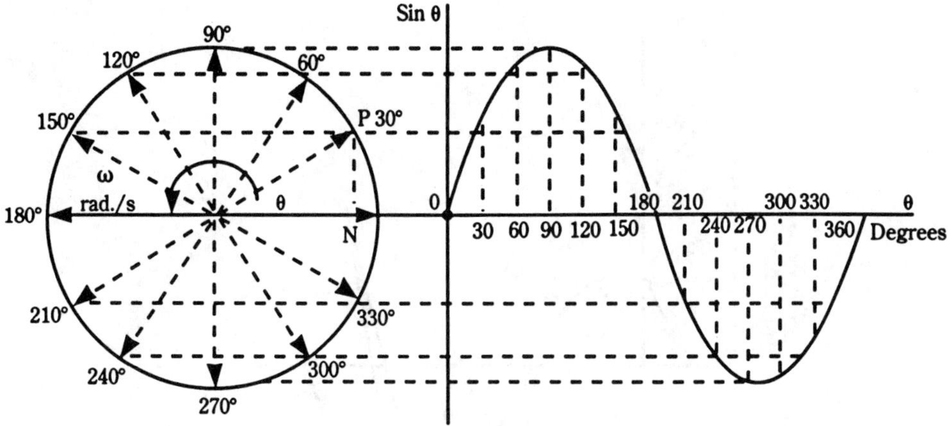

Fig. 2-7 A phasor representation of a sine wave.

Angular velocity:

$$\begin{aligned} \omega &= 2\pi f \\ &= 2 \times \pi \times 60 \qquad (2\text{-}6) \\ &= 377 \text{ rad./s, rounded off} \end{aligned}$$

2-4. Phase relationships

When two dc voltages, E_1, E_2, are in series, they are either in series-aiding or in series-opposing; only addition or subtraction is necessary to obtain their combined voltage. However, two ac sine-wave voltages of the same frequency might not reach similar points in their cycles at the same time. As an example, when an inductor and a resistor are in series across an ac source, the voltage across the inductor reaches its peak value when the voltage across the resistor is zero. In other words, the two voltages are a quarter of a cycle apart. The amount by which the two sine waves are out of step is referred to as their *phase difference,* which is either measured in degrees or radians. In this example, the shift of one quarter of a cycle is equivalent to a phase difference of 90° or $\pi/2$ radians.

In FIG. 2-8, the e_2 waveform reaches its peak, X, earlier in time than the e_1 waveform with its corresponding peak, Y. The difference between the two waveforms is ϕ radians, with e_2 leading e_1 (or e_1 lagging e_2). Phase differences can therefore be either leading or lagging, with their angles usually extending up to 180°. In the particular case where ϕ is 180° or π radians, the terms "leading" or "lagging" are not used because 180° leading has the same meaning as 180° lagging. In most cases, there is little point in using angles greater than 180° because, for example, a phase difference of 270° leading is equivalent to 90° lagging.

It is impossible to add together two or more series ac voltages (or currents if some form of parallel circuit is involved) without knowing their peak values and their phase relationships. Figure 2-9 shows the results of adding two ac voltages, each with a 10-V peak, but with phase differences that are in turn 0°, 90°, 120°, 180°; the resultant (sum) voltages have corresponding peak values of 20 V, 14.14 V, 10 V, and 0. Notice that in each case, the frequency of $e_1 + e_2$ is the same as the frequency of e_1 and e_2.

In the accompanying phasor diagrams, the angles between the phasors e_1, e_2 and $e_1 + e_2$ represent their phase differences. To determine the phasor $e_1 + e_2$, the following construction procedure is used:

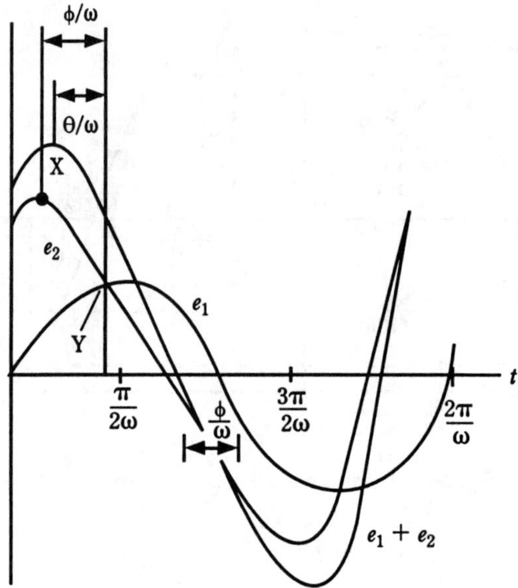

Fig. 2-8 Addition of two sine-wave voltages of the same frequency.

1. Through point Q, draw a line parallel to line OP.
2. Through point P, draw a line parallel to line OQ.
3. The two construction lines intersect at the point, R. Diagonal OR then represents phasor $e_1 + e_2$.

* **Question 2-9** A voltage phasor whose RMS value is 3 V, leads a second voltage phasor by 90°. If the RMS value of the second phasor is 4 V, the effective value of their phasor sum is:

A. 7 V B. 5 V C. 3.5 V D. 1 V E. 6 V

Answer Choice B. The effective value of the phasor sum is:

$$\sqrt{3^2 + 4^2} = \sqrt{9 + 16} = \sqrt{25} = 5 \text{ V}$$

2-5. Resistance in the ac circuit

If a sine wave is connected across a resistor, R (FIG. 2-10A), Ohm's Law applies throughout the cycle of the alternating voltage, *e*. When *e* is instantaneously zero, zero current flows in the circuit, but when the applied voltage reaches one of its peaks, X, the current is also a maximum in one direction. When we reach the peak (Y) of the other alternation, the current is again at its maximum value, but its direction is reversed. At all times, $e/i = R$; therefore, the sine waves of *e* and *i* are in phase (FIG. 2-10B) with a phase difference of zero degrees. This is indicated by the *e* and *i* phasors, which lie along the same horizontal line (FIG. 2-10C).

The instantaneous power, *p*, in the circuit is the product of the instantaneous voltage, *e*, and the instantaneous current, *i*. When *e* and *i* are simultaneously zero, the instantaneous power is also zero, but when both *e* and *i* reach their peaks together, the power reaches its peak value of $E_{max} \times I_{max}$ watts. When the voltage reverses polarity, the current reverses direction, but the resistor continues to dissipate (lost) power in the form of heat. All of the instantaneous power

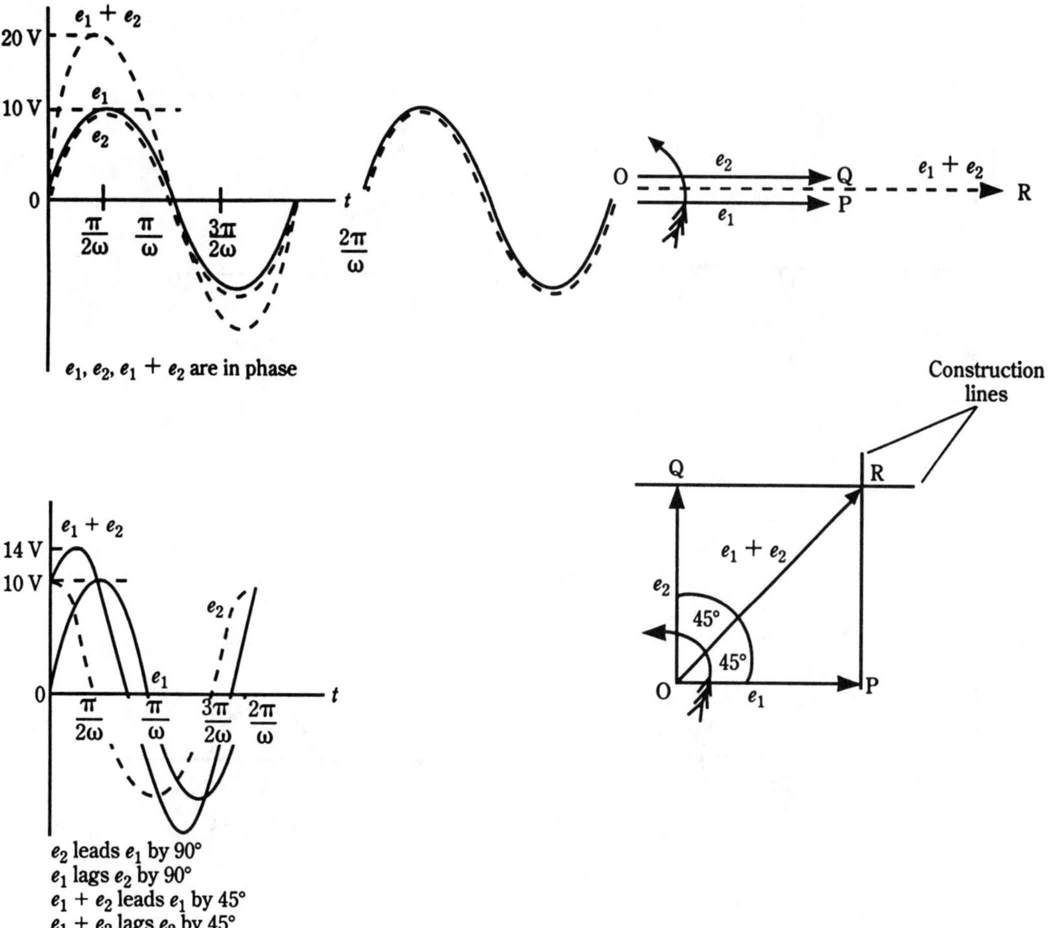

Fig. 2-9 Examples of phase relationships.

curve must be drawn above the zero line and its frequency is twice that of the applied voltage. The mean value of the power curve is a measure of the average power dissipated over the voltage cycle.

* **Question 2-10** In the circuit of FIG. 2-11, calculate the value of the maximum power that can be developed in the load, R_L.

A. 30 W B. 7.5 W C. 15 W D. 20 W E. 25 W

Answer Choice B. For maximum power transfer to the load:

$$R_L = 10 + 20 = 30\ \Omega. \text{ Maximum load power } = \frac{(30\text{ V})^2}{4 \times 30\ \Omega} = 7.5\text{ W}.$$

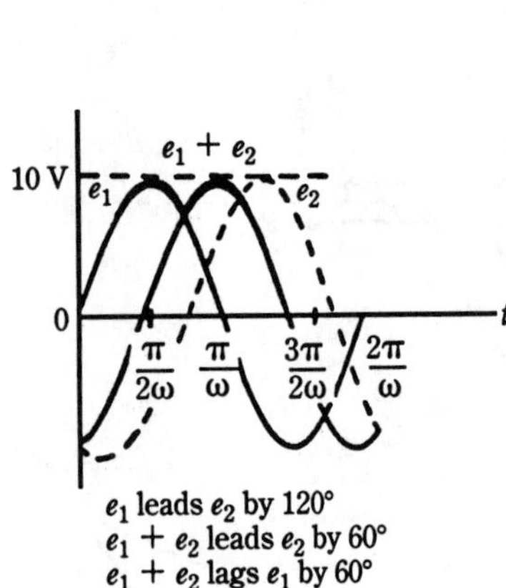

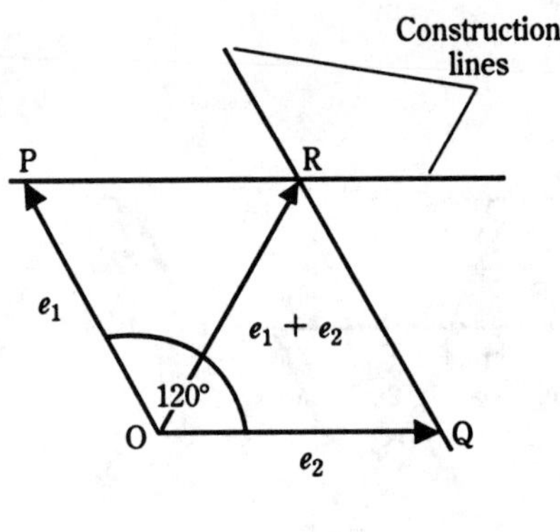

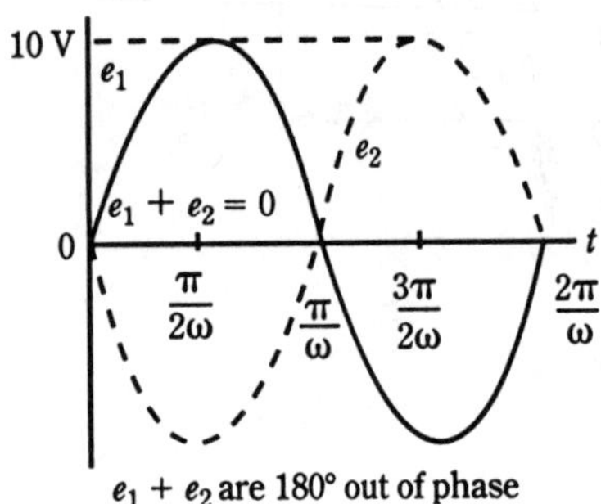

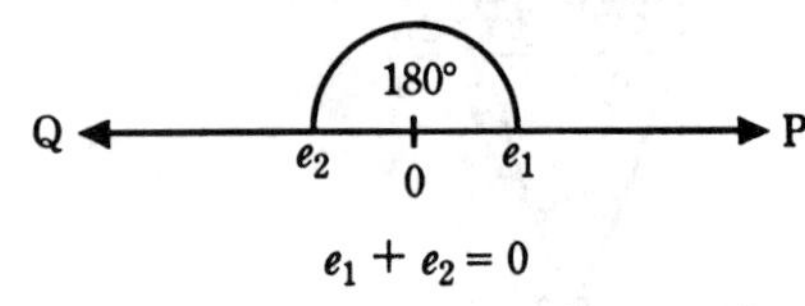

Fig. 2-9 Continued

2-6. Reactance

Inductive reactance

Assume in FIG. 2-12A that the inductor only possesses the property of inductance and that you can ignore its resistance. When an alternating current is flowing through the coil, the surrounding magnetic field is continually expanding and collapsing so that an induced voltage, v_L, has a value that must at all times exactly balance the instantaneous value of the source voltage, *e*. Therefore, when *e* is instantaneously at its peak value, the value of v_L is also at its peak. Because $v_L = -L \times$ (rate of change of current), the rate of change of the current is at its highest level. This occurs when the slope of the current sine wave is steepest at the point of zero time and zero current. Consequently, when *e* is at its peak value, *i* is instantaneously zero. Therefore, *e*, *i* are 90% out of phase (FIGS. 2-12B and C). This can be remembered by the word "*eLi*"; for an inductor, *L*, the instantaneous voltage, *e*, leads the instantaneous current, *i*, by 90°.

You cannot obtain the opposition to the current flow by dividing the instantaneous voltage

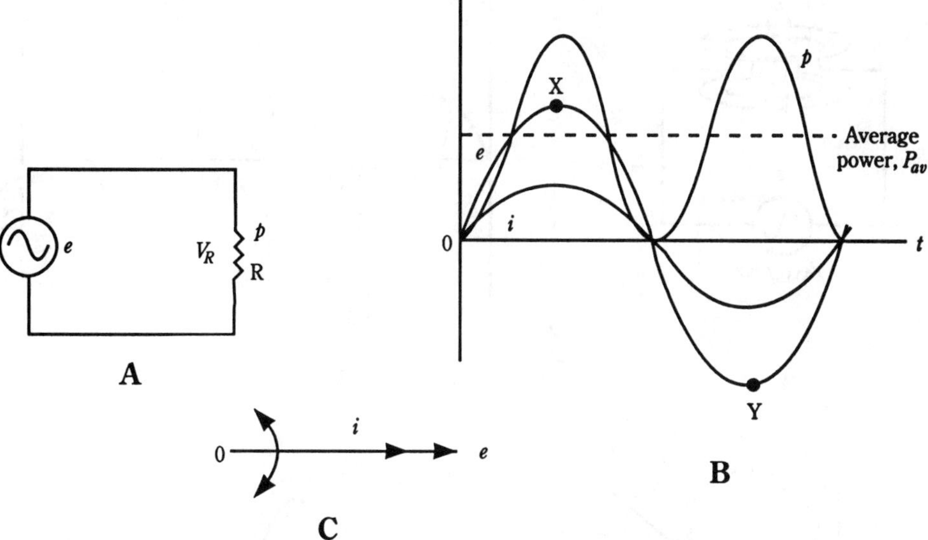

Fig. 2-10 The effect of resistance in an ac circuit.

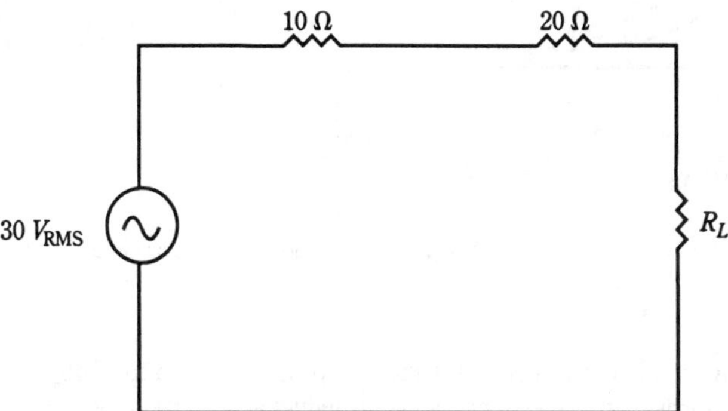

Fig. 2-11 The circuit for question 2-10.

by the instantaneous current. For example, at the 0° point, the value of *e*/*i* is infinite; at the 90° mark, *e*/*i* is 0. However, you can attempt to find the value of E_{RMS}/I_{RMS} because the effective values are derived from the complete cycles of the voltage and the current.

Assume that the source voltage and the inductance are kept constant, but the frequency is raised. The voltage induced in the coil must remain the same, but the magnetic field is expanding and collapsing more rapidly so that the required magnetic flux is less. As a result, the current is reduced and is inversely proportional to the frequency. For example, if the frequency is doubled, the value of the effective current is halved.

Now keep the source voltage and the frequency constant, but the inductor is replaced by another coil with a higher inductance. Because the induced voltage, v_L, is the same, the value of the rate of change of current must be less; therefore, the effective current is again reduced. Finally, by raising the value of the source voltage while the frequency and the inductance are unchanged, the induced voltage must be increased; consequently, the effective current is greater.

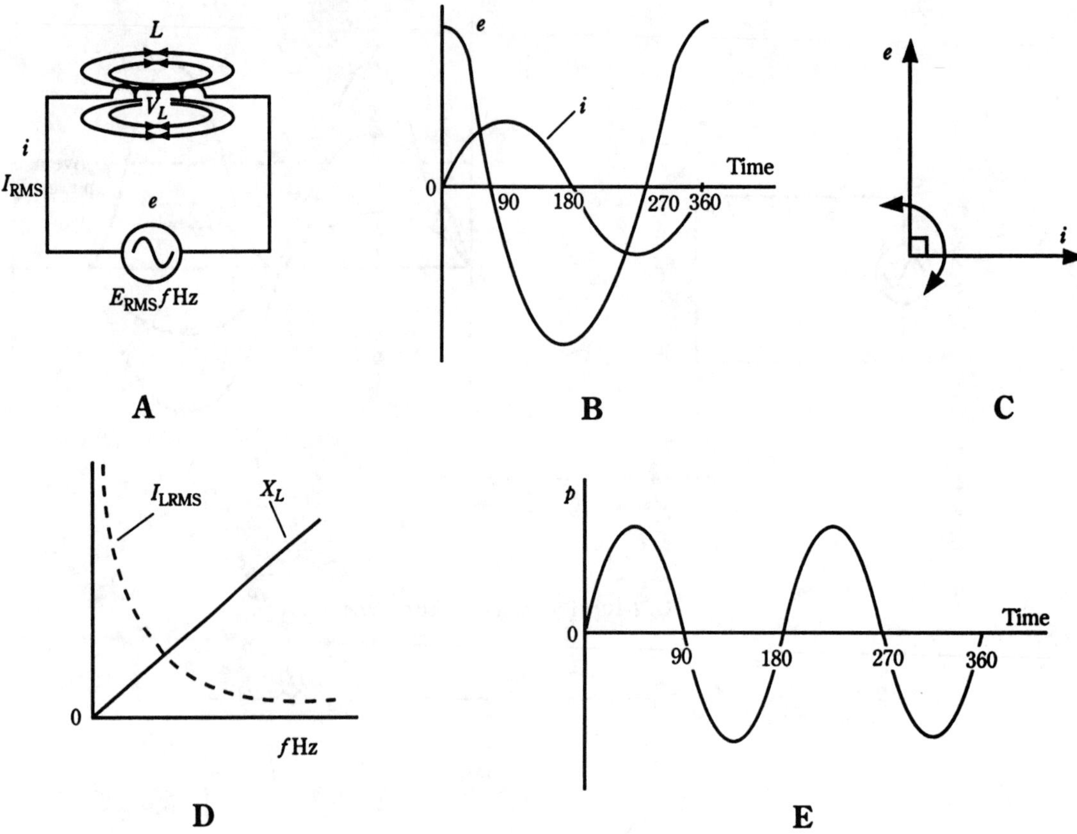

Fig. 2-12 The inductor in an ac circuit.

Summarizing, the effective current is directly proportional to the effective voltage, but it is inversely proportional to the frequency and the inductance. The opposition to the alternating current is therefore determined by the product of the frequency and the inductance. This opposition is called the *inductance reactance*, $X_L = E_{RMS}/I_{RMS}$, and is measured in ohms. The formula for the inductive reactance is $X_L = 2\ \pi fL\Omega$ and because X_L is directly proportional to the frequency, the graph of X_L versus frequency is a straight line (FIG. 2-12D).

The instantaneous power, *p*, is equal to the product of *e* and *i*. The graph of the instantaneous power, *p*, versus time is a second harmonic sine wave (FIG. 2-12E), whose average value is zero over the source voltage's cycle. During the first quarter cycle, the magnetic field is established around the inductor and the energy is drawn from the source. However, during the second quarter cycle, the magnetic field collapses and the energy is returned to the source. This action is repeated during the third and fourth quarter cycles so that the average power over the complete cycle is zero.

This highlights the difference between resistance and reactance. Both resistance and reactance limit the value of the alternating current, but while resistance dissipates (lost) power in the form of heat, reactance does not lose any power at all. The product of $E_{RMS} \times I_{RMS}$ is called the *reactive power (RP)*, which is measured in *volt-amperes reactive (VArs)*.

In the circuit of FIG. 2-12A:

Inductive reactance:
$$X_L = 2\pi fL \text{ ohms } (\Omega) \tag{2-13}$$

Current:
$$I_{RMS} = \frac{E_{RMS}}{X_L} \text{ amperes (A)} \tag{2-14}$$

Reactive power:
$$\begin{aligned} RP &= E_{RMS} \times I_{RMS} \\ &= E^2_{RMS}/X_L \\ &= I^2_{RMS} \times X_L \text{ volt-ampere reactive (VAr)} \end{aligned} \tag{2-15}$$

where: L = inductance (H)
f = frequency (Hz)
E_{RMS} = effective value of the source voltage (V)
I_{RMS} = effective value of the source current (A)

If three inductors L_1, L_2, and L_3 are connected in series across an ac voltage source, the total equivalent inductance is:

$$L_T = L_1 + L_2 + L_3 \text{ henrys (H)}$$

Therefore:
$$2\pi fL_T = 2\pi fL_1 + 2\pi fL_2 + 2\pi fL_3$$

and total equivalent inductive reactance:

$$X_{LT} = X_{L1} + X_{L2} + X_{L3} \text{ ohms } (\Omega) \tag{2-16}$$

For individual reactances in series, the total equivalent reactance is the sum of the individual reactances.

Similarly, for inductors in parallel:

$$X_{LT} = \frac{1}{\dfrac{1}{X_{L1}} + \dfrac{1}{X_{L2}} + \dfrac{1}{X_{L3}}} \text{ ohms } (\Omega) \tag{2-17}$$

Capacitive reactance

When an alternating current, i, is flowing in the circuit of FIG. 2-12A, the capacitor is continuously charging and discharging so that the voltage, v_C, across the capacitor must at all times exactly balance the instantaneous value of the source voltage, e. Therefore, when e is momentarily at its peak value, the value of v_C is also at its peak and the capacitor is fully charged. The current is then instantaneously zero; therefore, e and i are 90° out of phase (FIGS. 2-13B and C). This can be remembered by the word iCe; for an ideal capacitance, C, the instantaneous current, i, leads the instantaneous voltage, e, by 90°. Then, combine "iCe" with the word "eLi" for the inductor and create "eLi, the iCe man!"

Now derive the factors that determine the capacitor's opposition to the flow of alternating current. Assume that the source voltage and the capacitance are kept constant, but that the frequency is raised. This reduces the period so that the capacitor must acquire or lose the same amount of charge in a shorter time. The charging or discharging current must therefore be greater. In fact, the effective current is directly proportional to the frequency; if the frequency is doubled, the effective current is also doubled. By contrast, when the frequency is doubled for an inductor, the effective current is halved.

Now keep the source voltage and frequency constant, but raise the capacitance. The new capacitor will have to store or lose more charge in the same time so that the effective current is again increased. The values of the capacitance and the effective current are directly proportional; if the capacitance is halved, the effective current is also halved. Finally, by raising the source

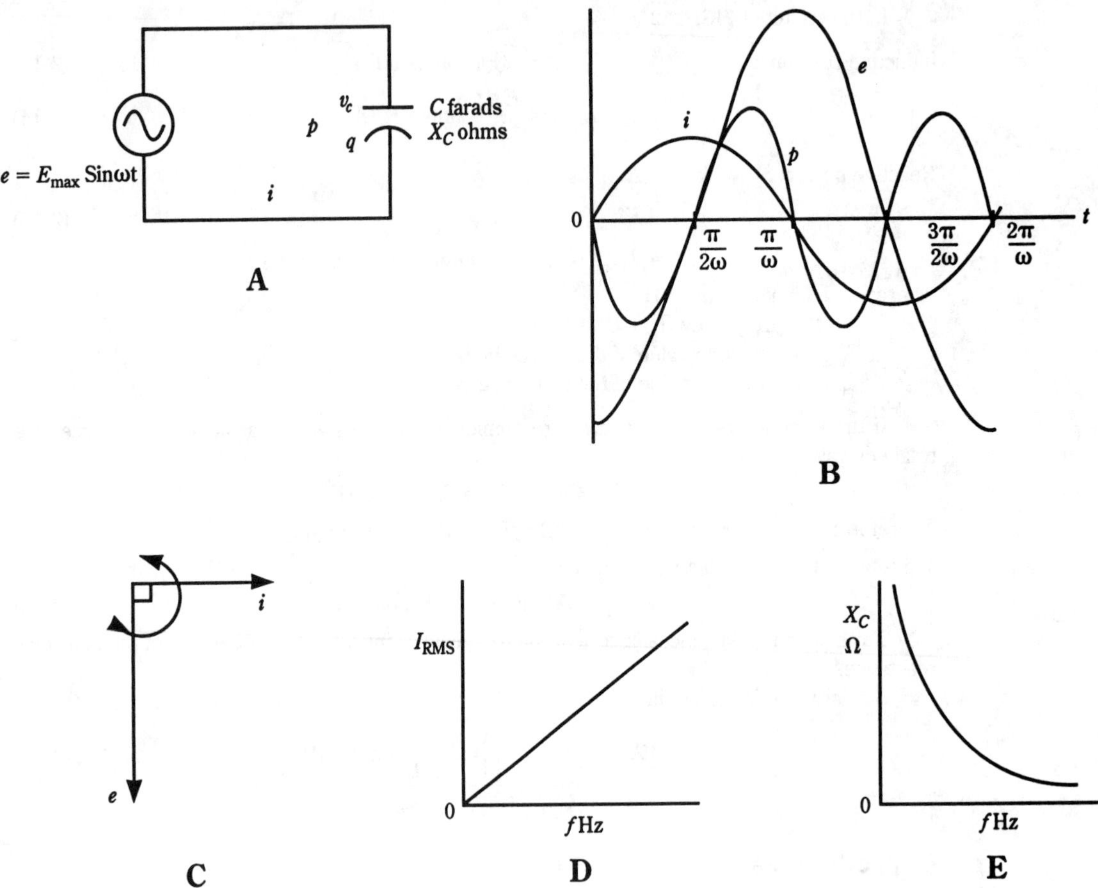

Fig. 2-13 The capacitor in an ac circuit.

voltage while the frequency and the capacitance are unchanged, the voltage across the capacitor must be greater, the capacitor must store more charge in the same period of time, and, consequently, the effective current is once more increased.

Summarizing, the value of the effective current is directly proportional to the voltage, the capacitance, and the frequency. The opposition to the alternating current flow is therefore inversely determined by the product of the frequency and the capacitance. This opposition is called the *capacitive reactance,* $X_C = E_{RMS}/I_{RMS}$ and is measured in ohms. The formula for the capacitive reactance is $X_C = 1/(2\pi fC)\ \Omega$. Because X_C is inversely proportional to the frequency, the graph of X_C versus frequency is the rectangular hyperbolic curve of FIG. 2-13E. By contrast, the effective current is directly proportional to the frequency so that the graph of I_{RMS} versus frequency is a straight line (FIG. 2-13D).

The instantaneous power, p, is equal to the product of e and i. The graph of the instantaneous power, p, versus time is a second harmonic sine wave (FIG. 2-13B) whose average value is zero over the source voltage's cycle. During one quarter cycle, the capacitor charges so that energy is drawn from the source and appears in the form of the electric field between the capacitor's plates. However, during the following quarter cycle, the capacitor discharges and the energy is returned to the source. The product of E_{RMS} and I_{RMS} is the reactive power, which is measured in VArs.

Like the inductor, the importance of the capacitor lies in the fact that its opposition to alternating current depends on frequency; as the frequency is raised, the effective current increases from zero to infinity (FIG. 2-13D) while the capacitive reactance decreases from infinity towards zero (FIG. 2-13E). Consequently, for given values of L and C there must always be a (resonant) frequency for which $X_L = X_C$; this fact is used in the LC tuning circuit which, for example, is capable of selecting a particular station through its ability to distinguish between one frequency and another.

In the circuit of FIG. 2-13E:

Capacitive reactance: $$X_C = \frac{1}{2\pi fC} \text{ ohms } (\Omega) \tag{2-17}$$

Current: $$I_{RMS} = \frac{E_{RMS}}{X_C} \text{ amperes (A)} \tag{2-18}$$

Reactive power: $$\begin{aligned} RP &= E_{RMS} \times I_{RMS} \\ &= E^2_{RMS}/X_C \\ &= I^2_{RMS} \times X_C \text{ volt-amperes reactive (VAr)} \end{aligned} \tag{2-19}$$

where: C = capacitance (F)
f = frequency (Hz)
E_{RMS} = effective value of the source voltage (V)
I_{RMS} = effective value of the source current (A)

If three capacitors C1, C2, C3 are connected in series across an ac voltage source, the total equivalent capacitance is given by:

$$\frac{1}{C_T} = \frac{1}{C_1} + \frac{1}{C_2} + \frac{1}{C_3} \text{ farads (F)}$$

Therefore: $$\frac{1}{2\pi fC_T} = \frac{1}{2\pi fC_1} + \frac{1}{2\pi fC_2} + \frac{1}{2\pi fC_3}$$

and total equivalent capacitive reactance:

$$X_{CT} = X_{C1} + X_{C2} + X_{C3} \text{ ohms } (\Omega) \tag{2-20}$$

For capactive reactances in series, the total equivalent reactance is the sum of the individual reactances. Similarly, for capacitors in parallel, the total capacitive reactance:

$$X_{CT} = \frac{1}{\dfrac{1}{X_{C1}} + \dfrac{1}{X_{C2}} + \dfrac{1}{X_{C3}}} \text{ ohms } (\Omega) \tag{2-21}$$

Question 2-11 A 110-V 60-Hz sine-wave voltage is applied across a 5-H inductor. If the frequency is increased to 120 Hz, the new value of the inductance is:

A. 5 H B. 10 H C. 2.5 H D. 20 H E. 1.25 H

Answer Choice A. Although the inductive reactance is directly proportional to the frequency, the inductance, L, is independent of any change in the frequency. Consequently, the value of the inductance remains at 5 H.

Question 2-12 Figure 2-14 shows the phase relationship between a source voltage and the accompanying source current. The circuit, across which the source is connected, contains:

A. resistance only B. inductance only C. capacitance only D. resistance and inductance in series E. resistance and capacitance in series

Answer Choice C. In FIG. 2-14, *i* leads *e* by 90°; therefore the circuit is entirely capacitive.

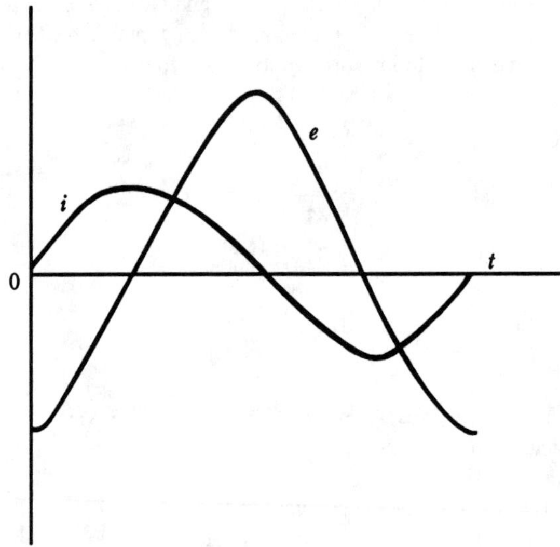

Fig. 2-14 Waveforms for question 2-12.

* **Question 2-13** Figure 2-15 shows the phase relationship between a source voltage and the accompanying current. The circuit, across which the source is connected, contains:

A. inductance only B. resistance only C. capacitance only D. resistance and capacitance in series E. inductance and resistance in series

Answer Choice A. In FIG. 2-15, *e* leads *i* by 90°; therefore, the circuit is entirely inductive.

* **Question 2-14** A 0.001-μF capacitor is connected across a sine-wave voltage source whose angular frequency, $\omega = 2\pi f = 1000$ rad/s. The reactance of this capacitor is:

A. 159 kΩ B. 628 kΩ C. 1 MΩ D. 1 kΩ E. 1590 kΩ

Answer Choice C.

Capacitive reactance:

$$X_C = \frac{1}{2\pi fC}$$

$$= \frac{1}{1000 \times 0.001 \times 10^{-6}} \quad (2\text{-}17)$$

$$= 1\ \text{M}\Omega$$

2-7. Impedance and power factor

Provided there is only a single sine-wave source, all ac circuits, however complex, can ultimately be analyzed into a resistance in series with a reactance, which can be either inductive or capaci-

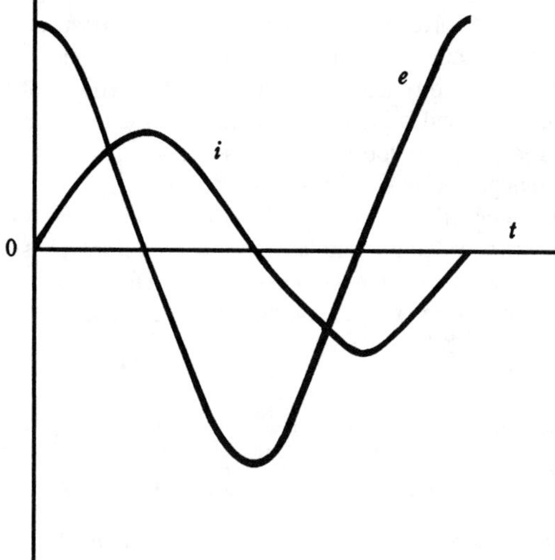

Fig. 2-15 Waveform for question 2-13.

tive. The total opposition to the flow of alternating current is therefore a resistance/reactance combination that is called the *impedance, z* (FIG. 2-16).

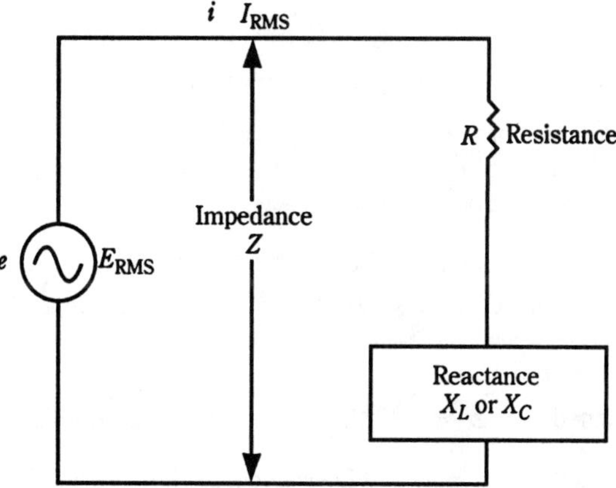

Fig. 2-16 Impedance of an ac circuit.

The impedance, *z*, is a phasor that is defined as the ratio of the source voltage phasor to the source current phasor. The magnitude, *Z*, of the impedance phasor is measured in ohms and is equal to the ratio of E_{RMS}:I_{RMS}. E_{RMS} and I_{RMS} are the effective values of the source voltage and the source current.

The phase angle, ϕ, of the impedance is the angle between the direction of *z* and the horizontal reference line. The value of this angle normally ranges from $-90°$ (capacitive reactance only) through 0° (resistance only) to $+90°$ (inductive reactance only).

In the general ac circuit, the resistive component dissipates (lost) power in the form of heat while the reactive component stores power in the form of either an electric field (capacitive reactance) or a magnetic field (inductive reactance). Therefore, the product of $E_{RMS} \times I_{RMS}$ does not represent the dissipated power and is instead referred to as the *apparent power,* as measured at the source in volt-amperes (VA). By contrast, the dissipated power is called the *true power* and the ratio of true power to apparent power is the *power factor.*

If an ac circuit is *inductive,* the phase angle is positive and the power factor is *lagging* (the source current lags the source voltage). With a *capacitive circuit* the phase angle is negative and the power factor is *leading* (the source current leads the source voltage). The value of the power factor extends from zero (reactance only) to unity (resistance only).

In FIG. 2-16:

Magnitude of the impedance: $$Z = \frac{E_{max}}{I_{max}} = \frac{E_{RMS}}{I_{RMS}} \text{ ohms } (\Omega) \quad (2\text{-}22)$$

$$\textit{True power} = I^2R \text{ watts (W)} \quad (2\text{-}23)$$

$$\textit{Reactive power} = I_2X \text{ volt-amperes reactive (VAr)} \quad (2\text{-}24)$$

$$\textit{Apparent power} = E_{RMS} \times I_{RMS} = I^2Z \text{ volt-amperes (VA)} \quad (2\text{-}25)$$

$$\textit{Power factor} = \frac{\textit{true power}}{\textit{apparent power}} = \frac{R}{Z} = \text{Cos. } \phi \quad (2\text{-}26)$$

$$\begin{aligned}\textit{True power} &= \textit{Apparent power} \times \textit{power factor} \\ &= E_{RMS} \times I_{RMS} \times \textit{power factor} \\ &= E_{RMS} \times I_{RMS} \times \text{Cos.}\phi \text{ watts (W)}\end{aligned} \quad (2\text{-}27)$$

where: E_{RMS} = effective value of the source voltage (V)
I_{RMS} = effective value of the source current (A)
ϕ = phase angle (degrees or radians)

Question 2-15 The impedance of an ac circuit is measured in:

A. siemens B. henrys C. farads D. ohms E. The unit depends on the nature of the components in the circuit

Answer Choice D. Impedance, $Z = \frac{E_{RMS}}{I_{RMS}}$ and is therefore measured in ohms.

Question 2-16 A 100-V 60-Hz supply voltage is connected to a relay whose resistance is 4 Ω. If the relay current is 0.2 A, the impedance of the relay is:

A. 4 Ω B. 20 Ω C. 50 Ω D. 20 Ω E. 500 Ω

Answer. Choice E.

Impedance: $$Z = \frac{E_{RMS}}{I_{RMS}} = \frac{100 \text{ V}}{0.2 \text{ A}} = 500\ \Omega \quad (2\text{-}22)$$

* **Question 2-17** The true power is calculated by knowing the:

A. RMS values of the source voltage and the source current
B. apparent power and the form factor
C. cosine of the phase angle
D. average values of the source voltage and the source current
E. both A and C are required

Answer Choice E. True power = $E_{RMS} \times I_{RMS} \times$ *power factor* = $E_{RMS} \times I_{RMS} \times$ Cos.ϕ watts (EQ. 2-27). Both choices A and C are required.

* **Question 2-18** In an ac circuit, the effective values of the source voltage and the source current are kept constant. Initially, the voltage and the current are in phase, but as they move out of phase, the:

A. apparent power increases
B. reactive power decreases
C. true power is unchanged
D. power factor increases
E. true power decreases

Answer Choice E. True power = $E_{RMS} \times I_{RMS} \times$ Cos.ϕ watts (EQ. 2-27). Because the cosine of a phase angle is less than unity, the value of the true power decreases.

* **Question 2-19** The true power in an ac circuit is determined by:

A. multiplying the effective value of the source voltage by the effective value of the source current
B. multiplying the square of the effective source current by the value of the impedance
C. multiplying the square of the effective source current by the resistance
D. dividing the square of the effective source voltage by the impedance
E. multiplying the square of the effective source current by the reactance

Answer Choice C. True power = I^2R watts.

* **Question 2-20** If the cosine of the phase angle is multiplied by the product of the effective source voltage and the effective source current, the result is the:

A. true power B. reactive power C. apparent power D. impedance E. energy consumed

Answer Choice A. True power = $E_{RMS} \times I_{RMS} \times$ Cos.ϕ watts.

* **Question 2-21** In the circuit of FIG. 2-17 the true power can be calculated from:

A. the product of V and A
B. the product of A^2 and $(R_1 + R_2)$
C. the power factor times the product of V and A
D. the result of dividing V^2 by $(R_1 + R_2)$
E. The true power cannot be calculated, but must instead by measured by a wattmeter

Answer Choice E. Because the values of the frequency and R_2 are unknown, the power factor cannot be calculated.

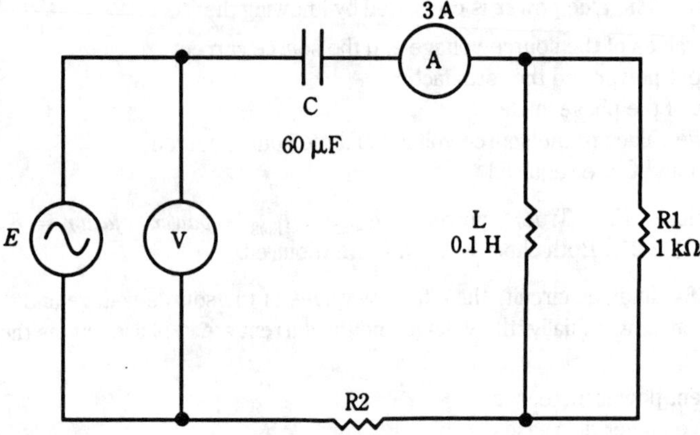

Fig. 2-17 The circuit for question 2-17.

2-8. Sine-wave input voltage to series combinations of L, C, and R

R and L in series

Assume that the value of X_L ($= 2\pi fL$ Ω) is greater than the value of R. Because R and L are in series, the same alternating current must flow through each component (FIG. 2-18A). The instantaneous voltage drop (v_R) across the resistor and the instantaneous current (i) through the resistor are in phase (FIG. 2-18B) so that their phasors lie along the same horizontal line (FIG. 2-18C). By contrast, the instantaneous voltage (v_L) across the inductor leads the instantaneous current (i) by 90° and consequently their phasors are perpendicular. The phasor sum of v_R and v_L is the supply voltage, e; the current, i, then lags the source voltage, e, by the phase angle, ϕ. This inductive circuit is then considered to have a lagging power factor (resistance, R/impedance, Z) and the phase angle is positive.

The total opposition to the alternating current flow is measured by the impedance phasor, z, which is defined as the ratio of the e phasor to the i phasor and is equal to the phasor sum of R and X_L (FIG. 2-18D).

The true power (TP) in watts is the power dissipated or lost as heat in the resistor; it is also the average value of the instantaneous power curve (FIG. 2-18B). The reactive, idle, or wattless power (RP) in volt-amperes reactive (VAr) is the power stored by the inductor as a magnetic field during one quarter of the ac cycle; this power is subsequently returned to the source during the next quarter cycle. The apparent power (AP) in volt-amperes (VA) is the product of the source voltage and the source current, and is the phasor sum of the true power and the reactive power (FIG. 2-18E). The power factor is the ratio of the true power to the apparent power and is equal to the cosine of the phase angle. If the value of the resistance is the same as that of the inductive reactance, the phase angle is 45° and the power factor is Cos. 45° = 0.707, lagging.

In the following equations, capital letters are used to indicate RMS values of voltage and current.

In FIG. 2-18A, total impedance:

$$Z = \sqrt{R^2 + X_L^2} \text{ ohms } (\Omega) \tag{2-28}$$

Current:

$$I = \frac{E}{Z} \text{ amperes (A)} \tag{2-29}$$

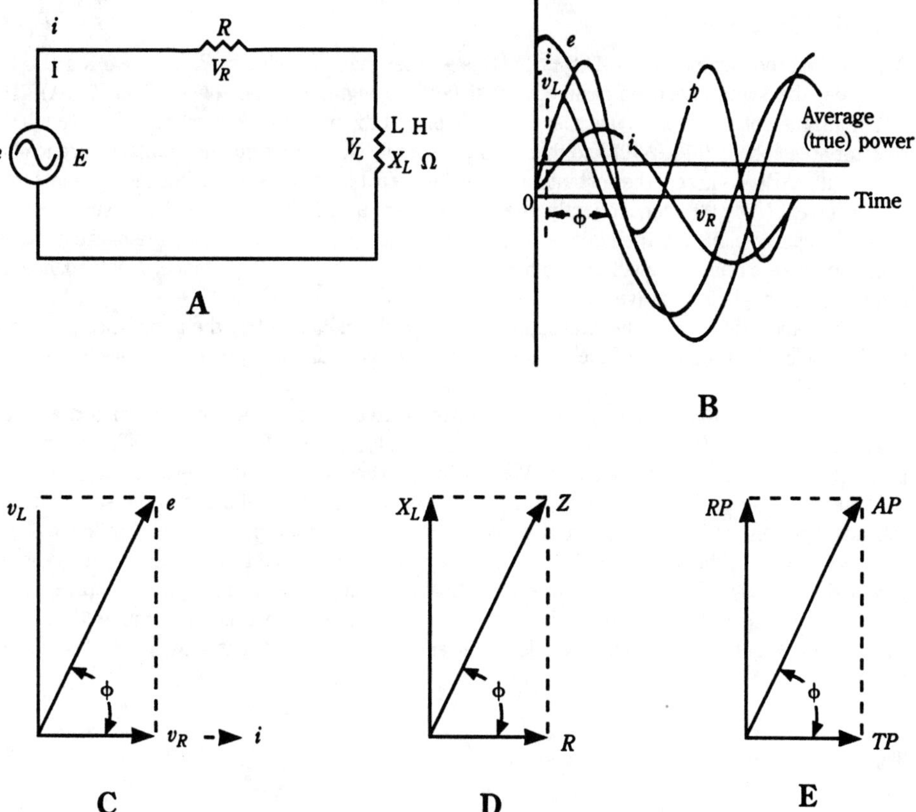

Fig. 2-18 The series combination of L and R in an ac circuit.

Voltage drop across the resistor: $V_R = I \times R$ volts (V) (2-30)

Voltage across the inductor: $V_L = I \times X_L$ volts (V) (2-31)

Source voltage: $E = \sqrt{V_R^2 + V_L^2}$ volts (V) (2-32)

$$\textit{True power} = I \times V_R = I^2R \text{ watts (W)} \quad (2\text{-}33)$$

$$\textit{Reactive power} = I \times V_L = I^2X_L \text{ volt-amperes reactive (VAr)} \quad (2\text{-}34)$$

$$\textit{Apparent power} = I \times E = I^2Z \text{ volt-amperes (VA)} \quad (2\text{-}35)$$

$$\textit{Apparent power} = \sqrt{(\textit{true power})^2 + (\textit{reactive power})^2} \text{ volt-amperes (VA)} \quad (2\text{-}36)$$

$$\textit{Power factor} = \frac{\textit{true power}}{\textit{apparent power}} = \text{Cos.}\,\phi\text{, lagging} \quad (2\text{-}37)$$

$$\textit{Phase angle, } \phi = \textit{Inv.Cos.}(\textit{power factor}) \text{ and is a positive angle} \quad (2\text{-}38)$$

R and C in series

Assume that the value of $X_C(= 1/(2\pi fC)\ \Omega)$ is greater than the value of R. Because R and C are in series, the same alternating current must flow through each component (FIG. 2-19A). The instantaneous voltage drop (v_R) across the resistor and the instantaneous current (i) through the resistor are in phase (FIG. 2-19B) so that their phasors lie along the same horizontal reference line (FIG. 2-19C). By contrast, the instantaneous voltage (v_C) across the capacitor lags the instantaneous current (i) by 90°; consequently, their phasors are perpendicular. The phasor sum of v_C and v_R is the supply voltage, e; the current, i, then leads the source voltage, e, by the phase angle, ø. This capacitive circuit is considered to have a leading power factor (resistance, R/impedance, Z) and the phase angle is negative.

The total opposition to the alternating current flow is measured by the impedance phasor, z, which is defined as the ratio of the e phasor to the i phasor, and is equal to the phasor sum of R and X_C (FIG. 2-19D).

The true power (TP) in watts is the power dissipated or lost as heat in the resistor; it is also the average value of the instantaneous power curve (FIG. 2-19E). The reactive, idle, or wattless power (RP) in volt-amperes reactive (VAr) is the power stored by the capacitor as an electric field during one quarter of the ac cycle; this power is subsequently returned to the source during the next quarter cycle. The apparent power (AP) in volt-amperes (VA) is the product of the source voltage and the source current, and is the phasor sum of the true power and the reactive power (FIG. 2-19F). The power factor is the ratio of the true power to the apparent power and is equal to the cosine of the phase angle. If the value of the resistance is the same as that of the capacitive reactance, the phase angle is $-45°$ and the power factor is Cos. $(-45°) = 0.707$, leading.

In FIG. 2-19A:

Total impedance: $$Z = \sqrt{R^2 + X_C^2} \text{ ohms } (\Omega) \quad (2\text{-}39)$$

Current: $$I = \frac{E}{Z} \text{ amperes (A)} \quad (2\text{-}40)$$

Voltage drop across the resistor: $$V_R = I \times R \text{ volts (V)} \quad (2\text{-}41)$$

Voltage across the capacitor: $$V_C = I \times X_C \text{ volts (V)} \quad (2\text{-}42)$$

Source voltage: $$E = \sqrt{V_R^2 + V_C^2} \text{ volts (V)} \quad (2\text{-}43)$$

$$\text{True power} = I \times V_R = I^2R \text{ watts (W)} \quad (2\text{-}44)$$

$$\text{Reactive power} = I \times V_C = I^2X_C \text{ volt-amperes reactive (VAr)} \quad (2\text{-}45)$$

$$\text{Apparent power} = X \times E = I^2Z \text{ volt-amperes (VA)} \quad (2\text{-}46)$$

$$\textit{Apparent power} = \sqrt{(\textit{true power})^2 + (\textit{reactive power})^2} \text{ volt-amperes (VA)} \quad (2\text{-}47)$$

$$\textit{Power factor} = \frac{\textit{true power}}{\textit{apparent power}} = \text{Cos.}\phi\text{, leading} \quad (2\text{-}48)$$

$$\textit{Phase angle, } \phi = \textit{Inv. Cos. (power factor)} \text{ and is a negative angle} \quad (2\text{-}49)$$

L and C in series

Assume that the value of $X_L(= 2\pi fL\ \Omega)$ is greater than the value of $X_C = 1/(2\pi fC)\ \Omega$. Because L and C are in series, the same alternating current must be associated with both the inductor and the capacitor (FIG. 2-20A). The instantaneous voltage (v_L) across the inductor leads the instantaneous current (i) by 90°, and the instantaneous voltage across the capacitor (v_C) lags i by 90° (FIG. 2-20B). Consequently, v_L and v_C are 180° out of phase and their phasors are pointing in opposite directions (FIG. 2-20C). Because it has been assumed that $X_L > X_C$, $v_L > v_C$ so that the supply

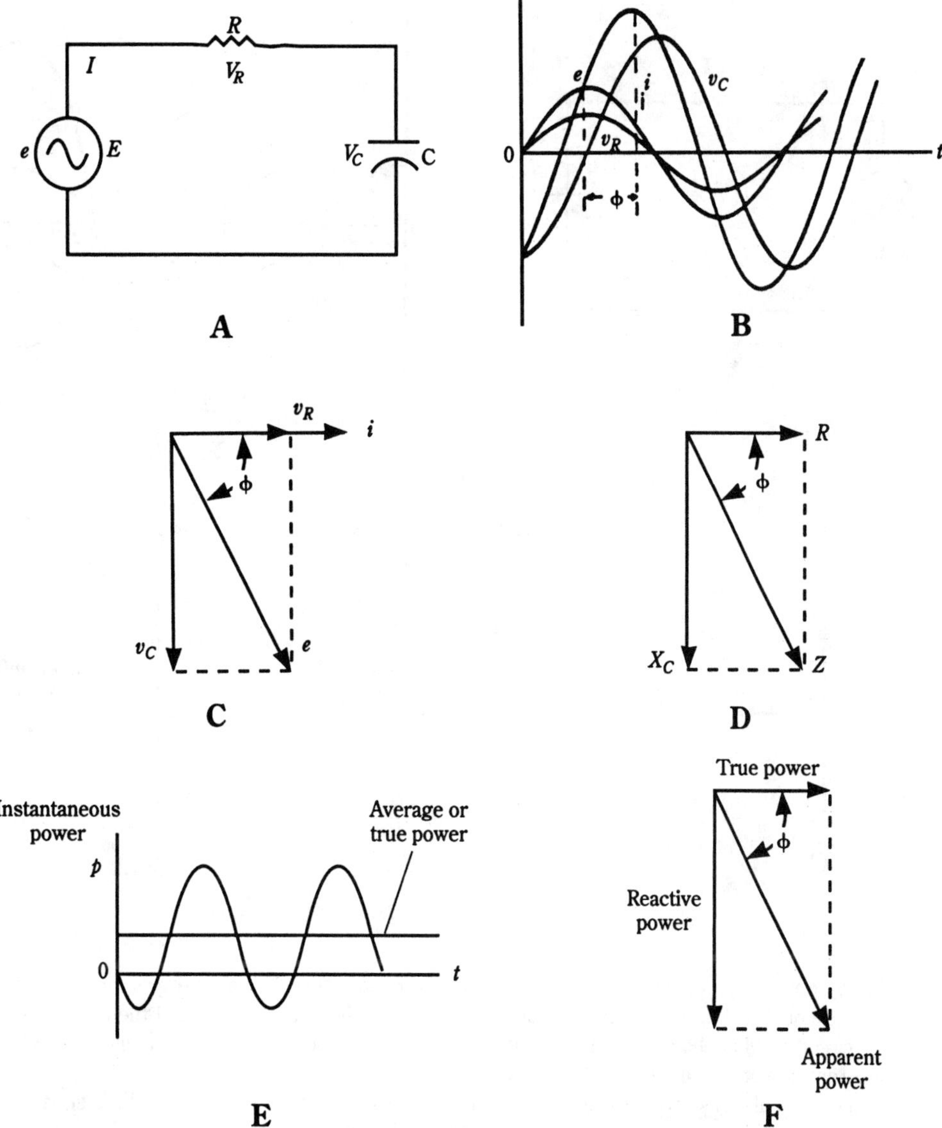

Fig. 2-19 The series combination of C and R in an ac circuit.

voltage, e, (which is the phasor sum of v_L and v_C) is in phase with v_L, but has a magnitude of $V_L - V_C$. Because i lags e by 90°, the circuit behaves inductively and has a lagging power factor with a phase angle of +90°. The magnitude of the impedance, Z, is found by combining X_L and X_C so that $Z = X_L - X_C\ \Omega$ (FIG. 2-20D).

Because the inductor and the capacitor are considered to be ideal components, there is no resistance present in the circuit and no true power is dissipated. The inductive reactive power (IRP) is greater than the capacitive reactive power (CRP) and the apparent power (AP) is entirely reactive, with a value equal to $IRP - CRP$ (FIG. 2-20E).

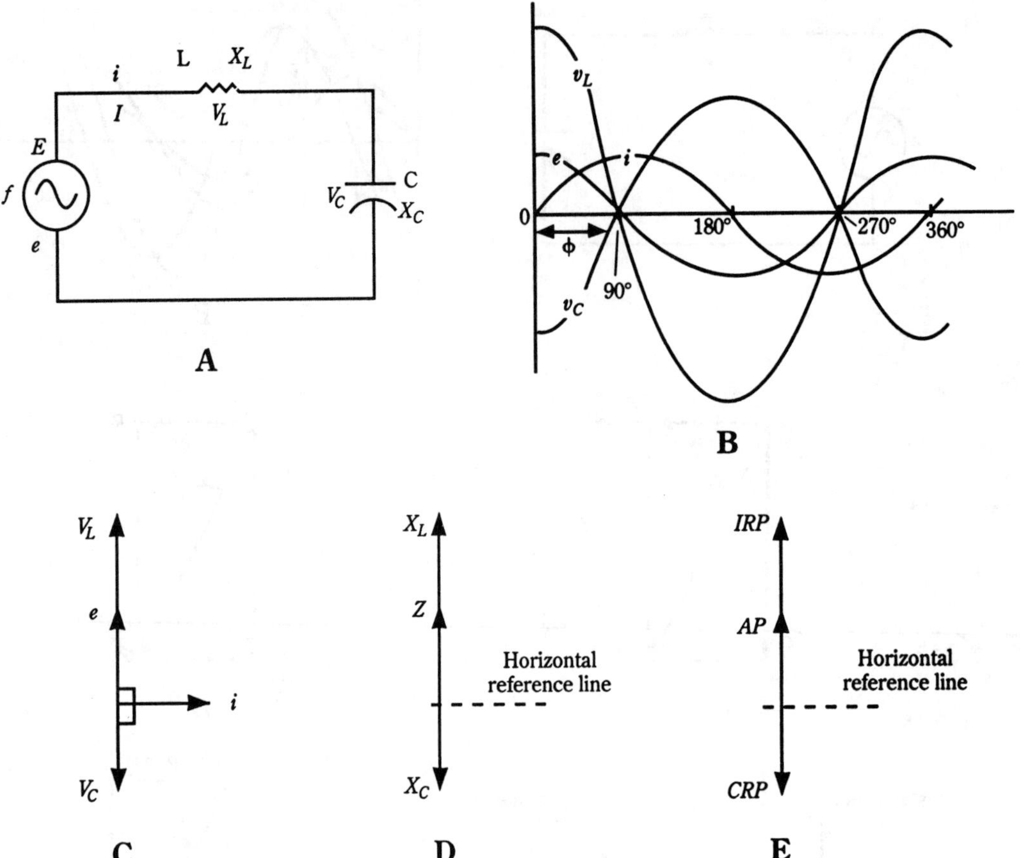

Fig. 2-20 The series combination of L and C in an ac circuit.

If, by contrast, you lowered the frequency to the point where X_C became greater than X_L; E would be equal to $V_C - V_L$; and Z would be $X_C - X_L$. The current, i, would then lead e by 90°, the circuit would behave capacitively with a leading power factor and a phase angle of $-90°$. The apparent power would equal $CRP - IRP$.

In the particular case where the frequency is chosen so that X_L is equal to X_C, V_L is equal to V_C, and Z is zero. The current would then be theoretically infinite.

In FIG. 2-20A:

Impedance: $$Z = X_L \sim X_C \text{ ohms } (\Omega) \quad (2\text{-}50)$$

The sign "~" means the "difference"; you are required to subtract the smaller quantity from the larger quantity so that the result is always positive. This takes into account the two cases: $X_L > X_C$ and $X_C > X_L$.

Current: $$I = \frac{E}{Z} \text{ amperes (A)} \quad (2\text{-}51)$$

Voltage across the inductor: $$V_L = I \times X_L \text{ volts (V)} \quad (2\text{-}52)$$

Voltage across the capacitor: $$V_C = I \times X_C \text{ volts (V)} \quad (2\text{-}53)$$

Source voltage: $$E = V_L \sim V_C \text{ volts (V)} \quad (2\text{-}54)$$

Because E is equal to the difference between V_L and V_C, it follows that either V_L or V_C or both V_L and V_C must be greater than the value of E. This voltage increase is possible because there is no power dissipated in the circuit.

$$\text{True power } (TP) = 0 \text{ watts (W)} \tag{2-55}$$

Inductive reactive power:
$$IRP = I \times V_L \text{ volt-amperes reactive (VArs)} \tag{2-56}$$

Capacitive reactive power:
$$CRP = I \times V_C \text{ volt-amperes reactive (VArs)} \tag{2-57}$$

Apparent power:
$$\begin{aligned} AP &= I \times E \\ &= IRP \sim CRP \text{ volt-amperes (VA(r)s)} \end{aligned} \tag{2-58}$$

It is permissible to measure the apparent power in VArs because the power is entirely reactive and there is no true power in the circuit.

$$\textit{Power factor} = 0 \text{ and is lagging if } X_L > X_C, \text{ but is leading if } X_C > X_L$$

At the particular frequency, f, for which $X_L = X_C$, $V_L = V_C$, $Z = 0$, and I is theoretically infinite.

Then:
$$2\pi fL = \frac{1}{2\pi fC}$$

This yields:
$$f = \frac{1}{2\pi\sqrt{LC}} \text{ hertz (Hz)} \tag{2-59}$$

where: L = inductance (H)
C = capacitance (F)

L,C, and R in series

Assume that X_L is greater than X_C and that R is less than $X_L - X_C$ in the circuit of FIG. 2-21A. Because all three components are in series, the instantaneous current, i, is the same throughout the circuit. In terms of phase relationships, v_R is in phase with i, v_L leads i by 90°, and v_c lags i by 90° (FIGS. 2-21B and C). The combined voltage across the inductor and the capacitor is represented by the phasor v_X, which is in phase with v_L and leads i by 90°. The current, i, lags the source voltage, e, which is the phasor sum of v_X and v_R. The current is therefore overall inductive, the power factor is lagging, and the phase angle, ø, is positive.

The net reactance, X, is equal to $X_L - X_C$, which is then combined with R to produce the impedance, Z (FIG. 2-21D). The total reactive power is the phasor sum of the inductive reactive power and the capacitive reactive power. When the total reactive power is combined with the true power, the result is the apparent power (FIG. 2-21E).

If X_C was greater than X_L, v_X would be in phase with v_C, and i would lead e by the phase angle, ø. The power factor would then be leading and ø would be a negative angle.

At the particular frequency, $f = 1/(2\pi\sqrt{LC})$ Hz, the reactances are equal and therefore cancel each other. The impedance is then equal to the resistance and the phase angle is zero. As a result, the values of the true power and the apparent power are the same.

In FIG. 2-21A:

Impedance:
$$Z = \sqrt{R^2 + (X_L \sim X_C)^2} \text{ ohms } (\Omega) \tag{2-60}$$

Current:
$$I = \frac{E}{Z} \text{ amperes (A)} \tag{2-61}$$

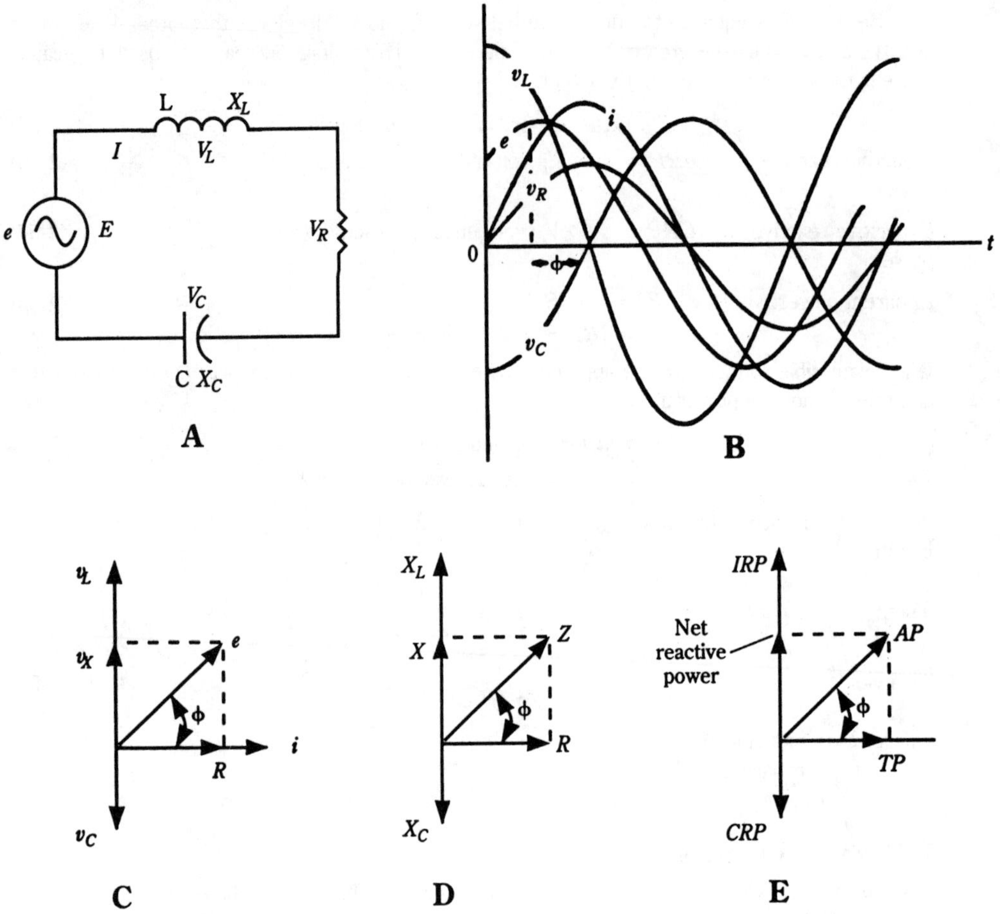

Fig. 2-21 The series combination of L, C, and R in an ac circuit.

Voltage across the resistor: $V_R = I \times R$ volts (V) (2-62)

Voltage across the inductor: $V_L = I \times X_L$ volts (V) (2-63)

Voltage across the capacitor: $V_C = I \times X_C$ volts (V) (2-64)

Source voltage: $E = \sqrt{V_R^2 + (V_L \sim V_C)^2}$ volts (V) (2-65)

True power: $TP = I \times V_R$ watts (W) (2-66)

Inductive reactive power: $IRP = I \times V_L$ volt-amperes reactive (VArs) (2-67)

Capacitive reactive power:

$CRP = I \times V_C$ volt-amperes reactive (VArs) (2-68)

Apparent power: $AP = I \times E$ (2-69)

$= \sqrt{TP^2 + (IRP \sim CRP)^2}$ volt-amperes (VA)

Power factor $= \dfrac{TP}{AP}$ and is lagging if $X_L > X_C$, but is leading if $X_C > X_L$. (2-70)

Phase angle, ϕ = Inv. Cos. (power factor) and is a positive angle when: $X_L > X_C$, but is a negative angle if $X_C > X_L$. When $R = X_L - X_C$, $\phi = +45°$ and when: $R = X_C - X_L$, $\phi = -45°$. (2-71)

* **Question 2-22** In FIG. 2-22, the resistor and the capacitor are connected in series across a sine-wave voltage source whose angular frequency: $\omega = 2\pi f = 1000$ rad./s. The total impedance of the circuit is:

A. 1 MΩ B. 2 MΩ C. $\frac{1}{\sqrt{2}}$ MΩ D. $\sqrt{2}$ MΩ E. 1.5 MΩ

Answer Choice D.

Reactance of the capacitor:

$$X_C = \frac{1}{2\pi fC} = \frac{1}{1000 \times 0.001 \times 10^{-6}} = 10^6\ \Omega = 1\ \text{M}\Omega \qquad (2\text{-}17)$$

Impedance of the circuit:

$$Z = \sqrt{R^2 + X_C^2} = \sqrt{1^2 + 1^2}\ \text{M}\Omega = \sqrt{2}\ \text{M}\Omega \qquad (2\text{-}39)$$

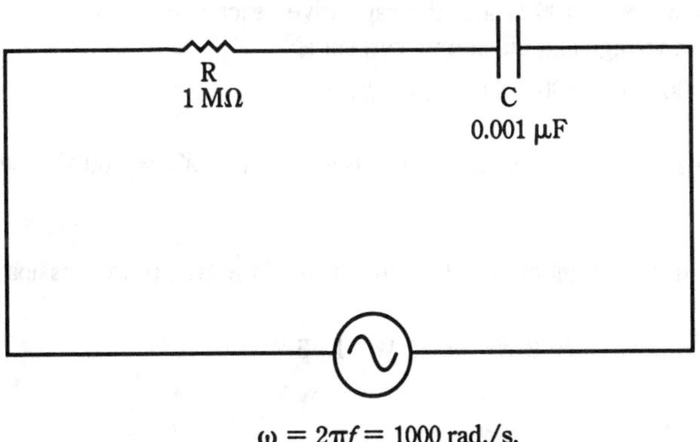

Fig. 2-22 The circuit for question 2-22.

* **Question 2-23** In FIG. 2-23, what is the phase relationship between the source voltage, E, and the source current, I?

A. E and I are in phase
B. E lags I
C. I leads E
D. E and I are 90° out of phase
E. The phase difference between E and I is 45°

Answer Choice E.

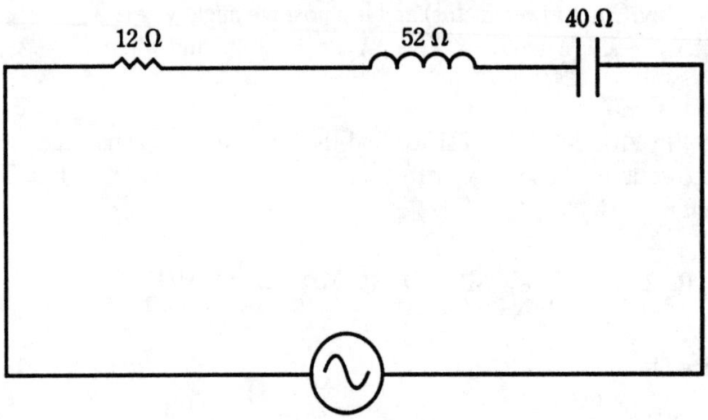

Fig. 2-23 The circuit for question 2-23.

Net reactance:

$$X = X_L - X_C$$
$$= 52 - 40 \qquad (2\text{-}50)$$
$$= 12\ \Omega$$

Therefore:

$$R = X = 12\ \Omega$$
$$\text{Phase angle, } \phi = +45°$$

The circuit is inductive so that *I* lags *E*.

* **Question 2-24** A resistor and a capacitor are connected in series across a sine-wave voltage source. If the resistance is 100 Ω and the capacitive reactance is 100 Ω, the phase difference between the source voltage and the source current is:

A. 0° B. +90° C. −90° D. +45° E. −45°

Answer Choice E. The circuit is capacitive. Because $R = X_C = 100\ \Omega$, the phase difference is −45°.

Question 2-25 In the circuit of FIG. 2-24, the value of the true power dissipated in the resistor is:

A. 6 W B. 5.6 W C. 9.2 W D. 11 W E. 5 W

Answer Choice C.

Voltage across the inductor:

$$V_L = I \times X_L \qquad (2\text{-}31)$$
$$= 0.1\text{ A} \times 600\ \Omega = 60\text{ V}$$

Voltage drop across the resistor:

$$V_R = \sqrt{E^2 - V_L^2}$$
$$= \sqrt{110^2 - 60^2} \qquad (2\text{-}32)$$
$$= 92.2\text{ V}$$

True power:

$$TP = I \times V_R$$
$$= 0.1\text{ A} \times 92.2\text{ V} \qquad (2\text{-}33)$$
$$= 9.2\text{ W, rounded off}$$

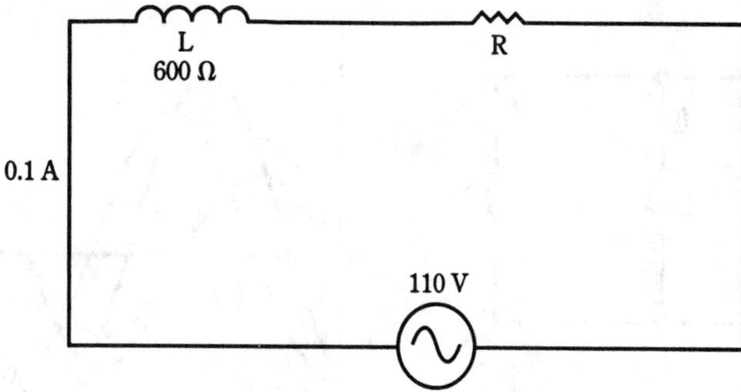

Fig. 2-24 The circuit for question 2-25.

* **Question 2-26** A 1-MΩ resistor and a 0.002-μF capacitor are connected in series across a sine-wave voltage source whose frequency is 60 Hz. The value of the circuit's impedance is:

A. 1 MΩ B. 2.33 MΩ C. 1.33 MΩ D. 1.66 MΩ E. 2.66 MΩ

Answer Choice D.

Capacitive reactance:
$$X_C = \frac{1}{2\pi f C}$$
$$= \frac{1}{2 \times \pi \times 60 \times 0.002 \times 10^{-6}} \quad (2\text{-}17)$$
$$= 1.33 \text{ M}\Omega\text{, rounded off}$$

Impedance:
$$Z = \sqrt{R^2 + X_c^2}$$
$$= \sqrt{1^2 + 1.33^2} \text{ M}\Omega \quad (2\text{-}39)$$
$$= 1.66 \text{ M}\Omega$$

2-9. Sine-wave input voltage to parallel combinations of L,C, and R

R and L in parallel

Because R and L are in parallel, the source voltage, e, is across each of the components and the source or supply current, i_S, will be the phasor sum of the two branch currents, i_R and i_L (FIGS. 2-25A and B). If you assume that the value of R is greater than the value of X_L, the resistor current ($I_R = E/R$) will be less than the inductor current ($I_L = E/X_L$). Because i_R is in phase with e and i_L lags e by 90°, the source current will lag the source voltage by the phase angle, ø (FIGS. 2-25B, C). The power factor will be lagging and the phase angle is positive (notice that in both the series and parallel combinations of R and L, the source current lags the source voltage; in each case, the phase angle is positive).

The true power, *TP*, is equal to E^2/R watts and is independent of the frequency. The reactive power, *RP*, is associated with the inductor while the apparent power (*AP*) at the source is the phasor sum of the true power and the reactive power (FIG. 2-25D).

In FIG. 2-25A:

Branch currents:
$$I_R = \frac{E}{R} \text{ amperes (A)} \quad (2\text{-}72)$$

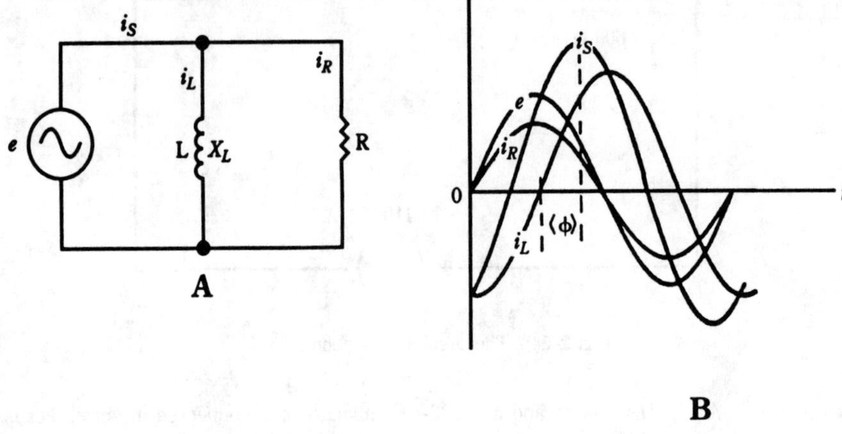

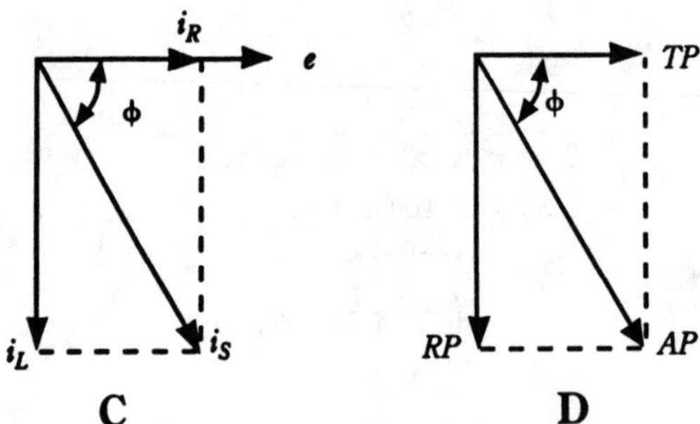

Fig. 2-25 The parallel combination of L and R in an ac circuit.

$$I_L = \frac{E}{X_L} \text{ amperes (A)} \tag{2-73}$$

Source current:
$$I_S = \sqrt{I_R^2 + I_L^2} \text{ amperes (A)} \tag{2-74}$$

Total impedance:
$$Z_T = \frac{E}{I_S} = \frac{R \times X_L}{\sqrt{R^2 + X_L^2}} \text{ ohms } (\Omega) \tag{2-75}$$

True power:
$$TP = E \times I_R = \frac{E^2}{R} \text{ watts (W)} \tag{2-76}$$

Notice that the true power is independent of the frequency.

Reactive power:
$$RP = E \times I_L = \frac{E^2}{X_L} \text{ volt-amperes reactive (VArs)} \tag{2-77}$$

Apparent power: $AP = E \times I_S$

$$= \frac{E^2}{Z_T}$$

$$= \sqrt{TP^2 + RP^2} \text{ volt-amperes (VA)} \qquad (2\text{-}78)$$

$$\text{Power factor} = \frac{TP}{AP} = \frac{Z_T}{R} \text{ and is lagging} \qquad (2\text{-}79)$$

$$\text{Phase angle, } \phi = \text{Inv.Cos.(power factor) and is a positive angle} \qquad (2\text{-}80)$$

If $R = X_L$, $\phi = +45°$ and the power factor is 0.707, lagging.

R and C in parallel

Because R and C are in parallel, the source voltage, e, is across each of the components and the source or supply current, i_S, will be the phasor sum of the two branch currents, i_R and i_C (FIGS. 2-26A and B). If you assume that the value of R is greater than the value of X_C, the resistor current ($I_R = E/R$) will be less than the capacitor current ($I_C = E/X_C$). Because i_R is in phase with e while i_C leads e by 90°, the source current will lead the source voltage by the phase angle, ϕ, (FIGS. 2-26B and C). The power factor will then be leading and the phase angle is negative.

The true power, TP, is equal to E^2/R watts and is independent of the frequency. The reactive power, RP, is associated with the capacitor, and the apparent power, AP, at the source is the phasor sum of the true power and the reactive power (FIG. 2-26D).

In FIG. 2-26A:

Branch current:

$$I_R = \frac{E}{R} \text{ amperes (A)} \qquad (2\text{-}81)$$

$$I_C = \frac{E}{X_C} \text{ amperes (A)} \qquad (2\text{-}82)$$

Source current:

$$I_S = \sqrt{I_R^2 + I_C^2} \text{ amperes (A)} \qquad (2\text{-}83)$$

Total impedance:

$$Z_T = \frac{E}{I_S}$$

$$= \frac{R \times X_C}{\sqrt{R^2 + X_C^2}} \text{ ohms } (\Omega) \qquad (2\text{-}84)$$

True power:

$$TP = E \times I_R = \frac{E^2}{R} \text{ watts (W)} \qquad (2\text{-}85)$$

Notice that the value of the true power is independent of the frequency.

Reactive power:

$$RP = E \times I_C = \frac{E^2}{X_C} \text{ volt-amperes reactive (VArs)}$$

Apparent power: $AP = E \times I_S$

$$= \frac{E^2}{Z_T}$$

$$= \sqrt{TP^2 + RP^2} \text{ volt-amperes (VA)} \qquad (2\text{-}86)$$

$$\text{Power factor} = \frac{TP}{AP} = \frac{Z_T}{R} \text{ and is leading} \qquad (2\text{-}87)$$

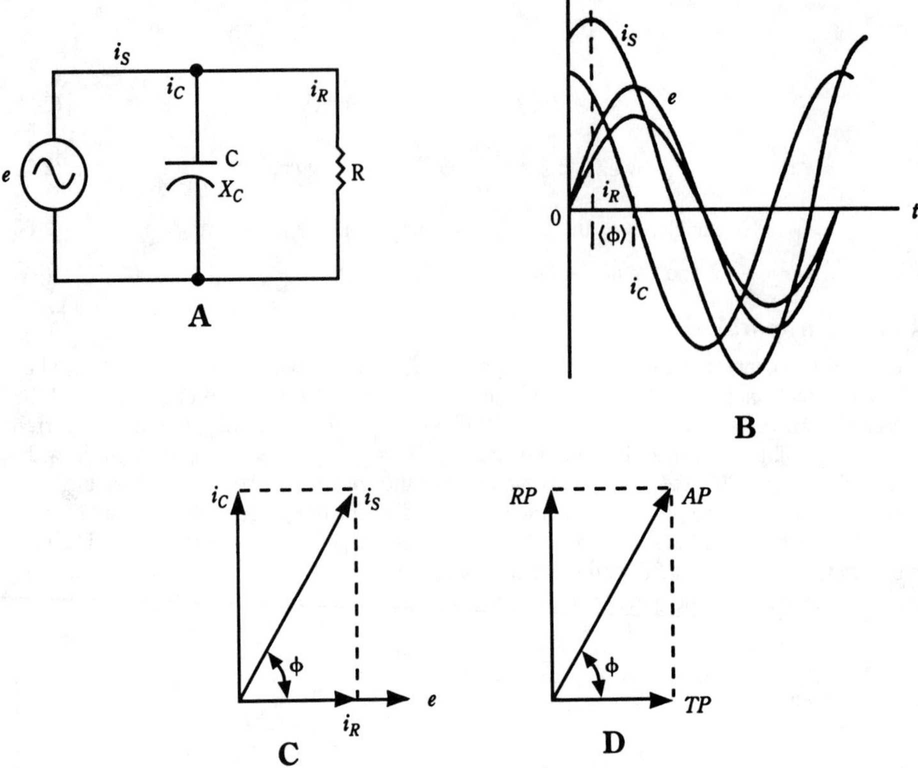

Fig. 2-26 The parallel combination of C and R in an ac circuit.

$$\text{Phase angle, } \phi = \text{Inv.Cos.(power factor) and is a negative angle} \quad (2\text{-}88)$$

If $R = X_C$, $\phi = -45°$ and the power factor is 0.707, leading.

L and C in Parallel

Because L and C are in parallel, the source voltage, e, is across each of the components and the source or supply current, i_S, will be the phasor sum of the two branch currents, i_L and i_C (FIGS. 2-27A and B). If you assume that the value of X_C is greater than the value of X_L, the capacitor current ($I_C = E/X_C$) will be less than the inductor current ($I_L = E/X_L$). Because i_C leads the source voltage by 90° while i_L lags the same source voltage by 90°, i_C and i_L are 180° out of phase (FIG. 2-27B) and their phasors are pointing in opposite directions (FIG. 2-27C). The phasor sum of i_L and i_C is the source current, i_S, which will be in phase with i_L and will lag the source voltage by 90°. The current therefore behaves inductively, the power factor is lagging and the phase angle is positive. Notice that this is opposite to the result obtained from the series L,C circuit, where if X_C was greater than X_L, the power factor was leading. This is because, in the parallel circuit, you are concerned with the branch currents, which are inversely proportional to the reactances. In the series circuit, you considered the component voltages, which were directly proportional to the reactances.

If X_L is greater than X_C, the capacitor current is greater than the inductor current; i_S is in

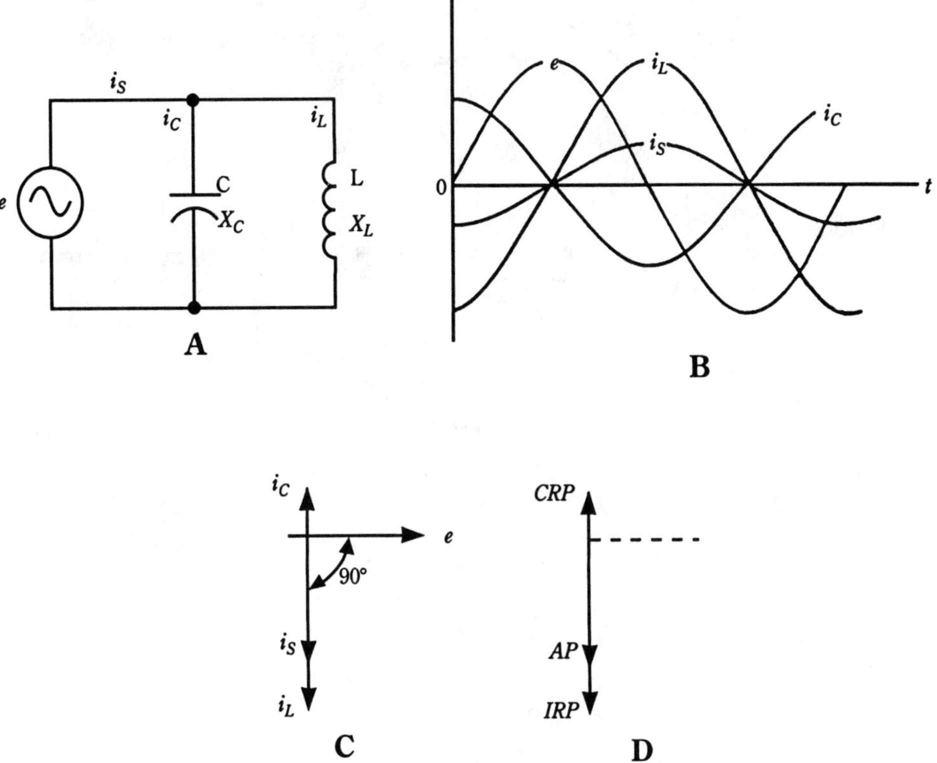

Fig. 2-27 The parallel combination of L and C in an ac circuit.

phase with i_C and leads the source voltage by 90°. The power factor is then leading and the phase angle is negative (FIG. 2-28).

Because the components are assumed to be ideal, there are no resistance losses associated with the circuit and the true power, *TP*, is zero. The apparent power (*AP*) is the phasor sum of the inductive reactive power (*IRP*) and the capacitive reactive power (*CRP*) (FIG. 2-27).

Notice at the particular frequency, *f*, for which the reactances are equal, the branch currents are also equal; therefore, the supply current is zero. The total impedance is then infinite and the parallel combination behaves as an open circuit. This is theoretically possible because the power in the circuit is entirely reactive and no true power is dissipated as heat.

In FIG. 2-27A:

Branch currents:

$$I_L = \frac{E}{X_L} \text{ amperes (A)} \tag{2-89}$$

$$I_C = \frac{E}{X_C} \text{ amperes (A)} \tag{2-90}$$

Source current:

$$I_S = I_L \sim I_C \text{ amperes (A)}$$

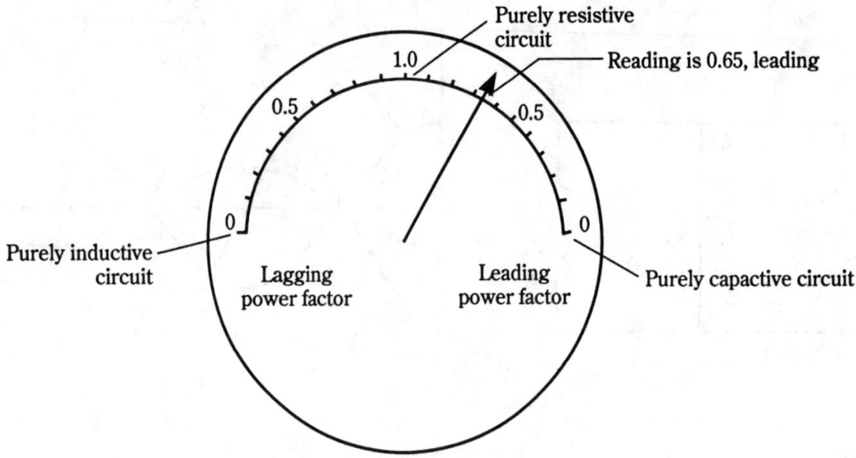

Fig. 2-28 The power factor meter.

Total impedance:

$$Z_T = \frac{E}{I_S} = \frac{X_L \times X_C}{X_L \sim X_C} \text{ ohms } (\Omega) \qquad (2\text{-}91)$$

True power:

$$TP = 0 \text{ watts (W)} \qquad (2\text{-}92)$$

Inductive reactive power:

$$IRP = E \times I_L \text{ volt-amperes reactive (VArs)} \qquad (2\text{-}93)$$

Capacitive reactive power:

$$CRP = E \times I_C \text{ volt-amperes reactive (VArs)} \qquad (2\text{-}94)$$

Apparent power:

$$AP = E \times I_S = IRP \sim CRP \text{ volt-amperes (VA(r)s)} \qquad (2\text{-}95)$$

$$\textit{Power factor} = 0, \text{ lagging}$$
$$\textit{Phase angle} = +90°$$

The reactances are equal at the frequency, *f*, for which:

$$f = \frac{1}{2\pi\sqrt{LC}} \text{ hertz (Hz)} \qquad (2\text{-}96)$$

where: L = inductance (H)
C = capacitance (F)

L,C, and R in parallel

Because all three components are in parallel across the source voltage, the source current, i_S, will be the phasor sum of the three branch currents, i_R, i_L, and i_C (FIGS. 2-29A and 2-29B). If you assume that the inductive reactance is greater than the capacitive reactance and that the value of the resistance is relatively large, the capacitor current ($I_C = E/X_C$) will be greater than the inductor current ($I_L = E/X_L$) and the resistor current ($I_R = E/R$) will be small. Because i_C leads the source voltage by 90° while i_L lags the same source voltage by 90°, i_C and i_L are 180° out-of-phase (FIG. 2-29B) and their phasors are pointing in opposite directions (FIG. 2-29C). The phasor sum of i_L and i_C is the total reactive current, i_X, which is in phase with i_C. The resistor current, i_R, is then combined with i_X to provide the source current, i_S, which leads the source voltage so that the power factor is leading and the phase angle, ϕ, is negative.

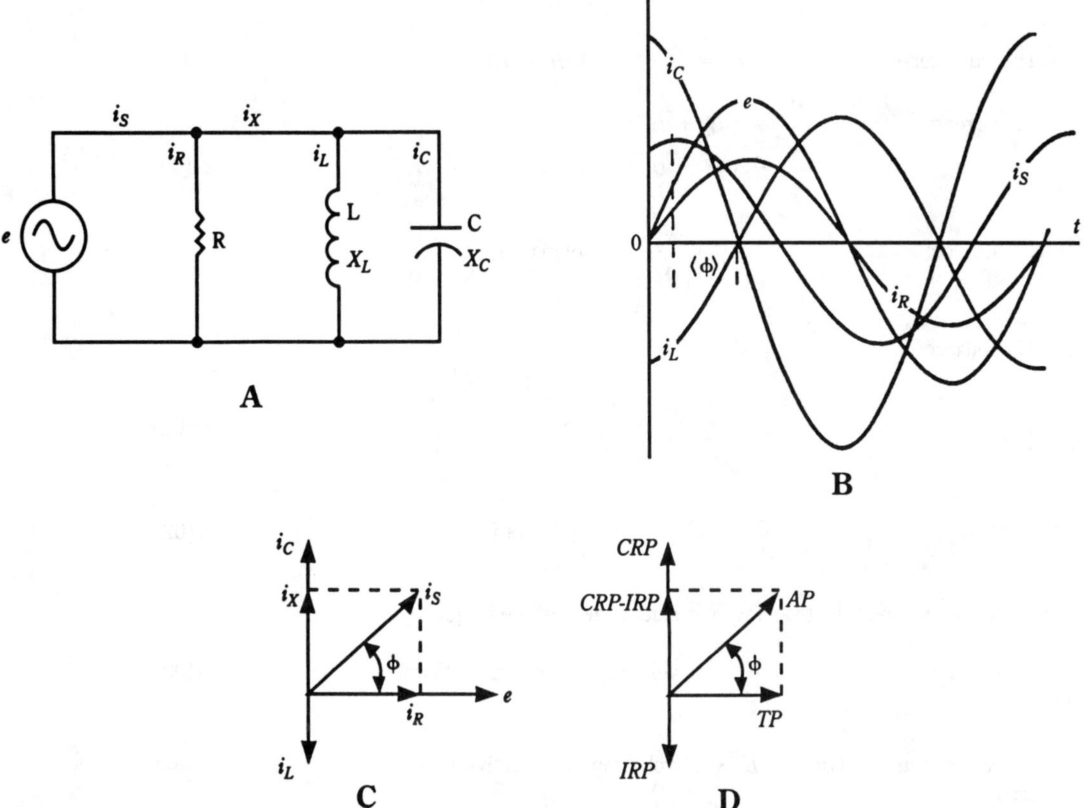

Fig. 2-29 The parallel combination of L, C, and R in an ac circuit.

If X_C is greater than X_L, the inductor current is greater than the capacitor current; i_X is in phase with i_L and i_S lags the source voltage by the positive phase angle, ϕ. The power factor is then lagging. The apparent power (*AP*) is the phasor sum of the true power (*TP*), the inductive reactive power (*IRP*), and the capacitive reactive power (*CRP*) (FIG. 2-29D).

At the particular frequency, *f*, for which the reactances are equal, the inductor and the capacitor currents cancel out (the parallel L, C combination behaves as an open circuit), and the source current is the same as the resistor current. The total impedance is then equal in value to the resistance. At frequencies above and below *f*, the parallel L, C combination behaves as a certain reactance value which, when placed in parallel with the resistance, produces a total impedance that is less than the value of the resistance. When these two statements are combined, the total impedance cannot be higher than the value of the resistance.

In FIG. 2-29A:

Branch currents: $I_R = \frac{E}{R}$ amperes (A) (2-97)

$I_L = \frac{E}{X_L}$ amperes (A) (2-98)

$I_C = \frac{E}{X_C}$ amperes (A) (2-99)

Total reactive current: $I_X = I_L \sim I_C$ amperes (A)

Source current: $I_S = \sqrt{I_R^2 + I_X^2}$

$= \sqrt{I_R^2 + (I_L \sim I_C)^2}$ amperes (A) (2-100)

Total reactance: $X_T = \frac{X_L \times X_C}{X_L \sim X_C}$ ohms (Ω)

Total impedance: $Z_T = \frac{E}{I_S}$

$= \frac{R \times X_T}{\sqrt{R^2 + X_T^2}}$ ohms (Ω) (2-101)

True power: $TP = E \times I_R = \frac{E^2}{R}$ watts (W) (2-102)

Notice that the value of the true power is independent of the frequency.

Inductive reactive power: $IRP = E \times I_L$ volt-amperes reactive (VArs) (2-103)

Capacitive reactive power: $CRP = E \times I_C$ volt-amperes reactive (VArs) (2-104)

Apparent power: $AP = E \times I_S$ (2-105)

$= \sqrt{TP^2 + (IRP \sim CRP)^2}$ volt-amperes (VA)

$$Power\ factor = \frac{TP}{AP}$$ and is leading (2-106)

Phase angle: ϕ = Inv. Cos. (power factor) and is a negative angle (2-107)

The frequency, *f*, for which the reactances are equal and the impedance is a maximum, is given by:

$$f = \frac{1}{2\pi\sqrt{LC}} \text{ hertz (Hz)} \qquad (2\text{-}108)$$

where: L = inductance (H)
C = capacitance (F)

* **Question 2-27** In the circuit of FIG. 2-30, the true power can be calculated from:

A. (reading of V) × (reading of A) × *power factor*
B. (reading of V) × (reading of A)
C. (reading of A)^2 × (R_3 + R_4)
D. (reading of V)^2 ÷ (R_3 + R_4)
E. (reading of A)^2 × R_3

Answer Choice A. Because the values of the frequency and the components are known, the power factor can be calculated.

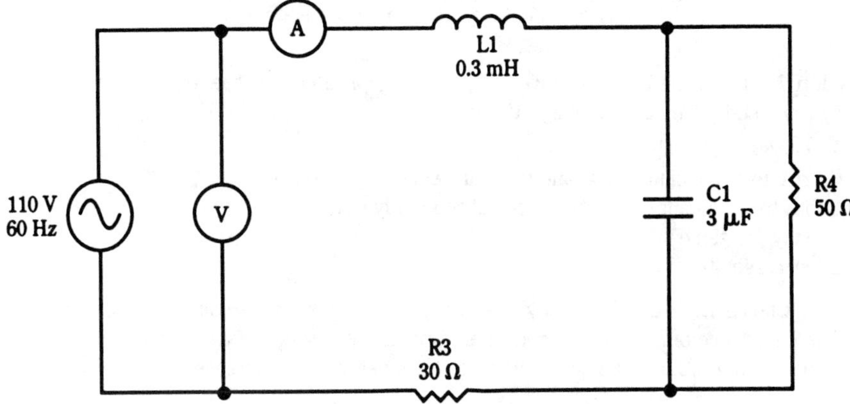

Fig. 2-30 The circuit for question 2-27.

* **Question 2-28** In the circuit of FIG. 2-31, how many watts are supplied from the sine-wave voltage source?

A. 0 W B. 1 W C. 10 W D. 20 W E. 30 W

Answer Choice A. Although the apparent power is 10 V × 1 A = 10 VA, the inductor and the capacitor are assumed to be ideal components with no resistive losses. Consequently, the true power in the circuit is zero (0 W).

* **Question 2-29** An ideal inductor and an ideal capacitor have no resistive losses and are connected in parallel across a sine-wave voltage source. Which of the following statements is true?

A. The power factor of the circuit is always unity
B. The phase angle of the circuit is 0° and is independent of the frequency
C. The source current is in phase with the source voltage
D. The source current is 180° out of phase with the source voltage
E. The power factor of the circuit is zero

Answer Choice E. Because the components have no resistive losses, there is no true power dissipated and the power factor of the circuit is therefore zero.

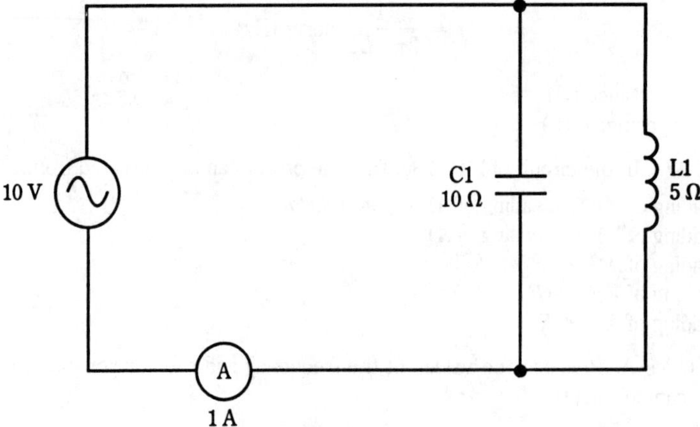

Fig. 2-31 The circuit for question 2-28.

* **Question 2-30** In the circuit of FIG. 2-32, E is held at a constant level, but the frequency is steadily increased. The output voltage V_o, will:

A. decrease steadily
B. rise to a maximum value and then subsequently decrease
C. fall to a minimum value and then subsequently rise
D. stay the same
E. increase steadily

Answer Choice E. If the frequency is steadily increased, the reactance of the capacitor, C, falls. The impedance of $R//C$ is reduced; therefore, there is less voltage drop across this parallel combination. It follows that the output voltage, V_o, must steadily increase.

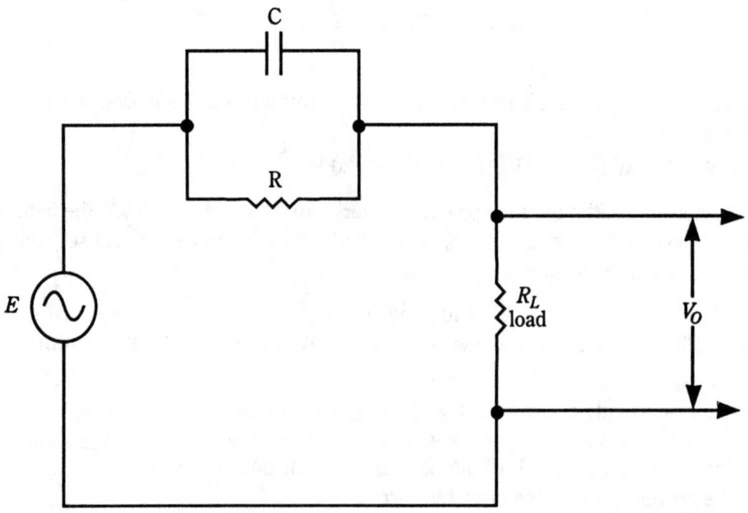

Fig. 2-32 The circuit for question 2-30.

2-10. The decibel

In the most recent General Radiotelephone Examinations, the Federal Communications Commission (FCC) has introduced a number of new questions that involve a knowledge of decibels. Because such a knowledge will shortly be required, it is appropriate to look at the decibel concept.

On many occasions, electronics and communications are concerned with the transmission of alternating power from one position to another. The various lines and items of equipment (which constitute the transmission system) introduce both power gains and losses.

Consider a network that joins an alternating source (for example, a radio-frequency (RF) generator) to a load. Let the input power be P_i and the output power be P_o. The ratio of the output power to the input power is the power ratio P_o/P_i (FIG. 2-33A). A network (such as an attenuator) introduces a loss, in which case P_o/P_i is less than unity. By contrast, an amplifier provides a gain so that P_o/P_i is greater than unity. If a number of these networks are connected in cascade (FIG. 2-33B), and the individual power ratios are known, the overall power ratio is obtained by multiplying together the individual power ratios.

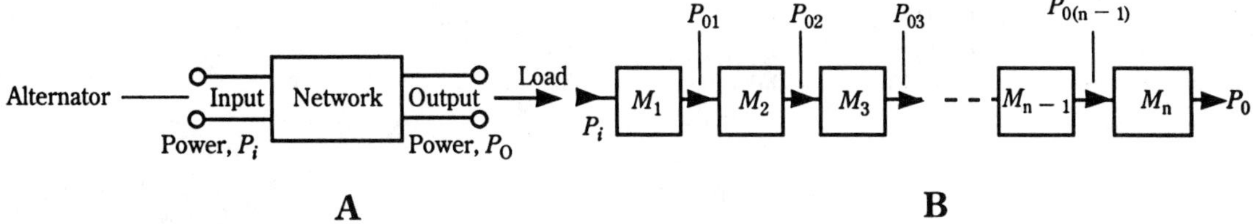

Fig. 2-33 The power ratio.

In a complex system that contains a variety of networks each contributing a gain or loss, the calculation of the overall power ratio might become extremely laborious. To simplify the calculation, the individual power ratios are expressed by a logarithmic unit, which enables the algebraic sum to be used in place of multiplication. The logarithmic unit used is the *decibel* (*dB*) and the power gain or loss of a network is then expressed as 10 log (P_o/P_i) dB, where "log" is used as an abbreviation for *common logarithm* to the base 10.

The common logarithm of a number is the power or exponent to which the base (10) must be raised in order that the result is equal to the value of the number. For example, log 100,000 = 5 because 10^5 = 100,000 whereas log 0.01 = log 1/100 = −2 because 10^{-2} = $1/10^2$ = 1/100. Therefore, a power gain of 100,000 is equivalent to 10 log 100,000 = 10 × 5 = 50 dB, while a power loss ratio of 0.01 corresponds to 10 log 0.01 = 10 × (−2) = −20 dB. If an attenuator whose power loss is 0.01 is followed by an amplifier with a power gain ratio of 100,000, the overall power ratio is 100,000 × 0.01 = 1000 or +30 dB. The same result is obtained by taking the algebraic sum of +50 dB and −20 dB = (+50 dB) + (−20 dB) = +30 dB. Corresponding power ratios and decibels are shown in TABLE 2-2.

Table 2-3 shows additional corresponding values of power ratios and decibels; these are needed to solve certain questions that have appeared in the most recent General Radiotelephone License examinations.

A larger logarithmic unit is the *bel,* which is equivalent to 10 decibels and was named after Alexander Graham Bell. The decibel was originally related to acoustics and was regarded as the smallest change in sound intensity that could be detected by the human ear.

The decibel is essentially a unit of power ratio and not of absolute power; however, if some

Table 2-2. Conversions of power, voltage, and current ratios to decibels.

Voltage E_o/E_i ratio, or current I_o/I_i ratio	Power ratio P_o/P_i	N decibels (dB)	
1000	1000000	60	Power gain
316	100000	50	
100	10000	40	
31.6	1000	30	
10	100	20	
3.16	10	10	
1	1	0	
0.316	0.1	−10	Power loss
0.1	0.01	−20	
0.0316	0.001	−30	
0.01	0.0001	−40	
0.00316	0.00001	−50	
0.001	0.000001	−60	

Table 2-3. Conversion of certain power ratios to decibels.

Power ratio P_o/P_1	N decibels (dB)
5.0	7
4.0	6
2.0	3
1.26	1
0.79	−1
0.5	−3
0.25	−6
0.2	−7

standard reference level of power is assumed to represent 0 dB, then any value of absolute power can be expressed as so many dB above or below this reference standard. Although various other standards are occasionally encountered, the standard most commonly adopted is 1 mW (0.001 W), which is delivered along a standard 600-Ω program transmission line. This means that 1 mW of single tone audio power is 0 dBm (dB, with respect to 1 mW). Then, 1 W, for example, is 10 log (1 W/1mW) = 10 log 1000 = 30 dBm, and 1 μW is 10 log (1 μW/1 mW) = 10 log (1/1000) = −30 dBm.

Zero VU (volume unit) has the same reference level of 1 mW; it therefore appears that the dBm and the VU are identical. However, the use of the dBm is normally confined to single frequencies (tones), and the VU is reserved for complex audio signals (such as speech or music). When you want to compare the powers developed in equal input and output resistances, it is sufficient to use their associated voltages and currents. The power gain or loss in decibels is then equal to 20 times the common logarithm of the voltage or current ratio.

In FIG. 2-33A:

The power gain or loss of a network is expressed as:

$$N = 10 \log (P_o/P_i) \text{ dB} \tag{2-109}$$

where: N = power gain or loss (dB)
P_o = output power (W)
P_i = input power (W)

Positive and negative values of N respectively represent power gains and losses.

Power ratio:

$$\frac{P_o}{P_i} = \text{inv.log}\left(\frac{N}{10}\right) \text{ or } 10^{N/10} \tag{2-110}$$

In FIG. 2-33B:

Overall power gain:

$$\frac{P_o}{P_i} = \frac{P_{o1}}{P_i} \times \frac{P_{o2}}{P_{o1}} \times \frac{P_{o3}}{P_{o2}} \times \ldots \times \frac{P_o}{P_{o(n-1)}} \tag{2-111}$$

Total dB gain:

$$N_T = N_1 + N_2 + N_3 \ldots + N_N \tag{2-112}$$

where N_T is the algebraic sum of the individual gains and losses.

Absolute power

Absolute power:

$$P = 10 \log \frac{P}{1 \text{ mW}} \text{ dBm} \tag{2-113}$$

Voltage and current ratios

Consider equal input and output resistances, R, for a particular stage (such as an amplifier or an attenuator). If the input and output voltages have RMS values of E_i and E_o and are associated with input and output RMS currents of I_i and I_o:

Input power: $P_i = E_i \times I_i = I_i^2 \times R = E_i^2/R$ watts

Output power: $P_o = E_o \times I_o = I_o^2 \times R = E_o^2/R$ watts

Therefore, the power gain in decibels is given by:

$$N = 10 \log\left(\frac{P_o}{P_i}\right) = 10 \log\left(\frac{I_o^2R}{I_i^2R}\right) = 10 \log\left(\frac{E_o^2/R}{E_i^2/R}\right)$$
$$= 20 \log\left(\frac{I_o}{I_i}\right) = 20 \log\left(\frac{E_o}{E_i}\right) \text{ dB} \tag{2-114}$$

The power gain in decibels is equal to 20 log (current ratio) or 20 log (voltage ratio), provided that the input and output resistances are the same.

* **Question 2-31** In terms of dBm a power level of 0.1 mW is equal to:

A. −10 dBm B. +10 dBm C. +20 dBm D. −20 dBm E. zero dBm

Answer Choice A.

Power level:

$$P = 10 \log \left(\frac{0.1 \text{ mW}}{1 \text{ mW}}\right) = 10 \log 0.1 = -10 \text{ dBm} \qquad (2\text{-}115)$$

* **Question 2-32** A 1-mW signal is the input to an attenuator which provides a loss of −40 dB. The power output of the attenuator is:

A. 0.1 μW B. 1 μW C. 10 μW D. 0.1 mW E. 0.01 μW

Answer Choice A.

$$\text{Power ratio} = 10^{-40/10} = 0.0001$$

$$\text{Power output} = 0.0001 \times 1 \text{ mW} = 10^{-4} \text{mW} = 0.1 \ \mu\text{W} \qquad (2\text{-}110)$$

* **Question 2-33** A power level of −20 dBm is equivalent to:

A. 100 mW B. 0.1 mW C. 10 μW D. 1 μW E. 100 μW

Answer Choice C.

$$\text{Power} = 10^{-20/10} = 0.01 \text{ mW} = 10 \ \mu\text{W} \qquad (2\text{-}110)$$

* **Question 2-34** A 1-mW signal is the input to an amplifier that provides an output of 100 mW. The amplifier's gain is:

A. +10 dB B. −10 dB C. +20 dB D. −20 dB E. +100 dB

Answer Choice C.

$$\text{Power ratio} = \frac{100 \text{ mW}}{1 \text{ mW}} = 100$$

Gain in dB:

$$N = 10 \log 100 = 10 \times 2 = +20 \text{ dB} \qquad (2\text{-}109)$$

* **Question 2-35** A transmitter has an output of 10 W at the fundamental frequency, whereas its second harmonic output is 0.1 W. By how much is the second harmonic output attenuated, with respect to the fundamental output?

A. 3 dB B. 100 dB C. 10 dB D. 20 dB E. 40 dB

Answer Choice D.

Gain in decibels:

$$N = 10 \log \frac{0.1 \text{ W}}{10 \text{ W}} = 10 \log 0.01 = -20 \text{ dB} \qquad (2\text{-}109)$$

Therefore, the amount of attenuation is 20 dB.

* **Question 2-36** A gain of 10 dB is equivalent to a power ratio of:

A. 2 B. 20 C. 10 D. 100 E. 5

Answer Choice C.

$$\text{Power ratio} = 10^{10/10} = 10 \tag{2-110}$$

* **Question 2-37** The input to a circuit is 120 mV, and its output is 1200 μV. Assuming that the input and the output resistances are the same, the amount of the attenuation is:

A. 10 dB B. 20 dB C. 30 dB D. 12 dB E. 40 dB

Answer Choice E.

Voltage ratio: $$\frac{V_o}{V_i} = \frac{1200\ \mu\text{V}}{120\ \text{mV}} = 0.01$$

Gain in decibels: $$N = 20 \log 0.01 = 20 \times (-2) = -40\ \text{dB} \tag{2-114}$$

Amount of attenuation is equal to 40 dB.

* **Question 2-38** A 250-mV signal encounters a circuit that produces 20-dB attenuation. The output signal is:

A. 1.25 mV B. 2.5 mV C. 0.25 mV D. 25 mV E. 12.5 mV

Answer Choice D.

$$\text{Voltage ratio} = 10^{-20/20} = 0.1 \tag{2-114}$$

$$\text{Output signal voltage} = 250 \times 0.1 = 25\ \text{mV}$$

* **Question 2-39** When a 100-mW signal is fed to an attenuator, the power level of the output signal is only 1 mW. The loss provided by the attenuator is:

A. 100 dB B. 50 dB C. 30 dB D. 20 dB E. 10 dB

Answer Choice D.

$$\textit{Power ratio} = \frac{1\ \text{mW}}{100\ \text{mW}} = 0.01$$

Gain in decibels: $$N = 10 \log 0.01 = 10 \times (-2) = -20\ \text{dB} \tag{2-109}$$

Therefore, the loss provided by the attenuator is 20 dB.

2-11. Series and parallel resonant circuits

Resonance in a series L,C,R circuit

The condition of electrical resonance in all circuits is defined as follows: any two-terminal (single-source) network containing resistance and reactance is said to be in resonance when the source voltage and the current drawn from the source are in phase. It follows from this definition that a resonant circuit has a phase angle of zero and a power factor of unity.

If the series LCR circuit of FIG. 2-34A is at resonance, the values of the inductive reactance and the capacitive reactance must be equal. Therefore, the phasor sum of v_L and v_C is zero (FIGS. 2-34B and C) so that $e = v_R$ and the circuit is purely resistive. The total impedance of the circuit is equal to the resistance and is at its minimum value (FIG. 2-34D); for this reason, the series resonant LCR combination is sometimes referred to as an *acceptor circuit.* It follows that, at resonance, the circuit current is at its maximum value, which is equal to E/R amperes.

Because the values of the inductive reactance and the capacitive reactance are both dependent on the frequency, there must be a particular resonant frequency for which the two reactances are equal. The manner in which the behavior of the series LCR circuit varies with frequency is illustrated by means of response curves (FIGS. 2-35A and B). These are the graphs of certain variables (such as impedance, current, voltages across inductor, capacitor, etc.) versus frequency. Such response curves are important because they show the circuit's ability to distinguish between one frequency and another.

Tuning a series LCR circuit means adjusting the value of the inductor or the capacitor until the resonant frequency is the same as the desired signal frequency. Take the amplitude modulation (AM) broadcast band as an example. Each station is assigned a particular operating frequency, and the frequencies of the nearest stations either side are 10 kHz away. Induced in the antenna (FIGS. 2-36A and B) of an AM receiver are literally hundreds of signals from all the radio waves in the vicinity. The purpose of the tuned circuit is to provide maximum response at the frequency of the wanted signal, but much smaller responses at the other unwanted signals. This is achieved by adjusting the capacitor until the resonant frequency is equal to the assigned frequency of the desired station.

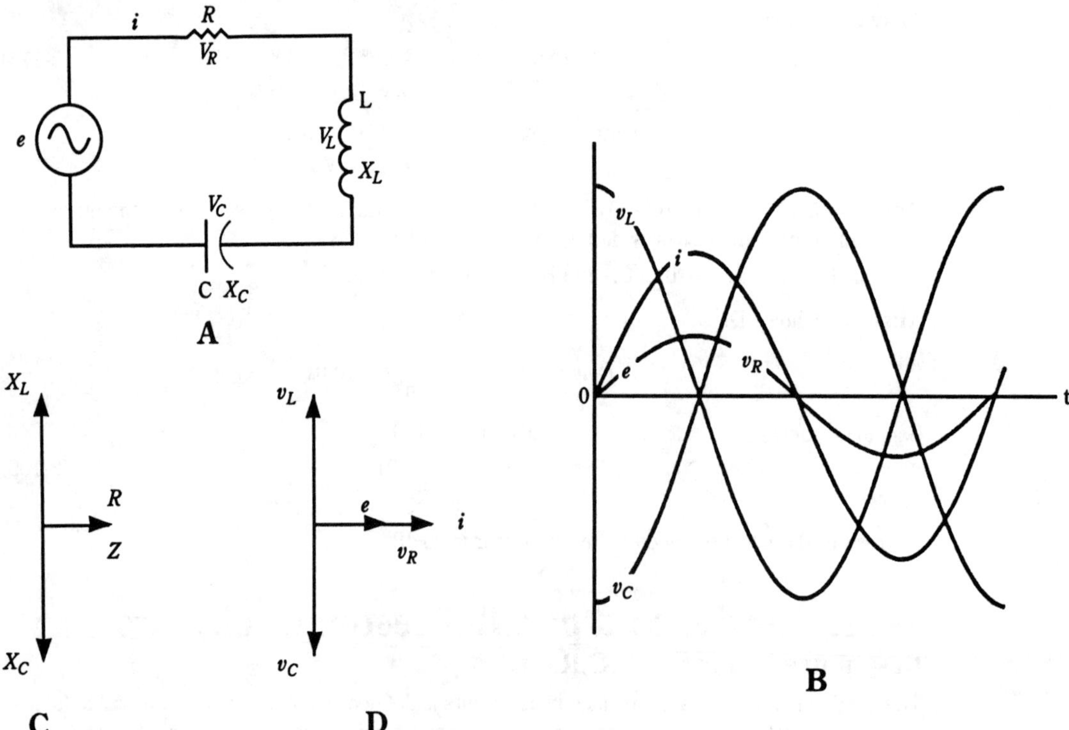

Fig. 2-34 The series L, C, R circuit at resonance.

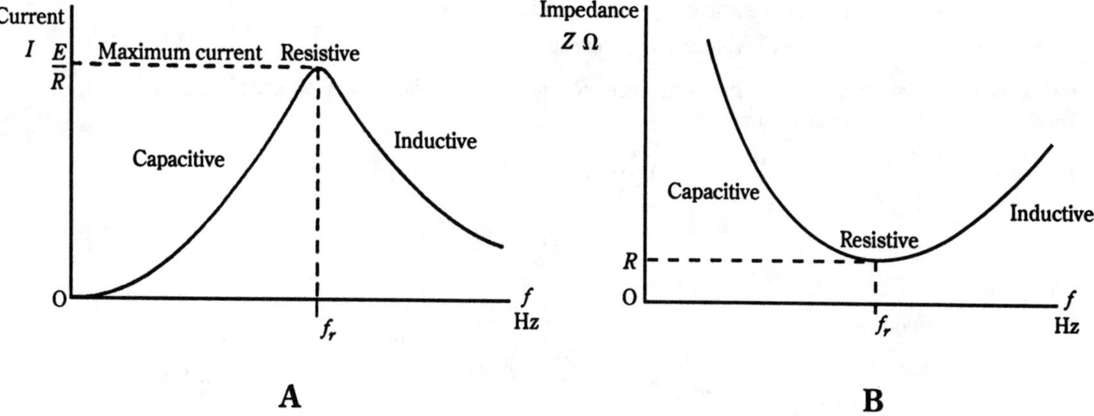

Fig. 2-35 The response curves of the series L, C, R circuit.

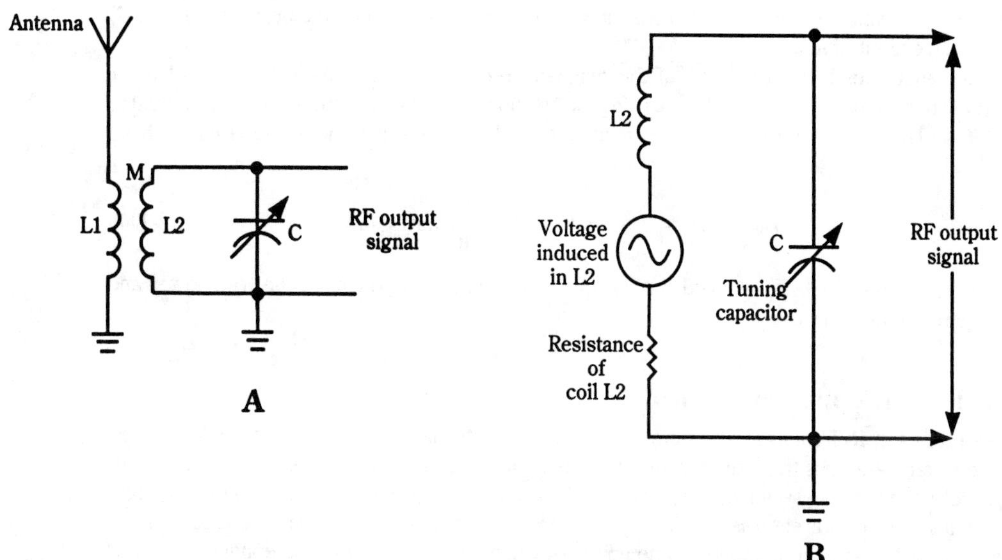

Fig. 2-36 The practical application of the series resonant circuit.

Notice that the circuit of FIG. 2-36B is a series arrangement because the wanted signal induced in the antenna drives a current through coil L1. The alternating magnetic flux surrounding L1 cuts the other coil so that an RF (radio frequency) voltage is induced in L2. This voltage is within the loop that contains coil L2 and capacitor C so that these components and their source voltage are in series.

At resonance in the circuit of FIG. 2-34A:

$$\text{Phase angle, } \phi \text{, is zero}$$

$$\text{Phasor } e = v_R$$

$$\text{Phasor sum of } v_L \text{ and } v_C \text{ is zero}$$

$$\text{Inductive reactance, } X_L = \text{capacitive reactance, } X_C$$
$$\text{Inductor voltage, } V_L = \text{capacitor voltage, } V_C$$

Impedance, Z, is equal in value to the resistance, R, and is at its minimum level. Current, I, is equal to E/R and is at its maximum level.

Because:

$$X_L = X_C$$
$$2\pi f_r L = \frac{1}{2\pi f_r C}$$

This yields:

Resonant frequency:

$$f_r = \frac{1}{2\pi\sqrt{LC}} = \frac{0.159}{\sqrt{LC}} \text{ hertz (Hz)} \qquad (2\text{-}116)$$

Then:

$$L = \frac{0.0253}{f_r^2 C} \text{ henrys (H) and } C = \frac{0.0253}{f_r^2 L} \text{ farads (F)}$$

Notice that the value of the resonant frequency is inversely dependent on the product of L and C, but is independent of R.

At frequencies below the value of the resonant frequency, X_C is greater than X_L, i leads e and the circuit behaves capacitively. At frequencies above the resonant frequency, X_L is greater than X_C, i lags e, and the circuit is net inductive. Only at resonance does the circuit behave resistively.

$$\textit{True power} = I^2R = E \times I = \frac{E^2}{R} \text{ watts (W)} \qquad (2\text{-}117)$$

Because the phase angle is zero and the power factor is unity, the values of the true power and the apparent power are the same.

Q, selectivity, and bandwidth

When a series LCR circuit is at resonance, the current has its maximum possible value for a given source voltage—across the inductor and the capacitor, are then developed equal, but 180° out-of-phase, voltages. These voltages might each be many times greater than the source voltage. The number of times greater is called the *voltage magnification factor,* which is referred to as Q. The Q factor is just a number and has no units. However, it is a measure of the inductor's merit in the sense that a "good" coil will have a high value of inductive reactance, compared to its resistance.

The main importance of Q is its indication of a series tuned circuit's selectivity; this is its ability to distinguish between the signal frequency to which it is resonant and other unwanted signals on nearby frequencies. It therefore follows that the higher the selectivity, the greater is the freedom from adjacent channel interference. The degree of the selectivity is related to the sharpness of the current response curve (the sharper the curve, the greater the selectivity) and can be measured by the frequency separation between two specific points on the curve (FIG. 2-37). The points arbitrarily chosen are those for which the true power in the circuit is one half of the maximum true power, which occurs when the circuit is resonant. These positions on the response curve are also referred to as the *3-decibel (dB) points* because a loss of 3 dB is equivalent to a power ratio of one half (TABLE 2-3). The frequency separation between these points is called the *bandwidth* (or *bandpass*) of the tuned circuit.

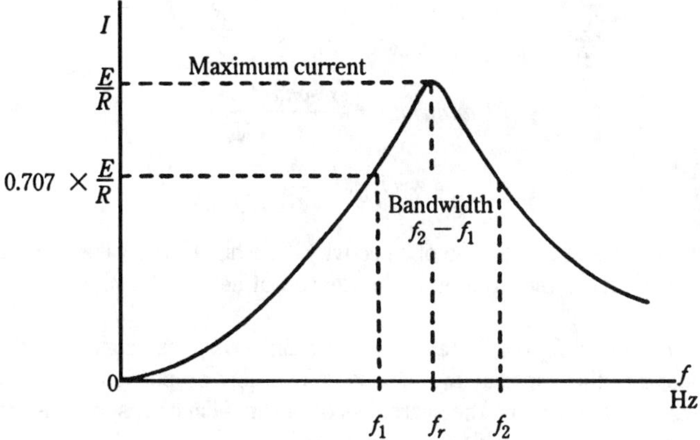

Fig. 2-37 The bandwidth of the series L,C,R circuit.

At the 3-dB points, the RMS circuit current will be $1/\sqrt{2}$ or 0.707 times the maximum RMS value of the current at resonance (do not confuse this result with the relationship between the RMS and the peak values of a sine-wave alternating current). In addition, the overall reactance at the 3-dB points is equal to the circuit's resistance; the phase angle is 45° and the power factor is Cos. $45° = 0.707$.

The narrower the bandwidth and the higher the resonant frequency, the sharper is the response curve and the greater is the selectivity. It follows that the Q value is a direct measure of the selectivity.

The voltage magnification factor at resonance:

$$Q = \frac{V_L}{E} = \frac{V_C}{E}$$

$$Q = \frac{I \times X_L}{I \times R} = \frac{X_L}{R} = \frac{2\pi f_r L}{R} = \frac{\textit{inductor's reactance}}{\textit{inductor's resistance}}$$

Because the resonant frequency: $f_r = \dfrac{1}{2\pi\sqrt{LC}}$ hertz (Hz) (2-116)

$$Q = \frac{2\pi L}{2\pi\sqrt{LC} \times R} = \frac{1}{R} \times \sqrt{\frac{L}{C}} \qquad \text{(2-118)}$$

Because the resonant frequency depends on the product of L and C, it follows that, for the given resonant frequency, there are an infinite number of possible pairs of values for L and C. However, because the Q value is determined by the ratio of L and C, there is, for particular values of f_r and Q, only a limited range of values for L and C (assuming that the value of R does not alter appreciably). For audio-frequency (AF) circuits involving a few kHz, Q is of the order of 10 to 20; with radio-frequency (RF) circuits, Q can exceed 100.

Bandwidth

It can be shown that: $\textit{Bandwidth} = f_2 - f_1 = \dfrac{R}{2\pi L}$ hertz (Hz) (2-119)

Therefore:
$$\frac{Bandwidth}{Resonant\ frequency} = \frac{R}{2\pi f_r L} = \frac{R}{X_L} = \frac{1}{Q}$$

$$Bandwidth = \frac{resonant\ frequency}{Q} \tag{2-120}$$

$$Q = \frac{resonant\ frequency}{bandwidth}$$

Q is a direct measure of the degree of selectivity. The higher the value of Q, the sharper is the current response curve, the greater is the degree of selectivity, and the narrower is the bandwidth.

The higher the value of R, the flatter is the impedance response curve and the lower is the selectivity. The slope of the impedance response is inversely proportional to R, but is directly proportional to $\sqrt{L/C}$. It follows that the sharpness of the impedance response is directly proportional to Q. These results are illustrated in FIGS. 2-38A and B.

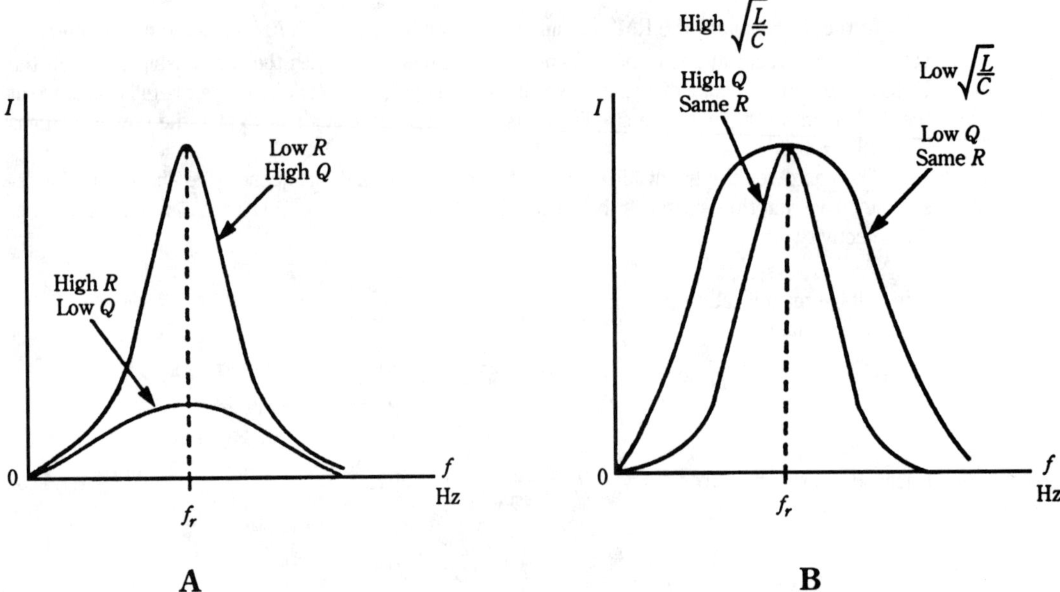

Fig. 2-38 The comparison between high-Q and low-Q circuits.

Skin Effect

Because $Q = 2\pi f_r L/R$, it would appear at first glance that the value of Q would increase indefinitely as the resonant frequency is raised and that the graph of Q versus f_r would be a straight line. However if the frequency is raised, the equivalent inductance changes due to the effect of the coil's distributed capacitance and the coil's resistance increases for a number of reasons:

- **Proximity effect** This is the effect of winding one turn on top of another. The greater mutual inductance results in an increased resistance.
- **Dielectric loss** This loss is caused by leakage currents that are associated with the insulation between the turns.

- **Core loss** If an iron dust core is present, the hysteresis and eddy current losses increase with frequency.
- **Mutual inductance** There will be losses associated with the currents induced in neighboring conductors, such as in screens that act as secondary circuits of virtually zero resistance.
- **Skin effect** Of these five reasons, skin effect is the most important. If a steady dc current is passing through a length of copper wire, the current density (A/m^2) is the same throughout the wire's cross-sectional area. This is also approximately true for the line frequency (60 Hz) and for audio frequencies (up to 15 kHz).

To consider the case of an RF current, assume that the conductor consists of a number of separate conductors that are welded together (FIG. 2-39). The RF current flowing through conductor A at the center of the wire produces an alternating magnetic field, which induces voltages in the surrounding conductors. By Lenz's Law, these voltages are such as to oppose the change that was responsible for their creation, namely the RF current. Consequently, there will be an increase in the impedance to the flow of RF current at the center of the wire. However, fewer conductors surround conductor B at the wire's perimeter; therefore, the impedance at this position is less. As the frequency is raised, the current retreats more and more to the circumference and is then confined to the wire's "skin." Consequently, the cross-sectional area available for the flow of current is reduced and the resistance is increased. The effect is quite dramatic; if a length of 2-mm diameter copper wire has a dc resistance of 1 Ω, its resistance at 10 MHz exceeds 80 Ω! At frequencies above 30 MHz, it is more practical to use hollow, rather than solid, conductors. Notice that the skin effect is less for conductors with a large surface area. For example, a flat sheet of copper will have less impedance than a wire of comparable length.

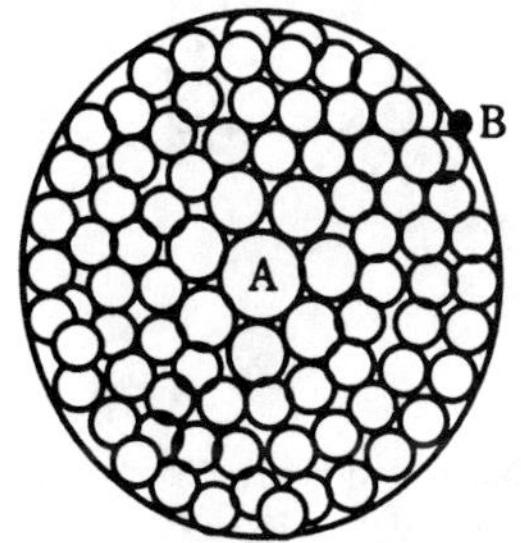

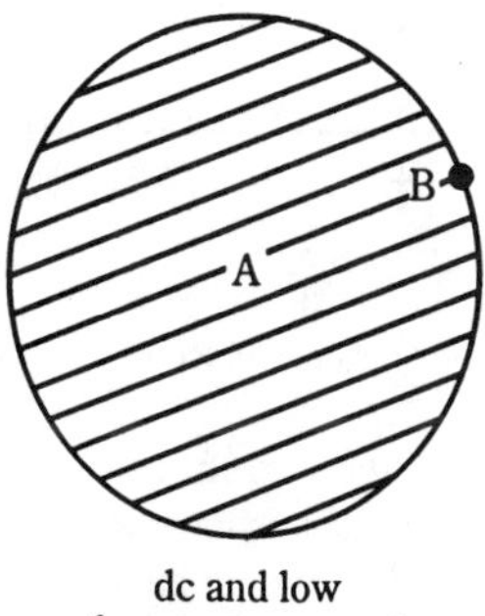

dc and low frequency current distribution

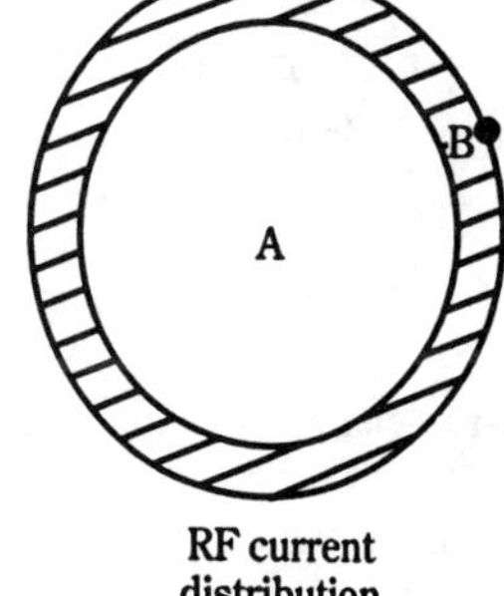

RF current distribution

Fig. 2-39 Skin effect.

It is clear that if the resistance increases rapidly as the frequency is raised, the Q of a coil will not increase indefinitely, but will reach a shallow peak and will decrease in value (FIG. 2-40). A coil is therefore designed to be used over a limited frequency range with the maximum value of Q occurring near the midfrequency of the band. However, at either end of the band, the Q value is still sufficient to provide an adequate degree of selectivity.

Resonance in a parallel L,C,R circuit

From the definition of resonance, the supply or source current, i_S, must be in phase with the source voltage, e (FIG. 2-41A). This will occur if the values of the inductor and capacitor currents

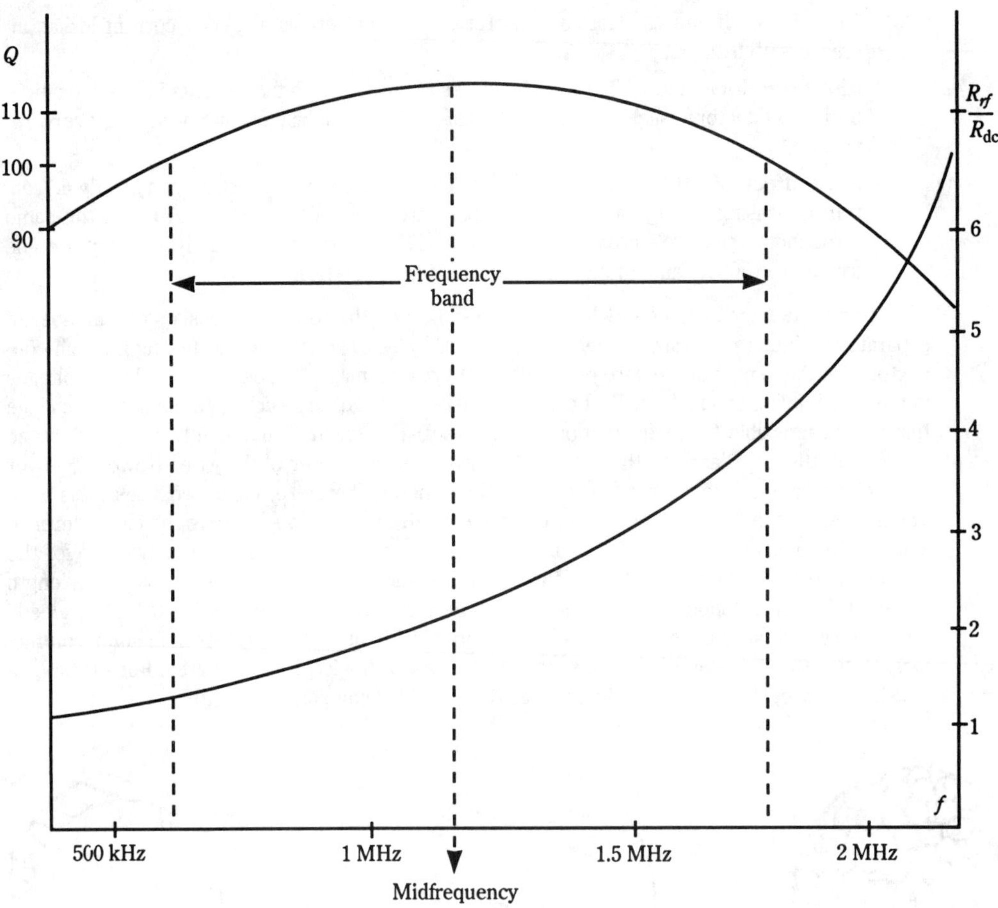

Fig. 2-40 Variation of the Q value and RF resistance with frequency.

are equal; only then will the phasor sum, i_x, of their currents be zero (remember that i_L and i_C are 180° out of phase). Then, the resistor current (which is independent of the frequency) will be the same as the supply current, whose value will be at its minimum level of E/R amperes. It follows that the total impedance, Z_T, of the complete circuit will be entirely resistive and have its maximum value of R ohms.

At resonance, the inductive and capacitive reactances are equal and the parallel LC combination behaves theoretically as an open circuit; the total impedance of the circuit is then equal to the resistance. At frequencies other than the resonant frequency, the LC combination behaves as a certain value of resistance, which when placed in parallel with the resistance, produces a total impedance that is less than the value of the resistance. Combining these two statements, the total impedance can never exceed the value of the resistance.

At frequencies below the resonant frequency, the capacitive reactance is greater than the inductive reactance, the capacitor current is less than the inductor current, and the circuit behaves inductively. At frequencies above the resonant frequency, the inductive reactance is greater than the capacitive reactance, the inductor current is less than the capacitor current and the circuit behaves capacitively. These results are the reverse of those for the series LCR circuit, which behaved capacitively for frequencies below f_r and inductively for frequencies above f_r. The current and the impedance response curves are illustrated in FIGS. 2-42A and B.

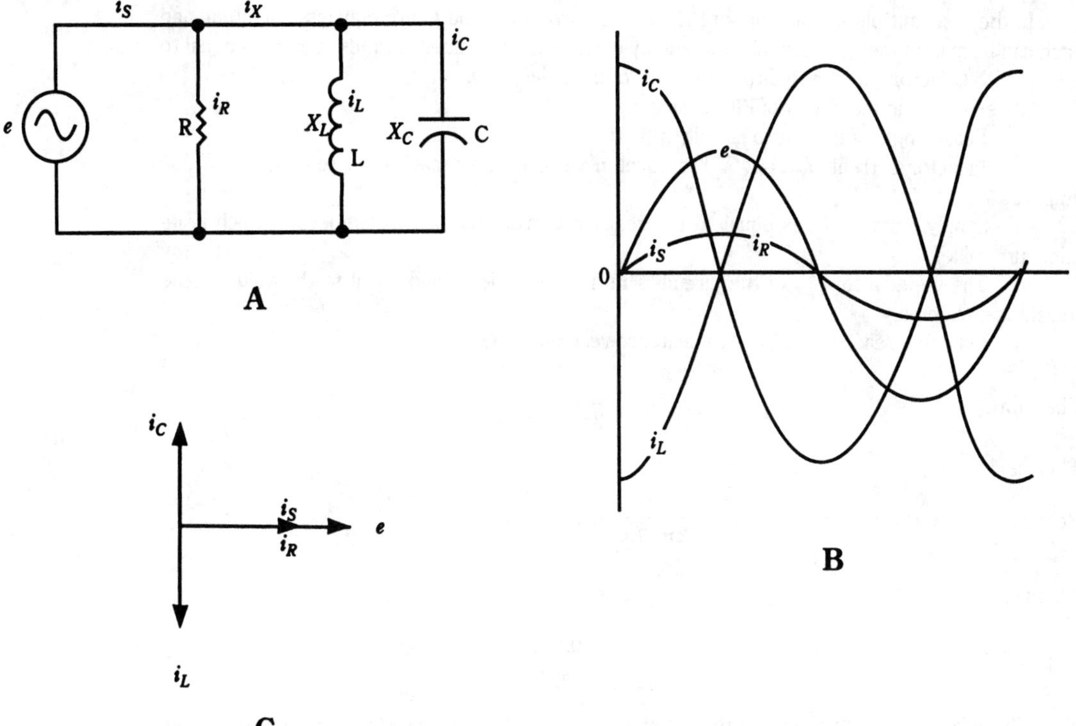

Fig. 2-41 The parallel resonant L, C, R circuit.

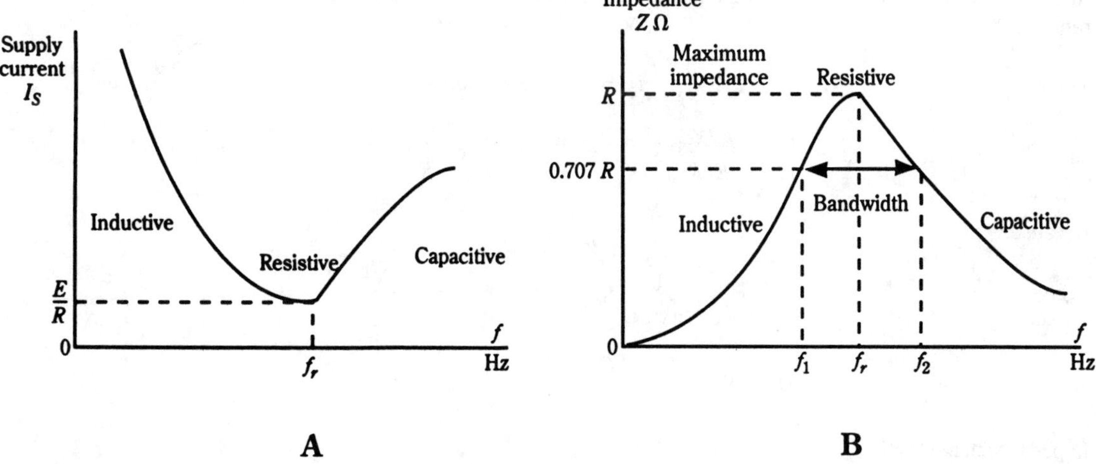

Fig. 2-42 Response curves of the parallel L, C, R circuit.

In the resonant phasor diagram of FIG. 2-41C, currents I_L and I_C are equal in magnitude and each can be many times greater than the supply current. The number of times greater is equal to the circuit's Q factor, which is a direct measure of the selectivity.

At resonance in the circuit of FIG. 2-41A:

Phase angle of the entire circuit, $\phi = 0°$.

Inductor current, I_L ($=E/X_L$) is equal in value to the capacitor current, I_C ($= E/X_C$) amperes.

Supply current, I_S, is equal to the resistor current, $I_R = E/R$ amperes, which is its minimum value.

The impedance, Z_T, of the circuit is its maximum level and equal to the value of the resistance, R ohms.

Inductive reactance, X_L = capacitance reactance, X_C.

Therefore:

$$2\pi f_r L = \frac{1}{2\pi f_r C}$$

This yields:

Resonant frequency:

$$f_r = \frac{1}{2\pi\sqrt{LC}} \text{ hertz (Hz)}$$

Then:

$$L = \frac{1}{4\pi^2 f_r^2 C} = \frac{0.0253}{f_r^2\, C} \text{ H}$$

and:

$$C = \frac{1}{4\pi^2 f_R L} = \frac{0.0253}{f_r^2 C} F$$

These last three equations are the same as the corresponding expressions for series resonance.

Current magnification

At resonance, currents I_L and I_C are equal in magnitude, and each is Q times the supply current, I_S.

Then:

$$I_L = \frac{E}{X_L},\ I_C = \frac{E}{X_C},\ I_S = I_R = \frac{E}{R} \text{ amperes}$$

and:

$$Q = \frac{I_L}{I_S} = \frac{E/X_L}{E/R} = \frac{R}{X_L} = \frac{R}{X_C}\left(\textit{not}\ \frac{X_L}{R} \text{ or } \frac{X_C}{R}\right) \quad (2\text{-}121)$$

Because:

$$Q = \frac{R}{X_L} = \frac{R}{2\pi f_r L}$$

and:

$$f_r = \frac{1}{2\pi\sqrt{LC}} \text{ hertz (Hz)}$$

$$Q = R \times \frac{2\pi\sqrt{LC}}{2\pi \text{ L}} = R \times \sqrt{\frac{C}{L}}$$

Impedance magnification:

$$R = QX_L = QX_C \quad (2\text{-}122)$$

From Equation 2-121:

The impedance at resonance is Q times the reactance of either the inductor or the capacitor. Notice that if an additional resistor is shunted across a resonant parallel L,C,R circuit, the impedance at resonance is reduced, the value of Q is lower, the bandwidth is greater, but the resonant frequency remains the same.

Selectivity

As in the case of the series L, C, R circuit, Q determines the sharpness of the response curve and is therefore the direct measure of the selectivity.

$$Q = \frac{\textit{resonant frequency}}{\textit{bandwidth}} = \frac{f_r}{f_2 - f_1} \tag{2-123}$$

The bandwidth is defined from the impedance response curve as the frequency separation between the points, where the total impedance of the circuit is 0.707 times the maximum impedance, R. From this definition:

$$\textit{Bandwidth} = f_2 - f_1 = \frac{1}{2\pi RC} \text{ hertz (Hz)} \tag{2-124}$$

where C and R are respectively measured in farads and ohms. The concept of the half-power points cannot be used in the case of the parallel L, C, R circuit because the true power is always E^2/R watts and is independent of the frequency.

In TABLE 1-6, $R_L >> R_i$ when a high voltage was developed across the load. Because the impedance of a parallel L, C, R circuit has a maximum value at resonance, such a circuit can be used as the load of a transistor amplifier (FIG. 2-43), which is operated at radio frequencies. If the current passing through the load contains a number of frequencies, the output voltage across the load will only be high at the particular frequency to which the load is resonant.

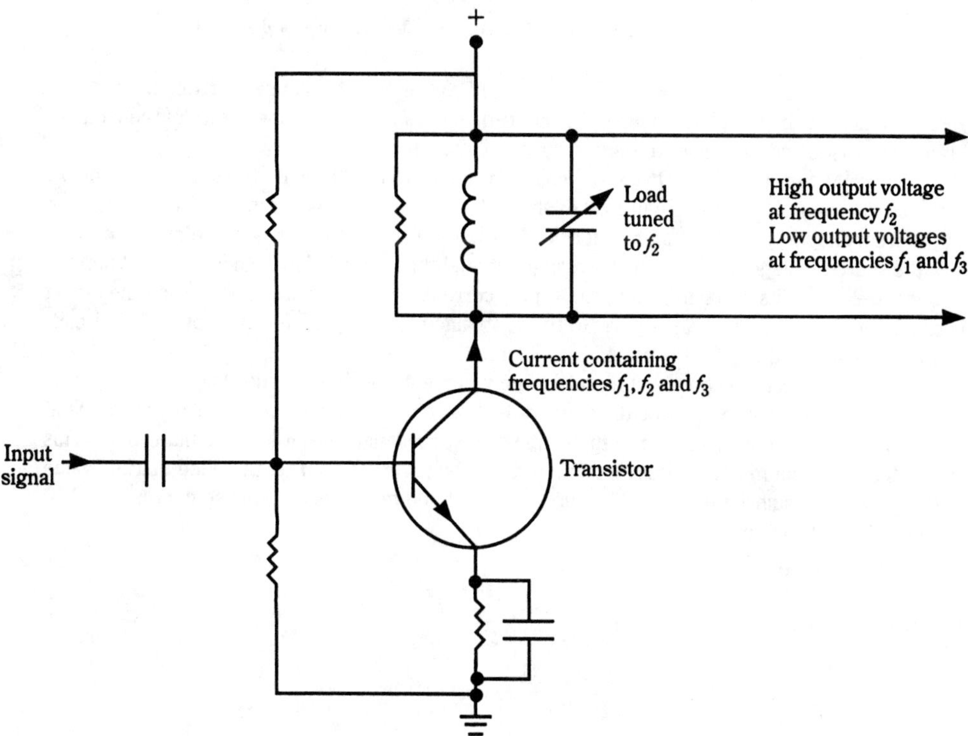

Fig. 2-43 The parallel resonant L, C, R circuit as the load on a transistor amplifier.

Parallel resonant "tank" circuit

The parallel resonant tank circuit consists of a practical inductor with its series resistance, in parallel with a capacitor whose losses are assumed to be negligible (FIG. 2-44A). Such a circuit is commonly used as the collector load of certain transistor RF (radio frequency) amplifiers; in such stages, a high value of load impedance is required at the frequency to which the circuit is tuned.

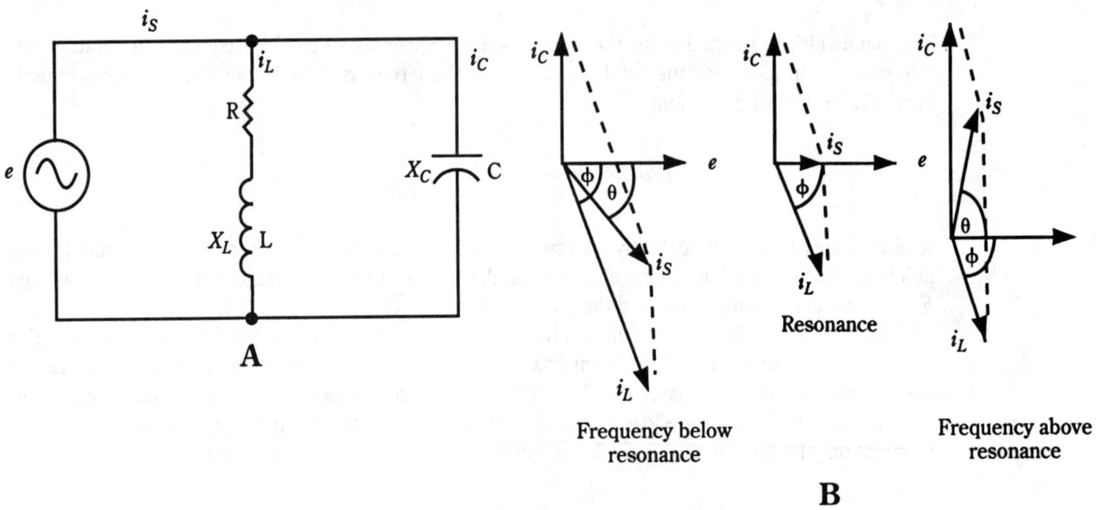

Fig. 2-44 The tank circuit and its phasor diagrams.

Because the inductor branch contains both reactance and resistance, current, i_L, lags the source voltage, e, by the phase angle, ø. If the frequency is raised, the impedance of the inductor branch increases and the angle, ø, moves closer to 90°.

The capacitor current, i_C, leads the source voltage, e, by 90° while the supply current, i_S, is the phasor sum of i_C and i_L. Figure 2-44B shows the changes that occur in the circuit's behavior as the frequency is varied. At all frequencies below the resonant frequency, the supply current lags the source voltage by the total phase angle, θ, and the circuit behaves inductively. When the frequency exceeds its resonant value, the supply current leads the source voltage and the circuit is capacitive. These results are similar to those obtained for the parallel resonant L,C,R circuit, but are opposite to those for the series L,C,R circuit.

At resonance, the supply voltage and supply current are in phase so that the angle, θ, is zero. As suggested by the phasor diagrams of FIG. 2-44B, the supply current at resonance is at its minimum level; consequently, the total impedance at resonance is at its maximum value. This last statement is not mathematically exact, but it can be regarded as true, provided that the value of the Q factor is sufficiently high. The supply current and impedance response curves are illustrated in FIGS. 2-45A and B.

In the circuit of FIG. 2-44A:

Resonant frequency:

$$f_r = \frac{1}{2\pi}\sqrt{\frac{1}{LC} - \frac{R^2}{L^2}}$$

$$\approx \frac{1}{2\pi\sqrt{LC}} \text{ hertz (Hz)} \qquad (2\text{-}125)$$

provided that the value of $Q > 10$.

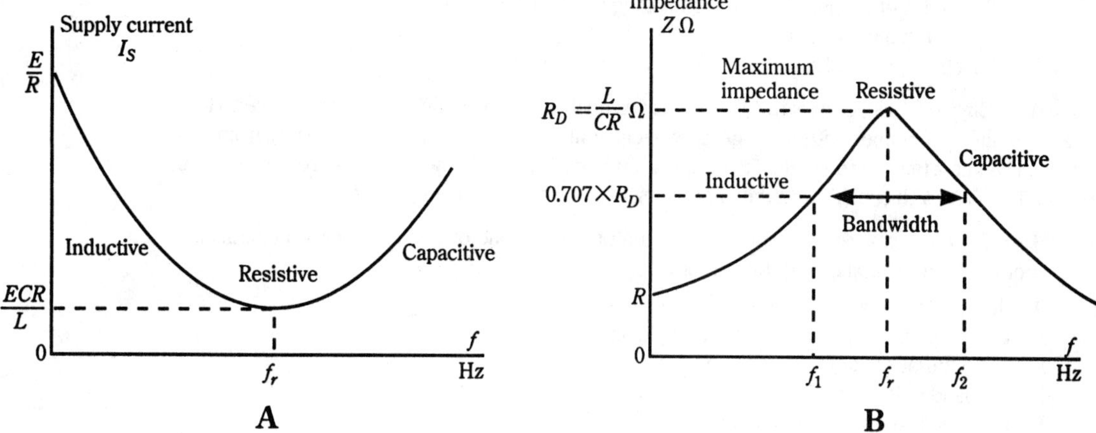

Fig. 2-45 Response curves of the tank circuit.

Note with FCC Questions the formula used to determine the resonant frequency, is always $f_r = 1/(2\pi\sqrt{LC})$ Hz.

Total impedance at resonance: $$Z_T = R_D = \frac{L}{CR} \text{ ohms } (\Omega) \tag{2-126}$$

The quantity of L/CR Ω is called the *dynamic resistance,* R_D, because it only appears under operating conditions. The value of the dynamic resistance is virtually equal to the maximum level of the impedance at resonance.

The true power in the tank circuit may either be expressed as $I_S^2 \times L/CR$ watts or $I_L^2 \times R$ watts. Therefore:

$$\frac{I_L^2}{I_S^2} = \frac{L/CR}{R} = \frac{L}{R^2C} = Q^2$$

or: $$I_L (\approx I_C) = Q \times I_S \text{ amperes (A)} \tag{2-127}$$

The capacitor current is nearly the same as the inductor current. Consequently, at resonance a large circulating or "flywheel" current is associated with the inductor and the capacitor, and this current is Q times the supply or line current. It follows that the value of the dynamic resistance is approximately equal to Q times the inductive reactance or Q times the capacitive reactance. Moreover, because:

$$Z_T \approx Q \times X_L$$

and

$$X_L = Q \times R$$

$$Z_T \approx Q^2 \times R \text{ ohms } (\Omega) \tag{2-128}$$

The Q factor is the measure of the tank circuit's selectivity and equals resonant frequency/bandwidth. From the impedance response curve, the bandwidth is defined as the frequency separation between those points where the circuit's total impedance is equal to 0.707 times the dynamic resistance (the total impedance at resonance). Refer to FIG. 2-45B.

* **Question 2-40** Which of the following has the lowest impedance at the frequency of 100 MHz?

A. a 6-inch length of AWG #22 copper wire
B. a 6-inch length of aluminum wire whose cross-sectional area is one circular mil

C. a thin sheet of copper that is 6 inches long and 2 inches wide
D. a 0.01-μF paper capacitor
E. a 6-inch length of silver wire whose cross-sectional area is one circular mil

Answer Choice C. No legitimate calculations will enable you to obtain the correct answer. However, the sheet of copper with its large cross-sectional area will not suffer appreciably from skin effect. The important word is "thin"; the question does not specify how thin; therefore, you can reduce the sheet's thickness until the sheet vanishes and there is no impedance!

* **Question 2-41** A resonant circuit consists of a practical inductor and a capacitor in parallel. If a resistor is added in parallel with the circuit:

A. the impedance at resonance decreases
B. the resonant frequency is appreciably decreased
C. the value of the Q factor is raised
D. the bandwidth is lower
E. Choices C and D are both true

Answer Choice A. When the resistor is added in parallel, the impedance of the circuit is decreased.

* **Question 2-42** A tank circuit is caused to resonate at 12 MHz by its tuning capacitor. The circuit is now retuned to 24 MHz. The ratio of the new capacitance to the original capacitance is:

A. 1:4 B. 1:2 C. 4:1 D. 2:1 E. 1:8

Answer Choice A. The resonant frequency, $f_r = 1/(2\pi\sqrt{LC})$ Hz and is therefore inversely proportional to the square root of the capacitance. Consequently, the capacitance must be reduced to one quarter of its original value. The required ratio is 1:4.

* **Question 2-43** It is required to increase the bandwidth of a series L,C,R circuit without altering the resonant frequency. This result can be achieved by:

A. lowering the value of L
B. increasing the value of C
C. raising the ratio, L:C, without altering the value of the product, $L \times C$
D. lowering the value of Q
E. lowering the value of the resistance.

Answer Choice D. Choices A and B will cause the resonant frequency to change. Choices C and E will raise the value of Q and therefore decrease the bandwidth. The Q factor must be lowered to increase the bandwidth.

* **Question 2-44** In the circuit of FIG. 2-46 the reading of the voltmeter connected across the inductor, is:

A. 1 V B. 100 V C. 200 V D. 50 V E. 1000 V

Answer Choice B. Because $X_L = X_C = 100\ \Omega$, the series circuit is resonant and the total impedance, $Z = R = 100\ \Omega$. The current is: $100\ \text{V}/100\ \Omega = 1$ A and the voltage across the inductor $= 1\ \text{A} \times 100\ \Omega = 100$ V.

Notice: There is 100 V each across the resistor, the inductor, and the capacitor. The voltages across the inductor and the capacitor are 180° out of phase and therefore cancel. The voltage across the resistor then balances the source voltage.

* **Question 2-45** The tendency for high-frequency alternating currents to retreat toward the surface of a conductor, rather than exist across the entire cross-sectional area, is called:

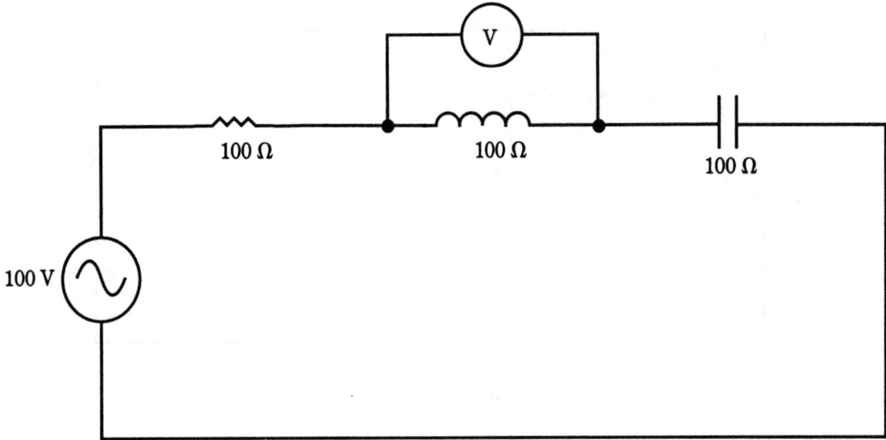

Fig. 2-46 The circuit for question 2-44.

A. proximity effect B. surface attraction C. skin effect. D. perimeter effect
E. reluctance

Answer Choice C.

* **Question 2-46** A series L,C,R circuit consists of a 6-Ω resistor, a 5 μH inductor and a 5-pF capacitor. The resonant frequency of this circuit is:

A. 3.18 MHz B. 31.8 MHz C. 318 kHz D. 31.8 kHz E. 318 MHz

Answer Choice B.

Resonant frequency: $f_r = \dfrac{1}{2\pi\sqrt{LC}}$

$$= \frac{1}{2 \times \pi \times \sqrt{5 \times 10^{-6} \times 5 \times 10^{-12}}} \text{ hertz (Hz)} \quad (2\text{-}116)$$

$$= \frac{10^9}{2 \times \pi \times 5} \text{ hertz (Hz)}$$

$$= 31.8 \text{ MHz}$$

Question 2-47 In the circuit of FIG. 2-47, the series and parallel L,C circuits are at resonance. The value of the source current is:

A. 288 A B. 0.5 A C. 0.2 A D. 2 A E. The value of the source current cannot be determined from the information given

Answer Choice D. Because the inductors and capacitors are assumed to have no resistance losses, the series L,C combination behaves as a short circuit, whereas the parallel combination is equivalent to an open circuit. Consequently, the source current equals 24 V/12 Ω = 2 A.

* **Question 2-48** A marine transmitter is connected to ground through:

A. a single copper conductor
B. AWG #22, #24 or higher gage wire

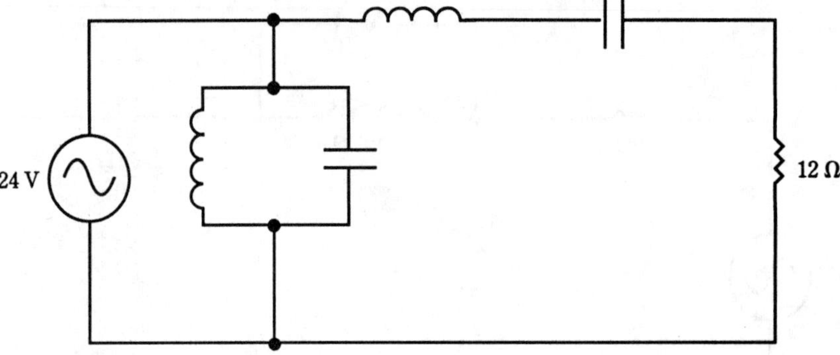

Fig. 2-47 The circuit for question 2-47.

C. multistrand wire whose length is as short as possible
D. multistrand wire with each strand insulated from its neighbors
E. a braided copper strip

Answer Choice C. Because of its larger surface area, multistrand wire suffers less from skin effect than a single conductor.

Question 2-49 A parallel L, C, R circuit is used as the load of an RF amplifier. Initially, the tuning capacitor is set so that the circuit's resonant frequency is below that of the input signal. If the capacitance is gradually reduced so that the circuit's resonant frequency at first equals the input signal frequency and afterwards exceeds it, the output voltage across the load:

A. increases from a low value to a maximum value and afterwards falls back to a low value
B. increases from a low value to a maximum value at resonance and afterwards stays at the same level
C. decreases from a high value to a minimum value at resonance, and afterwards stays at the same level
D. does not change as the capacitance is reduced
E. decreases from the high value to the minimum value and afterwards rises back to the high value.

Answer Choice A. When the parallel L, C, R circuit is resonant at the input signal frequency, its impedance rises to its maximum value. Then, the voltage across the load will also be at its maximum level.

* **Question 2-50** At high frequencies in the UHF band, the value of a fixed composition resistor appears to:

A. be a short circuit
B. be an open circuit
C. decrease in value
D. increase in value
E. possess a high value of inductance

Answer Choice C. The self-capacitance of the resistor is in parallel with the resistance and therefore at high frequencies, the value of this resistance is reduced.

2-12. Transformers

Mutually coupled coils

In previous sections, you have discussed the inductors that have a magnetic flux linked with their own turns and therefore possess the property of self-inductance. Now, consider the situation where the magnetic flux associated with one coil links with the turns of another coil. Such inductors are said to be magnetically, inductively, mutually, or transformer coupled, and possess the property of mutual inductance, whose letter symbol is M and whose unit is the henry (H). In the circuits of the previous sections, there were a pair of input terminals (2-port network). You now have a pair of input and another pair of output terminals; this is referred to as a *4-port network*.

The alternating i_1, in the coil #1 (FIG. 2-48) creates an alternating flux, only part of which links with the coil #2. This causes an induced voltage, v_2, whose size depends on the rate of change of the current, i_1, and on the mutual inductance, M, between the coils. The mutual inductance is 1 H, if, when the current, i_1, is instantaneously changing at the rate of one ampere per second, the induced voltage, v_2, is one volt. The factors that determine the mutual inductance include the number of turns, N_1 and N_2, the cross-sectional area of the coils, their separation, the orientation of their axes and the nature of their cores. Consequently, the induced voltage, $v_2 = M \times$ rate of change of i_1.

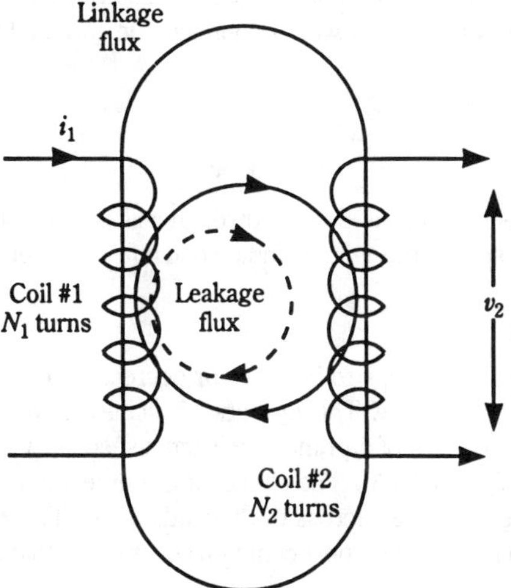

Fig. 2-48 Mutually coupled coils.

If the alternating current, i_1, has a sinusoidal waveform with a frequency of f hertz, $V_{2RMS} = 2\pi fmI_{RMS}$ (compare $V_{LRMS} = 2\pi fLI_{RMS}$ for the property of self-inductance). When the two coils are wound in the same sense, v_2 lags i_1 by 90°, but if the two coils are wound in the opposite sense, v_2 leads i_1 by 90°. Notice that the property of the mutual inductance is reversible in the sense that if the same rate of change in the current, i_1, is flowing in coil #2, then the voltage induced in the coil #1 is: $v_1 = M \times$ rate of change in the current, i_1.

In cases where the coils are tightly wound, one on top of the other, with a common soft iron core, the leakage flux is extremely small and can therefore be neglected. Assuming perfect flux linkage between the coils (corresponding to zero flux leakage), the mutual inductance is given by:

Mutual inductance: $$M = \frac{\mu_o \mu_r N_1 N_2 A}{l} \text{ henrys (H)} \qquad (2\text{-}117)$$

where: A = cross-sectional area for each coil (m^2)
μ_r = relative permeability of the soft iron
l = the coil's length (m)
μ_o = permeability of free space ($4\pi \times 10^{-7}$H/m)

The self-inductance of coil #1 is:

$$\text{Self-inductance, } L_1 = \frac{\mu_o \mu r N_1^2 A}{l} \text{ henrys (H)}$$

and the self-inductance of coil #2 is:

$$\text{Self-inductance, } L_2 = \frac{\mu_o \mu r N_2^2 A}{l} \text{ henrys (H)}$$

This yields: $$M^2 = L_1 L_2 \qquad (2\text{-}118)$$

and: $$\text{Mutual inductance, } M = \sqrt{L_1 L_2} \text{ henrys (H)} \qquad (2\text{-}119)$$

If the leakage flux is not negligible, then only a fraction, k, of the total flux links with the two coils. This fraction, k, whose value cannot exceed unity, is called the *coefficient of coupling* or the *coupling factor.* Its value can be close to unity if a common soft iron core is used for the two coils, but it can be very small (less than 0.01) with a nonmagnetic core and the two coils widely separated (loose coupling).

Coupling factor: $$k = \frac{M}{\sqrt{L_1 L_2}} \qquad (2\text{-}120)$$

Notice that if a steady direct current is flowing through coil #1, the linkage flux will be constant in magnitude and direction so that the voltage induced in coil #2 is zero.

Power transformers

The purpose of a power transformer is to increase or decrease the value of the ac line or supply voltage without altering the frequency. This operation is achieved with a high level of efficiency.

A power transformer consists of a primary coil and a secondary coil whose number of turns are, respectively, N_p and N_s (FIG. 2-48). The alternating source voltage, E_p, is applied across the primary coil, and the load is connected across the secondary coil. These two coils can each consist of thousands of turns, which are wound on a common soft-iron so that the leakage flux is reduced to a low value.

In the case of the ideal transformer, the leakage flux is zero so the mutual inductance, $M = \sqrt{L_p L_s}$, and the coupling factor k, is unity. When an alternating current, I_p, flows in the primary coil, it creates a magnetic flux, which links with the secondary coil and induces the secondary voltage, E_s. With zero flux leakage, the same volts per turn are associated with both the primary and secondary coils. It follows that if the number of secondary turns exceeds the number of primary turns, the secondary voltage is greater than the primary voltage, and you have a so-called "step-up" transformer. Similarly, if the number of secondary turns is less than the number of primary turns, the secondary voltage is smaller than the primary voltage and the transformer is of the *step-down* type. The terms *step-up* and *step-down* normally refer to the voltage and not the current. From the phase point of view, the primary and secondary voltages are 180° out of phase, provided that the two coils are wound in the same sense.

An ideal power transformer has zero power losses; therefore, the power input to the primary circuit equals the power output from the secondary circuit. It follows that a step-up of the voltage level from the primary circuit to the secondary circuit must be accompanied by a corresponding reduction in the current level.

By contrast, with the ideal transformer, the practical transformer suffers from the following losses:

- The *copper loss,* which is the power dissipated in the resistances of the primary and secondary windings.
- The *iron loss,* which is dissipated in the core. This lost energy is subdivided into:
  - ~ the *eddy-current loss,* which is caused by the moving magnetic flux, which cuts the core and induces circulating currents within the metal. The loss is reduced by laminating the core into thin slices with each slice insulated from its neighbor.
  - ~ the *hysteresis loss,* which is caused by the rapid magnetizing, demagnetizing, and remagnetizing of the core during the cycle of the primary current.

For practical power transformers, the total losses are less than 10% of the primary power.

When a load resistance is connected across the secondary coil, the secondary current creates an alternating magnetic flux, which, by Lenz's Law, opposes and partially cancels the primary flux. As a result, the primary current increases and an effective resistance of value E_p/I_p ohms is presented to the primary source; this ohmic value is the resistance *reflected* from the secondary circuit into the primary circuit, owing to the presence of the secondary load.

Notice that if a steady direct current flows in the primary coil, the leakage flux will be constant in magnitude and direction so that the voltage induced in the secondary coil is zero. However, if the steady dc voltage applied to the primary coil is "chopped" to produce a square wave, the transformer responds to this type of input and some form of alternating voltage (not, however, a simple sine wave) will be induced in the secondary coil; the secondary voltage is then rectified to provide a final output dc voltage, which is larger than the dc input voltage.

For the ideal power transformer: Turns ratio,
$$\frac{N_p}{N_s} = \frac{E_p}{E_s} \tag{2-121}$$

Because an ideal transformer has no losses:
$$\text{Primary power, } P_p = \text{ secondary power, } P_s \tag{2-122}$$
$$E_p \times I_p = E_s \times I_s \text{ watts (W)}$$

Combining EQS. 2-121 and 2-122:
$$\frac{E_p}{E_s} = \frac{I_s}{I_p} = \frac{N_p}{N_s}$$

Primary voltage:
$$E_p = \frac{E_s I_s}{I_p} = \frac{E_s N_p}{N_s} \text{ volts (V)} \tag{2-123}$$

Primary current:
$$I_p = \frac{E_s I_s}{E_p} = \frac{I_s N_s}{N_p} \text{ amperes (A)} \tag{2-124}$$

Secondary voltage:
$$E_s = \frac{E_p I_p}{I_s} = \frac{E_p N_s}{N_p} \text{ volts (V)} \tag{2-125}$$

Secondary current: $$I_s = \frac{E_p I_p}{E_s} = \frac{I_p N_p}{N_s} \text{ amperes (A)} \quad (2\text{-}126)$$

If the secondary is loaded with a resistance, R_s:

$$R_s = \frac{E_s}{I_s} \text{ ohms } (\Omega)$$

Because: $$E_p = \frac{E_s N_p}{N_s} \text{ (EQ. 2-123) and } I_p = \frac{I_s N_s}{N_p} \quad (2\text{-}124)$$

$$\begin{aligned} R_p &= \frac{E_p}{I_p} \\ &= \frac{E_s N_p / N_s}{I_s N_s / N_p} \\ &= \frac{E_s}{I_s} \times \left(\frac{N_p}{N_s}\right)^2 \\ &= R_s \times \left(\frac{N_p}{N_s}\right)^2 \text{ ohms } (\Omega) \end{aligned} \quad (2\text{-}127)$$

where R_p = effective resistance presented to the primary source.

The equation: $$\frac{E_p}{I_p} = R_s \times \left(\frac{N_p}{N_s}\right)^2$$

is represented by the equivalent circuit of FIG. 2-49C. The expression: $R_s \times (N_p/N_s)^2$ is the effective resistive load that is presented to the primary source and is referred to as the value of the resistance reflected from the secondary circuit into the primary circuit owing to the introduction of the secondary load. If you choose the turns ratio so that the value of the reflected resistance, $R_s \times (N_p/N_s)^2$, is equal to the internal resistance of the primary source, the secondary load is then matched to the primary source for maximum power transfer to the secondary load.

If R_p is the resistance associated with the primary source, the matched condition is:

$$R_p = R_s \times \left(\frac{N_p}{N_s}\right)^2 \text{ and } R_s = R_p \times \left(\frac{N_s}{N_p}\right)^2 \text{ ohms } (\Omega)$$

or: $$\left(\frac{N_p}{N_s}\right)^2 = \frac{R_p}{R_s} \text{ and turns ratio, } \frac{N_p}{N_s} = \sqrt{\frac{R_p}{R_s}} \quad (2\text{-}128)$$

Radio frequency transformers

The iron losses of a transformer increases dramatically as the frequency is raised; therefore at radio frequencies any use of a solid iron core is prohibited. Consequently, there is a considerable flux leakage so that the coupling factor, k, is typically less than 0.1 and the turns ratio of the primary and secondary windings have little significance.

At the high end of the RF spectrum, the primary and secondary windings have self-inductances of only a few microhenrys. Each winding has a small number of turns that are separately wound on a nonmagnetic core, such as plastic; the separation between the windings then determines the degree of mutual coupling and the value of the coupling factor. The schematic symbol for this type of RF transformer is [symbol].

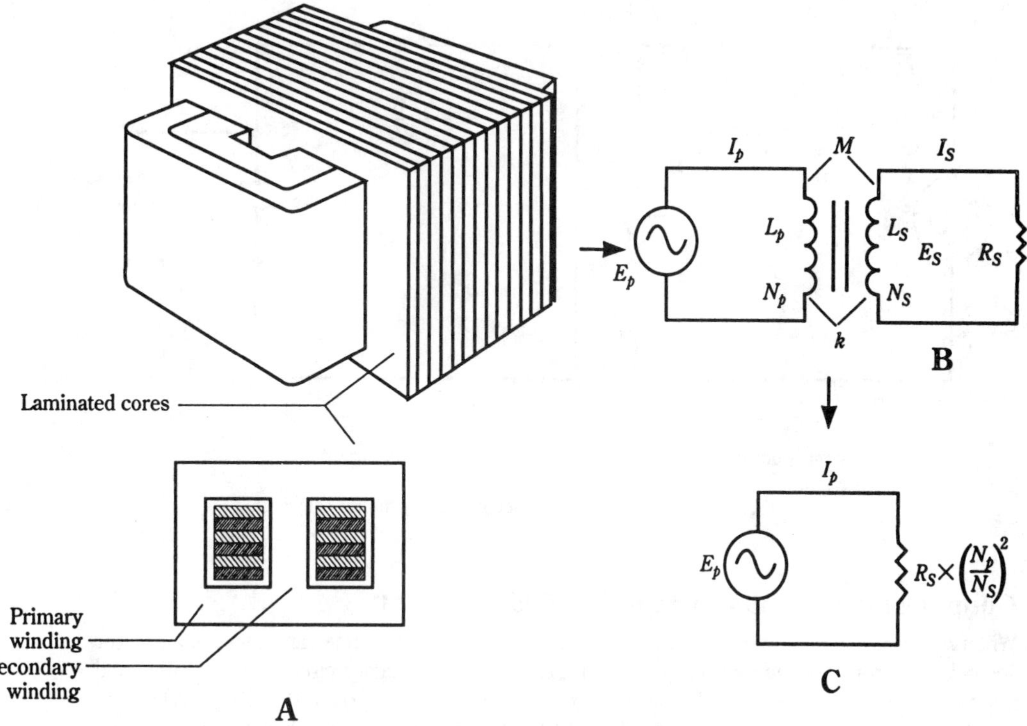

Fig. 2-49 The power transformer.

At frequencies around 1 MHz, the self-inductances of the primary and secondary windings are of the order of 100 μH. Such a transformer uses an iron-dust core in which granules are insulated from each other and are then compressed to form a solid slug. The value of the mutual inductance can be increased by inserting the slug deeper into the windings. An alternative type of core uses a ceramic material, known as *ferrite.* The magnetic properties of ferrite are similar to those of iron, but ferrite is an insulator that helps to reduce the eddy current loss. The schematic symbol for this transformer is:

RF transformer coupling with tuned primary and secondary circuits

Figure 2-50 shows identical primary and secondary circuits, which are magnetically coupled by the mutual inductance, M, and are each resonant to the same frequency, f_o. It is required to consider the changes in the behavior of the circuits as the values of M and the coupling factor k are increased. Theoretically, these increases could be obtained by starting with the coils far apart, then moving them closer together. In practice, the variation in the coupling factor is determined by the depth of penetration that is achieved by the iron-dust slugs.

Low values of coupling (k = 0.005 approximately)

Under these conditions of loose coupling, the voltage induced in the secondary winding is low so that there is only a small secondary current that will have little effect on the primary circuit. The shapes of the response curves will not differ appreciably from those that are obtained with the circuits tuned and excited separately.

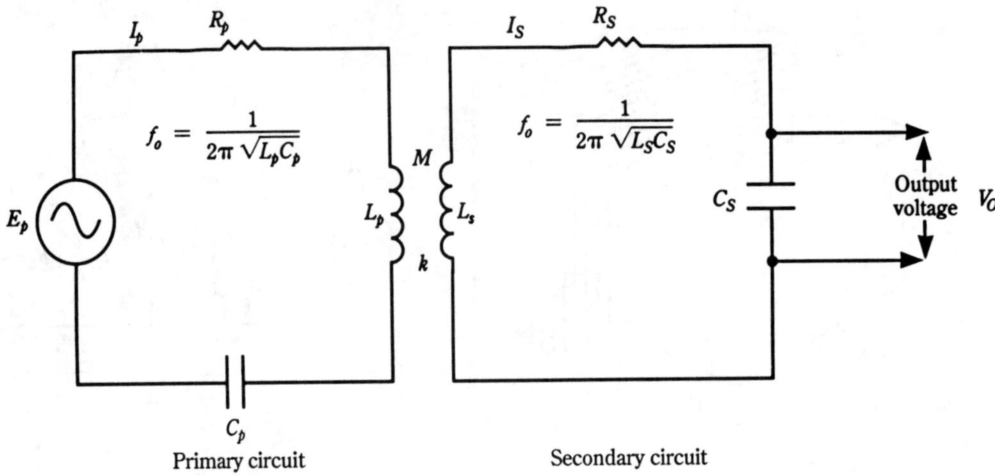

Fig. 2-50 Tuned primary-tuned secondary mutual coupling.

Coupling factor of approximately $0.005 < k < 0.01$

When k is increased, the voltage induced in the secondary winding rises and there is a greater secondary current. At the frequency, f_o, both primary and secondary circuits are resistive and more resistance will be reflected from the secondary circuit into the primary circuit. This has two effects; the primary resonant current falls and the effective Q value is reduced so that the response curve broadens. These conditions continue until the coupling factor reaches a certain critical value at which the reflected resistance from the secondary at the resonant frequency, f_o, is equal to the primary resistance. This is a matched condition so that there is maximum RF power transfer from the primary circuit to the secondary circuit.

Coupling factor of the order 0.01 and above

With tight coupling, the value of the reflected impedance is larger (near resonance); consequently, the primary and secondary circuits have a considerable effect on each other. Because the primary and secondary are tuned to the same frequency, f_o, the nature of the reactance in both circuits is the same for any frequency. Consequently, at frequencies below resonance both circuits are capacitive; the secondary reactance will reflect into the primary circuit as a certain value of inductive reactance. At a particular frequency, f_1, which depends on the value of the coupling factor, this reflected inductive reactance cancels the primary's reactance to produce a resonant "hump" in the primary response curve. A second resonant hump occurs at another frequency, f_2, so that: $f_2 - f_o = f_o - f_1$. This effect of tight coupling is known as *double-humping* or *split-tuning,* which occurs in both primary and secondary circuits (FIGS. 2-51A, B). At the resonant frequency, f_o, both circuits are resistive. Because resistance reflects as resistance, the resonant responses at f_o in both the primary and secondary circuits decrease as k is increased.

Frequency separation between the resonant "humps" is given by:

$$f_2 - f_1 = k f_o \text{ hertz (Hz)} \qquad (2\text{-}129)$$

$$\text{Bandwidth at the half-power points} = \sqrt{2}kf_o \qquad (2\text{-}130)$$

Transformer coupling with tuned primary, tuned secondary circuits is used to provide the wide bandwidth required by the intermediate amplifiers of certain receivers. In AM communica-

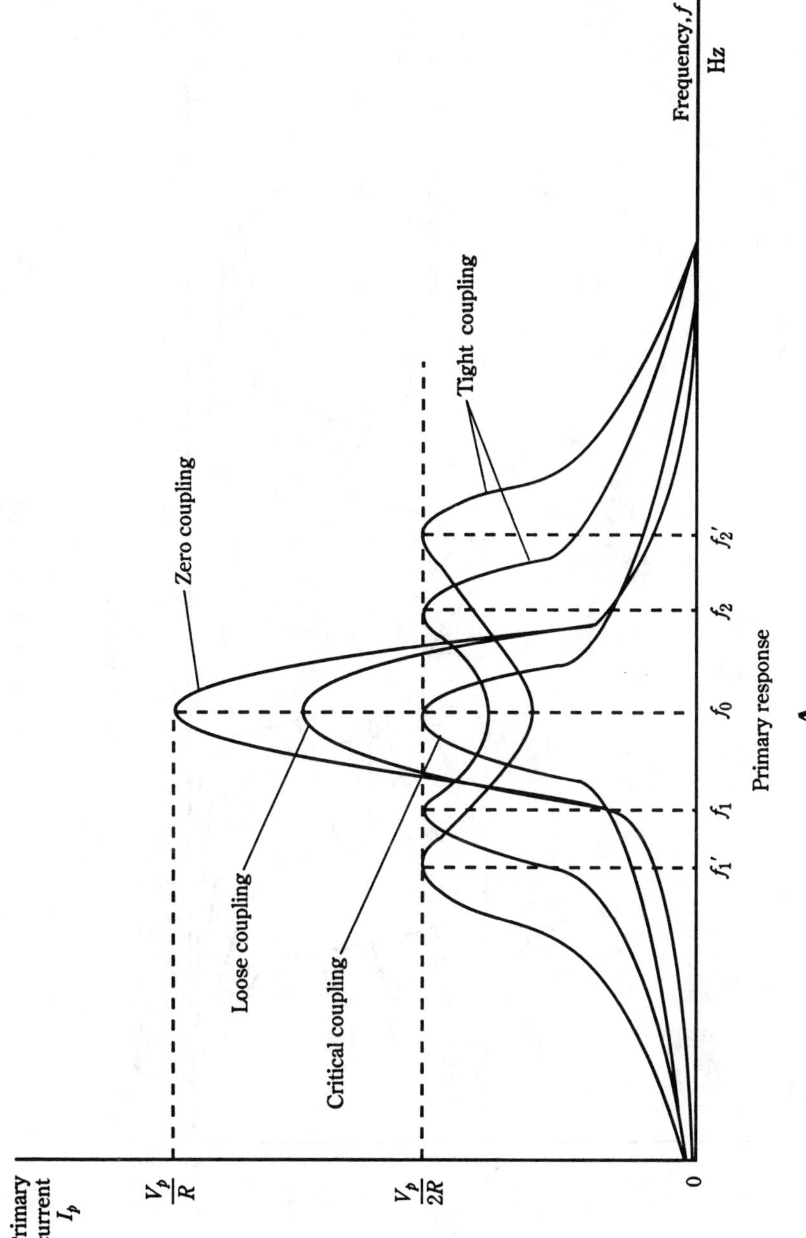

Fig. 2-51 Response curves of the tuned primary, tuned secondary circuits.

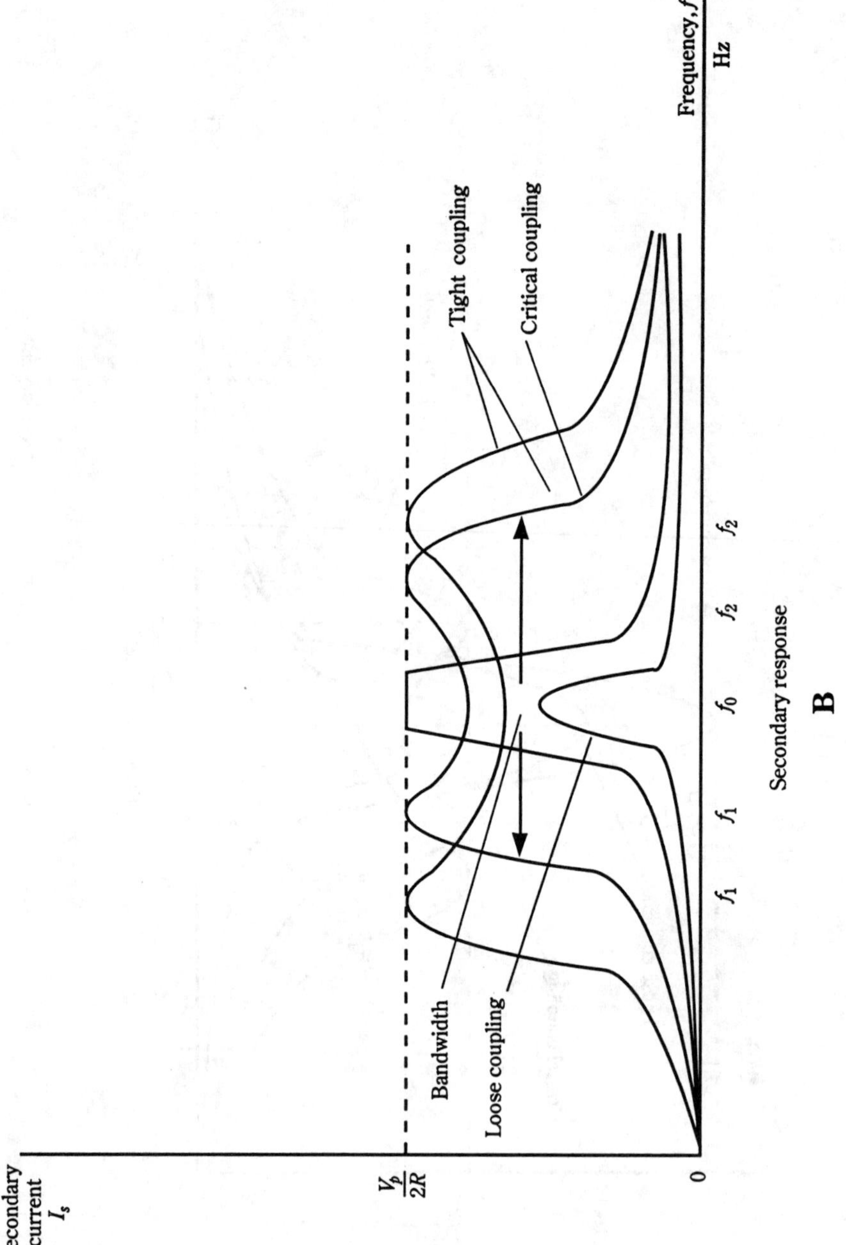

Fig. 2-51 Continued

tions receivers, the necessary bandwidth is only a few kilohertz so that the coupling factor is reduced to below the critical value.

By contrast, TV and radar receivers need wide bandwidths and therefore the coupling factor is increased above the critical level so that the split-tuning occurs. A typical IF amplifier circuit is shown in FIG. 2-52; through network analysis, this circuit can be reduced to the basic arrangement of FIG. 2-50.

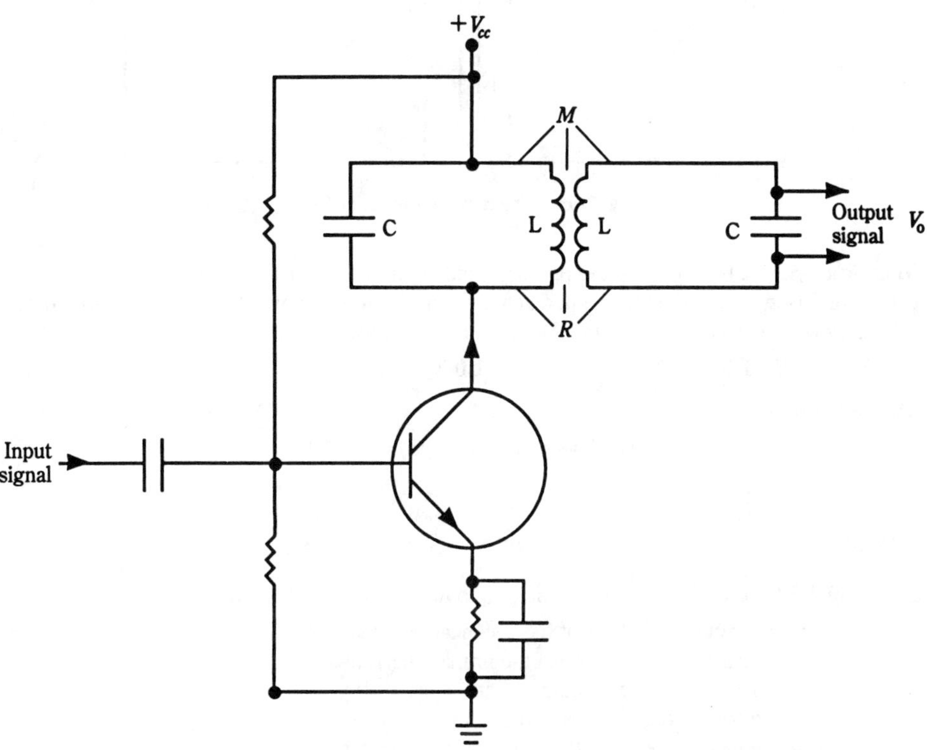

Fig. 2-52 The circuit of the intermediate amplifier.

* **Question 2-51** In the circuit of FIG. 2-53, the value of the current flowing through the 33-kΩ resistor is:

A. 22 mA B. 20 mA C. 0.6 mA D. 12 mA E. 132 mA

Answer Choice B.

Secondary voltage:

$$E_s = 110 \times \frac{2400}{400} \tag{2-126}$$

$$= 660 \text{ V}$$

Secondary current:

$$I_s = \frac{660 \text{ V}}{33 \text{ k}\Omega}$$

$$= 20 \text{ mA}$$

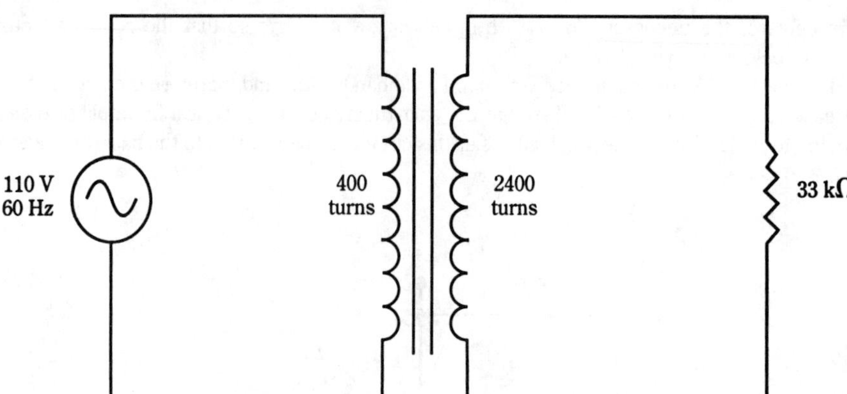

Fig. 2-53 The circuit for question 2-51.

* **Question 2-52** The supply to the primary winding of the power transformer is 100 V, 60 Hz. The secondary winding is center tapped and a voltage of 300 V is measured from one side of the secondary winding to the center tap. The transformer's turns ratio is:

A. 3:1 B. 1:3 C. 1:6 D. 6:1 E. 1:0.3

Answer Choice C.

$$\text{Total secondary voltage} = 2 \times 300 = 600\text{ V}$$

Turns ratio:

$$\frac{N_p}{N_s} = \frac{E_p}{E_s} = \frac{100\text{ V}}{600\text{ V}} = 1{:}6$$

* **Question 2-53** If the turns ratio of a step-up power transformer is 1:5:

A. the primary current is 20% of the secondary current
B. the secondary current is 20% of the primary current
C. the primary and secondary currents are equal
D. the secondary voltage is 20% of the primary voltage
E. the secondary current is 500% of the primary current

Answer Choice B. Let the primary voltage be 100 V and let a 100-Ω load be connected across the secondary winding. The secondary voltage is then 5 × 100 = 500 V and the secondary current is: 500 V/100 Ω = 5 A. The secondary power is: 500 V × 5 A = 2500 W; therefore, the primary power is also 2500 W (assuming no losses in the transformer). Primary current is 2500 W/100 V = 25 A. The secondary current (5 A) is 20% of the primary current (25 A).

* **Question 2-54** Eddy currents are:

A. the result of skin effect in the transformer's windings
B. caused by the effect of hysteresis in the iron core
C. produced as a result of the alternating magnetic flux cutting the iron core of a power transformer
D. reduced as the frequency is increased
E. reduced by the use of a solid iron core

Answer Choice C.

* **Question 2-55** In radio circuits, leads should be kept as short as possible so that:

A. skin effect is reduced
B. there is less hysteresis effect
C. stray coupling is minimized
D. there is less eddy current loss
E. there is less dielectric loss

Answer Choice C.

* **Question 2-56** In an RF transformer with tuned primary-tuned secondary circuits, the coupling factor is increased beyond its critical value. As a result of this "tight" coupling:

A. there is maximum power transferred from the primary circuit to the secondary circuit
B. the center frequency of each circuit is increased
C. the center frequency of each circuit is lowered
D. the bandwidth is increased
E. the gain of the transformer is increased

Answer Choice D. The bandwidth is equal to $\sqrt{2}\, kf_o$ Hz. If k is increased, the bandwidth is greater and the degree of selectivity is reduced.

* **Question 2-57** The IF amplifier of a communications receiver contains an RF transformer with tuned primary-tuned secondary circuits. If the bandwidth is too high so that the selectivity is inadequate:

A. increase the coupling factor to beyond its critical value
B. increase the value of the intermediate frequency
C. decrease the value of the intermediate frequency
D. decrease the coupling factor to below its critical value
E. reduce the amount of the signal input to the amplifier

Answer Choice D. The transformer is over-coupled; therefore, the coupling factor must be reduced to below its critical value.

* **Question 2-58** The output audio stage of a receiver requires a load of 4000 Ω, which must be matched to the loudspeaker impedance of 10 Ω. The required turns ratio of the audio transformer is:

A. 400:1 B. 20:1 C. 1:25 D. 25:1 E. 40:1

Answer Choice C.

Turns ratio:

$$\frac{N_p}{N_s} = \sqrt{\frac{R_p}{R_s}} = \sqrt{\frac{4000}{10}} = \sqrt{400} = 20:1. \qquad (2\text{-}128)$$

Notice that the audio transformer is step-down.

2-13. Filters

Principles of filters

A network that is designed to attenuate certain frequencies, but pass others is called a *filter.* A filter therefore possesses at least one *pass band,* a band of frequencies for which the attenuation theoretically is zero, and at least one stop band, a band of frequencies for which the attenuation in decibels is finite. The frequencies that separate the various pass and stop bands are called the *cut-off values.*

An important characteristic of all filters is that they are constructed from purely reactive elements because otherwise, the attenuation could never become zero. Certain networks that contain resistances and reactances have a filtering action, but they are not filters in the true sense. An *ideal filter* presents zero attenuation in the pass band and infinite attenuation in the stop band. For example, the ideal low-pass filter has an attenuation-versus-frequency characteristic (FIG. 2-54).

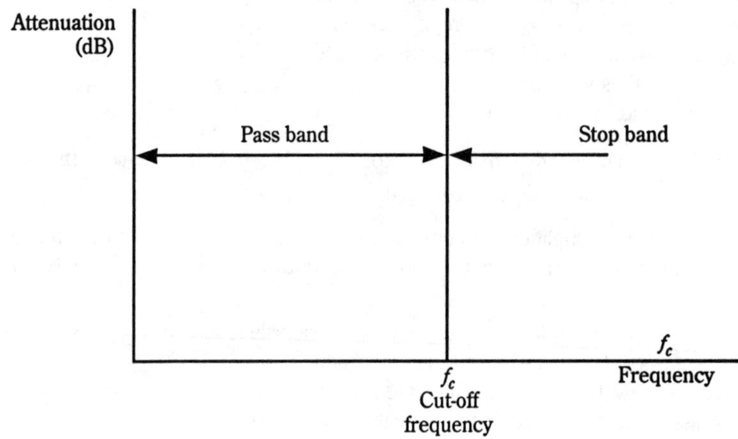

Fig. 2-54 The attenuation-versus-frequency characteristic of an ideal low-pass filter.

The ideal characteristic cannot be achieved in practice because of filter losses, such as are caused by the inductor's effective resistance. Furthermore, there can be a mismatch at certain frequencies between the filter and its terminating load. This also affects the shape of the attenuation characteristic.

As shown in FIG. 2-55, a filter can be regarded as being composed of a number of repeating T and π sections; Z_1 is referred to as the filter's series impedance and Z_2 is the shunt impedance.

Constant-*k* low-pass filter

The constant-*k* variety is a simple or prototype filter, for which the *k* factor ($= \sqrt{z_1 z_2}$) is a fixed value that is independent of the frequency.

An example of a constant-*k* filter is the low-pass circuit of FIG. 2-56. At low frequencies, V_L is small and V_C exceeds V_i (because V_L and V_C are 180° out of phase). It is possible therefore for V_o to equal V_i; this means theoretical zero attenuation. At high frequencies, V_L is large so that V_C and V_o are low and the attenuation is high. Figure 2-57 shows the resulting characteristic and it can be shown that the cut-off frequency is given by:

$$\text{Cutoff frequency, } f_c = \frac{1}{\pi\sqrt{LC}} \text{ hertz (Hz)} \qquad (2\text{-}129)$$

High-pass filter

With this type of filter, L and C are interchanged and the basic T section appears in FIG. 2-58.

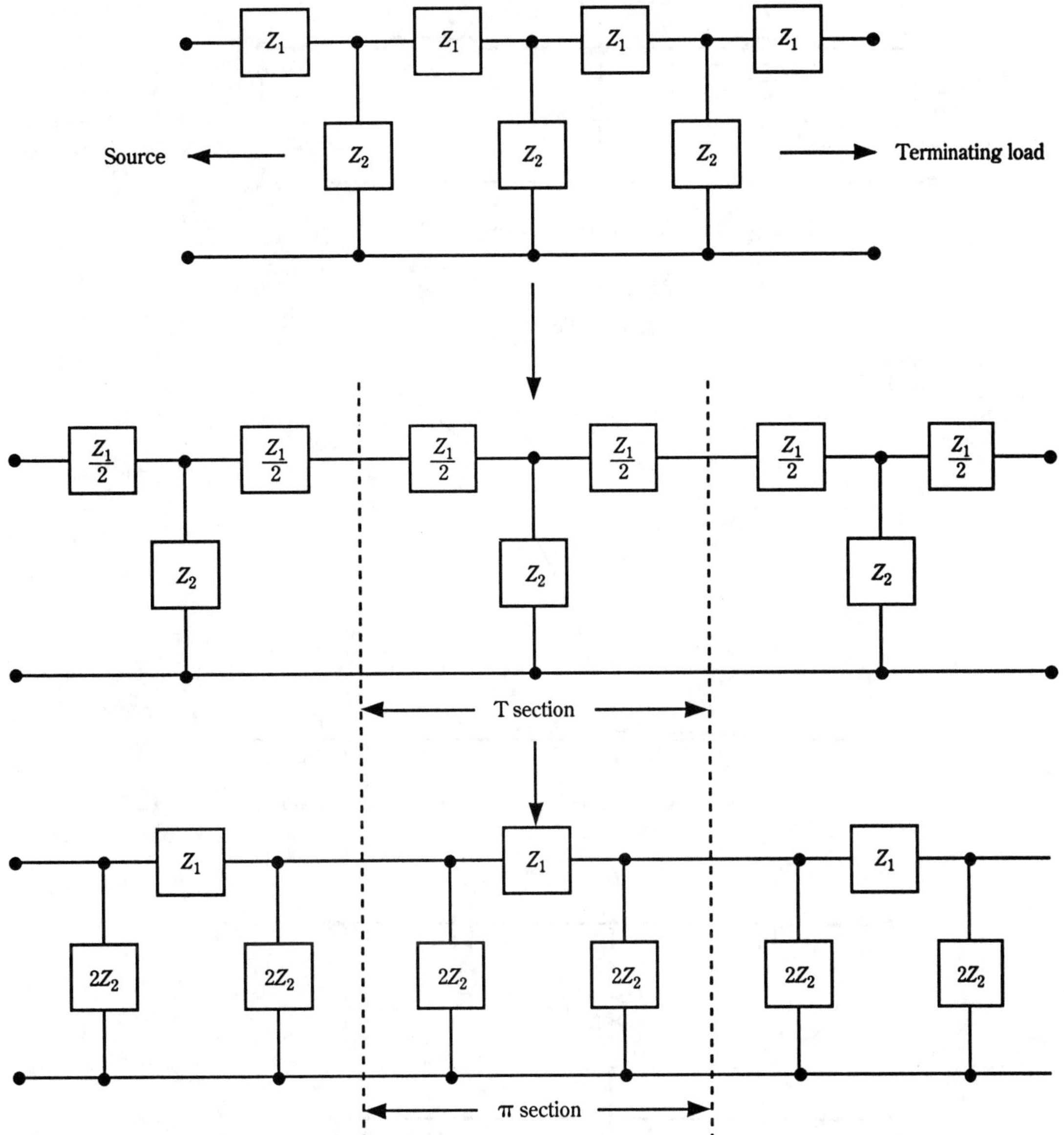

Fig. 2-55 Filters expressed in terms of T and π sections.

The cut-off frequency is given by: $f_c = \dfrac{1}{4\pi\sqrt{LC}}$ hertz (Hz) (2-130)

and the associated attenuation versus frequency curve appears in FIG. 2-59.

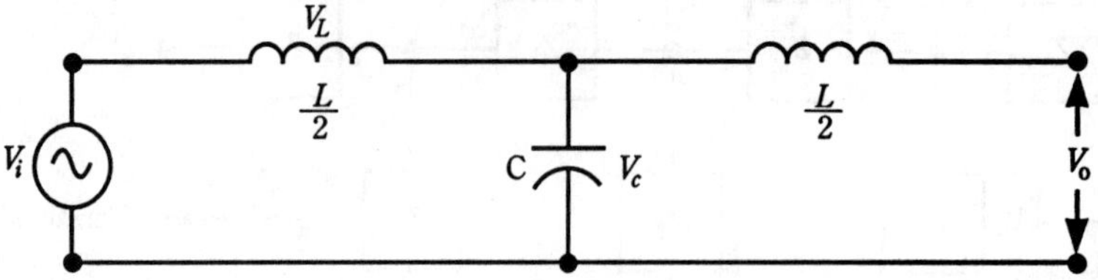

Fig. 2-56 T-section of a low-pass constant-k filter.

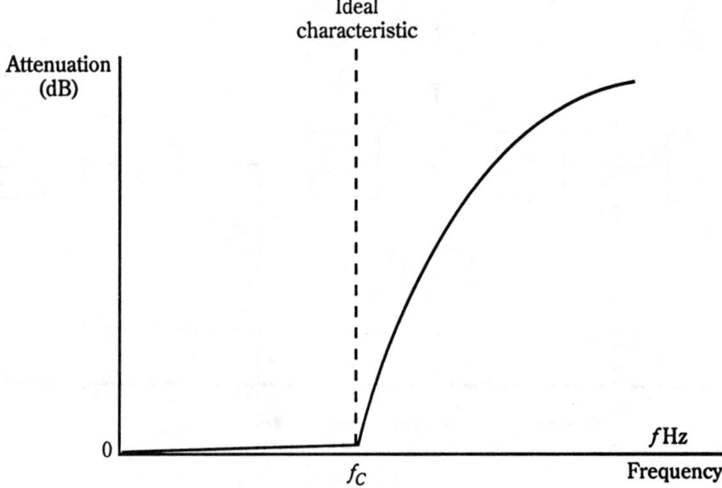

Fig. 2-57 The attenuation-versus-frequency characteristic of a constant-k low-pass T section.

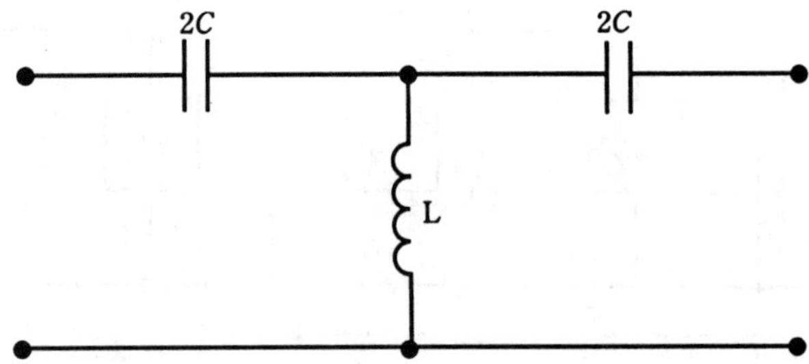

Fig. 2-58 T section of a high-pass constant-k filter.

Band-pass filter

This type of filter must have two cut-off values because it is designed to pass a band of frequencies with zero attenuation. Its basic pass-band T section appears in FIG. 2-60.

At low frequencies, the section behaves as a high-pass filter (FIG. 2-61A); at the high frequencies, the section appears to be a low-pass filter (FIG. 2-61B). Consequently, there is a high degree of attenuation for both low and high frequencies.

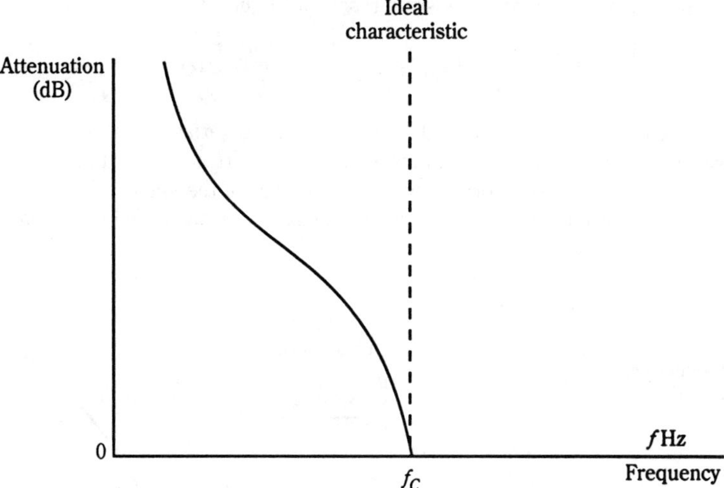

Fig. 2-59 The attenuation-versus-frequency characteristic of a constant-k high-pass filter.

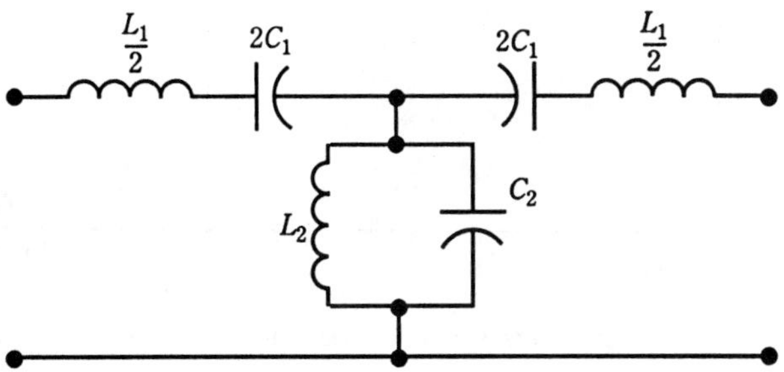

Fig. 2-60 The T section of a band-pass contant-k filter.

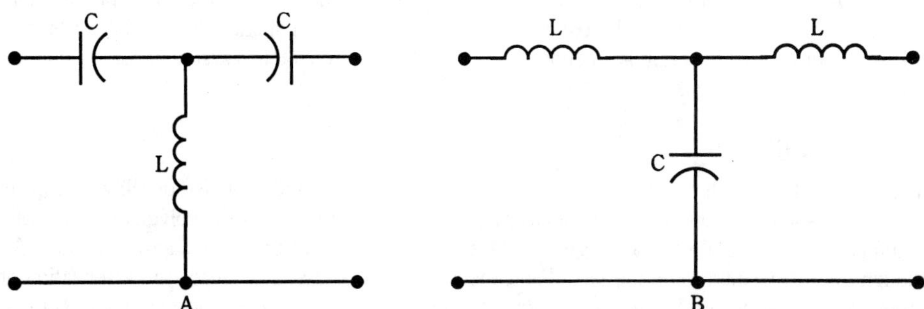

Fig. 2-61 The behavior of the band-pass T section at low and high frequencies.

The series and shunt arms have the same resonant frequency:

$$f_o = \frac{1}{2\pi\sqrt{L_1C_1}} = \frac{1}{2\pi\sqrt{L_2C_2}} \text{ hertz (Hz)} \qquad (2\text{-}131)$$

For both low and high frequencies, the reactance of the series arm is high and that of the shunt arm is low so that there is a degree of finite attenuation. However, at the frequency, f_o, the impedance of the series arm is theoretically zero while that of the shunt arm is infinite; consequently, there is zero attenuation. The resulting attenuation-versus frequency curve appears in FIG. 2-62.

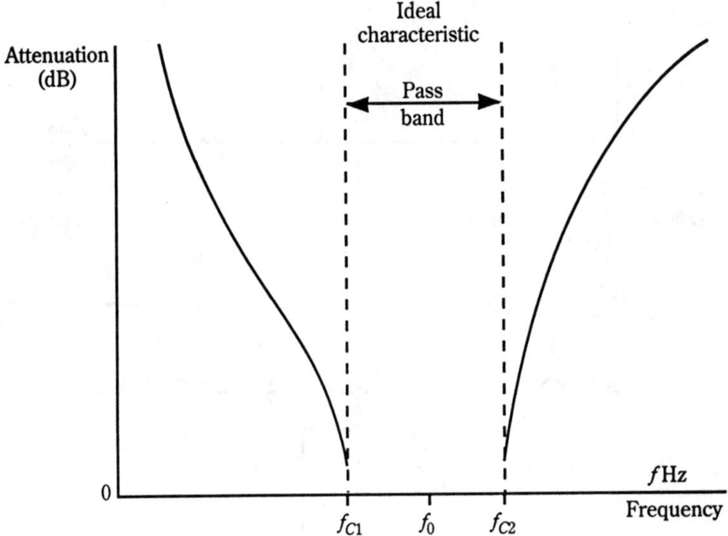

Fig. 2-62 The attenuation-versus-frequency characteristic of a constant-k band-pass filter.

Band-stop filter

The *band-stop filter* is designed to "stop" a band frequencies; therefore, it must also possess two cut-off values. Compared with the band-pass type, the series and shunt arms are interchanged; therefore, the basic T section is as shown in FIG. 2-63. Its attenuation-versus-frequency characteristic appears in FIG. 2-64.

m-derived filters

The main problem with constant-*k* filters is that the attenuation does not rise or fall very rapidly near the cut-off frequencies. It would appear at first glance that this could be solved by connecting a number of identical T sections together. This would not disturb the matching of the filter. Although the attenuation over the pass band theoretically would still be zero, the attenuation at other frequencies would be greatly increased. Unfortunately, because of losses in the components, the attenuation in the pass band of a practical filter is not zero, and the attenuation-versus-frequency curve becomes badly "rounded" near the cut-off value (FIG. 2-65).

It is therefore required to design a new filter section that has the same cut-off frequency as that of the constant-*k* and is matched to its terminating load, but it will have an improved (sharper)

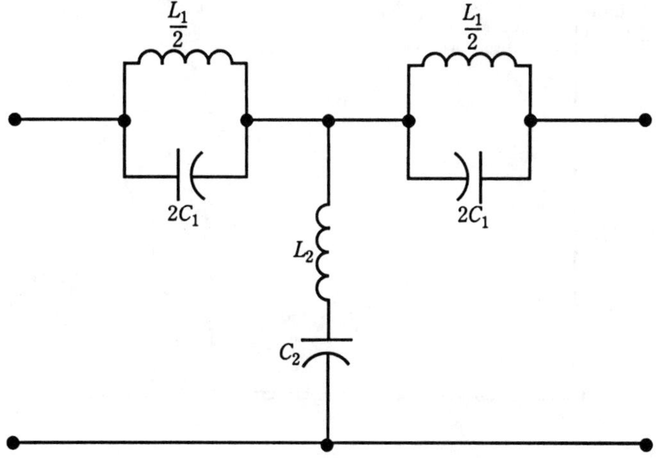

Fig. 2-63 The T-section of a band-stop constant-k filter.

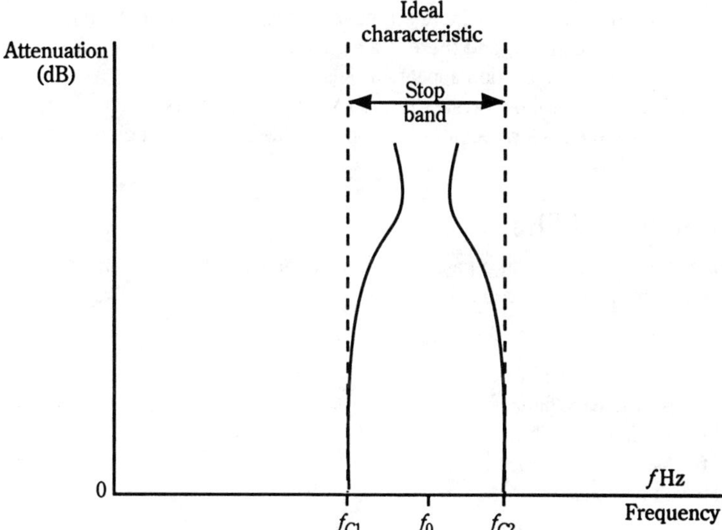

Fig. 2-64 The attenuation-versus-frequency characteristic of a constant-k band-stop filter.

attenuation-versus-frequency characteristic. This is the purpose of the *m*-derived filter; *m* is a mathematical parameter that has a value that lies between zero and unity.

Low-pass *m*-derived filter

A T section for a low-pass *m*-derived filter appears in FIG. 2-66A. At low frequencies, the combination of the reactance of C_2 in series with the reactance of L_2 behaves capacitively and therefore provides a pass band.

The attenuation band begins at the cut-off frequency, f_c, but above this value, the reactance

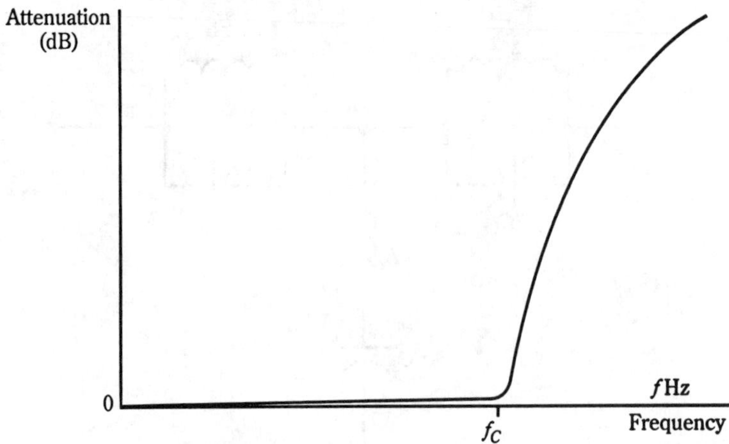

Fig. 2-65 The attenuation-versus-frequency characteristic of a practical constant-k low-pass filter.

of C_2 resonates with the reactance of L_2 at another frequency, f_∞; therefore, a short circuit theoretically exists in the shunt arm, and infinite attenuation is the result. For still higher frequencies, the shunt arm behaves inductively, and there is a high degree of attenuation (FIG. 2-67). An alternative form of the *m*-derived T section appears in FIG. 2-66B.

The shape of the attenuation-versus-frequency characteristic is much "sharper" near the cut-off value; therefore, the *m*-derived filter is a considerable improvement over the LC prototype variety.

High-pass *m*-derived filter

The T section for the *m*-derived high-pass filter appears in FIGS. 2-68A and B. The corresponding attenuation-versus-frequency curve is shown in FIG. 2-68C.

* **Question 2-59** The circuit in FIG. 2-69 represents a (an):

A. constant-*k* high-pass filter
B. constant-*k* low-pass filter
C. *m*-derived high-pass filter
D. constant-*k* band-pass filter
E. *m*-derived low-pass filter

Answer Choice A. Refer to FIG. 2-58.

* **Question 2-60** The circuit in FIG. 2-70 represents a:

A. two-section constant-*k* high-pass filter
B. constant-*k* band-pass filter
C. constant-*k* band-stop filter
D. two-section *m*-derived filter
E. two-section constant-*k* low-pass filter

Answer Choice D. The circuit can be redrawn as in FIG. 2-71, and it represents a two-section *m*-derived low-pass filter (FIG. 2-66).

* **Question 2-61** The main advantage of an *m*-derived filter over the corresponding prototype circuit, is its:

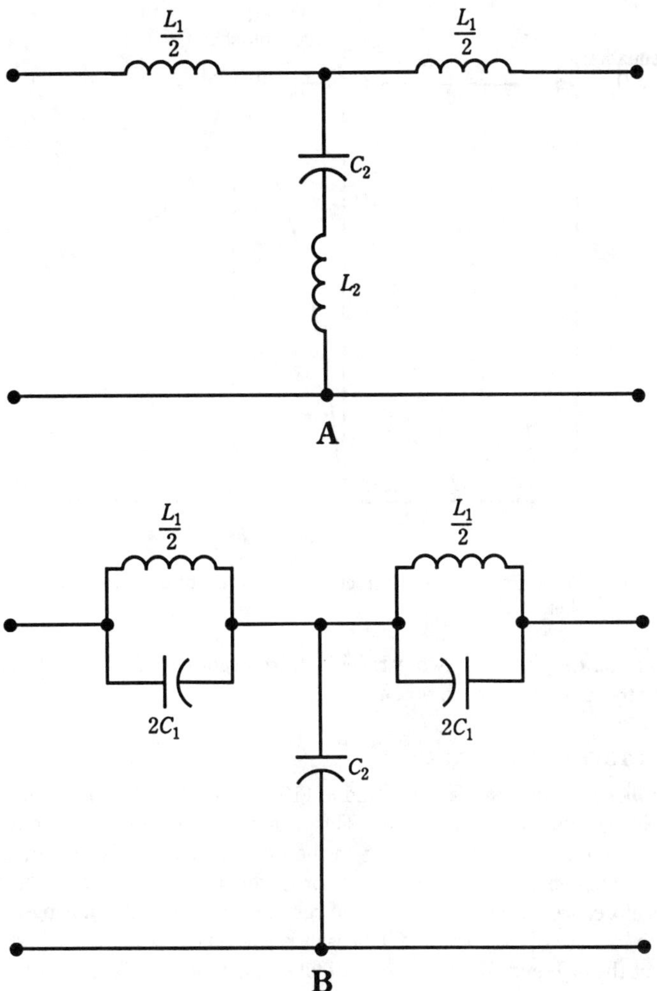

Fig. 2-66 T sections of low-pass m-derived filters.

A. simplicity of design
B. ability to be terminated by a high resistance load
C. sharper cutoff characteristic
D. low Q value
E. low resonant frequency

Answer Choice C.

2-14. Ac measurements

Moving-iron ammeters and voltmeters

Moving-iron ammeters and voltmeters can be divided into two types:

- The *attraction type,* in which a piece of soft iron is attracted toward a solenoid.

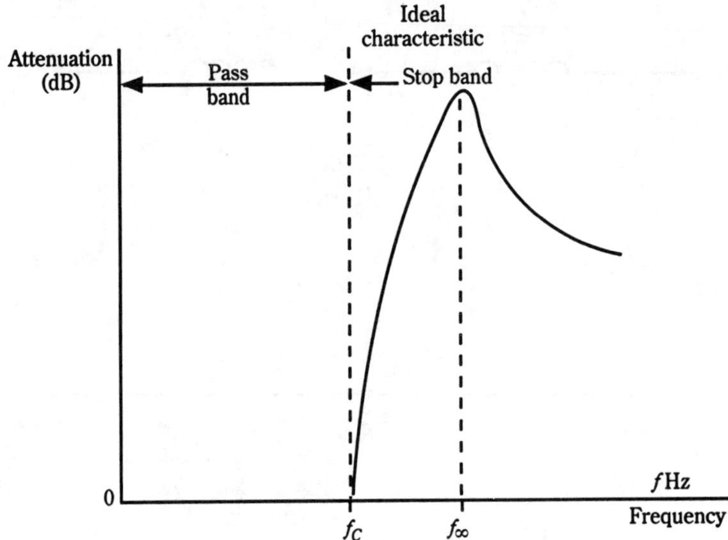

Fig. 2-67 The attenuation-versus-frequency characteristic of an m-derived low-pass filter.

- The *repulsion type,* in which two parallel, soft-iron vanes are magnetized inside a solenoid, and they therefore repel each other.

Attraction moving-iron meter

The *attraction moving-iron meter* is illustrated in FIG. 2-72A. The current to be measured flows through the coil and sets up a magnetic flux. This field magnetizes the soft iron disc and draws it into the center of the coil. The force acting on the iron depends on the flux density and on the coil's magnetic field intensity, both of which are proportional to the current. The torque and the deflection, therefore, are not proportional to the current alone (as in the moving-coil meter movement), but to the square of the current. The result is a nonlinear scale that is cramped at the low end, but open at the high end. However, by careful shaping the iron disc, the scale's linearity can be improved.

The restoring torque of the controlling device is supplied by a spring or sometimes by gravity. The damping device is commonly obtained by the use of an air piston.

Repulsion moving-iron meter

Two iron vanes are situated axially in a short solenoid (FIG. 2-72B). One vane is fixed and the other is movable and attached to a pivot that also carries the pointer. When the current flows through the coil, the vanes are equally magnetized and repel each other. The repulsion creates a deflection of the needle on the scale, which is calibrated for direct reading. The force of repulsion is dependent on the flux density of each iron vane and is directly proportional to the square of the current; therefore, the scale is again nonlinear. The restoring and damping systems are similar to those of the attraction type.

In the measurement of ac, the deflecting torque for both the attraction and repulsion meters is proportional to the square of the instantaneous current; therefore, it varies from zero to a peak value at a rate that is equal to twice the alternating frequency. Because of its inertia, the moving system takes up a position that corresponds to the mean torque. The deflection is then proportional to the square of the current's RMS value.

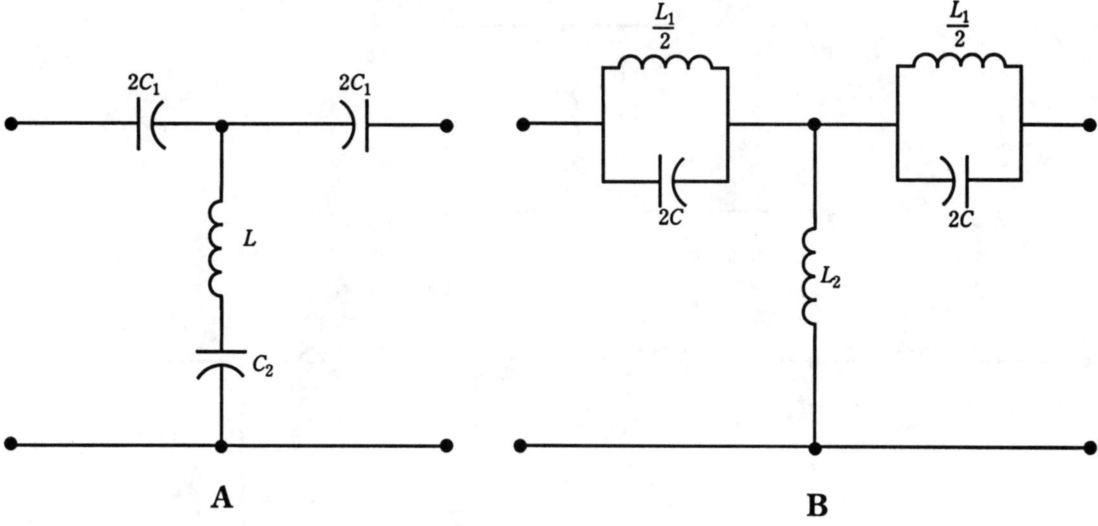

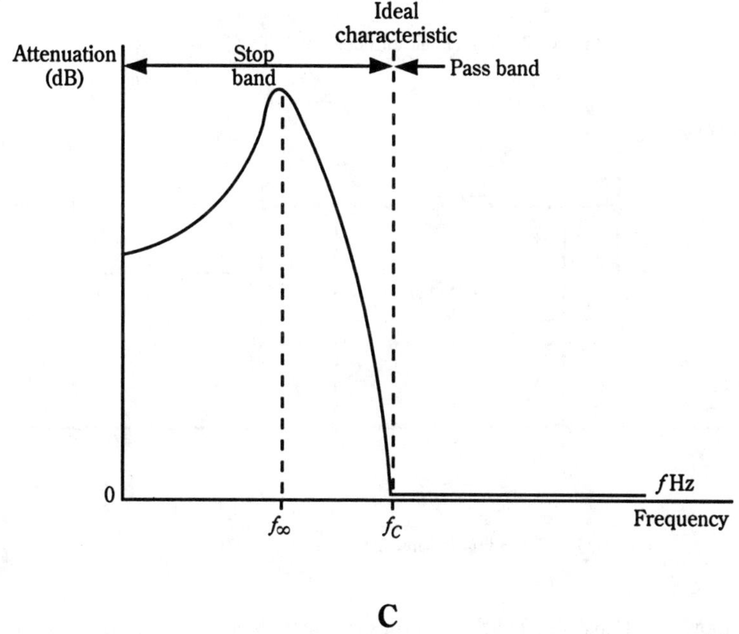

Fig. 2-68 The T section and attenuation-versus-frequency characteristic for the m-derived high-pass filter.

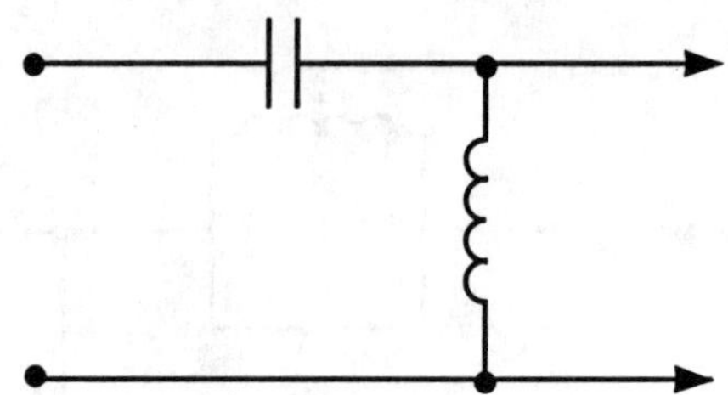

Fig. 2-69 The circuit for question 2-59.

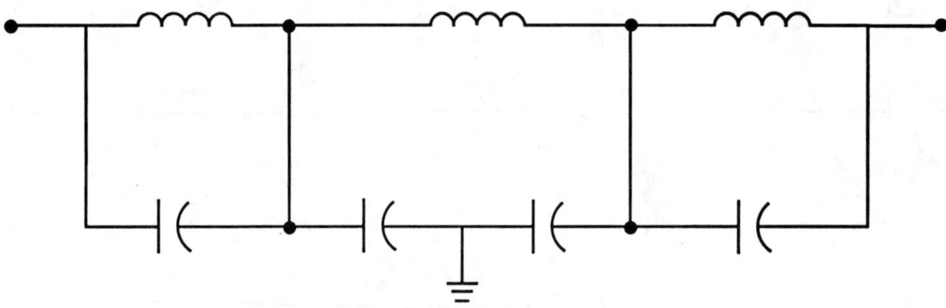

Fig. 2-70 The circuit for question 2-60.

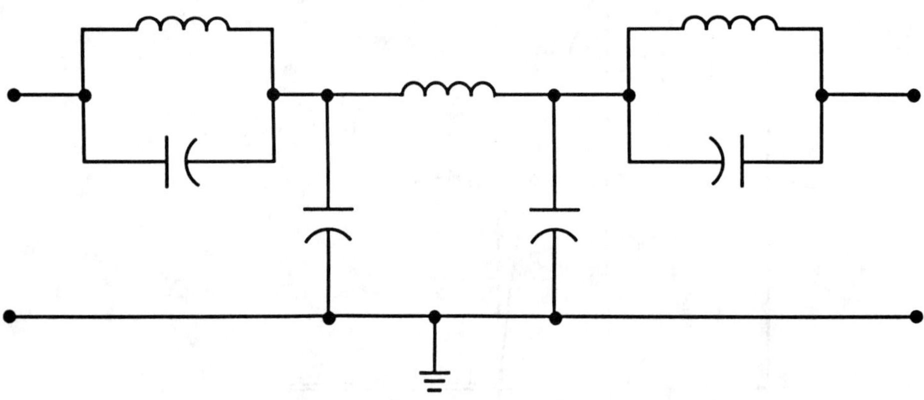

Fig. 2-71 The circuit for answer to question 2-60.

Unlike the moving-coil instrument, the moving iron meter can be used for both dc and ac measurements. If the current contains both dc and ac components, the effective reading is equal to:

$$\sqrt{I_{dc}^2 + I_{RMS}^2}$$

Because the strength of the deflection torque depends on the number of ampere turns for the coil, it is possible to arrange for various ranges by winding different numbers of turns on the coil. Also, by varying the type of wire used, the meter's resistance can be changed so that there is no

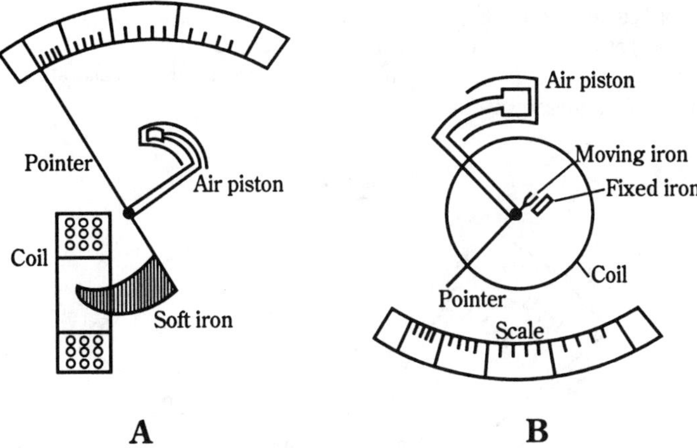

Fig. 2-72 Moving-iron instruments.

need for shunt and swamp resistances. The moving-iron milliammeter can be converted to a voltmeter by adding a suitable noninductive series resistor.

Apart from their advantage of being able to measure both dc and ac, the moving-iron instruments also are relatively cheap and robust, but their operation is only satisfactory at line frequencies. Moreover, they have low sensitivity, are affected by stray magnetic fields, and are liable to hysteresis error when used to measure ac.

The thermocouple meter

The principle of the *thermocouple meter* is based on the *Seebeck effect,* which was discovered originally in 1821. If a circuit consisting of different metals is at the same temperature throughout, there is no resulting EMF. However, if a junction between two dissimilar metals is maintained at a different temperature from the rest of the circuit, a *thermoelectric EMF* is generated, and a current then can be driven through a conventional moving-coil meter movement.

The construction of the meter is shown in FIG. 2-73. The current to be measured passes between X and Y and raises the temperature of the heater wire. Attached to the center of this wire is the thermocouple junction, J; bismuth and antimony are commonly used as the dissimilar metals, though many other combinations are possible. As the temperature rises, the thermoelectric EMF increases and drives a greater current through the meter movement. The amount of deflection on the scale depends on a heating effect that is proportional to the square of the measured current. The meter scale is therefore nonlinear so that it is cramped at the low end and open at the high end.

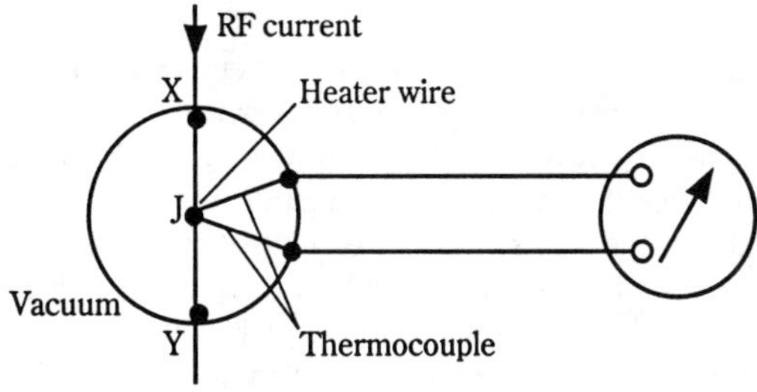

Fig. 2-73 The thermocouple meter.

This type of "current-squared" meter is suitable for reading both dc and the RMS value of ac. Its particular importance lies in the measurement of RF currents, such as occur in the antenna systems of transmitters (FIG. 2-74). Once this type of meter has been calibrated, the calibration is accurate from dc up to microwave frequencies.

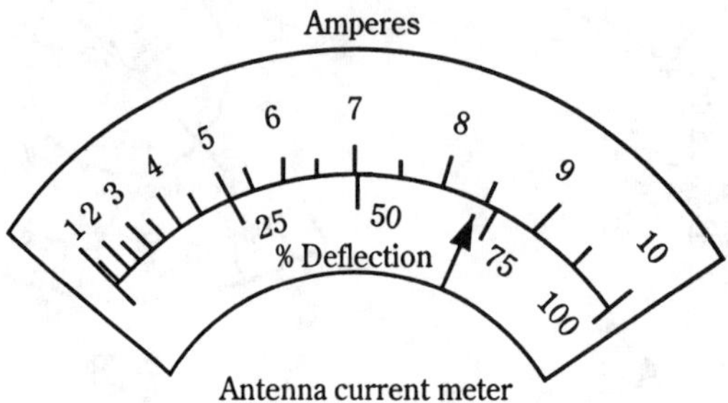

Fig. 2-74 The current-squared meter.

Electrodynamometer movement and the wattmeter

In the moving-coil meter movement, the flux that is associated with the permanent magnet is fixed in direction; consequently, this type of meter (unless used in conjunction with a rectifier) can be used only for dc measurements. However, if the permanent magnet is replaced by an electromagnet, the direction of the flux can be reversed. This is shown in the *electrodynamometer* movement of FIG. 2-75A, in which two fixed coils, F and F′, provide the electromagnet. The moving coil, M, is then carried by a spindle, and the controlling torque is exerted by spiral hair-springs, H and H′, which also lead the current into and out of the moving coil.

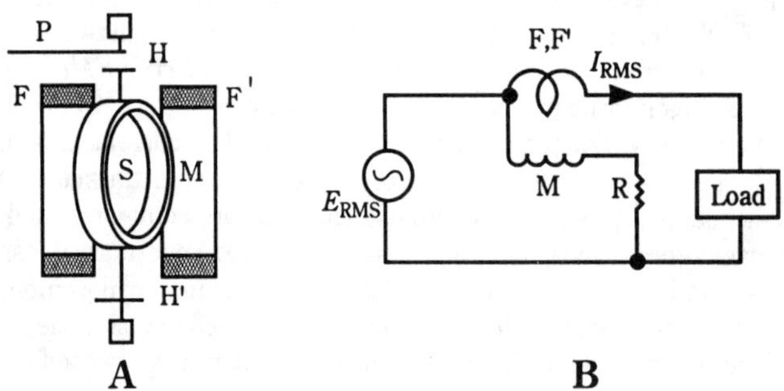

Fig. 2-75 The electrodynamometer movement and the wattmeter.

For dc measurements, the electrodynamometer movement has no advantage over the D'Arsonval type. Compared with ac moving-iron instruments, dynamometer ammeters and voltmeters are less sensitive and more expensive, and they are rarely used. However, dynamometer wattmeters are important because they are the most common way to measure power directly in ac circuits. Figure 2-75B shows the way in which the wattmeter is connected into the circuit. The fixed coils are joined in series with the load so that they carry the instantaneous load current. The moving coil is in series with a high-value noninductive multiplier resistor, so the current through the moving coil is proportional to and nearly in phase with the source voltage. The instantaneous torque on the moving coil is proportional to the product of the instantaneous current through the fixed (current) coils and the instantaneous current through the moving (voltage) coil; it is therefore proportional to the instantaneous power taken by the load.

The controlling torque that is provided by the hairsprings depends directly on the deflection, which is proportional to the power; consequently, electrodynamometer wattmeters have linear scales.

If the load contains both resistance and reactance, the instantaneous power waveform is a second harmonic curve (FIG. 2-18B). When the curve is above the zero horizontal line, the torque on the moving coil is clockwise, but its direction is reversed when the curve falls below the line. The inertia of the voltage coil and the pointer does not allow the deflection to follow the variations in the instantaneous torque. The rest position of pointer, P, therefore will represent the average (true) power taken by the load. In other words, the wattmeter automatically takes into account the power factor of the circuit. Therefore, the true power recorded by the wattmeter is:

$$\text{True power } (TP) = E \times I \times \textit{power factor} \quad (2\text{-}132)$$
$$= E \times I \times \text{Cos.}\phi \text{ watts (W)}$$

where: E = RMS value of the source voltage
I = RMS value of the load current
ϕ = phase angle between the source voltage and the load current

When the load is entirely reactive, the clockwise and counterclockwise torques exactly balance so that the wattmeter reads zero. However, heavy currents can be flowing in the fixed and moving coils so that the instrument must have both voltage and current ratings.

The power factor of the load can be determined by dividing the wattmeter reading by the product of the source voltage and the load current. However, power-factor meters continuously indicate the value of the power factor and whether it is leading or lagging (FIG. 2-28).

The cathode-ray oscilloscope

The basic triggered-sweep cathode-ray oscilloscope (CRO) is probably the most flexible, general-purpose measuring instrument in use today, and, perhaps, for some time in the future. The key element of the CRO is the electrostatic cathode-ray tube, which operates with a high degree of vacuum and in which a stream of electrons is produced by a heated cathode. This acts together with other metallic elements to form the *electron gun.* The stream of electrons is accelerated by high voltages toward the inside surface of the tube face. Light is produced when the electrons strike the fluorescent screen that coats this inside surface.

Between the beginning of the electron gun and the fluorescent screen are a number of electrodes held at positive potentials, with respect to the cathode. Some of these focus the electron beam to a point at the screen. A control on the front panel can be used to improve the focus and affect the size and appearance of the spot seen by the operator. Other electrodes cause the electron beam to be deflected. One pair of electrodes, called the *X plates,* causes a horizontal deflection, which is proportional to the impressed voltage. A second pair, the *Y plates,* causes vertical deflection (FIG. 2-76A), whose amount depends on the length of the vertical plates and their separation, the values of the vertical deflection voltage, and the horizontal accelerating voltage, as well as the distance between the vertical plates and the screen.

An electrostatic CRT commonly has a sensitivity that is about 1 mm of vertical deflection for each volt applied to the Y plates with 1 kV of horizontal accelerating voltage. If V_Y = 100 V and V_X = 10 kV, the vertical deflection is 1 × (100/10) mm = 1 cm. In other words, the sensitivity is 100 V/cm for a horizontal accelerating voltage of 10 kV.

In the most commonly used mode of operation, the horizontal deflection is linear and is produced by a sawtooth voltage waveform applied to the X plates. The beam, and the spot that it produces, move equal distances in equal intervals of time. For slow movements, the spot can be

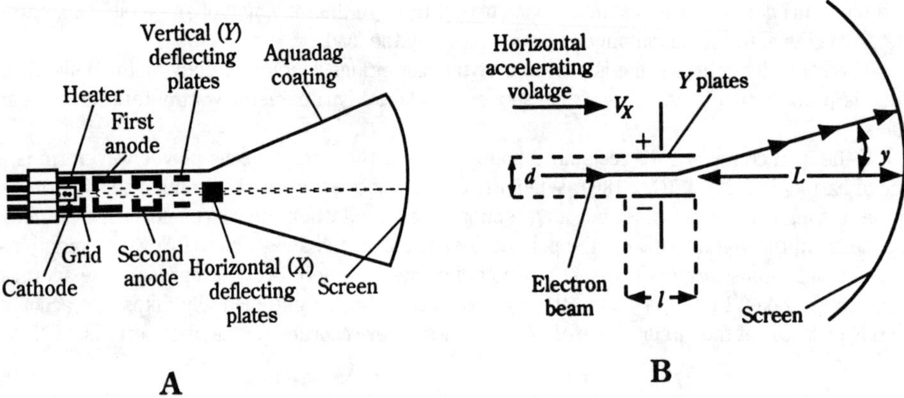

Fig. 2-76 The cathode-ray tube.

seen moving to the right, leaving a rapidly disappearing trail. Upon reaching the end of its travel on the right, the spot disappears and quickly reappears on the left to repeat its linear journey. With fast movements of the beam, required for most electronic measurements, the beam cannot be seen, but its trace (repeated hundreds, thousands, or even millions of times per second) appears as a solid horizontal line. For the purpose of measurement, a TIME/DIV control knob on the front panel determines the time that is required for the spot to travel the horizontal distance between two major division marks. On most modern oscilloscopes, the major division marks are separated by 1 cm.

The vertical deflection of the beam is usually caused by an amplified signal to be observed and measured. The amount of amplification, and the deflection, is controlled by a knob on the CRO panel. This VOLTS/DIV control determines the amount of input voltage that is required to deflect the electron beam vertically through a distance of one major division (usually 1 cm).

The combined horizontal sweep motion and vertical signal deflection give a graphic picture of the signal waveform. If a dc voltage is applied to the vertical plates, the appearance on the screen is a horizontal line, which is deflected upward, according to the polarity of the deflecting voltage.

In FIG. 2-76B:

Vertical deflection: $$y = \frac{LlV_Y}{2d\,V_X} = K \times V_Y \text{ millimeters (mm)} \tag{2-133}$$

Sensitivity of the CRT: $$K = \frac{Ll}{2d\,V_X} \text{ millimeters per deflection volt for each 1 kV of horizontal accelerating voltage} \tag{2-134}$$

where: y = vertical deflection (mm)
L = distance between the vertical plates and the screen (mm)
l = length of the vertical plates (mm)
d = separation between the plates (mm)
V_Y = vertical deflection voltage (V)
V_X = horizontal accelerating voltage provided by the "gun" (kV)

Notice that the amount of vertical deflection depends neither on the charge nor on the mass of the particle being deflected. Therefore, electrons and negative residual gas ions are subjected to the same deflection.

* **Question 2-62** Figure 2-77 shows the display on the face of an oscilloscope. If the horizontal TIME/DIV control is set to 50 μs/div., the frequency of the sine-wave voltage is:

A. 5 MHz B. 50 MHz C. 500 kHz D. 50 kHz E. 5 kHz

Answer Choice E. The period, T, covers four major divisions which are equivalent to a time interval of $4 \times 50 = 200$ μs.

$$\begin{aligned} \text{Frequency, } f &= \frac{1}{T} \\ &= \frac{1}{200 \times 10^{-6}\text{s}} \qquad (2\text{-}1) \\ &= \frac{10^6}{200} \text{ hertz (Hz)} \\ &= 5 \text{ kHz} \end{aligned}$$

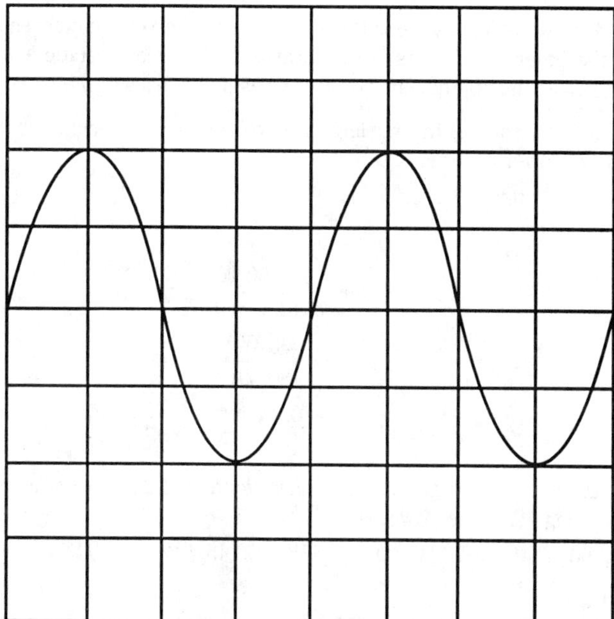

Fig. 2-77 The waveform for question 2-62.

* **Question 2-63** In QUES. 2-62, the vertical VOLTS/DIV control is set to 10 mV per division. The RMS value of the sine-wave voltage is:

A. 20 mV B. 40 mV C. 28.3 mV D. 14.1 mV E. 7.1 mV

Answer Choice C. The peak value covers two major divisions, which are equivalent to 2×10 mV = 20 mV.

$$\begin{aligned} \textit{RMS value} &= 0.707 \times \textit{peak value} \\ &= 0.707 \times 20 \qquad (2\text{-}11) \\ &= 14.1 \text{ mV, rounded off} \end{aligned}$$

* **Question 2-64** The beam intensity of a cathode-ray tube is primarily controlled by the:

A. heater voltage
B. grid-to-cathode voltage
C. horizontal accelerating vo!tage
D. second anode voltage
E. horizontal deflection voltage

Answer Choice B. When the grid is made more negative with respect to the cathode, the beam current is reduced; this in turn lowers the beam intensity.

* **Question 2-65** The beam of a cathode ray tube is brought to a focus at the screen by:

A. changing the horizontal accelerating voltage
B. altering the voltage on one anode, with respect to the other anode(s)
C. varying the grid-to-cathode voltage
D. equalizing the horizontal and vertical deflection voltages
E. reducing the beam current

Answer Choice B. If three anodes are in the electron gun, the voltage difference between the middle anode and the other two results in the formation of an electrostatic lens. This voltage difference can then be varied until the lens brings the beam to a focus at the screen.

* **Question 2-66** At an ac source, the readings are: voltmeter 12 V, ammeter 9 A, wattmeter 90 W. The value of the power factor is:

A. 1.0 B. 0.9 C. 0.75 D. 0.83 E. 0.95

Answer Choice D.

$$\textit{Power factor} = \frac{90\ \text{W}}{12\ \text{V} \times 9\ \text{A}} = \frac{90\ \text{W}}{180\ \text{VA}} = 0.83 \qquad \text{(2-132)}$$

* **Question 2-67** At an ac source the readings are: voltmeter 220 V, milliammeter 300 mA, power factor 0.6, leading. The true power is:

A. 66 W B. 60 W C. 39.6 W D. 25.5 W E. 45.4 W

Answer Choice C.

$$\textit{True power} = E \times I \times \textit{power factor} = 220\ \text{V} \times 0.3\ \text{A} \times 0.6 = 39.6\ \text{W} \qquad \text{(2-132)}$$

2-15. Nonsinusoidal waveforms

Previous sections of this chapter have only covered sinusoidal voltages and currents. However, what about other alternating waveforms, such as the square wave and the sawtooth wave (FIGS. 2-78A and B)? Is a new method of analysis required for each type of alternating source? Fortunately, it is not. In the 18th century, a French mathematician by the name of Jean Baptiste Fourier (1768–1850) was trying to solve a problem involving the flow of heat. He developed a means of analysis by which any finite, continuous, and periodic waveform can be analyzed into a series of sine waves. The general series contains a fundamental sine wave, whose frequency is the same as that of the periodic waveform; together with the fundamental wave are harmonic components. The derivation of the Fourier series is sometimes known as *harmonic analysis*.

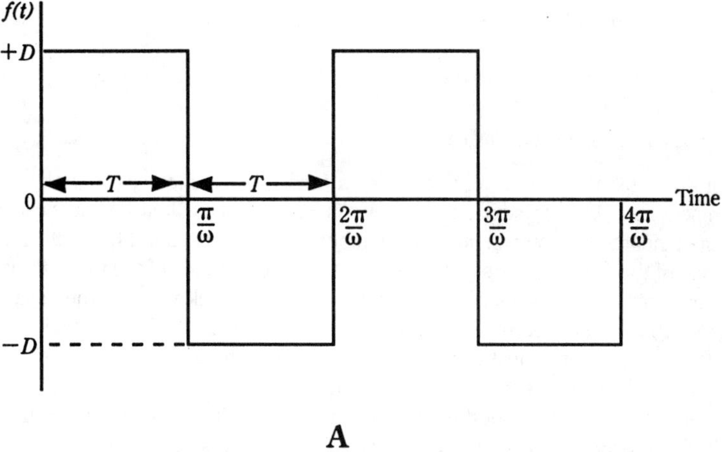

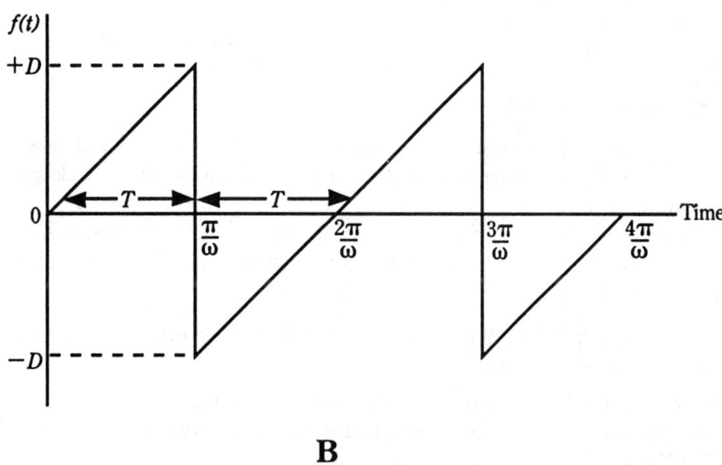

Fig. 2-78 The symmetrical square and sawtooth waveforms.

The Fourier series

The Fourier theorem can be stated formally as: "Any finite, continuous single-valued function, $f(t)$, that has a period of 2π radians (360°) can be expressed by the series:

$$f(t) = a_o + A_1\text{Sin.}(\omega t + \phi_1) + A_2\text{Sin.}(2\omega t + \phi_2) + A_3\text{Sin.}(3\omega t + \phi_3) + \ldots \quad (2\text{-}134)$$

$$= a_o + a_1 \text{ Cos.}\omega t + a_2 \text{ Cos.}2\omega t + a_3 \text{ Cos.}3\omega t + \text{---}$$
$$+ b_1\text{Sin.}\omega t + b_2\text{Sin.}2\omega t + b_3\text{Sin.}3\omega t + \text{---}$$

A waveform frequently encountered in electronics and communications is that of the symmetrical square wave (FIG. 2-78A). This waveform is symmetrical in the sense that the two time intervals (T) are equal. Its Fourier series is:

$$f(t) = \frac{4D}{\pi}\left(\text{Sin.}\omega t + \frac{1}{3}\text{ Sin.}3\omega t + \frac{1}{5}\text{ Sin.}5\omega t + \text{---}\right) \qquad (2\text{-}135)$$

where: D = peak value of the square wave

From EQ. 2-135 the square wave contains a fundamental sine wave together with odd harmonic components. An approximation to the square wave can then be synthesized by adding together the fundamental component and a number of the harmonics (FIG. 2-79). For example, if the amplitude of the fundamental sine wave is 10 V, the amplitudes of the third, fifth, and seventh harmonics are (respectively) 3.33 V, 2 V, and 1.43 V; the peak value of the square wave is 10 V × π/4 = 7.85 V, rounded off. The amplitudes of the higher order harmonics only decrease slowly so that the synthesis must contain a large number of harmonics in order to achieve a close approximation to the square wave.

Another practical example of the periodic waveform is the symmetrical positive sawtooth of FIG. 2-78B. Such a waveform is applied to a cathode-ray tube so that the beam is deflected horizontally and causes the spot on the screen to move across from left to right with a constant velocity. Its Fourier series is:

$$f(t) = \frac{2D}{\pi}\left(\text{Sin.}\omega t - \frac{1}{2}\text{ Sin.}2\omega t + \frac{1}{3}\text{ Sin.}3\omega t + \text{---}\right) \qquad (2\text{-}136)$$

where: D = peak value of the sawtooth waveform

In this case, the series contains a fundamental sine wave with all harmonics, both odd and even. Again, a large number of harmonics must be synthesized to achieve a close approximation to the sawtooth waveform.

The complete Fourier expansion of EQ. 2-134 contained both sine and cosine terms. However, because of the symmetries of the square and sawtooth waveforms, no cosine terms were included in their series.

* **Question 2-68** Which of the following frequency groups are contained in the harmonic analysis of a 250-kHz symmetrical square wave?

A. 250 kHz, 500 kHz, 750 kHz, and all harmonic frequencies
B. 250 kHz, 500 kHz, 1000 kHz, and additional even harmonic components
C. 250 kHz, 125 kHz, 62.5 kHz, and 31.25 kHz
D. 250 kHz, 750 kHz, 1250 kHz, 1750 kHz, and additional odd harmonic components
E. 250 kHz, 500 kHz, 1000 kHz, 2000 kHz, and 4000 kHz

Answer Choice D. The harmonic analysis of the symmetrical square wave contains a fundamental sine wave (at the same frequency as the square wave) together with all odd harmonic components.

* **Question 2-69** Which of the following groups of frequencies can be used to synthesize an approximation to a 25 MHz symmetrical square wave?

A. 25 MHz, 75 MHz, 125 MHz, 175 MHz, and 225 MHz
B. 25 MHz, 50 MHz, 75 MHz, 100 MHz, and 125 MHz
C. 25 MHz, 50 MHz, 100 MHz, 150 MHz, and 200 MHz

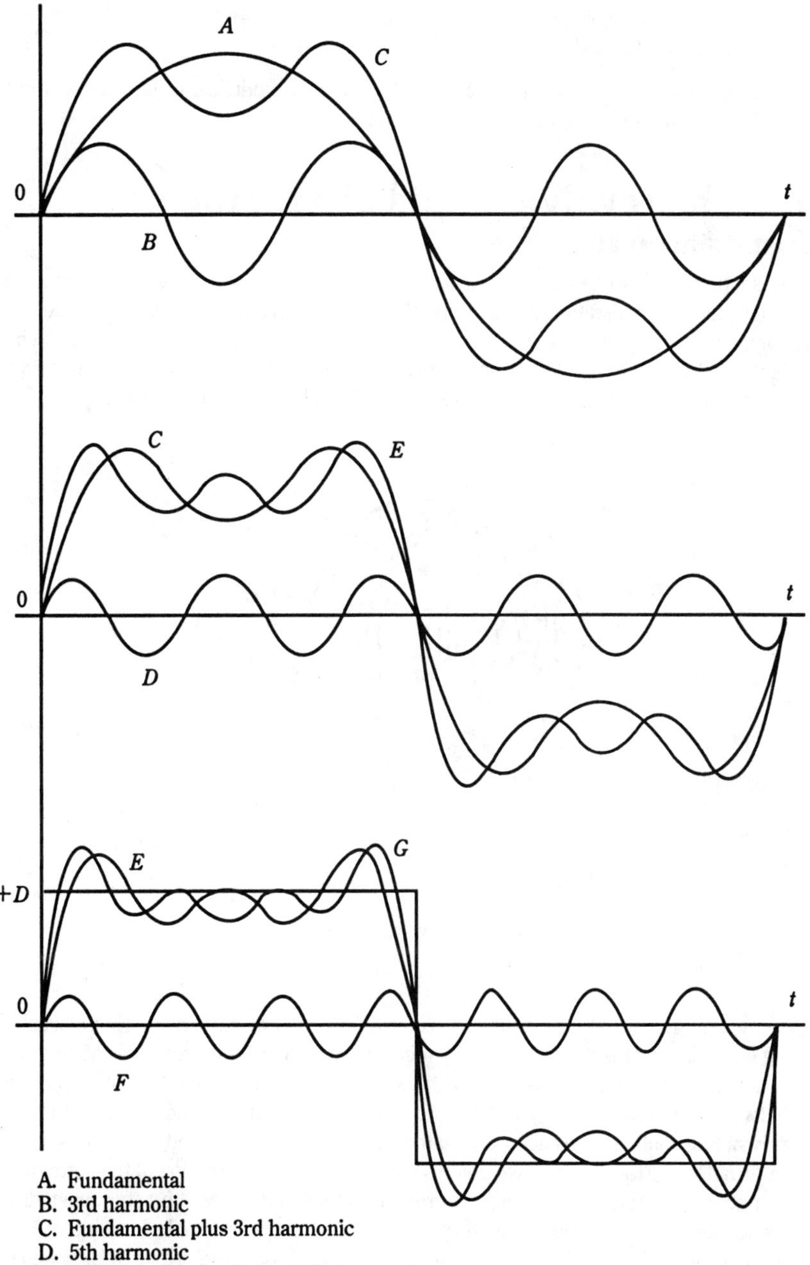

Fig. 2-79 The synthesis of the symmetrical square wave.

D. 25 MHz, 12.5 MHz, 6.25 MHz, 3.125 MHz, and 1.5625 MHz
E. 25 MHz, 125 MHz, 225 MHz, 325 MHz, and 400 MHz

Answer Choice A. To synthesize an approximation to a symmetrical square wave, the fundamental and all odd harmonic components are required.

2-16. The revolving field alternator

The practical alternator

In the first section of this chapter, the basic alternator contained a revolving armature whose conductors cut the flux of a stationary magnetic field. The alternating voltage generated then was taken through sliprings to the load. The contacts between these sliprings and the carbon brushes were subject to friction wear and sparking; moreover, they were liable to arc over at high voltages. These problems are overcome in the revolving field alternator of FIG. 2-80.

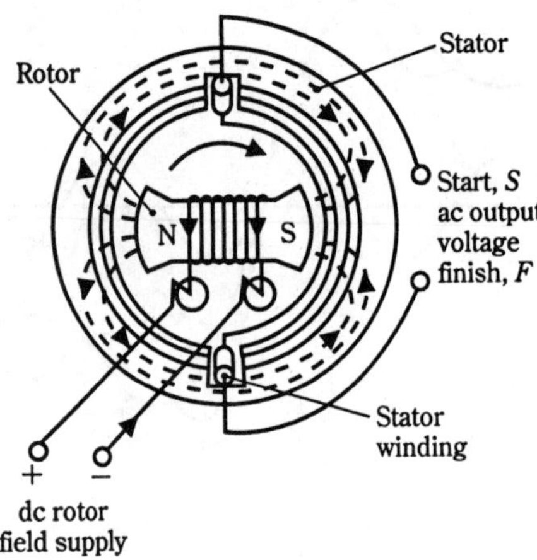

Fig. 2-80 The revolving field alternator.

In this type of generator, a dc source drives a direct current through sliprings, brushes, and the winding on a rotor that is driven around by mechanical means. This creates a rotating magnetic field that cuts the conductors embedded in the surrounding stator. An alternating voltage then appears between the ends (S and F) of a stator winding. Because S and F are fixed terminals, there are no sliding contacts, and all of the stator winding can be insulated continuously.

The alternator of FIG. 2-80 has two poles so that one complete rotation of the rotor generates one cycle of ac in the stator. Therefore, in order to generate 60 Hz, the rotor must turn at 60 revolutions per second: $60 \times 60 = 3600$ rpm. However, in the four-pole machine of FIG. 2-81, one revolution produces two cycles of ac voltage; therefore, it only requires a rotor speed of 1800 rpm to generate a 60-Hz output. It follows that:

$$\text{Generated frequency, } f = \frac{np}{60} \text{ hertz (HZ)} \qquad (2\text{-}137)$$

where: n = rotor speed in rpm
p = number of pairs of poles

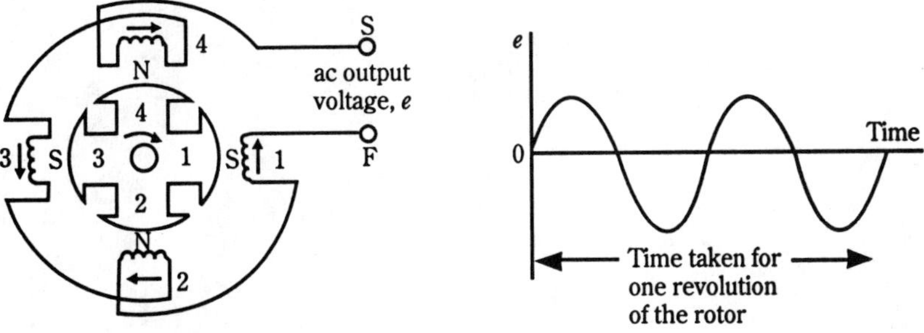

Fig. 2-81 The revolving field alternator with a 4-pole rotor.

The power delivered to a resistive load by a single-phase alternator is fluctuating at twice the line frequency. This presents a problem because the load on the mechanical source of energy, and the necessary torque, are not constant. Notice that the field current of the rotor can be increased to raise the output voltage without changing the value of the frequency.

* **Question 2-70** An alternator operates with a separately excited rotor. Without changing the frequency, the output voltage can be raised by increasing the:

A. rotor's speed
B. number of commutator segments
C. number of poles
D. number of brushes
E. rotor's field current

Answer Choice E.

3

Semiconductor diodes and power supplies

In this chapter you will learn:

- about the features of the silicon power diode and its use as a "one-way" device.
- to compare the properties of half-wave and full-wave power supplies.
- how the zener diode is used as a voltage-regulating device.
- how the varistor and the thermistor are able to provide voltage regulation.
- how the varactor diode is a device whose capacitance is voltage controlled.
- about the use of a tunnel diode in a low-power microwave oscillator.

3-1. The silicon diode

The modern power rectifier device is the *silicon diode,* which basically uses a pn junction to provide the "one-way" action. The p-type material is produced by doping pure silicon with an acceptor or a trivalent impurity such as indium, gallium, or boron. The n-type silicon is created by doping with a donor or pentavalent impurity of arsenic, antimony, or phosphorus. Although both n-type and p-type materials are electrically neutral, the majority charge carriers in the n-type and p-type semiconductors are, respectively, negative electrons and positive holes.

When the silicon pn junction is formed, there is a movement of the majority carriers across the junction. At room temperature, this creates an internal potential barrier of about 0.7 V across a depletion region, which is in the immediate vicinity of the junction and is devoid of majority charge carriers. In order to forward-bias the junction, it is necessary to connect the positive terminal of a voltage source to the p region and the negative terminal to the n region (FIG. 3-1A). However, the applied bias must exceed the 0.7-V internal potential before appreciable forward current will flow (FIG. 3-1B).

For a general-purpose silicon diode, with the p region as the anode and the n region as the cathode, a forward voltage, V_F, of about 1 V will correspond to a forward current, I_F, of several hundred mA. The small voltage drop across the conducting silicon diode is its real advantage,

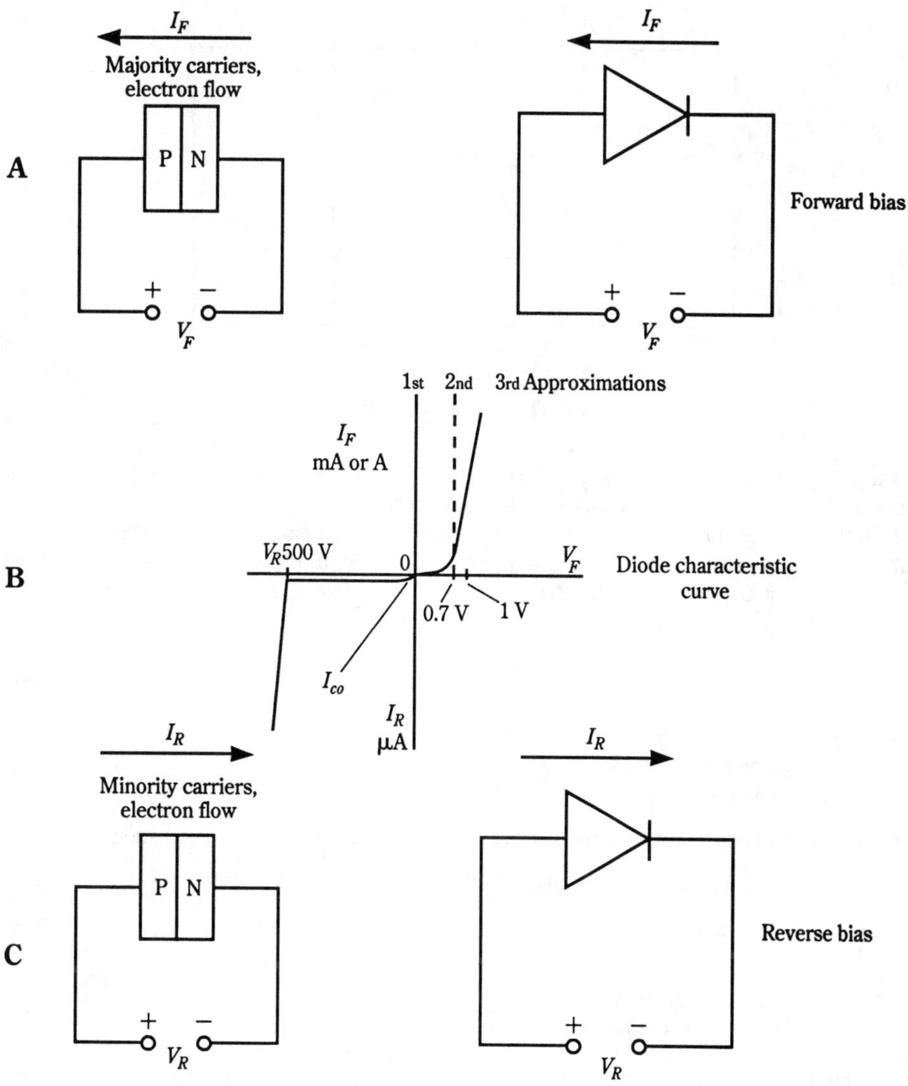

Fig. 3-1 The silicon diode.

when compared with other rectifier devices because even with high forward currents, the power dissipation will be low.

To create a reverse bias (FIG. 3-2), the positive terminal of a voltage source is connected to the n region (cathode) and the negative terminal to the p region (anode). If only the majority carriers were involved, there would be zero reverse current; however, thermal energy creates minority carriers (electrons in the p region and holes in the n region) so that there is a small reverse current, I_{co}, whose value rises rapidly and saturates at about 1 µA. However, the saturated value of I_{co} depends on the diode's temperature and will approximately double for every 10° Celsius rise. Typically, a reverse bias, V_R, of about 250 V to 500 V can be applied with only a small reverse current, I_R. However, with excessive reverse voltage there is a breakdown point at

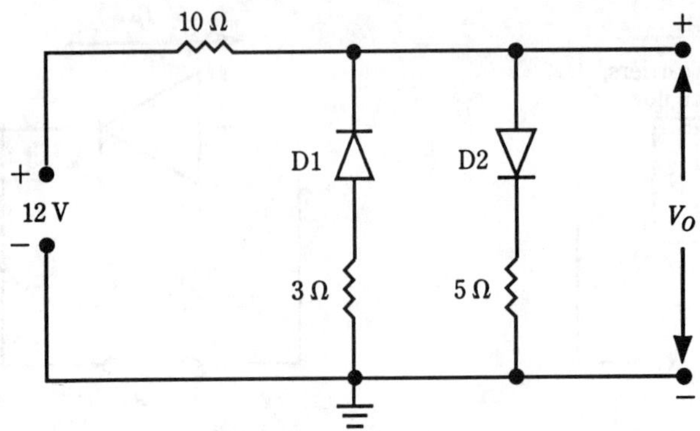

Fig. 3-2 The circuit for question 3-1.

which there is a rapidly increasing flow of reverse current; this action is the principle behind the zener diode, which is used for voltage-regulation purposes.

In the roughest or first approximation, the forward-biased diode is regarded as a short circuit. To a second approximation, take into account the 0.7-V drop across the diode. In the third approximation, you include the bulk resistance of the semiconductor material from which the diode is made. The equation for the third approximation is:

$$I_F = \frac{V_F - 0.7\text{ V}}{R_B} \text{ amperes (A)} \tag{3-1}$$

where: I_F = forward current (A)
V_F = forward voltage (V)
R_B = bulk resistance (Ω)

In the FCC examinations, you are normally required to use the second approximation.

$$\text{Power dissipated in the diode, } P_D = V_F \times I_F \text{ watts (W)} \tag{3-2}$$

When the diode is reverse-biased:

$$\textit{Reverse resistance} = \frac{V_R}{I_R} \text{ ohms (Ω)} \tag{3-3}$$

where: V_R = reverse voltage (V)
I_R = reverse current (A)

* **Question 3-1** In the circuit of FIG. 3-1, determine the value of the output voltage, V_o:
A. 4.5 V B. 3.8 V C. 3.1 V D. 5 V E. 3.5 V

Answer Choice A. The diode D1 is reverse-biased and therefore does not conduct (to a first approximation). Using the second approximation, the voltage drop across the diode D2 is 0.7 V and the remaining 12 − 0.7 = 11.3 V is divided between the 10-Ω and 5-Ω resistors. Using the voltage-division rule, the *IR* drop across the 5-Ω resistor is: 11.3 V × 5 Ω/(5 Ω + 10 Ω) = 3.8 V and the output voltage is: V_o = 3.8 + 0.7 = 4.5 V.

* **Question 3-2** In the circuit of FIG. 3-3, the value of the voltage drop across the resistor R3 is:
A. 4.3 V B. 5.7 V C. 0.4 V D. 0.7 V E. 5 V

Answer Choice E. The diode is reverse-biased and therefore behaves as an open circuit (to a first approximation). By the voltage division rule, the *IR* drop across the resistor R3 is:

$$V_{R3} = 10\text{ V} \times \frac{300\ \Omega}{100\ \Omega + 200\ \Omega + 300\ \Omega}$$
$$= 5\text{ V}$$

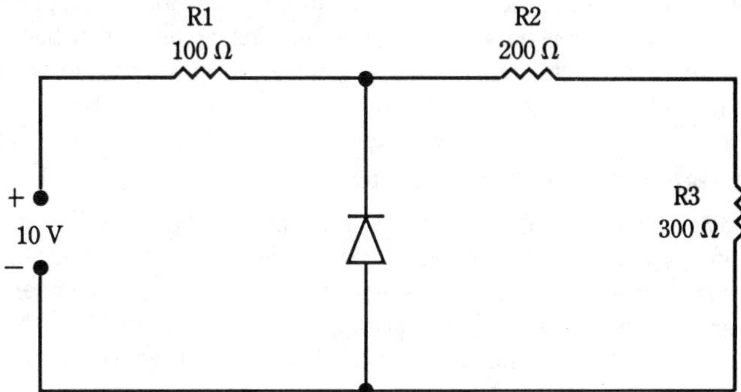

Fig. 3-3 The circuit for question 3-2.

* **Question 3-3** In the circuit of FIG. 3-4, calculate the value of the voltage drop across resistor R1:

A. 6.7 V B. 0.7 V C. 10 V D. 9.3 V E. 0 V

Answer Choice D. Diode D2 is reverse-biased and does not conduct (to a first approximation). Diode D1 is forward-biased and has a voltage drop of 0.7 V. Therefore, the voltage drop across R1 is 10 − 0.7 = 9.3 V.

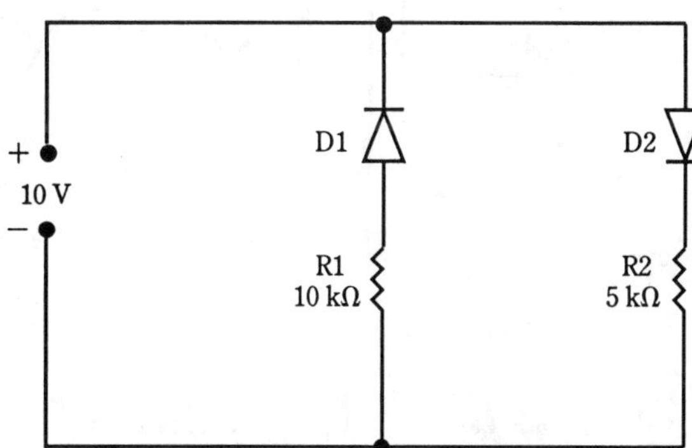

Fig. 3-4 The circuit for question 3-3.

3-2. Half-wave rectifier circuits

The circuits of communications systems, such as transmitters and receivers, normally need dc voltages for their operations. With mobile systems, these voltages can be derived from batteries or motor generators. For stationary communications equipment, it is customary to obtain the required power from the standard 60-Hz supply. It is therefore necessary to convert the ac

110-V RMS line voltage to the required steady dc level. This function is fulfilled by a power-supply unit that contains a power transformer to step the 60-Hz voltage up or down to the necessary level. The secondary voltage is then applied to a rectifier circuit, which converts the ac sine wave into a fluctuating dc output. Before such an output is normally of any use, it must be applied to a low-pass filter so that the result is a steady dc level with an acceptable ripple superimposed. Finally, the unit can contain some form of regulation circuit so that the dc level is stabilized against variations in the load current drawn from the power supply and against fluctuations in the ac line voltage.

Single-phase half-wave rectifier circuit

The basic half-wave rectifier circuit is illustrated in FIG. 3-5. The secondary ac voltage of the power transformer is applied across the series combination of the diode and the load, R_L; normally, R_L is not just a resistor, but it represents the combination of a number of circuits (for example, amplifiers) to which the dc output is supplied. The value of R_L is then the result of dividing the output voltage by the total dc load current drawn from the power supply.

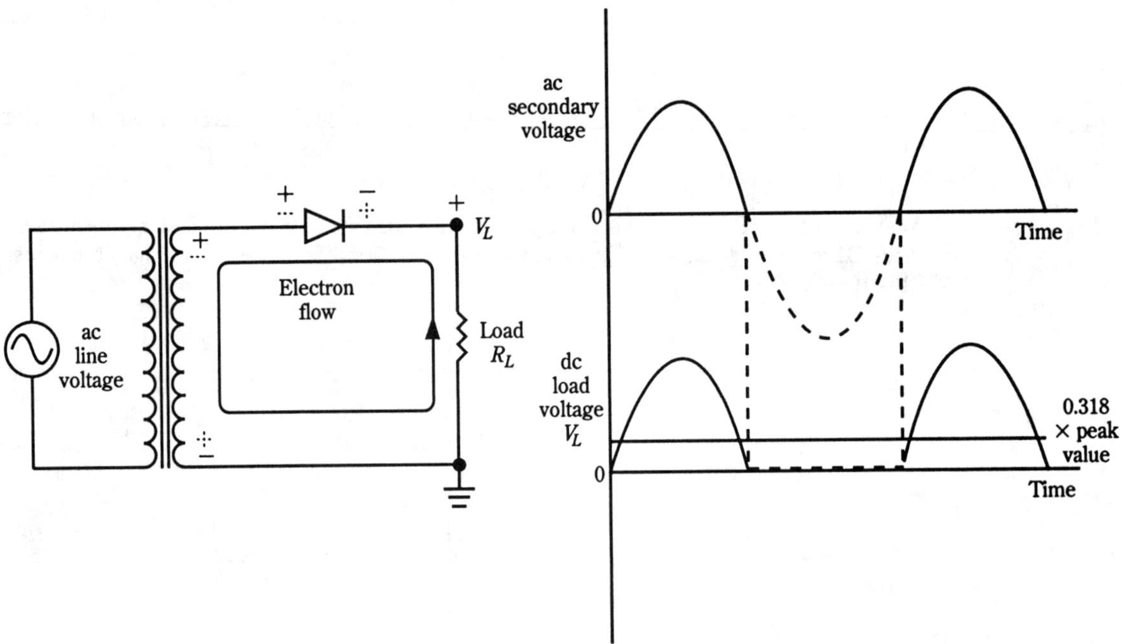

Fig. 3-5 The half-wave rectifier circuit.

During the secondary voltage's "positive" half cycle, which is shown as a solid line, it is assumed that the top of the secondary voltage is positive, with respect to ground. The silicon diode is forward-biased so that an electron flow (of the order of mA or A) will occur and a voltage will be developed across the load. If the small voltage drops across the diode and the resistance of the secondary winding are ignored, the half cycle of the voltage across R_L will be a replica of the secondary half cycle.

During the other "negative" half cycle, which is indicated by the broken line, the top of the secondary winding is negative, with respect to ground, the diode is reverse-biased, and only a small current (of the order of μA) will flow. If this current is ignored, the voltage across R_L is zero. The negative half cycle then appears across the diode and you must take care not to exceed its reverse-voltage rating.

The load voltage across R_L can be described as a fluctuating positive dc output, which is composed of half cycle "pulses" with an average value of $0.318 \times$ the peak value. In order to obtain a negative output, with respect to ground, the diode connections must be reversed.

A battery composed of secondary cells can be charged from a fluctuating dc voltage, but such an output cannot be used to operate communications stages, such as amplifiers, oscillators, and mixers. These stages require a dc level that must fluctuate as little as possible. To achieve this objective, the fluctuating output from the rectifying device is passed to a low-pass filter, whose output is subsequently applied across the load. For this purpose, the most commonly used filters are:

- The *capacitor input filter,* which is normally used in situations where either the load current is small or is virtually constant as in a communications receiver.
- The *choke input filter,* which appears in power supplies designed to accommodate wide variations in a heavy load current; such might be the case in communications transmitters. However, the choke input filter can only be used with full-wave rectifier circuits.

Figure 3-6 shows a half-wave rectifier circuit that has been modified to include the input capacitor, C, of a low-pass filter. When the diode conducts during part of the "positive" half cycle, its current charges the capacitor towards the peak value of the secondary voltage. The charging path of the capacitor travels through the secondary of the transformer and the conducting diode. The resistance of this path is small so that the corresponding time constant is low and the capacitor charges rapidly. When the secondary voltage falls below the potential difference, V_C, to which the capacitor has been charged (point X), the diode ceases to conduct and the capacitor discharges through the load, R_L. However, the value of C is chosen so that the time constant of the capacitor's discharge is high compared with the period of the ac line voltage. For example, if $C = 40$ μF and $R_L = 5$ kΩ, their time constant is $CR_L = 5 \times 10^3 \times 40 \times 10^{-6}$s $= 0.2$ s, which is 12 times greater than the period of a 60-Hz supply. The operation of the circuit depends on the short time constant for the charging of the capacitor and the high time constant for its discharge.

As a result of the time constant that is provided C and R_L, the capacitor only discharges slowly and its voltage loss is small over the interval from point X to point Y. At point Y, the secondary voltage again rises above the potential difference across the capacitor; the diode once more conducts and rapidly recharges the capacitor.

As illustrated, the charging current consists of short-duration pulses, but the pulse's peak current and its average level over the complete cycle must not exceed the diode's rated values. Notice that in FIG. 3-6, the voltage drop across the silicon diode has been ignored so that the waveform of V_C follows the secondary voltage during the charging interval from point Y to point X. The V_C waveform therefore contains a steady level, which is close to the peak value of the secondary voltage. For example, if the secondary voltage is 30 V RMS with a peak value of $30 \times 1.414 = 42.42$ V, the output dc voltage under load conditions might be 38 V.

Either side of the dc level is a fluctuation, which is referred to as the *ripple.* The waveform of the ripple is complex, but the rate at which it repeats is the same as the frequency of the ac secondary voltage. Consequently, if the line frequency is 60 Hz, the ripple's fundamental frequency component will also be 60 Hz. The amount of the ripple is measured by:

$$\textit{Percentage ripple} = \frac{\textit{rms value of the ripple's fundamental component}}{\textit{dc output voltage}} \times 100\%$$

The lower the level of the percentage ripple, the better is the filtering action of the capacitor. It would appear that you could indefinitely lower the ripple by raising the value of the capacitor.

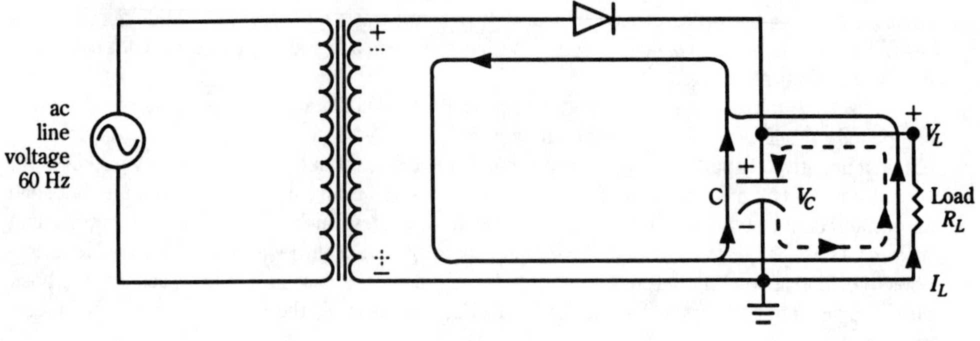

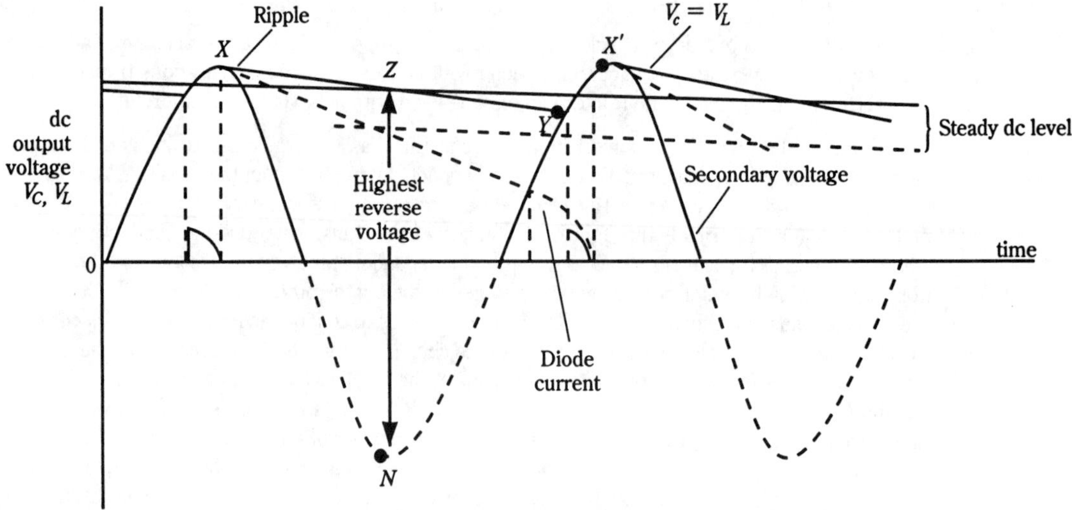

Fig. 3-6 The capacitor input filter.

However, not only might this increase the cost and physical size of the capacitor, it would require a larger diode current during the recharging interval. This illustrates one of the "trade-offs" that must be considered in the operation of a power supply.

In the V_C waveform of FIG. 3-6, point Z is of particular interest. At this instant, the diode is not conducting, but the secondary's "negative" peak combines with the value of V_C to produce the highest reverse voltage across the diode. The amount of this reverse voltage (represented by the line ZN) is approximately equal to twice the peak value of the secondary voltage and must not exceed the diode's rating.

If the secondary voltage is 1000 V RMS, the maximum reverse voltage under open-circuit conditions is $2 \times 1000 \times 1.414 = 2828$ V. Instead of using a special simple diode with a reverse voltage rating of more than 3000 V, it is possible to connect diodes of the same type in series (FIG. 3-7). The voltage of 2828 V would then be divided between the reverse resistances of the three diodes. However, even for the same type of diode, the values of these reverse resistances can vary widely. The resistors, R, have the same high values and are inserted to ensure that the maximum reverse voltage is equally distributed between the diodes. The capacitors, C, provide a bypass path for voltage surges, which otherwise might cause excessive forward currents to flow in the diodes. As well as the series arrangement, diodes can also be connected in parallel so that each diode can carry a share of the total forward current; this will enable the total diode dissipation to be divided among the individual diodes.

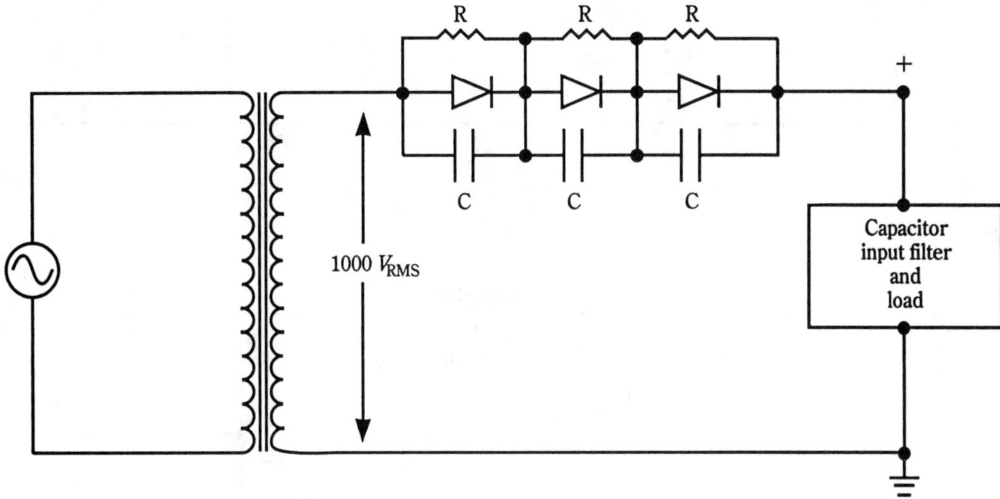

Fig. 3-7 Diodes in series.

In most cases, the filtering action provided by a single capacitor is inadequate and a pi (π) section (FIG. 3-8A) is then used to lower the ripple percentage. The section is completed by the filter choke, L_1, and the filter capacitor, C_1. The input capacitor voltage, V_C, which consists of the mean dc level and the ac ripple, is applied across the series-parallel combination of $L_1C_1R_L$ with the output developed across C_1 and R_L in parallel (FIG. 3-8B). Assume that the dc level of V_C is 100 V and the peak-to-peak value of the ripple is 10 V so that V_C fluctuates between 95 and 105 V. For a 60-Hz line voltage, the iron-cored filter choke typically has an inductance value near 10 H, and its dc resistance is 50 Ω. Because the capacitors are operating in a dc circuit with no reversal of polarity, it is customary to use the electrolytic type with values from 20 to 40 μF and with leakage resistances of several MΩ.

As far as the 100-Vdc level is concerned, it will be divided between the 50-Ω resistance of L_1 and the parallel combination of C_1's leakage resistance and the resistance, R_L, of the load. Because $R_L = 5\ \text{k}\Omega$, the leakage resistance of C_1 can be ignored and the output dc voltage by the VDR (voltage division rule) is: $\dfrac{100\ \text{V} \times 50\ \Omega}{5\ \text{k}\Omega + 50\ \Omega} = 99\ \text{V}$. Consequently, there is only 1 Vdc voltage drop across the filter choke and the potential at D, with respect to ground, is greater than the potential at E by that amount. The final dc output voltage can be connected across a voltage divider network in order to supply a number of different voltages to various loads.

The ripple has a fundamental 60-Hz component; at this frequency, a 10-H filter choke would have an inductive reactance of $X_{L1} = 2 \times \pi \times 60\ \text{Hz} \times 10\ \text{H} = 3770\ \Omega$. If $C_1 = 20\ \mu\text{F}$, its capacitance reactance, X_{C1}:

$$\frac{1}{2 \times \pi \times 60\ \text{Hz} \times 20 \times 10^{-6}\ \text{F}} = 130\ \Omega$$

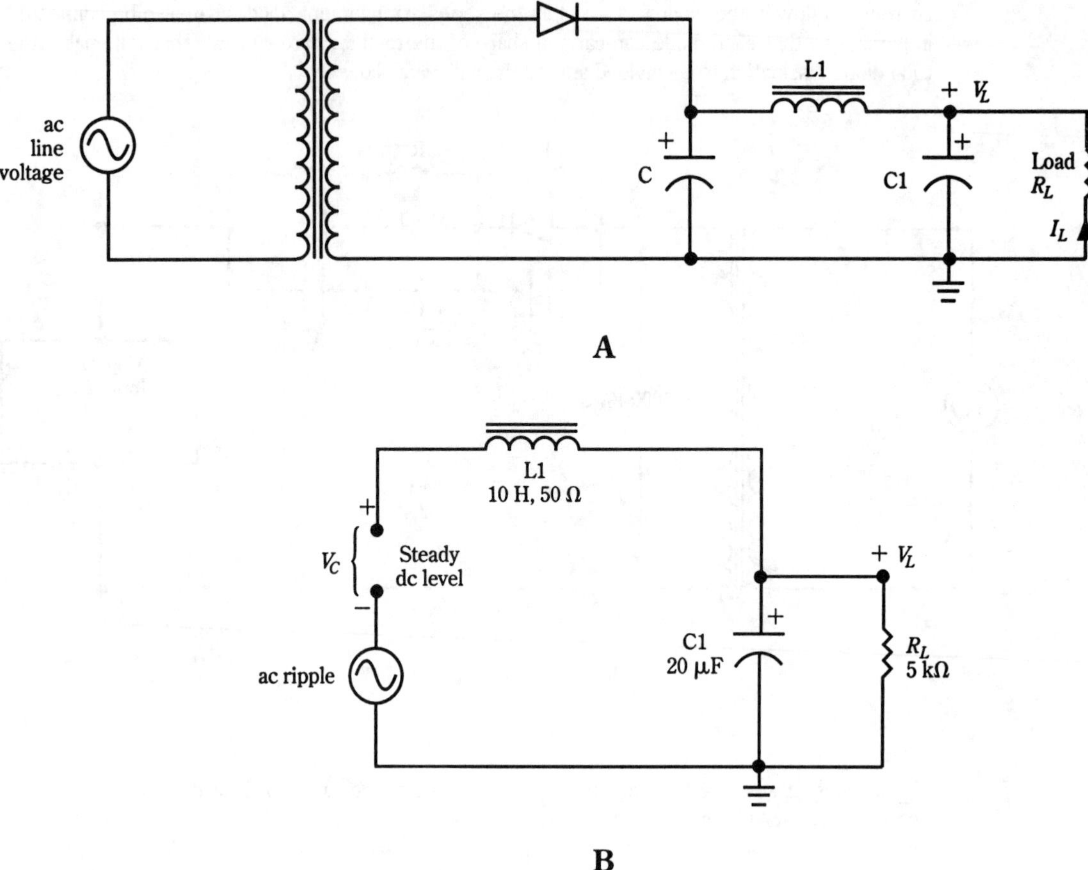

Fig. 3-8 The capacitor-input low-pass filter.

this is much smaller than the value of the parallel resistance, R_L, whose effect can therefore be ignored as far as the ripple is concerned. The peak-to-peak ripple voltage appearing in the output is:

$$\frac{10\text{ V} \times 130\ \Omega}{3770\ \Omega - 130\ \Omega} = 0.36\text{ V}$$

so that the ripple has been reduced by a factor of 28. This result is an approximation because the ripple waveform contains harmonics, which the low-pass filter attenuates even more than the fundamental frequency.

By doubling the values of L_1 and C_1 the ripple would be lowered by a factor of four; however, it would be more effective and economical to repeat the filter (FIG. 3-9), which would reduce the ripple by a further factor of 28 without any appreciable fall in the dc output voltage.

A cheaper and smaller alternative to the filter choke is a resistor whose value is comparable with the choke's reactance. However, there could be a considerable dc voltage drop across the filter resistor; such a resistor is normally confined to those cases where the load current is small.

The next point to discuss is the degree of regulation that is provided by a half-wave power

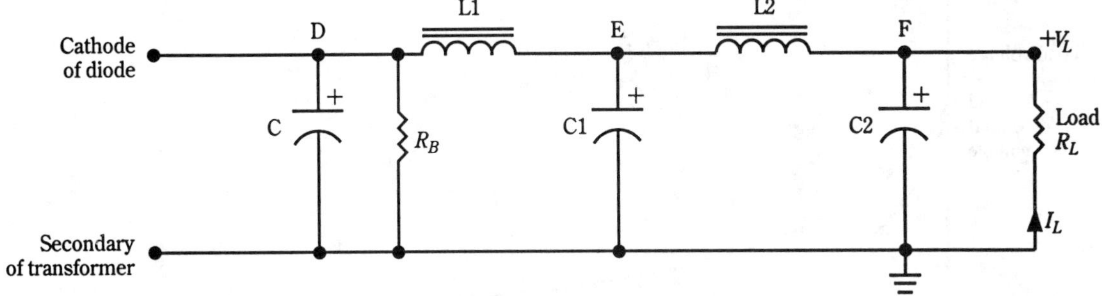

Fig. 3-9 The two-section low-pass filter.

supply with a capacitor input filter. In FIG. 3-6, assume that there is an increase in load current at the instant represented by point X. This increase in load current is accompanied by a decrease in the load resistance, R_L, so that the value of the time constant, R_LC, is lowered and the capacitor discharges more rapidly. The result is threefold:

1. There is an increase in the ripple percentage, but this can probably be reduced to an acceptable level by the low-pass filter.
2. The pulse of the diode current has a greater peak value and a longer duration.
3. The dc output voltage falls appreciably as the load current is increased. Consequently, the percentage of voltage regulation is high.

$$\text{Percentage voltage regulation} = \frac{E_{NL} - E_{FL}}{E_{FL}} \times 100\%$$

where: E_{NL} = dc output voltage under no-load or minimum-load conditions (V)
E_{FL} = dc output voltage under full-load conditions (V)

Ideal regulation corresponds to a zero percentage. The graph of the output voltage versus the load current would then be a horizontal line.

The third statement indicates that the regulation of a capacitor input filter is poor as a result of the action of the filter itself. In addition, the regulation will be worsened by the additional dc voltage drops across filter chokes L_1 and L_2. Therefore (FIG. 3-9), the highest positive voltage (with respect to ground) occurs at point D, the intermediate value exists at the point E, and the lowest value would be measured across R_L (point F). The difference between the voltages (with respect to ground) at points D and E, is the voltage drop across L_1, and the voltage drop across L_2 accounts for the difference between the voltages at points E and F. A typical regulation curve for a half-wave rectifier with a capacitor input filter is shown in FIG. 3-10.

Finally, a point of safety! When the ac power is shut off and the load is removed from the rectifier circuit, capacitors C, C_1, and C_2 can remain charged for an appreciable time. To avoid possible shock, it is customary to include a bleeder resistor, R_B, which will rapidly discharge the capacitors when the load is removed. Such a resistor has a high value so that it has no appreciable shunting effect on the load. In fact, if the bleeder resistor burns out, there will be no noticeable change in the dc output voltage.

* **Question 3-4** In a power supply, the bleeder resistor burns out. What effect does this have on the circuit during normal operation?

A. there is a considerable increase in the amount of ripple in the output voltage
B. the percentage regulation increases significantly

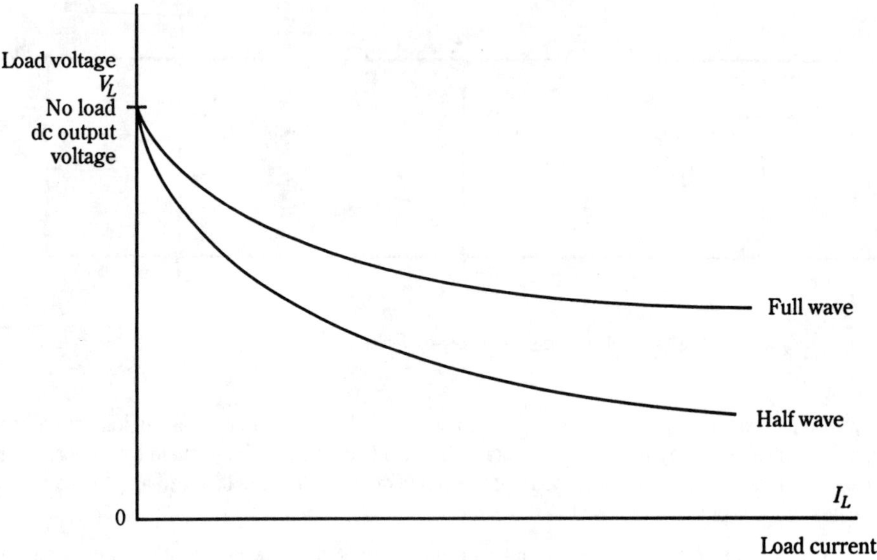

Fig. 3-10 The regulation curve of a half-wave rectifier with a capacitor input filter.

C. the diodes might be destroyed
D. the power transformer will be damaged unless it is protected by a fuse
E. there is no appreciable effect on the output dc voltage

Answer Choice E.

* **Question 3-5** Under no-load conditions, a half-wave rectifier circuit with a capacitor input filter has a dc output voltage of 9 V. What is the effective value of the ac voltage input to the rectifier circuit?

A. 9 V B. 12.7 V C. 6.4 V D. 7.3 V E. 5.8 V

Answer Choice C. The input capacitor charges towards the peak voltage of the ac input. Therefore, the effective value is $0.707 \times 9 = 6.4$ V, rounded off.

* **Question 3-6** In the circuit of FIG. 3-7, the function of the three resistors, R, is to:

A. ensure that there is the same forward voltage across each diode
B. reduce the amount of ripple across each diode
C. protect the diodes from the effects of voltage surges
D. ensure that the same reverse voltage is across each diode
E. choices A and C are true

Answer Choice D.

3-3. Full-wave rectifier circuits

Single-phase full-wave rectifier circuit

By contrast to the half-wave rectifier, the basic full-wave circuit (FIG. 3-11) uses two diodes and the secondary winding of the power transformer carries a center tap, which is usually grounded. During the solid line or "positive" half cycle of the secondary voltage, the "top" of the secondary

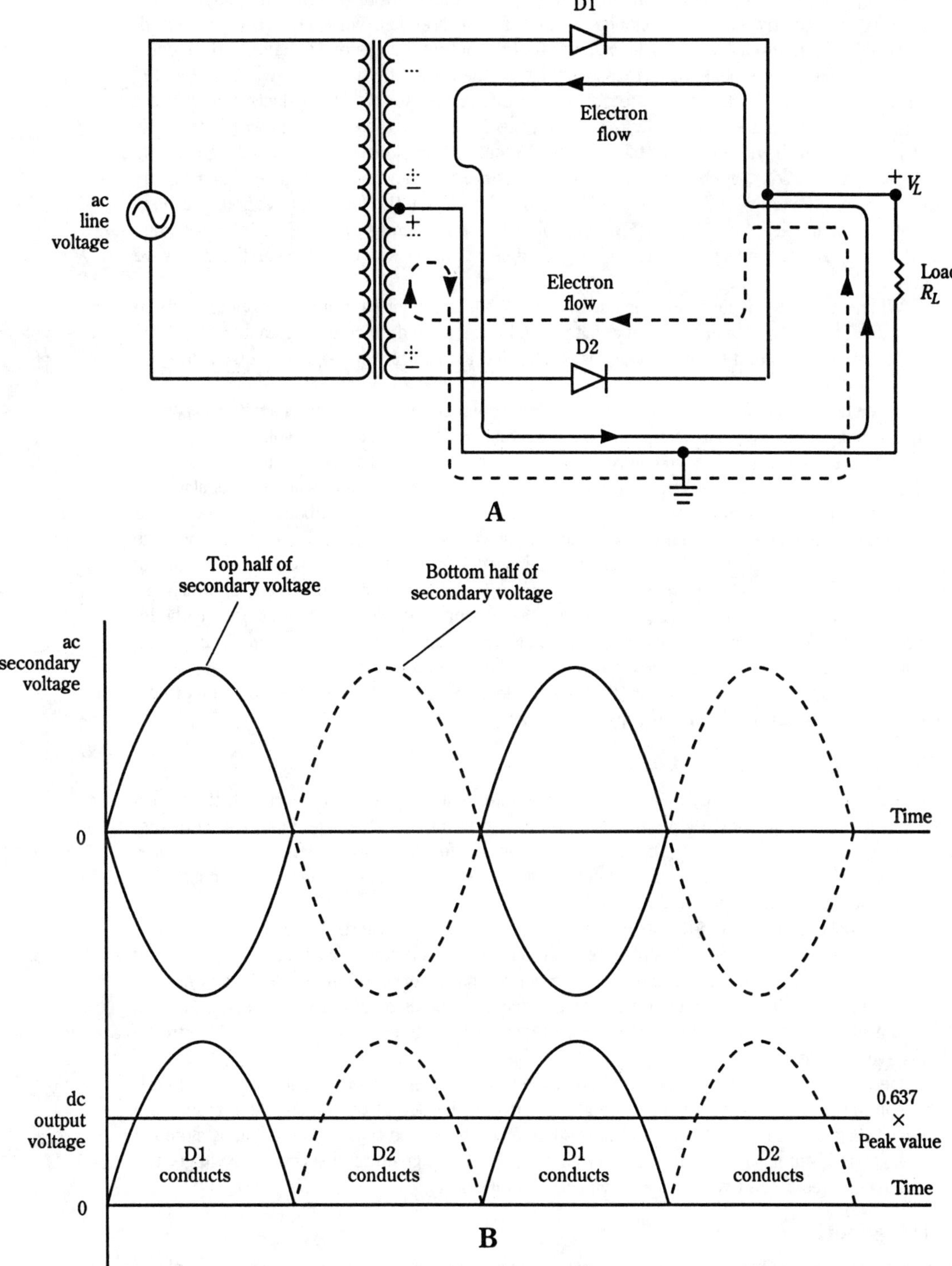

Fig. 3-11 A basic full-wave rectifier circuit.

is positive, with respect to the grounded center tap, and the "bottom" carries an equal negative voltage. Consequently, diode D_1 conducts in the forward direction, while D_2 is reverse-biased. The direction of the "solid" electron flow shows that the output is a positive voltage, with an equal value to one half of the peak value measured across the complete secondary winding. For the "negative" half cycle (broken line), the polarities are reversed so that D_2 conducts and D_1 is cut off (ignoring any reverse current flow). However, the direction of the electron flow through R_L is unchanged so that the dc voltage is still positive. The output waveform is fluctuating dc, consisting of positive alternations, each of which is one half of the total secondary voltage. Ignoring any reverse flow, the voltage drops across D_1D_2 when conducting in the forward direction, the average of the voltage across R_L is 63.7% of its peak value; this is equal to 31.8% of the peak value for the complete secondary winding and is the same result as was obtained for the half-wave rectifier.

When a capacitor input filter is included (FIG. 3-12), the input capacitor charges toward the peak value of ½ × the total secondary voltage and is recharged twice during each cycle of the line voltage. Therefore, if the line voltage is 60 Hz, the rate at which the ripple voltage repeats is 120 Hz.

When one of the diodes is reverse-biased under open-circuit load conditions with a capacitor input filter, its reverse voltage is equal to the peak value of the full secondary voltage.

With the same secondary voltage, the discharge time of the full-wave circuit is shorter than in the half-wave circuit; consequently, the full-wave ripple percentage is less and the regulation in the full-wave circuit is superior to that of the half-wave rectifier. However, because of the center tap required, you can only obtain the same dc output voltage by doubling the secondary voltage in the full-wave arrangement. This might cause insulation problems if we require an output of several kV. The half-wave arrangement is therefore preferred for high dc voltages, which are associated with a light load current (for example, the horizontal accelerating voltage for a cathode-ray tube). One other point of comparison—the half-wave rectifier can be operated directly from the ac line voltage, and the full-wave arrangement requires a power transformer.

As a summary, the capacitor input filter provides a high dc output voltage and a low ripple percentage; however, its degree of voltage regulation is poor.

The choke input filter

We have already learned that with a capacitor input filter in a full-wave rectifier circuit, the diodes conduct alternately in short-duration pulses, but for most of the cycle, the input capacitor discharges slowly through the load. This action is responsible for the poor regulation of the capacitor input filter, which is therefore used in power supplies where either the load current is constant or the current varies, but always has a low value.

The choke input filter (FIG. 3-13) is used in power supplies where the load current is high and varies over a wide range; an amplifier operated under class B conditions is an example of such a load. The action of the choke input filter requires that a forward current is always flowing through one diode. Thus, in the full-wave rectifier circuit, one diode starts to conduct as soon as the other diode is cut off. It also follows that the choke input-filter action cannot occur with the half-wave arrangement.

Because the conducting diode can be regarded as equivalent to a low resistance, large variations in the load resistance will produce little change in the output dc voltage. As a result, the voltage regulation of the choke-input filter is superior to that of the capacitor-input filter, although the choke-input filter has a higher percentage of ripple. For a given total secondary voltage, the regulation curves of the two filters are compared in FIG. 3-14.

Bridge rectifier circuit

The conventional full-wave arrangement described in the previous section, is really a two-phase half-wave circuit in which each diode rectifies one half of the secondary voltage and these two ac

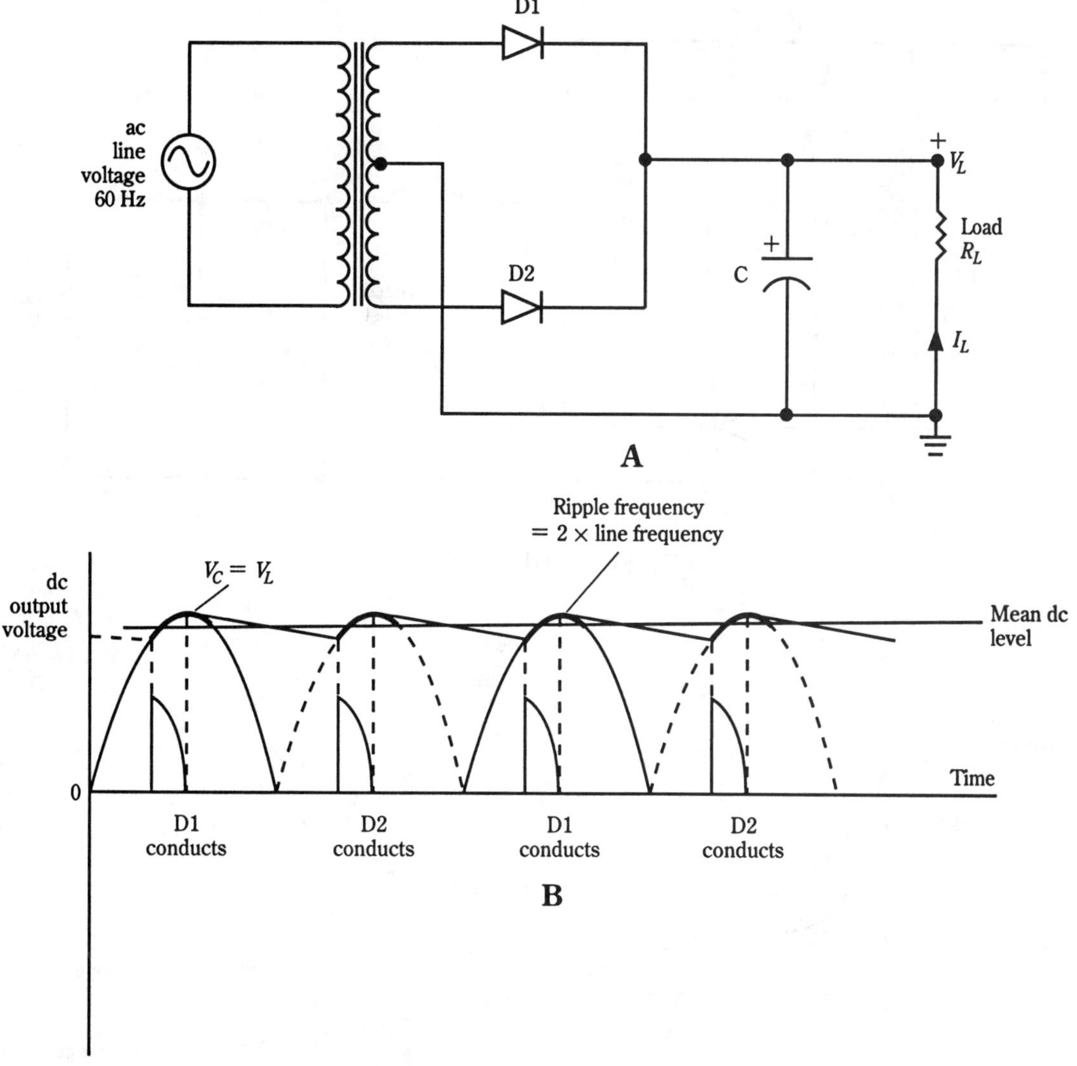

Fig. 3-12 A full-wave rectifier with a capacitor-input filter.

voltages are 180° out of phase. The "true" full-wave rectifier is the bridge circuit, which is illustrated in FIGS. 3-15A,B,C; here, the same circuit has been drawn in two different ways. Notice that in the bridge arrangement, the opposite pairs of diodes are connected in the same direction. The two diodes joined to the "top" of the secondary winding are connected in opposite directions and the same applies to the two diodes attached to the "bottom" of the secondary winding.

During the "solid" line half cycle, the "top" of the secondary winding is assumed to be positive, with respect to the bottom. Diodes D1 and D2 conduct, while diodes D3 and D4 are reverse-biased. The direction of the electron flow, as indicated, results in a positive output voltage across the load, R_L. For the other ("broken" line) half cycle, the conditions are reversed; diodes D2 and D4 conduct, but diodes D1 and D3 are now reverse-biased. However, the electron flow that is associated with R_L remains unchanged so that the polarity of the dc output voltage is still positive. The result is similar to the full-wave rectifier circuit that was described earlier, but in the bridge

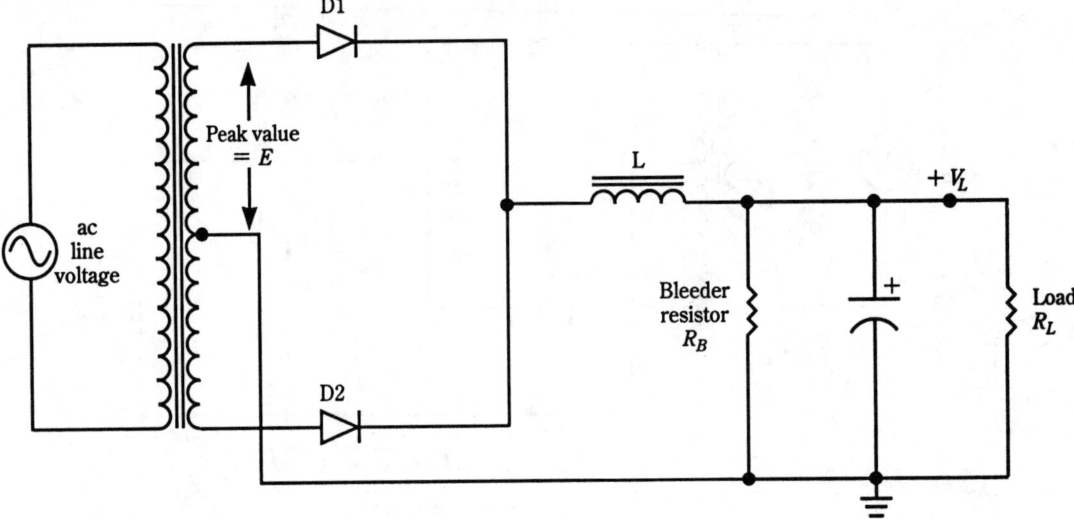

Fig. 3-13 The choke-input filter.

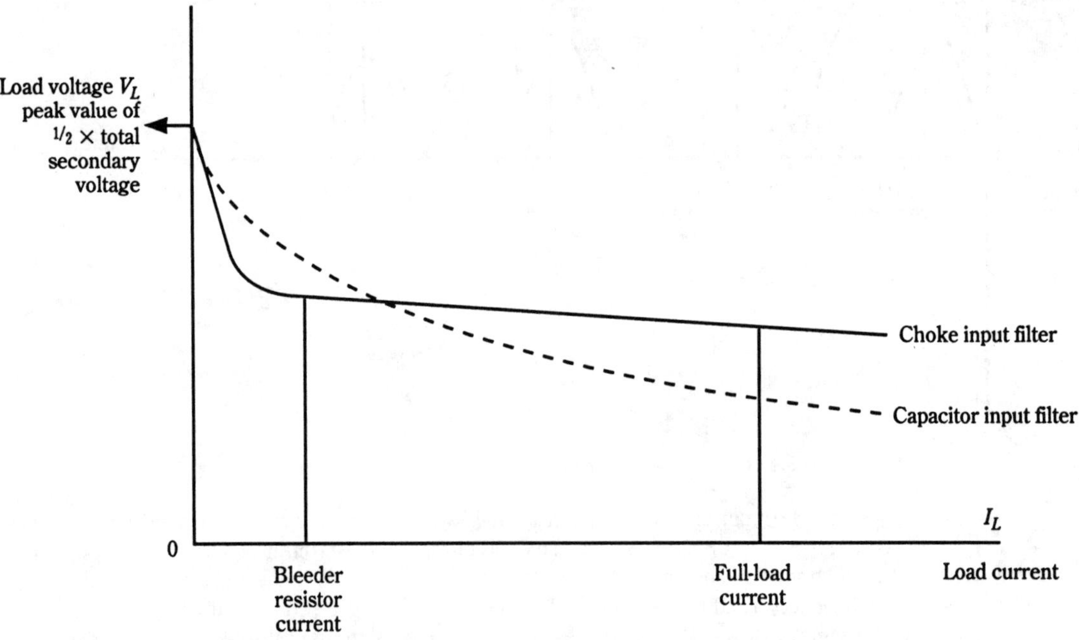

Fig. 3-14 The regulation curves of the choke input filter and the capacitor input filter.

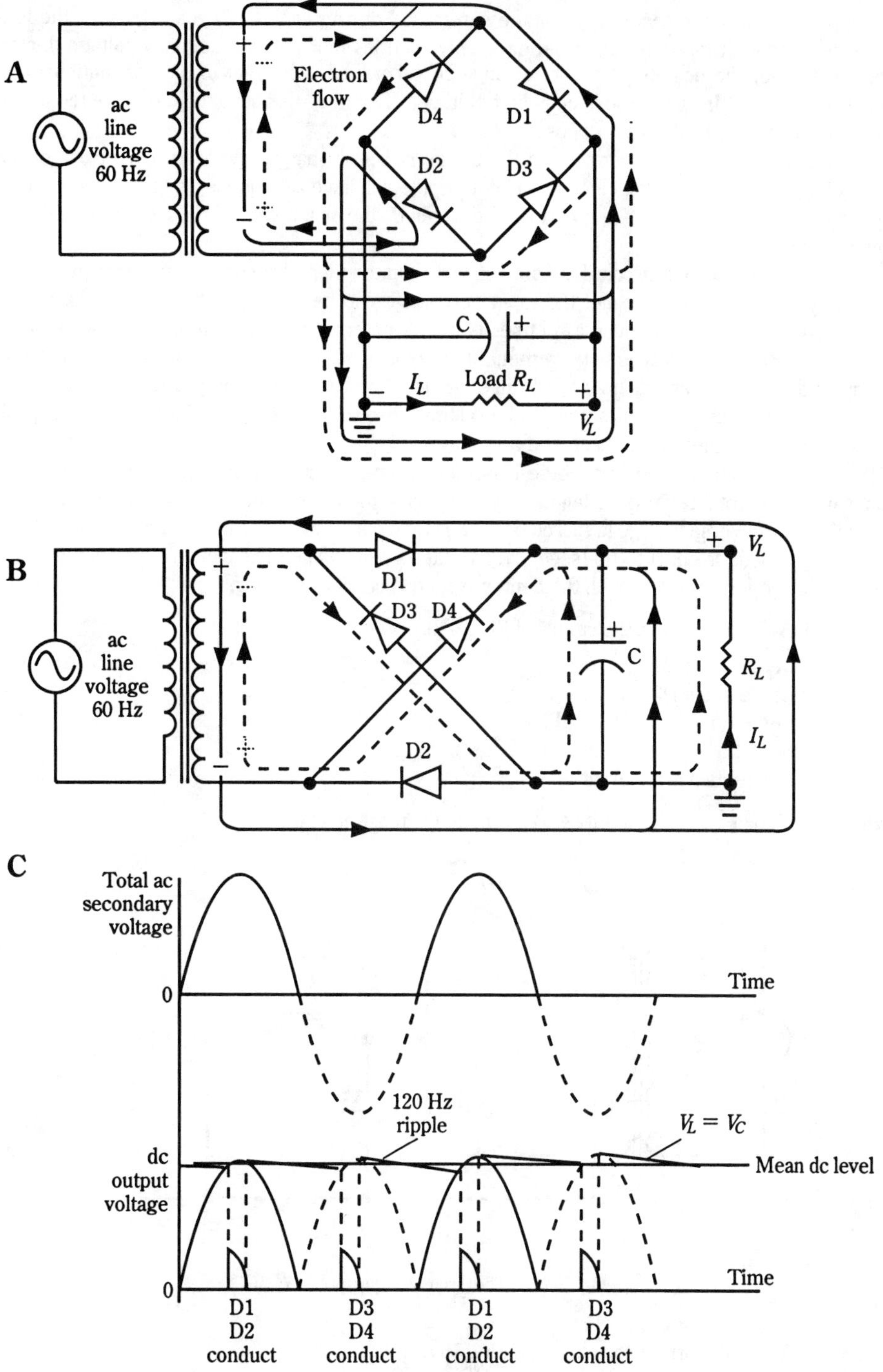

Fig. 3-15 The bridge rectifier.

arrangement, all of the secondary voltage is rectified during each half cycle. Because the full-wave rectifier with its center-tap secondary only rectifies half of the secondary voltage during each half cycle, the dc output from the bridge circuit will be twice that of the conventional full-wave rectifier for the same total secondary voltage; of course, this advantage is achieved at the expense of using four diodes as opposed to two.

Because the input capacitor, C, of the bridge circuit is charged twice for each cycle of the line voltage, the fundamental component of its ripple will have a frequency that is a second harmonic of the line frequency. As previously described, the ripple can be reduced by including a low-pass filter.

The bridge-rectifier circuit does not require a center-tapped secondary winding; therefore, no transformer is necessary and the input ac voltage can be directly connected to the bridge rectifier. One major use of such a rectifier is in voltmeters, which contain a moving-coil meter movement. Because this type of movement only responds directly to dc, an ac voltage must first be applied to a rectifier, such as the bridge circuit. The rectified dc output then activates the meter movement and the voltmeter can be calibrated so that the scale reads the effective, peak or peak-to-peak values of the measured ac voltage.

When one pair of diodes is reverse-biased under open-circuit load conditions with a capacitor input filter, the total reverse voltage is equal to twice the peak value of the secondary voltage. However, the reverse voltage is shared between two diodes so that the maximum reverse voltage across each diode is equal to the secondary voltage's peak value. The same result was obtained for the conventional rectifier with the center-tapped secondary winding.

* **Question 3-7** To correct the circuit of FIG. 3-16:

A. reverse diode D1
B. reverse diode D2
C. reverse both diodes D1 and D2
D. change the polarity of the output dc voltage
E. no correction is necessary

Answer Choice A. Refer to FIG. 3-12A. Diode D1 must be reversed.

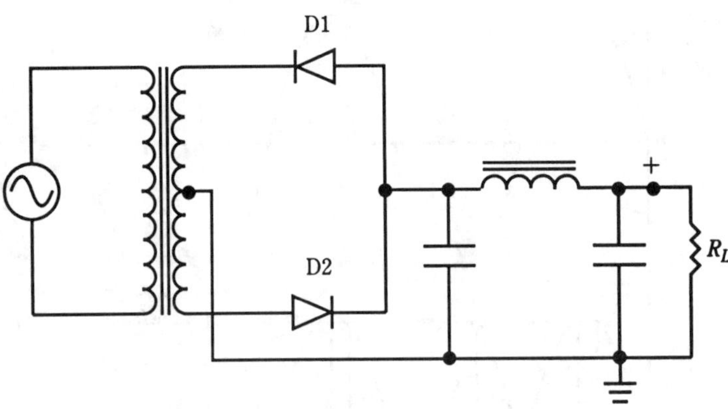

Fig. 3-16 The circuit for question 3-7.

* **Question 3-8** To correct the circuit of FIG. 3-17:

A. reverse diode D4
B. reverse diode D2

C. reverse both diodes D2 and D4
D. reverse both diodes D1 and D3
E. reverse diode D1

Answer Choice C. Refer to FIG. 3-15A. Reverse both diodes D2 and D4.

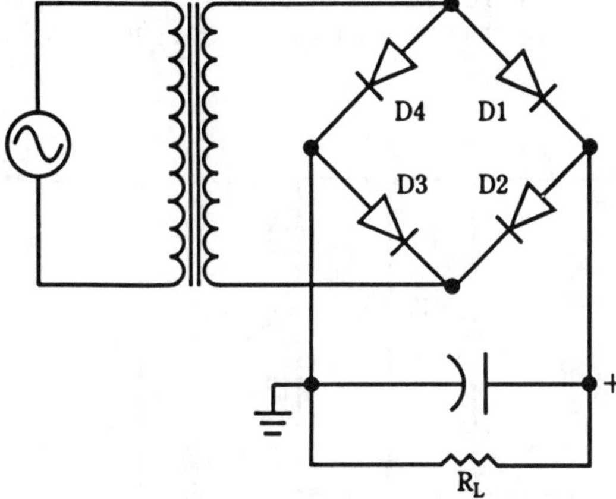

Fig. 3-17 The circuit for question 3-8.

* **Question 3-9** When compared to the full-wave rectifier circuit that contains two diodes, the bridge arrangement:

A. provides a lower dc output voltage
B. uses a minimum of three diodes
C. does not require a power transformer for its operation
D. does not require a center tap on the secondary winding of the power transformer
E. choices C and D are true

Answer Choice E.

3-4. The zener diode

A silicon *zener diode* is heavily doped so that the width of its depletion region is reduced. At a certain level of reverse voltage, the electric field intensity across the depletion region is sufficiently strong to eject some valence electrons from their outer orbits; this is the so-called "zener effect." If the reverse voltage is further increased, some of these liberated electrons are accelerated to high velocities and then collide with other valence electrons, which are similarly ejected. This results in an avalanche effect, which causes the reverse breakdown voltage to remain practically constant as the diode current increases. The breakdown graph of I_R versus V_R is nearly vertical so that the zener diode approximates to a constant voltage device. By controlling the amount of doping, the available manufactured range of the breakdown voltage extends from 2 to 200 V. This diode can be used to provide voltage regulation or to establish a voltage reference level.

The basic zener-diode voltage-regulator circuit is shown in FIG. 3-18A. Its purpose is to stabilize the value of the load voltage, V_L, against changes in the source voltage, E, and/or changes in the load current, I_L. The diode operates with reverse bias in the breakdown region (FIG. 3-18B) where to a first approximation, the diode's reverse current, I_Z, is independent of the diode voltage, V_Z, which is equal to the load voltage, V_L. The resistance, R allows the diode to operate well within the breakdown region. At the same time, it regulates the load voltage by dropping the difference between V_Z and the unregulated dc source voltage, E. For example, if there is a substantial increase in the value of E, V_Z only rises slightly to produce a large increase in I_Z. The greater voltage drop across resistor R then absorbs most of the increase in the unregulated voltage. Similarly, if the load current exceeds its normal value, V_Z falls slightly so that the decrease in I_Z largely compensates for the increase in the load current.

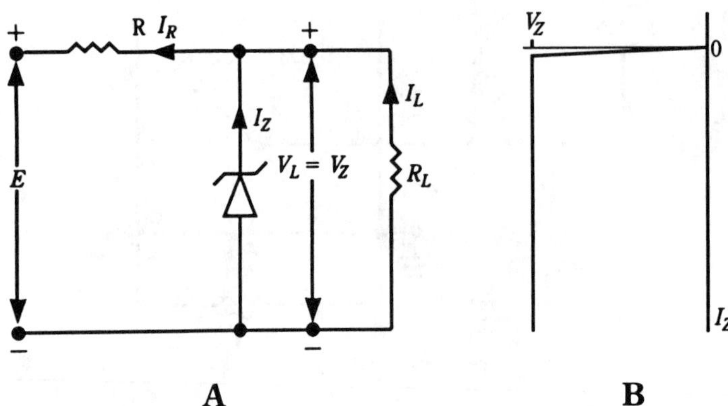

Fig. 3-18 The Zener diode voltage-regulator circuit.

In FIG. 3-18A:

Resistor current: $$I_R = I_L + I_Z \text{ milliamperes (mA)} \tag{3-4}$$

Load current: $$I_L = \frac{V_L}{R_L} = \frac{V_Z}{R_L} \text{ milliamperes (mA)} \tag{3-5}$$

Consequently: $$I_R = \frac{E - V_Z}{R} = \frac{E - V_L}{R} \text{ milliamperes (mA)} \tag{3-6}$$

The previous equations refer to the roughest or first approximation. However, because the breakdown curve is not completely vertical, a second approximation will involve the zener diode's resistance, R_Z, which is derived from the slope of its characteristic. Therefore:

Load voltage: $$V_L = V_Z + I_Z R_Z \text{ volts (V)} \tag{3-7}$$

Finally, the power dissipation in the zener diode is given by:

Zener diode power dissipated: $$P_Z = I_Z V_Z \text{ watts (W)} \tag{3-8}$$

The value of P_Z must not exceed the diode's rating.

* **Question 3-10** In the circuit of FIG. 3-19, the voltage across resistor R1 is:

A. 3 V B. 4 V C. 0.7 V D. 6 V E. 9 V

Answer Choice E. The zener diode provides a 3-V reference level. Therefore, the voltage across R1 is 12 − 3 = 9 V.

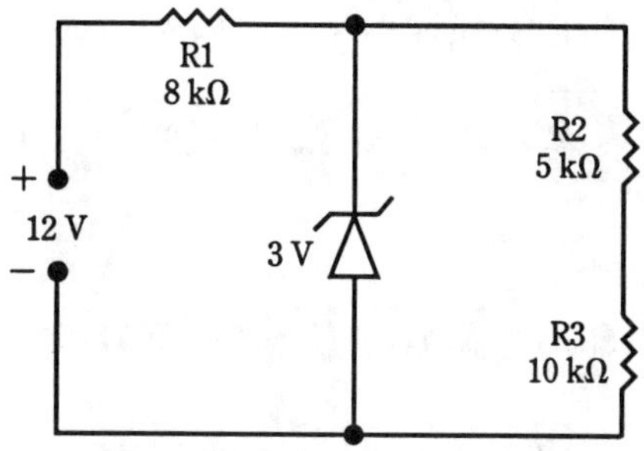

Fig. 3-19 The circuit for questions 3-10 and 3-11.

* **Question 3-11** In QUES. 3-10, the voltage across resistor R2 is:

A. 3 V B. 2 V C. 1 V D. 0.7 V E. 3.7 V

Answer Choice C. The zener diode provides a reference level so that the total voltage across R2 and R3 in series is 3 V. By the VDR, the voltage across R2 is 3 V × 5 kΩ/(5 kΩ + 10 kΩ) = 1 V.

* **Question 3-12** In the circuit of FIG. 3-20, the voltage across resistor R2 is:

A. 1 V B. 3.5 V C. 1.2 V D. 2 V E. 2.4 V

Answer Choice A. The zener diode provides a reference level so that the total voltage across R2 and R3 in series is 3 V. By the VDR, the voltage across R2 is 3 V × 10 Ω/(10 Ω + 20 Ω) = 1 V.

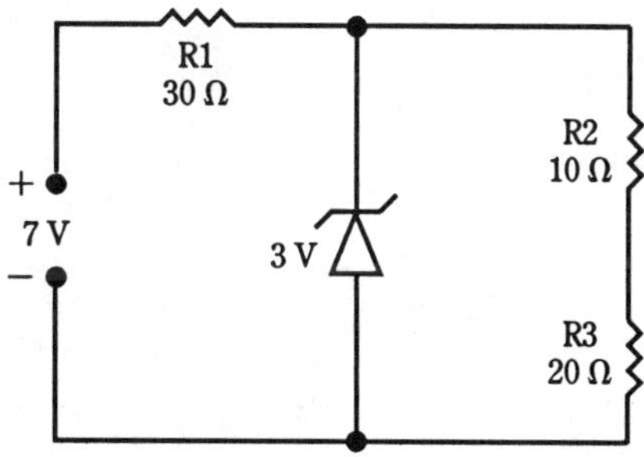

Fig. 3-20 The circuit for question 3-12.

* **Question 3-13** Zener diodes are used:

A. to provide practically constant dc output voltages with variations in the load currents
B. to provide practically constant dc output voltages with variations in the line voltages
C. to act as voltage-reference levels
D. with breakdown voltages, which extend from 2 to 200 V
E. all of the above choices are true

Answer Choice E.

* **Question 3-14** Which of the following is the symbol for a zener diode?

A. B. C. D. E.

Answer Choice D.

3-5. The varistor and the thermistor

The varistor

The *varistor* is a semiconductor device, which consequently does not obey Ohm's Law. A doped semiconductor material has both majority and minority charge carriers, but the minority current is only important at the higher voltages; this result is a nonlinear voltage-versus-current characteristic, which is illustrated in FIG. 3-21. As the voltage is increased, the varistor's equivalent resistance falls and there is a negative coefficient of resistance, with respect to voltage. The varistor can then be used to protect semiconductor components from high-voltage surges and to regulate a voltage source (FIG. 3-22A).

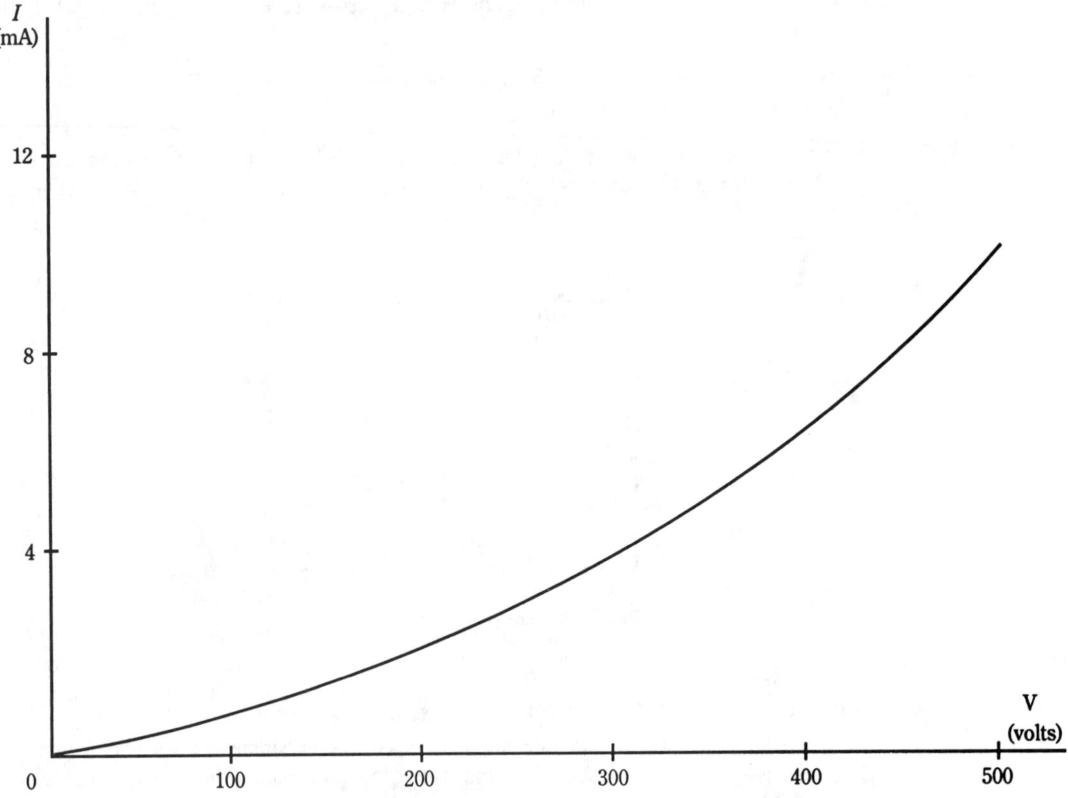

Fig. 3-21 The current-versus-voltage characteristic of a varistor.

If the unregulated voltage increases, the resistance of the varistor falls. The varistor current then exceeds its normal value and there will be a greater voltage drop across the series resistor, R_S. This absorbs most of the rise in the unregulated voltage and the output voltage is only slightly above its regulated value.

The thermistor

The *thermistor* is another semiconductor device that is doped to provide a considerable number of minority charge carriers as a result of thermal energy. It follows that the thermistor has a well-defined negative temperature coefficient of resistance over its operating range. Assume that the thermistor replaces the varistor in the voltage-regulator circuit of FIG. 3-22B. When the unregulated voltage rises, there is an increase in the thermistor's power dissipation so that its temperature rises and its resistance falls. The thermistor current then exceeds its normal value and the greater voltage drop across R_S absorbs most of the rise in the unregulated voltage. In addition to voltage regulation, thermistors are used to protect circuits against surges and to stabilize the operation of certain transistor amplifiers.

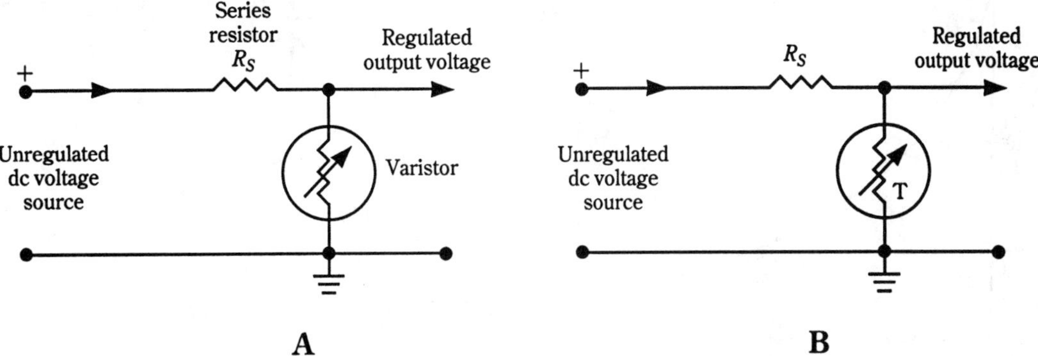

Fig. 3-22 The varistor and thermistor voltage-regulation circuits.

* **Question 3-15** A varistor can be used:

A. as a voltage-regulating device
B. to keep a load voltage practically constant as the load current varies
C. to keep a load voltage practically constant as the unregulated supply voltage fluctuates
D. to protect semiconductor components from voltage surges
E. all of the above choices are true

Answer Choice E.

* **Question 3-16** A varistor is a semiconductor device:

A. whose capacitance varies with the applied voltage
B. that can be used to achieve voltage regulation
C. that has a high positive temperature coefficient of resistance
D. whose resistance is controlled by the applied voltage
E. choices B and D are true

Answer Choice E.

3-6. The varactor diode

Because of the presence of the depletion layer, there is a certain capacitance that exists at a pn junction. If a diode is reverse-biased and the amount of bias is then increased, the depletion layer widens and the junction capacitance decreases. These semiconductor devices that are used to behave as voltage-controlled variable capacitors, are referred to as *varactor* or *varicap diodes.*

The characteristic of a typical varactor diode is shown in FIG. 3-23. The range of the reverse bias, V_r, is limited between zero and the point at which avalanche breakdown occurs.

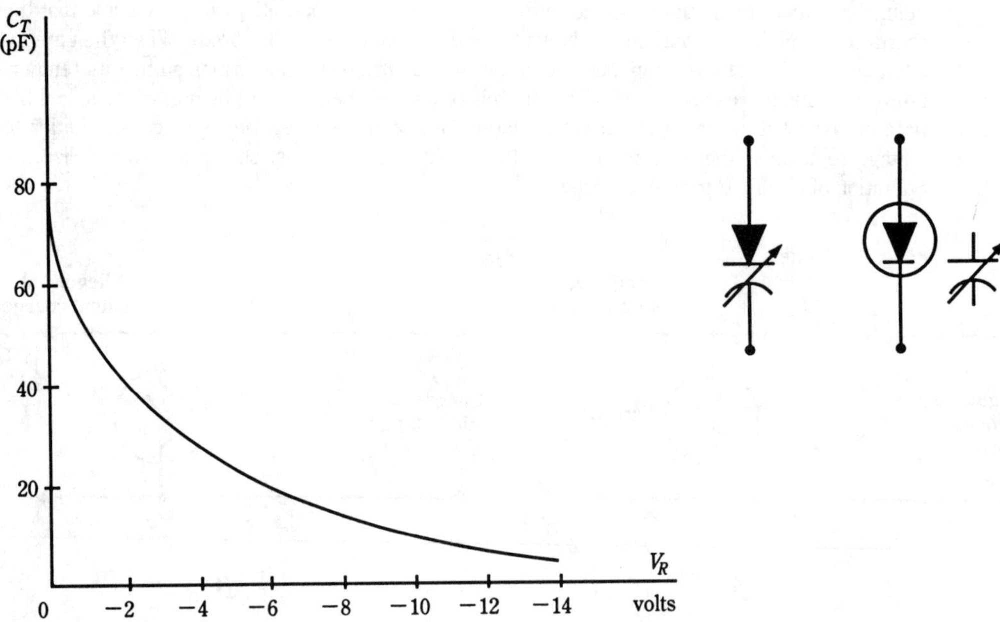

Fig. 3-23 The characteristic and symbols of a varactor diode.

Notice that there is a sharp initial drop in the value of the junction or transition capacitance, C_T, and that the characteristic of C_T versus V_r has a marked curvature. This degree of curvature allows the varactor diode to be used for frequency multiplication in the microwave region.

The original microwave varactor diodes were manufactured from silicon. However, silicon has largely been replaced by gallium arsenide because of its higher mobility of charge carriers.

To summarize, varactor diodes can be used

1. to generate frequency modulation (FM) by the direct method
2. to generate phase modulation (PM) by the indirect method
3. for frequency multiplication in the microwave region
4. as control devices in AFC circuits
5. as a "pump" in parametric amplifiers

* **Question 3-17** The semiconductor device whose capacitance is voltage-controlled, is the:

A. varactor diode B. reactance diode C. tunnel diode D. zener diode E. avalanche diode

Answer Choice A.

* **Question 3-18** A varactor diode is used:

A. to provide amplitude modulation (AM) of an RF carrier
B. to provide pulse modulation (PM) of an RF carrier
C. for frequency division in the microwave region

D. as an alternative to the tunnel diode
E. to provide frequency modulation (FM) of an RF carrier

Answer Choice E.

* **Question 3-19** Which of the following is the symbol for a varactor diode?

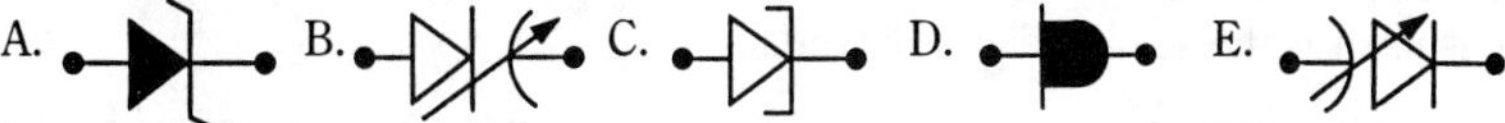

Answer Choice B.

* **Question 3-20** A varactor diode is used:

A. to generate frequency modulation (FM)
B. to generate phase modulation (PM)
C. for frequency multiplication in the microwave region
D. as a control device in an AFC circuit
E. all of the above choices are true

Answer Choice E.

3-7. The tunnel diode

When a charged capacitor is connected across an inductor, the result is a damped oscillator circuit. If an additional resistor is connected to the LC combination, the circuit losses are increased and the damping is more severe. The extra resistor represents positive resistance in the sense that as the voltage across the resistor decreases, the current decreases, so both changes are in the same direction. However, if you are able to add negative resistance across the LC circuit, the effect would be reversed and a continuous oscillation would result. But what is *negative resistance*? It is a region of some device's characteristic so that as the voltage across the device decreases, the current through the device increases; the two changes are now in the opposite direction. As an example, the tunnel diode has a characteristic that includes a negative-resistance region, and can therefore be used in the oscillator circuit of FIG. 3-24.

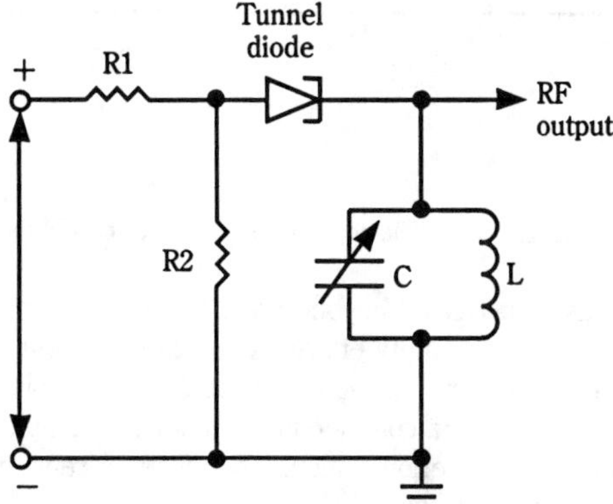

Fig. 3-24 The tunnel-diode oscillator.

Although the tunnel diode uses a pn junction, its manufacture differs from that of the basic semiconductor diode in two important respects:

- The level of doping extends from 100 times to several thousand times that of the conventional diode.
- As the result of the high levels of doping, the depletion layer at the junction is extremely thin and is only 100 μm wide (about 1% of the normal thickness). Consequently the transit time for the device is extremely short—especially because gallium arsenide (rather than silicon) is used as the semiconductor material.

For appreciable current to flow in a conventional diode, it must be provided with a forward bias (several hundred mV), which exceeds the barrier potential. This allows the electrons (majority charge carriers) in the n region to possess the required energy to cross in to the p region. However, with the tunnel diode, a small forward voltage of only tens of mV will provide the electrons with sufficient energy to "tunnel" their way through the extremely thin depletion layer. These majority charge carriers literally "punch" through with velocities that are much higher than those associated with ordinary diodes. In the process, the electrons lose virtually none of their energy. In the forward-voltage-versus-current characteristic of FIG. 3-25A, it describes the action of the tunnel diode between points O and P. At point P (where the peak current I_p occurs), the energy levels of the electrons in the n region are the same as the vacant energy-level states of the valence electrons in the p region; consequently, the maximum number of electrons can tunnel through the depletion layer.

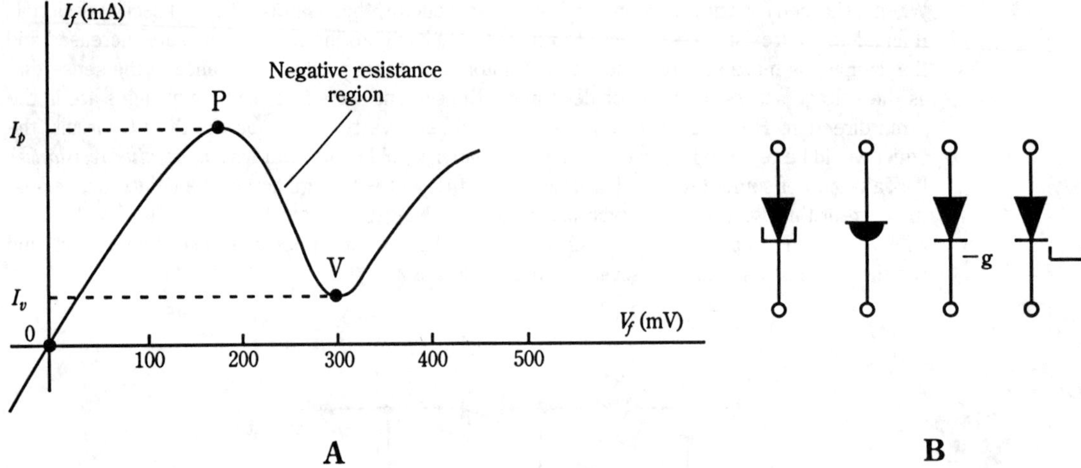

Fig. 3-25 The characteristic and symbols of the tunnel diode.

When the forward bias is increased beyond point P, the energy-level state of the valence electrons is further reduced, so the empty energy levels in the p region drop below the energy levels of the electrons in the n region. The action of the forbidden zone then comes into play so that between points P and V there is a continuous reduction in the number of electrons that are capable of tunneling through the depletion region. The diode current then falls to a minimum at point V (where the valley current I_v occurs).

Between the points P and V, the tunnel diode exhibits its property of dynamic negative resistance because as the forward voltage is increased over this section, the forward current is reduced.

Beyond point V, the tunneling action ceases entirely and ordinary diode current occurs as the result of the forward bias overcoming the potential barrier. Notice that the tunnel diode's reverse current is much higher because of the heavy doping; however, this has little significance because the tunnel diode is not normally reverse-biased. The common tunnel diode symbols are shown in FIG. 3-25B. Tunnel-diode oscillators are capable of producing low-power outputs in the microwave region.

* **Question 3-21** A tunnel diode is used in a microwave oscillator circuit because:

A. it has a negative temperature coefficient of resistance
B. it is lightly doped and has a wide depletion region
C. its equivalent capacitance changes as the applied voltage fluctuates
D. its characteristic contains a negative-resistance section
E. its current increases as the applied voltage increases over its operating range

Answer Choice D.

4

Transistors and other semiconductor devices

In this chapter you will learn:

- about the principles and characteristics of bipolar transistors and the relationships among the emitter, base, and collector currents.
- how to identify the leads of a transistor and the pins of a microchip.
- the principles of base bias and voltage divider bias.
- to compare the features of the common base, common emitter, and common collector configurations.
- about the operations of the class-A power amplifier, the class-B push-pull amplifier, and the Class-C RF power amplifier.
- why Class-C operation can be used to achieve frequency modulation.
- about the principles and characteristics of the junction field-effect transistor.
- about the principles of metal-oxide semiconductor field-effect transistors in their depletion and enhancement modes.
- how bipolar transistors are used in conjunction with zener diodes to achieve voltage regulation.
- the necessary criteria for an RF circuit to sustain a continuous oscillation.
- about the properties of quartz crystals and their use in the Miller and Pierce oscillators.
- how the multivibrator and blocking oscillator circuits are used to produce a sawtooth voltage.
- about the principles that underlie the action of various operational amplifiers.
- the features of such devices as the silicon-controlled rectifier, the silicon-controlled switch, the diac, and the triac.

4-1. Introduction to the bipolar transistor

The action of ***bipolar transistors*** involves two sets of charge carriers; these are the positive charge carriers (holes) and the negative charge carriers (electrons). Bipolar transistors are also of two types, ***pnp*** and ***npn***, whose symbols are shown in FIG. 4-1A. Each of these possesses three sections, which are called the *emitter*, the *base*, and the *collector*; the arrow in each symbol indicates the direction of conventional flow (the opposite direction to that of the electron flow).

The bipolar transistor can be roughly compared to a triode with emitter, base, and collector corresponding respectively to the cathode, control grid, and plate or anode. For normal amplifier conditions, the voltages are applied to the transistor so as to forward-bias the emitter-base junction, but to reverse-bias the collector-base junction. For the pnp transistor (FIG. 4-1B), this requires that the emitter is positive (with respect to the base), which is in turn positive (with respect to the collector). These polarities are reversed for the npn transistor. Some of the methods of producing the correct dc bias voltages for the emitter-base and collector-base junctions are covered in the next section. Under either static or signal conditions, emitter current, (I_E), base current (I_B), and collector current (I_C) flow in a bipolar transistor circuit (FIG. 4-1A). Applying Kirchhoff's current law:

$$I_E = I_C + I_B,\ I_C = I_E - I_B,\ I_B = I_E - I_C \tag{4-1}$$

Under normal operating conditions, I_B is typically less than 5% of either I_E or I_C, and I_C is only slightly less than I_E.

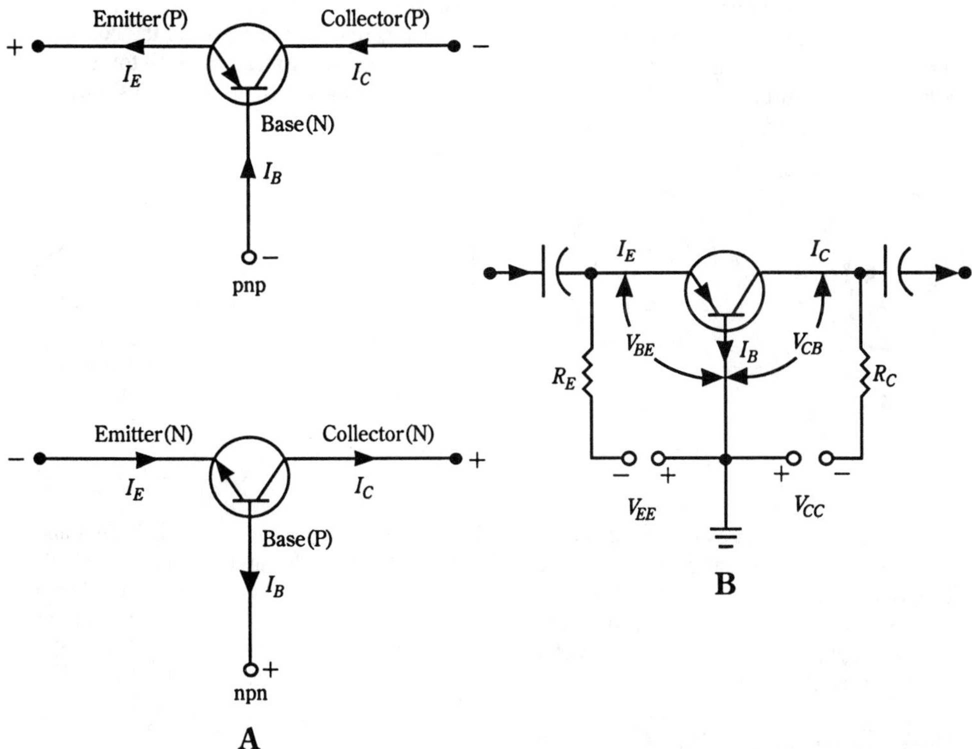

Fig. 4-1 The principles of the bipolar transistor.

In the construction of an npn transistor, the emitter region is small, but heavily doped, and the base is thin and lightly doped. The collector is relatively lightly doped, but physically large because most of the power dissipated occurs in this region; it follows that the transistor is not a symmetrical device so that the emitter and the collector are not interchangeable. Under amplifier conditions, the forward bias applied to the emitter-base junction causes a large number of majority charge carriers (electrons in the conduction band) to move across from the emitter into the base. There is some recombination between the electrons and the holes in the base region, and, as a result, there is a small external base current. However, most of the electrons pass through the base and cross into the collector region. The reverse bias applied to the collector-base junction provides an electric field, which drives the electrons through the collector region and is responsible for producing the external flow of the output current. In other words, the operation of the transistor as an amplifying device requires that the emitter current controls the collector current.

Apart from its operation as an amplifier, a transistor can function in two other states:

1. **Cut-off** Both emitter-base and collector-base junctions are reversed-biased so that any collector current is extremely small.
2. **Saturation** Both emitter-base and collector-base junctions are forward-biased. The emitter current will then no longer control the collector current, but any small change in collector-base voltage will cause a very large change in collector current.

Under extreme saturation conditions, the collector current might be so large that the transistor can be destroyed. However, in some digital circuits, transistors are commonly switched between cut-off and saturation without damage to the device.

To identify the three leads at the base of the transistor, refer to the details of the housing. Frequently, a red or silver dot indicates the collector; in power transistors, the collector is normally connected to the casing. Four examples of the bottom views of transistors are shown in FIGS. 4-2A, B, C, and D.

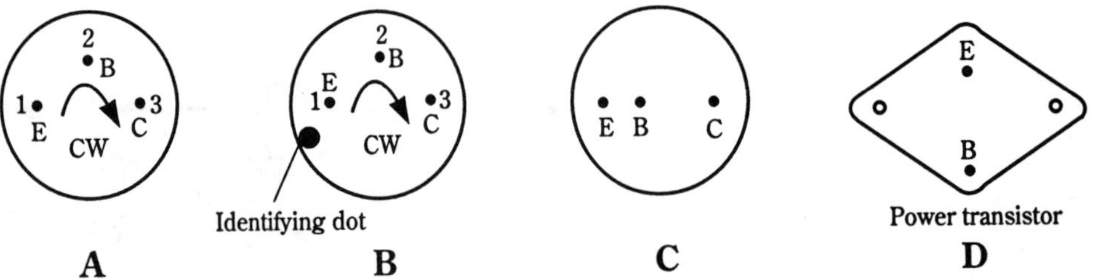

Fig. 4-2 The bottom views of transistor housings.

Where the leads are arranged in a circle, lead 1 is found from the gap or identifying dot and the count from the bottom view then proceeds in the clockwise (CW) direction (FIGS. 4-2A, B). The same applies to a microchip (FIGS. 4-3A, B), where pin 1 is located by a dot or notch. From the top view, identify the pins by counting in the CCW direction (FIG. 4-3A), but from the bottom view, the count must be in the CW direction. The same method of counting also applies to the pins at the base of a tube.

Collector characteristics

One bipolar transistor is distinguished from another by means of its collector characteristics. These are the graphs of the collector-emitter voltage (V_{CE}) versus the collector current, I_C, for a

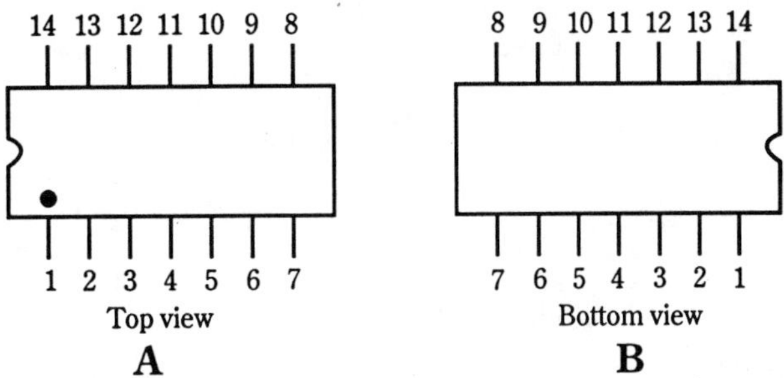

Fig. 4-3 Identifying the pins of a microchip.

fixed value of the base current, I_B. A family of such curves are either obtained experimentally or from a transistor curve tracer. A typical set of such characteristics is displayed in FIG. 4-4.

Consider point P on the $I_B = 30\ \mu\text{A}$ characteristic. At this point $I_C = 3$ mA, $I_B = 30\ \mu\text{A}$ and therefore $I_E = I_C + I_B = 3\text{ mA} + 30\ \mu\text{A} = 3.03$ mA. The current gain from emitter to collector is designated as α_{dc} (Greek alpha) and is defined by:

$$\alpha_{dc} = \frac{I_C}{I_E} \tag{4-2}$$

$$= \frac{3}{3.03} \approx 0.99$$

Typical values for α_{dc} range from 0.95 to 0.995.

The current gain from base to collector is designated as β_{dc} (Greek beta) and is defined by:

$$\beta_{dc} = \frac{I_C}{I_B}$$

$$= \frac{3\text{ mA}}{30\ \mu\text{A}} \tag{4-3}$$

$$= 100$$

Typical values for β_{dc} range from 50 to 200.

Notice that α_{dc} and β_{dc} are only numbers and have no units. Moreover, their values are not constant, but are sensitive to temperature variations. For example, if the temperature increases, more majority charge carriers are produced by thermal energy; therefore, the values of I_E, I_B, and I_C all rise.

From EQ. 4-2:

$$\text{Current gain, } \alpha_{dc} = \frac{I_C}{I_E}$$

$$= \frac{I_C}{I_B + I_C} \tag{4-1}$$

$$= \frac{I_C/I_B}{1 + I_C/I_B}$$

$$= \frac{\beta_{dc}}{1 + \beta_{dc}} \tag{4-4}$$

This yields: $$\text{Current gain, } \beta_{dc} = \frac{\alpha_{dc}}{1 - \alpha_{dc}} \quad (4\text{-}5)$$

In the example: $$\alpha_{dc} = \frac{100}{1 + 100} \approx 0.99$$

and: $$\beta_{dc} = \frac{0.99}{1 - 0.99} \approx 100$$

From FIG. 4-1B, it is clear that:

$$V_{CE} = V_{CB} + V_{BE} \quad (4\text{-}6)$$

Because, for a silicon transistor, $V_{BE} \approx 0.7$ V:

$$V_{CB} = V_{CE} - 0.7\text{ V} \quad (4\text{-}7)$$

For an appreciable collector current to flow, it is necessary that V_{CB} is positive so that the collector-base junction is reverse-biased. As shown in FIG. 4-4, the collector current increases sharply until $V_{CE} > 1$ V and then levels off. For higher values of V_{CE}, there will only be a small rise in I_C because some additional electrons reach the collector, rather than being captured by holes in the base region.

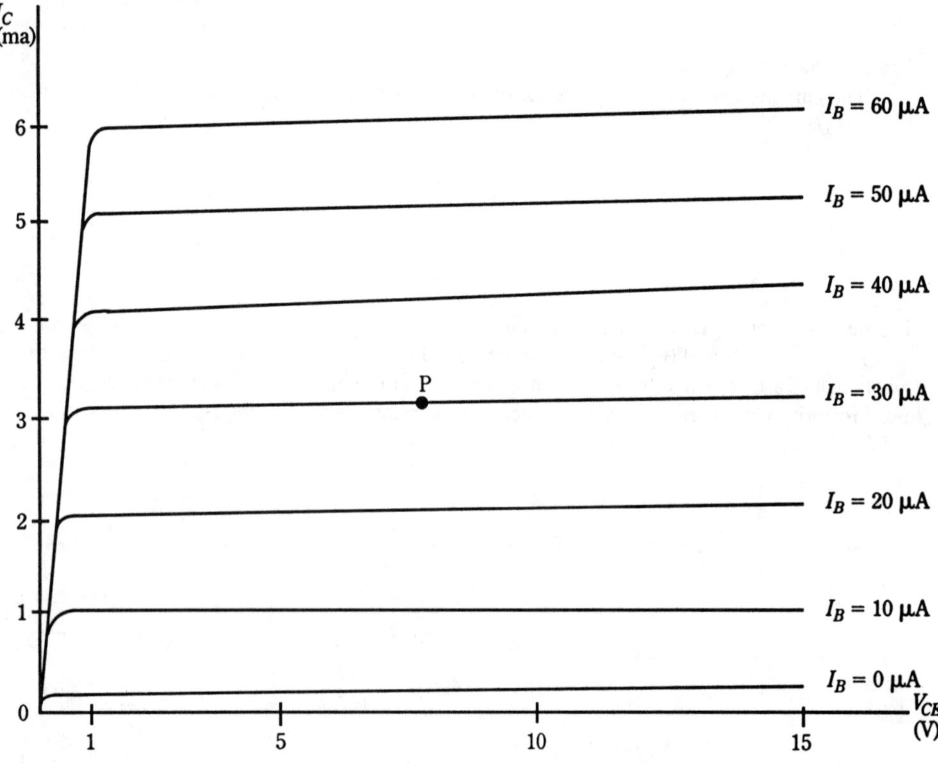

Fig. 4-4 The collector characteristics of a bipolar transistor.

* **Question 4-1** Which electrode of a triode tube can be compared with the collector region of a bipolar transistor?

A. plate B. control grid C. cathode D. filament E. screen grid

Answer Choice A.

* **Question 4-2** Which electrode of a triode tube can be compared with the base region of a bipolar transistor?

A. cathode B. plate C. screen grid D. control grid E. filament

Answer Choice D.

* **Question 4-3** Which electrode of a indirectly heated triode tube can be compared with the emitter region of a bipolar transistor?

A. heater B. screen grid C. control grid D. plate E. cathode

Answer Choice E.

* **Question 4-4** When a bipolar transistor is operating as a linear amplifier device, the:

A. emitter-base junction and the collector-base junction are both forward-biased
B. emitter-base junction and the collector-base junction are both reverse-biased
C. emitter-base junction is forward-biased and the collector-base junction is reverse-biased
D. emitter-base junction is reverse-biased and the collector-base junction is forward-biased
E. emitter-base junction is forward-biased and the collector-emitter junction is reverse-biased

Answer Choice C.

* **Question 4-5** A bipolar transistor is operated with both the emitter-base junction and the collector-base junction in the reverse-biased condition. As a result, the:

A. transistor is cut off
B. transistor is in its saturation mode
C. transistor is acting as a linear amplifying device
D. transistor might be ruined
E. choices B and D are true

Answer Choice E.

* **Question 4-6** In FIG. 4-5, the symbol is that of a:

A. npn junction transistor
B. junction field-effect transistor
C. DE MOSFET
D. pnp junction transistor
E. E MOSFET

Answer Choice A.

* **Question 4-7** In FIG. 4-6, the symbol is that of a:

A. junction field-effect transistor
B. pnp junction transistor
C. E MOSFET
D. E MOSFET
E. npn junction transistor

Answer Choice B.

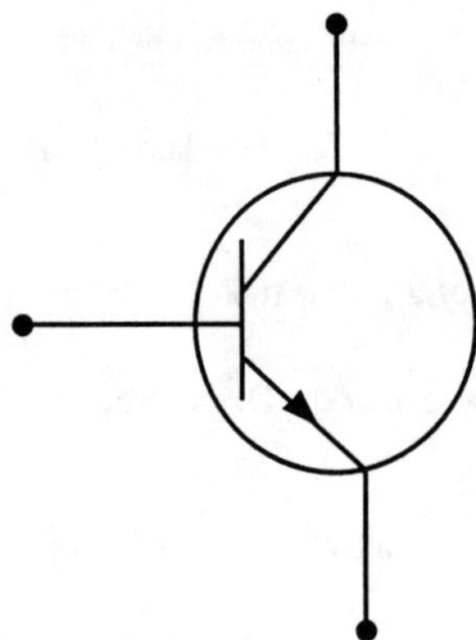

Fig. 4-5 The symbol for question 4-6.

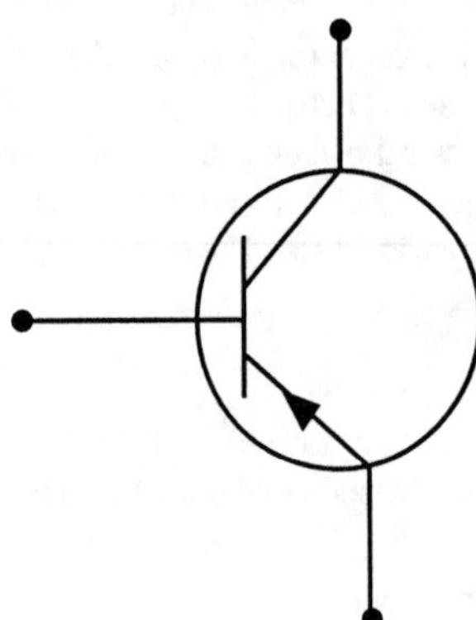

Fig. 4-6 The symbol for question 4-7.

* **Question 4-8** In FIG. 4-7, the transistor is:

A. reverse-biased on the base
B. forward-biased on the collector
C. reverse-biased on the emitter
D. forward-biased
E. reverse-biased

Answer Choice D.

* **Question 4-9** In FIG. 4-8, identify pin 10 of the microchip:

A. a B. b C. c D. d E. e

Answer Choice B. In the bottom view, pin 1 is identified by *e*. Counting clockwise from pin 1, pin 10 is indicated by *b*.

* **Question 4-10** In FIG. 4-9, identify pin 9 of the microchip:

A. a B. b C. c D. d E. e

Answer Choice A. In the top view of the microchip, pin 1 is identified by the dot (*e*). Counting counterclockwise from pin 1, pin 9 is identified by *a*.

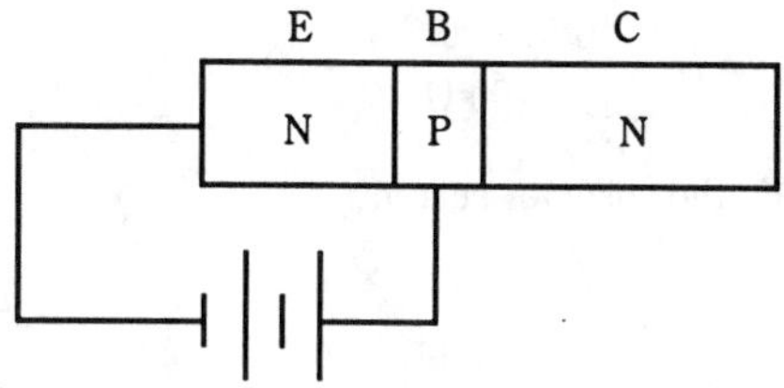

Fig. 4-7 The circuit for question 4-8.

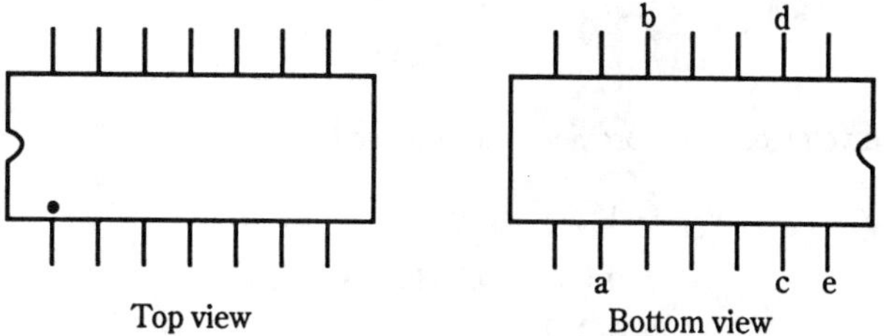

Fig. 4-8 The pin identification for question 4-9.

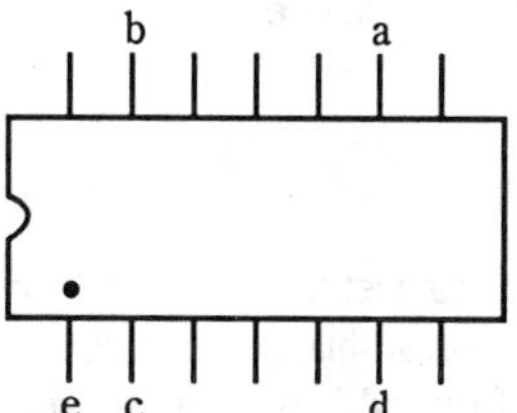

Fig. 4-9 The pin identification for question 4-10.

4-2. Dc biasing of the bipolar transistor

The input signal to the base of a linear amplifier can have any one of variety of waveforms (such as a sine wave, a square wave, a sawtooth wave, a pulse, voice, or music). The term *linear* means that the output magnified signal from the collector has a waveform that closely resembles that of the input signal; in other words, the amount of distortion is kept to a minimum. If you plot the graph of the instantaneous output voltage versus the instantaneous input voltage, the appearance is a close approximation to a straight line.

To operate a bipolar transistor under linear (class A) conditions, it is necessary to establish the required dc values for the emitter, base, and collector currents. This is achieved by applying the correct levels of forward bias to the emitter-base junction and reverse bias to the collector-base junction.

At this stage, only consider small-signal amplifiers, whose input waveforms are typically measured in millivolts. Figure 4-1B shows the circuit of such an amplifier in which V_{EE} provides the forward bias for the emitter-base junction, while V_{CC} reverse-biases the collector-base junction.

As an example, let $V_{EE} = 6$ V, $R_E = 10$ kΩ, $R_C = 15$ kΩ, $V_{CC} = +15$ V. It is normally assumed in the FCC examinations that $V_{BE} = 0.7$ V so that the emitter current:

$$I_E = \frac{6\ \text{V} - 0.7\ \text{V}}{10\ \text{k}\Omega} = 0.53\ \text{mA}$$

If the value of α_{dc} is 0.95, the collector current:

$$\begin{aligned} I_C &= 0.95 \times I_E \\ &= 0.95 \times 0.53 \\ &= 0.5035\ \text{mA} \end{aligned}$$

Base current:

$$\begin{aligned} I_B &= I_E - I_C \\ &= 0.53 - 0.5035 \\ &= 0.0265\ \text{mA} \end{aligned} \tag{4-1}$$

Collector-base voltage, which provides the reverse bias:

$$\begin{aligned} V_{CB} &= V_{CC} - I_C R_C \\ &= 15\ \text{V} - 0.5035\ \text{mA} \times 15\ \text{k}\Omega \\ &= 7.4475\ \text{V} \end{aligned}$$

These quiescent (no-signal) values are provided through the use of two dc voltage sources with the value of V_{EE} appreciably less than that of V_{CC}. Clearly, it would be more efficient if both bias voltages could be obtained from a single supply. Therefore, look at two methods of achieving this goal.

Base Bias

For the normal operation of a bipolar transistor, the emitter-base junction must be forward-biased while the collector-base junction is reverse-biased. The circuit (FIG. 4-10) contains an npn transistor, whose emitter-base junction is forward-biased by the source, V_{CC}. This voltage is connected in series with R_B between base and ground, and, for this reason, the arrangement is referred to as *base bias*. In order that the amplifier should behave in a linear manner, it is necessary that the dc or quiescent (no signal) conditions should remain as stable as possible. Unfortunately, base bias is sensitive to the value of β_{dc}, which in turn is affected by temperature variations.

For example, let $R_B = 200\ \text{k}\Omega$, $V_{CC} = +12\ \text{V}$, $V_{BE} = 0.7\ \text{V}$, $R_C = 3\ \text{k}\Omega$, and $\beta_{dc} = 50$:

Voltage drop across R_B:

$$\begin{aligned} V_{RB} &= 12 - 0.7 \\ &= 11.3\ \text{V} \end{aligned}$$

Base current:

$$\begin{aligned} I_B &= \frac{11.3\ \text{V}}{200\ \text{k}\Omega} \\ &= 56.5\ \mu\text{A} \end{aligned}$$

The base current is unaffected by temperature variations. However, the collector current:

$$\begin{aligned} I_C &= \beta_{dc} \times I_B \\ &= 50 \times 56.5\ \mu\text{A} \\ &= 2.825\ \text{mA} \end{aligned}$$

Collector voltage:

$$\begin{aligned} V_C &= 12\ \text{V} - 2.825\ \text{mA} \times 3\ \text{k}\Omega \\ &= 3.525\ \text{V} \end{aligned}$$

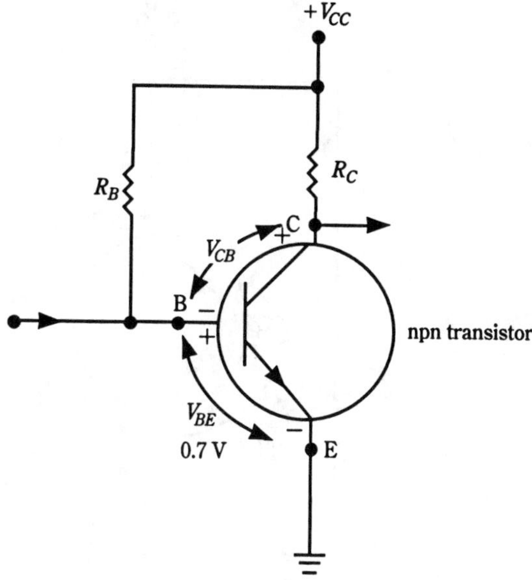

Fig. 4-10 Base bias.

Because $I_C \approx I_E = \beta_{dc} \times I_B$, the values of the collector and emitter currents are directly proportional to the value of β_{dc} and are therefore seriously affected by temperature variations. Notice that $V_C = V_{CE}$ and has a low-voltage value when the transistor is conducting.

Voltage divider bias

The voltage-divider circuit is the most important and the most commonly used of all the base-biased arrangements. Resistors R1 and R2 form a voltage divider (FIG. 4-11), and are connected between the collector supply voltage (V_{CC}) and ground. The voltage drop across R2 then provides the necessary forward bias for the emitter-base junction. The inclusion of R_E is essential because this resistor primarily determines the value of the emitter current, I_E. It follows that the voltage-divider arrangement provides a stable value of I_E that is almost independent of any fluctuations in the value of β_{dc}. In addition, this type of bias only requires a single voltage source (V_{CC}). For example, let $R_1 = 20\ \text{k}\Omega$, $R_2 = 10\ \text{k}\Omega$, $R_E = 3.3\ \text{k}\Omega$, $R_C = 5.6\ \text{k}\Omega$, $V_{BE} = 0.7$ V, and $V_{CC} = +30$ V.

Using the voltage division rule (VDR), the voltage between base and ground:

$$V_B = 30\ \text{V} \times \frac{20\ \text{k}\Omega \times 10\ \text{k}\Omega}{20\ \text{k}\Omega + 10\ \text{k}\Omega}$$

$$= 10\ \text{V}$$

Voltage at the emitter:

$$V_E = 10 - 0.7$$

$$= 9.3\ \text{V}$$

Emitter current:

$$I_E = \frac{9.3\ \text{V}}{3.3\ \text{k}\Omega}$$

$$= 2.8\ \text{mA}$$

Collector voltage:

$$V_C \approx +30\ \text{V} - 2.8\ \text{mA} \times 5.6\ \text{k}\Omega$$

$$= +14.2\ \text{V}$$

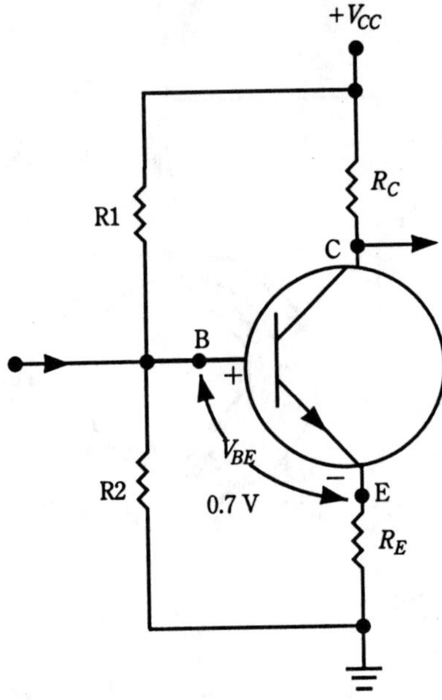

Fig. 4-11 Voltage divider bias.

Collector-emitter voltage:

$$V_{CE} = V_C - V_E$$
$$= 14.2 - 9.3$$
$$= 4.9\text{ V}$$

Collector-base voltage:

$$V_{CB} = V_C - V_B$$
$$= 14.2 - 10$$
$$= 4.2\text{ V}$$

Notice that the value of β_{dc} did not enter into these calculations.

* **Question 4-11** What, if anything, is wrong with the circuit of FIG. 4-12?

A. the emitter-base bias battery must be reversed
B. the collector-base bias battery must be reversed
C. the voltage of the emitter-base bias battery is too large
D. the voltage of the collector-base bias battery is too large
E. the circuit is correct, as shown

Answer Choice C. Under normal conditions, the value of V_{EE} is less than that of V_{CC}.

* **Question 4-12** What, if anything, is wrong with the circuit of FIG. 4-13?

A. replace the pnp transistor with an equivalent npn transistor
B. reverse the collector battery
C. remove R1
D. interchange the emitter and the collector
E. the circuit is correct, as shown

Answer Choice E. The circuit shows a pnp transistor that uses base bias. The polarity of the battery is correct.

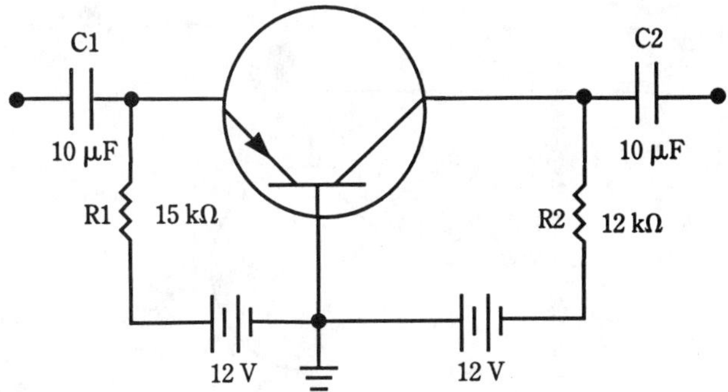

Fig. 4-12 The circuit for question 4-11.

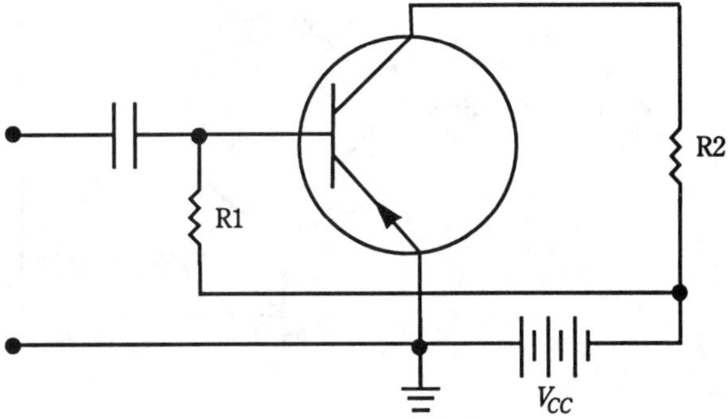

Fig. 4-13 The circuit for question 4-12.

* **Question 4-13** If the temperature of a transistor increases, the:

A. surrounding circuit is not affected
B. base current decreases
C. emitter current decreases
D. collector current increases
E. value of β_{dc} is unchanged

Answer Choice D

* **Question 4-14** In the circuit of FIG. 4-14, $R_1 = R_2$, $R_3 = R_4$ and the two transistors are identical. If switch S1 is closed, but switch S2 is open, both of the lamps (L1 and L2) are lit. If both S1 and S2 are closed:

A. both lamps are lit
B. neither lamp is lit
C. only L1 is lit
D. only L2 is lit
E. the two lamps are lit alternately

Answer Choice C. If both S1 and S2 are closed, the two emitter-base junctions will be provided with forward (base) bias. Therefore, both transistors conduct and lamp L1 is lit. However, the

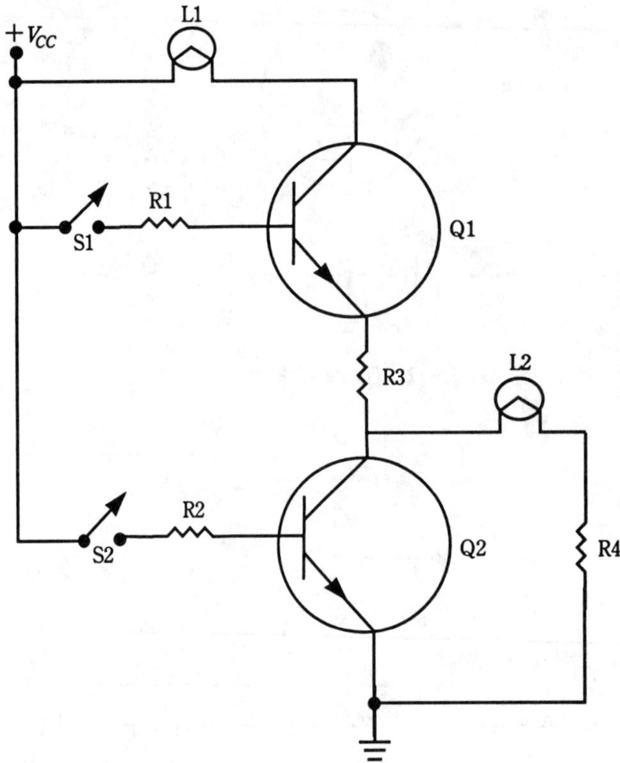

Fig. 4-14 The circuit for question 4-14.

V_{CE} voltage of Q2 will be too low to light L2 because the main flow of current will occur through Q2, R3, Q1, L1, and V_{CC}.

* **Question 4-15** In the circuit of FIG. 4-15, the voltage at the base relative to ground is:

A. + 5 V B. + 4.3 V C. + 0.7 V D. + 20 V E. 15 V

Answer Choice B.

By the voltage rule, the base voltage:

$$V_B = +20\text{ V} \times \frac{5\text{ k}\Omega}{5\text{ k}\Omega + 15\text{ k}\Omega}$$

$$= +5\text{ V}$$

4-3. Transistor amplifier configurations

Because a bipolar transistor has three regions, you can feed the input signal to one region, take the output signal from a second region, and then regard the third region as common or grounded. This leads to three possible configurations:

1. **The common-base (CB) amplifier** The input signal is fed to the emitter, the output amplified signal is taken from the collector, and the base is grounded.

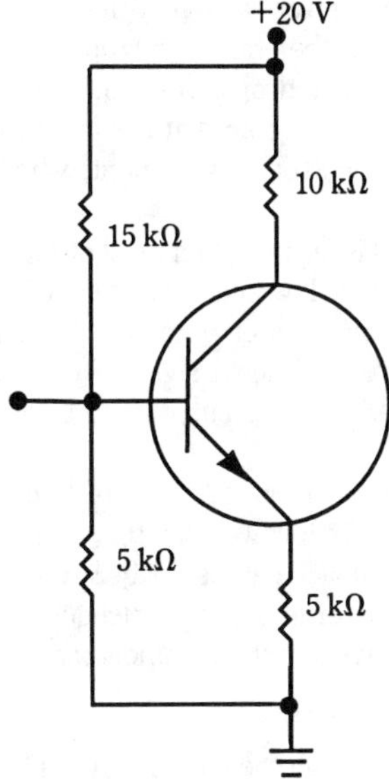

Fig. 4-15 The circuit for question 4-15.

2. **The common-emitter (CE) amplifier** The input signal is fed to the base, the output amplified signal is taken from the collector, and the emitter is grounded.
3. **The common-collector (CC) or emitter-follower circuit** The input signal is fed to the base, the output signal is taken from the emitter, and the collector is grounded (as far as the signal is concerned).

These three configurations are now compared, in regard to input and output impedances, voltage gain, and the phase relationship between the input and output signals.

The common-base amplifier

In the common-base arrangement, the base of the npn transistor is grounded and the input signal, v_e, is applied to the emitter (FIG. 4-16); the output signal, v_c, then appears between the collector and ground.

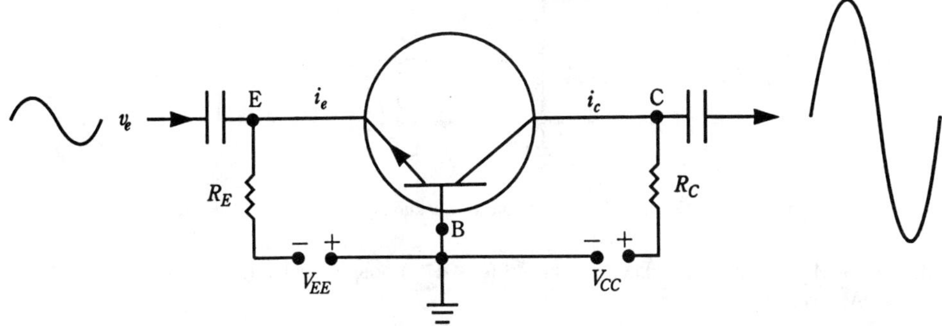

Fig. 4-16 The common-base configuration.

If the input signal drives the emitter (*n* region) more positive, the forward voltage on the emitter-base junction is lower so that the emitter current is reduced. This, in turn, will decrease the collector current so that the voltage drop across the collector load will be less. The collector voltage, v_c, will therefore be more positive so that the input and the output signals are in phase. This is in contrast to the common emitter arrangement, where the input and output signals are 180° out of phase.

Because the small input signal is facing a high level of the signal emitter current, i_e, the input impedance of the CB amplifier is very low and is typically of the order of 100 Ω or less. This is the principal disadvantage of this configuration because a low input impedance has a loading effect on the previous stage, which supplies the input signal. By contrast, the amplified output signal is associated with the slightly smaller collector current, i_c. Consequently, the output impedance is of the order of a few kilohms.

Because the base is grounded, there is little possibility of feedback from the output collector circuit to the input emitter circuit. It follows that the common base circuit is unlikely to self-oscillate. However, if a positive feedback path is deliberately provided, the common-base configuration will behave as a stable oscillator in the higher frequency bands.

To summarize the main properties of the common-base amplifier:

- Input and output signals are in phase.
- Appreciable voltage gain, although the current gain is less than unity.
- Very low input impedance.
- Relatively high output impedance.

* **Question 4-16** In the amplifier circuit of FIG. 4-17:

A. the batteries must be reversed
B. the emitter-base battery voltage is too high
C. the collector-base battery voltage is too high
D. there is no voltage gain from emitter to collector
E. The output signal is in phase with the input signal

Answer Choice E.

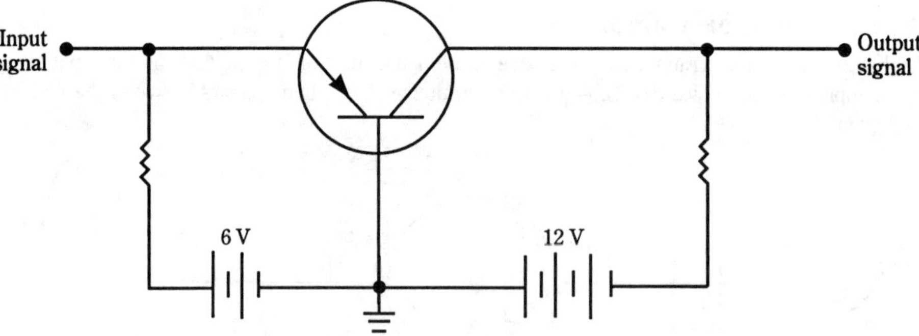

Fig. 4-17 The circuit for questions 4-16 and 4-17.

* **Question 4-17** In the amplifier circuit of FIG. 4-17, a positive pulse is applied to the input terminal. As a result:

A. the transistor is destroyed
B. there is virtually no effect on the collector current

C. the emitter current decreases
D. the base current decreases
E. the collector current increases

Answer Choice E.

* **Question 4-18** The circuit of FIG. 4-17:

A. will not provide voltage amplification
B. represents a common emitter stage
C. uses a pnp transistor
D. is improperly grounded
E. introduces 180° phase change between the input and output signals

Answer Choice C.

* **Question 4-19** A common base amplifier has a:

A. high input impedance
B. 180° phase difference between its input and output signals
C. low output impedance
D. low input impedance
E. high current gain

Answer Choice D.

* **Question 4-20** Which of the following stages has an appreciable voltage gain, an input impedance of the order of 100 Ω or less, a relatively high output impedance, its input and output signals in phase, and little possibility of self-oscillation?

A. common emitter amplifier
B. common collector stage
C. common base amplifier
D. JFET amplifier
E. MOSFET amplifier

Answer Choice C.

* **Question 4-21** A common-base arrangement uses a pnp transistor and is biased for linear amplification. On the positive half cycle of the input sine-wave signal:

A. the collector-base voltage decreases
B. the output signal from the collector is a negative half cycle
C. there is a power loss and a current gain
D. the base current decreases
E. the collector current increases

Answer Choice E. The positive half cycle of the input signal will increase the instantaneous forward bias applied to the emitter-base junction; as a result, the emitter, base, and collector currents all increase.

The common emitter amplifier

The base-driven stage is the most frequently used type of transistor amplifier. In FIG. 4-18, the input signal, v_b, is applied between the base of an npn transistor and ground while the amplified output signal, v_c, appears between the collector and ground.

If the input signal drives the base more positive, with respect to ground, the forward voltage across the emitter-base junction will be higher so that the emitter current is increased. This, in

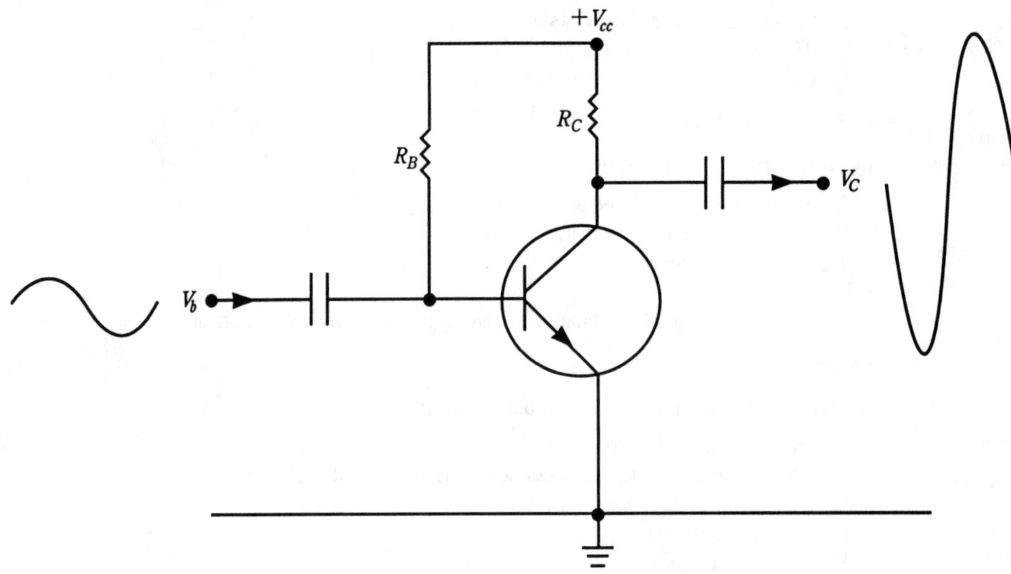

Fig. 4-18 The common emitter amplifier.

turn, will raise the level of the collector current so that a greater voltage drop will be across the collector load, R_C. As a result, the signal collector voltage, v_c, will be less positive, so the input and output signals are 180° out of phase. This is not important as far as voice or music is concerned because phase has no effect on the human ear.

Because the input signal is only facing the low level of the signal base current, i_b, the input impedance of the CE amplifier is quite high and is about 100 times greater than the input impedance of the CB amplifier. This is one of the main advantages of the CE stage because its high input impedance has less loading effect on the previous stage, which supplies the input signal. The output impedance of the CE amplifier is also high and comparable with that of the CB configuration. The voltage gain from base to collector can be 100 or more and the current gain is of a similar order.

If a CE stage is used at high radio frequencies, there is a possibility of feedback from the collector to the base through their junction capacitance. It might then be necessary to neutralize the amplifier in order to prevent self-oscillation (chapter 5).

To summarize the main properties of the common-emitter amplifier:

1. Input and output signals are 180° out of phase.
2. High voltage and current gains.
3. High input impedance.
4. High output impedance.

* **Question 4-22** In order to correct the common-emitter amplifier circuit of FIG. 4-19:

A. reverse the collector battery
B. reverse both batteries
C. reverse the base battery
D. the ground point must be shifted
E. the circuit is correct as shown

Answer Choice C. The base battery is providing reverse bias instead of the required forward bias.

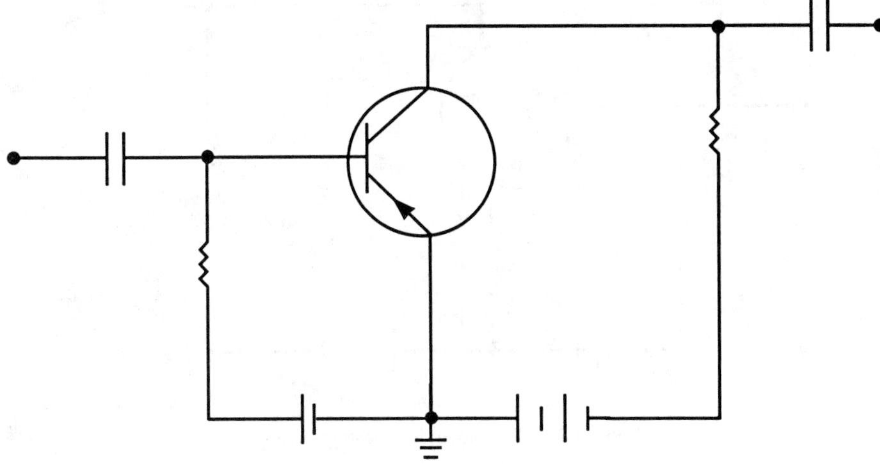

Fig. 4-19 The circuit for question 4-22.

* **Question 4-23** An audio-amplifier uses a pnp transistor in a common-emitter configuration. If the collector-base junction is forward-biased, the:

A. stage will behave as a conventional linear amplifier
B. emitter-base circuit would operate in the cut-off mode
C. transistor might be ruined
D. transistor is operating in the saturation mode
E. choices C and D are true

Answer Choice E.

* **Question 4-24** The circuit of FIG. 4-20:

A. provides a 180° phase reversal between the input and output signals
B. provides no phase change between the input and output signals
C. represents a common-emitter configuration
D. has a very low input impedance
E. represents a common-collector configuration

Answer Choice A. The circuit is a common-emitter amplifier; therefore, there is a 180° phase change between the input and output signals.

* **Question 4-25** In order to correct the common-emitter amplifier circuit of FIG. 4-21:

A. reverse the collector battery
B. reverse both batteries
C. reverse the base battery
D. shift the ground point
E. the circuit is correct, as shown

Answer Choice B. The transistor is of the pnp variety and both batteries provide incorrect bias so that the emitter-base junction is cut off.

* **Question 4-26** Which of the following stages has high voltage and current gains, high input and output impedances, as well as input and output signals that are 180° out of phase?

A. common-emitter amplifier
B. common-collector stage

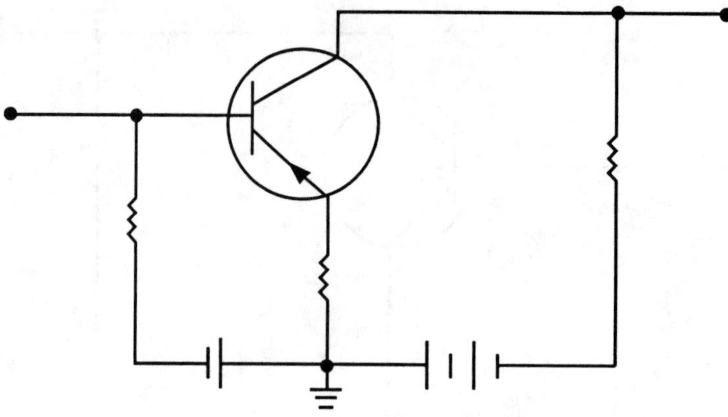

Fig. 4-20 The circuit for question 4-24.

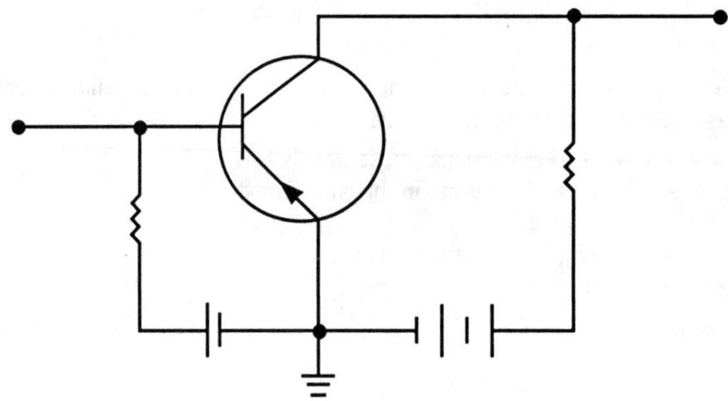

Fig. 4-21 The circuit for question 4-25.

C. common-base amplifier
D. emitter-follower
E. none of the above choices is true

Answer Choice A.

* **Question 4-27** In the circuit of FIG. 4-22:

A. the transistor is used in a common-collector configuration
B. there is no phase change between the input and output signals
C. the transistor is used in a common-base configuration
D. there is a 180° phase change between the input and output signals
E. the amplifier is incorrectly biased

Answer Choice D. The circuit shows a common-emitter configuration; consequently, there is a 180° phase reversal between the input and output signals.

* **Question 4-28** The circuit of FIG. 4-22 has:

A. a low input impedance and low voltage gain
B. a low input impedance and high voltage gain

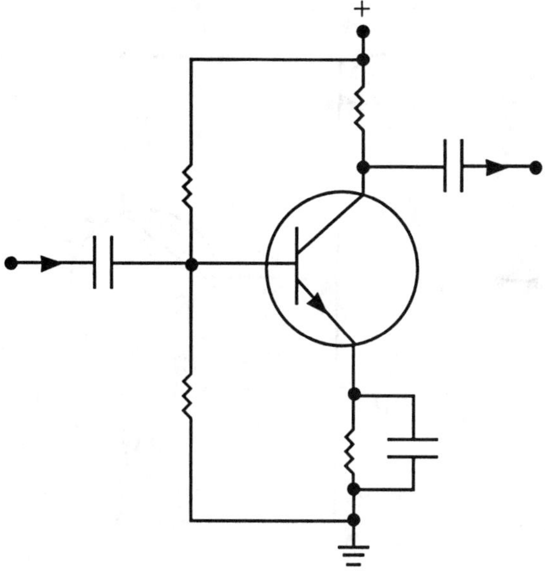

Fig. 4-22 The circuit for questions 4-27 and 4-28.

C. a high input impedance and a low voltage gain
D. a high input impedance and a high voltage gain
E. equal input and output impedances

Answer Choice D.

The common-collector (emitter-follower) stage

The emitter-follower is sometimes referred to as the *common collector (CC) stage.* In FIG. 4-23, the input signal is applied between the base and ground while the output signal is taken from the emitter and ground; the collector is normally joined directly to the V_{CC} supply. The voltage gain from the base to the emitter is less than unity, but the CC arrangement has a very high input impedance and a low output impedance. The emitter-follower is therefore primarily used for impedance matching by allowing a high-impedance source to feed a low-impedance load. In this way, it behaves as a matching transformer, but with the advantages of a better frequency response, greater simplicity, and a lower cost. This also means that the emitter-follower can provide some degree of isolation between two stages.

Assume that the input signal is driving the p-type base more positive, with respect to ground. This increases the forward voltage applied to the emitter-base junction so that the emitter current increases. This increase of current passes through the emitter resistor, R_E; as a result, the emitter voltage becomes more positive, with respect to ground. The emitter output signal is therefore in phase with the input base signal. In other words, the emitter output "follows" the base input. However, the whole of the output signal is applied as negative or degenerative feedback to the input signal. This is the reason for the very high input impedance, the low output impedance, and the voltage gain of less than unity.

To summarize the important features of the emitter-follower stage:

- Very high input impedance.
- Low output impedance.

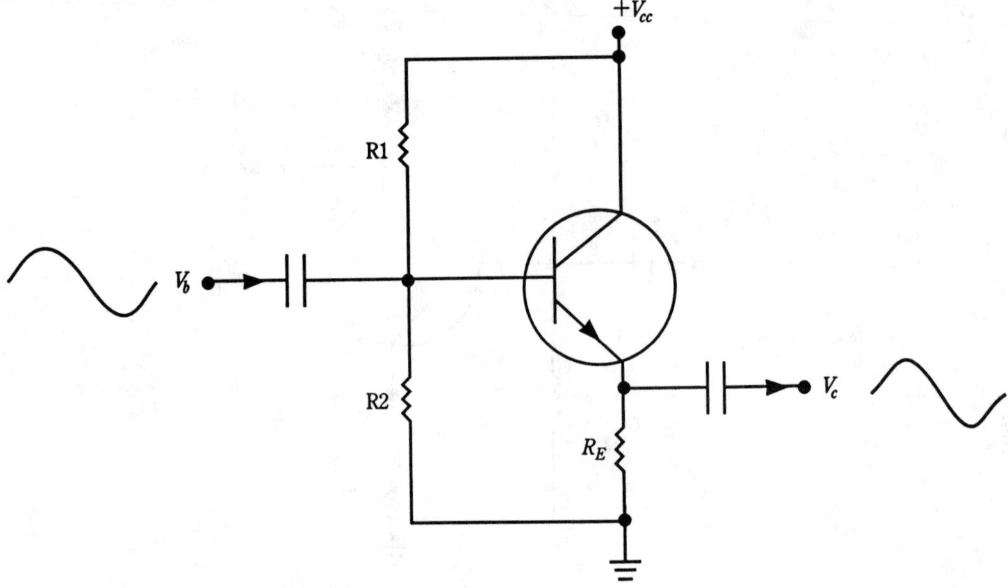

Fig. 4-23 The common collector (emitter-follower) stage.

- Voltage gain of less than unity.
- Input and output signals are in phase.
- High current gain.

* **Question 4-29** Which of the following stages has a very high input impedance, a low output impedance, a voltage gain of approximately 0.98, and no phase change between its input and output signals?

A. common-collector stage
B. common-emitter amplifier
C. common-base amplifier
D. emitter-follower
E. choices A and D are true

Answer Choice E.

* **Question 4-30** An emitter-follower circuit can be used to provide:

A. a high voltage gain
B. a high output impedance
C. a low input impedance
D. matching between a low-impedance source and a high-impedance load
E. a high degree of isolation between two stages

Answer Choice E.

* **Question 4-31** The circuit shown in FIG. 4-24 is a:

A. signal doubler
B. balanced collector-emitter amplifier
C. phase inverter

D. collector-feedback amplifier
E. collector-emitter follower

Answer Choice C. R_E acts as the load of an emitter-follower circuit so that output 1 is in phase with the base input signal. Because the collector current is only slightly less than the emitter current, output 2 is virtually the same size as output 1, but this output from the collector is 180° out of phase with the base input signal. You therefore have two equal outputs that are 180° out of phase and the circuit is called a *phase inverter*, which is capable of providing the required voltages for a push-pull amplifier.

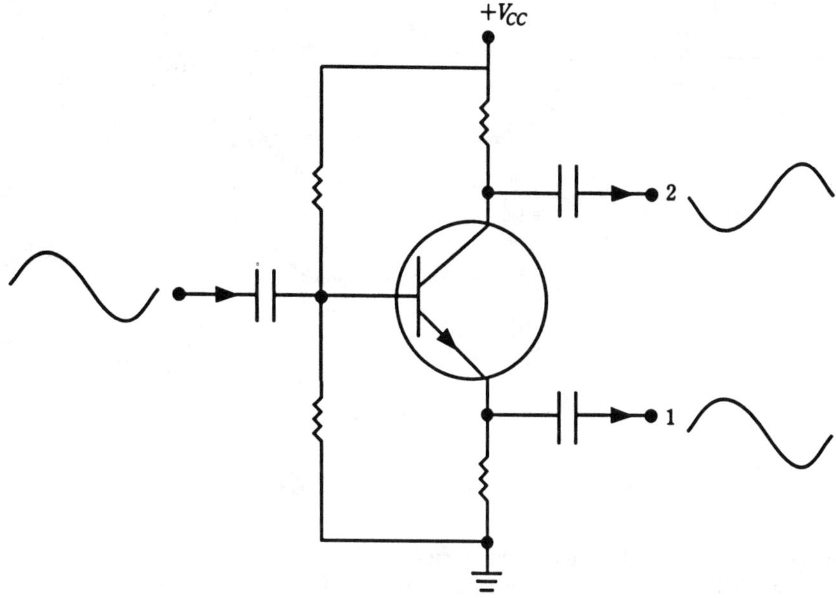

Fig. 4-24 The circuit for question 4-31.

4-4. The class-A power amplifier

Figure 4-25A illustrates a receiver's output stage whose load is a low-impedance loudspeaker. The step-down transformer is used to match the speaker to the required value of the collector load. Under optimum conditions, the circuit will deliver audio power to the loudspeaker with the minimum amount of signal distortion.

The collector characteristics of a power transistor are shown in FIG. 4-25B. Initially, the quiescent or no-signal conditions are analyzed to determine the dc value, V_{CEQ}, of the collector-emitter voltage. If the resistance of the transformer's primary winding is ignored, a vertical dc load line can be drawn and a convenient Q point can be selected to determine the dc level (I_{CQ}) of the collector current. The effective collector load of the loudspeaker is given by:

$$R_L \times \left(\frac{N_P}{N_S}\right)^2$$

and determines the slope of the ac load line.

When the input signal is applied to the base, the operating conditions move up and down the

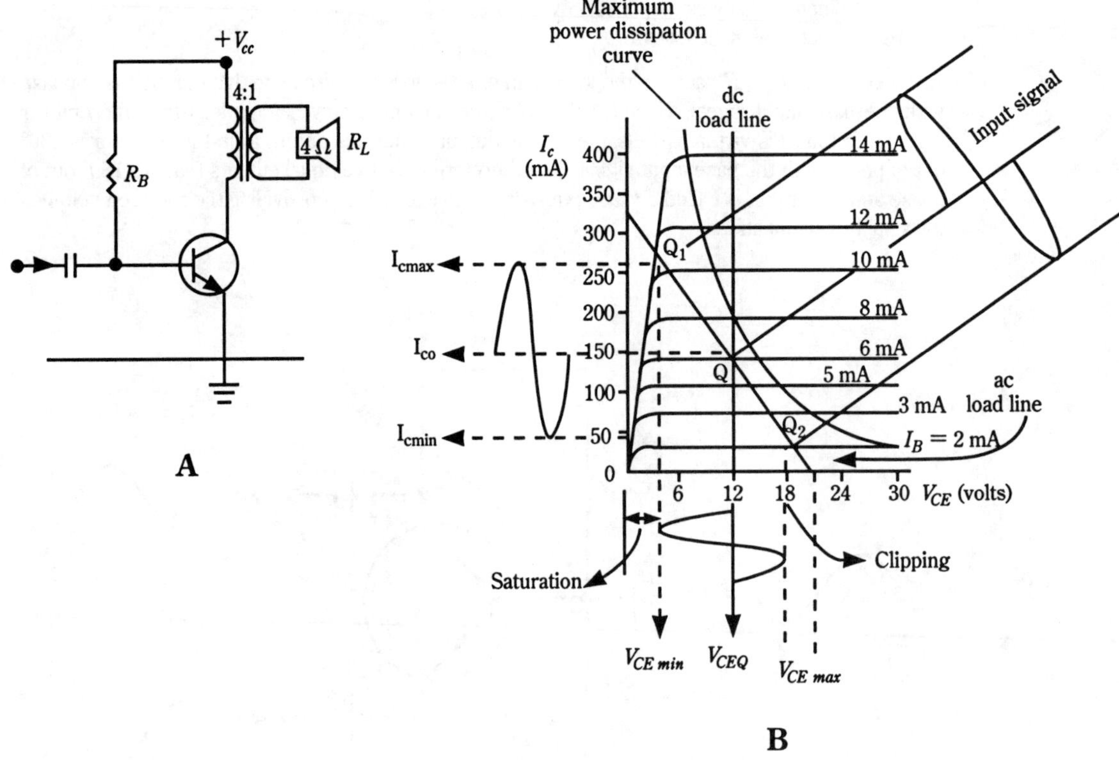

Fig. 4-25 The class-A power amplifier.

ac load line. To allow for the greatest input signal, it is important that Q is approximately in the center of this line. This is class-A operation, in which the collector current flows throughout the cycle of the base-signal voltage. However, the amount of the input signal is limited by saturation on the positive alternation (point Q_1) and by cut-off clipping on the negative alternation (point Q_2). You must also be careful that the transistor's maximum V_{CE} and power ratings are not exceeded on the operating section of the ac load line. This is ensured by keeping the load line below the curve that represents the transistor's maximum power rating.

In the circuit of FIG. 4-25A, dc power is drawn from the V_{CC} supply and part of this power is converted to the audio signal power, which is delivered to the loudspeaker. The remainder of the power is mostly dissipated as heat in the transistor's collector region. The percentage efficiency is defined by:

$$\textit{Percentage efficiency} = \frac{\textit{audio signal power output}}{\textit{dc power input}} \times 100\% \qquad (4\text{-}2)$$

The theoretical maximum efficiency under class-A conditions is 50%. However, in a practical amplifier, the highest efficiency is of the order of 25% to 30%.

In FIG. 4-25B, you will observe that the collector characteristics are not evenly spaced; the positive half cycle of the input sine wave is amplified more than the negative half cycle. The output waveform is therefore distorted and can be analyzed into a fundamental component with harmonics that represent the distortion. Most of the distortion is associated with the second harmonic component, so:

$$\textit{Percentage of second-harmonic distortion} = \frac{\textit{effective value of the second-harmonic component}}{\textit{effective value of the fundamental component}} \times 100\% \qquad (4\text{-}3)$$

Under class-A conditions, the percentage of second-harmonic distortion is of the order of 2% or less.

* **Question 4-32** A sine-wave signal is applied to a transistorized class-A amplifier. For how many degrees of the signal cycle does the collector current flow?

A. 360° B. 270° C. 180° D. 120° E. 90°

Answer Choice A. Collector current flows throughout the cycle of the input signal.

* **Question 4-33** The percentage efficiency of a practical class-A amplifier is:

A. 60% B. 50% C. 78.5% D. 85% E. 25%

Answer Choice E.

* **Question 4-34** Class-A operation of a amplifier stage is signified by:

A. minimum distortion
B. centering its Q point on the load line
C. low efficiency
D. continuous collector current flows throughout the cycle of the input signal
E. all of the above choices are true

Answer Choice E.

4-5. The class-B push-pull audio amplifier

Figure 4-26A illustrates a class-B push-pull audio amplifier. In this figure, the input signals to the two bases are 180° *out of phase,* while the output transformer is connected between the collectors so that the collector currents drive in opposite directions through the primary winding. As a result, the input signal to the loudspeaker is determined by the value of $i_{c1} - i_{c2}$; therefore, the collector currents combine to produce a practically undistorted output signal from the secondary winding.

In the class-A operation of the last section, the Q point was located at the middle of the ac load line so that the collector current flowed continuously throughout the cycle of the input signal. Although the distortion was kept to a minimum, the efficiency of the class-A circuit was only of the order of 20% to 30%. To increase the efficiency up to between 50% and 60%, operate under class-B conditions, whereby the Q point is theoretically lowered to the bottom of the ac load line (FIG. 4-26B) so that $V_{CEQ} = V_{CC}$ and $I_{CQ} = 0$. In other words, the forward bias on each transistor is zero. However, there is unacceptable (cross-over) distortion near the cut-off region; in practice, each transistor is provided with a small forward "trickle" bias by the voltage divider (R1 and R2).

As a further compromise between distortion and efficiency, you can operate an audio push-pull circuit in class-AB, where the corresponding Q point on the ac load line lies half-way between the two points that represent class-A and class-B (FIG. 4-26B).

Under class-B conditions, each transistor conducts for about one half cycle of its input signal. Because the two base signals are 180° out of phase, the transistors conduct alternately; in other words, there is a "cross-over" between the two transistors. The two half cycles then combine to produce the complete sine-wave output that appears across the loudspeaker.

Compared with a single power transistor that is operated under class-A conditions, the push-pull amplifier offers the following advantages:

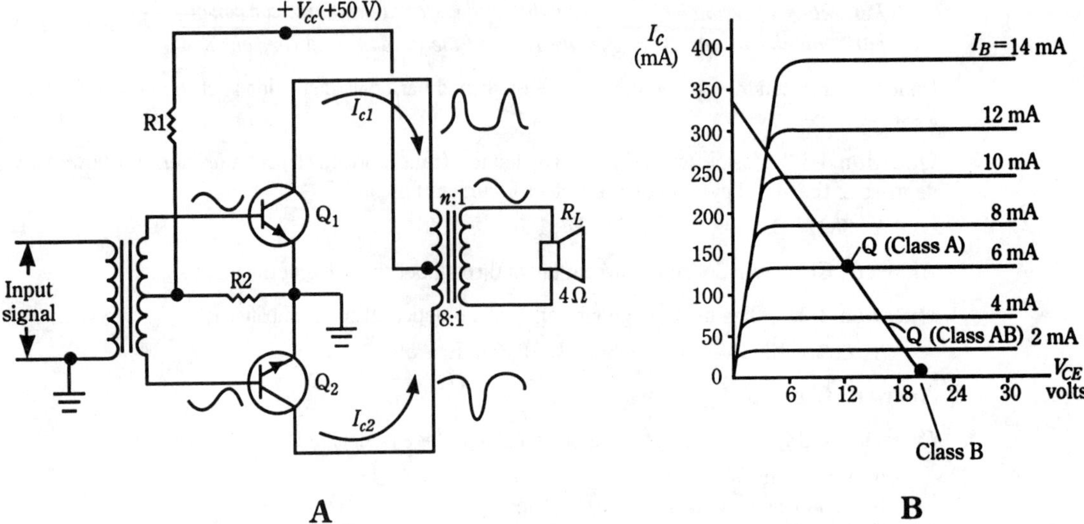

Fig. 4-26 The class-B push-pull power amplifier.

- There is no resultant dc current to cause partial saturation of the output transformer's iron core. If the core would partially saturate, the output signal would be distorted.
- Because of nonlinearity in the transistor characteristics, the collector-current waveforms cannot be pure sine waves and are therefore, to some extent, distorted. This distortion is in the form of harmonic components, both odd and even. The even harmonic components of i_{c1} and i_{c2} are in phase and will therefore cancel in the output transformer. The elimination of even harmonic distortion is the major advantage of the push-pull arrangement.
- The efficiency (50% to 60%) of the class-B push-pull stage is much higher than that of the single-transistor class-A amplifier (20% to 30%). Therefore, for a given dc power input, the push-pull stage can provide a greater signal power output.
- The maximum input signal voltage to the class-B push-pull stage is approximately four times greater than the maximum input signal to the class-A amplifier. All of these advantages are achieved at the expense of using a matched pair of transistors. If one transistor becomes defective, both should be replaced.

Class-B operation is also used for RF linear stages, which are capable of amplifying an amplitude modulated (AM) signal with minimum distortion of the modulation envelope.

* **Question 4-35** One of the main advantages of a push-pull audio amplifier over a stage that uses a single transistor, is the elimination:

A. of odd and even harmonic distortion
B. of odd harmonic distortion only
C. of even harmonic distortion only
D. of the fundamental component and even harmonic distortion
E. of the fundamental component and odd harmonic distortion.

Answer Choice C.

* **Question 4-36** Class B operation is associated with:

A. a practical efficiency between 50% and 60%
B. a Q point near cut-off
C. elimination of even harmonic distortion
D. the requirement for a matched pair of transistors in an audio push-pull amplifier
E. all of the above choices are true

Answer Choice E.

* **Question 4-37** When an input signal is present, the circuit of FIG. 4-27 is operated as a class-B stage. In the absence of an input signal, the forward bias applied to the emitter-base junction is:

A. 15 V B. 5 V C. 4.3 V D. 0.7 V E. 10 V

Answer Choice D. Because the emitter is grounded, the bias in the absence of a signal is 0.7 V.

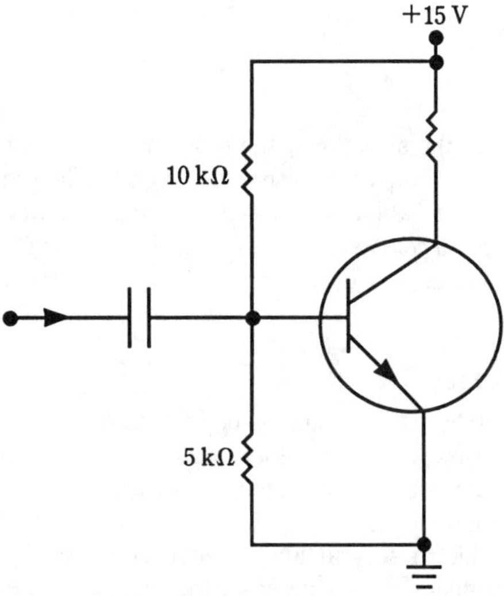

Fig. 4-27 The circuit for question 4-37.

4-6. The class-C RF power amplifier

Figure 4-28 shows a class-C RF power amplifier that is operated at a high efficiency of 80% or more; in other words, 80% of the dc power drawn from the V_{CC} supply is converted into the RF signal power output.

The circuit uses signal bias in which base current flows either side of the positive alternation's peak. This base current charges the capacitor, C_B, but when the current ceases, the capacitor discharges through R_B. However, the time constant R_BC_B is high, compared with the period of the input signal. As a result, the dc voltage across R_B is approximately equal to the peak value of the input signal and applies a reverse bias to the emitter-base junction. Care must be taken that this reverse bias does not exceed the emitter-to-base breakdown voltage.

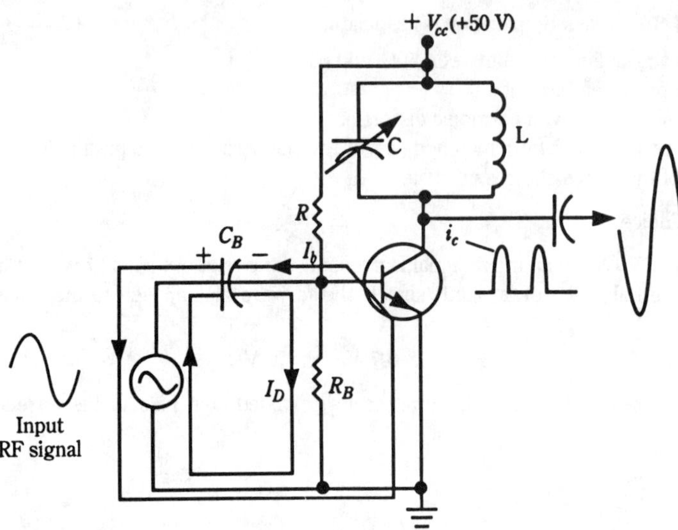

Fig. 4-28 The class-C RF power amplifier.

Because of the action of the signal bias, the collector current consists of narrow pulses at the same repetition rate as the frequency of the input signal. When these pulses are applied to the high-*Q* resonant-tuned circuit, the result is a circulating or "fly-wheel" current that oscillates between L and C and develops a complete sine wave for the output voltage between the collector and ground. Only a small mean level of collector current is drawn from the V_{CC} supply so that the amplifier's efficiency is high.

Frequency multipliers

For reasons of frequency stability, it is common practice to operate a transmitter RF oscillator stage at low frequency and low power, and then build up the frequency and the power in the following stages. To increase the frequency, multiplier stages (sometimes called *harmonic generators*) are used. Their circuitry is similar to that of FIG. 4-28, but their class-C operation is achieved with a bias level, which is several times the normal value. This reduces the angle of the output current flow and the efficiency, but increases the strength of the harmonic content. So, instead of the tank circuit being tuned to the fundamental frequency of the input base signal, the "tank" can be tuned to a particular harmonic contained in the output current waveform. To a first approximation, the output voltage of the multiplier stage will be an undistorted sine wave whose frequency is a whole number of times (twice for a doubler stage, three times for a tripler, etc.) the frequency of the input signal on the base. Because the output frequency from the collector circuit is different from the input frequency to the base circuit, frequency-multiplier stages are not required to be neutralized.

For a doubler stage, the angle of output current flow is typically 90°, the bias level is approximately 10 times the normal value, and the efficiency is 50%. A tripler stage has about the same efficiency, but the bias level is approximately twenty times the normal value, so the angle of the output current flow is reduced to 75°.

The push-push doubler stage

The *push-push arrangement* (FIG. 4-29) only occurs in RF circuitry. The two bases are again fed 180° out of phase with the input sine-wave signal. In contrast with the push-pull circuit, the collectors are joined together to one end of the tank circuit, so the output signal is proportional to the sum of the two collector currents. Consequently, all signal components that were eliminated from the output of the push-pull circuit will appear in the output of the push-push circuit, and vice-versa. As a result, the output of the push-push arrangement will contain only even harmonics. Therefore, the circuit is mainly used as a doubler with the tank circuit tuned to the second harmonic of the input frequency. Notice that for simplicity, the class-C bias arrangements have not been included in FIG. 4-29.

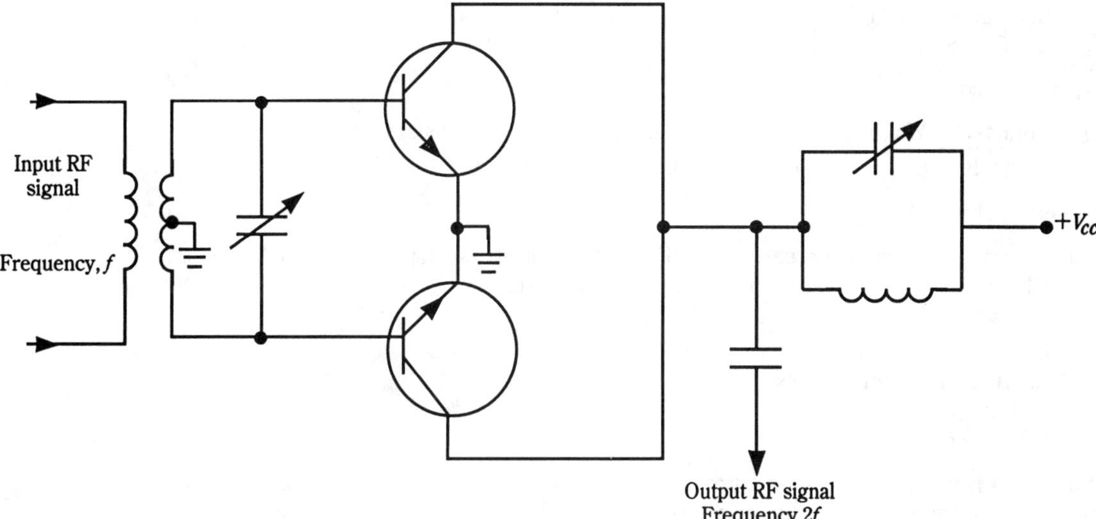

Fig. 4-29 The push-push doubler stage.

Compared with the single-transistor doubler, the tuning of the tank circuit to the second harmonic will be more easily achieved in the push-push circuit because the fundamental frequency and the third harmonic have been eliminated from the output. Because the push-push stage is a harmonic generator, it does not need to be neutralized.

* **Question 4-38** A Class-C RF amplifier stage:

A. operates with a high level of forward bias
B. provides minimum distortion of the collector current waveform
C. produces a collector output voltage that consists of narrow pulses
D. has a high level of efficiency
E. uses a resistor as its collector load

Answer Choice D.

* **Question 4-39** A class-C amplifier stage:

A. has a low level of efficiency
B. has a small input signal
C. operates with a bias near to the cut-off value
D. causes the waveform of the collector current to be severely distorted
E. has a low power output when compared with class-A or class-B stages

Answer Choice D.

* **Question 4-40** Frequency multiplier stages are operated in:

A. class A B. class AB C. class B D. class C E. class D

Answer Choice D.

* **Question 4-41** Which of the following transistorized stages might need to be neutralized?

A. audio amplifiers
B. push-pull audio amplifiers
C. class-C RF power amplifiers
D. frequency multipliers
E. RF oscillators

Answer Choice C.

* **Question 4-42** Which of the following classes has the highest efficiency?

A. A B. AB_1 C. B D. C E. AB_2

Answer Choice D.

* **Question 4-43** A transistorized class-C RF power amplifier has a tank circuit as its collector load. The output voltage waveform from the collector consists of:

A. narrow negative pulses
B. narrow positive pulses
C. half-cycle negative pulses
D. half-cycle positive pulses
E. entire cycles

Answer Choice E. The collector current waveform consists of narrow spikes that "flick" impulse the tank circuit into continuous oscillation. A circulating current then flows between the inductor and the capacitor and a sine-wave voltage output appears between the collector and ground.

* **Question 4-44** Class-C operation produces frequency multiplication because:

A. the stage is highly efficient
B. the collector load is a tank circuit
C. the emitter-base forward bias is very high
D. the collector current waveform is severely distorted and therefore contains components that are harmonics of the input frequency
E. the input signal is badly distorted

Answer Choice D.

* **Question 4-45** The circulating or fly-wheel current in a tank circuit recreates the sinusoidal voltage waveform in:

A. class-A audio amplifiers
B. class-AB audio amplifiers
C. phase inverters
D. class-B push-pull audio amplifiers
E. class-C RF power amplifiers

Answer Choice E.

* **Question 4-46** A class-C collector current waveform contains a:

A. dc level together with ac fundamental and even harmonic components
B. dc level together with ac fundamental and odd harmonic components

C. dc level together with ac fundamental and harmonic components, both odd and even
D. dc level and only an ac fundamental component
E. dc level and subharmonic components

Answer Choice C.

* **Question 4-47** In a class-C amplifier stage with a tank circuit as its load, the:

A. output current waveform is severely distorted
B. output voltage waveform is severely distorted
C. efficiency is low
D. input signal is small
E. choices A and B are true

Answer Choice A.

* **Question 4-48** In a push-push doubler stage:

A. the two bases are fed 180° out of phase and the collectors are joined together to one end of the tank circuit
B. the two bases are fed in phase and the collectors are joined together to one end of the tank circuit
C. the two bases are fed 180° out of phase and the tank circuit is connected between the collectors
D. the two bases are fed in phase and the tank circuit is connected between the collectors
E. the two bases are fed 180° out of phase and the emitters are joined together to one end of the tank circuit

Answer Choice A.

* **Question 4-49** Figure 4-30 illustrates a frequency-multiplier (tripler) stage. What happens if the capacitor, C, open-circuits?

A. the transistor is cut off
B. the transistor is driven into saturation
C. the RF power output increases
D. the RF power output decreases
E. the capacitor only determines the circuit's dc conditions; therefore, there is no appreciable change in the RF power output

Answer Choice D. If the capacitor, C, open-circuits, negative feedback is developed across the resistor, R. Therefore, the RF power output decreases.

4-7. The junction field-effect transistor

The action of the pnp or npn bipolar transistor involves two types of charge carrier—the electron and the hole. The *FET* is a unipolar transistor because its operation requires only one charge carrier that can be either the electron or the hole.

The two common types of FETs are the *junction field-effect (JFET)* and the *metal-oxide semiconductor transistor (MOSFET)*; the latter is sometimes referred to as an *insulated-gate field-effect transistor (IGFET)*.

The JFET is essentially a doped silicon bar, which is referred to as a *channel* and behaves as a resistor. The doping can either be p-type or n-type, so it is either a p-channel or an n-channel JFET. At the ends of the channel are two terminals that are referred to as the *source* and the *drain*. When a particular drain-source voltage (V_{DS}) is applied between the end terminals, the

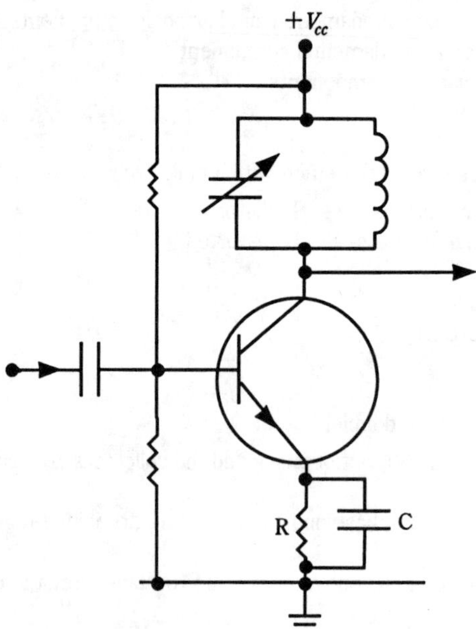

Fig. 4-30 The circuit for question 4-49.

amount of current flow (I_D) between the source and the drain depends on the channel's resistance. The value of this resistance is controlled by a gate that can either consist of two n-type regions diffused into a p-type channel or two p-type regions diffused into an n-type channel. In either case, the two regions are commonly joined to provide a single gate (two separate gates can be used in some mixer circuits). Cut-away views of both types with their schematic symbols are shown in FIGS. 4-31A and B. In these schematic symbols, the vertical lines can be regarded as the channel; the arrow then points toward an n-channel, but away from a p-channel. The gate line can either be symmetrically positioned, with respect to the source and the drain, or it can be drawn closer to the source.

If a reverse-bias voltage is applied between the gate and the source of an n-channel JFET, depletion layers will surround the two p-regions that form the gate. If the reverse bias is increased, the depletion layers will spread more deeply into the channel until they almost touch. The channel's resistance will then will be extremely high so that the gate current is very small.

The reverse-biasing of the gate-source junction can be compared to applying a negative voltage to a triode's grid, relative to its cathode. Like the tube, the FET is a voltage-controlled device in the sense that only the input voltage to the gate controls the output drain current. This is in contrast with the bipolar transistor, where the base-emitter junction is forward-biased; the input voltage then controls the input current, which in turn determines the output current. Moreover, the JFET and the triode are normally "on" because a large drain current flows when there is zero voltage between the gate and the source. By contrast, the bipolar transistor is a normally "off" device because no collector current flows when the emitter-base voltage is zero.

With reverse-biasing of the gate-source junction, very little gate current flows. Thus, the input impedance to a JFET is of the order of several megohms; this is a definite advantage of the FET over the bipolar transistor whose input impedance is relatively low. However, when compared with the JFET, the output current of a bipolar transistor is much more sensitive to changes in the input voltage; the result is a lower voltage gain that is available from the JFET.

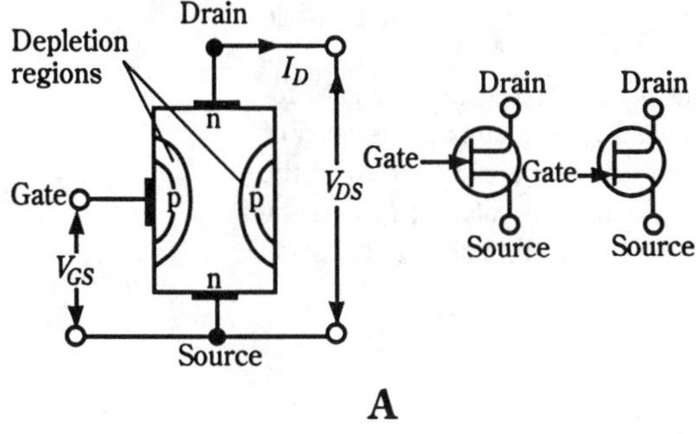

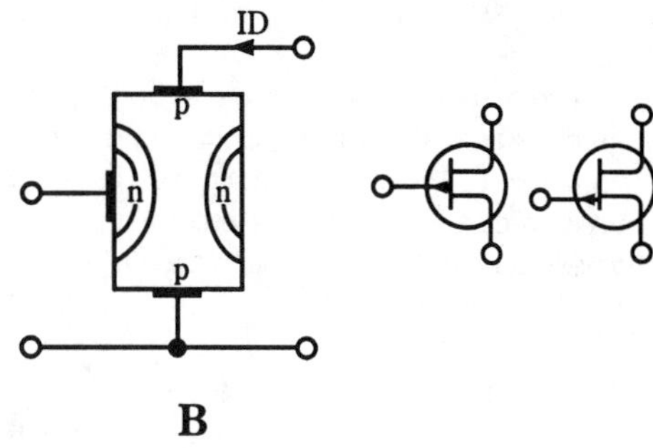

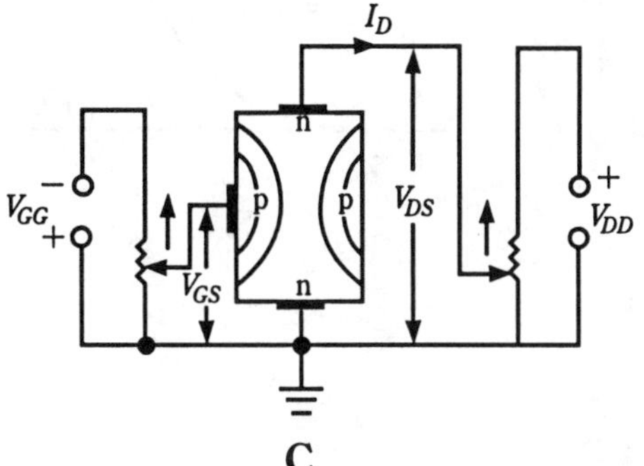

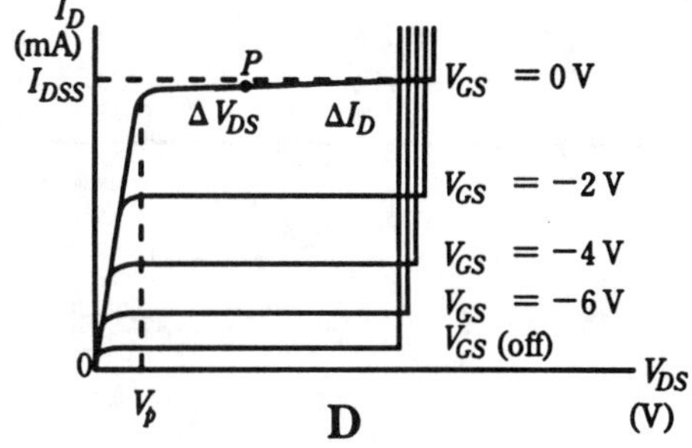

Fig. 4-31 The junction field-effect transistor.

In FIG. 4-31C, the voltage (V_{DS}) between the source and the drain of the n-channel JFET, is gradually increased from zero; at the same time, the voltage between the gate and the source, V_{GS}, is 0 V, which is referred to as the *shorted-gate condition.* Initially, the available channel is broad so that the drain current, I_D, is directly proportional to V_{DS} and rises rapidly as V_{DS} is increased. However, the drain voltage creates a reverse bias on the junction between the channel and the gate. The increase in V_{DS} causes the two depletion regions to widen until finally they almost come into contact. This occurs when V_{DS} equals a value called the ***pinch-off voltage,*** V_p (FIG. 4-31D); the available channel is then very narrow so that the drain current is limited (pinched-off). Further raising of V_{DS} above the pinch-off value will only produce a small increase in the drain current. This situation continues until the drain voltage equals $V_{DS(max)}$; at this point, an avalanche effect occurs and the JFET breaks down. Over the operating range between V_p and $V_{DS(max)}$, the approximately constant value of the drain current with the shorted gate is referred to as the I_{DSS} (drain-to-source current with shorted gate).

For each different negative value of V_{GS}, a different drain-current curve can be obtained. This family of curves is illustrated in FIG. 4-31D. Ultimately, V_{GS} can be sufficiently negative so that the drain current is virtually cut off and equal to zero; this value of gate-source voltage is therefore referred to as $V_{GS(off)}$.

At the cut-off condition, the depletion layers nearly touch; this also occurred when V_{DS} was equal to V_p. Therefore, $V_{GS(\text{off})}$ has the same value as V_p, although $V_{GS(\text{off})}$ is a negative voltage while V_p is positive.

The *transconductance curve* is the graph of the drain current, I_D, plotted against the gate-to-source voltage, V_{GS}, while maintaining the drain-to-source voltage, V_{DS}, at a constant level. For example, in FIG. 4-32A, the drain voltage is set to 12 V while the gate is initially shorted to the source so that $V_{GS} = 0$. The recorded drain current would then equal the value of I_{DSS}. If the reverse gate voltage is now increased from zero, the drain current will fall until ultimately cut-off is reached when $V_{GS} = V_{GS(\text{off})}$.

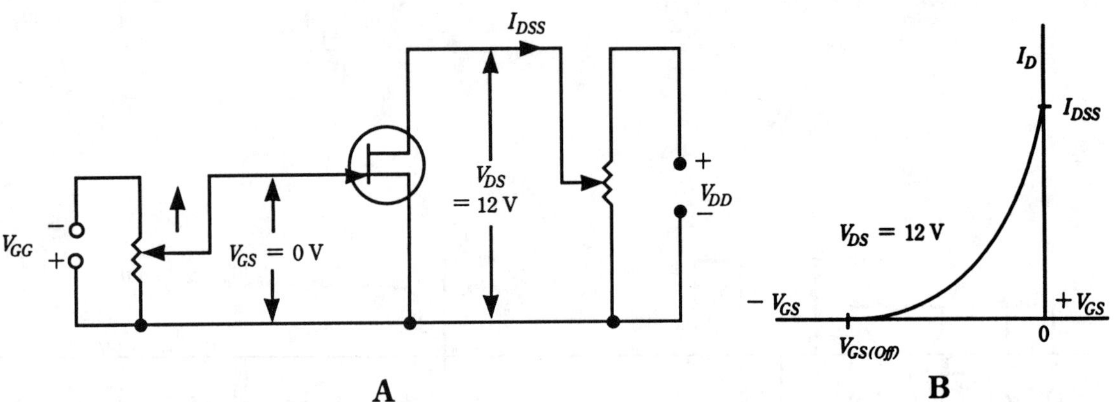

Fig. 4-32 The JFET's transconductance curve.

Methods of biasing the JFET gate bias

The gate-bias method is similar to the bias of bipolar transistors. In FIG. 4-33A, the drain current is given by:

$$I_D = \frac{V_{GG} - V_{GS}}{R_S} \approx \frac{V_{GG}}{R_S} \text{ milliamperes (mA)} \tag{4-4}$$

provided $V_{GG} >> V_{GS}$.

Equation 4-4 means that the values of V_{GG} and R_S can be chosen to establish a value of I_D that is independent of the JFET characteristics.

Voltage divider bias

This method avoids the requirement of a separate V_{GG} supply. By comparing the circuits of FIG. 4-33A and B, the equivalent gate supply voltage:

$$V_{GG} = V_{DD} \times \frac{R_2}{R_1 + R_2} \text{ volts (V)} \tag{4-5}$$

and the equivalent gate resistance:

$$R_G = \frac{R_1 R_2}{R_1 + R_2} \text{ ohms } (\Omega) \tag{4-6}$$

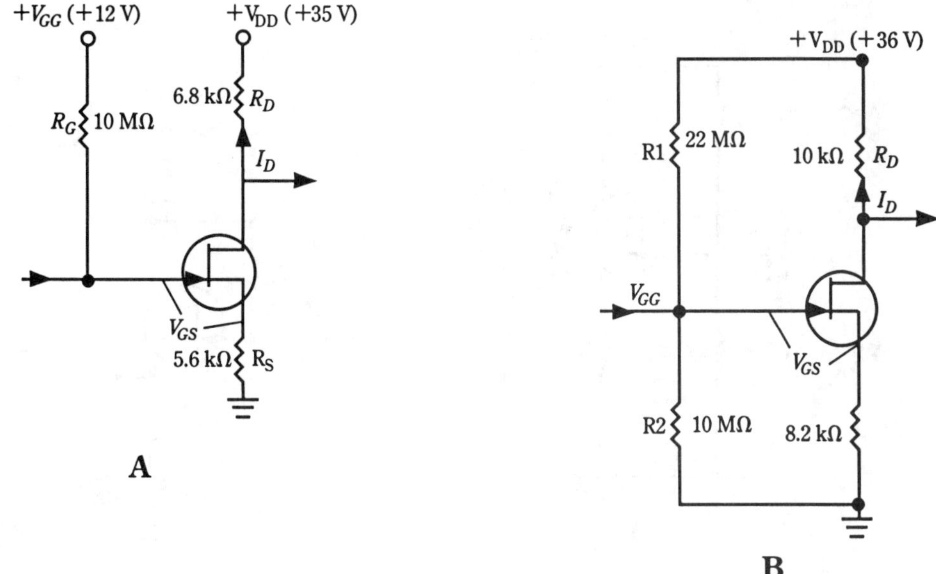

Fig. 4-33 Common methods of biasing the JFET.

The JFET amplifier and the source follower

The principles of the JFET amplifier are shown in FIG. 4-34A (lowercase letters are used to indicate signal values). The signal, v_g, to be amplified is applied between the gate and the source and produces variations, i_d, in the drain current. The resultant voltage variations across the drain load, r_d, produce voltage variations of opposite polarity between gate and ground. This output signal, v_d, is 180° out of phase with the input signal. The same phase inversion occurred with the common-emitter arrangement of a bipolar transistor amplifier. However, the input impedance of the JFET stage is of the order of megohms, while the input impedance to the common-emitter amplifier is only a few kilohms.

Figure 4-34B represents a source follower, which can be compared to the common-collector stage. Because of the negative feedback developed across r_s, the voltage gain is slightly less than unity. However, the same negative feedback also results in the source follower having an extremely high input impedance, but a low output impedance.

* **Question 4-50** The symbol of FIG. 4-35 refers to a (an):

A. npn bipolar transistor B. pnp bipolar transistor C. p-channel JFET D. n-channel JFET E. D MOSFET

Answer Choice D. Refer to FIG. 4-30.

* **Question 4-51** The action of a JFET can be compared with that of a:

A. diode B. triode C. tetrode D. pentode E. hexode

Answer Choice B.

* **Question 4-52** A circuit with a very low input impedance and a relatively high output impedance is the:

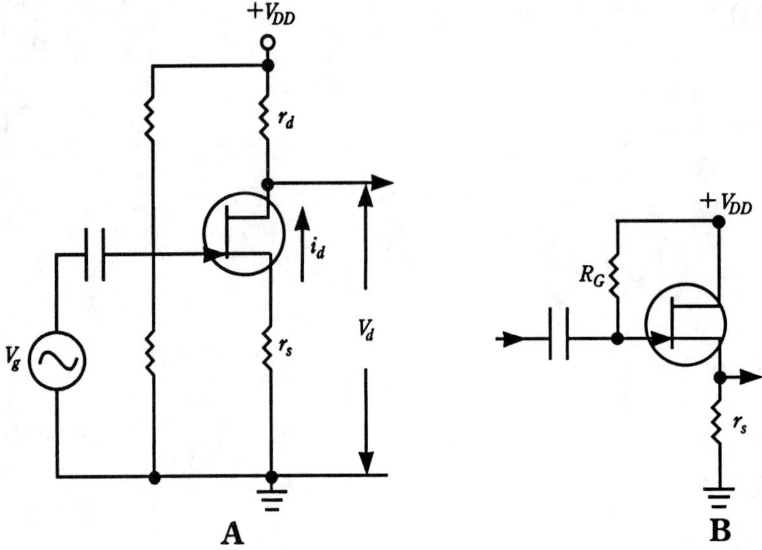

Fig. 4-34 The JFET amplifier and the source follower.

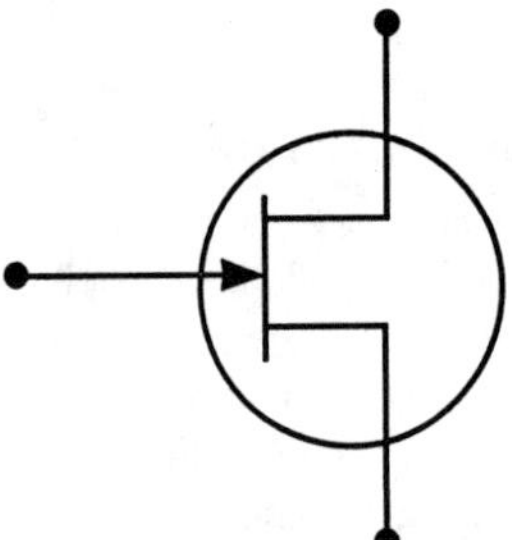

Fig. 4-35 The symbol for question 4-50.

A. JFET amplifier
B. source follower
C. common-emitter amplifier
D. common-base amplifier
E. common-collector stage

Answer Choice D.

* **Question 4-53** The circuit of FIG. 4-36 has a:

A. voltage gain of less than unity
B. low input impedance
C. low output impedance
D. high input impedance
E. poor frequency response

Answer Choice D. The JFET has a low gate current and therefore a very high input impedance.

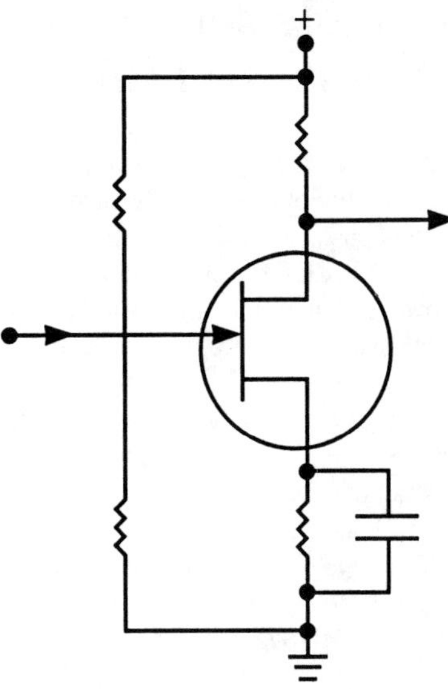

Fig. 4-36 The circuit for question 4-53.

* **Question 4-54** The circuit of FIG. 4-37 has a:

A. very high input impedance
B. low output impedance
C. high voltage gain
D. high output impedance
E. choices A and B are true

Answer Choice E. The circuit is that of a source follower that has a very high input impedance and a low output impedance.

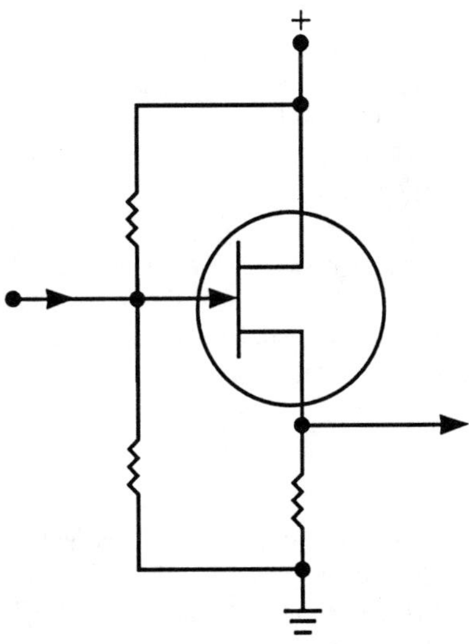

Fig. 4-37 The circuit for question 4-54.

4-8. The metal-oxide semiconductor field-effect transistor (MOSFET)

To avoid excessive gate current, it is necessary to apply a negative bias to a gate of JFET. However, with a MOSFET, the gate current is still virtually zero—even if the gate is positive, with respect to the source. This is made possible by the MOSFET's construction.

In FIG. 4-38A, the n-channel MOSFET has only one p-region, which is called the *substrate.* The substrate might have its own terminal (four-terminal device) or it might be internally connected to the source (three-terminal device); here it is assumed that the source and the substrate are either internally or externally connected. This is illustrated in the schematic symbol of FIG. 4-38B. As with the JFET, the arrow in the symbol points toward the n-channel. The action of the substrate is to reduce the width of the channel through which the electrons pass from source to drain. On the other side of the narrow channel, a thin layer of silicon dioxide (a metal oxide) is deposited and acts as an insulator. A metallic gate is then spread over the opposite surface of the silicon-dioxide layer. Because the gate is now insulated from the channel, the device is sometimes referred to as an *insulated-gate FET (IGFET).*

In the operation of the n-channel MOSFET, the drain supply voltage, V_{DD}, causes electrons to flow from source to drain through the channel while the gate voltage controls the channel's resistance. If a negative voltage is applied to the gate, with respect to the source (FIG. 4-38C), electrostatic induction will cause positive charges to appear in the channel. These charges will be in the form of positive ions that have been created by the repulsion of the conduction-band electrons away from the gate; in other words, the number of conduction-band electrons existing in the n-channel has been reduced or depleted. If the gate is made increasingly negative, there will be fewer and fewer conduction-band electrons available until ultimately the MOSFET is cut off. This action is very similar to that of the JFET; because a negative gate causes a depletion of conduction electrons, this manner of operating a MOSFET is called the *depletion mode.*

Because the channel and the gate are insulated from each other, it is possible to apply a positive voltage to the MOSFET gate (FIG. 4-38D). The result will be to induce negative charges into the n-channel; these will be in the form of additional conduction-band electrons that are drawn into the channel by the action of the positive gate. The total number of conduction-band electrons has therefore been increased or enhanced; consequently, this manner of operation for the MOSFET is called the *enhancement mode.*

Unlike the JFET, the MOSFET can be operated with either a positive or a negative gate voltage; in either mode of operation, the input resistance of a MOSFET is very high and is typically of the order of hundreds of GΩ.

Apart from the necessity of reversing the polarity of the drain and gate supply voltages, the operations of p-channel and n-channel MOSFET's are identical.

The appearance of the MOSFET's characteristic curves is similar to those of the JFET and is illustrated in FIGS. 4-39A and B. The only difference is the extension of the gate voltage into the positive region of the enhancement mode.

The DE MOSFET amplifier

The type of MOSFET that can either operate in the depletion or the enhancement mode, conducts when $V_{GS} = 0$, with a drain current equal to I_{DSS}. For this reason, the device is called a *normally "on"* or *depletion-enhancement (DE) MOSFET.* Such a MOSFET can be operated with zero bias because the dc operating point can be chosen at $V_{GS} = 0$ (FIG. 4-40). When the signal is applied to the gate, the operation of the MOSFET will swing back and forth between the depletion and the enhancement modes.

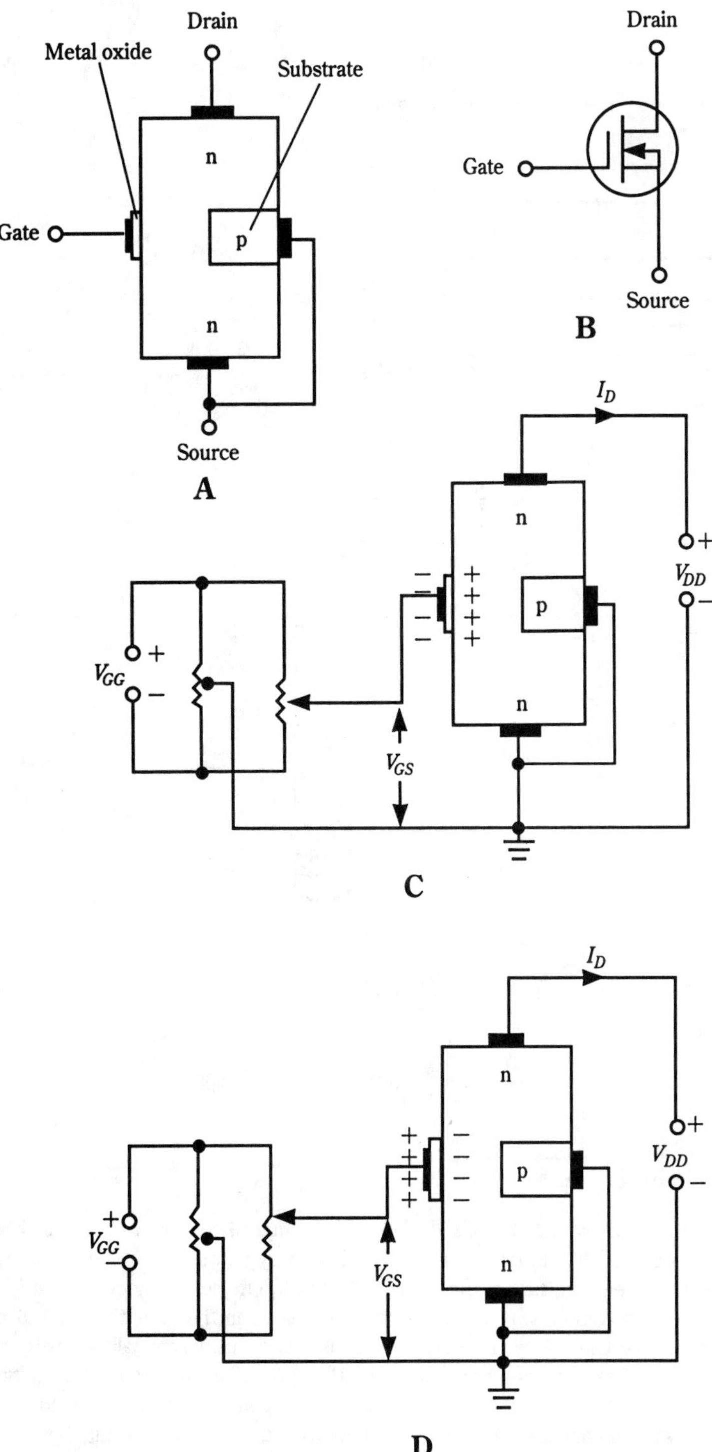

Fig. 4-38 The DE MOSFET.

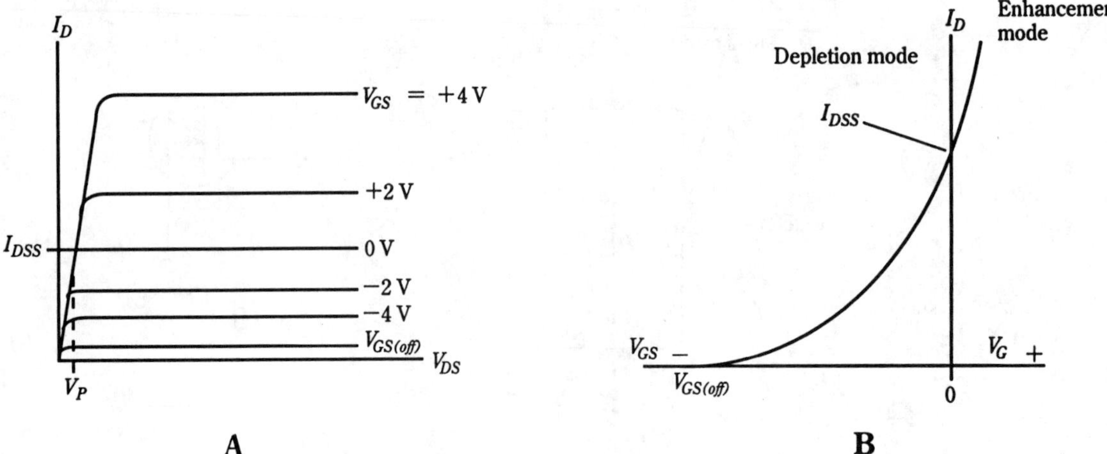

Fig. 4-39 The characteristics of the DE MOSFET.

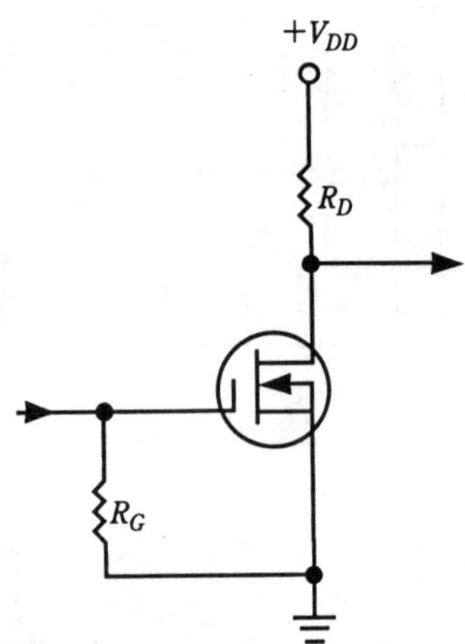

Fig. 4-40 The DE MOSFET amplifier.

The E MOSFET

In the *Enhancement Only (E) MOSFET,* there is no longer a continuous n-channel between the drain and the source. The substrate stretches all the way across the metal-oxide layer (FIG. 4-41A) so that no current can flow if the MOSFET is in the depletion mode. When V_{GS} = 0 V, a small number of conduction-band electrons will be created in the substrate by thermal energy, but the current flow caused by the drain supply is still extremely small. Consequently, the E MOSFET is also referred to as a *normally "off" MOSFET.* This normally off condition is shown in the schematic symbol (FIG. 4-41B) by the broken line, which represents the channel. Because FIG. 4-41A shows an n-channel E MOSFET, the arrow in the schematic symbol points toward the channel; with a p-type E MOSFET, the arrow points away from the channel.

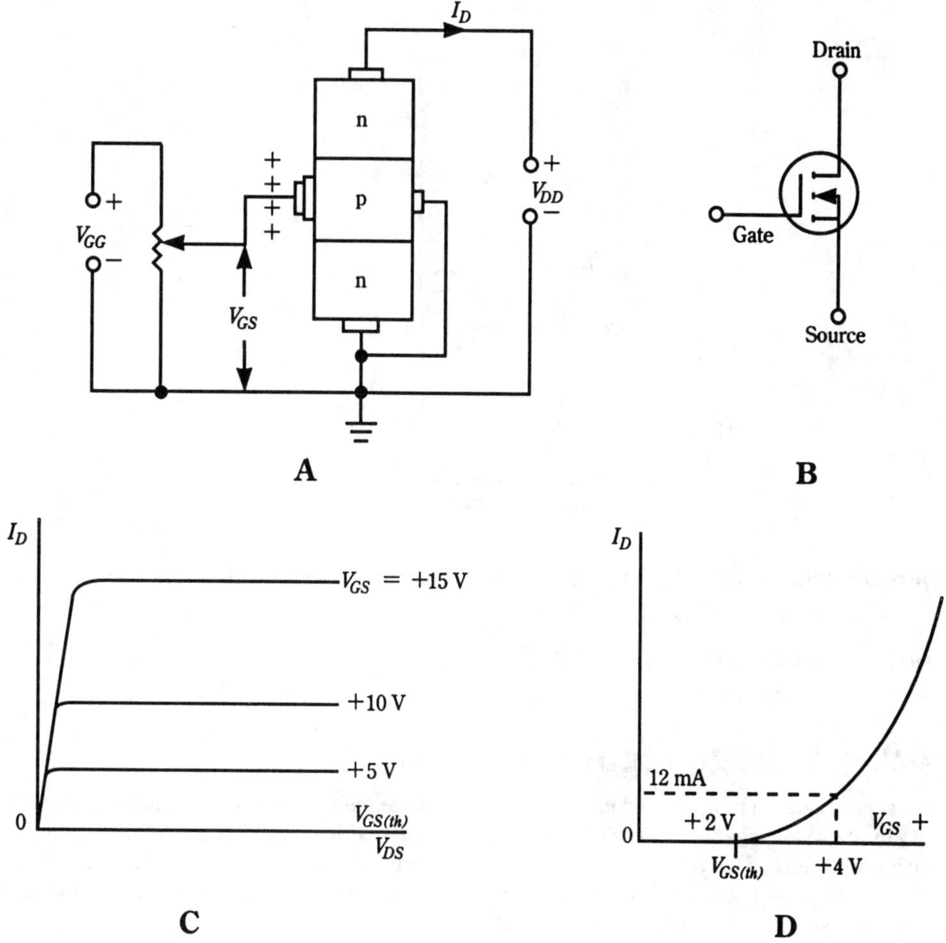

Fig. 4-41 The E MOSFET and its characteristics.

To produce an appreciable flow of drain current, it is necessary to apply a positive voltage to the gate. If this voltage is low, the charges induced in the substrate are negative ions, which are created by filling holes in the p-substrate with valence electrons. When the positive gate voltage is increased above a certain *minimum* threshold level, ($V_{GS} > V_{GS(th)}$), the additional induced charges are conduction-based electrons that exist in a thin n-type inversion layer next to the metal oxide and allow an appreciable flow of electrons from source to drain. The characteristics of an E MOSFET are shown in FIGS. 4-41C and D.

A typical E-MOSFET amplifier circuit is shown in FIG. 4-42. The resistor, R_G, allows the necessary positive bias to be applied to the gate, so $V_{GS} > V_{GS(th)}$.

* **Question 4-55** In FIG. 4-43, which of the symbols represent a DE MOSFET?

A. a B. b C. c D. d E. e

Answer Choice D. Refer to FIG. 4-38B.

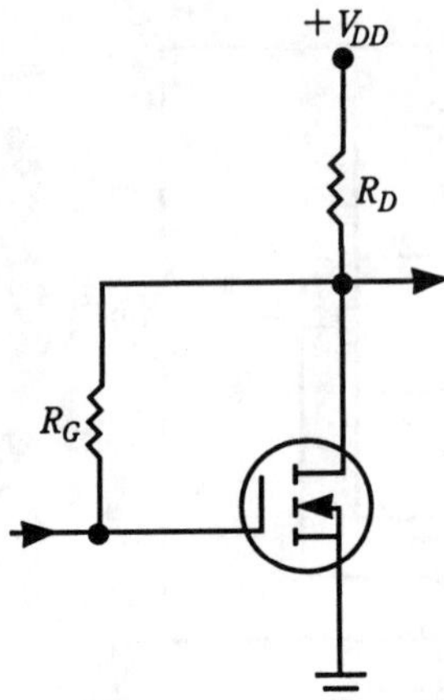

Fig. 4-42 The E MOSFET amplifier.

* **Question 4-56** In FIG. 4-43, which of the symbols represents an E MOSFET?

A. a B. b C. c D. d E. e

Answer Choice E. Refer to FIG. 4-41B.

4-9. Voltage regulator circuits

The zener diode is primarily used in power supplies where the load current is small and does not vary over a wide range. By using a transistor in conjunction with a zener diode, the current range can be increased and the regulation percentage can be reduced. Such electronic voltage regulators are referred to as either *shunt* or *series* regulators; these classifications are determined by the circuit position of the transistor in relation to the load.

Shunt voltage regulator

The basic shunt-regulator circuit is shown in FIG. 4-44, where the npn transistor, Q1, is in parallel across the load. The collector is directly joined to the positive side of the regulated dc output voltage, and the emitter is connected to the negative (grounded) side through the zener diode, CR1. This diode is biased to its breakdown voltage by the resistor, R_2, and it therefore maintains a constant reference level at Q1's emitter. The base is connected to the wiper of the potentiometer, R_1, which is adjusted so that the base is positive, with respect to the fixed emitter voltage. The emitter-base junction is therefore forward-biased and the transistor will conduct with its collector current value determined by R_1's setting. Because the collector current flows through the series resistor, R, the potentiometer's setting also determines the level of the dc output voltage.

If the unregulated input voltage rises or the load current falls, there will be a slight increase in the dc output voltage. This will raise the forward bias that is applied to the emitter-base junction of Q1; as a result, the collector current will be greater and this increase will compensate for the original change in the values of E or I_L. Similarly, if, for any reason, the dc output voltage tends

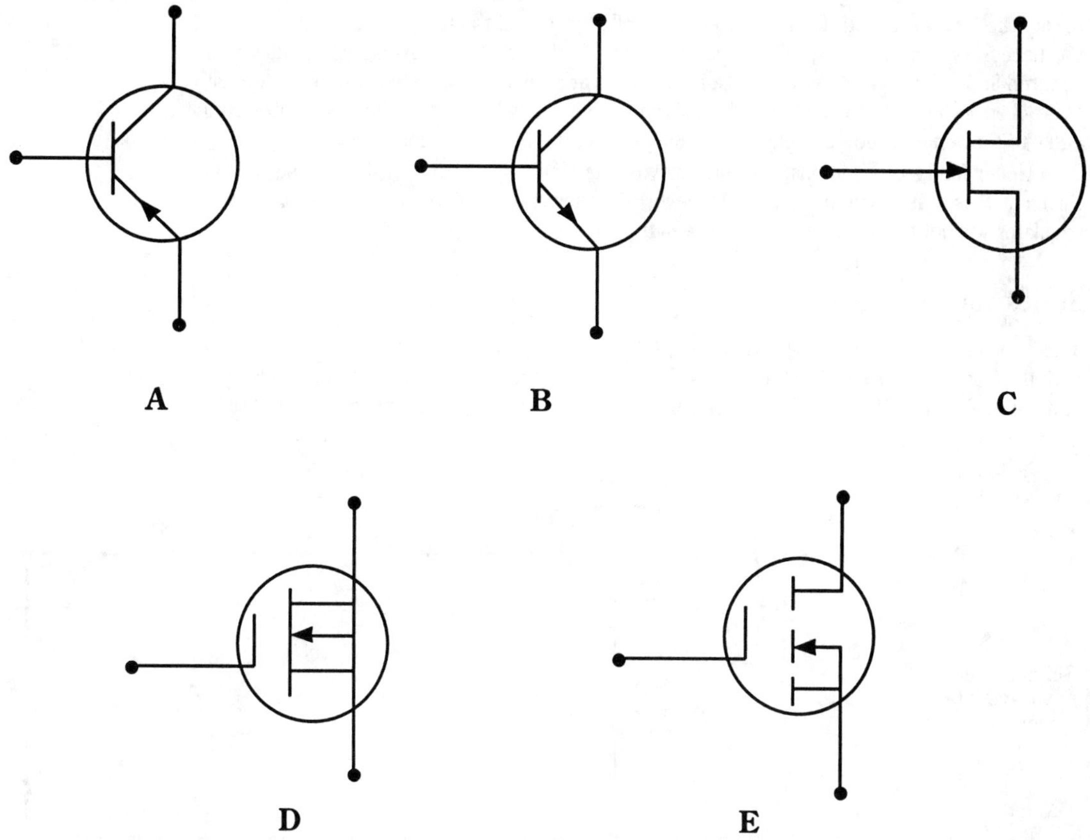

A **B** **C**

D **E**

Fig. 4-43 The symbols for questions 4-55 and 4-56.

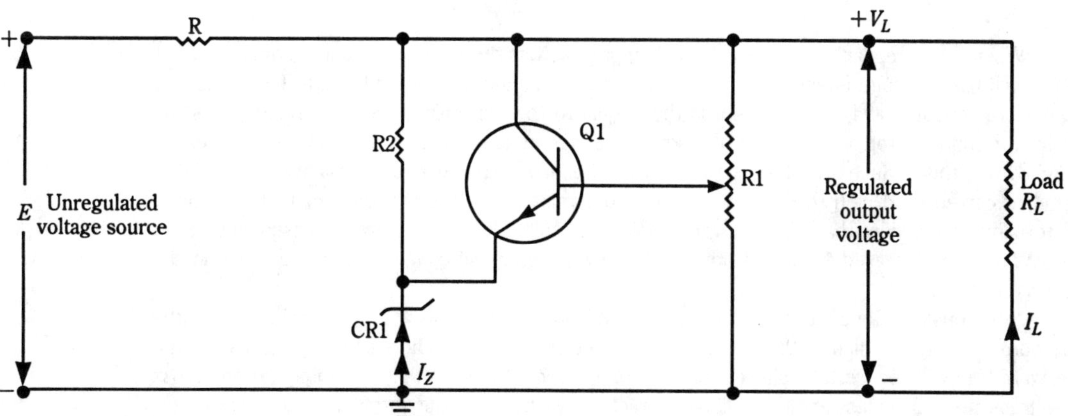

Fig. 4-44 The shunt-voltage regulator.

to fall, the forward bias to Q1 is reduced, the collector current is less, and its decrease provides the necessary compensation. The action is similar to that of the zener-diode circuit, which was covered in Section 3-4. However, because a small variation in forward bias can provide relatively large changes in collector current, the current-range capability of the shunt-regulator circuit is equal to the zener diode's current range multiplied by the β factor of the transistor.

Under full-load conditions, the efficiency of the shunt regulator is high because the current through Q1 is at its minimum level. Moreover, if a short circuit occurs across the load, the shunt regulator will not be subjected to excessive current.

Series voltage regulator

The basic regulator circuit is shown in FIG. 4-45, where npn transistor Q1 is connected in series with the load and also acts as a variable resistor. In conjunction with R_1, the zener diode operates at its breakdown voltage, and it therefore maintains a constant potential at the base of Q1.

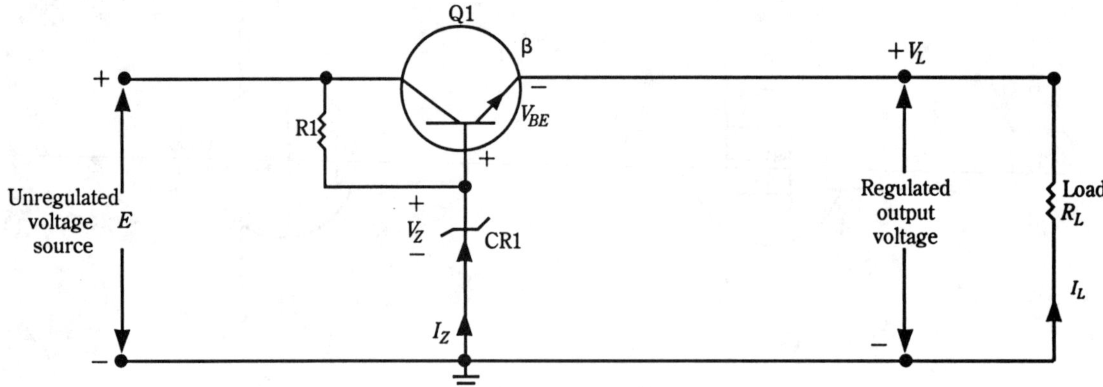

Fig. 4-45 The series-voltage regulator.

When the unregulated source voltage is applied across the series combination of Q1 and R_L, the fixed base voltage is such that the emitter-base junction is forward-biased. The transistor therefore conducts and the dc output is then equal to the unregulated source voltage, less the collector-emitter drop across Q1. If the source voltage increases, the value of V_L also increases slightly and this reduces the forward bias to Q1's emitter-base junction. As a result, a smaller emitter current is driven through R_L and this compensates for the tendency of V_L to increase. Alternatively, consider that Q1's equivalent collector-emitter resistance has increased so that, by the VDR, the increased voltage drop across the transistor will compensate for the rise in the source voltage.

Now consider the effect of an increase in the load current. This will cause a slight fall in the dc output voltage, which is the same as Q1's emitter potential. The resultant increase in the forward bias will reduce the collector-emitter resistance. It follows that the voltage drop across the transistor will be less and this will counteract any decrease in the output voltage.

The operation of the series regulator is based on the principle of negative feedback. The resultant degree of circuit stability is the main advantage of series regulators over shunt regulators and is the reason why series regulators are more widely used. However, the circuit of FIG.

4-45 has no inherent protection against excessive current, so if a short circuit occurs across the output voltage, the transistor will be severely overloaded. Another disadvantage of this regulator circuit is its inability to respond quickly to small voltage changes.

* **Question 4-57** In the circuit of FIG. 4-46, the voltage across the resistor, R, is:

A. 15 V B. 6 V C. 0.7 V D. 9 V E. 21 V

Answer Choice D. Because $E = 15$ V and the zener-diode voltage is 6 V, the voltage drop across $R = 15 - 6 = 9$ V.

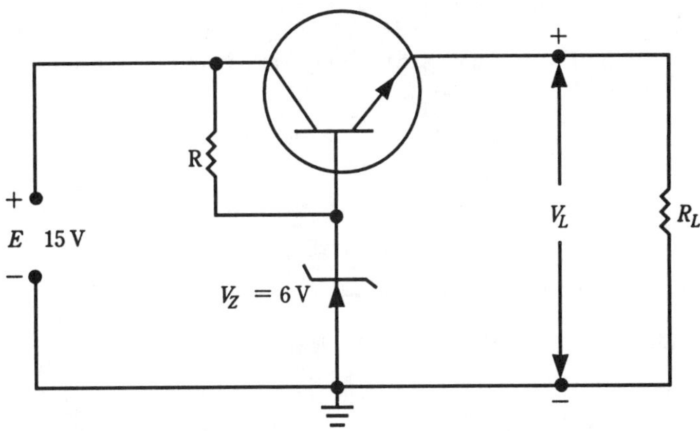

Fig. 4-46 The circuit for questions 4-57 and 4-58.

* **Question 4-58** In the circuit of FIG. 4-46, the output voltage, V_L, across the load, R_L, is:

A. 6 V B. 6.7 V C. 5.3 V D. 15 V E. 9 V

Answer Choice C. The emitter-base junction is forward-biased so that $V_{BE} = 0.7$ V and the base is positive, with respect to the emitter. Because the zener diode voltage is 6 V, the output voltage, V_L, across the load, R_L, is: $6 - 0.7 = 5.3$ V.

4-10. Oscillators

An amplifier in a radio-frequency (RF) transmitter is responsible for raising the power level of its input signal. Tracing backwards from the transmitter's final amplifier, you will ultimately arrive at a stage that is capable of producing a continuous RF power output, without any input from a preceding stage. Such a stage is called an *oscillator;* its primary function is to generate a given waveform (sine, square, pulse, sawtooth, triangular, etc.) at a constant peak-to-peak value and at a specific frequency. These desirable traits are achieved by the partial conversion of a dc input power into an RF output power. The requirements are:

- The voltage feedback from the output circuit is the signal to the input circuit. It must provide the correct action at the input so as to aid the operation of the circuit. This is known as *positive* or *regenerative feedback.*

- The amount of the positive feedback must be sufficient to compensate for the losses that naturally occur in the circuit.

An oscillator circuit must also contain a dc supply for its operation, an active device (op amp, transistor, or tube), a frequency-determining network, and a positive feedback path. The various oscillators can then be classified according to the method of providing the positive feedback.

Positive or regenerative feedback

Positive feedback can be used to increase the gain of an amplifier circuit. This is illustrated in FIG. 4-47, where V_i is the input signal from the preceding stage. Such a signal is applied between the base of a transistor and ground. The output signal, V_o, appears between the collector and ground and a fraction, beta (β), of this output is fed back to the input circuit, so this feedback voltage, $+\beta V_o$, is in phase with V_i; β is called the *feedback factor,* which can either be expressed as a decimal, fraction, or percentage.

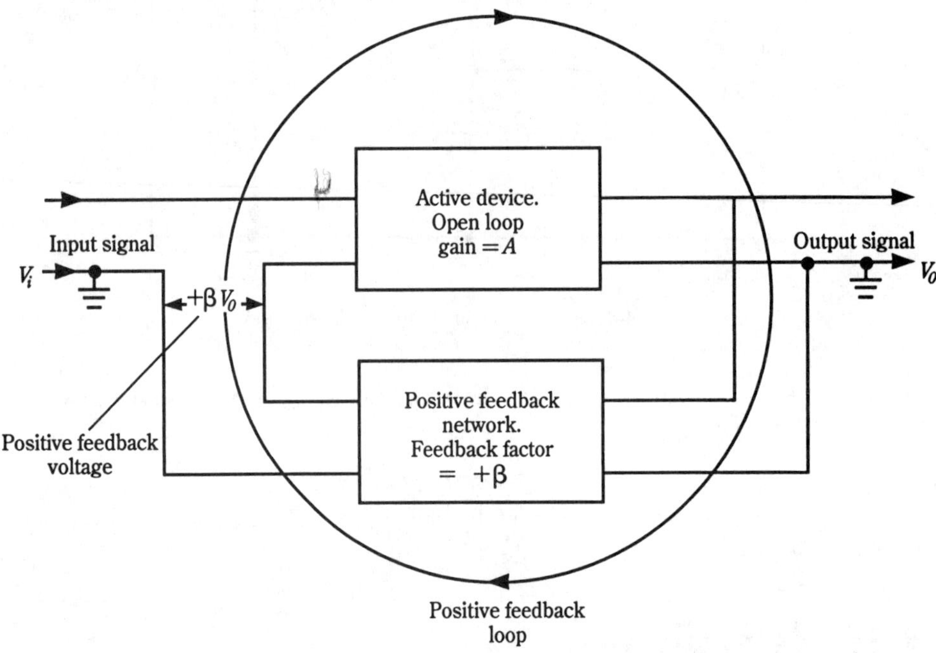

Fig. 4-47 Positive feedback in an amplifier circuit.

In order for the feedback to be positive, there must be a total of 360° phase shift (equivalent to zero phase shift) around the feedback loop, base → collector → base. The total signal voltage, when applied between the base and emitter, is the sum of the input signal, V_i, and the positive feedback voltage, $+\beta V_o$. Because the voltage gain (open-loop gain) of the active device is A:

$$\text{Output signal: } V_o = A \times (V_i + \beta V_o) \qquad (4\text{-}7)$$

This yields:

$$A' = \frac{V_o}{V_i} = \frac{A}{1 - A\beta} \qquad (4\text{-}8)$$

where A' is the overall voltage gain with the positive feedback present (closed loop gain). There are three possible conditions that are associated with EQ. 4-4.

- If A and β are chosen so that the value of $A\beta$ is less than 1, then A' is greater than A and the amplifier's gain has been increased as a result of the positive feedback. Such is the case with the so-called regenerative amplifier.

- If $A\beta = 1$ (for example $A = 10$ and $\beta = 0.1$ or 10%), A' is theoretically infinite. Thus, the circuit can provide a continuous output without any input signal from the previous stage. This is the condition for a stable oscillator.

- If $A\beta > 1$, the oscillator is unstable. The output, V_o, increases, which reduces the value of A until the equilibrium condition of $A\beta = 1$ is reached.

The condition of oscillation is therefore $A\beta = 1\angle 0°$, sometimes referred to as the ***Barkhausen*** or ***Nyquist criterion***. The inclusion of "$\angle 0°$" in the polar value of $A\beta$ means that the resultant phase shift around the loop is 0°; consequently, the feedback is positive. By contrast, an angle of 180° would indicate that the feedback is negative.

In a sine-wave oscillator, the frequency-determining network is (in most cases) some form of tuned LC circuit (FIG. 4-48A). If a charged capacitor is connected across an inductor, the capacitor will discharge and establish a magnetic field around the inductor. When the discharge is completed, the magnetic field collapses and a counter EMF is induced in the coil. This EMF will recharge the capacitor, whose voltage has its polarity reversed, when compared with the original condition. The sequence of events is then repeated so that an alternating sine-wave current exists between the inductor and the capacitor. This is sometimes referred to as the *flywheel effect,* which occurs at the frequency, f_o, of free oscillation. The formula for f_o is:

$$\text{Frequency, } f_o = \frac{1}{2\pi}\sqrt{\frac{1}{LC} - \frac{R^2}{4L^2}} \approx \frac{1}{2\pi\sqrt{LC}} \text{ hertz (Hz)} \tag{4-9}$$

where R is the resistance of the coil.

Owing to the power dissipated as heat in the coil's resistance, the flywheel current is in the form of a damped oscillation (FIG. 4-48B) that gradually decays to zero. In order to sustain a continuous oscillation, you must supply positive feedback to the tuned circuit and thereby compensate for the losses that naturally occur.

Figure 4-49 shows the principle of positive feedback in an oscillator circuit. Assume that the input signal is 1 V RMS and the voltage gain of the active device is 10; the output signal is 10 V RMS. If the feedback factor is 1⁄10 or 10%, the 10-V output signal will be responsible for creating the 1-V input signal (this does not mean that only 9 V is left at the output signal). This argument sounds rather like the chicken and the egg, so the question arises "how does the circuit get started in the first place?" There are two possible answers:

1. When the dc power supply is applied, the resulting transient conditions will cause the tuned circuit to be shocked into oscillation. The positive feedback takes control and builds up the oscillation.

2. All active devices are inherently noisy. Because the noise is spread through the frequency spectrum, it will contain a component at the frequency of oscillation. This component will

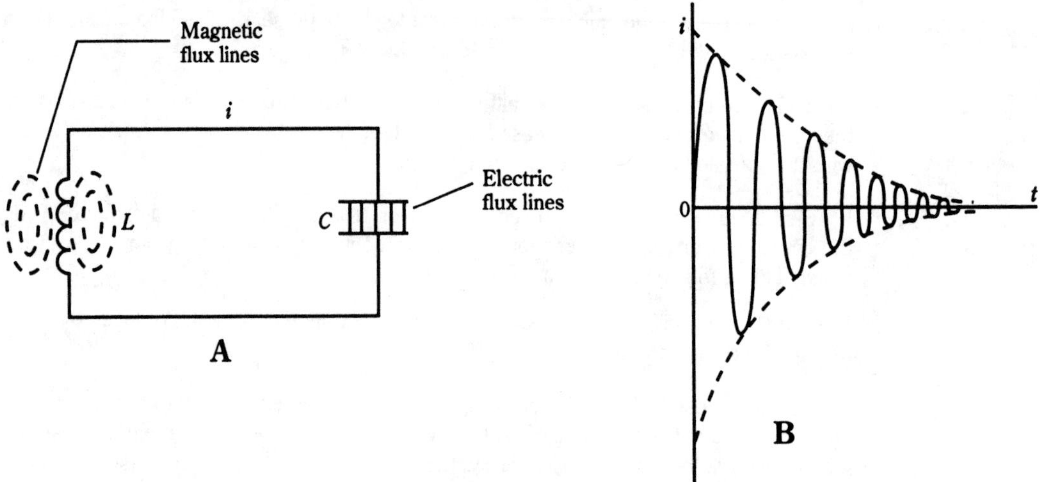

Fig. 4-48 Damped oscillation in an LC circuit.

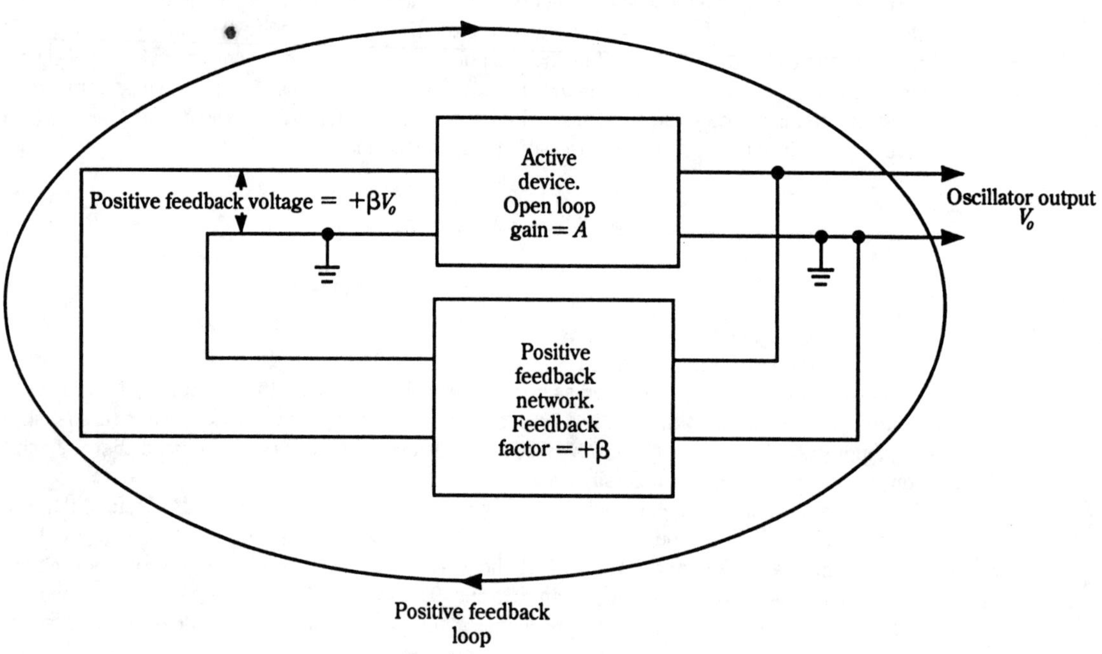

Fig. 4-49 The principle of the oscillator.

trigger the positive feedback network, increasing the oscillation until the equilibrium condition of $A\beta = 1/0°$ is reached.

You have studied the requirements for an oscillator circuit to operate successfully. Now, you can look at some oscillator circuits and see how the requirements are fulfilled.

Direct-feedback Hartley and Colpitts oscillators

In Hartley oscillators, the feedback voltage is developed across a component that is common to both the output and input circuits. Figure 4-50 shows one form of the Hartley oscillator. Notice that the circuit contains a tapped coil, which is the distinguishing feature of this type of oscillator. The coil is common to both the input and output circuits because the portion L1 belongs to the output circuit, and L2 is part of the input circuit.

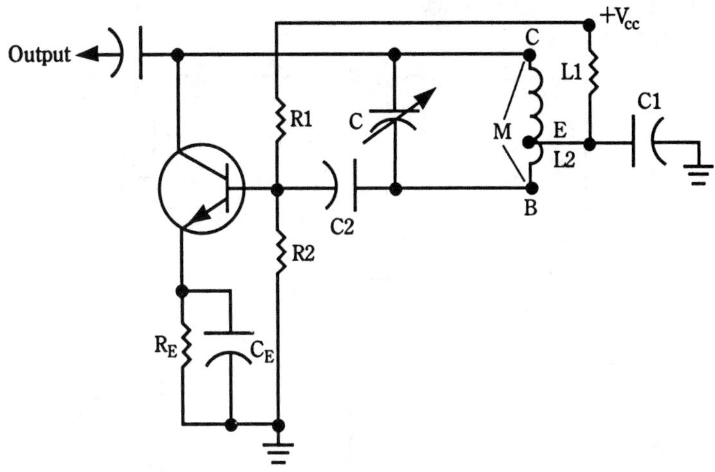

Fig. 4-50 The Hartley oscillator.

In the circuit of FIG. 4-50, the capacitor, C1, is a bypass capacitor to prevent the RF current from entering the V_{CC} supply. The tapping point, E, is effectively at RF ground, and is therefore at emitter potential (as far as the oscillation is concerned). The top of L1 (point C) is directly joined to the collector, and the bottom of L2 (point B) is connected to the base through the bypass capacitor, C2, which prevents the V_{CC} voltage from being applied to the base through L2. Because the npn transistor is arranged in the common-emitter (CE) configuration, there is 180° phase change from the base to the collector as a result of the amplifying action. Because points C and B are at opposite ends of the tapped coil, these points carry RF voltages that are 180° out of phase, with respect to the tapping point, E (RF ground). Consequently, there is a further 180° phase change across the coil, and a total shift of 360° around the loop of base → collector → base. The feedback is therefore positive with the feedback voltage developed across L2 and applied between the base and emitter.

The amount of feedback, and hence the oscillator's output from the collector, can be easily determined by the position of the tapping point on the coil. The higher the position of the tapping point, the greater the amount of feedback and the higher the oscillator's output. Because the feedback is easily controlled, the Hartley circuit oscillates readily over a wide range of frequencies. Notice that R1 is included to provide forward bias, which allows the transistor to conduct when the V_{CC} supply is switched on.

The generated frequency is approximately:

Frequency of oscillation: $$f_o = \frac{1}{2\pi\sqrt{(L_1 + L_2 + 2M)C}} \text{ hertz (Hz)} \qquad (4\text{-}10)$$

where M is the mutual inductance between L1 and L2.

Although there is normally mutual coupling between L1 and L2, the circuit will still oscillate through direct feedback, even if L1 and L2 are shielded from each other.

Owing to nonlinear operation of the transistor, the oscillator will generate harmonic voltages that appear between the collector (point C) and RF ground (point E). In FIG. 4-51, these harmonic voltages are divided between C and L2. For high harmonic frequencies, the reactance, C, is low while the reactance of L2 is high. Consequently, there is appreciable feedback across L2, and the Hartley oscillator's output is rich in harmonics. In some applications, the presence of harmonics is a definite disadvantage, but in other circuits they serve a useful purpose.

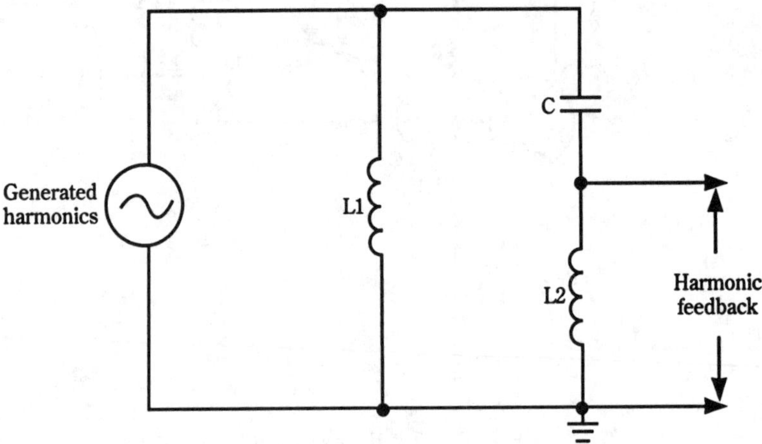

Fig. 4-51 Harmonic feedback in the Hartley oscillator.

The Colpitts oscillator is very commonly used—especially in the high-frequency range of hundreds of MHz; a JFET version is shown in FIG. 4-52. Notice the presence of the capacitive voltage divider, C1, C2, which is the distinguishing feature of the Colpitts oscillator. In the Hartley circuit, the direct feedback was taken across the inductor, L2: in the Colpitts oscillator, the positive feedback is developed across the capacitor, C2. It is common practice to vary the values C1 and C2, so their ratio remains constant and the feedback factor does not change with frequency.

All arrangements of the Colpitts oscillator are shunt-fed, because the active device could not conduct if the positive dc supply was series-connected to the lead that joins capacitors C1 and C2.

Examine the n-channel JFET version in detail. There is 180° phase change from the gate to the drain because of the amplifying action of the device. Because points D (drain) and G (gate) are connected to opposite ends of the tuned circuit, these points will carry RF voltages that are 180° out of phase, with respect to the grounded point, S (source). Consequently, there is a further 180° phase change across the tuned circuit and a total of 360° (zero) phase shift around the positive feedback loop, gate → drain → gate. C_g and R_g provide signal bias by the use of gate current.

In FIG. 4-52, capacitors C1, and C2 are in series across coil L, and the tuning capacitor, C3, is in parallel. Therefore, ignoring the parameters of the active device, the output frequency from the drain is given by:

Frequency of oscillation: $$f_o = \frac{1}{2\pi\sqrt{LC_T}} \text{ hertz (Hz)}$$

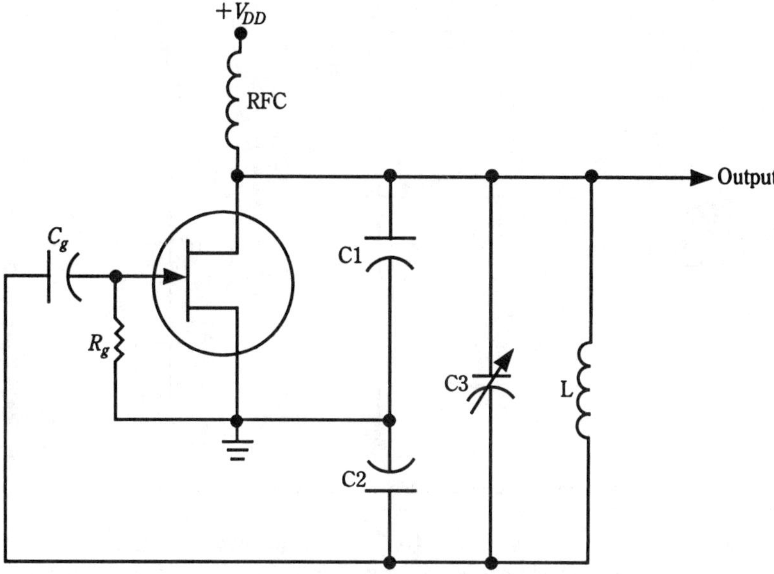

Fig. 4-52 The Colpitts oscillator.

where:

$$C_T = C_3 + \frac{C_1C_2}{C_1 + C_2} \qquad (4\text{-}10)$$

Capacitor C3 can be omitted, and the circuit can then be tuned by varying either C1 or C2 (or both). However, any changes in the capacitive divider might alter the amount of feedback and the amplitude of the oscillator's output.

The harmonics generated by the nonlinear operation of the JFET appear between points D and S (FIG. 4-53). These voltages are divided between L and C2, and because the reactance of L is high for the harmonic frequencies while that of C2 is low, there will be little harmonic feedback developed across C2. Consequently, the output waveform is virtually devoid of harmonics; this is a major advantage in some applications.

Notice that because both the Hartley and Colpitts oscillators can be tuned through an entire frequency range, they are called *variable-frequency oscillators (VFOs).*

The crystal and the piezoelectric effect

A crystal oscillator is used to obtain the higher degree of frequency stability that is required by transmitters that are licensed by the FCC. A properly cut crystal possesses the characteristics of a resonant circuit and can therefore be used in place of a tuned circuit as the frequency-controlling element.

Before discussing the use and operation of a crystal in a circuit, it is best to discuss some of the properties and the manufacture of the various types of crystal. Controlling the frequency by means of crystals is based on the piezoelectric effect. When certain crystals are compressed or stretched in specific directions electric charges appear on the surface of the crystal. Conversely, when such crystals are placed between two metallic surfaces, across which a difference of poten-

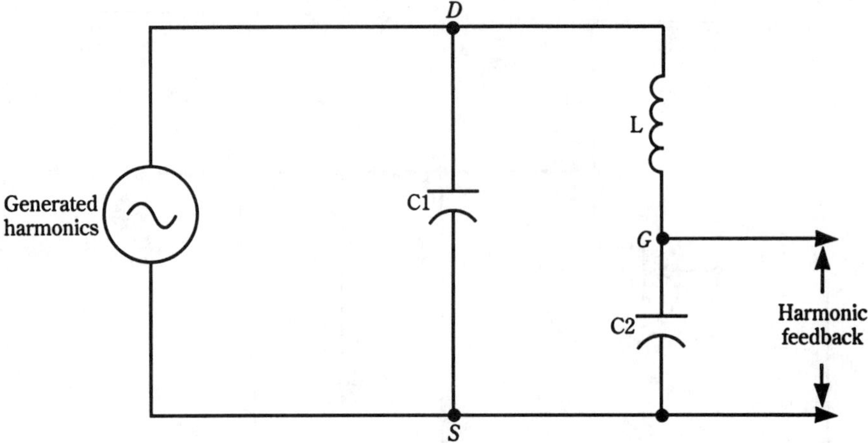

Fig. 4-53 Harmonic feedback in the Colpitts oscillator.

tial exists, the crystals expand or contract. This interrelation between the electric and the mechanical properties of a crystal is termed the *piezoelectric effect.* If a slice of crystal is stretched along its length so that its width contracts, opposing electrical charges appear across its faces and a difference of potential is generated. If a slice of crystal is compressed along its length so that its width expands, the charges across its faces will reverse polarity. Consequently, if alternately stretched and compressed, the slice of crystal becomes a source of alternating voltage.

The effect is reversible; if an alternating voltage is applied across the faces of a crystal, it will vibrate mechanically. The amplitude of these vibrations will be vigorous when the frequency of the ac voltage is equal to the natural mechanical frequency of the crystal. These fundamental frequencies are governed by such factors as the dimensions of the crystal and (in particular) its thickness. If all mechanical losses are overcome, the vibrations at this natural frequency will sustain themselves and generate an electrical oscillation at a constant frequency. Accordingly, a crystal can be substituted for the tuned tank circuit in certain solid-state oscillators.

Practically all crystals exhibit the piezoelectric effect, but only a few are suitable as the equivalent of tuned circuits for frequency-control purposes. Among these crystals are quartz, Rochelle salt, and tourmaline. *Rochelle salt* is the most active piezoelectric substance because it generates the greatest amount of voltage for a given mechanical strain. However, the operation of a Rochelle-salt crystal is affected to a large extent by heat, aging, mechanical shock, and moisture.

Tourmaline is almost as good as quartz over a considerable frequency range, and is somewhat better than quartz between 3 and 90 MHz, but it has the advantage of being a semi-precious stone, and its cost is therefore prohibitive.

Quartz, although less active than Rochelle salt, is used universally for oscillator frequency control because it is inexpensive, mechanically rugged, and expands very little with heat. Crystals used in oscillator circuits are cut from natural or artificially grown quartz crystals that have the general form of a hexagonal prism (FIG. 4-54A), whose cross-section is shown in FIG. 4-54B.

The line that joins the points at each end (or apex) of the crystal, is known as the *optical* or *Z-axis.* Stresses along this axis produce no piezoelectric effect. The X-axes pass through the hexagonal edges and the cross-sectional area at right-angles to the Z-axes. Such axes are known as the *electrical axes,* which are the directions of the greatest piezoelectric activity.

The Y-axes, which are perpendicular to the faces of the crystal, as well as the Z-axes, are called the *mechanical axes.* A mechanical stress in the direction of any Y-axis produces an electro-

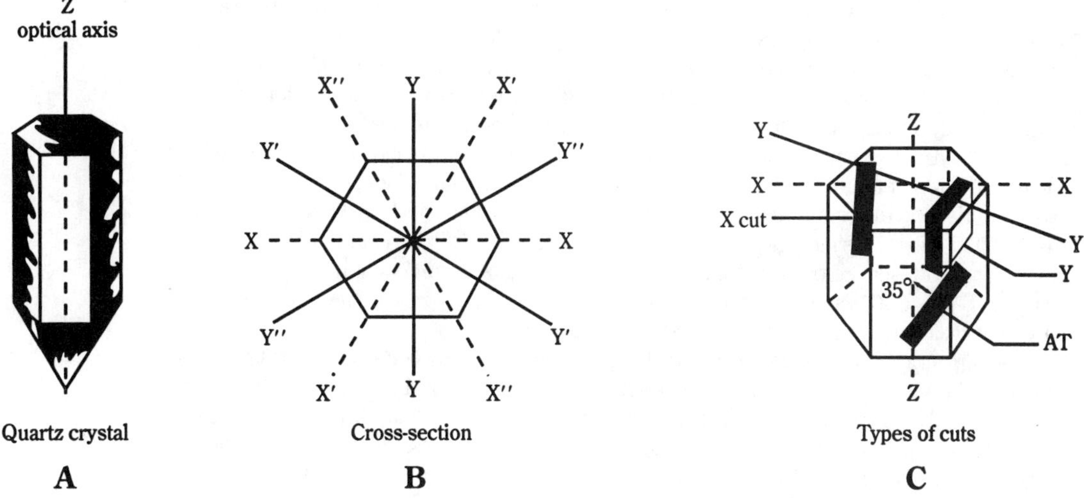

Fig. 4-54 Axes and cuts of the quartz crystal.

static stress, or charge, in the direction of the Z-axis, which is perpendicular to the Y-axis involved. The polarity of the charge depends on whether the mechanical strain is a compression or a tension. An electrostatic stress, or voltage applied in the direction of any electrical axis produces a mechanical strain (either an expansion or a contraction) along that mechanical axis that is at right-angles to the electrical axis. For example, if a crystal is compressed along a Y-axis, a voltage will appear on the faces of the crystal along the X-axis. If a voltage is applied along the X-axis of a crystal, it will expand or contract in the direction of the Y-axis. This interconnection between the mechanical and the electrical properties is exhibited by practically all sections cut from a piezoelectric crystal.

Crystal wafers can be sliced from the mother crystal in a variety of directions along the axes. These are known as *cuts* and are identified by designations such as X, Y, AT, GT, etc. (FIG. 4-54C). Each has certain advantages, but, in general, the crystal should operate at the intended frequency, have a single operating frequency, and possess minimum frequency variations as a result of temperature changes.

Both the X- and Y-cuts have unfavorable temperature characteristics; the FCC requires that such cuts are enclosed in a thermostatically controlled oven with a maximum temperature variation of ± 0.1°C. Better characteristics can be obtained by cutting wafers at different angles of rotation about the X-axis; the Y-cut serves as the 0° reference because it is lined up with both the X- and Z-axes and lies in a plane formed by those axes. By rotating this slice from its starting point, a number of different cuts can be formed.

Crystals in oscillator circuits must be cut and ground to accurate dimensions. Crystals can also be cut in various shapes. Crystals in the lower frequency range are square or rectangular and some of the crystals in the higher frequency range are disc shaped, similar to a coin. The type of cut determines how active the crystal will be, and for a given crystal cut, the thinner the crystal, the higher is its resonant frequency. For example, the thickness of a 25-MHz quartz crystal is only about 1 millimeter. This is the top limit for a fundamental frequency because thinner crystals would tend to fracture easily.

The resonant frequency of quartz crystals is practically unaffected by changes in the load. Like most other materials, however, quartz expands slightly with an increase in temperature. The expansion affects the resonant frequency of the crystal.

The *temperature coefficient* of the crystal refers to the increase or decrease in the resonant frequency as a function of temperature. The temperature coefficients vary widely from one crystal cut to another. A positive temperature coefficient is assigned to those cuts that provide an increase in the frequency with an increase in the temperature. A negative coefficient refers to those crystals that decrease their natural resonant frequency when the temperature increases. One cut, the GT, has a practically zero temperature coefficient over a wide range of temperature changes. The temperature coefficient also depends on the surrounding temperature at which it is measured. Heating the crystal can be caused by external conditions, such as the high temperature of transmitter tubes. Heating can also be caused by excessive RF currents flowing through the crystal. The slow shift of the resonant frequency that results from crystal heating is called *frequency drift.* This drift is avoided by the use of crystals with a nearly zero temperature coefficient, and also by maintaining the crystal at a constant temperature.

The temperature coefficient of the crystal is measured in ±Hz/MHz/°C or parts per million per degree Celsius. The amount of frequency drift is the product of the coefficient, the crystal's frequency in MHz, and the temperature change in degrees Celsius. This change is positive if the temperature increases, but is negative if the temperature decreases. For example, if the temperature coefficient of a 2-MHz crystal is − 10 Hz/MHz/°C and the temperature drops from 40° to 35°C, the total frequency shift = (− 10 Hz/MHz/°C) × 2 MHz × (35°C − 40°C) = + 100 Hz. Consequently, the crystal's fundamental frequency has risen to 2 MHz + 100 Hz = 2.0001 MHz.

To maintain the extremely close frequency tolerances required, the general practice is to construct the entire oscillator assembly in such a manner as to provide for nearly constant temperatures. This practice helps to prevent excessive frequency drift. Power-supply voltages are also kept as constant as possible by suitable voltage regulation circuits. In particular, the quartz crystal is operated within a constant-temperature oven. The oven is electrically heated and temperature controlled by special thermostats. The entire assembly usually is constructed of an aluminum shell that is enclosed by thick layers of suitable material to insulate the assembly. For extreme stability, the entire compartment can be placed inside still another temperature-controlled box. In this way, frequency stabilities as high as 1 part in 10,000,000 or better can be attained. Even with low temperature-coefficient crystals used in broadcast stations, the FCC requires that their temperature is maintained to within ± 1.0°C.

At its resonant frequency, a crystal behaves like a series-tuned circuit, as far as the electrical circuits associated with it are concerned. The crystal and the holder (FIG. 4-55A) can be replaced by an equivalent circuit (FIG. 4-55B). C_H represents the capacitance of the mounting or holder with the crystal in place between the metallic electrodes. The series combination of $L, R,$ and C, represents the equivalent of the vibrational characteristics of the quartz crystal. The inductance, L, is the electrical equivalent of the crystal's mass, which is effective in the vibration. The capacitance is the electrical equivalent of the mechanical elasticity, and R represents the equivalent of the mechanical friction during vibration. The capacitance of the holder, C_H, is about 100 times as great as the vibration capacitance, C, of the crystal itself.

Typical values of $L, C,$ and R are respectively of the order of henrys, picofarads, and kilohms. For example, if $L = 1$ H, $C = 1$ pF and $R = 1$ kΩ, the value of Q is:

$$Q = \frac{1}{R} \times \sqrt{\frac{L}{C}}$$

$$= \frac{1}{10^3} \times \sqrt{\frac{1}{1 \times 10^{-12}}} = 1000$$

Crystals can have Q-factors of several thousand, which is large compared to the typical Q value (up to 300) of a conventional LCR circuit. A high-Q means superior frequency stability, and therefore crystal oscillators are much more stable than any of the VFOs; as a secondary reason,

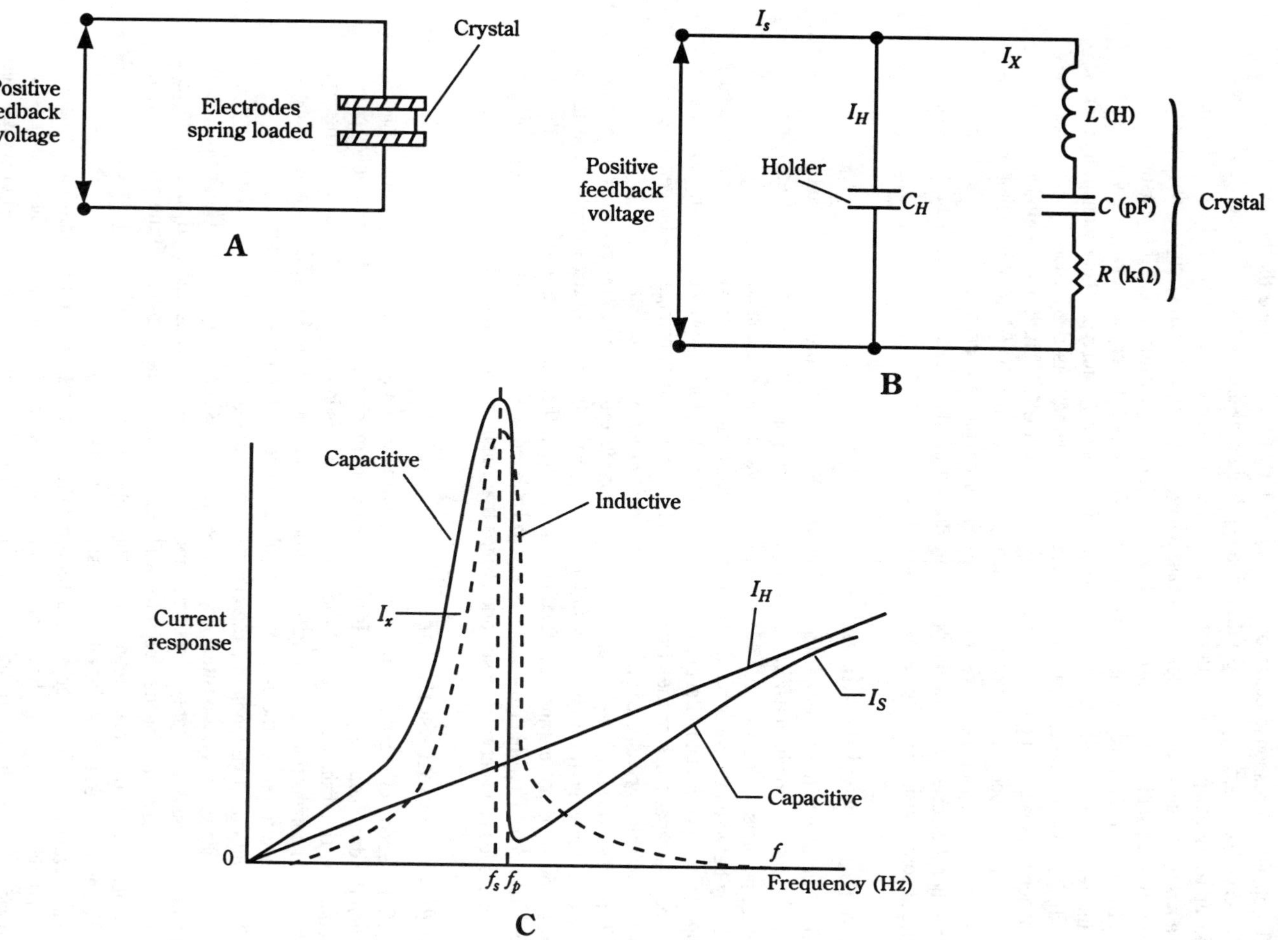

Fig. 4-55 The response curve of the crystal and its holder.

the temperature coefficient of the crystal is extremely low and can be virtually zero, provided that the crystal is maintained at the correct temperature.

To obtain the response curve of I_S versus f (FIG. 4-55C), combine the holder current, I_H, with the crystal current, I_X, and take their phase relationships into account. For a capacitor, there is a linear relationship between its current and the frequency. For the crystal, the current response has the familiar "bell" shape that is associated with a series LCR circuit. Below resonance the crystal is capacitive, but above resonance, it is inductive. After taking the phasor sum of I_X and I_H to produce I_S, it is revealed that the combination of the crystal and the holder has two resonant frequencies. There is a series resonant frequency, f_s, and a parallel resonant frequency, f_p, which, because of the crystal's high-Q, are close together. As the frequency increases, the combination is capacitive up to the point of series resonance (f_s), but it behaves inductively over the narrow region between f_s and the point of parallel resonance, f_p. Above parallel resonance, the combination is again capacitive. In some oscillator circuits, the crystal and its holder can function in either the series mode or the parallel mode, but in other circuits, the crystal and its holder operate at some position on the response curve between f_s and f_p.

The Miller crystal oscillator

The JFET version of the Miller oscillator is shown in FIG. 4-55. In order for the circuit to oscillate, the gate and drain circuits must be net inductive, with respect to the generated frequency. It is therefore possible to replace the gate circuit by a crystal-holder combination, which will behave inductively between the series and parallel resonant frequencies. Positive feedback then occurs through the drain-gate capacitance, and signal bias for the JFET is provided by the combination of R_g and the capacitance of the crystal holder. To produce small changes in the generated frequency, a variable low-value capacitor can be connected across the crystal.

The Miller version is a popular crystal oscillator since the vibration is confined to the input circuit. Consequently, for a given excitation of the crystal, this type of oscillator will create the greatest power output because the feedback occurs from the drain to the gate and not through the crystal itself. The Miller oscillator is also reliable because the crystal is located in the gate circuit and is less subject to stresses and strains that might cause it to crack and fail.

The Pierce crystal oscillator

The JFET version of the Pierce oscillator is shown in FIG. 4-56. The crystal is now connected between the drain and the gate so it is more subject to mechanical stress than the Miller circuit; consequently, the main application of the Pierce oscillator is in low-power RF circuits. The crystal's holder, in conjunction with the gate resistor, R_g, generates signal bias. C is a blocking capacitor that is used to reduce the amount of dc voltage developed across the crystal.

To provide positive feedback, the crystal-holder combination must behave inductively, and therefore oscillates at some position on the response curve between f_s and f_p. The indirect feedback path is through the gate-source capacitance and phasor analysis shows that the gate tank circuit must be *capacitive* for the circuit to oscillate. Because of the presence of the active device's output capacitance, the gate circuit is naturally capacitive; consequently, the tank circuit is not essential, and can be replaced by either a resistor or a RFC.

The advantages of the Pierce oscillator are its lack of need for an output tank circuit, and its ability to oscillate easily over a broad range of frequencies by using a number of different crystals. The disadvantage is the comparatively low-power operation, so it is mainly used in crystal calibrators, test equipment, receivers, and transmitters, whose output power is only a few watts.

The astable multivibrator

The multivibrator circuit of FIG. 4-58 consists of two common-emitter stages, which are cross-connected for positive feedback. The resultant instability causes the transistors to cut on and off

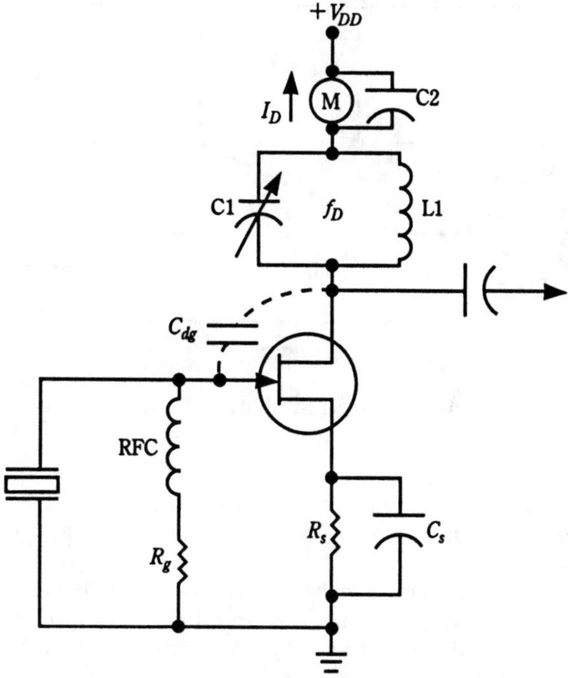

Fig. 4-56 The Miller crystal oscillator.

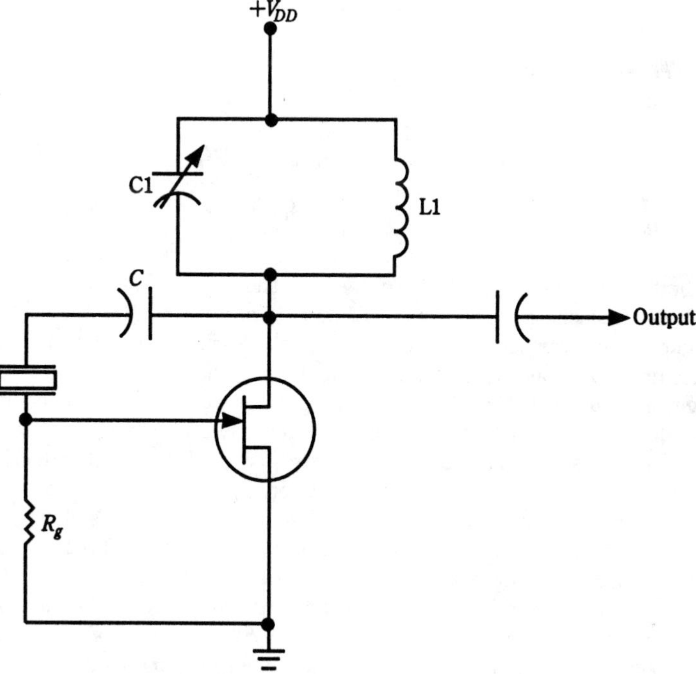

Fig. 4-57 The Pierce crystal oscillator.

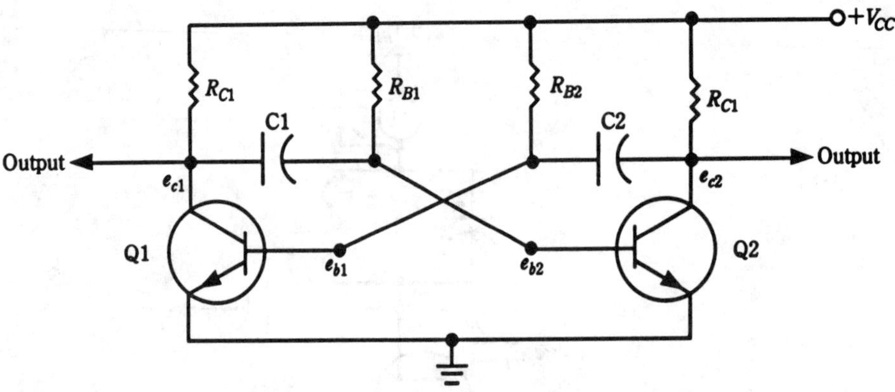

Fig. 4-58 The transistorized astable multivibrator.

alternatively so that approximate square-wave voltage outputs appear at the collectors; the base waveforms have a sawtooth appearance. Because the circuit has two unstable states, it is astable and will therefore freely run.

When resistor R1 has been driven to the cut-off condition as a result of the positive feedback action, the base potential e_{b1} is approximately equal to $-V_{CC}$. The capacitor C2 will then discharge through R_{B2} and Q2, so e_{b1} will rise toward $+V_{CC}$ with a time constant of approximately $C2R_{B2}$. When e_{b1} becomes slightly positive, Q1 will switch on, and the positive feedback action will drive Q2 to the cut-off condition. Because e_{b1} reaches approximately its halfway mark in rising from $-V_{CC}$ to a slightly positive potential on its way toward $+V_{CC}$, Q1 is cut off for a time interval of approximately $0.7C_2R_{B2}$.

$$\textit{The multivibrator frequency} = \frac{1}{\textit{total period}} = \frac{1}{0.7\,(C_1R_{B1} + C_2R_{B2})} = \frac{1}{1.4\,CR_B} \text{ hertz (Hz)} \tag{4-11}$$

if the multivibrator is symmetrical, with $C_1 = C_2 = C$, and $R_{B1} = R_{B2} = R_B$.

Multivibrator frequencies range from a few hertz to nearly 100 kHz. The square wave outputs from the collectors can be used to switch other electronic circuits on and off; such square waves are also rich in harmonics and can be applied to an amplifier to test its frequency response.

Although an astable multivibrator is freely running, the changeover from one unstable state to the other can be timed to the arrival of a positive-going synchronizing pulse that is fed to the base of one of the transistors. That transistor will then start conducting earlier than it would have done so under freely running conditions. For this to occur, the frequency of the synchronizing pulse must be higher than the natural frequency of the multivibrator. It is also possible for the synchronizing pulse frequency to be much higher than the multivibrator frequency; for example, a multivibrator whose frequency is approximately 1 kHz, can be triggered by a 10-kHz pulse. Then, 9 out of 10 pulses would be inactive, but the tenth would trigger the multivibrator. This represents a 10:1 "count-down" factor and is known as *frequency division,* which results in the multivibrator's output frequency being a subharmonic of the synchronizing frequency.

The blocking oscillator

Blocking describes a condition, in which a circuit oscillates for a period of time; this is followed by a quiescent interval during which no oscillation occurs. After the quiescent interval, the circuit again oscillates, so the sequence is oscillation, no oscillation, oscillation, no oscillation, and so on indefinitely.

Oscillators that use signal bias tend to block, provided that there is a large amount of positive feedback and too high a time constant for the capacitor's discharge. The strong feedback oscillation causes the capacitor to charge, and drives the bias point far into the cut-off region of the active device. This reduces the device's gain to the point where the Barkhausen criterion is no longer fulfilled. As soon as the oscillation starts to decline, the bias under normal conditions rapidly decreases and the condition for continuous oscillation is restored. However, if the time constant of the capacitor's discharge is too high, the bias cannot decrease fast enough and the oscillation ceases. During the quiescent interval that follows, the capacitor discharges slowly until the active device again conducts to initiate a further burst of oscillation; the sequence is repeated indefinitely.

The blocking oscillator (FIG. 4-59) is an extreme example of this sequence. A very large amount of positive feedback is ensured by the high degree of coupling between L1 and L2; this is achieved by the common soft iron core, on which the two coils are wound. C and R create the high time constant for the signal bias, but one end of R is connected to $+V_{CC}$ in order to provide a starting bias. Diode D1 is included to prevent negative transient voltages from forward-biasing the collector-base junction.

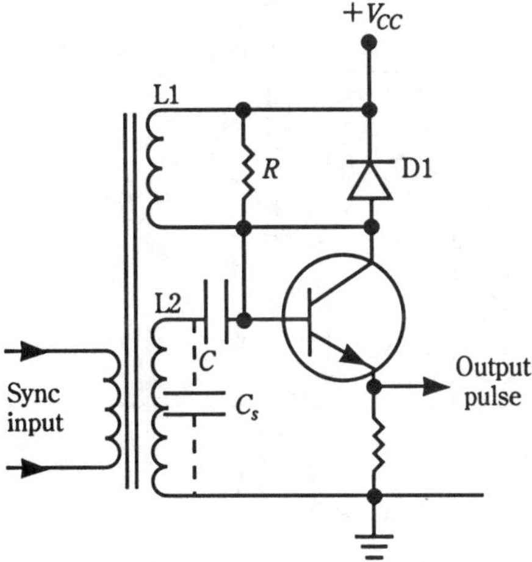

Fig. 4-59 The blocking oscillator.

When the circuit is switched on, the initial collector current creates a magnetic flux that surrounds L1 and therefore cuts L2. This shocks into oscillation a tuned circuit that is primarily formed by L2 and its self-capacitance, C_s; the resonant frequency of this circuit is typically of the order of MHz. On the first positive swing of this oscillation, the base current charges C, and the bias point is driven well into the cut-off region. Oscillation then ceases and C starts to discharge slowly through R. Eventually, the transistor will rise above its cut-off level so that the collector current again flows and the sequence is repeated. An approximate sawtooth waveform is then present at the base, and a narrow pulse is obtainable from the emitter. The natural frequency of the pulses is primarily determined by the RC time constant.

Although the blocking oscillator is a freely running circuit, it can be triggered by a variety of synchronizing voltages (such as a sine wave, pulse, etc.). The synchronizing input causes the base to rise above cut-off earlier than it would have done under freely running conditions; it follows that the synchronizing frequency must be higher than the blocking oscillator's natural frequency.

The blocking oscillator can be used as the discharge circuit for a deflection generator in a TV receiver and to form the pulse in a radar transmitter.

Parasitic oscillations

Parasitic oscillations occur at low frequencies or very high frequencies of the order of hundreds of MHz; in either case, these oscillations are in no way related to the design frequency. Such oscillations can appear in either RF amplifiers or oscillators and their presence can be detected by high or erratic readings in the dc meters that are located in the stage's input and output circuits. The importance of these oscillations lies in the additional power that is absorbed from the dc supply; this in turn will cause a greater power dissipation in the active device.

High-frequency parasitic oscillations are caused by stray inductance and capacitance associated with the leads, components, and active devices. These stray values can form some type of tuned-output tuned-input oscillator (FIG. 4-60). The parasitic oscillation that the circuit generates can be eliminated by:

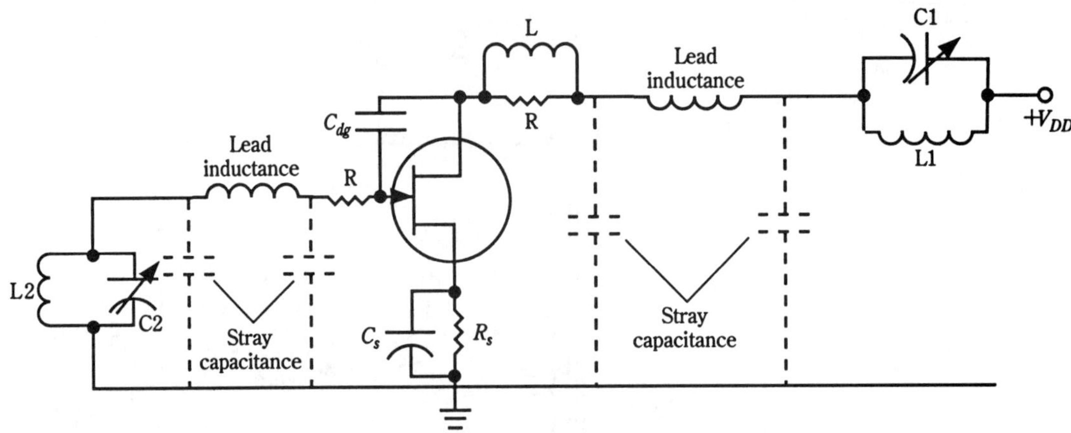

Fig. 4-60 The generation of parasitic oscillations.

- the inclusion of low-value damping resistors, *R*, which are connected as close as possible to the active device. These lower the *Q* of the stray tank circuits (the visible tank circuits L1/C1 and L2/C2 behave as short circuits at these very-high frequencies), so the amount of positive feedback through the drain-gate capacitance, C_{dg}, is no longer sufficient to sustain the unwanted oscillation.
- wrapping a few turns of copper wire around the damping resistor. At the high parasitic frequencies, this forms an RF coil, L, which is connected in parallel with the resistor. The purpose of the RF coil is to introduce a phase shift into the feedback loop so that the Barkhausen criterion is no longer fulfilled for the parasitic oscillation. However, at the design frequency, the inductor, *L*, would virtually short out the damping resistor.

The presence of low-frequency parasitic oscillation is commonly caused by the inclusion of RF chokes in the input and output circuits. The solution is either to replace one of the chokes with a resistor or to make the value of the output choke higher than that of the input choke.

* **Question 4-59** In a crystal oscillator, the frequency can be varied by a change in the temperature and also by:

A. a change in the value of the dc supply voltage
B. a change in the value of the emitter resistor
C. a change in the value of the inductance in the plate tank circuit
D. a change in the value of the capacitance in the plate tank circuit
E. a change in the component values that provide the signal bias

Answer Choice A.

Question 4-60 A test to determine whether an oscillator is generating its output, is to check:

A. that drain current is flowing
B. the value of the signal bias on the gate
C. that source current is flowing
D. the dc value of the drain voltage
E. for a high value of the dc supply voltage

Answer Choice B.

Question 4-61 Identify the circuit shown in FIG. 4-61:

A. audio frequency amplifier
B. Armstrong oscillator
C. neutralized RF amplifier
D. Hartley oscillator
E. Colpitts oscillator

Answer Choice D.

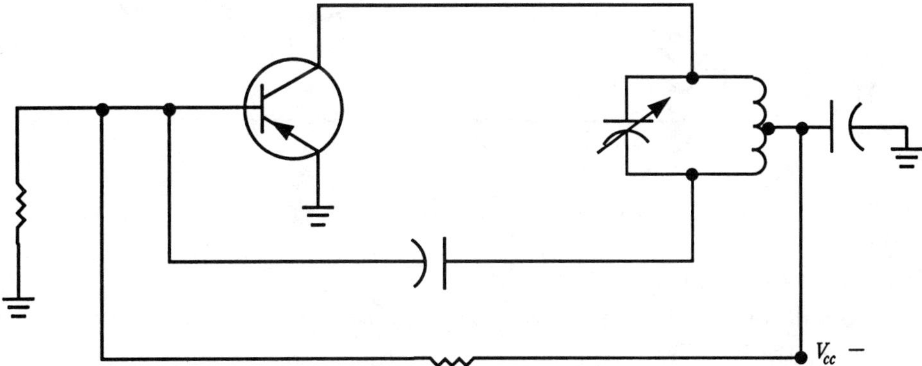

Fig. 4-61 The circuit for question 4-61.

* **Question 4-62** In a n-channel FET oscillator circuit, electron current would flow:

A. from V_{DD} to the drain
B. from the drain to the source

C. from gate to ground through the resistor that provides signal bias
D. from ground to gate through the resistor that provides signal bias
E. from the drain to the gate

Answer Choice C.

Question 4-63 For successful operation, a Hartley oscillator requires:

A. sufficient positive feedback to overcome the circuit losses
B. a very low-*Q* tank circuit
C. indirect capacitive feedback from the output circuit to the input circuit
D. a tank coil that is grounded at its midpoint
E. a capacitive voltage divider

Answer Choice A.

Question 4-64 In the circuit of FIG. 4-62, an approximate sawtooth waveform can be monitored between points:

A. A and E B. E and B C. A and D D. C and E E. A and B

Answer Choice D.

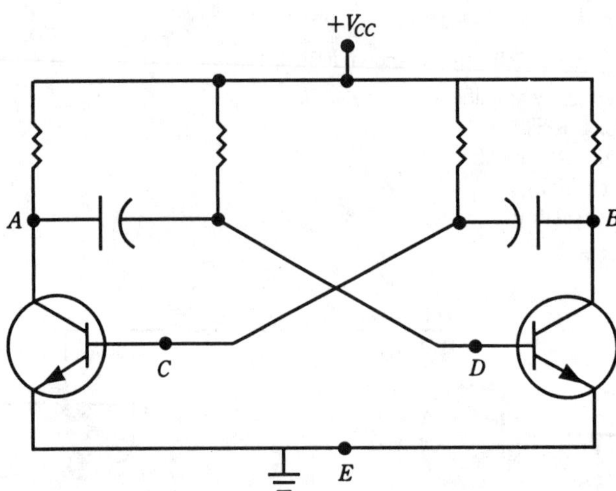

Fig. 4-62 The circuit for question 4-64.

Question 4-65 Signal bias in a JFET oscillator:

A. is the result of the time constant provided by the resistor/capacitor combination in the gate-source circuit
B. depends on the flow of source current to generate the bias
C. depends on the amplitude of the oscillation
D. prevents any flow of the drain current
E. choices A and C are true

Answer Choice E.

* **Question 4-66** What substance in its crystalline form can be used in oscillators?

A. silicon B. germanium C. carbon D. quartz E. sapphire

Answer Choice D.

* **Question 4-67** The frequency of a crystal oscillator is shifted slightly if:

A. a resistor is added in series with the crystal
B. an inductor is added in series with the crystal
C. a capacitor is added in series with the crystal
D. an inductor is added in parallel with the crystal
E. a capacitor is added in parallel with the crystal

Answer Choice E.

Question 4-68 The frequency of a transistorized multivibrator is determined primarily by:

A. the collector supply voltage, V_{CC}
B. the junction capacitances of the transistors
C. the collector load resistors
D. the time constants formed by the coupling capacitors and the base resistors
E. the parameters of the transistors

Answer Choice D.

* **Question 4-69** What happens to a shunt-fed JFET Hartley oscillator if a short circuit is across the RF choke, which is connected to the drain?

A. There is no charge in either the amplitude or the frequency of the oscillation
B. The amplitude of the oscillation increases
C. The circuit ceases to oscillate
D. The output frequency increases
E. The output frequency falls

Answer Choice C.

Question 4-70 The Hartley oscillator:

A. uses indirect feedback
B. is especially suitable for generating frequencies greater than 100 MHz
C. has an output waveform that is rich in harmonics
D. uses a capacitive voltage divider
E. uses mutual coupling exclusively to provide the positive feedback

Answer Choice C.

Question 4-71 A transmitter uses a 3-MHz crystal with a temperature coefficient of + 10 Hz/MHz/°C. If the crystal oscillator is followed by three doubler stages, what is the transmitter's output frequency if the temperature falls by 20°C?

A. 24 MHz B. 24.0016 MHz C. 23.9984 MHz D. 24.0048 MHz E. 23.9952 MHz

Answer Choice E. The frequency shift at the oscillator stage is $+\ 10$ Hz/MHz/°C $\times$ 3 MHz $\times$ (-20°C) $= -600$ Hz. Output frequency shift $=$ (-600 Hz) $\times 2 \times 2 \times 2 = -4800$ Hz. Transmitter's output frequency $=$ 3 MHz $\times 2 \times 2 \times 2 -$ 4800 Hz $=$ 23.9952 MHz.

Question 4-72 To reduce high-frequency parasitic oscillation:

A. the circuit must be neutralized
B. low-value damping resistors are connected to the active device
C. RF chokes are connected in series with the low-value damping resistors
D. an additional resistor is connected between the input and output circuits of the active device
E. both B and C

Answer Choice B.

Question 4-73 The circuit of FIG. 4-63 represents a crystal oscillator that is operating on the third overtone. If the crystal has a fundamental frequency of 1 MHz, the output frequency is:

A. 1 MHz B. 2 MHz C. 3 MHz D. 4 MHz E. 333 kHz

Answer Choice C. The output frequency is: $3 \times 1 = 3$ MHz.

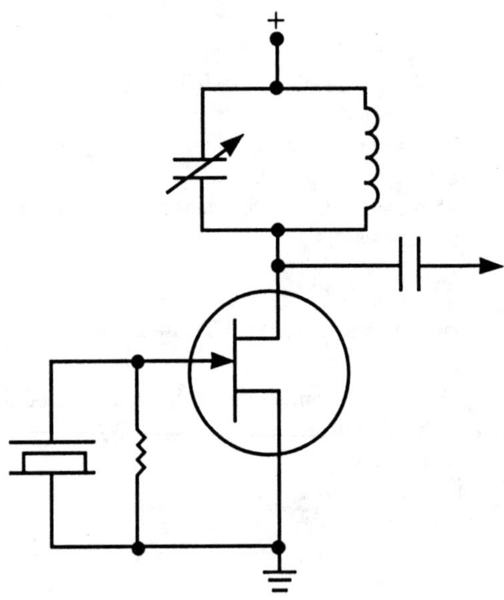

Fig. 4-63 The circuit for questions 4-73 and 4-74.

* **Question 4-74** In QUES. 4-73, the positive feedback occurs through:

A. the drain-to-gate capacitance
B. the gate-to-source capacitance
C. the drain-to-source capacitance
D. direct feedback
E. capacitive filtering

Answer Choice A.

Question 4-75 Parasitic oscillations can occur in a (an):

A. transmitter B. receiver C. RF amplifier D. RF oscillator E. all of the above

Answer Choice E.

4-11. Operational amplifiers

Operational amplifiers are designed to simulate certain mathematical operations (such as addition, subtraction, differentiation, and integration). Examples of such circuits are:

Inverting operational amplifier

In the circuit of FIG. 4-64A, the input signal, V_i, is fed through an impedance, Z_i, to a linear solid-state amplifier whose voltage gain is extremely high (of the order of 10,000). This voltage gain is shown as $-A$; the minus sign indicates that the output signal, V_o, is inverted, with respect to the input signal. The impedance, Z_f, provides feedback from the output circuit to the input circuit with the same feedback current, i_{fb}, flowing through the series combination of Z_f and Z_i.

In FIG. 4-64A, the open-loop gain, A, of the op amp is very large so that there is only a small voltage at the "-" input terminal. It follows that the voltage across Z_f is virtually equal to the output voltage, V_o, while the negative feedback voltage across Z_i is equal to V_i. Because the same feedback current, i_{fb}, flows through Z_f and Z_i:

$$V_o = i_{fb} \times Z_f$$

$$V_i = -i_{fb} \times Z_i$$

Voltage gain with feedback:

$$A' = \frac{V_o}{V_i} = -\frac{Z_f}{Z_i} \qquad (4\text{-}11)$$

If Z_f and Z_i are resistors, voltage gain with feedback:

$$A' = -\frac{R_f}{R_i} \qquad (4\text{-}12)$$

Noninverting operational amplifier

The circuit of FIG. 4-64B represents a noninverting operational amplifier in which the output voltage, V_o, is in phase with the input signal, V_i. Impedances Z_f and Z_i form a voltage-divider circuit for the output voltage. The negative feedback voltage across Z_i is virtually equal to the input voltage, V_i.

Then:

$$V_i = V_o \times \frac{Z_i}{Z_i + Z_f} \text{ volts (V)}$$

Voltage gain with feedback:

$$A' = \frac{V_o}{V_i} = \frac{Z_i + Z_f}{Z_i} = 1 + \frac{Z_f}{Z_i} \qquad (4\text{-}13)$$

If Z_f and Z_i are resistors, voltage gain with feedback:

$$A' = 1 + \frac{R_f}{R_i} \qquad (4\text{-}14)$$

Summing (addition) amplifier

In the summing amplifier (FIG. 4-64C), the gain for each input signal is $-R_f/R_i$.

Output signal:

$$V_o = -R_f\left(\frac{V_{i1}}{R_{i1}} + \frac{V_{i2}}{R_{i2}} + \frac{V_{i3}}{R_{i3}}\right) \text{ volts (V)} \qquad (4\text{-}15)$$

Differential (subtraction amplifier)

For the differential amplifier (FIG. 4-64D):

Output signal:

$$V_o = -\frac{R_f}{R_i}\left(V_{i1} - V_{i2}\right) \text{ volts (V)} \qquad (4\text{-}16)$$

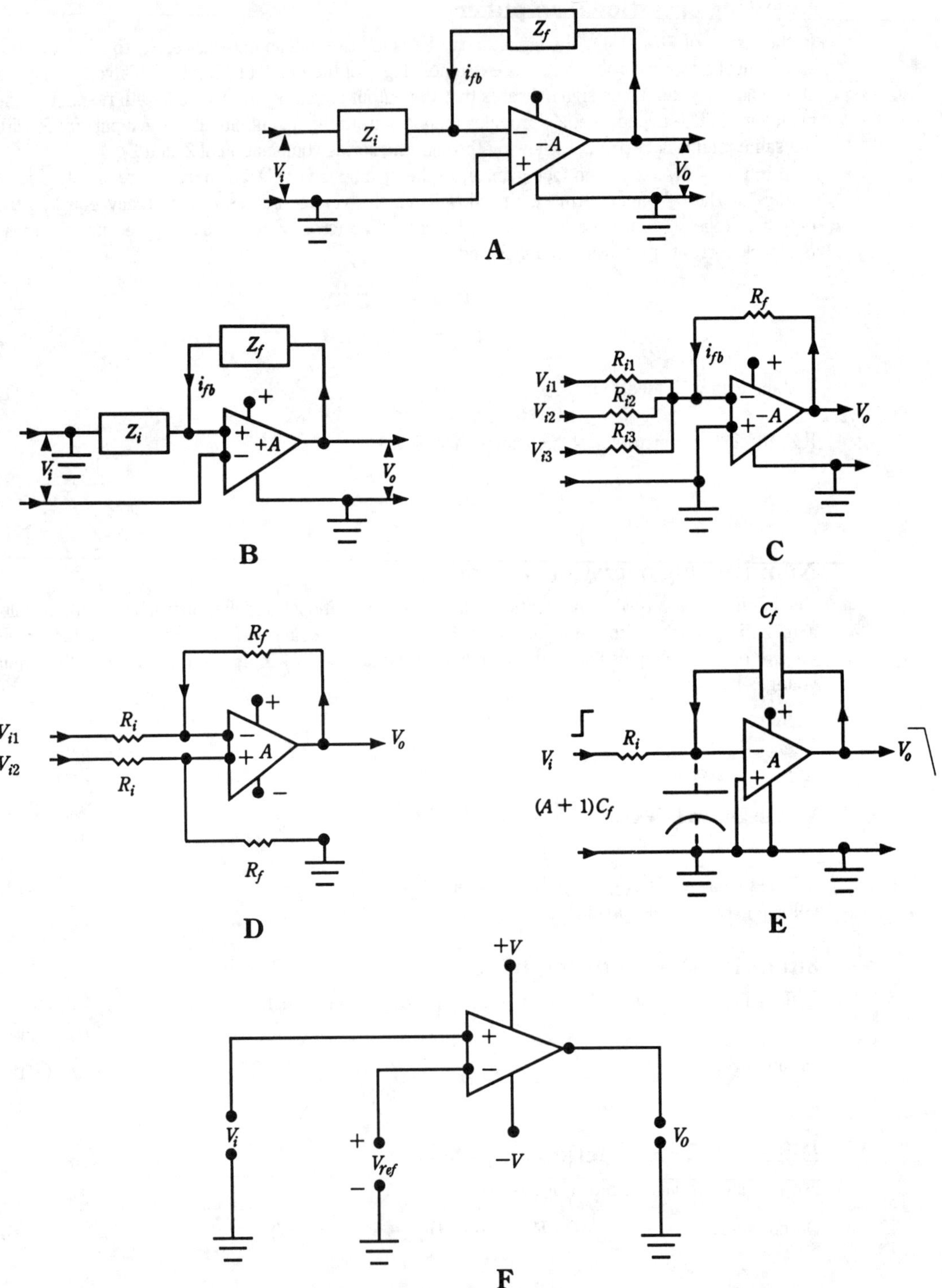

Fig. 4-64 Examples of operational amplifiers.

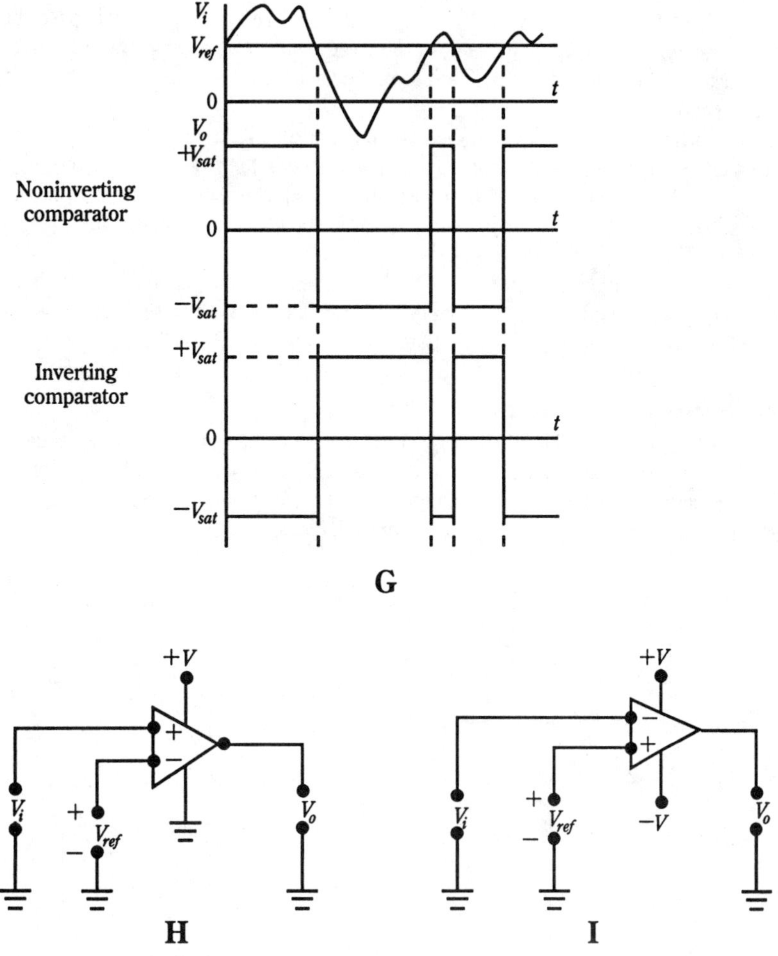

Fig. 4-64 Continued

Integrating amplifier

In the operational amplifier of FIG. 4-64E, C_f is a capacitor and the amplifier is then capable of integration. Owing to the Miller effect, the input capacitance will be equal to: $(A + 1)C_f$. If the input signal, V_i, is a step voltage (as shown), the voltage at the amplifier input terminal will slowly rise and the output signal, V_o, will be an amplified linear fall, which will represent the result of integrating V_i. If C_f is replaced by a suitable inductor, L_f, the op amp will be capable of differentiation.

The comparator circuit

The circuit of FIG. 4-64F shows a noninverting comparator, which is used to determine whether an input voltage, V_i, is greater or less than the reference voltage, V_{ref}. When V_i is greater than V_{ref}, the comparator circuit is driven into positive saturation and the output, V_o, is equal to $+ V_{sat}$, which is about 1 V less than + V. By contrast, when V_i drops below V_{ref}, the comparator is driven into negative saturation and its output, V_o, is $- V_{sat}$ (about 1 V above − V). Because it is virtually impossible to hold the input steady at $V_i = V_{ref}$, V_o will not rest at V_{ref}, but will pass through the level of the reference voltage. As a result of the large gain of the op amp (which is not providing linear amplification), a variation of 1 mV or less in the value of V_i will cause V_o to change by several volts (FIG. 4-64G).

To summarize, for the noninverting comparator, output V_o is equal to $+V_{sat}$ when V_i is connected to the "+" input terminal of the op amp and exceeds the reference voltage, V_{ref}, which is connected to the "−" input terminal. By contrast, V_o is equal to $-V_{sat}$ when V_i drops below V_{ref}.

A simplified form of a noninverting comparator is shown in FIG. 4-64H. When $V_i > V_{ref}$, $V_o = +V_{sat}$, but when $V_i < V_{ref}$, the value of V_o is zero.

In the inverting comparator circuit of FIG. 4-64I, the input, V_i, is connected to the "−" input terminal while V_{ref} is joined to the "+" input terminal. Consequently, the output, V_o, will be inverted (FIG. 4-64G), when compared with that of the circuit in FIG. 4-64F.

Voltage follower

The circuit of FIG. 4-65 is called a *voltage follower* because the output signal V_o equals the input signal V_i. The purpose of such a circuit is to transfer a signal associated with a high output impedance to a low impedance load with a voltage gain of virtually unity. Consequently, the voltage follower is basically an op amp, which is used for impedance matching.

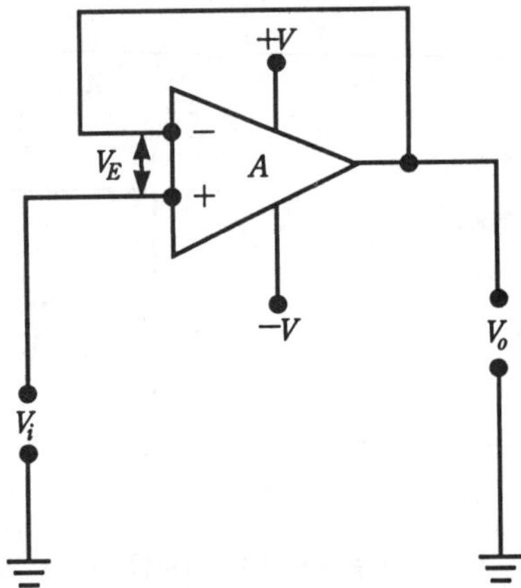

Fig. 4-65 The voltage follower.

Notice that there is no feedback resistor. Therefore, there is 100% negative feedback to the inverting terminal. When a signal is applied to the noninverting input terminal, the op amp at once causes the inverting input, V_E, to fall to nearly zero so that the V_i and V_o are virtually equal. For example, if V_i is +10 V, V_o might be 9.999 V, so the inverting input is −0.001 V, which allows for an open loop gain of 10,000. The same principles apply to both dc and ac voltage followers.

* **Question 4-76** In FIG. 4-64A, Z_f is a 150-kΩ resistor and Z_i is a 10 kΩ resistor. Assuming that the value of A is large, the gain of this operational amplifier is:

A. +15 B. −15 C. +16 D. −16 E. +15.5

Answer Choice B. The gain of the inverting amplifier is $-R_f/R_i$ (EQ. 4-12) = −150/10 = −15.

* **Question 4-77** In FIG. 4-64B, Z_f is a 150-kΩ resistor and Z_i is a 10-kΩ resistor. Assuming that the value of A is large, the gain of this op amp is:

A. +15 B. −15 C. +16 D. −16 E. −15.5

Answer Choice C. The gain of the noninverting amplifier is $1 + R_f/R_i$ (EQ. 4-14) = 1 + 150/10 = + 16.

* **Question 4-78** In the circuit of FIG. 4-64F, $V_i = +2.7$ V, $V_{ref} = +1.3$ V, V = 15 V. The value of V_o is:

A. +2.7 V B. +1.3 V C. −14 V D. −15 V E. +14 V

Answer Choice E. The circuit is that of a noninverting comparator, which is driven into positive saturation. Therefore, V_o is approximately + 14 V.

* **Question 4-79** In the circuit of FIG. 4-64H, $V_i = +2.5$ V, $V_{ref} = +4.0$ V, V = +6 V. The value of V_o is:

A. +2.5 V B. +4.0 V C. +1.5 V D. 0 V E. +6 V

Answer Choice D. The circuit is that of a modified noninverting comparator, which is driven into negative saturation so that the value of V_o is zero.

* **Question 4-80** In the circuit of FIG. 4-64H, $V_i = +4.0$ V, $V_{ref} = +2.5$ V, V = +6 V. The value of V_o is:

A. +2.5 V B. +4.0 V C. +1.5 V D. 0 V E. +6 V

Answer Choice E. The circuit is that of a modified noninverting comparator, which is driven into positive saturation so that the value of V_o is +6 V.

* **Question 4-81** In the circuit of FIG. 4-64I, $V_i = +5$ V, $V_{ref} = +3$ V, V = 12 V. The value of V_o is:

A. +5 V B. +3 V C. +8 V D. +12 V E. −12 V

Answer Choice E. The circuit is that of an inverting comparator. Because $V_i > V_{ref}$, the circuit is driven into negative saturation so that $V_o = -12$ V.

* **Question 4-82** In the circuit of FIG. 4-65, $V_i = +4$ V, $V = 12$ V. The value of V_o is:

A. +4 V B. −4 V C. +12 V D. −12 V E. −8 V

Answer Choice A. The circuit is that of a voltage follower. Therefore, the value of V_o is +4 V.

4-12. Other discrete semiconductor devices

The silicon-controlled rectifier

The *silicon-controlled rectifier (SCR)* is constructed of alternate p-type silicon and n-type semiconductor layers with metallic connections to the anode, cathode, and gate (see FIG. 4-66A). The SCR symbol appears in FIG. 4-66B. Visualize the layers of the SCR as forming two transistors (FIG. 4-67). When the base voltage of Q2, with reference to the emitter, is low, the collector current of Q2, and hence the base current of Q1, are also low, so the SCR appears as an open circuit between the anode and the cathode.

Raising the gate voltage causes gate current (base current of Q2) to flow, resulting in Q2 collector current, Q1 base current, and Q1 conduction. If the SCR voltage applied between the anode and cathode is sufficiently large, with a given amount of gate current, the overall action is regenerative, the SCR voltage will drop, and the current will increase. Moreover, the gate current ceases to have any control over the SCR operation.

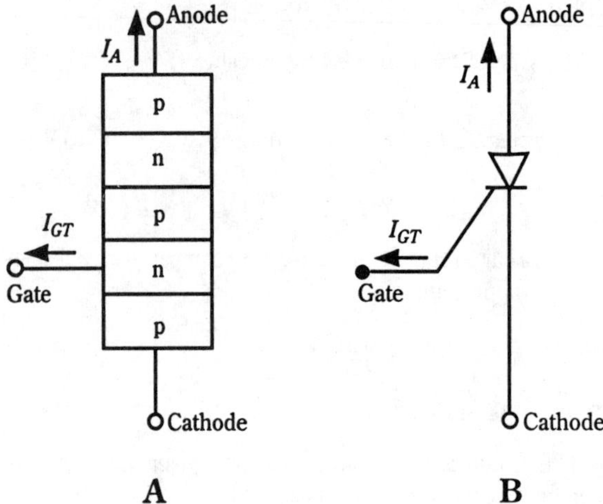

Fig. 4-66 The silicon-controlled rectifier and its symbol.

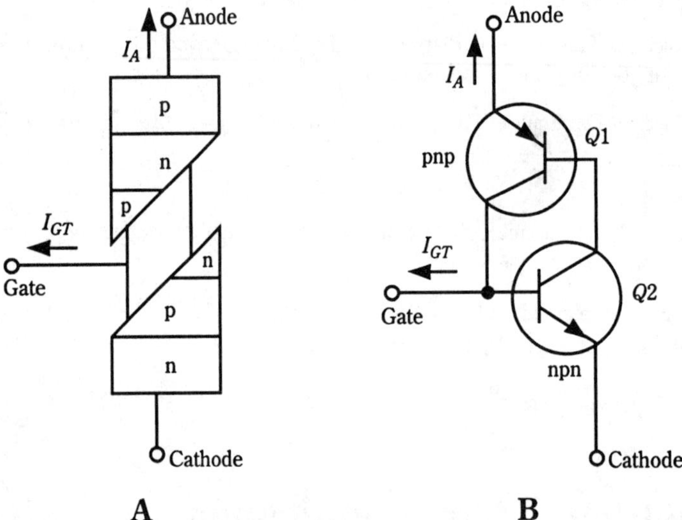

Fig. 4-67 The two-transistor equivalent of the silicon-controlled rectifier.

Figure 4-68 summarizes the SCR characteristics and emphasizes the results of having different gate currents, I_{G0}, I_{G1}, and I_{G2}. V_F is the "forward" (forward-bias direction) SCR anode-to-cathode voltage. Notice that, for I_{G2}, the characteristic resembles that of a forward-biased diode.

When the SCR is on, it cannot be turned off by removing the gate signal. Two possibilities exist for turning the SCR off. The first, *anode current interruption,* can be accomplished by opening the anode circuit or by placing a direct short circuit between the anode and cathode. The second method, *forced commutation,* requires that current be forced from the anode to the cathode in the direction opposite to that used to turn the SCR on.

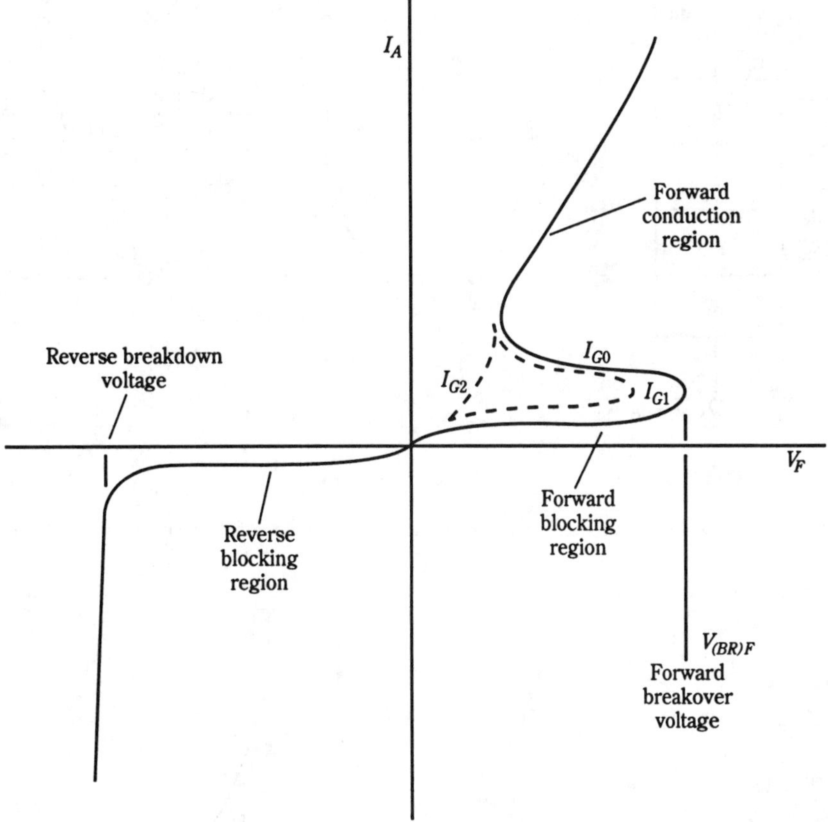

Fig. 4-68 The characteristics of the silicon-controlled rectifier.

The silicon-controlled switch

The *silicon-controlled switch (SCS)* semiconductor device resembles the SCR, except that an anode gate is added (FIG. 4-69). The SCS can turn the device on with a negative voltage, or off with a positive voltage. Usually, the anode gate current for turn-on is much larger than the required cathode gate current. In addition to reduced turn-off time, the SCS has the advantage of increased control. The SCS is limited to low-power ratings, as compared with the SCR.

The diac

The bidirectional diode thyristor permits triggering with either polarity of voltage on the two electrodes, called *anodes*. Figure 4-70 shows that the breakdown voltage for the characteristic is V_{BR}. The double diode in the circuit symbol is misleading because conduction is implied, as by a forward-biased diode, without the presence of breakdown. A bidirectional characteristic is particularly useful in ac circuits. However, no direct control of breakdown (conduction) is possible.

The triac

Adding a gate to the basic diac structure forms the *bidirectional triode thyristor (triac)*. Triacs behave much like diacs, except that gate current (positive or negative) can control the breakdown

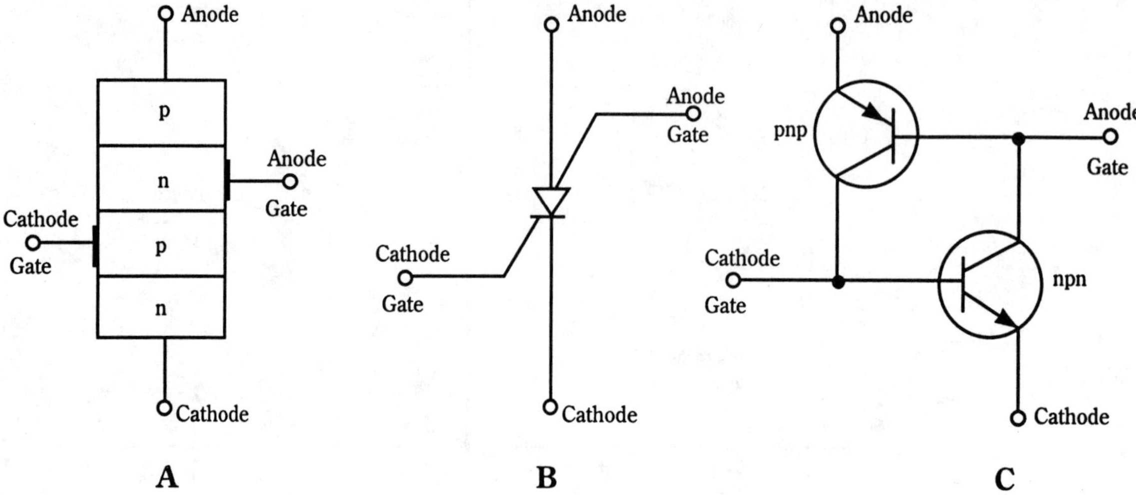

Fig. 4-69 The construction, symbol, and transistor equivalent circuit of the silicon-controlled switch.

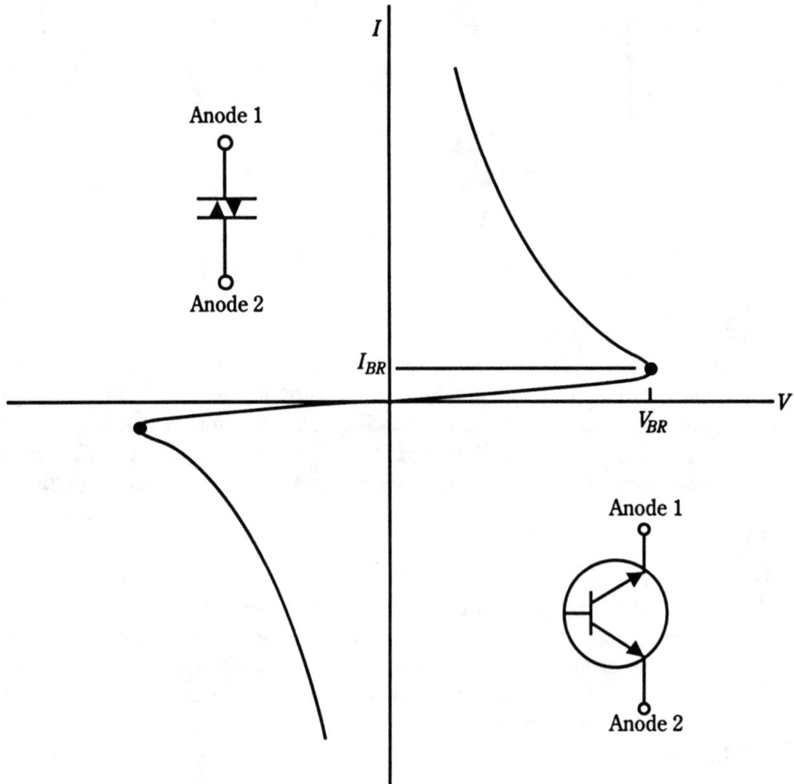

Fig. 4-70 The Diac symbol and its characteristics.

point. Like the diac, the triac continues to conduct until the applied voltage drops to a level of about 1 V. For ac, conduction occurs for a partially controllable fraction of each alternation. The symbol and characteristics for triacs are shown in FIG. 4-71.

* **Question 4-83** Which of the following is the symbol for the bidirectional diode thyristor (diac)?

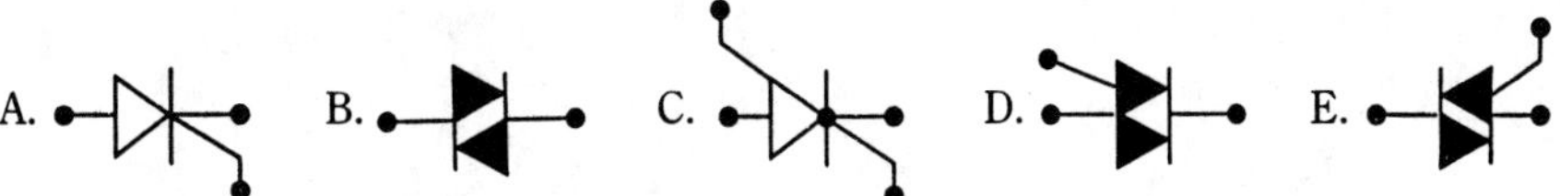

Answer Choice B. Refer to FIG. 4-70.

* **Question 4-84** Referring to QUES. 4-83, which is the symbol for the bidirectional triode thyristor (triac)?

A. a B. b C. c D. d E. e

Answer Choice E. Refer to FIG. 4-71.

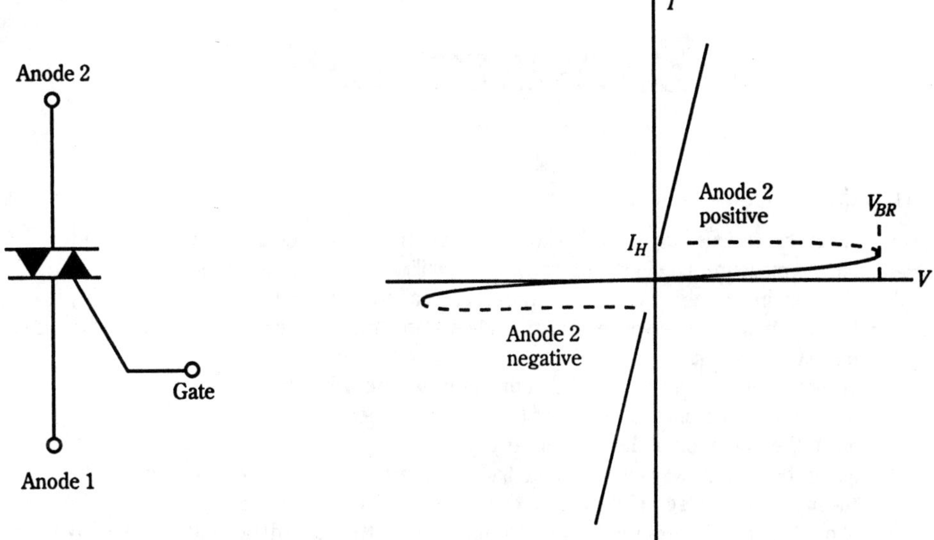

Fig. 4-71 The Triac symbol and its characteristics.

5 Transmitters

In this chapter you will learn:

- about the various stages, which are present in the block diagram of a CW transmitter.
- how to measure the degree of frequency stability in an RF oscillator stage.
- the meaning of the percentage of variance, as a measurement of frequency stability.
- how the buffer stage isolates the crystal oscillator from the loading effect of the first intermediate amplifier.
- about the operation and purpose of the intermediate RF amplifiers.
- how frequency amplifiers are used to raise the carrier frequency.
- about the operation of the transmitter's final stage.
- about the various ways in which the harmonics are reduced in the final stage.
- the meaning of telegraphy and how code is used to convey information.
- about the functions of the various components in the schematic diagram of a CW transmitter.

5-1. Block diagram of a transmitter

In chapters 1 and 2, you investigated the passive properties of resistance, inductance, capacitance, and their effects in dc and ac circuits.

In chapters 3 and 4, the passive elements were combined with the semiconductor devices (diodes, BJTs, and FETs) to produce stages that were capable of such operations as rectification, amplification and oscillation. Now you can join together a number of such stages to produce a transmitter system that is capable of fulfilling a specific purpose to radiate an RF wave into space at an assigned frequency and at a particular power level. Figure 5-1 shows the block diagram of the transmitter's RF section, which is responsible for generating the required carrier power. Now the purpose and operation of each block is covered.

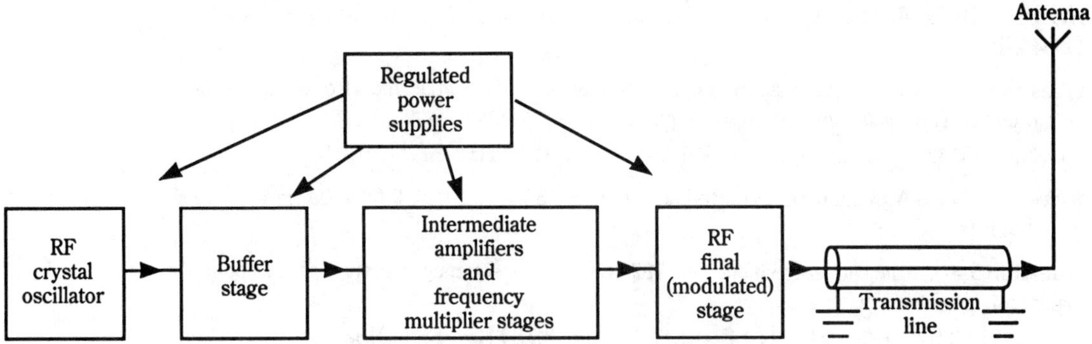

Fig. 5-1 A block diagram of the CW transmitter.

5-2. The oscillator stage

The FCC assigns a certain carrier frequency to a particular station; at the same time, the FCC requires that the output frequency is maintained within narrow tolerance limits. For example, in the AM broadcast band, a station is assigned a carrier frequency of 980 kHz with an allowed tolerance of ± 20 Hz. Consequently, the output frequency must not rise above 980 kHz $\pm$ 20 Hz $=$ 980.02 kHz or fall below 980 kHz $-$ 20 Hz $=$ 979.98 kHz. This narrow tolerance is obeyed by using a crystal oscillator and enclosing the crystal in a thermostatically controlled oven (Section 4-10). The same tolerance of ± 20 Hz applies to marine transmitters, which operate in the MF band.

In addition to quoting the permitted variation in hertz, the frequency tolerance can also be measured as a percentage (%) or in parts per million (ppm) of the carrier frequency. These two methods of measurement are related by:

$$\textit{Percentage of tolerance} = \frac{\textit{parts per million}}{10^4}$$

$$= \textit{ppm} \times 10^{-4}\% \tag{5-1}$$

$$\textit{Parts per million} = \textit{percentage} \times 10^4 \tag{5-2}$$

For example, if a 2-MHz carrier has a percentage tolerance of 0.002%, its frequency tolerance is $0.002 \times 10^4 = 20$ ppm or $\pm 2 \times 20 = \pm 40$ Hz.

The oscillator stage is operated under conditions that can lie between class AB and class C and provides a power output that can extend up to a few watts. In addition, the oscillator is normally operated from a highly regulated and well-filtered dc power supply.

* **Question 5-1** A transmitter is assigned a carrier frequency of 156.8 MHz. If the operating frequency deviates from the assigned frequency by 1 ppm, the amount of the frequency deviation is:

A. 1.568 kHz B. 15.68 kHz C. 15.68 Hz D. 156.8 Hz E. 1.568 Hz

Answer Choice D. The amount of the deviation is $156.8 \times 10^6 \times 1/10^6$ Hz $=$ 156.8 Hz.

* **Question 5-2** An aircraft transmitter has an assigned frequency of 156.4 MHz and a frequency tolerance of ± 10 ppm. What is the value of the maximum permitted frequency deviation?

A. 1.564 kHz B. 156.4 Hz C. 15.64 kHz D. 15.64 Hz E. 1.564 Hz

Answer Choice A. Maximum permitted deviation = $156.4 \times 10^6 \times 10/10^6$ Hz = 1564 Hz = 1.564 kHz.

* **Question 5-3** A transmitter has an assigned frequency of 156.8 MHz and a frequency tolerance of ±0.002%. The maximum permitted frequency deviation is:

A. 3.136 kHz B. 3.136 Hz C. 313.6 Hz D. 31.36 Hz E. 31.36 kHz

Answer Choice A. Maximum permitted deviation = $156.4 \times 10^6 \times 0.002/100$ Hz = 3136 Hz = 3.136 kHz.

* **Question 5-4** If the carrier frequency is 2182 kHz with a frequency tolerance of ±10 ppm, the maximum permitted deviation is:

A. 218.2 Hz B. 2.182 kHz C. 21.82 Hz D. 2.182 Hz E. 0.2182 Hz

Answer Choice C. Maximum permitted deviation = $2182 \times 10^3 \times 10/10^6$ Hz = 21.82 Hz.

* **Question 5-5** Express a frequency tolerance of ±0.01% in parts per million (ppm):

A. ± 1000 ppm B. ± 100 ppm C. ± 10 ppm D. ± 1 ppm E. ± 10,000 ppm

Answer Choice B.

$$\begin{aligned}\text{Frequency tolerance in ppm} &= \pm 0.01\% \times 10^4 \\ &= \pm 100 \text{ ppm}\end{aligned} \quad (5\text{-}2)$$

* **Question 5-6** Express a frequency tolerance of ± 10 ppm as a percentage:

A. ± 1% B. ± 0.1% C. ± 0.01% D. ± 0.001% E. ± 0.0001%

Answer Choice D.

$$\begin{aligned}\textit{Percentage tolerance} &= \pm \frac{10}{10^4} \\ &= \pm 1 \times 10^{-3} \quad (5\text{-}1) \\ &= \pm 0.001\%\end{aligned}$$

5-3. The buffer stage

To improve the frequency stability still further, the oscillator is followed by a buffer stage (FIG. 5-2), which has a very high input impedance and is typically operated under class A, AB, A or B conditions. The power gain of the buffer stage is low, but it presents to the oscillator a constant (rather than a varying) load; this is an important factor in stabilizing the frequency generated by the oscillator stage.

* **Question 5-7** One reason for including the buffer stage is to:

A. increase the power output of the oscillator stage
B. behave as a harmonic generator
C. present a varying load to the oscillator stage
D. improve the efficiency of the oscillator stage
E. improve the frequency stability of the oscillator stage

Answer Choice E.

* **Question 5-8** One reason for including a buffer stage in a transmitter is to:

A. provide a low output impedance to the intermediate power amplifiers
B. stabilize the power supply to the oscillator stage

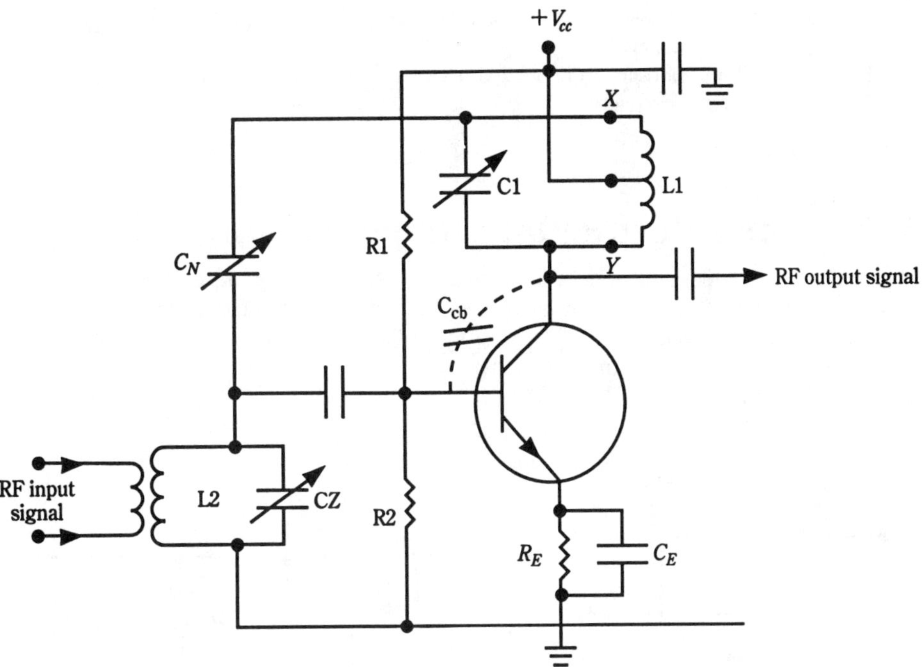

Fig. 5-2 The class-C intermediate RF power amplifier stage.

C. stop the oscillator from generating parasitic oscillations
D. present a constant load to the oscillator stage
E. present a low input impedance to the oscillator stage

Answer Choice D.

* **Question 5-9** Features of a transmitter's buffer stage include:

A. reduction of harmonics
B. high gain
C. harmonic generation
D. low input impedance
E. improvement in the frequency stability of an oscillator stage

Answer Choice E.

* **Question 5-10** In a transmitter, a constant and stable load for the oscillator can be provided by a:

A. class-C intermediate stage
B. push-pull class-C stage
C. frequency multiplier
D. buffer stage
E. push-push stage

Answer Choice D.

* **Question 5-11** The purpose of a buffer amplifier is to:

A. prevent the oscillator from being overloaded by the preceding stage
B. isolate a preceding stage from the loading effect of the following stage

C. prevent frequency instability in the oscillator stage because of the variations in the loading effect of the following stage
D. prevent RF interference from being transferred from the antenna to the oscillator stage
E. choices B and C are true

Answer Choice E.

5-4. The intermediate RF power amplifiers

The main function of these stages is to increase the power level of the carrier. Because efficiency is of vital importance, each stage is invariably operated under class-C conditions and uses a tank circuit as the collector load (FIG. 5-3). Owing to feedback from the output circuit to the input circuit, such stages might need to be neutralized.

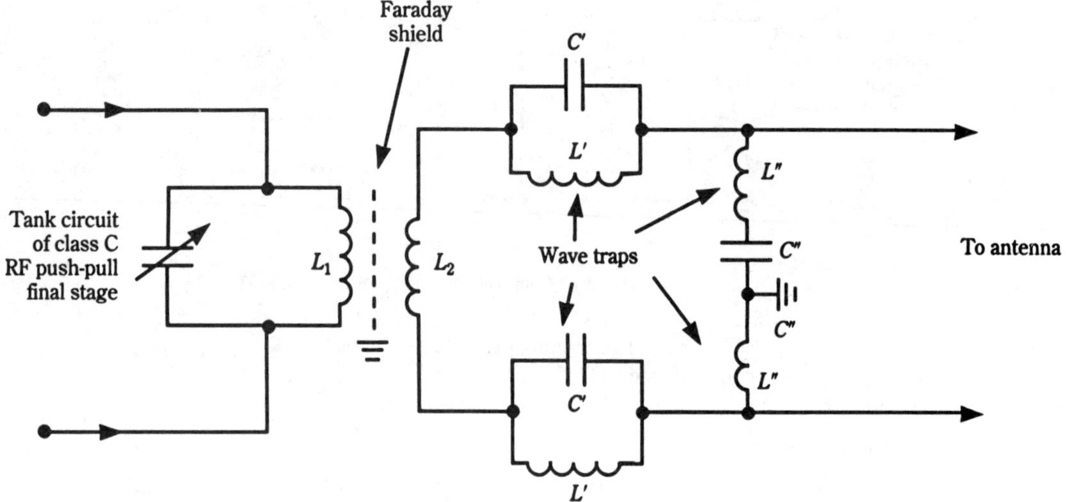

Fig. 5-3 Methods of achieving harmonic attenuation.

Because of the existence of the depletion region at the collector-base junction, there must be a collector-to-base capacitance (C_{cb}). This capacitance provides, particularly at high (radio) frequencies, a path between the collector and the base circuits so that the output signal at the collector can drive a current back into the base circuit and develop a feedback voltage across the impedance of the input circuit; this phenomenon is commonly referred to as *Miller effect.* If this indirect feedback voltage is of sufficient magnitude and has the correct phase (positive feedback), the circuit might no longer function solely as an amplifier, but will also be capable of generating a spurious oscillation. This can occur if the collector load (the tank circuit L1, C1) behaves inductively. However, if the collector-tank circuit presents a capacitive impedance, the phase of the feedback voltage is reversed (negative feedback) and the amplifier's gain is reduced. Neither of these effects will occur if the collector tank circuit is at resonance and behaves resistively; however, this circuit might drift to either side of resonance and become inductive or capacitive. The bipolar transistor can therefore be unstable as an RF amplifier, unless the circuit is neutralized. The presence of spurious oscillation can be found by moving a neon bulb in the vicinity of the amplifier; where the bulb glows, a spurious oscillation must exist.

A typical neutralization circuit is shown in FIG. 5-3. Here, the purpose is not to eliminate the feedback through the C_{cb}, but to cancel its effect by an opposite feedback through the neutralizing capacitor, C_N. In this collector neutralization circuit, a center tap on the collector tank coil, L1, is connected to $+V_{CC}$ and is therefore effectively at RF ground. Points X and Y are at opposite ends of L1; therefore, the RF potentials at these points are equal in magnitude, but are 180° out of phase. The feedback from the voltage at Y through the collector-to-base capacitance is then cancelled by the opposite feedback from the voltage at X through the neutralizing capacitor, C_N. During the neutralizing procedure, the collector supply voltage, $+V_{CC}$, is removed so that the spurious oscillation is not masked by the amplified signal; the value of C_N is then varied until complete cancellation of the feedback is achieved. Notice that a common-base amplifier does not need to be neutralized because the grounded base acts as a shield between the output collector circuit and the input emitter circuit.

If the transmitter is operating in the VHF band, it is impossible to find a crystal that will oscillate at the required frequency. For example, let the required carrier frequency be 100 MHz. Because the upper frequency limit for a crystal's fundamental vibration is only about 25 MHz, you cannot use class-C amplifiers alone for the intermediate stages, but must instead include some frequency multipliers. In this example, one solution is to use a 12.5-MHz crystal and insert three doubler stages in the intermediate amplifiers. The total product factor is: $2 \times 2 \times 2 = 8$; therefore, the output frequency is: 8×12.5 MHz $= 100$ MHz. Because the output frequency from a doubler or a tripler is a multiple of the input frequency, there is no effective feedback from the collector circuit; consequently, frequency multipliers do not need to be neutralized. Also, if the tolerance of the output frequency is ± 2 kHz, the tolerance at the crystal oscillator is ± 2 kHz/8 $= \pm 250$ Hz. In other words, the amount of tolerance is changed, but the percentage of the tolerance $\pm \frac{2 \text{ kHz}}{100 \text{ MHz}} \times 100 = \pm \frac{250 \text{ Hz}}{12.5 \text{ MHz}} \times 100 = \pm 0.002\%$, remains unchanged. The actual deviation of the output frequency from its assigned value is measured by the percentage of variance.

$$\frac{\textit{Percentage}}{\textit{of variance}} = \frac{\textit{assigned frequency} \sim \textit{operating frequency}}{\textit{assigned frequency}} \times 100\% \tag{5-3}$$

In this equation, only unmodulated values can be used.

* **Question 5-12** The frequency tolerance of a 2-MHz oscillator is $\pm 0.002\%$. Between the crystal oscillator and the output amplifier of the transmitter are the three doubler stages. The maximum permitted deviation of output frequency is:

A. 3.2 kHz B. 320 Hz C. 32 kHz D. 0.32 MHz E. 32 Hz

Answer Choice B. Output frequency $= 2 \times 2 \times 2 \times 2 = 16$ MHz. Maximum permitted deviation of the output frequency is $16 \times 10^6 \times 0.002/100$ Hz $= 320$ Hz.

* **Question 5-13** A transmitter's output frequency is 2182 kHz. If three doubler stages are between the oscillator and the final stage, the oscillator's frequency is:

A. 2182 kHz B. 1091 kHz C. 545.5 kHz D. 272.75 kHz E. 136.4 kHz

Answer Choice D.

$$\begin{aligned} \textit{Oscillator frequency} &= \frac{2182}{2 \times 2 \times 2} \\ &= 272.75 \text{ kHz} \end{aligned}$$

* **Question 5-14** The base in an RF amplifier is grounded in order to:

A. raise the input impedance
B. lower the output impedance

C. obtain maximum power output
D. raise the amplifier's efficiency
E. avoid the requirement of neutralizing the stage

Answer Choice E.

* **Question 5-15** A transmitter's output frequency is 16 MHz, with a tolerance of $\pm 0.002\%$. Three doubler stages exist between the final amplifier and the oscillator. The maximum permitted frequency deviation at the oscillator is:

A. 320 Hz B. 400 Hz C. 40 Hz D. 80 Hz E. 160 Hz

Answer Choice C. Oscillator frequency $= 16$ MHz$/(2 \times 2 \times 2) = 2$ MHz. Maximum permitted deviation at the oscillator is $2 \times 10^6 \times 0.002/100 = 40$ Hz.

* **Question 5-16** Neutralization is not required in:

A. audio amplifiers
B. frequency-multiplier stages
C. CB amplifiers when the base is grounded
D. push-push stages
E. all of the above choices are true

Answer Choice E.

* **Question 5-17** A crystal oscillator is operated at its fundamental frequency of 184 kHz. If the transmitter's output frequency is 2208 kHz, the required combination of harmonic generators is:

A. three doubler stages
B. three doubler stages and a tripler stage
C. one doubler stage and two tripler stages
D. one doubler stage and one quadrupler stage
E. two doubler stages and one tripler stage

Answer Choice E. The required product factor for the multiplier stages is $2208/184 = 12$, which would require two doubler stages and a tripler stage $(2 \times 2 \times 3 = 12)$.

* **Question 5-18** A transmitter has an assigned frequency of 50 MHz but its operating frequency is 50.01 MHz. The percentage of variance is:

A. 0.02% B. 0.002% C. 0.001% D. 0.01% E. 0.05%

Answer Choice A.

$$\textit{Percentage of variance} = \frac{50.01 - 50}{50} \times 100 \qquad (5\text{–}3)$$
$$= 0.02\%$$

* **Question 5-19** A transmitter has an assigned carrier frequency of 16 MHz with a tolerance of ± 200 ppm. Between the final amplifier and the oscillator are three doubler stages. The maximum permitted frequency deviation at the oscillator is:

A. 40 Hz B. 400 Hz C. 800 Hz D. 1600 Hz E. 3200 Hz

Answer Choice B.

$$\textit{Oscillator frequency} = \frac{16}{2 \times 2 \times 2} = 2 \text{ MHz}$$

$$\textit{Maximum permitted frequency deviation} = 2 \times 10^6 \times 200/10^6$$
$$= 400 \text{ Hz}$$

* **Question 5-20** Neutralization of an RF amplifier stage might be necessary in order to:

A. increase the amplifier's gain
B. reduce the amplifier's gain
C. prevent the generation of spurious oscillation
D. reduce the level of the output harmonics
E. prevent the generation of parasitic oscillations

Answer Choice C.

5-5. The RF final stage

The *RF final stage* is the most important stage in the entire RF section because it is responsible for delivering the rated power output of the transmitter to the antenna system. The FCC assigns an authorized power output to a particular station, but at the same time there is a certain power tolerance. For example, the power tolerance for AM broadcast stations extends from 5% above to 10% below. Thus, for a station with an assigned power of 10 kW, the actual operating power can extend up to 10.5 kW and down to 9 kW. The operating power can be determined by the direct method, as described in Section 10-4.

$$\textit{Operating power} = I_A{}^2 R_A \text{ watts (W)} \tag{5-4}$$

where: I_A = antenna current at the feedpoint (A)
R_A = resistance of the resonant antenna (Ω)

In addition, the readings of the supply voltage (E) for the final stage and its associated dc level of current (I) are entered in the station log. The dc current meter must be shunted by an RF bypass capacitor so that the reading is not affected by the RF components that are contained in the current waveform. The product of E and I is equal to the dc power input to the final stage. If this product is multiplied by the efficiency factor F, the result is the operating power, as calculated by the indirect method.

$$\textit{Operating power} = E \times I \times F \text{ watts (W)} \tag{5–5}$$

where: E = dc supply voltage (V)
I = dc level of output current (A)
F = efficiency factor

Because the final stage produces the highest level of RF power, this amplifier must be operated under class-C conditions with an efficiency of up to 90%; this will inevitably create harmonic components of the carrier frequency. However, harmonic radiation from the antenna must be kept to a minimum in order to prevent interference with other stations. The following means can be used to reduce the harmonics to a level that is normally at least 40 dB below the carrier power.

- The use of a push-pull RF circuit for the final stage. Such an arrangement will eliminate all even harmonics of the carrier frequency.
- The insertion of a Faraday shield between the tank coil and the coupling coil to the transmission line (FIG. 5-3). This screen is grounded at its base so that the capacitive coupling between the two coils is considerably reduced and will no longer permit the transfer of high-frequency harmonic components to the antenna system.
- If a certain strong harmonic component appears across the coupling coil, it can be prevented from reaching the transmission line by using series and parallel wave traps (FIG. 5-3). At this particular harmonic frequency, the parallel wave trap (L′, C′) behaves as a theoretical open circuit, and the series wave trap (L″, C″) acts as a short circuit.

- The bias on the final stage can be reduced so that the angle of the output current flow is increased and the associated harmonics are weaker.

The antenna system is a load on the tank circuit of the final stage; therefore, it lowers the value of its Q factor. As a result, the responses to the various harmonic components are increased. The degree of coupling between L_1 and L_2 is therefore adjusted to compromise between the power transfer to the antenna system and the degree of harmonic response; a loaded Q value of the order of 10 to 15 is typical.

* **Question 5-21** A transmitter is operating on a frequency of 122.5 MHz with an assigned power of 100 W. A strong fourth harmonic (490 MHz) component has a radiated power of 5 W. If the 490-MHz component is fed through a filter with a 7-dB loss, what is the new value of the harmonic's radiated power?

A. 0.7 W B. 3.5 W C. 0.2 W D. 1 W E. 4.3 W

Answer Choice D. A loss of 7 dB is equivalent to a power ratio of 1/5 (TABLE 2-3). Harmonic radiated power = 5 × 1/5 = 1 W.

* **Question 5-22** The radiated carrier power from a transmitter is 500 W. If the radiated power of the second harmonic component is 0.5 W, the degree of the harmonic attenuation relative to the carrier is:

A. 5 dB B. 7 dB C. 30 dB D. 20 dB E. 50 dB

Answer Choice C. Power ratio = 500/0.5 = 1000. Amount of attenuation = 10 log 1000 = 30 dB.

* **Question 5-23** The radiated carrier power from a transmitter is 1 kW. If the second harmonic component has been attenuated to 40 dB below the carrier power, the power in the second harmonic is:

A. 0.4 W B. 0.1 W C. 10 W D. 4 W E. 1.4 W

Answer Choice B. Attenuation of 40 dB is equivalent to a power ratio of antilog (− 40 dB/10) = 10^{-4} = 0.0001. The second harmonic power = 1 kW × 0.0001 = 1000 × 0.0001 W = 0.1 W.

* **Question 5-24** A 50-MHz transmitter has a radiated carrier power of 100 W. Because of inadequate neutralization a 49.9-MHz spurious emission with a power of 5 W is passed through a filter that provides a loss of 7 dB. The radiated power of the spurious emission is:

A. 1 W B. 0.7 W C. 0.5 W D. 0.35 W E. 1.5 W

Answer Choice A. A loss of 7 dB is equivalent to a power ratio of 1/5 (TABLE 2-3). The radiated power of the spurious emission is 5 × 1/5 = 1 W.

Question 5-25 A dc supply voltage to a transmitter's final stage is 1220 V and the associated dc level of current is 320 mA. If the output carrier power is 250 W, the efficiency factor is:

A. 0.69 B. 0.59 C. 0.66 D. 0.73 E. 0.64

Answer Choice E.

$$\textit{Dc power input to the final stage} = 1220 \text{ V} \times 320 \text{ mA} = 390.4 \text{ W}$$

Efficiency factor:

$$F = \frac{250 \text{ W}}{390.4 \text{ W}} = 0.64 \text{ or } 64\% \qquad (5\text{-}5)$$

Notice that the efficiency factor can either be expressed as a decimal fraction or as a percentage.

Question 5-26 The known values for a transmitter are as follows: dc supply voltage to the final stage = 500 V, associated dc level of current for the final stage = 0.4 A, antenna current at the feedpoint = 3.2 A, antenna resistance at resonance = 15 Ω, efficiency factor = 0.7. Calculate the value of the operating power by the direct method:

A. 140 W B. 154 W C. 200 W D. 173 W E. 168 W

Answer Choice B.

By the direct method:

$$\begin{aligned}\text{Operating power} &= I_A{}^2R_A \\ &= (3.2\ \text{A})^2 \times 15\ \Omega \qquad (5\text{-}4) \\ &= 150\ \text{W}\end{aligned}$$

Notice that by the indirect method:

$$\begin{aligned}\textit{Operating power} &= E \times I \times F \\ &= 500\ \text{V} \times 0.4\ \text{A} \times 0.7 \qquad (5\text{-}5) \\ &= 140\ \text{W}\end{aligned}$$

* **Question 5-27** The known values for a transmitter are: dc supply voltage to the final stage = 600 V, associated dc level of current for the final stage = 0.3 A, antenna current at the feedpoint = 3 A, Antenna resistance at resonance = 15 Ω. Calculate the value of the efficiency factor:

A. 0.75 B. 0.80 C. 0.72 D. 0.65 E. 0.55

Answer Choice A. By the direct method:

$$\textit{Operating power} = (3\ \text{A})^2 \times 15\ \Omega = 145\ \text{W}$$

$$\begin{aligned}\textit{Dc power input to the final stage} &= 600\ \text{V} \times 0.3\ \text{A} \qquad (5\text{-}4) \\ &= 180\ \text{W}\end{aligned}$$

Efficiency factor:

$$\begin{aligned}F &= \frac{145\ \text{W}}{180\ \text{W}} \\ &= 0.75\end{aligned}$$

Question 5-28 The operating power of a transmitter is increased by:

A. increasing the level of reverse signal bias on the final stage
B. reducing the degree of coupling between the final stage and the antenna load
C. raising the value of the dc supply voltage to the final stage
D. reducing the amount of signal drive to the final stage
E. lowering the value of the efficiency factor

Answer Choice C. Because the operating power is equal to $E \times I \times F$ watts, raising the value of the dc supply voltage will increase the operating power.

Question 5-29 The dc power input to the final stage of a transmitter is calculated by:

A. multiplying the RMS value of the input signal by the dc level of output current
B. multiplying the operating power by the efficiency factor
C. multiplying the dc supply voltage by the RMS value of the antenna current
D. multiplying the antenna resistance by the square of the final stage's dc current and dividing the result by the efficiency factor
E. none of the above choices is true

Answer Choice E.

5-6. The continuous-wave transmitter

The system of oscillator, buffer amplifier, intermediate amplifiers, frequency multipliers, and a final stage is only capable of generating the RF carrier, which, by itself, contains no information and is designated as a *NON* (unmodulated carrier—absence of any modulation—no information) *emission.* This arrangement is known as a *Continuous Wave (CW)* transmitter in which the carrier can be keyed to produce "mark" and "space" intervals. This coded form of communication is known as *telegraphy,* as opposed to *telephony,* which is voice transmission. For example, the morse code for the letter a is . _ , which is illustrated in FIG. 5-4. The designation for this form of telegraphy is A1A (telegraphy on/off keying, without the use of a modulating AF tone). A complete list of the FCC emission designations appears in chapter 6.

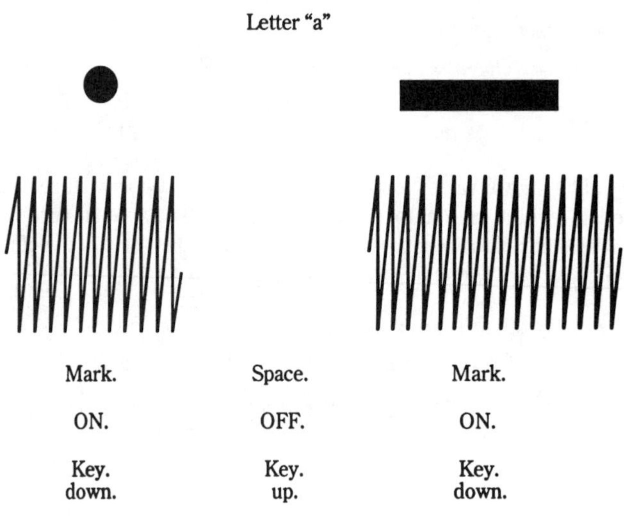

Fig. 5-4 Telegraphy using morse code.

To key a CW transmitter, a bias is applied to most, if not all, of the transmitter's class-C amplifiers. For example, the keying bias can be a negative voltage that is applied to the p-bases of npn transistors. When the key is pressed down ("mark"), the negative voltage is not applied to the bases; the transmitter functions normally and a continuous wave is radiated from the antenna. As soon as the key is released ("space") the keying bias is applied, most of the stages close down and, there is no radiated wave.

This coverage of the CW transmitter is concluded by analyzing a typical schematic diagram (FIG. 5-5). This diagram contains a (tripler) frequency multiplier, an intermediate power amplifier or driver, and the final stage, which is coupled to the transmission line and the antenna. The output frequency lies in the *very high frequency (VHF)* band.

The functions of the various components are as follows:

L1/C1 form a tuned circuit that is tuned to the incoming signal frequency (for example, 15 MHz).

C2/R2 provide the necessary time constant for the signal bias, which allows Q1 to operate under class-C conditions. The collector current's waveform therefore consists of narrow spikes, and these contain a strong third harmonic (45 MHz) component.

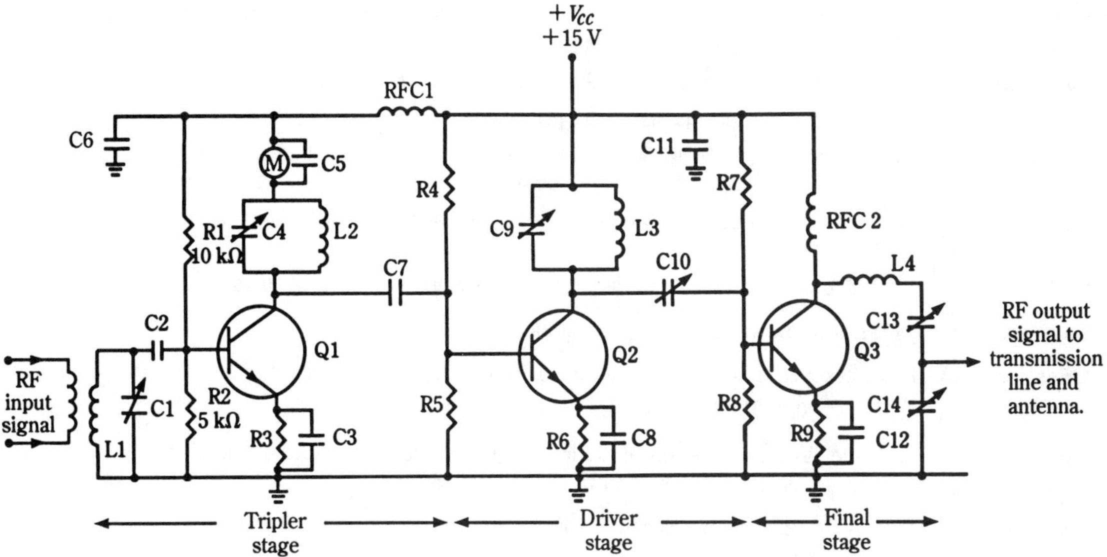

Fig. 5-5 The schematic diagram of a VHF transmitter's last three stages.

R1/R2/R3 forward-bias Q1 so that this transistor is conducting in the absence of the incoming signal. Capacitor C3 is included to prevent any negative (degenerative) feedback being developed across R3. Should any such feedback exist, the gain of the tripler stage would be reduced.

L2/C4 form the collector load. This tank circuit is tuned to the third harmonic (45 MHz) of the input signal.

M is a current meter that records the dc level of the collector current. When the tank circuit is tuned to resonance at the third harmonic, its impedance rises to its maximum value and the RF current falls to its lowest level. Because Q1 is operated under class-C conditions, the minimum RF current is associated with a minimum level of dc current. When the value of C_4 is varied through resonance, the meter will show a "dip" in its reading; this is commonly known as *tuning for the dip.* C5 is a bypass capacitor to prevent the reading of M from being affected by the RF components contained in the collector current.

RFC1/C6 form a decoupling network so that the RF components in the collector current are bypassed to ground via C_6 and do not enter the dc supply ($+V_{CC}$). If the RF current is allowed to pass through the V_{CC} supply, it can develop an RF voltage across the supply's internal impedance. This RF voltage fluctuation will then be fed to all of the other stages that use the same dc voltage. As a result, there will be undesirable feedback between these stages.

C7/R5 provide signal bias for Q2 and couple the 45-MHz signal from the collector of Q1 to the base of Q2. C7 is also a blocking capacitor, which prevents the dc voltage at the collector of Q1 from being applied to the base of Q2.

R4/R5/R6/C8 supply forward bias to Q2 in the absence of the 45-MHz signal.

C9/L3 is the collector load for Q2. This tank circuit is tuned to resonance at 45 MHz.

C10 provides signal bias in conjunction with resistor R8. The variation in the value of C_{10}, controls the amount of (signal) drive to the base of Q3.

R7/R8/R9/C12 supply forward bias to Q3 in the absence of the 45-MHz signal.

C11 is an RF bypass capacitor whose purpose is the same as that of C6.

RFC2 forms part of the collector load. The final stage is a shunt-fed amplifier with the tuned circuit in parallel with transistor Q3.

L4/C13/C14 acts as the tuned circuit, which is tuned to resonance at 45 MHz by capacitor C13.

C14 is used to match the antenna load to the load required by the final stage.

Questions 5-30 to 5-40 refer to the schematic diagram of FIG. 5-5.

* **Question 5-30** In the absence of any input signal, the dc voltage across resistor R2 is:

A. 5 V B. 4.3 V C. 0.07 V D. 10 V E. 15 V

Answer Choice A. In the absence of the signal, R1 and R2 provide voltage-divider bias so that the voltage across resistor R2 is: 15 V × 5 kΩ/(5 kΩ + 10 kΩ) = 5 V.

* **Question 5-31** What is the function of capacitor C13?

A. to tune Q3's collector load
B. C13 is part of a high-pass filter to attenuate the harmonics
C. C13 is the neutralizing capacitor
D. C13 matches the antenna load to the value of load required by the final stage
E. C13 prevents the generation of parasitic oscillations

Answer Choice A.

* **Question 5-32** What is the purpose of capacitor C14?

A. C14 is part of a bandpass filter to accentuate the harmonics
B. C14 is the neutralizing capacitor
C. C14 is an anti-parasitic component
D. C14 matches the antenna load to the value of load required by the final stage
E. C14, in conjunction with C13, form a capacitive voltage divider to prevent positive feedback

Answer Choice D.

* **Question 5-33** Which of the following events would have the least effect on the circuit's performance?

A. C13 open-circuits
B. R3 open-circuits
C. C11 open-circuits
D. C4 open-circuits
E. C14 short-circuits

Answer Choice C. C11 is a bypass decoupling capacitor; if this component open-circuits, there might be some intercoupling between the stages, but this would not have a severe effect on the circuit's performance. All the other choices result in zero output to the transmission line.

* **Question 5-34** What is the effect on the circuit's performance if C3 open-circuits?

A. parasitic oscillations increase
B. the transmitter's output frequency increases
C. the transmitter's output frequency decreases

D. the transmitter's output power increases
E. the transmitter's output power decreases

Answer Choice E. If C3 open-circuits, a negative feedback voltage is developed across R3. This reduces the gain provided by Q1; therefore, the transmitter's power output decreases.

* **Question 5-35** What is the effect on the circuit's performance if a short circuit is developed across R3?

A. the transmitter's output frequency decreases
B. the transmitter's output frequency increases
C. Q1 is cut off
D. the stability of the Q1 tripler stage is reduced
E. the transmitter's power output increases

Answer Choice D. If R3 short-circuits, transistor Q1 is no longer provided with voltage-divider bias and the stability of the circuit is reduced.

* **Question 5-36** As capacitor C4 is tuned through resonance at the third harmonic frequency:

A. the reading of the RF current meter, M, falls to a minimum value
B. the reading of the RF current meter, M, rises to a maximum value
C. the reading of the dc current meter, M, is zero throughout the tuning procedure
D. the reading of the dc current meter, M, dips
E. the reading of the dc current meter, M peaks

Answer Choice D.

* **Question 5-37** What is the purpose of capacitor C5?

A. to act as a capacitor shunt to extend the RF current range of the meter, M
B. to prevent current surges from damaging the meter, M
C. to bypass the RF components contained in the collector current so that these components do not affect the readings of the meter, M
D. to bypass the harmonics contained in the collector current so that only the fundamental component passed through the meter, M
E. C5 is an anti-parasitic component

Answer Choice C.

* **Question 5-38** When tuning a CW transmitter (such as shown in the schematic diagram of FIG. 5-5), the first step is to:

A. connect a dummy antenna
B. switch on all stages and then transmit your call sign
C. tune all stages with the transmitter's antenna connected
D. check the output frequency of the oscillator stage
E. apply full voltage to the final stage

Answer Choice A. It is important to carry out the tuning procedure in radio silence so that there is minimum interference with other stations.

* **Question 5-39** If a short circuit develops across RFC2, the:

A. transmitter's output frequency increases, but the RF power output remains the same
B. transmitter's output frequency decreases, but the RF power output remains the same
C. transmitter's RF power output falls to a very low level
D. transmitter's RF power output increases
E. transistor Q3 is cut off

Answer Choice C. Because of the presence of C11, the collector of Q3 will be virtually at RF ground, although its dc voltage is +15 V. Consequently, the transmitter's RF power output falls to a very low level.

* **Question 5-40** If the harmonics radiated by the transmitter are too strong:

A. increase the amount of signal bias on the final stage
B. reduce the value of C_{13}
C. increase the value of C_{14}
D. adjust the value of C_{10} to reduce the amount of signal bias on the transistor Q3
E. either choice B or C is correct

Answer Choice D. Adjust the value of C_{10} to reduce the amount of the input signal to the base of Q3. This will lower the amount of the signal bias and increase the angle of flow for the collector current. The harmonic amplitudes will then be reduced.

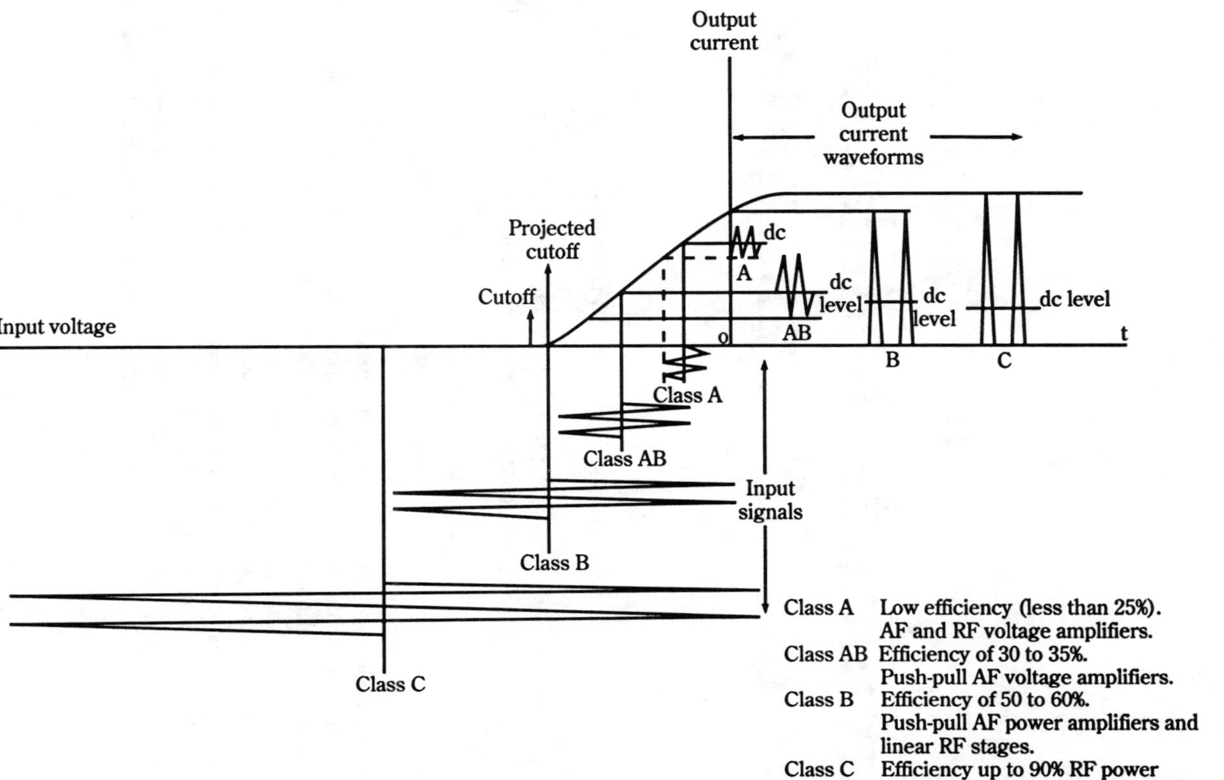

Fig. 5-6 A comparison between class-A, class-AB, class-B, and class-C operation.

6

Amplitude modulation and the AM transmitter

In this chapter you will learn:

- about the principles of amplitude modulation in conveying information from a transmitter to a receiver.
- how to measure the percentage of amplitude modulation and the degree of carrier shift.
- that an AM signal is composed of the carrier and sidebands, which require a certain bandwidth.
- how the sidebands are displayed on a spectrum analyzer.
- how the total sideband power depends on the percentage modulation.
- about the block diagram of an AM transmitter and its various stages.
- to distinguish between high and low level modulation.
- how amplitude modulation is achieved in the collector circuit of the final RF stage.
- why amplitude modulation produces an increase in the antenna current.
- about the reasons for intermodulation interference.
- about the simplex and duplex methods of two-way communications.
- why single-sideband operation is extensively used and about its emission designation, emission designators, and frequency tolerances.
- the ways in which a transmitter's frequency is measured against a suitable standard.
- about the use of the phonetic alphabet when communications are difficult or the signals are weak.

6-1. Amplitude modulation

Chapter 5 showed that the CW transmitter was only capable of conveying information in the form of a code. For telephony, you must modulate the carrier in such a way that the information (voice, music, etc.) is transported or "carried" from the transmitter to the receiver.

Modulation means controlling some feature of the RF carrier by the audio signal so that the receiver is able to reproduce the information (speech, music, etc). Because the carrier can be regarded as a high-frequency sine wave, it only possesses three features that can be modulated—amplitude, frequency, and phase (such quantities as period and wavelength are directly related to the frequency). In amplitude modulation, the instantaneous amplitude (voltage) of the RF wave is linearly related to the instantaneous magnitude (voltage) of the AF signal and the rate of amplitude variation is equal to the modulating frequency.

In FIG. 6-1A, the modulating signal is a single sine wave or test tone, which is used to amplitude-modulate an RF carrier. The extent of modulation is measured by the percentage modulation, as defined by:

$$\textit{Percentage modulation} = \frac{E_{max} - E_o}{E_o} \times 100\% \tag{6-1}$$

where: E_o = amplitude of the modulated carrier (V)
E_{max} = maximum amplitude of the AM signal (V)

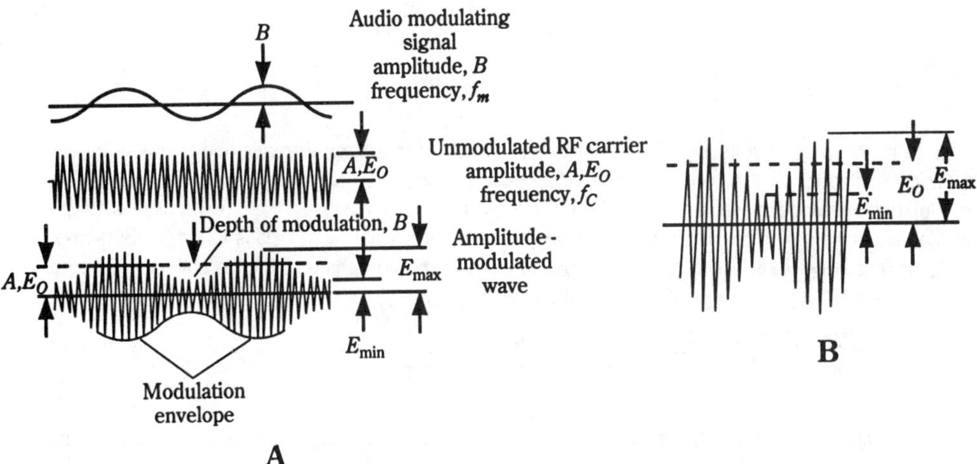

Fig. 6-1 The AM signal when modulated by a test tone.

Equation 6-1 expresses the percentage modulation for positive peaks of the modulating test tone; this is also referred to as *upward modulation.*

The percentage modulation on negative (downward) modulation peaks is:

$$\textit{Percentage modulation} = \frac{E_o - E_{min}}{E_o} \times 100\% \tag{6-2}$$

where: E_{min} = *minimum amplitude of the AM signal*

If the modulation is symmetrical about the E_o level, as in FIG. 6–1A:

$$E_o = \frac{E_{max} + E_{min}}{2} \tag{6-3}$$

Equations 6-1 and 6-3 yield:

$$\textit{Percentage modulation} = \frac{E_{max} - \dfrac{E_{max} + E_{min}}{2}}{\dfrac{E_{max} + E_{min}}{2}} \times 100\%$$

$$= \frac{E_{max} - E_{min}}{E_{max} + E_{min}} \times 100\% \qquad (6\text{-}4)$$

$$= \frac{E_{max} - E_{min}}{2E_o} \times 100\%$$

In FIGS. 6-1A and B it is clear that:

$$E_{max} = A + B \qquad (6\text{-}5)$$

and:

$$E_{min} = A - B \qquad (6\text{-}6)$$

where: $A = E_o$ = amplitude of unmodulated carrier (V)
B = depth of modulation (V)

From EQS. 6-4, 6-5 and 6-6:

$$\text{Degree of modulation, } m = \frac{\textit{percentage of modulation}}{100}$$

$$= \frac{(A + B) - (A - B)}{(A + B) + (A - B)} \qquad (6\text{-}7)$$

$$= \frac{B}{A}$$

For a variety of reasons, the modulation envelope for a symmetrical tone contains asymmetrical distortion that is referred to as *carrier shift.* In *negative carrier shift,* the troughs of the modulation envelope are greater than the peaks and this will cause a decrease (compared with the unmodulated value) in the dc current reading of a collector-modulated class-C stage. Similarly, with *positive carrier shift,* the envelope's peaks exceed the troughs and the dc collector current will increase. The percentage of carrier shift is defined by:

$$\textit{Percentage of carrier shift} = \frac{\textit{dc level (modulated)} - \textit{dc level (unmodulated)}}{\textit{dc level (unmodulated)}} \times 100\% \qquad (6\text{-}8)$$

The percentage of carrier shift should not exceed 5%.

Increasing the amplitude of the test tone raises the percentage modulation, improves the signal-to-noise ratio at the receiver, and results in a higher audio power output. However, if the modulation percentage is increased to 100% and beyond (overmodulation), the modulation envelope is severely distorted and this distortion will ultimately appear in the output from the loudspeaker. Overmodulation also results in the generation of spurious frequencies that will cause interference to adjacent channels. Figure 6-2A shows the AM waveforms for various modulation percentages.

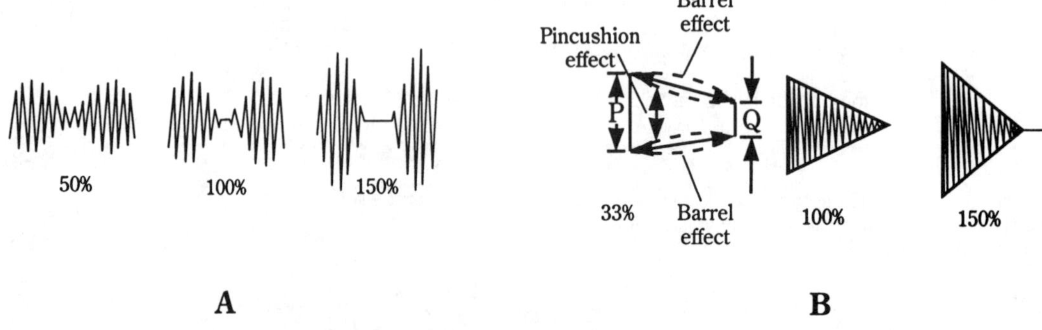

Fig. 6-2 The waveforms of the AM signal for different percentages of modulation.

Other than measuring the percentage modulation from the AM waveform, it is common practice to use a trapezoidal display on an oscilloscope. This is achieved by feeding the AM signal to the vertical deflecting (Y) plates and the audio signal to the horizontal deflecting (X) plates. In addition to measuring percentage modulation, this method will clearly indicate whether there exists the required linear relationship between the instantaneous amplitude of the RF carrier and the instantaneous magnitude of the tone signal. Nonlinearity will appear either as a "barrel" or a "pin-cushion effect" on the trapezoidal display (FIG. 6-2B). The percentage of modulation is given by:

$$\textit{Percentage modulation} = \frac{P - Q}{P + Q} \times 100\% \qquad (6\text{-}9)$$

for 50% modulation, $P = 3\,Q$ (not $2\,Q$).

When AM is being used to transmit speech or music, the percentage of modulation varies from instant to instant. Permitted values can then be quoted for:

- The minimum percentage modulation on average peaks of the audio signal.
- The maximum modulation percentage on negative modulation peaks.
- The maximum modulation on positive modulation peaks.
- The maximum carrier shift.

For example, for marine transmitters, the modulation on positive and negative peaks must be maintained between 75% and 100%. By contrast, aviation transmitters must maintain their modulation between 70% and 100%.

* **Question 6-1** In FIG. 6-3, the percentage modulation of the AM signal is:

A. 100% B. 80% C. 40% D. 50% E. 60%

Answer Choice D. On the scale provided, $E_{max} = 1.5$ E and $E_{min} = 0.5$ E. Because the modulation appears to be symmetrical:

$$\textit{Percentage modulation} = \frac{E_{max} - E_{min}}{E_{max} + E_{min}} \times 100\%$$

$$= \frac{1.5\text{ E} - 0.5\text{ E}}{1.5\text{ E} + 0.5\text{ E}} \times 100 \qquad (6\text{-}4)$$

$$= \frac{1}{2} \times 100 = 50\%$$

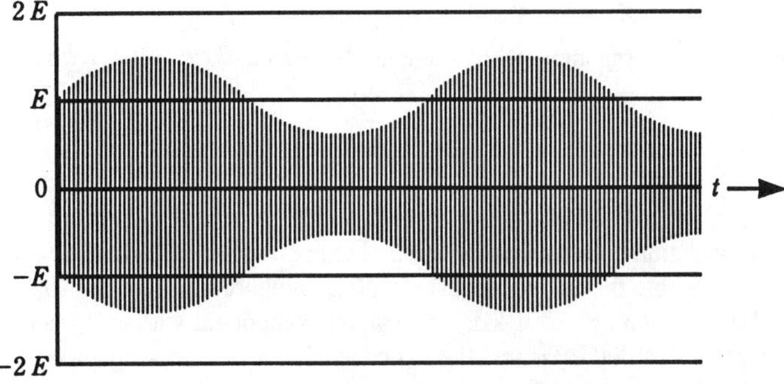

Fig. 6-3 The waveform for question 6-1.

* **Question 6-2** The carrier of an AM transmitter is the:

A. transmitter's output signal when the modulation is zero
B. transmitter's output signal when the modulation is present
C. output signal from the crystal oscillator
D. RMS value of the AM signal
E. transmitter's output signal when the modulation percentage is 50%

Answer Choice A. Because the percentage of modulation for a voice transmission changes from instant to instant, only unmodulated values are normally entered into the station's log.

6-2. AM sidebands and bandwidth

Figure 6-4 illustrates the result of amplitude-modulating an RF carrier (amplitude A, frequency f_c) by an audio test tone (amplitude B, frequency f_m). As previously discussed, the degree of modulation, $m = B/A$ (EQ. 6-7). Analysis reveals that the AM (voltage) signal is entirely RF in nature (no audio voltage is present) and contains the following three components:

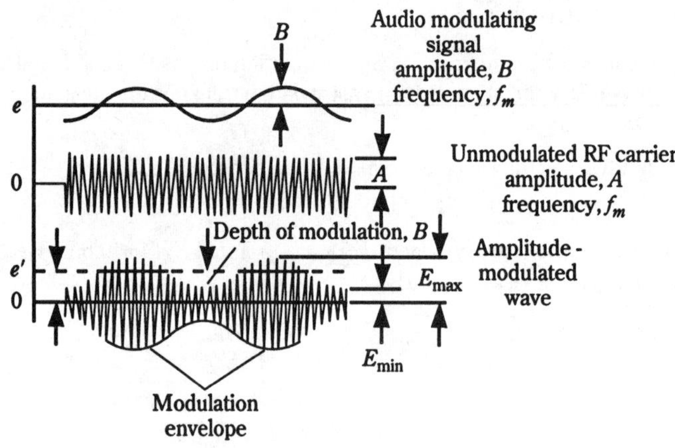

Fig. 6-4 The AM signal.

- An *upper sideband* component whose amplitude is $B/2 = mA/2$ and whose frequency is $f_c + f_m$.
- A *carrier,* whose amplitude is A and whose frequency is f_c.
- A *lower sideband* component whose amplitude is $B/2 = mA/2$ and whose frequency is $f_c - f_m$.

When these three RF components are literally added together, the resultant waveform is that of the AM signal.

As an example, let a 100-V 1-MHz carrier be 50% amplitude modulated by a 1-kHz test tone. The act of modulation creates the sidebands that contain the signal's intelligence so that the AM signal is composed of: the upper sideband with an amplitude of $0.5 \times 100/2 = 25$ V at a frequency of 1 MHz + 1 kHz = 1001 kHz, the carrier component with an amplitude of 100 V at a frequency of 1 MHz = 1000 kHz, and the lower sideband with an amplitude of 25 V at a frequency of 1 MHz − 1 kHz = 999 kHz. The instantaneous maximum voltage is 100 + 25 + 25 = 150 V, and the minimum voltage is 100 − 25 − 25 = 50 V.

Now assume that the carrier and sidebands are each associated with an antenna load of 100 Ω. The power, P_C, in the rf carrier is (100 V)^2/100 Ω = 100 W, whereas the power in each sideband is (25 V)^2/100 Ω = 6.25 W. The total sideband power, P_{SB}, is then 2 × 6.25 = 12.5 W. This result can also be obtained from the formula:

Total sideband power:

$$P_{SB} = \frac{1}{2} m^2 P_C \text{ watts (W)} \tag{6-10}$$

In the example, $m = 0.5$. Therefore:

$$P_{SB} = \frac{1}{2} \times (0.5)^2 \times 100$$

$$= 12.5 \text{ W}$$

If the percentage of modulation is increased to 100%, the carrier power remains at 100 W, but the total sideband power is increased to 0.5 × 1^2 × 100 = 50 W. The total RF power (carrier and sidebands) in the AM signal is 100 + 50 = 150 W, of which two thirds reside in the carrier and only one third in the sidebands.

The AM signal is accommodated within a certain bandwidth that is defined as the frequency difference between the upper and lower sidebands. In the example, the bandwidth required is 1001 − 999 = 2 kHz, which is equal to twice the frequency of the modulating tone. When the signal is speech or music that contains many instantaneous frequencies of varying amplitudes, each audio component will produce a pair of sidebands, and the bandwidth occupied by the AM signal will be the frequency difference between the highest upper sideband and the lowest lower sideband transmitted. Consequently, the bandwidth is equal to twice the highest audio modulating frequency.

Bandwidth:

$$BW = 2 \times \textit{highest modulating frequency} \tag{6-11}$$

Notice that if the carrier was modulated by a 3-kHz tone that possessed a strong second harmonic, the highest modulating frequency would be 2 × 3 = 6 kHz and the required bandwidth would be 2 × 6 = 12 kHz.

The presence of the carrier and the sidebands can be displayed on a spectrum analyzer. This item of test equipment is in the form of a receiver (chapter 7) with a very narrow bandwidth that is normally determined by a filter. A simplified block diagram of a spectrum analyzer is shown in FIG. 6-5.

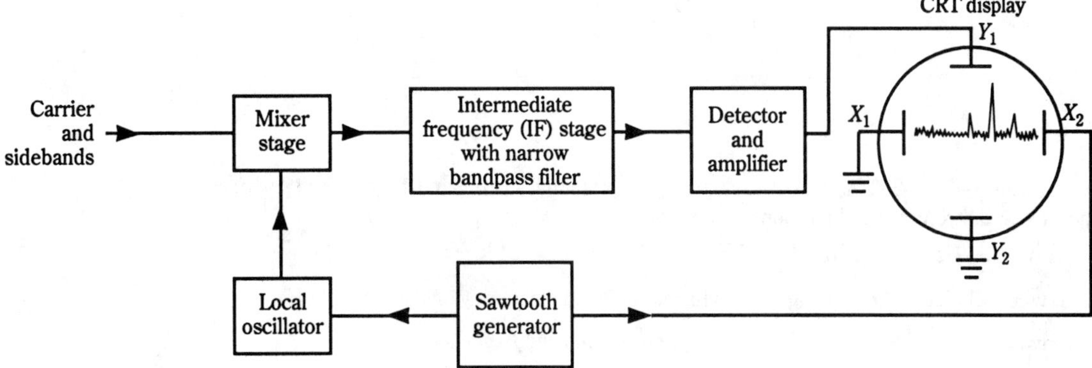

Fig. 6-5 A simplified block diagram of a spectrum analyzer.

The output of the sawtooth generator causes the local oscillator's frequency to sweep in a linear manner. At the same time, the sawtooth voltage is applied to the horizontal (X) deflection plates of the CRT so that the horizontal axis of the display represents a frequency, rather than a time scale. During the sweep, there will come a time when the difference between the carrier frequency and the local oscillator output is equal to the value of the intermediate frequency (IF). The filter output is then detected, amplified, and fed to the vertical (Y) deflection plates. The result is a vertical "spike," whose shape is determined by the narrow bandwidth of the receiver and characteristic of the filter. At different times, the same action will be repeated for the two sidebands and the display will therefore show three "spikes" (FIG. 6-6). The vertical scale is calibrated in decibels, relative to the zero level, where small random spikes are present as a result of noise. Apart from showing the existence of the sidebands, the spectrum analyzer can also be used to detect the presence of spurious oscillations, parasitic oscillations, and harmonics.

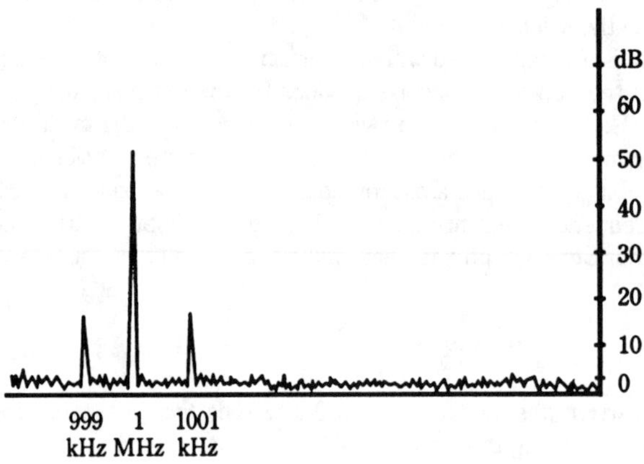

Fig. 6-6 A spectrum analyzer display.

Question 6-3 A 500-W 3-MHz transmitter is 80% amplitude-modulated by a pure tone. The total power in the sidebands is:

A. 320 W B. 400 W C. 200 W D. 160 W E. 80 W

Answer Choice D. Total sideband power:

$$P_{SB} = \frac{1}{2} \times m^2 \times P_C$$

$$= \frac{1}{2} \times (0.8)^2 \times 500 \qquad (6\text{-}10)$$

$$= 160 \text{ W}$$

* **Question 6-4** A 250-W 4-MHz transmitter is amplitude-modulated by a 1.5-Hz tone, which possesses a strong second harmonic. The required bandwidth is:

A. 1.5 kHz B. 3 kHz C. 6 kHz D. 12 kHz E. 24 kHz

Answer Choice C. The strong second harmonic has a frequency of: 2 × 1.5 = 3 kHz.

Bandwidth:

$$BW = 2 \times \textit{highest modulating frequency}$$

$$= 2 \times 3 \qquad (6\text{-}11)$$

$$= 6 \text{ kHz}$$

Notice that the assigned bandwidth of a marine double-sideband AM transmitter is 8 kHz, which means the highest audio frequency transmitted is only 4 kHz. This is adequate for voice communication, but it would be insufficient for the transmission of music.

* **Question 6-5** A 1-MHz carrier is amplitude modulated by a pure 200-Hz audio test tone. Which of the following combinations of frequencies represent the total content of the AM signal?

A. 1 MHz and 200 Hz
B. 999.8 kHz and 1000.2 kHz
C. 1 MHz, 999.8 kHz, 1000.2 kHz, and 200 Hz
D. 1 MHz and 1000.2 kHz
E. 999.8 kHz, 1000 kHz, and 1000.2 kHz

Answer Choice E. The frequency of the lower sideband is $f_c - f_m = 1000\text{ kHz} - 200\text{ Hz} = 999.8\text{ kHz}$. The frequency of the upper sideband is: $f_c + f_m = 1000\text{ kHz} + 200\text{ Hz} = 1000.2\text{ kHz}$. The AM signal contains the carrier and both sidebands; the required combination of frequencies is therefore 999.8, 1000, and 1000.2 kHz.

* **Question 6-6** An AM transmitter has an assigned carrier frequency of 25 MHz. Measurements reveal that the actual carrier frequency under unmodulated conditions is 25.00025 MHz, but it shifts to 24.99950 MHz when the modulation is applied. Which of the following statements is correct?

A. if the allowed frequency tolerance is 0.003%, the transmission is illegal
B. if the allowed frequency tolerance is 0.001%, the transmission is legal
C. if the allowed frequency tolerance is 0.002%, the transmission is illegal
D. if the authorized frequency tolerance is 0.0005%, the transmission is legal
E. the question is in error because the carrier frequency cannot change when the modulation is applied

Answer Choice B. Modulated values of the carrier frequency are ignored.

$$\begin{aligned} \textit{Percentage of variance} &= \frac{25.00025 - 25}{25} \times 100\% \\ &= 0.001\% \end{aligned}$$

* **Question 6-7** The display of FIG. 6-7 indicates that the input to the spectrum analyzer is a:

A. 15-MHz sine-wave signal
B. 15-MHz positive sawtooth signal
C. 15-MHz square-wave signal
D. 15-MHz triangular signal
E. 15-MHz negative sawtooth signal

Answer Choice A. Because neither the second harmonic (30 MHz) nor the third harmonic (45 MHz) is present, the input signal cannot be a square wave, a triangular wave or a sawtooth. The input must therefore be a 15-MHz sine wave.

* **Question 6-8** The "spike" shown in the display of FIG. 6-7 has a shape that is:

A. determined by the narrow bandwidth of the spectrum analyzer's receiver
B. the positive alternation (180°) of a sine wave
C. one quarter cycle (90°) of a sine wave
D. determined by the characteristic of a narrow band pass filter
E. choices A and D are true

Answer Choice E.

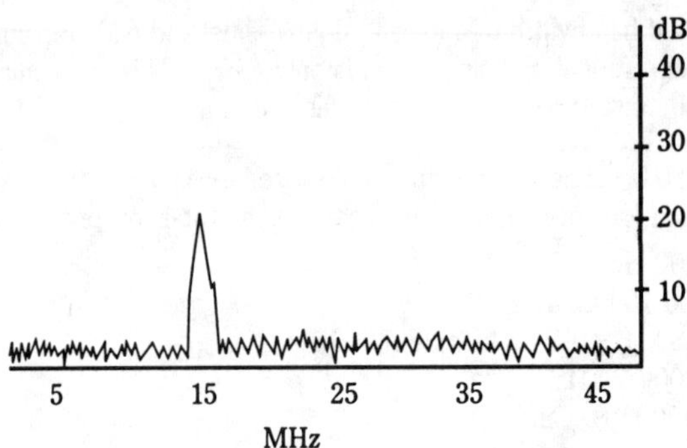

Fig. 6-7 The display for questions 6-7 and 6-8.

* **Question 6-9** A 1-kW 2-MHz carrier is 60% amplitude-modulated by a 1-kHz test tone. If the modulation is increased to 80%, what is the percentage increase in the total sideband power?

A. 33⅓% B. 67% C. 25% D. 50% E. 78%

Answer. Choice E.

Total sideband power for 60% modulation:

$$P_{SB} = \frac{1}{2} \times (0.6)^2 \times 1000 = 180 \text{ W} \qquad (6\text{-}10)$$

Total sideband power for 80% modulation:

$$P_{SB} = \frac{1}{2} \times (0.8)^2 \times 1000 = 320 \text{ W} \qquad (6\text{-}10)$$

Percentage increase in the total sideband power, is:

$$\frac{320 - 180}{180} \times 100 = \frac{1400}{18} = 78\%$$

Question 6-10 During average peaks of the audio signal, a high level of modulation is necessary in an AM transmitter in order to:

A. provide a high level of signal-to-noise ratio at the receiver
B. provide a high level of audio power for the receiver's loudspeaker
C. widen the bandwidth of the AM signal
D. reduce the bandwidth of the AM signal
E. choices A and B are true

Answer Choice E.

* **Question 6-11** A 500-W transmitter is 100% amplitude-modulated by a pure tone. The amount of the power in the lower sideband is:

A. 250 W B. 125 W C. 62.5 W D. 500 W E. 50 W

Answer Choice B.

Total sideband power:

$$P_{SB} = \frac{1}{2} \times 1^2 \times 500 \qquad (6\text{-}10)$$
$$= 250 \text{ W}$$

$$\text{Power in lower sideband} = \frac{250}{2} = 125 \text{ W.}$$

* **Question 6-12** The ratio of a modulated signal to the noise level is 20:1. This is equivalent to:

A. 20 dB quieting B. 10 dB quieting C. 3 dB quieting D. 30 dB quieting
E. 13 dB quieting

Answer Choice E. A power ratio of 20 = 2 × 10. From TABLE 2-3, a power ratio of 2 is equal to 3 dB, and a power ratio of 10 is the same as 10 dB. Therefore, a power ratio of 20 can be expressed as 3 + 10 = 13 dB quieting.

6-3. The AM transmitter

The CW transmitter of chapter 5-1 contains only RF stages. For telephony, you need an *audio frequency (AF) section,* which is shown in the block diagram of FIG. 6-8. Start by looking at the microphone, which is required for voice communication, then follow with a discussion of the audio stages and the modulation of the final RF stage.

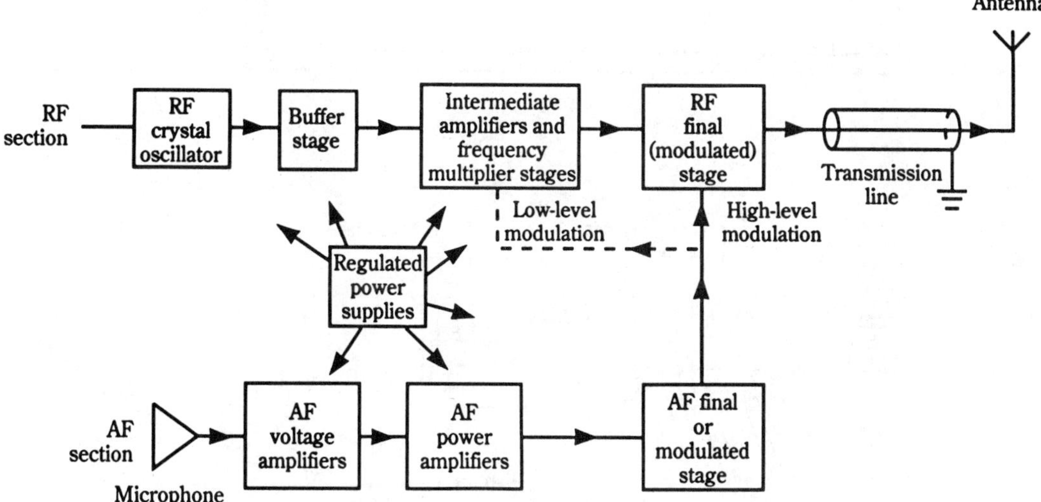

Fig. 6-8 The block diagram of AM transmitter.

The microphone

Every microphone consists basically of a *diaphragm,* which vibrates in the presence of a sound wave and some form of transducer capable of converting the mechanical vibration into an electrical signal. Some microphones have their diaphragms stretched in order to improve the frequency response; this is achieved by making the diaphragm's natural resonant frequency higher than the upper limit of the audio range.

The *dynamic (moving coil)* microphone is shown in FIG. 6-9. Joined with the diaphragm is a circular coil with its turns passing between the poles of a permanent magnet. When the diaphragm vibrates, the coil cuts the magnetic flux, so there is an induced voltage, which is the electrical equivalent of the sound wave. This type of microphone is commonly used in studios.

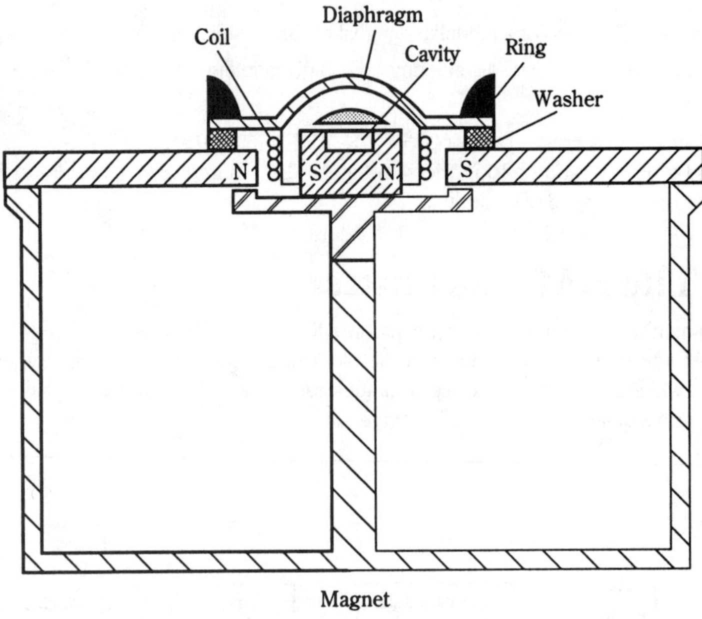

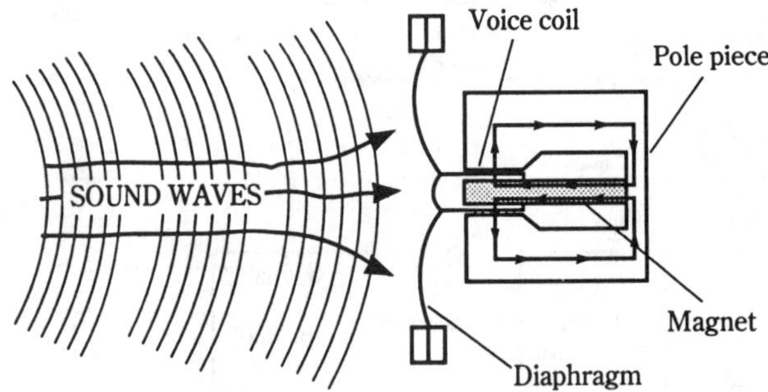

Fig. 6-9 The dynamic microphone.

The features of this type of microphone include:

- Low output impedance
- Wide frequency response
- No dc power supply necessary
- Relatively low level of output
- Relatively unaffected by humidity and temperature
- Low hum
- Light weight, but rugged construction

The *carbon microphone* is shown in FIG. 6-10. Attached to the diaphragm is a "button" that contains fine carbon granules. Vibration of the diaphragm varies the pressure on the granules and alters the resistance of the "button." A low-voltage (6 V) battery is connected in series with the "button" and the primary of an audio transformer. The primary current, and therefore the secondary voltage, will then correspond to the movement of the diaphragm created by the sound wave.

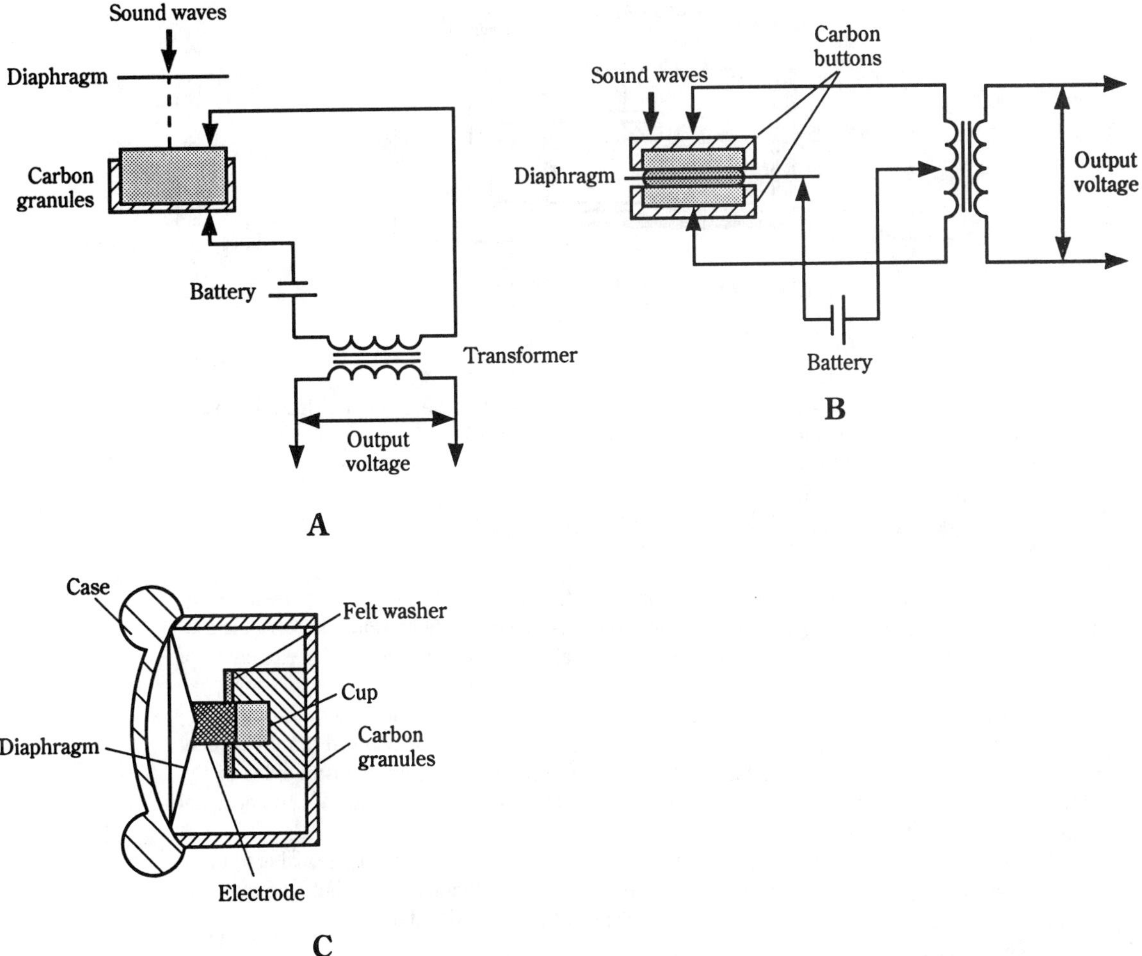

Fig. 6-10 The carbon microphone. A. single button. B. double button. C. side view.

Features include:

- Very high sensitivity associated with a high level of output
- Poor frequency response, which is the main reason why the carbon microphone is no longer widely used
- Background hissing present in the microphone's output
- Carbon granules are subject to "packing" with excessive moisture (the microphone must not be allowed to get wet)

- Low output impedance (100 Ω or less)
- Inexpensive.

The *crystal microphone* is shown in FIG. 6-11. In this type of microphone, the transducer is commonly a series of Rochelle salt crystals, which display the piezoelectric effect and are wax impregnated in an airtight container.

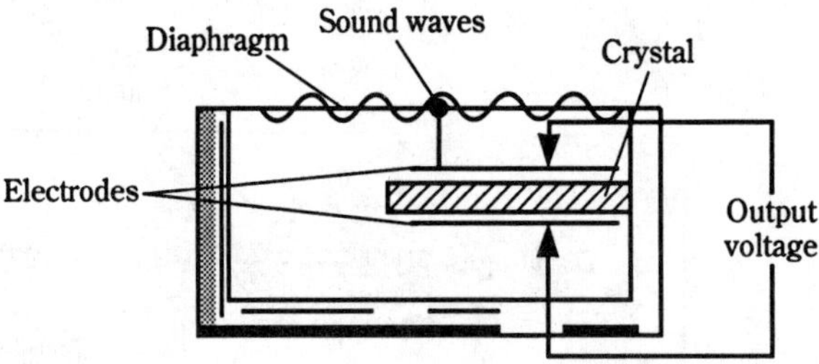

Fig. 6-11 The crystal microphone.

Features include:

- Adversely affected by excessive heat (the microphone must be protected from hot sunlight), shock, and humidity (Rochelle salt dissolves in water)
- Good frequency response
- Absence of background noise
- High-impedance output, which might allow hum pickup
- No power supply required

In the *ceramic microphone,* the principle and construction are similar to the crystal microphone, except for the use of certain ceramic materials instead of Rochelle salt. The ceramic materials act as transducers in the same way as the crystals, but are less affected by extremes of temperature, humidity, and shock.

The *velocity (ribbon) microphone* is shown in FIG. 6-12. This type of microphone is commonly used in a studio. The diaphragm is a very light aluminum ribbon, which is allowed to move freely in a magnetic field. When the sound wave causes a pressure difference on opposite sides of the ribbon, a velocity gradient causes the ribbon to vibrate. The corresponding audio electrical signal is then induced into the ribbon.

The output impedance of this type of microphone is extremely low, so the signal is fed to a step-up transformer. This not only raises the output level to a practical value, but also matches the low microphone impedance to the surge impedance of a standard audio line.

Features include:

- Blasting or wind might affect the delicate ribbon. Its use is confined to indoor studios.
- No power supply required
- Low level of background noise
- Good frequency response
- High level of output
- Not affected by temperature and humidity

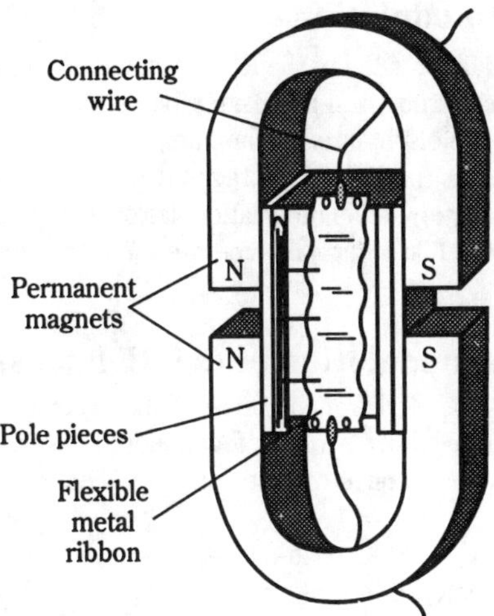

Fig. 6-12 The velocity microphone.

Audio voltage amplifiers

The output from a microphone is typically of the order of millivolts. Therefore, it is necessary to build up this signal by a number of audio voltage amplifiers. The early stages are operated in class-A mode with single active devices, but the later stages are more likely to be class-A or class-AB push-pull amplifiers.

In the block diagram of FIG. 6-8, the sideband power is supplied from the final audio amplifier, which is the *modulator stage* and is commonly operated in a class-B push-pull arrangement. Such a stage is preceded by one or more audio power amplifiers.

Summarizing, the dc power input to the final stage is converted at a certain efficiency to the RF carrier power. The same efficiency applies in the conversion of the modulator's output audio power to the total power contained in the sidebands (FIG. 6-13).

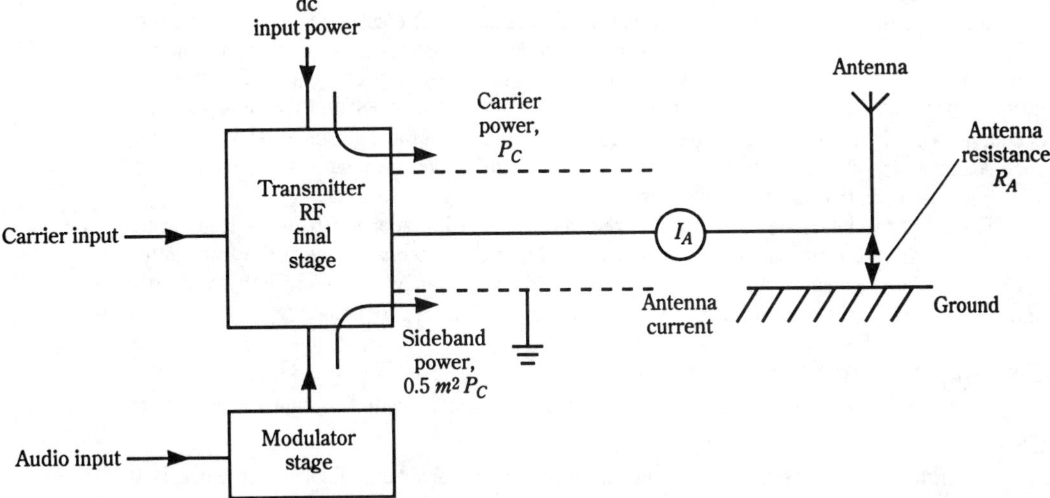

Fig. 6-13 The conversion of the modulator's audio-power output into sideband power.

High- and low-level modulation

When the output of the modulator is fed to the RF final stage, the result is "high level" modulation, which has the disadvantage of requiring a considerable amount of audio power. It is possible to generate the AM signal in one of the intermediate amplifiers ("low-level" modulation); less audio power is needed, but none of the following stages can be operated in class C or be used for frequency multiplication. After low-level modulation has occurred, all following amplifiers must be so-called "linear stages," which are normally operated in class B with its lower efficiency, compared with class C.

Collector amplitude modulation of the RF final stage

When the assigned power of an AM transmitter is of the order of kilowatts, the final stage uses tubes. However, if the carrier power is only a few hundred watts, it is possible to use a transistorized final stage and to achieve collector modulation by feeding the audio signal into the dc line from the V_{CC} supply.

Figure 6-14 shows a final class-C push-pull stage in which the secondary of the modulator's output transformer is connected in series with the V_{CC} supply line. Consequently, the voltage applied to the collectors is a combination of dc and the audio signal. Assume that the collector supply voltage to the modulated stage is 100 V and the audio secondary voltage is a sine wave with a peak value of 90 V. The instantaneous voltage supplied to the collector circuits then fluctuates between $100 + 90 = 190$ V and $100 - 90 = 10$ V. Because the RF output from a class-C amplifier depends on the value of its supply voltage, there will be a maximum power output when the applied voltage is 190 V and the minimum power output is when the applied voltage is 10 V.

By optimizing such parameters as the collector load's tank circuit, the level of signal bias, the turns ratio of the modulator transformer and the antenna load, it is possible to obtain an approximate linear relationship between the instantaneous amplitude of the output RF signal and the instantaneous value of the audio voltage. The required conditions for amplitude modulation are then fulfilled.

Intermodulation

Assume that a transmitter, TX1, is operating on a carrier frequency, f_1; near by is a second transmitter, TX2, whose carrier frequency is f_2. It is therefore possible for the TX2 transmission to be intercepted by the TX1 antenna so that both RF signals will exist in the first transmitter's RF final stage, which is operated under class-C conditions. A complex form of mixing occurs and there will be a large number of intermodulation products, whose carrier frequencies are of the form $+ mf_1 \pm nf_2$, where m and n equal 0, 1, 2, 3, 4 . . . and so on. The same type of mixing will, of course, occur in the final stage of the second transmitter. All of these harmonic sum and difference components will carry one or the other or both of the modulating signals and might cause severe interference to other transmissions.

The effects of intermodulation can be reduced by inserting appropriate wave traps in the antenna circuits of the two transmitters. For example, in the antenna circuit of the transmitter, TX1, there will be a wave trap that is tuned to the carrier frequency, f_2; consequently, very little of the f_2 transmission is passed through to the final stage of the first transmitter.

Two-way communication systems

The following methods can be used to establish two-way communications between a pair of stations:

- **Simplex** At each station, the transmitter and the receiver use the same antenna. Both stations operate on the same frequency so that simultaneous transmission in both directions is not feasible.

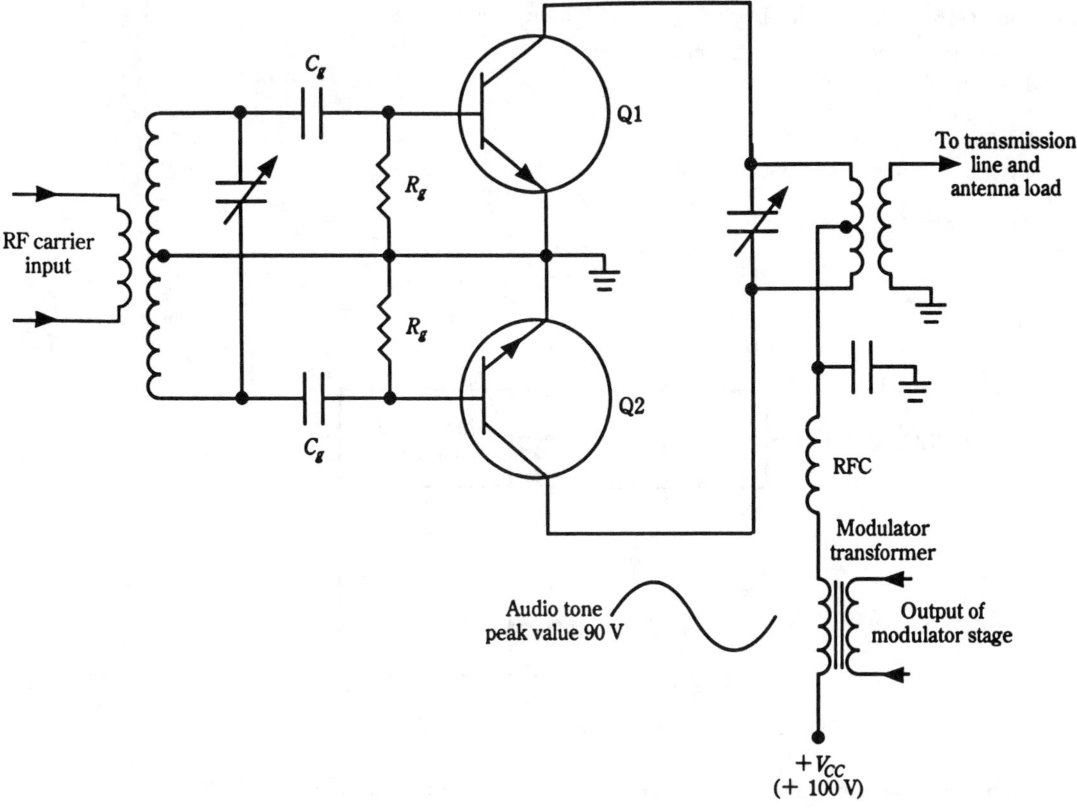

Fig. 6-14 The collector amplitude modulation.

- **Duplex** The stations operate on two different frequencies so that simultaneous communication in both directions is possible.

* **Question 6-13** An AM signal can be amplified by a:

A. frequency-multiplier stage
B. class-C push-pull amplifier
C. class-C intermediate rf amplifier
D. class-C RF final stage
E. class-B linear RF amplifier

Answer Choice E.

* **Question 6-14** If the RF final stage of a marine transmitter is 100% modulated by a pure tone, the ratio of the (audio) modulator-stage power output to the modulated-stage dc power input is:

A. 1:1 B. 1:2 C. 2:1 D. $1{:}\sqrt{2}$ E. 1:3

Answer Choice C. Assume that the unmodulated carrier power is 100 W and the efficiency of the final stage is 80%. Dc power input is therefore 100/0.8 = 125 W.

Total sideband power: $$P_{SB} = \frac{1}{2} \times 1^2 \times 100 = 50 \text{ W} \qquad (6\text{-}10)$$

The modulator's output power is 50/0.8 = 62.5 W and the required ratio is 125/62.5 W = 2:1.

Question 6-15 The simplified block diagram of FIG. 6-15 represents a (an):

A. low-level modulated AM transmitter
B. direct FM transmitter
C. indirect FM transmitter
D. PM transmitter
E. high-level modulated AM transmitter

Answer Choice E.

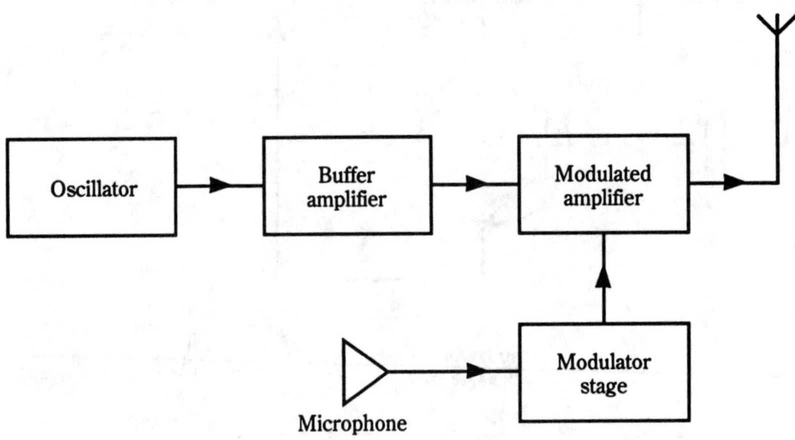

Fig. 6-15 The block diagram for question 6-15.

Question 6-16 Amplitude modulation created in an amplifier before the final RF stage is called:

A. indirect modulation
B. direct modulation
C. low-level modulation
D. intermediate modulation
E. high-level modulation

Answer Choice C.

Question 6-17 Which of the following might cause packing of the granules in a carbon microphone?

A. connecting the microphone to the battery with the polarity reversed
B. moisture
C. too high a level of current
D. speaking close to the microphone in a loud voice
E. choices B and C are true

Answer Choice E.

Question 6-18 In amplitude modulation, sidebands:

A. represent undesirable distortion of the carrier wave
B. are the audio frequencies contained in the AM signal
C. contain the intelligence that is present in the AM signal
D. are created by the effect of the audio modulation on the amplitude of the RF signal in the modulated stage
E. choices C and D are true

Answer Choice E.

Question 6-19 An RF amplifier can be operated under linear class-B conditions (as opposed to class C) in order to:

A. amplify an AM signal
B. generate only even harmonics
C. generate only odd harmonics
D. increase the efficiency
E. increase the harmonic content in the output signal

Answer Choice A.

Question 6-20 When low-level modulation is used in an AM transmitter, the RF stages following the modulated stage, cannot be:

A. harmonic generators
B. operated in class A
C. operated on class B
D. operated in class C
E. choices A and D are true

Answer Choice E.

Question 6-21 When a class-C RF amplifier is collector AM-modulated, its average dc level collector current does not change. This indicates:

A. a normal condition
B. either positive or negative carrier shift
C. excessive drive to the base
D. insufficient drive to the base
E. insufficient audio modulation

Answer Choice A. When modulation is applied, the carrier component is unchanged. Therefore, the dc input power remains the same.

Question 6-22 When an AM transmitter uses high-level modulation, the audio signal is introduced into the:

A. oscillator stage (direct method)
B. phase modulator (indirect method)
C. intermediate RF amplifier
D. buffer stage
E. RF final stage

Answer Choice E.

Question 6-23 Which of the following microphones uses a very light strip of corrugated aluminum suspended in a magnetic field?

A. crystal B. dynamic C. velocity D. carbon E. ceramic

Answer Choice C.

* **Question 6-24** A two-way communications system, in which both stations operate on the same frequency, is called:

A. simplex B. uniplex C. duplex D. biplex E. diplex

Answer Choice A.

* **Question 6-25** A two-way communications system, in which the stations operate on different frequencies, is called:

A. biplex B. diplex C. duplex D. simplex E. polyplex

Answer Choice C.

* **Question 6-26** The antennas of two AM transmitters are close together. As a result, the two modulated signals are mixed in the final RF stages of both transmitters. The resultant effect on other stations is called:

A. intermodulation interference
B. harmonic interference
C. spurious interference
D. crossmodulation interference
E. parasitic interference

Answer Choice A.

* **Question 6-27** The type of two-way communications that allows for simultaneous transmission and reception, is:

A. diplex B. simplex C. duplex D. uniplex E. biplex

Answer Choice C.

* **Question 6-28** A CB transmitter is causing interference with TV channels 2 through 6. This is caused by:

A. intermodulation
B. crossmodulation
C. spurious oscillations
D. parasitic oscillations
E. harmonic interference

Answer Choice E. Because the frequencies of CB channels lie between 26.965 MHz and 27.405 MHz, the TV channels are experiencing harmonic interference.

6-4. Percentage change in AM antenna current

The act of amplitude modulation creates the additional sideband power; therefore, the total RF power associated with the antenna is greater under modulated conditions. The higher the degree of modulation, the greater is the amount of the sideband power.

The antenna current is directly proportional to the square root of the total RF power, and will increase with the degree of modulation. Problems involving the percentage changes in the antenna current and the sideband power can be solved by assuming convenient and compatible values for the unmodulated carrier power, the antenna current, and the effective antenna resistance. A suitable set of values is:

$$\begin{aligned} \textit{Unmodulated carrier power} &= 100 \text{ W} \\ \textit{Unmodulated antenna current} &= 1 \text{ A} \\ \textit{Effective antenna resistance} &= 100\ \Omega \end{aligned}$$

As an example, if the modulation percentage produced by a single tone is 50%, the total sideband power is $1/2 \times 0.5^2 \times 100$ W = 12.5 W and the total RF power is 100 + 12.5 = 112.5 W. The new antenna current is: $\sqrt{112.5 \text{ W}/100\ \Omega} = \sqrt{1.125} = 1.0607$ A. If the percentage modulation is now increased to 100%, the new sideband power $= 1/2 \times 1^2 \times 100$ W = 50 W, the new total RF power is: 100 + 50 = 150 W and the new antenna current is: $\sqrt{150 \text{ W}/100\ \Omega} = \sqrt{1.5} = 1.2247$ A. Consequently, when compared with the unmodulated condition, the antenna current increases by 6.07% for 50% modulation and 22.47% for 100% modulation. If the percentage modulation is increased from 50% to 100%, the sideband power increases by:

$$\frac{50 \text{ W} - 12.5 \text{ W}}{12.5 \text{ W}} \times 100\% = 300\%$$

and the percentage increase in the antenna current is:

$$\frac{(1.2247 - 1.0607) \times 100}{1.0607} = 15.4\%$$

If the degree of modulation is increased from zero to a value, *m*, the percentage increase in antenna current is given by:

$$\textit{Percentage increase} = \left(\sqrt{1 + \frac{m^2}{2}} - 1\right) \times 100\% \qquad (6\text{–}12)$$

For example, if $m = 1$ (100% modulation):

$$\begin{aligned} \textit{Percentage increase,} &= \left(\sqrt{1 + \frac{1}{2}} - 1\right) \times 100 \\ &= (1.225 - 1) \times 100 \\ &= 22.5\% \end{aligned}$$

Question 6-29 The percentage of modulation for an AM transmitter is increased from 0 to 80%. The percentage increase in the antenna current is:

A. 15% B. 18% C. 19.5% D. 17.5% E. 16%

Answer Choice A. Percentage increase in antenna current:

$$\begin{aligned} \% \text{ increase} &= \left(\sqrt{1 + \frac{m^2}{2}} - 1\right) \times 100 \\ &= \left(\sqrt{1 + \frac{(0.8)^2}{2}} - 1\right) \times 100 \qquad (6\text{-}12) \\ &= \left(\sqrt{1.32} - 1\right) \times 100 \\ &= 15\%, \text{ rounded off} \end{aligned}$$

Question 6-30 The percentage of modulation for an AM transmitter is increased from 50% to 80%. The percentage increase in the antenna current is:

A. 6.5% B. 8.3% C. 10.6% D. 11.5% E. 12.4%

Answer Choice B.

Using the suggested values in this section, the antenna current (I_A), when 50% modulated, is:

$$\begin{aligned} I_A &= \sqrt{112.5 \text{ W}/100\ \Omega} \\ &= 1.061 \text{ A} \end{aligned}$$

For 80% modulation:

$$\begin{aligned} I_A &= \sqrt{132 \text{ W}/100\ \Omega} \\ &= 1.149 \text{ A} \end{aligned}$$

$$\begin{aligned} \textit{Percentage increase} &= \frac{1.149 - 1.061}{1.061} \times 100 \\ &= 8.3\%, \text{ rounded off} \end{aligned}$$

6-5. Single-sideband modulation

The sidebands in an AM wave represent the audio information and in order to convey this information, it is not essential for the carrier and both sets of sidebands are transmitted.

There are various types of AM emission and each type must be considered separately, in regard to the power content of the sidebands and the bandwidth. For example, in the single-sideband suppressed carrier (SSSC) system of FIG. 6-16, designated J3E (formerly A3J), all of the RF power is concentrated in one set of sidebands (either the upper set or the lower set). This improves the signal-to-noise ratio at the receiver, and it reduces the required bandwidth. However, when compared with double-sideband operation (A3E), the SSSC system demands a much higher degree of frequency stability for the carrier generated in the transmitter's oscillator and also requires that a carrier component be reinserted at the receiver.

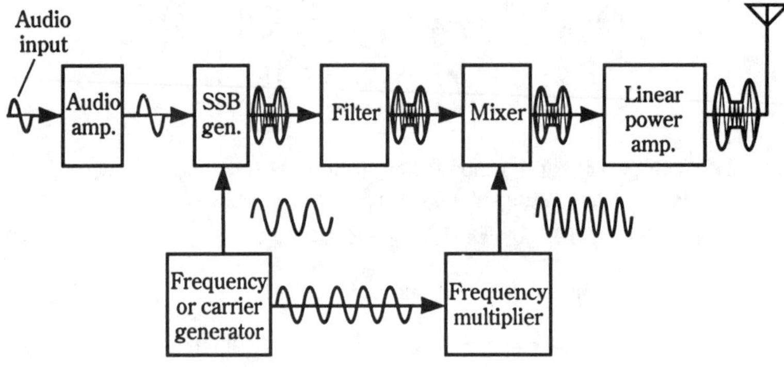

Fig. 6-16 The SSB transmitter.

The advantage of power saving with the SSSC system lies in the fact that all of the RF carrier power can be concentrated in one set of sidebands, rather than being distributed over the carrier and two sets of sidebands; this is the reason for the improvement in the signal-to-noise ratio at the receiver. In addition, the bandwidth required for an SSSC system is only half of that required for comparable double-sideband operation.

For example, if a 100-W carrier is 100% (A3E) modulated by a single tone, the power in each of the sidebands is 25 W. If the whole of the 100 W unmodulated carrier power is concentrated in one sideband, the power advantage is equivalent to:

$$\begin{aligned} 10 \log_{10} \left(\frac{100 \text{ W}}{25 \text{ W}}\right) &= 10 \log_{10} 4 \\ &= 6 \text{ dB} \end{aligned}$$

If the bandwidth of the A3E emission was 8 kHz, the required bandwidth for the comparable J3E emission is only 8 kHz/2 = 4 kHz.

The power advantage causes an improved signal-to-noise ratio at the receiver.

Other single-sideband emission designations are:

- **R3E** Single-sideband with reduced (or pilot) carrier.
- **H3E** Single-sideband with full carrier power.

Because the sideband frequencies are very close to that of the carrier, it is only possible to balance out the carrier and eliminate one set of sidebands if the stage is operating at a low frequency. This is shown in FIG. 6-16; after filtering out one set of sidebands, the output frequency is increased with the aid of the frequency multiplier and mixer stages. Table 6-1 shows a list of the designations for the more commonly used emissions.

Table 6-1. Emission designations.

In 1987 the FCC introduced new emission designations into its rules and regulations. Each type of emission is now designated by three symbols of which the first and third symbols are letters and the second or middle symbol is a number. The meanings of these symbols are:

First symbol (letter)	Type of modulation.
Second symbol (number)	Nature of signal.
Third symbol (letter)	Type of information.

FIRST SYMBOL

A	Amplitude modulation, double sideband, full carrier.
C	Vestigial sideband.
F	Frequency modulation.
G	Phase modulation.
H	Single sideband, full carrier.
J	Single sideband, suppressed carrier.
K	Pulse amplitude modulation.
L	Pulse width (duration) modulation.
M	Pulse position modulation.
N	Unmodulated carrier.
P	Unmodulated pulse sequence.
R	Single sideband, reduced carrier.

SECOND SYMBOL

0	Absence of any modulation.
1	Telegraphy ON/OFF keying without the use of a modulating AF tone.
2	Telegraphy by ON/OFF keying of a modulating AF tone, or by the ON/OFF keying of the modulated emission.
3	Analog voice communication.

THIRD SYMBOL

A	Telegraphy (aural reception).
B	Telegraphy (reception by automatic machine).
C	Facsimile.
D	Telemetry, data transmission.
E	Telephony.
F	Television (video signal).
N	No information.

EXAMPLES OF EMISSIONS

A1A	Telegraphy by ON/OFF keying, previously designated as A1.
A3C	AM facsimile, previously designated as A4.
A3E	Amplitude modulated, double sideband, telephony. Previously designated as A3.

Table 6-1. Continued.

C3F	Vestigial sideband transmission for television's video signal. Previously designated as A5C.
F1B	Frequency-shift keying (FSK). Previously designated as F1.
F3C	FM facsimile. Previously designated as F4.
F3E	FM telephony. Previously designated as F3.
G3E	Phase-modulated (PM) telephony. Previously designated as F3.
H3E	Single sideband, full carrier. Previously designated as A3H.
J3E	Single sideband, suppressed carrier (SSSC). Previously designated as A3J.
NON	Unmodulated carrier, No information, Previously designated as A0.
R3E	Single sideband, reduced carrier. Previously designated as A3A.

Notice that for a J3E emission, the carrier must be suppressed to a power level that is at least 40 dB below the peak envelope carrier. Similarly, for a R3E emission, the carrier must be reduced to a power level that is 18 dB below the peak envelope power.

In addition to the emission designations, there are also emission designators that indicate the necessary bandwidth, as opposed to the authorized bandwidth. Some examples of emission designators are shown in TABLE 6-2.

Table 6-2. Emission designators and authorized bandwidths for various classes of emission.

Class of emission	Emission designator	Authorized bandwidth (kHz)
A1A	160HA1A	0.4
A3E	6K00A3E	8.0
F1B	280HF1B	0.3
F3E	16K0F3E	20.0
G3E	16K0G3E	20.0
H3E	2K80H3E	3.0
J3E	2K80J3E	3.0
R3E	2K80R3E	3.0
F3N	20M0F3N	20000.0

In an emission designator, there are three figures and a letter that precede the emission designation. The letter is either H (Hertz) or K (kilohertz) or M (megahertz) and indicates the unit in which the necessary bandwidth is measured. In addition, "K" and "M" are positioned to show the location of the decimal point. For example:

- Emission designator 160HA1A has a necessary bandwidth of 160 Hz
- Emission designator 6K00A3E has a necessary bandwidth of 6.00 kHz
- Emission designator 16K0F3E has a necessary bandwidth of 16.0 kHz
- Emission designators 2K80H3E, 2K80J3E, 2K80R3E all have a necessary bandwidth of 2.80 kHz
- Emission designator 20M0F3E has a necessary bandwidth of 20.0 MHz

For particular marine stations, the authorized classes of emission and tolerance are shown in TABLE 6-3.

Table 6-3. Tolerances and classes of emission for the marine-frequency bands.

Frequency band	Classes of emission	Tolerance
1605–27500kHz	H3E, J3E, R3E	20 Hz
156–162 MHz	G3D, G3E	10 ppm
216–220 MHz	F1B, F2B, F2C, F3C	5 ppm

* **Question 6-31** The letters "SSSC" represent:

A. suppressed sideband, single carrier
B. suppressed sideband, suppressed carrier
C. single sideband, single carrier
D. single sideband, suppressed carrier
E. suppressed sideband, single channel

Answer Choice D.

* **Question 6-32** The emission designator for a marine SSSC transmitter with a authorized bandwidth of 3 kHz, is:

A. 3K00J3E B. 3K00R3E C. 3K00A3E D. 2K80H3E E. 2K80J3E

Answer Choice E. Refer to TABLE 6-2.

* **Question 6-33** Which of the following emission designators has the greatest necessary bandwidth?

A. 160HA1A B. 300HJ2B C. 2K66A2A D. 2K80H3E E. 1K40H2A

Answer Choice D. The designator 2K80H3E has a necessary bandwidth of 2.80 kHz, which is greater than that of any of the other choices.

* **Question 6-34** Which of the following emission designators has the greatest necessary bandwidth?

A. 160HJ3N B. 280HJ2B C. 300HF1B D. 160HA1A E. 1K40H2B

Answer Choice E. In the order of the choices, the necessary bandwidths are 160 Hz, 280 Hz, 300 Hz, 160 Hz, and 1.4 kHz.

* **Question 6-35** Which of the following emission designators has the greatest necessary bandwidth?

A. 2K80J3E B. 2K66H3N C. 16K0F3E D. 300HJ2B E. 6K00A3E

Answer Choice C. In the order of choices, the necessary bandwidths are 2.80 kHz, 2.66 kHz, 16.0 kHz, 300 Hz and 6.00 kHz.

* **Question 6-36** The frequency tolerance of a marine J3E transmitter in the band of 1650–27500 kHz is:

A. ±10 Hz B. ±20 Hz C. ±20 ppm D. ±10 ppm E. ±5 ppm

Answer Choice B. Refer to TABLE 6-3.

* **Question 6-37** The frequency tolerance of a marine transmitter operating within the band of 156 to 162 MHz, is:

A. ±10 ppm B. ±10 Hz C. ±20 Hz D. ±20 ppm E. ±5 ppm

Answer Choice A. Refer to TABLE 6-3.

* **Question 6-38** The frequency tolerance of a marine transmitter operating within the band of 216 to 220 MHz, is:

A. ±10 ppm B. ±10 Hz C. ±20 Hz D. ±20 pm E. ±5 ppm

Answer Choice E. Refer to TABLE 6-3.

* **Question 6-39** The emission designation, J3E, represents:

A. single sideband, suppressed carrier, telegraphy
B. single sideband, reduced carrier, telephony
C. single sideband, full carrier, telephony
D. double sideband, telephony
E. single sideband, suppressed carrier, telephony

Answer Choice E. Refer to TABLE 6-1.

* **Question 6-40** The emission, R3E, represents:

A. single sideband, suppressed carrier, telephony
B. double sideband, reduced carrier, telephony
C. single sideband, full carrier, telephony
D. double sideband, telephony
E. single sideband, reduced carrier, telephony

Answer Choice E. Refer to TABLE 6-1.

Question 6-41 An A3E transmitter has a bandwidth of 10 kHz. If the emission designation is changed to H3E, but the modulating signal remains the same, the new bandwidth is:

A. 3 kHz B. 2.8 kHz C. 4 kHz D. 5 kHz E. 6 kHz

Answer Choice D. The bandwidth is halved and its new value is 10 kHz/2 = 5 kHz.

Question 6-42 The emission designation H3E, represents:

A. single sideband, full carrier, telephony
B. single sideband, half carrier, telephony
C. single sideband, reduced carrier, telephony
D. single sideband, suppressed carrier, telephony
E. single sideband, half carrier, telegraphy

Answer Choice A. Refer to TABLE 6-1.

* **Question 6-43** What is the authorized bandwidth of a marine J3E emission?

A. 4 kHz B. 3 kHz C. 6 kHz D. 8 kHz E. 2.8 kHz

Answer Choice B. Refer to TABLE 6-2.

* **Question 6-44** In a marine J3E emission, by how many decibels must the carrier be suppressed below the peak envelope power?

A. 30 dB B. 40 dB C. 50 dB D. 60 dB E. 70 dB

Answer Choice B.

* **Question 6-45** What is the authorized bandwidth of a marine A3E emission?

A. 8 kHz B. 4 kHz C. 10 kHz D. 5.4 kHz E. 6 kHz

Answer Choice A. Refer to TABLE 6-2.

* **Question 6-46** In a marine R3E emission, the carrier is reduced below the peak envelope power by:

A. 8 dB B. 10 dB C. 12 dB D. 15 dB E. 18 dB

Answer Choice E.

* **Question 6-47** What is the authorized bandwidth of a marine R3E emission?

A. 4 kHz B. 3 kHz C. 6 kHz D. 8 kHz E. 2.8 kHz

Answer Choice B. Refer to TABLE 6-2.

* **Question 6-48** What is the authorized bandwidth of a marine H3E emission?

A. 2.8 kHz B. 8 kHz C. 3 kHz D. 6 kHz E. 4 kHz

Answer Choice C. Refer to TABLE 6-2.

* **Question 6-49** Which of the following frequencies falls within the band allocated to marine J3E emissions?

A. 500 kHz B. 10 MHz C. 20 MHz D. 30 MHz E. choices B and C are true

Answer Choice E. Refer to TABLE 6-3. The frequency band for J3E emissions is 1605 to 27500 kHz. Both 10 and 20 MHz fall within this band.

6-6. The frequency monitor

The frequency tolerance of a marine J3E station is ±20 Hz. The FCC requires that every station has a means of determining the number of Hz that the actual radiated carrier frequency differs from the assigned value. Such a device has to be approved by the FCC and is known as a *frequency monitor.* This auxiliary unit contains a crystal-controlled oscillator that is entirely separate from the AM transmitter. The amount by which the carrier frequency is too high or too low is shown on the frequency deviation indicator (FIG. 6-17A); this must be checked at intervals and the readings that are entered in the transmitter log.

The basic principle of the frequency monitor is shown in the block diagram of FIG. 6-17B. A crystal oscillator with a thermostatically controlled oven produces a stable frequency that differs from the authorized carrier frequency by 1 kHz. The output of the crystal oscillator is fed to a mixer stage that is also supplied with a sample of the carrier voltage, derived from an unmodulated stage of the transmitter. The frequency of the mixer's output to the discriminator circuit is the difference of 1 kHz ± any shift of the carrier frequency from its assigned value. The discriminator is of the tuned-high (1050 Hz)/tuned-low (950 Hz) or Travis variety so that the magnitude and polarity of its dc output is determined by the instantaneous shift in the carrier frequency. This dc output is then passed to the monitor's indicating device with its center zero scale.

Periodically, the accuracy of the frequency monitor is measured. An external check is made of the radiated carrier frequency and the result is compared with the simultaneous reading of the frequency monitor. The error in the frequency monitor can then be corrected by adjusting the monitor oscillator frequency (although the oscillator is crystal-controlled, the frequency can be varied a few Hz by adjusting the value of the trimmer capacitor across the crystal).

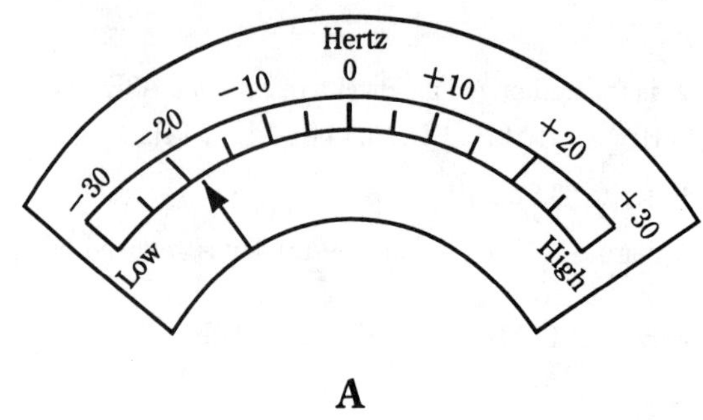

A

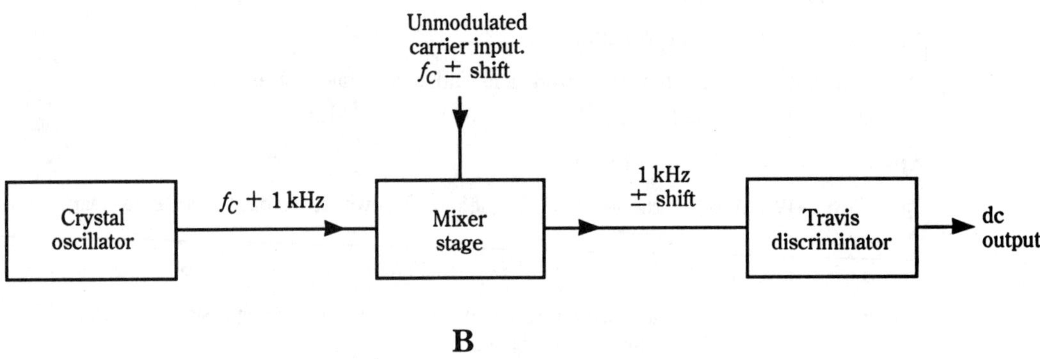

B

Fig. 6-17 The frequency monitor.

A more accurate method of determining a transmitter's output frequency involves the use of an instrument that contains a secondary frequency standard in the form of a crystal oscillator. This oscillator has in turn been calibrated against a primary standard, such as the transmitter WWV, which is maintained by the National Bureau of Standards at Fort Collins, Boulder, Colorado. WWV transmits carriers continuously on 2.5, 5, 10, 15, and 20 MHz; each of these carriers is accurate to within 1 Hz.

To check the frequency of the crystal's oscillation:

1. The secondary standard is activated and then allowed a warm-up period (0.5 to 1 hour) so that the circuits can stabilize.
2. A receiver is tuned to one of the WWV carriers.
3. Crystal harmonics are fed to the receiver. If one of these harmonics beats with the WWV signal to produce a zero beat, the crystal oscillator must be generating its correct frequency. If an audio note is heard, adjust the trimmer across the capacitor to obtain a zero beat.

Apart from WWV, another primary standard is WWVH located on Kauai Island, Hawaii. This station radiates a continuous carrier at frequencies of 2.5, 5, 10, and 15 MHz.

Question 6-50 The primary frequency standard transmitter in the United States that radiates a continuous 20-MHz carrier, is called:

A. WWV B. WWB C. WWVH D. FCCV E. choices A and C are true

Answer Choice A. Only WWV radiates a continuous 20-MHz carrier.

* **Question 6-51** When calibrating a secondary frequency standard against the primary standard, WWV, which of the following steps is wrong or unnecessary?

A. allow a ½- to 1-hour warm-up period for the secondary standard
B. tune the receiver to WWV
C. beat the WWV signal with one of the crystal's harmonics and obtain the zero beat
D. calibrate the receiver's tuning with WWV
E. adjust the value of the trimmer capacitor across the crystal in order to achieve the zero beat.

Answer Choice D. The receiver is only required to intercept the WWV signal and does not need to be calibrated.

Question 6-52 An external frequency check of an AM station reveals that at a particular time, the carrier frequency was 8 Hz low. The transmitter log showed that at the same time, the carrier frequency was 10 Hz high. What was the error in the station's frequency monitor?

A. 2 Hz high B. 2 Hz low C. 18 Hz high D. 18 Hz low E. none of the above

Answer Choice C.

$$\begin{aligned} \textit{Error in the frequency monitor} &= +\ 10\text{ Hz} - (-\ 8\text{ Hz}) \\ &= +\ 18\text{ Hz} \\ &= 18\text{ Hz high} \end{aligned}$$

* **Question 6-53** When measuring a transmitter's frequency against a suitable standard, the frequency to be measured is taken from the:

A. oscillator stage
B. buffer stage
C. intermediate amplifiers
D. final frequency-multiplier stage
E. final RF stage

Answer Choice E.

* **Question 6-54** To make certain that a marine transmitter's carrier frequency is within its assigned tolerance limits:

A. zero beat the output frequency with an approved standard
B. use a frequency counter to determine the crystal oscillator's frequency
C. zero beat the output frequency with one of WWV's carriers
D. use an absorption wavemeter
E. use a grid-dip meter

Answer Choice A.

6-7. The phonetic alphabet

The *phonetic alphabet* uses a particular code word to substitute for each letter of the alphabet. When it is necessary to spell difficult proper names or other words that cannot easily be understood, the phonetic alphabet can be used to reduce the number of errors and speed up communications. This is particularly true when communications are difficult or when signals are weak. As an example, the use of the words "Bravo" and "Victor" will enable the receiving station to distinguish clearly between the letters "B" and "V," which are similar in sound and can be easily confused. The international code of signals uses the following phonetic alphabet:

Letter	Code word	Letter	Code word	Letter	Code word
A	Alpha	J	Juliet	S	Sierra
B	Bravo	K	Kilo	T	Tango
C	Charlie	L	Lima	U	Uniform
D	Delta	M	Mike	V	Victor
E	Echo	N	November	W	Whiskey
F	Foxtrot	O	Oscar	X	X-Ray
G	Golf	P	Papa	Y	Yankee
H	Hotel	Q	Quebec	Z	Zulu
I	India	R	Rome		

* **Question 6-55** Which of the following combinations represent the first three words in the modern phonetic alphabet?

A. alpha, bravo, charlie
B. able, baker, charlie
C. ack, beer, charlie
D. alpha, beta, charlie
E. alpha, baker, charline

Answer Choice A.

* **Question 6-56** Which of the following actions should be taken when communications are difficult or when signals are weak?

A. increase the power of the transmitter
B. switch to the calling frequency
C. increase the percentage of modulation
D. use the phonetic alphabet
E. shout into the microphone as loudly as possible

Answer Choice D.

7
AM receivers

In this chapter you will learn:

- about the various requirements that a communications receiver must satisfy to provide adequate reception.
- about the disadvantages of operating a tuned radio frequency (TRF) receiver at high frequencies.
- how the supersonic heterodyne (superhet) receiver overcomes the TRF disadvantages by using the principle of frequency conversion.
- about the problem of image channel interference.
- how an initial RF stage is used to improve the receiver's signal-to-noise ratio.
- why the intermediate amplifier stages are able to provide a high degree of selectivity and sensitivity.
- the purpose and operation of the detector stage.
- the advantages and disadvantages of using automatic gain control (AGC).
- the advantage and disadvantage of using a squelch circuit.
- about the phenomenon of crossmodulation and how it can be eliminated in the RF stage.
- how to measure a receiver's selectivity.
- how to measure a receiver's sensitivity.
- about the purpose of including a beat frequency oscillator (BFO) in the superhet receiver.

7-1. Introduction to AM receivers and the TRF receiver

As you learned in chapter 6, the antenna of a double-sideband AM transmitter radiates both carrier and sideband power into space. The power levels involved can range from less than one watt to several kilowatts. However, the power intercepted by the receiving antenna is extremely small (of the order of picowatts) so that the associated voltages are measured in microvolts or possibly millivolts if the receiver is close to the transmitter. Literally hundreds of other (unwanted) signals are induced in the receiver's antenna, owing to all the radio waves in the vicinity. Static noise also amplitude modulates the incoming signal so that the receiver must have a high signal-to-noise ratio within its bandwidth.

The main requirements of an AM receiver are:

- **High selectivity** This means that the receiver will be capable of accepting the wanted carrier with its sidebands while rejecting all other signals outside the receiver's bandwidth—especially those on nearby frequencies. The higher is the receiver's degree of selectivity, the greater is its freedom from adjacent channel interference. Such selectivity is achieved by including tuned circuits in many of the receiver's stages.
- **High sensitivity** This measures the ability of the receiver to pick up a weak signal from a station. With a weak signal, the amplifiers of a receiver might be required to provide a voltage gain of more than one million.
- **Detection** This is the essential feature of an AM receiver. The AM signal contains no audio component and it is therefore necessary to reverse the modulation process that occurred in the transmitter. This reversal is carried out in the detector or demodulator stage. The input to the detector is the amplified AM signal, but the output is the audio voice information whose waveform closely resembles that of the modulating signal at the transmitter.
- **High signal-to-noise ratio** Noise, principably static, is external to the receiver, but there is also internal noise because of the active devices and their associated components. Noise is the ultimate limitation on a receiver's ability to intercept a weak signal. Once the signal is submerged below the noise level, both noise and signal are equally amplified within the receiver's bandwidth and the signal cannot then be distinguished from the noise. The signal-to-noise ratio is primarily determined in the receiver's first stage because both the signal and the noise are then followed by the full gain of the subsequent stages. An adequate signal-to-noise ratio is of the order of 20 dB.

To realize some of the difficulties in meeting these requirements, look at the tuned radio frequency (TRF) receiver, which is still used in the LF and lower MF bands.

Tuned radio-frequency (TRF) receiver

A block diagram of the *tuned radio-frequency (TRF)* AM receiver is shown in FIG. 7-1. The selectivity is mainly controlled by the three RF voltage amplifiers, each of which has a tuned circuit to provide the required degree of selectivity. Before the detector stage, there is another tuned circuit so that there are a total of four such circuits whose capacitors are mechanically ganged for simultaneous tuning; these circuits determine the receiver's overall Q factor.

The main problems associated with the TRF receiver are:

- **Limited sensitivity** The receiver's RF voltage amplifiers must compromise between gain and selectivity. If the degree of mutual coupling, M, (FIG. 7-2) is adjusted for maximum gain, the value of the loaded Q is only half that of the unloaded Q. The RF stages must therefore be loosely coupled in order to maintain the necessary degree of selectivity. Consequently, the voltage gain of a single RF amplifier is limited to 25 or less.
- **Limited selectivity** Assume that you want to design a TRF receiver over the range of 650 kHz to 30 MHz, which is divided into five bands. If the bandwidth is 10 kHz, the required overall Q value at 650 kHz is only 650 kHz/10 kHz = 65, but at 30 MHz, the required Q value rises to 30 MHz/10 kHz = 3000, which is clearly impossible. Consequently, the use of a TRF receiver is limited to the LF and lower MF bands.

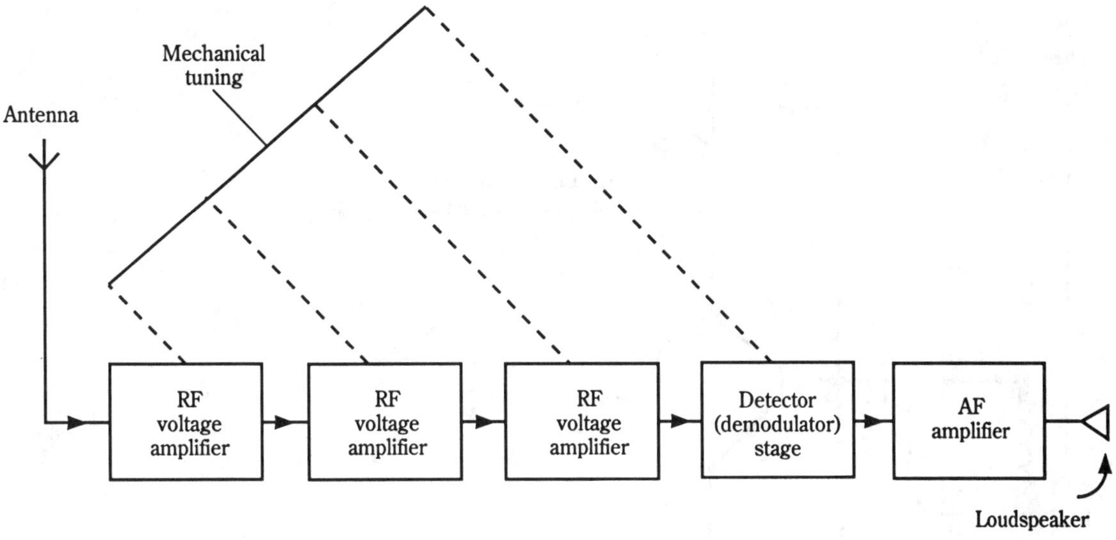

Fig. 7-1 The tuned radio frequency (TRF) receiver.

- **Self-oscillation** It is possible to raise the sensitivity and the selectivity by adding more RF amplifiers. However, all these stages are tuned to the same frequency. Consequently, there is the danger of feedback occurring between the amplifiers. For example, if the total gain is 10,000 and 1/10,000 of the output of the final amplifier's output is applied as positive feedback to the initial amplifier's input circuitry, all the stages will self-oscillate so that reception becomes impossible. This problem can even occur if the RF stages are carefully shielded from one another.

The problems of the TRF receiver are solved in the *supersonic heterodyne (superhet) receiver.* This is the modern type of receiver, which is used for broadcast, communications, radar, and TV reception.

* **Question 7-1** The diagram of FIG. 7-3 refers to the:

A. mixer stage B. RF amplifier C. AF amplifier D. oscillator stage E. detector stage

Answer Choice E.

* **Question 7-2** High selectivity occurs when the degree of coupling between a receiver's RF stages, is:

A. tight
B. critical
C. adjusted for maximum power transfer
D. adjusted for maximum voltage gain
E. loose

Answer Choice E.

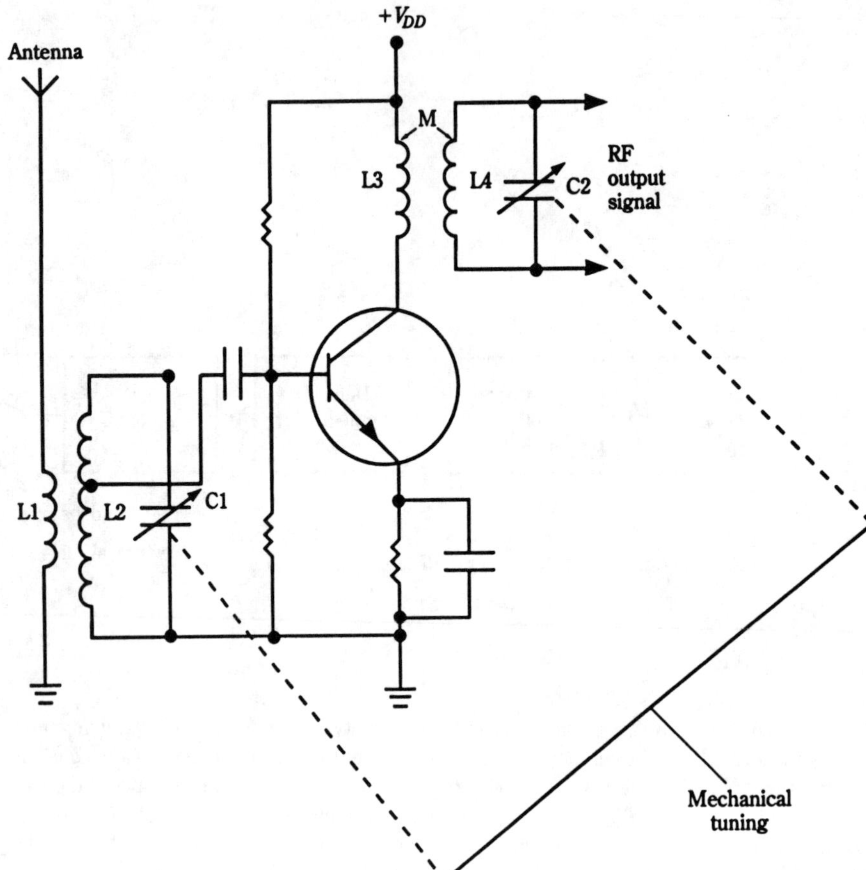

Fig. 7-2 The circuit of a receiver's RF voltage amplifier.

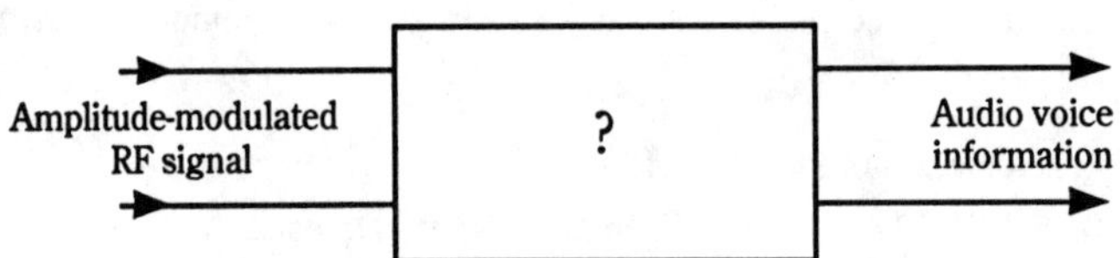

Fig. 7-3 The diagram for question 7-1.

Question 7-3 One disadvantage of a TRF receiver is:

A. unsatisfactory reception of strong signals
B. poor sensitivity at low frequencies
C. the requirement of a local oscillator for the reception of telephony
D. poor selectivity at high frequencies
E. the requirement for a detector stage

Answer Choice D.

* **Question 7-4** When no signal is being received, the loudspeaker is not entirely silent because of the presence of:

A. parasitic oscillations in some of the receiver stages
B. interference from the video signals of TV transmitters
C. negative feedback in each stage
D. spurious frequencies because of improper neutralization
E. internal receiver noise

Answer Choice E.

Question 7-5 In a multistage receiver, the RF amplifier's are normally shielded in order to:

A. avoid undesired coupling between the various stages
B. prevent the radiation of spurious emissions from the antenna
C. prevent the generation of parasitic oscillations in the various stages
D. introduce negative feedback, which will stabilize the operation of the amplifiers
E. provide positive feedback, which will increase the receiver's sensitivity

Answer Choice A.

* **Question 7-6** Receiver interference is not reduced by including a (an):

A. insulating enclosure around the receiver
B. crystal filters
C. wave trap
D. RF stage
E. noise limiter

Answer Choice A.

7-2. The AM superhet receiver and frequency conversion

Figure 7-4 represents the block diagram of an AM superhet receiver in the MF band. The purpose of the mixer and the local oscillator is to achieve frequency conversion. In this process, the receiver is tuned to a particular signal and the carrier frequency is then converted to a fixed intermediate frequency (IF), which is 455 kHz in the AM broadcast band. Therefore, for all incoming carrier frequencies, the IF stages always operate on the same fixed intermediate (low) frequency and can be designed to provide high selectivity and sensitivity. Moreover, because the RF amplifier, local oscillator, and IF stages all operate at different frequencies, there is little danger of self-oscillation because of unwanted feedback.

As indicated in FIG. 7-4, the RF tuned circuits of the initial amplifier, the mixer, and the local oscillator, are mechanically ganged so that as the RF amplifier and the input circuit of the mixer are tuned to the desired signal frequency, the local oscillator stage generates its own frequency and produces a continuous RF output that differs in frequency from the incoming carrier by the value of the intermediate frequency (IF). The term *intermediate* means that the value of the IF lies between the RF and AF frequencies.

The output of the oscillator and the incoming signal are both fed to the mixer stage, which contains a nonlinear device. In general, when two signals of different frequencies are mixed together (this mixing process is sometimes called *heterodyning*, or *beating*), the result contains a component at their different frequency, which is equal to the intermediate frequency. The mixer output circuit can therefore be tuned to the intermediate frequency. This will automatically eliminate the unwanted components that were created by the mixing process. During the frequency

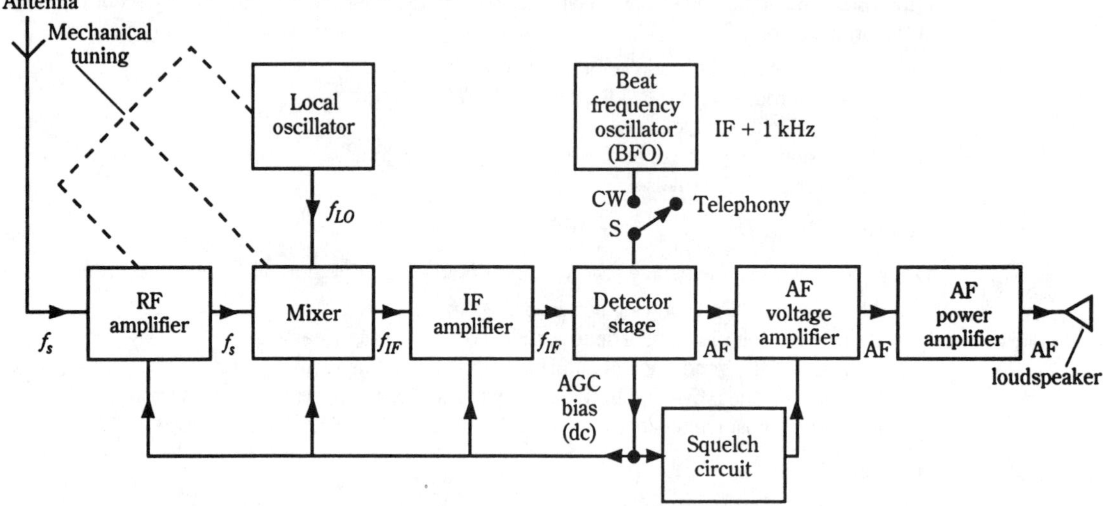

Fig. 7-4 The AM superheterodyne receiver.

conversion, the modulation originally carried by the wanted signal is transferred to the intermediate frequency component in the mixer's output. However, if the local oscillator frequency is greater than the incoming signal frequency (known as *tracking above*), the upper sidebands carried by the incoming carrier frequency will become the lower sidebands in the IF amplifiers and vice-versa.

In an AM receiver operating in the MF band, the local oscillator always tracks above in order to reduce the physical size that is required for the local oscillator tuning capacitor. However, in TV and FM receivers, which operate in the VHF and UHF bands, the local oscillator can track either above or below.

Image channel

Consider that a superheterodyne receiver is tuned to a carrier frequency of 640 kHz in the MF band. Because the IF is 455 kHz, the local oscillator will generate 640 + 455 = 1095 kHz. Assume that an unwanted signal has a carrier frequency of 1095 + 455 = 1550 kHz. If this signal is sufficiently strong to reach the mixer stage, it will beat with the local oscillator output, and its carrier frequency will also be converted to the IF. Once this has occurred, the IF stages will be unable to separate the wanted and the unwanted signals; both will be detected and both will be heard on the loudspeaker. The unwanted signal of 1550 kHz is an example of an image channel because its frequency is the image of the wanted signal in the "mirror" of the local oscillator frequency (the frequency of the wanted signal is the same amount below the local oscillator frequency as the image channel is above). The frequency of an image channel therefore differs from the wanted carrier frequency by an amount equal to twice the IF.

* **Question 7-7** A VHF receiver is tuned to 156.8 MHz and has an IF frequency of 10.7 MHz. If the local oscillator tracks above, the frequency of the image channel is:

A. 178.2 MHz B. 167.5 MHz C. 146.1 MHz D. 21.4 MHz E. 135.4 MHz

Answer Choice A. *Frequency of the image channel* = 156.8 + 2 × 10.7 = 178.2 MHz.

* **Question 7-8** The local oscillator of a VHF receiver is generating a 167.7-MHz output. If the receiver is tuned to 157.0 MHz, the frequency of the image channel is:

A. 21.4 MHz B. 178.4 MHz C. 146.3 MHz D. 135.6 MHz E. 189.1 MHz

Answer Choice B.

$$\begin{aligned} \textit{Intermediate frequency} &= 167.7 - 157 \\ &= 10.7 \text{ MHz} \\ \textit{Image-channel frequency} &= 167.7 + 10.7 \\ &= 178.4 \text{ MHz} \end{aligned}$$

* **Question 7-9** Figure 7-5 shows the block diagram of an AM superhet receiver that is tuned to 1 MHz. If this receiver is experiencing image-channel interference, the frequency of the interfering station is:

A. 1910 kHz B. 90 kHz C. 1.91 MHz D. 1455 kHz E. choices A and C are true

Answer Choices A and C are both true. Choice E.

$$\begin{aligned} \textit{Image-channel frequency} &= 1 \text{ MHz} + 2 \times 455 \text{ kHz} \\ &= 1.91 \text{ MHz} \\ &= 1910 \text{ kHz} \end{aligned}$$

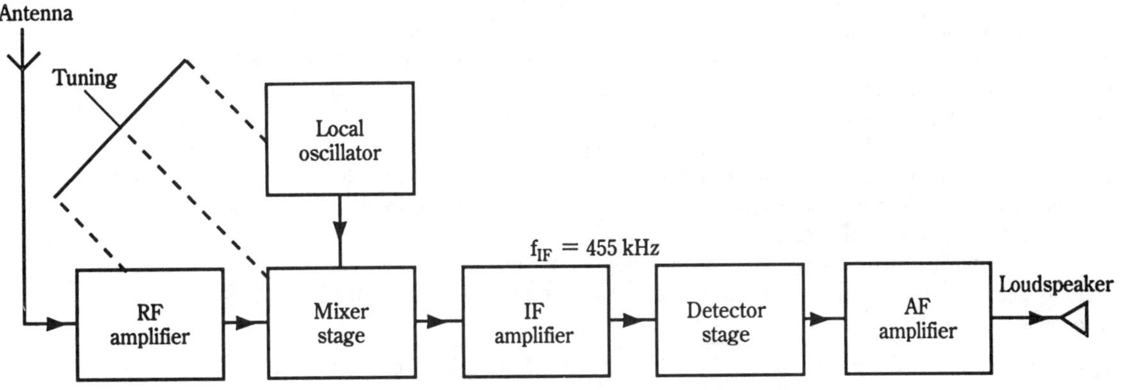

Fig. 7-5 The block diagram for questions 7-5 and 7-6.

* **Question 7-10** In FIG. 7-5 the local oscillator is generating a frequency of 2675 kHz. The receiver is tuned to a carrier frequency of:

A. 2220 kHz B. 1765 kHz C. 3030 kHz D. 3585 kHz E. 90 kHz

Answer Choice A.

$$\begin{aligned} \textit{Carrier frequency} &= 2675 - 455 \\ &= 2220 \text{ kHz} \end{aligned}$$

* **Question 7-11** An AM superhet is tuned to receive an A3E emission, which is defined as:

A. double-sideband amplitude-modulation telegraphy
B. single-sideband reduced-carrier telephony
C. single-sideband full-carrier telephony
D. single-sideband suppressed-carrier telephony
E. double-sideband amplitude-modulation telephony

Answer Choice E.

Question 7-12 A superhet receiver has an IF of 455 kHz and is experiencing image-channel interference on a frequency of 1570 kHz. The receiver is tuned to:

A. 1115 kHz B. 660 kHz C. 2025 kHz D. 2480 kHz E. 910 kHz

Answer Choice B. The carrier frequency of the wanted signal is: $1570 - 2 \times 455 = 660$ kHz.

7-3. The RF stage

Many superhets do not have an RF stage; such is the case with broadcast receivers, which normally are tuned to a strong signal, while at the same time, any adjacent channels are comparatively weak. By contrast, a communications receiver might be required to intercept a weak signal in the presence of strong neighboring channels.

Figure 7-2 shows the simplified schematic diagram of a receiver's RF stage. Because the incoming signal is only of the order of microvolts, the amplifier is operated under class-A conditions and the degree of coupling between L3 and L4 is "loose" so that the tuned circuit, L4/C2, is not subject to any appreciable loading and its selectivity remains high. The presence of the RF stage therefore increases the receiver's selectivity and sensitivity. Moreover the JFET and its associated circuitry are designed to achieve a high gain, while introducing the least possible amount of internal noise. Because the noise at the input of the RF stage is followed by the whole gain of the receiver, this noise will have more effect than that which is introduced by a subsequent stage. It follows that a high value of the signal-to-noise ratio can be established in the RF amplifier and this value is then maintained to within 5% throughout the receiver.

The frequency of an image channel differs from that of the wanted channel by twice the value of the IF. When the superhet is tuned to the wanted channel, the presence of the RF stage will greatly enhance the receiver's ability to reject the image channel, whose frequency is so far removed from that of the wanted channel.

The existence of an RF stage improves the degree of isolation between the local oscillator and the antenna. As a result, there is very little radiation from the antenna at the local oscillator frequency.

* **Question 7-13** An RF stage is coupled to the antenna and precedes the mixer stage of a superhet receiver. One advantage of including this RF stage, is:

A. improved signal-to-noise ratio
B. improved image channel rejection
C. better selectivity
D. greater sensitivity
E. All of the above choices are true

Answer Choice E.

* **Question 7-14** For a communications receiver, image-channel interference must be eliminated in the:

A. RF stage B. IF amplifiers C. detector stage D. audio amplifiers
E. squelch circuit

Answer Choice A.

7-4. The mixer stage and the local oscillator

In the circuit of FIG. 7-6, transistor Q1 provides the necessary mixing action and is also the amplifying device for the Armstrong local oscillator. Positive feedback is produced by the mutual coupling, M, between coils L1 and L2. The tuned circuit, L2/C2/C_T, determines the local oscillator frequency (f_{Lo}) and is coupled by C3/R_E to the emitter of Q_1. At the same time, the RF signal (f_s) is fed to the base circuit so that the sum of these two RF voltages is applied in series between the base-emitter junction. This circuit then behaves as a nonlinear device so that the mixing action generates several frequencies that are present in the collector current. These include f_s, f_{Lo}, $f_s + f_{Lo}$, $f_{Lo} - f_s$, as well as other unwanted mixer products.

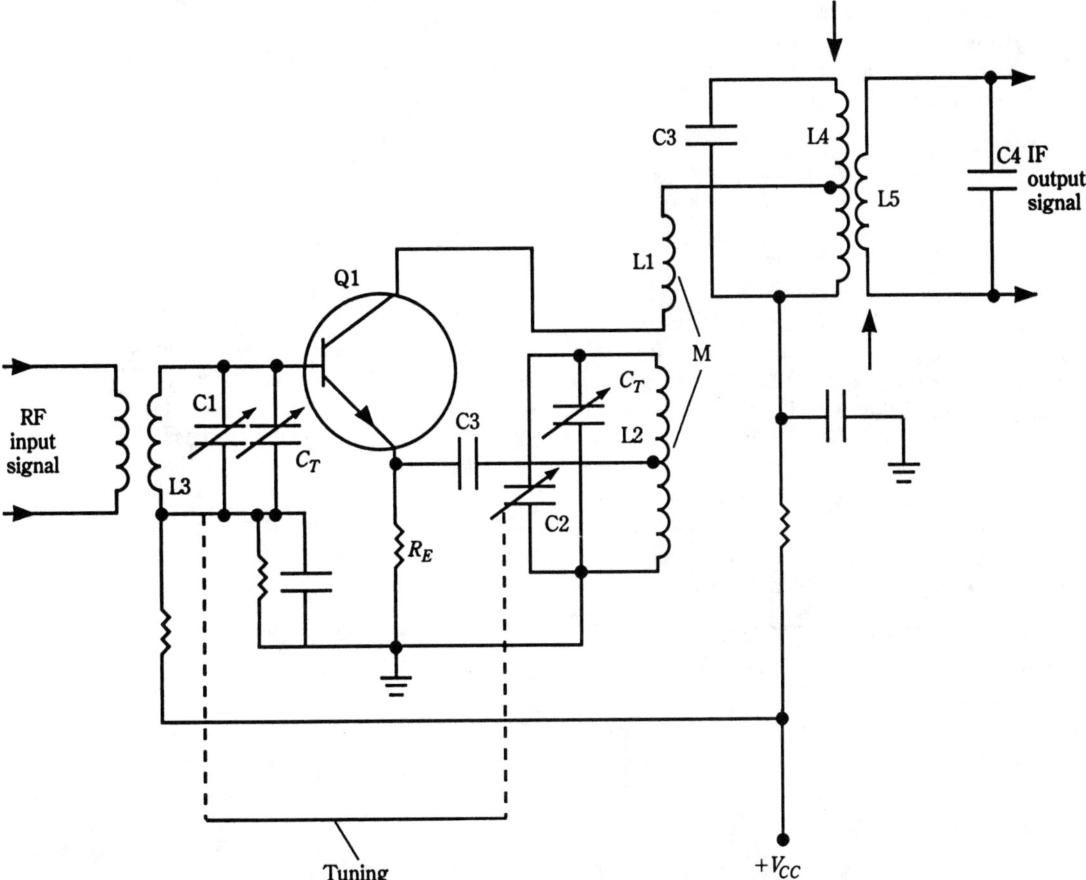

Fig. 7-6 The circuit diagram of the mixer and local oscillator. The circuit for question 7-16.

The difference frequency, $f_{Lo} - f_s$, is equal to the intermediate frequency, f_{IF}, and this component is selected by tuned circuits L4/C3 and L5/C4.

Notice the presence of the trimmer capacitance, C_T; these capacitors are adjusted during the receiver's alignment to ensure that the local oscillator frequency accurately tracks above the frequency of the RF signal to which the receiver is tuned.

* **Question 7-15** The mixer stage of an AM superhet receiver:

A. provides high gain for the input RF signal
B. provides high gain for the local-oscillator signal
C. acts as a nonlinear device

D. produces the sum and difference frequencies of the local oscillator signal and the incoming RF signal
E. choices C and D are correct

Answer Choice E.

* **Question 7-16** The circuit of FIG. 7-6:

A. provides AGC bias
B. represents a second detector stage
C. is used for frequency conversion
D. combines RF and IF amplifiers into one stage
E. contains a Colpitts oscillator

Answer Choice C.

7-5. The IF amplifier

Strong adjacent channel interference will not be adequately rejected by the RF stage (if present) and must therefore be eliminated in the IF amplifier(s). It follows that the response curve of a class-A IF amplifier (FIG. 7-7) must have steep sides, as well as a flat top to allow for the necessary bandwidth. These needs are fulfilled by the tuned-primary, tuned-secondary coupling between L1/C1 and L2/C2. However, it is important that the coupling between L1 and L2 should not exceed its critical value. Overcoupling will cause "split-tuning," and the bandwidth of the response curve will be far too wide. During alignment, the slugs of L1 and L2 are adjusted so that the coupling factor, k, is about 0.8 times the critical value.

Notice that if the IF stages are unable to reject a very strong unwanted signal that is operating on a particular frequency, it might be possible to eliminate this interference by introducing tunable wave traps into the antenna circuit.

* **Question 7-17** Strong interference from one particular station can be eliminated with:

A. wave traps in the antenna circuitry
B. noise limiters
C. squelch circuits
D. negative feedback
E. bypass capacitors

Answer Choice A.

* **Question 7-18** The phenomenon of "split-tuning" in a receiver's IF stages is corrected by:

A. increasing the value of the coupling factor
B. introducing a Faraday screen between the two coils
C. inserting the iron dust slugs deeper into the coils
D. reducing the value of the coupling factor to below its critical level
E. the use of "tight" coupling

Answer Choice D.

* **Question 7-19** In FIG. 7-7, the coupling between L1 and L2 is increased up to the critical value. As a result, the:

A. bandwidth of the response curve increases
B. value of the coupling factor decreases
C. stage's voltage gain decreases

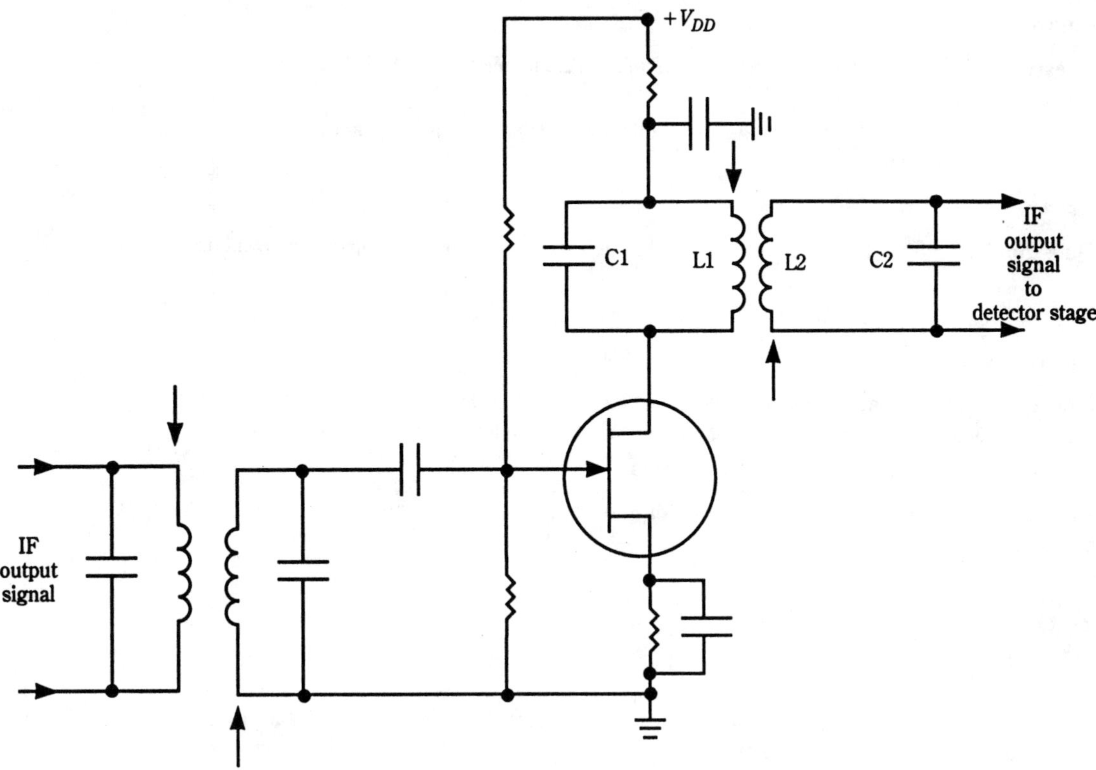

Fig. 7-7 The circuit diagram of an intermediate-frequency amplifier. The circuit for question 7-19.

D. amount of RF power transferred to the following stage is decreased
E. response at the IF frequency is reduced

Answer Choice A.

* **Question 7-20** An AM receiver's ability to accept the wanted signal while rejecting unwanted signals on nearby frequencies, is called its:

A. image-channel rejection
B. adjacent-channel rejection
C. channel sensitivity
D. intermodulation rejection
E. crossmodulation rejection

Answer Choice B.

* **Question 7-21** The tuned-primary and tuned-secondary circuits of an IF amplifier are tightly coupled. As a result:

A. the amplifier has a narrow bandwidth
B. the secondary response at the intermediate frequency is increased
C. the amplifier has a wide frequency response
D. there is maximum power transfer from the primary circuit to the secondary circuit
E. the amplifier's overall Q is increased

Answer Choice C.

* **Question 7-22** The stages that mainly determine a communications receiver's sensitivity and selectivity are the:

A. IF amplifiers B. mixer stage C. detector stage D. audio amplifiers E. RF amplifiers

Answer Choice A.

* **Question 7-23** The IF amplifier of a communications receiver is operated under the conditions of:

A. class A B. class AB C. class B D. class C E. class D

Answer Choice A.

* **Question 7-24** A communications superhet is receiving an A3E 2 MHz transmission, in which the highest audio frequency is 4 kHz. The required bandwidth for the IF stages is at least:

A. 4 kHz B. 2004 kHz C. 2008 kHz D. 2 kHz E. 8 kHz

Answer Choice E. The required bandwidth is equal to twice the value of the highest audio frequency or 2×4 kHz $= 8$ kHz.

7-6. The detector stage

This is the essential stage of any receiver. Into the detector or demodulator stage (FIG. 7-8) is fed the amplitude-modulated IF signal; emerging from the detector is the audio information, such as voice, music, or a single tone for test purposes. In other words, the detector stage reverses the modulation process carried out at the transmitter. In the crystal set of the 1920s, it was the combination of the galena crystal and the tungsten "cat's whisker," which acted as a rectifying contact and provided the necessary nonlinearity for detection to occur.

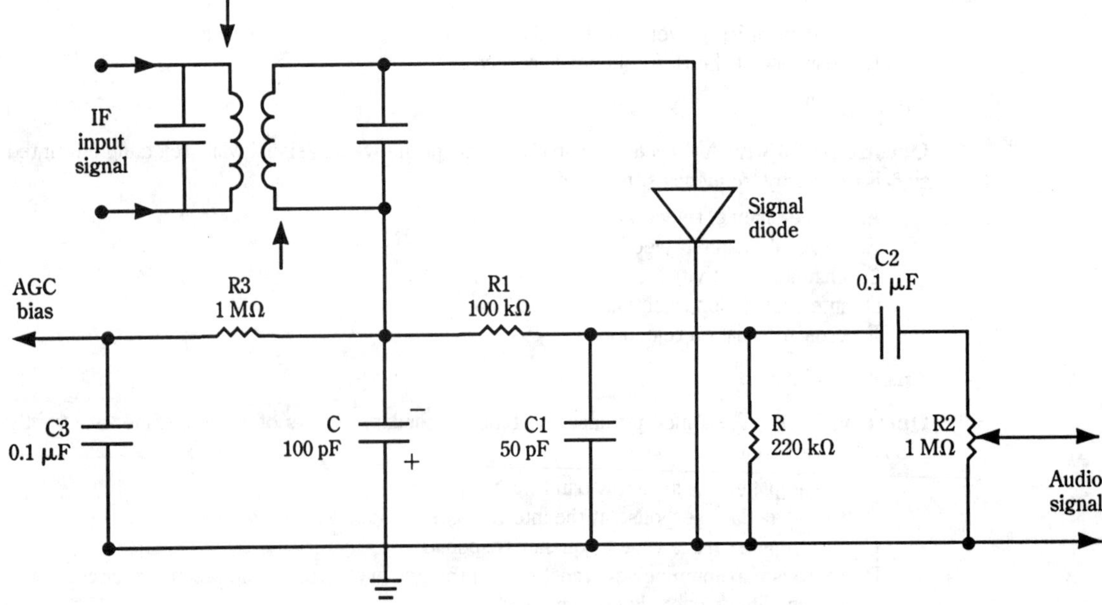

Fig. 7-8 The detector stage. The circuit for question 7-27.

Referring to FIG. 7-9, the signal diode is the nonlinear device that will pass pulses of current when the AM signal is applied. The diode current charges capacitor C, which subsequently discharges through R and R1 with a time constant of 100 pF × (220 kΩ + 100 kΩ) = 32 μs. This time constant is more than 10 times greater than the period of the IF (period = 1/455 kHz = 2.2 μs) but is about 40 times less than the period of the 1-kHz modulating tone (period = 1/1 kHz = 1000 μs) that amplitude modulates the IF carrier. Consequently, the voltage, V_C, across the capacitor, C, follows the envelope of the AM signal. As shown in the waveform of FIG. 7-9, V_C contains the audio tone, a dc level, and some IF ripple. The ripple is attenuated by the low-pass filter, R1C1, while the dc level is blocked by capacitor C2. As a result, the audio tone appears across the 1-MΩ potentiometer, which acts as a volume control. Subsequently, the tone signal is built up to loudspeaker strength by a combination of audio voltage and power amplifiers.

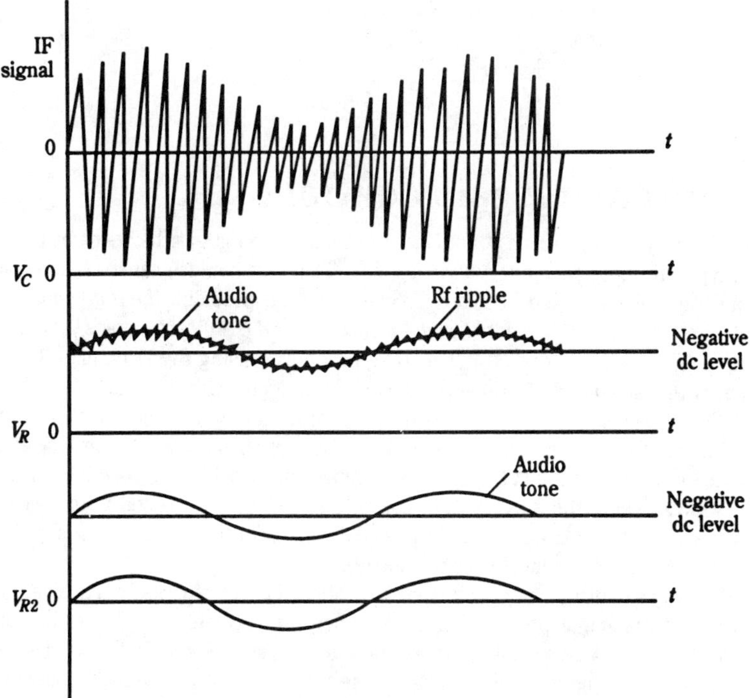

Fig. 7-9 The voltage waveforms of the detector stage.

* **Question 7-25** The circuit of FIG. 7-10 represents an AM receiver's:

A. AGC rectifier B. mixer stage C. squelch circuit D. detector stage
E. modulator circuit

Answer Choice D. Refer to FIG. 7-8.

* **Question 7-26** The input to a detector stage is an amplitude-modulated (A3E) IF signal. The output from the stage is:

A. a lower frequency carrier
B. the audio voice information

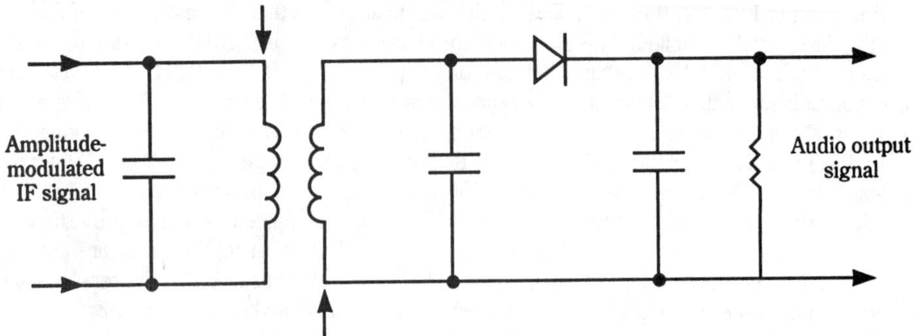

Fig. 7-10 The circuit diagram for question 7-25.

C. a morse-code signal
D. None of the above choices is true

Answer Choice B.

7-7. Automatic gain control (AGC)

Because of changes in propagation conditions, the carrier strength at the receiver fluctuates at a rate that is typically about once every two seconds. This variation can cause objectionable fading in the sound output from the loudspeaker. To overcome this problem, the *automatic gain control (AGC),* which is sometimes called *automatic volume control (AVC),* maintains an approximately constant signal voltage at the detector. This is achieved by biasing the circuits of the RF, IF, and mixer stages with a dc voltage that is derived from the detector circuit (FIG. 7-8). As a result, any increase in the carrier signal slightly increases the bias; this tends to counteract the increased signal by reducing the receiver's amplification (and vice-versa). In other words, the signal at the detector does increase slightly, but not nearly as much as it would have done if the AGC had not been present. In addition, the AGC system allows the receiver to be tuned from a weak signal to a strong signal without the danger of loudspeaker "blasting" (or from a strong signal to a weak signal without adjusting the manual volume control).

The advantages of using an AGC system are obtained at the expense of receiver sensitivity; this loss of sensitivity might present a problem when the receiver is trying to pick up a weak signal. To overcome this disadvantage, it is common to use *delayed AGC,* in which no bias is produced until a certain input signal level is reached. Notice that the "delay" is involved with a signal magnitude and *not* time.

The control that the AGC circuit exerts over the output signal depends on the amount of bias generated and the number of stages controlled. The control is therefore greater if the AGC circuit contains an additional amplifier for the IF signal or the bias.

In the detector circuit of FIG. 7-8, the AGC bias is developed across capacitor C. However, voltage V_C contains the audio signal and an IF ripple; these unwanted components are removed by the R3/C2 filter, which has a time constant of 0.1 s. This time constant enables the AGC bias to follow the fluctuations in the carrier signal strength. Delayed AGC requires a separate diode whose cathode is biased by a positive voltage. Until the input signal level is such that the anode voltage exceeds the cathode potential, the diode cannot conduct, and no AGC bias is generated.

* **Question 7-27** In FIG. 7-8, the AGC circuit has the disadvantage of:

A. increasing the sensitivity for strong signals
B. increasing the selectivity

C. reducing the image channel rejection
D. reducing the sensitivity for weak signals
E. increasing the fluctuations in the output signal to the loudspeaker

Answer Choice D.

* **Question 7-28** The purpose of delayed AGC is to:

A. increase the sensitivity for weak signals
B. increase the sensitivity for strong signals
C. reduce the selectivity
D. increase the image-channel rejection
E. introduce a time delay before applying the AGC bias

Answer Choice A.

* **Question 7-29** When a communications receiver is tuned to a strong signal, the delayed AGC bias is measured and found to be − 2.4 V. If the receiver is now retuned to a very weak signal, the new bias is:

A. − 2.4 V B. − 1.5 V to − 2.0 V C. − 1.0 V to − 1.5 V D. − 0.5 V to − 1.0 V
E. 0

Answer Choice E. The very weak signal will not be able to overcome the delay bias on the AGC diode.

* **Question 7-30** When a communications receiver is tuned to a strong signal, the AGC bias is measured and found to be zero. The fault cannot be caused by a (an):

A. defective IF stage
B. open circuit in the AGC's filter capacitor
C. defective local oscillator
D. short circuit across the AGC's filter capacitor
E. defective RF stage

Answer Choice B.

7-8. The squelch circuit

In the absence of a carrier, the AGC level is virtually zero so that the receiver is operating with maximum sensitivity. Consequently, the noise within the receiver's bandwidth is amplified to an objectionable degree. This can be an annoying situation for an operator who is required to man the receiver on a continuous basis. To eliminate this problem, a squelch (muting or quieting) circuit cuts off the receiver's audio output when no carrier is present.

A typical squelch circuit is shown in FIG. 7-11. A dc amplifier, Q1, controls the operation of the first audio amplifier which follows the detector stage. Once the AGC bias falls below a certain level, the transistor, Q1, is forward-biased so that its collector current flows through resistor R2. The voltage drop across this resistor provides sufficient reverse bias to cut off the transistor, Q2, so that excessive noise is prevented from reaching the loudspeaker. The low level of AGC bias, at which Q1 conducts is determined by setting the potentiometer, R1. It follows that a very weak signal might be unable to cut off Q2 and will therefore not be received. This is the main disadvantage of using a squelch circuit.

* **Question 7-31** The purpose of the receiver's squelch circuit is to:

A. prevent fluctuations in the AGC bias level
B. overcome fluctuations in the level of the RF signal arriving at the receiving antenna

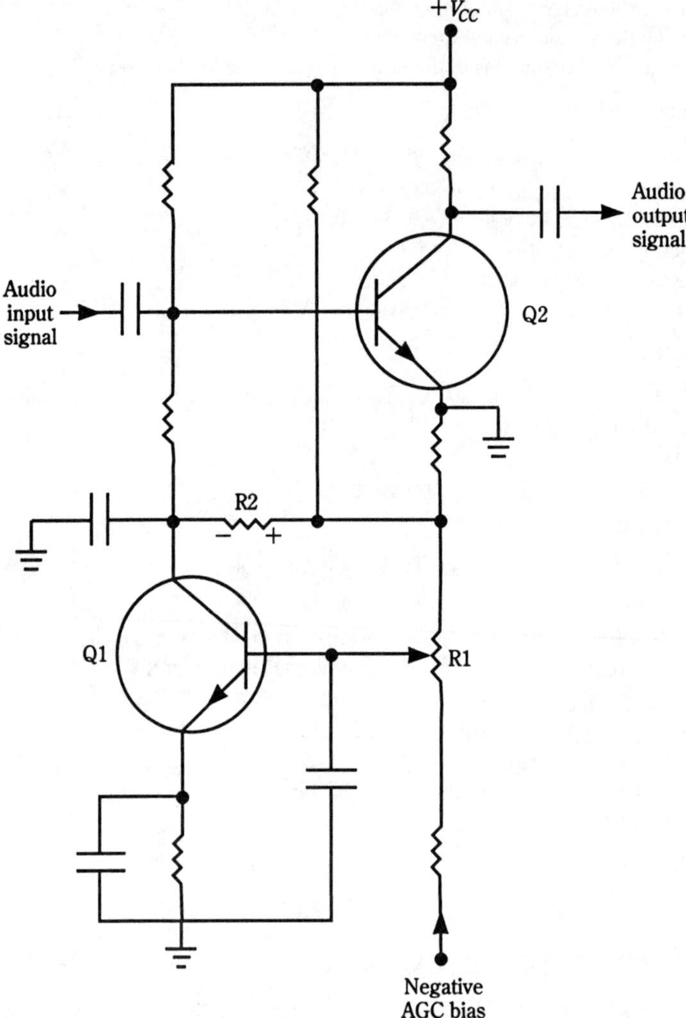

Fig. 7-11 The squelch circuit.

C. prevent amplified noise from reaching the loudspeaker during the absence of an incoming signal
D. reduce the receiver's sensitivity for all incoming signals
E. reduce the receiver's selectivity for all incoming signals

Answer Choice C.

* **Question 7-32** If a communications receiver is attempting to intercept a very weak signal:

A. the squelch circuit should be turned off
B. delayed AGC should be used
C. the AGC bias level must be increased
D. the squelch circuit should be switched on
E. choices B and D are true

Answer Choice A.

* **Question 7-33** The disadvantage of using a squelch circuit is that:

A. noise is reduced to a minimum in the absence of an incoming signal
B. the effect of AGC is reduced for strong signals
C. very weak signals might not be received
D. receiver sensitivity is reduced for strong signals
E. receiver selectivity is reduced for strong signals

Answer Choice C.

7-9. Crossmodulation

Apart from adjacent-channel and image-channel interference an AM receiver might experience the phenomenon of crossmodulation in which the modulation of an unwanted transmission is transferred to the carrier of the wanted signal. This effect might occur either externally to the receiver or within the receiver itself. In the external case, the wanted signal and a strong unwanted signal induced RF voltages in metal structures that are in the vicinity of the receiving antenna. If there is a discontinuity in one of these structures (for example, a rusty joint), there is a rectifying contact that will provide some degree of nonlinearity. When the nonlinear current versus voltage equation contains a third-order term, the result is crossmodulation. If the assumed current versus voltage equation is $i = a + bV + cV^2 + dV^3 + \ldots$, then the third order or cubic term, dV^3, contains the crossmodulation components. When a crossmodulation component at the wanted signal frequency is reradiated from the metal structure, it is intercepted by the receiving antenna after which it is impossible to eliminate the unwanted modulation and both signals appear on the loudspeaker.

Internal crossmodulation occurs in the first RF stage of the receiver. If this amplifier has an output-current-versus-input-voltage relationship, which contains a third order term, a crossmodulation component will be passed through to the following stages. To avoid this effect, the current versus voltage graph should be as close as possible to a parabola; this is a second-order curve, which has an equation of the form: $i = a + bV + cV^2$ so that no third-order term is present.

It is important to realize that the unwanted modulation will only appear in the receiver's output if the wanted carrier signal is present. A striking example is provided by "musical morse," in which the interfering music modulation has been transferred to the morse carrier. Consequently, the music will go "on" and "off" with the "mark" and "space" intervals of the morse signal. This is in contrast with adjacent- or image-channel interference; in these instances, the music is heard continuously in the background.

* **Question 7-34** In the vicinity of a receiver the modulation of an unwanted signal is transferred to the desired carrier. This effect is called:

A. image-channel interference
B. adjacent-channel interference
C. crossmodulation
D. intermodulation
E. modulation mixing

Answer Choice C.

* **Question 7-35** Crossmodulation in a receiver must be eliminated in the:

A. IF stages B. mixer stage C. detector stage D. audio amplifiers E. RF stage

Answer Choice E.

7-10. Measurement of an AM receiver's selectivity

Every receiver has an overall selectivity curve (FIG. 7-12). The vertical axis shows the amount of attenuation that is applied to unwanted signals whose carrier frequencies differ by a certain amount from the desired signal frequency. The horizontal axis indicates the differences (above or below) between the frequency of the desired carrier and the frequencies of the unwanted adjacent signals. At point P, the unwanted carrier frequency is 20 kHz above that of the desired signal and the corresponding attenuation is 43 dB. The selectivity could be quoted as "43-dB attenuation (−43 dB) for 20-kHz adjacent-channel rejection."

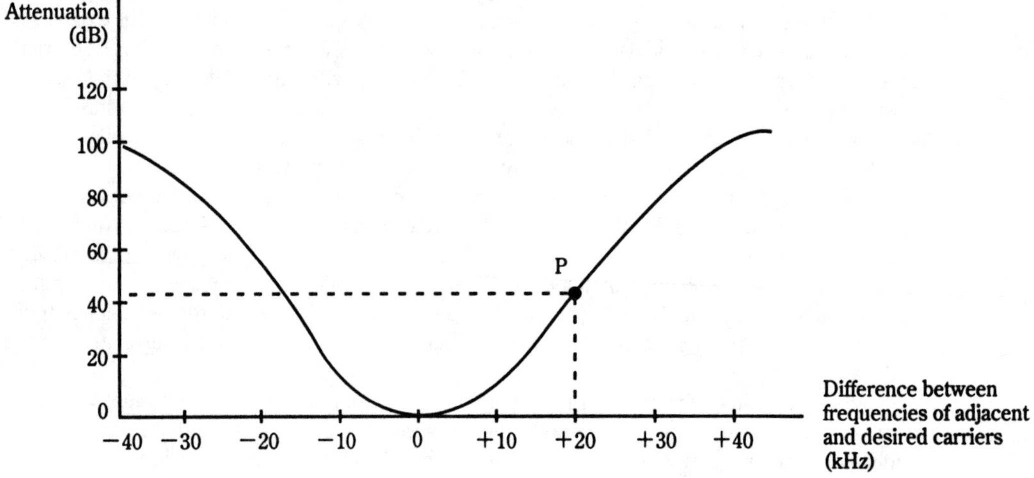

Fig. 7-12 An AM receiver's selectivity curve.

* **Question 7-36** Which of the following represents the highest degree of selectivity for an AM receiver?

A. −70-dB adjacent-channel sensitivity
B. −50 dB for 20-kHz adjacent-channel rejection
C. −40 dB for 30-kHz adjacent-channel rejection
D. −60 dB for 20-kHz adjacent-channel rejection
E. −60 dB for 30-kHz adjacent-channel rejection

Answer Choice D. Refer to FIG. 7-12.

7-11. Measurement of an AM receiver's sensitivity

A receiver's *sensitivity* measures its ability to amplify a weak signal. The RF signal induced in the antenna is of the order of microvolts, whereas the audio-output power from the final stage is measured in watts or milliwatts. A comparison between the audio power output and the voltage of the input RF signal, provides us with a measure of the sensitivity. The following standards are commonly used:

- The incoming carrier is 30% amplitude modulated by a 400-Hz test tone. This signal is applied to the receiver's first stage by a coupling network, which acts as a dummy antenna.
- The standard audio output power is a level of 50 mW, which is dissipated in a resistive load with the same value as the loudspeaker's impedance.

The sensitivity is either expressed directly in microvolts or in decibels that are referred to a standard of 1 V. For example, at a frequency that lies within the receiver's range, you can quote the sensitivity as "15 μV or 20 log(15×10^{-6}) = -96 dB below 1 volt for an audio power of 50 mW." You can also add the minimum requirement for the audio output's signal-to-noise ratio so that the sensitivity then becomes "15 μV for an output of 50 mW with a minimum signal-to-noise ratio of 20 dB."

If the equivalent resistance of the dummy antenna is known, the carrier voltage can be converted to an RF power, which is expressed in dBm. In this example, let the resistance of the dummy antenna be 70 Ω. The input RF power is $(15 \times 10^{-6}\ \text{V})^2/70\ \Omega = 3.2$ pW or 10 log(3.2 pW/1 mW) = -85 dBm. The sensitivity can then be quoted as "-85 dBm, 1.2 MHz for an output of 50 mW, with a minimum signal-to-noise ratio of 20 dB."

* **Question 7-37** The sensitivity of an AM receiver can be expressed in terms of:

A. 10 μV for a standard audio power level of 50 mW, with a minimum signal-to-noise ratio of 20 dB
B. 60 dB of attenuation at a frequency of 20 kHz above the incoming signal
C. 8 μV for an audio power level of 20 dBm
D. the ratio expressed in decibels of the audio output power to the RF input power
E. the overall receiver's voltage gain, expressed in decibels

Answer Choice A.

7-12. The beat frequency oscillator (BFO)

To receive a CW A1A transmission, it is necessary to create an audio note that appears on the loudspeaker and is interrupted in accordance with the morse code. Demodulation of an A1A signal produces no audio component, apart from a clicking sound that is caused by the rapid rise and fall of the "mark" intervals. An experienced operator can read key clicks, but it is much better to listen to a note, whose frequency is normally 1 kHz. For this reason, the *beat frequency oscillator (BFO)* is used (FIG. 7-4). This stage is not used for voice reception, but is set to generate a continuous RF output at a frequency whose value differs by 1 kHz from the IF. For example, if the IF is 455 kHz, the BFO would generate either 454 kHz or 456 kHz.

For CW reception, the switch, S, is closed and the detector stage behaves as a mixer circuit for the IF signal and the BFO output. During "mark" intervals, the 455 kHz IF carrier beats with the 456 kHz BFO output to produce a 1-kHz difference frequency, which is passed to the audio stages and causes a 1000-Hz note to appear on the loudspeaker or in the headphones. By contrast, a "space" interval will produce no audio note. Therefore, the interruptions in the note correspond to the original keying at the transmitter.

* **Question 7-38** The purpose of a beat frequency oscillator (BFO) is to:

A. generate a 1-kHz note for CW reception
B. aid in the reception of weak voice-modulated signals
C. generate a signal whose frequency is the same as that of the IF
D. generate an output whose frequency differs from the incoming carrier frequency by the value of the IF
E. generate an output whose frequency differs from that of the IF by 1 kHz

Answer Choice E.

* **Question 7-39** An AM superhet receiver is tuned to a CW A1A carrier whose frequency is 1 MHz. If the IF is 455 kHz, the output frequency of the BFO is:

A. 1 kHz B. 1001 kHz C. 999 kHz D. 454 kHz E. either choice B or C is correct

Answer Choice D. The BFO output frequency is 455 ± 1 = 454 kHz or 456 kHz.

* **Question 7-40** A beat frequency oscillator (BFO):

A. is a crystal oscillator that is contained within a TRF receiver
B. is used to detect telephony
C. produces an audio signal in the loudspeaker when the BFO's output is mixed with the local oscillator's output
D. is a crystal oscillator that substitutes for the local oscillator on fixed-frequency reception
E. is used to create an audio note in the loudspeaker during the reception of a CW telegraphy signal

Answer Choice E.

8
Frequency modulation and the FM transmitter

In this chapter you will learn:

- about the principles of frequency modulation, as well as the meanings of frequency deviation and modulation index.
- about the sideband structure of an FM signal.
- about the factors that determine the bandwidth of an FM signal.
- how the features of phase modulation differ from those of frequency modulation.
- about the block diagram of a direct FM transmitter.
- how a varactor-diode modulator or a reactance JFET modulator are both capable of generating direct FM.
- how pre-emphasis is used to improve the signal-to-noise ratio at the receiver.
- why an automatic frequency control (AFC) circuit is normally included in a direct FM transmitter.
- about the block diagram of an indirect FM transmitter.
- how a varactor diode is used to produce phase modulation in an indirect FM transmitter.
- how the audio correction network converts a PM signal into an FM signal.
- how frequency-shift keying is used to transmit telegraphy and how facsimile is used for the transmission of fixed images.

8-1. Frequency modulation

With *frequency modulation,* the instantaneous frequency of the RF wave is varied in accordance with the modulating signal, while the amplitude of the RF wave is kept constant. The RF power output and the antenna current of the FM transmitter are therefore independent of the modulation.

In the FM wave (FIG. 8-1), the instantaneous amount of the *frequency shift* or deviation away from its average unmodulated value is linearly related to the instantaneous magnitude (voltage) of the modulating signal; the rate at which the frequency deviation (f_d) occurs is equal to the modulating frequency. Notice that the amount of the frequency shift in the RF wave is independent of the modulating frequency. Therefore, if they are of the same amplitude, modulating tones of 200 and 400 Hz will provide the same amount of frequency shift in the FM wave. However, in FM transmitters, the audio frequencies above 800 Hz are progressively accentuated (pre-emphasized) in order to improve their signal-to-noise ratio at the receiver. The degree of pre-emphasis is measured by the time constant of an RC circuit, whose audio output increases with frequency. This time constant is specified by the FCC as 75 μs. In order to restore the tonal balance, the receiver's discriminator output is fed to an RC de-emphasis circuit with the same time constant.

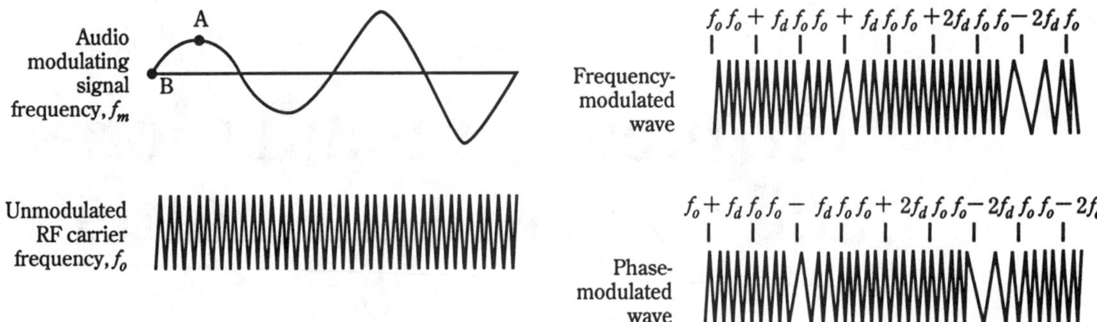

Fig. 8-1 Frequency and phase modulation.

When 100% modulation of an FM wave occurs, the amount of frequency shift reaches the maximum value allowed for the particular communications system. This maximum value is called the *frequency deviation*, which, in the FM broadcast services (emission designation F3E), is a shift of 75 kHz on either side of the unmodulated carrier frequency. The output-frequency swing for 100% modulation by a single test tone is therefore ±75 kHz. However, in the aural transmitter of a TV station, 100% modulation corresponds to a frequency deviation of 25 kHz; in the marine services, the frequency deviation is only 5 kHz. The percentage modulation and the amount of frequency shift are directly proportional so that 40% modulation in the FM broadcast service would correspond to an output frequency swing of $\pm 40 \times 75/100 = \pm 30$ kHz. The amount of the frequency deviation and the percentage modulation can be checked by using a deviation meter.

For FM, the degree of modulation is defined by:

$$\text{Modulation index, } m = \frac{f_d}{f_m} \tag{8-1}$$

where: f_m = modulating frequency (Hz)
f_d = frequency deviation (Hz)

During the transmission of speech and music, the value of the instantaneous modulation index can vary from less than 1 to over 100. However, for a particular system, there is a certain modulation index value, which is called the *deviation ratio* and is determined by:

$$\textit{Deviation ratio} = \frac{f_d \textit{ corresponding to 100\% modulation}}{\textit{highest transmitted value of } f_m} \tag{8-2}$$

For commercial FM broadcast, the transmitted audio range is 50 Hz to 15 kHz. Because the frequency deviation value for 100% modulation is 75 kHz, the deviation ratio is 75 kHz/15 kHz = 5, which is the typical value for a *wide-band FM system.* By contrast, marine FM transmitters operate on a *narrow-band* system, in which the frequency deviation for 100% modulation is 5 kHz and the highest audio frequency is 3 kHz; consequently, the value of the deviation ratio is only 5 kHz/3 kHz = 1.67.

Sideband structure

Assume that an RF carrier, whose frequency is f_c, is modulated by a single test tone (frequency, f_m). Using Fourier analysis, the resultant FM signal (FIG. 8-1) can be analyzed into the following components:

Third order, upper sideband, frequency $f_c + 3f_m$
Second order, upper sideband, frequency $f_c + 2f_m$
First order, upper sideband, frequency $f_c + f_m$
carrier component, frequency f_c
First order, lower sideband, frequency $f_c - f_m$
Second order, lower sideband, frequency $f_c - 2f_m$
Third order, lower sideband, frequency $f_c - 3f_m$

Although the modulating signal is only a single tone, there are theoretically an *infinite* number of sidebands which, in turn, would require an infinite bandwidth. Fortunately, there are only a limited number of sidebands, which contribute significantly to the information carried by the FM signal. In practice, the significant sidebands are limited to those that are greater than 1% of the unmodulated carrier voltage.

The amplitudes of the individual sidebands and the carrier are determined by the value of the modulation index. Assuming that the index is a whole number, the total number of significant sidebands (upper and lower) is equal to $2(m + 1)$. Because each sideband is separated from its neighbor by the modulating frequency, f_m:

$$\text{Required bandwidth} = 2(m + 1)f_m \text{ hertz (Hz)} \qquad (8\text{-}3)$$

For example, consider the case of a 100-MHz carrier which is modulated by a 2.5-kHz test tone. If the frequency deviation is: 5 kHz, the modulation index is: 5 kHz/2.5 kHz = 2 and the total number of sidebands is 2(2 + 1) = 6. Then, the necessary bandwidth is: 6 × 2.5 = 15 kHz. This example illustrates the case of a marine FM transmitter whose authorized bandwidth is 20 kHz.

Because the required bandwidth for FM (15 kHz) is much greater than that of the comparable AM signal (2 × 3 = 6 kHz), it is only possible to operate FM systems at high frequencies in the VHF band (and above). Because the amplitude of the FM signal is constant, the total power when modulation occurs, is equal to that of the unmodulated carrier. This same power level is merely redistributed between the carrier and the two sets of sidebands.

If the FM carrier is modulated by more than one tone, the upper sidebands are no longer the mirror images of the lower sidebands. Both sets of sidebands are required for the FM signal to be successfully demodulated so that any form of single-sideband FM is impossible.

Question 8-1 A 100-MHz FM carrier is 100% modulated by a single tone. The ratio of the peak envelope power to the unmodulated carrier power is:

A. 4:1 B. 2:1 C. $\sqrt{2}$:1 D. 3:1 E. 1:1

Answer Choice E. For FM, the power remains the same during modulation. Consequently, the ratio is 1:1.

* **Question 8-2** For a marine 150-W FM transmitter, 100% modulation corresponds to a frequency deviation of 5 kHz. If the modulating signal is a 2-kHz test tone, the frequency swing corresponding to 80% modulation is:

A. 4 kHz B. 2.5 kHz C. 2 kHz D. 1 kHz E. 500 Hz

Answer Choice A. Modulation of 80% corresponds to a frequency swing of: (80/100) × 5 = 4 kHz.

Question 8-3 In QUES. 8-2, the value of the modulation index is:

A. 0.5 B. 1.0 C. 1.5 D. 2.0 E. 2.5

Answer. Choice D.

Modulation index:

$$m = \frac{f_d}{f_m} = \frac{4\text{ kHz}}{2\text{ kHz}} = 2 \qquad (8\text{-}1)$$

Question 8-4 In QUES. 8-2 and 8-3, the required bandwidth for the FM signal is:

A. 8 kHz B. 12 kHz C. 4 kHz D. 16 kHz E. 10 kHz

Answer Choice B.

$$\text{Required bandwidth} = 2(m + 1)f_m = 2(2 + 1) \times 2\text{ kHz} = 12\text{ kHz} \qquad (8\text{-}3)$$

* **Question 8-5** If a carrier is frequency modulated by a single test tone, the frequency separation between a sideband and its neighboring sideband is equal to:

A. the modulating frequency
B. twice the modulating frequency
C. the carrier frequency divided by the modulation index
D. the frequency deviation
E. the frequency deviation multiplied by the modulation index

Answer Choice A. Because the frequencies of the sidebands are $f_c \pm f_m$, $f_c \pm 2f_m$, $f_c \pm 3f_m$ and so on, each sideband is separated from its neighbor by the value of the modulating frequency, f_m.

Question 8-6 An FM signal is 60% modulated by a single 200-Hz test tone and the resultant frequency deviation is 3 kHz. If the frequency of the test tone is increased to 300 Hz, what is the new value of the frequency deviation (neglecting any effect of pre-emphasis)?

A. 3 kHz B. 5 kHz C. 4.5 kHz D. 3.3 kHz E. 3.1 kHz

Answer Choice A. If the effect of pre-emphasis is neglected, the deviation is independent of the value of the modulating frequency. The frequency deviation therefore remains at 3 kHz.

* **Question 8-7** If a carrier is frequency modulated by a single test tone, the maximum value of the modulation index is directly proportional to the:

A. carrier amplitude B. carrier frequency C. modulating frequency
D. amplitude of the tone E. none of the above

Answer Choice D. The modulation index, $m = f_d/f_m$, and the maximum value of the instantaneous frequency, f_d, is directly proportional to the tone's amplitude.

Question 8-8 For test purposes, a 100 W marine FM transmitter is 80% modulated by a 2-kHz tone. Including the carrier and sidebands, the total power in the modulated FM signal is:

A. 200 W B. 132 W C. 116 W D. 164 W E. 100 W

Answer Choice E. Because of the RF power in an FM signal is independent of the modulation, the total power remains at 100 W.

Question 8-9 The deviation ratio of an FM transmitter is the ratio of the:

A. maximum frequency swing to the highest modulating frequency
B. operating frequency to the assigned frequency
C. frequency swing to the modulating frequency
D. highest modulating frequency to the minimum frequency deviation
E. lowest modulating frequency to the maximum frequency deviation

Answer Choice A.

Question 8-10 In an FM transmitter, the amplitude of the modulating test tone is doubled, but its frequency is halved. If the effect of pre-emphasis is neglected, the frequency deviation is:

A. halved B. doubled C. unchanged D. quadrupled E. quartered

Answer Choice B. If pre-emphasis is neglected, the frequency deviation is solely determined by the tone's amplitude.

Question 8-11 In an FM transmission, the modulating frequency of the test tone is 2 kHz. If there are 8 significant upper sidebands, the bandwidth is:

A. 32 kHz B. 16 kHz C. 8 kHz D. 4 kHz E. 2 kHz

Answer Choice A. There is a total of $2 \times 8 = 16$ significant sidebands. The bandwidth is therefore $16 \times 2 = 32$ kHz.

* **Question 8-12** If a carrier is frequency modulated by a test tone, the amount of the frequency deviation is mainly determined by the:

A. amplitude of the tone
B. modulating frequency
C. carrier amplitude
D. carrier frequency
E. both choices A and B are true

Answer Choice A.

* **Question 8-13** When a carrier is frequency modulated by a test tone, the percentage of modulation can be determined by:

A. observing the waveform of the FM signal
B. using a deviation meter
C. creating a trapezoidal display on an oscilloscope
D. taking readings of the frequency monitor
E. using a frequency counter

Answer Choice B.

* **Question 8-14** The amplitude of an FM modulating test tone is maintained at a constant level, but its frequency is lowered. As a result:

A. the value of the modulation index is reduced
B. there are a greater number of significant sidebands
C. the amplitude of the carrier is reduced
D. the percentage of modulation is increased
E. the frequency separation between adjacent sidebands is increased

Answer Choice B. The frequency deviation stays the same, but the value of the modulation index, m ($= f_d/f_m$) is increased. Consequently, the number [$= 2(m + 1)$] of significant sidebands is greater.

8-2. Phase modulation

In phase modulation (FIG. 8-1), the instantaneous phase of the RF carrier wave is varied in accordance with the modulating signal, while the amplitude of the RF wave is kept constant. The instantaneous amount of the phase shift away from its unmodulated value is linearly related to the instantaneous magnitude (voltage) of the modulating signal. Because a rate of change of phase is equivalent to a shift in frequency, the PM wave is similar in appearance to the FM wave and, in fact, they cannot be distinguished, except by reference to the modulating signal. The important differences are:

- With PM, the output frequency swing is proportional to the product of the amplitude and the frequency of the modulating signal. In FM, the swing is proportional to the amplitude alone. Therefore, if the carrier is being modulated by a single tone and the tone amplitude and the frequency are both doubled, the output frequency swing in the PM signal would be quadrupled (neglecting any effect of pre-emphasis).
- Relative to the cycle of the modulating signal, the instantaneous maximum (and/or minimum) frequency positions are 90° apart in the FM and PM waves. In FIG. 8-1, point A in the modulating signal corresponds to the instantaneous maximum frequency in the FM wave. For the PM wave, the maximum frequency occurs at point B, which is 25% of a cycle or 90° from point A.

The main importance of PM is its use in the indirect method of creating FM. For reasons of frequency stability (and to avoid the requirement for an AFC system), it is common practice in many FM transmitters to use a master crystal oscillator, whose frequency is fixed and which therefore cannot be directly modulated. The modulated stage comes after the crystal oscillator and consists of a circuit that actually creates phase modulation. However, before reaching the modulated stage, the audio signal is passed through a correction network (not to be confused with the pre-emphasis circuit), whose voltage output is inversely proportional to the frequency, and which introduces an approximate 90° phase shift. Then, as far as the undistorted audio signal input to the correction network is concerned, the output from the modulated stage is the required FM signal, but with regard to the output from the correction network, the modulated stage produces PM. Clearly, FM and PM are closely related; in fact, each is an example of *angle modulation.* However, the FCC designates phase-modulated telephony as a G3E emission, whereas frequency-modulated telephony is designated as F3E.

* **Question 8-15** Which of the following is an example of angle modulation?

A. double sideband, amplitude modulation
B. frequency modulation
C. single sideband, amplitude modulation
D. phase modulation
E. choices B and D are correct

Answer Choice E.

* **Question 8-16** A carrier is phase modulated by a test tone. If the amplitude and the frequency of the tone are both doubled, the amount of frequency deviation is:

A. doubled B. multiplied by four C. unchanged D. halved E. divided by four

Answer Choice B. For a PM wave the frequency deviation is directly proportional to the product of the tone amplitude and the modulating frequency. The frequency deviation is therefore multiplied by $2 \times 2 = 4$.

8-3. The direct FM transmitter

As briefly covered earlier, there are two methods of frequency modulating an RF carrier in a communications system. The first is:

The direct method

This method is illustrated in FIG. 8-1. The modulation process is carried out at the oscillator stage, which must therefore be of the variable frequency type (such as the Colpitts oscillator) and not crystal-controlled. Modulation at this early stage has two advantages:

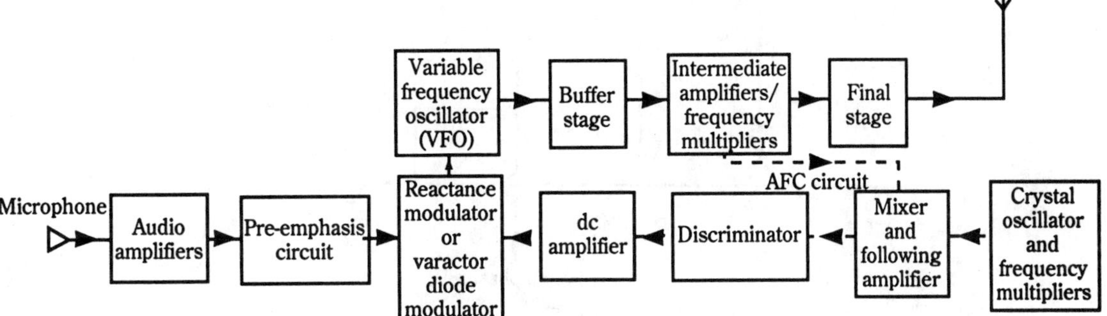

Fig. 8-2 The block diagram of an FM transmitter using the direct method.

- The power level is low so that the microphone is only followed by one or two audio voltage amplifiers.
- Unlike AM signals, an FM signal can be fed to a class-C stage, which can either be an amplifier or a frequency multiplier. The instantaneous RF shift controlled by the audio signal is then multiplied by the same product factor as the carrier frequency. As an example, an FM transmitter has an output carrier frequency of 94.5 MHz with an instantaneous frequency deviation of 60 kHz. If the stages following the oscillator contain two doublers and a tripler, the product factor is $2 \times 2 \times 3 = 12$. The VFO generates: $94.5/12 = 7.875$ MHz and the frequency deviation at the oscillator is only: $60/12 = 5$ kHz.

Now look at the stages and circuits that appear in a direct FM transmitter, but not in an AM transmitter.

The JFET reactance modulator

The circuit of FIG. 8-3A is a solid-state version of the earlier reactance tube modulator. The RF voltage, v_o, is developed across the VFO's tank circuit and is applied to the phase-shift circuit of

C and R in series. If $X_C >> R$, the current, i, will lead v_o by approximately 90°; however, the gate voltage, v_g, across the resistor, R, is in phase with i and therefore leads v_o by 90°. Because the drain current, i_d, is in phase with v_g (FIG. 8-3B), i_d leads v_o by nearly 90° so that the JFET presents a certain value of capacitive reactance and a corresponding capacitance to the voltage, v_o. This equivalent capacitance is in parallel with the oscillator's tank circuit and will therefore determine the instantaneous value of the generated frequency.

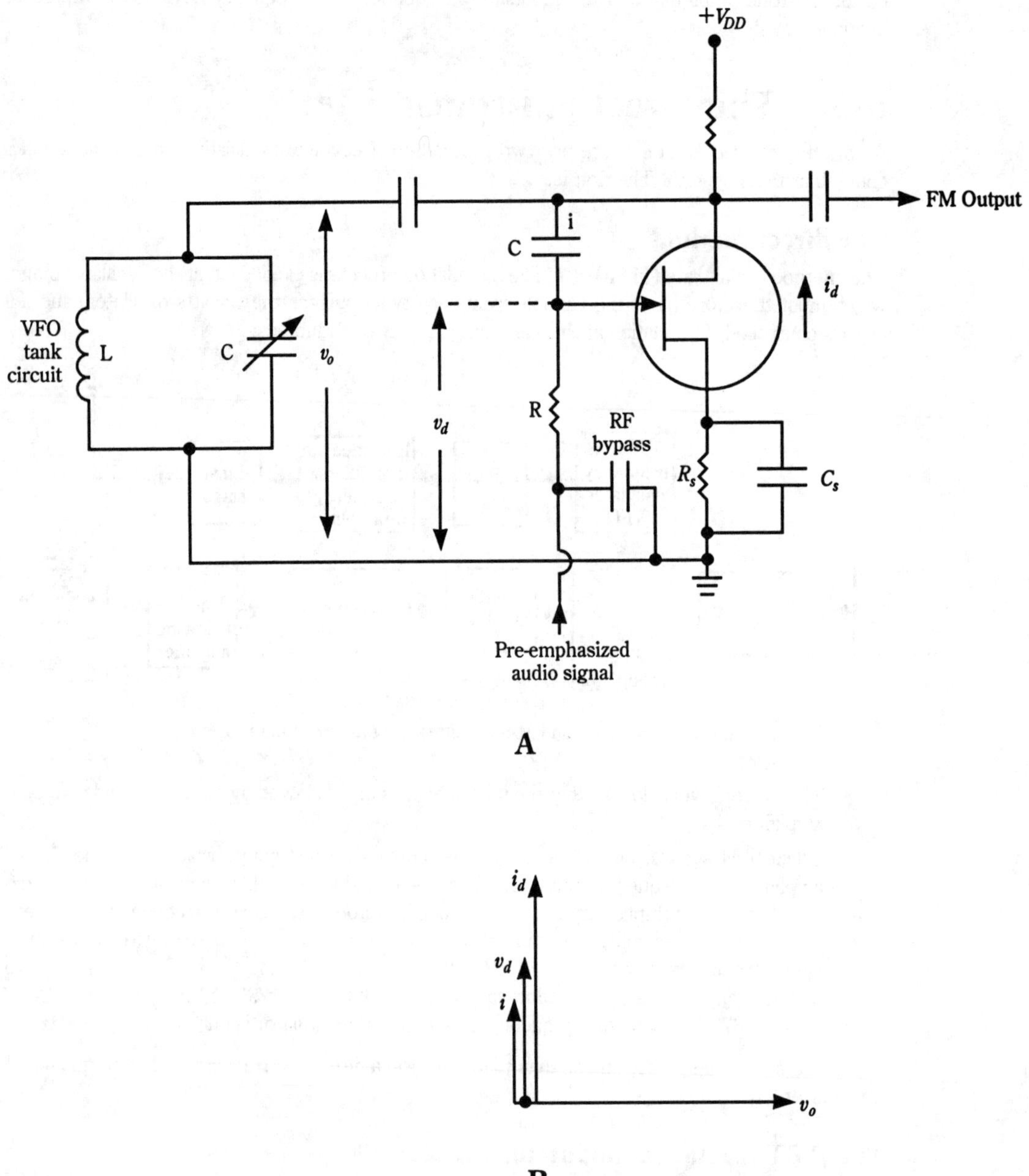

Fig. 8-3 The reactance JFET modulator.

When the audio signal is fed to the gate, it amplitude modulates the drain current and produces variations in the JFET's equivalent capacitance. For example, at the peak of the audio tone, the drain current is instantaneously at its maximum value so that the JFET's equivalent capacitance also rises to a maximum. As a result, the total capacitance associated with the tank circuit increases to its highest level and the instantaneous generated frequency is at its minimum value, $f_c - f_d$.

The JFET, as described, behaves as a capacitive-reactance modulator. However, if R and C are interchanged and $R >> X_C$, v_d will lag v_o by nearly 90° and the circuit will become an inductive-reactance modulator.

The varactor diode modulator

The varactor diode modulator also provides frequency modulation by the direct method. The varactor diode is reverse-biased and as the amount of the bias is increased, the depletion layer widens, and the junction capacitance decreases. These semiconductor devices, which are used to behave as voltage-controlled variable capacitors, are referred to as either *varactor* or *varicap diodes.* The characteristic of a typical varactor diode with its accepted symbols, is illustrated in FIG. 8-4. The range of the reverse bias, V_r, is limited to between zero and the point at which avalanche breakdown occurs. Notice that there is a sharp initial drop in the value of the junction or transition capacitance, C_T, and that the characteristic of C_T versus V_r has a marked curvature. This degree of curvature allows the varactor diode to be used for frequency multiplication in the microwave region.

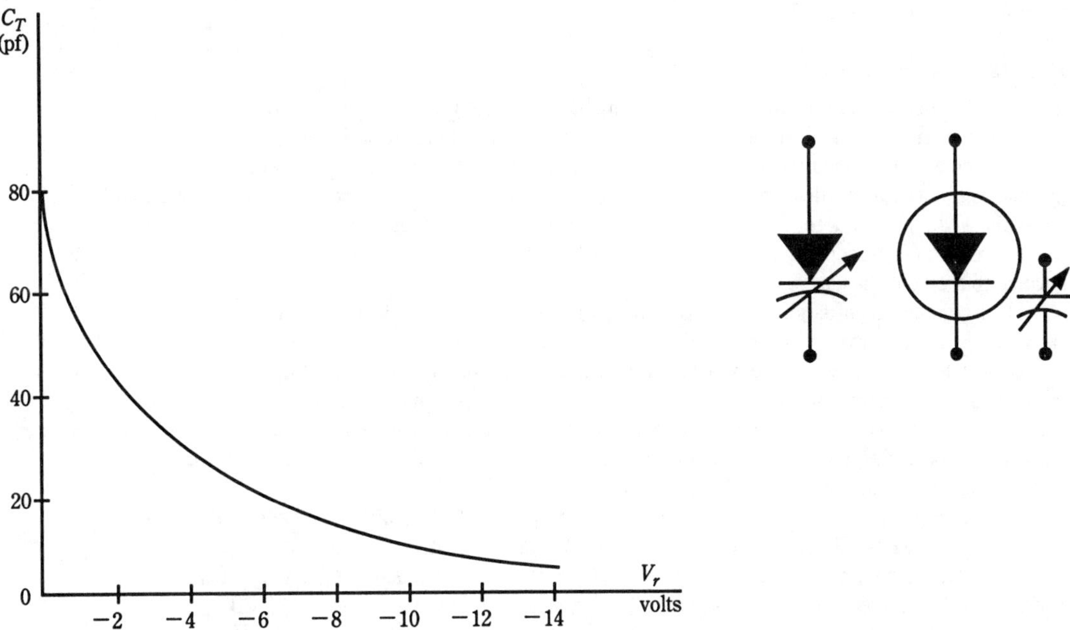

Fig. 8-4 The characteristic and symbols of a varactor diode.

Figure 8-5 shows the varactor-diode circuit for generating an FM signal by the direct method. The voltage divider R_1/R_2 provides the necessary reverse bias for the diode whose capacitance is in parallel with the oscillator's tank circuit and therefore determines the instantaneous value of the output frequency. The audio signal varies the diode's bias and the corresponding fluctuations in C_T are responsible for generating the required FM signal. At point X on the audio waveform, the reverse bias is increased, the value of C_T is reduced, and the instantaneous output frequency falls to its lowest value. Provided $C_T << C$, the amount of RF shift is directly proportional to the value of C_T.

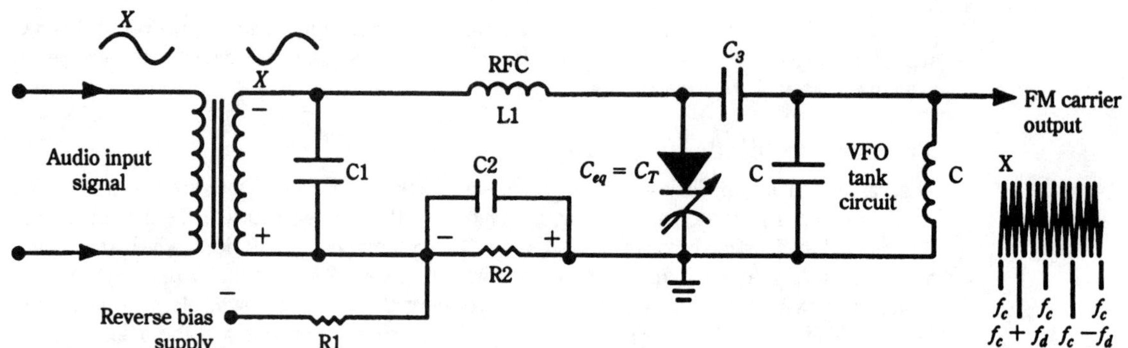

Fig. 8-5 The varactor-diode modulator circuit.

The RF choke, L_1, and the capacitor, C_1, form a low-pass filter whose purpose is to prevent interference between the RF and AF circuits. Capacitor C_2 is an AF and RF bypass capacitor so that there is no signal feedback to the dc bias supply. C_3 is a blocking capacitor which prevents the reverse bias from being applied to the oscillator stage.

Pre-emphasis circuit

The high-frequency components of speech contribute most toward intelligibility. Unfortunately, these components generally have the lowest amplitude. In addition, noise in an FM system has more effect on the higher modulating frequencies; it follows that if the audio frequencies are gradually accentuated at the transmitter, their signal-to-noise ratios are improved at the receiver. After the FM signal is detected by the discriminator (chapter 9), these same audio frequencies must receive a corresponding degree of gradual attenuation in order to restore the correct tonal balance to the voice signal.

The gradual accentuation of the audio frequencies at the transmitter is referred to as *pre-emphasis,* and the corresponding attenuation at the receiver is called *de-emphasis.* A common circuit designed to achieve pre-emphasis is shown in FIG. 8-6A. If the modulating frequency is increased, the reactance of capacitor C falls so that the impedance of the parallel RC combination is reduced. Consequently, the audio voltage drop across this impedance decreases and the output voltage will increase. The amount of pre-emphasis is measured by the decibel gain between a high-frequency output voltage and the output voltage at 30 Hz.

When the decibel gain versus frequency graph is plotted (FIG. 8-6B), the result is the pre-emphasis curve whose shape is determined by the RC time constant of 75 kΩ × 0.001 μF = 75 μs; this value of the time constant is the FCC standard for FM transmitters. At the audio frequency of 2120 Hz, the pre-emphasis gain is 3 dB, and at 15 kHz the gain rises to 17 dB.

The AFC circuit

In the direct method, the audio information produces frequency variations in the oscillator's output. For commercial purposes, it is essential that the oscillator has a high degree of frequency stability, which can be achieved through an AFC (automatic frequency control) circuit. In FIG. 8-2, a small amount of the FM signal from the intermediate stages is passed to a mixer, which is

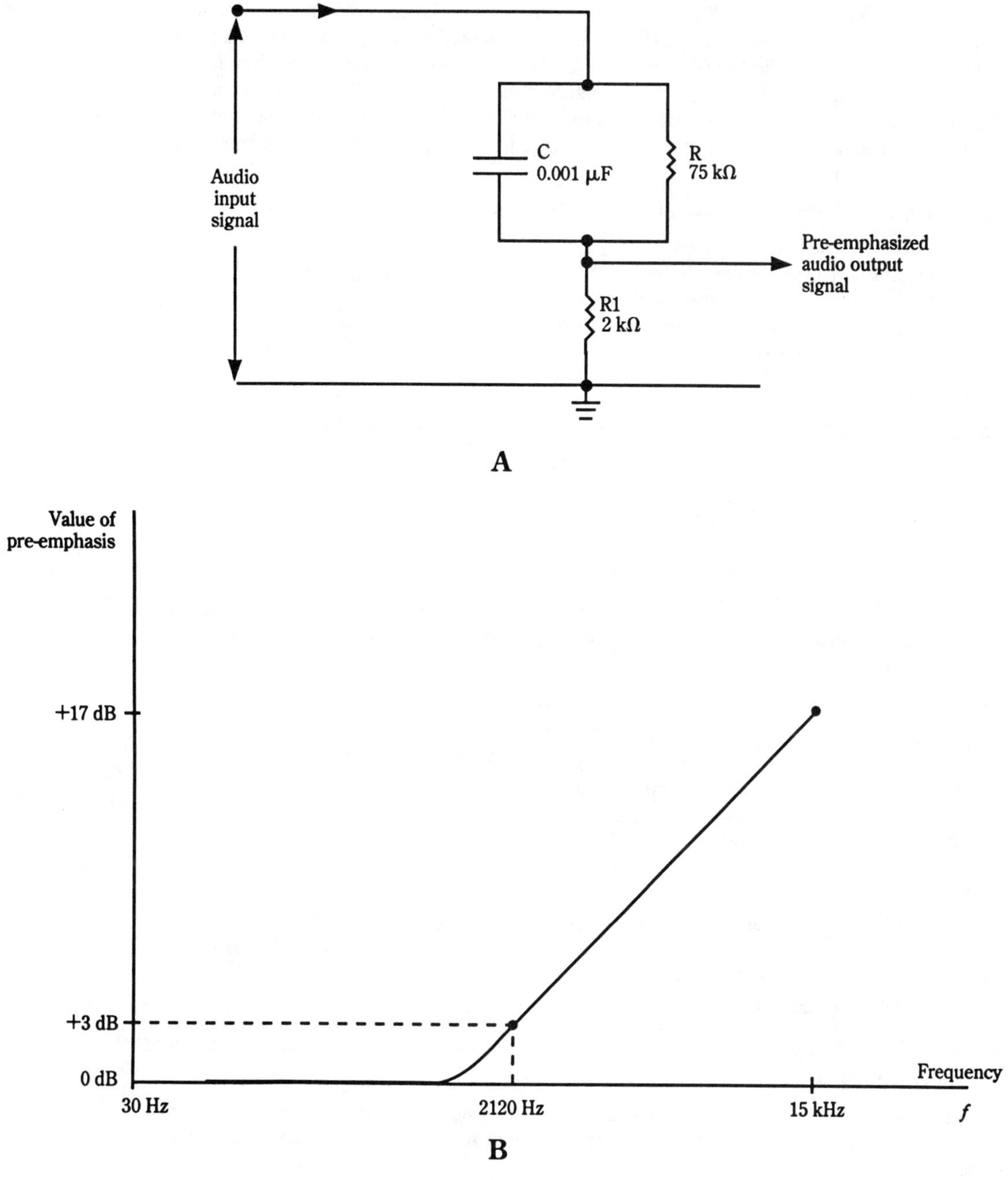

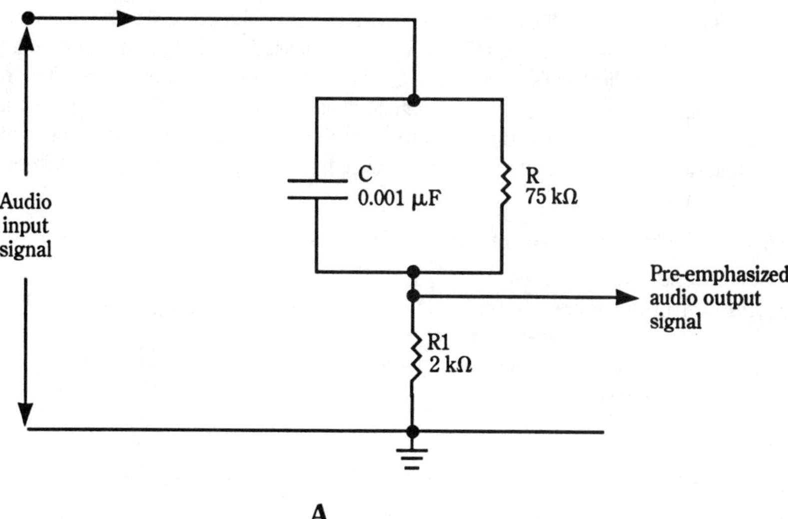

A

Value of
pre-emphasis
+17 dB
+3 dB
0 dB
Frequency
30 Hz
2120 Hz
15 kHz
f

B

Fig. 8-6 The pre-emphasis circuit.

also fed with a signal from a crystal oscillator and its harmonic generator. The mixer's output is a signal at the difference frequency, which is typically between 10% and 20% of the VFO's frequency. This difference frequency is amplified before being fed to a tuned high/tuned low discriminator (chapter 9). If the difference frequency is at its correct value, the output from the discriminator is zero. When the difference frequency rises above the correct value, the discriminator output is a dc voltage, which is amplified before being passed to another varactor diode; this diode is connected across the VFO's tank circuit and is only used for AFC purposes. The result is to drive the carrier's frequency back to its assigned value. In order that the AFC circuit is not affected by the modulating signal, the discriminator's output circuit has a high time constant and will therefore follow the slow fluctuations in the carrier frequency, but not the rapid frequency changes because of modulation.

* **Question 8-17** The main advantage of FM over AM is its:

A. narrower bandwidth
B. greater propagation range
C. total freedom from adjacent-channel interference
D. total freedom from image-channel interference
E. better signal-to-noise-ratio

Answer Choice E.

* **Question 8-18** Which of the following is best for long distance FM communications?

A. narrow-band system
B. a UHF carrier frequency, as opposed to one in the VHF band
C. a single-sideband FM system
D. wide-band system
E. few frequency-multiplier stages in the transmitter

Answer Choice A. In a narrow-band system, the information is contained in a small number of strong significant sidebands. This results in a greater propagation range than that possessed by a wide-band system.

* **Question 8-19** In an FM transmitter, the number of sidebands:

A. increases with a higher value of the modulation index
B. decreases with an increase in the modulating frequency
C. increases with the amplitude of the modulating signal
D. increases with a higher degree of pre-emphasis
E. all of the above choices are true

Answer Choice E.

* **Question 8-20** The oscillator of an FM transmitter is operating on a frequency of 8 MHz. If there are two doubler stages and one tripler stage between the oscillator and the RF final stage, the frequency of the transmitter's output carrier is:

A. 32 MHz B. 48 MHz C. 16 MHz D. 96 MHz E. 64 MHz

Answer Choice D. The product factor of the multiplier stages is $2 \times 2 \times 3 = 12$. Therefore, the output carrier frequency is $12 \times 8 = 96$ MHz.

* **Question 8-21** In QUES. 8-20, 100% modulation corresponds to an output frequency deviation of 5 kHz. If the output carrier is 60% modulated by a single tone, the frequency deviation at the oscillator is:

A. 250 Hz B. 500 Hz C. 750 Hz D. 1 kHz E. 3 kHz

Answer Choice A. 60% modulation corresponds to an output frequency deviation of $(60/100) \times 5 = 3$ kHz. The deviation at the oscillator is $3/12$ kHz $= 250$ Hz.

* **Question 8-22** Pre-emphasis is used in FM transmitters to improve the signal-to-noise ratio of:

A. low modulating frequencies
B. all modulating frequencies
C. high modulating frequencies
D. the carrier
E. all the significant sidebands

Answer Choice C. The high modulating frequencies are accentuated by the pre-emphasis circuit.

* **Question 8-23** Figure 8-7 shows the diagram of a:

A. low-pass filter
B. *m*-derived filter
C. pre-emphasis circuit
D. de-emphasis circuit
E. band-pass filter

Answer Choice C. Refer to FIG. 8-6A.

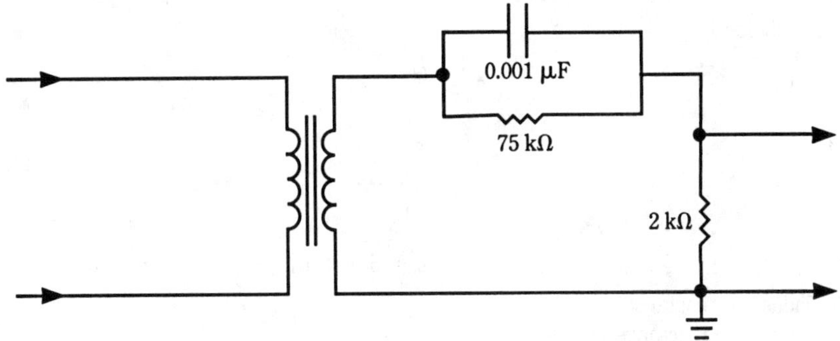

Fig. 8-7 The circuit for question 8-23.

* **Question 8-24** The pre-emphasis circuit in an FM transmitter is used to:

A. accentuate low AF components to improve their signal-to-noise ratio
B. attenuate high AF components to improve their signal-to-noise ratio
C. attenuate low AF components to improve their signal-to-noise ratio
D. accentuate high AF components to improve their signal-to-noise ratio
E. amplify low AF components and attenuate high AF components

Answer Choice D. Refer to FIG. 8-6B.

Question 8-25 Which of the following might contain a pre-emphasis circuit?

A. FM receiver B. VHF AM transmitter C. single-sideband transmitter D. AM receiver E. FM transmitter

Answer Choice E.

* **Question 8-26** The emission designation for FM telephony is:

A. G3E B. J3E C. F3E D. R3E E. H3E

Answer Choice C.

* **Question 8-27** Which of the following systems contains a VFO and a varactor-diode modulator?

A. direct FM transmitter
B. indirect FM transmitter
C. AM transmitter
D. SSB transmitter
E. FM receiver

Answer Choice A. Refer to FIG. 8-2.

* **Question 8-28** In a direct FM transmitter, a 5-MHz oscillator is modulated by a 300-Hz test tone, which produces a swing of ±1 kHz. If the intermediate amplifiers contain two triplers and a doubler stage, what is the value of the frequency deviation at the output stage?

A. 1 kHz B. 3 kHz C. 6 kHz D. 9 kHz E. 18 kHz

Answer Choice E. Frequency deviation at the output stage:

$$f_d = 3 \times 3 \times 2 \times 1\text{ kHz} = 18\text{ kHz}$$

Question 8-29 In QUES. 8-28, the value of the output modulation index is:

A. 6 B. 60 C. 10 D. 167 E. 3.3

Answer Choice B.

Modulation index:

$$m = \frac{f_d}{f_m} = \frac{18\text{ kHz}}{300\text{ Hz}} = 60 \qquad (8\text{–}1)$$

Question 8-30 In the reactance JFET modulator circuit, the JFET behaves as a (an):

A. inductive reactance
B. capacitive reactance
C. conductance
D. variable resistance
E. either choice A or B

Answer Choice E.

* **Question 8-31** A varactor diode can be used in a (an):

A. direct FM modulator circuit
B. AFC circuit in a direct FM transmitter
C. frequency-multiplier device in the microwave region
D. phase-modulator circuit
E. all of the above choices are true

Answer Choice E.

* **Question 8-32** The percentage modulation of an FM transmitter is determined by the:

A. amplitude of the carrier
B. modulating frequency
C. carrier frequency
D. amplitude of the modulating signal
E. phase angle of the modulating signal

Answer Choice D.

* **Question 8-33** The reactance-modulated oscillator of an FM transmitter operates on 4905 kHz and the output operating frequency is 98.1 MHz. If the output-frequency deviation frequency is 5 kHz, the frequency swing at the oscillator stage is:

A. ± 5 kHz B. ± 500 kHz C. ± 250 kHz D. ± 1 kHz E. ± 100 kHz

Answer Choice C.

$$\textit{Product factor of the multiplier stages} = \frac{98.1 \text{ MHz}}{4905 \text{ kHz}} = 20$$

$$\textit{Oscillator's frequency swing} = \pm\frac{5 \text{ kHz}}{20} = \pm 250 \text{ Hz}$$

* **Question 8-34** The rate at which the frequency swings in an FM transmitter is determined by the:

A. amplitude of the modulating signal
B. modulating frequency
C. carrier frequency
D. phase angle of the modulating signal
E. carrier amplitude

Answer Choice B.

Question 8-35 In an FM transmitter, a frequency deviation of 5 kHz corresponds to 100% modulation. If the transmitter is 50% modulated by a 7000-Hz test tone and the modulating frequency is then reduced to 5000 Hz, the value of the frequency deviation at both frequencies (neglecting pre-emphasis) is:

A. 2.5 kHz at both frequencies
B. 2.5 kHz at 7000 Hz and 1.8 kHz at 5000 Hz
C. 5 kHz at both frequencies
D. 1.8 kHz at 7000 Hz and 2.5 kHz at 5000 Hz
E. 10 kHz at both frequencies

Answer Choice B.

$$\textit{Frequency deviation for 50\% modulation} = (50/100) \times 5 = 2.5 \text{ kHz}$$

Neglecting the effect of pre-emphasis, the frequency deviation is the same at both frequencies.

* **Question 8-36** Pre-emphasis in an FM transmitter means that:

A. the higher audio frequencies (above about 2000 Hz) are progressively accentuated as the audio frequency is increased
B. audio frequencies in the vicinity of 2000 Hz are accentuated
C. the higher audio frequencies (above about 2000 Hz) are progressively attenuated as the audio frequency is increased
D. the frequency band between 2000 Hz and 15000 Hz is uniformly accentuated
E. frequencies up to 2000 Hz are accentuated, but higher frequencies are attenuated

Answer Choice A.

8-4. The indirect FM transmitter

The main problem with the direct method is the complexity of the AFC circuit that is required to achieve the necessary degree of frequency stability. Such stability is mainly determined by the drifts in the crystal oscillator and the input tuned circuits of the discriminator. The indirect method overcomes these difficulties by using a highly stable crystal oscillator to generate the unmodulated carrier; the modulation process is subsequently carried out at a later stage, which produces phase modulation (FIG. 8-8). As explained earlier, the phase modulation can then be converted to the required frequency modulation by the audio-correction network.

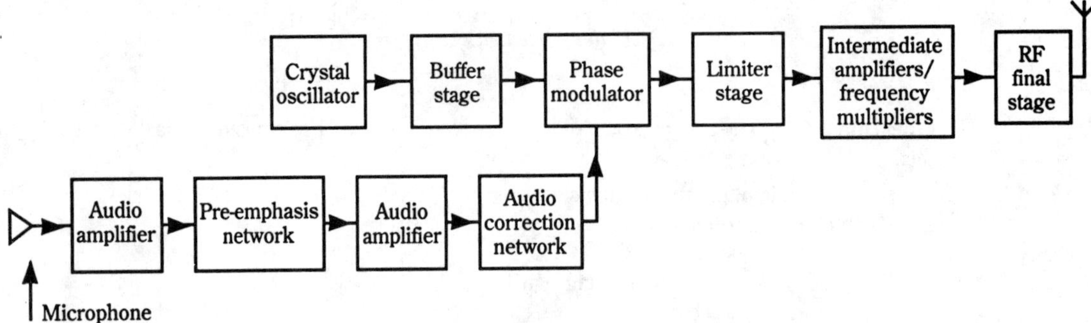

Fig. 8-8 The block diagram of an FM transmitter using the indirect method.

The phase modulator

A simplified version of the phase-modulator circuit is shown in FIG. 8-9. The RF input from the crystal oscillator drives a current, i, through the capacitor, C, and the collector tank circuit across which a voltage e_c, is developed. Because C has a low value of a few picofarads, its reactance is so high that i and e_c both lead v_i by 90°. At the same time, v_i is fed to the base of Q1; the collector current, i_c, is in phase with v_i and passes through the tank circuit, L1C1. A second voltage, e_m, will therefore be developed across the tank circuit and the modulator's output signal is the resultant of e_c and e_m, which are 90° out of phase.

The audio signal is also fed to the Q1 base and amplitude modulates the collector current and the value of e_m; however the value of e_c remains unchanged. The effect of modulation by a single tone is shown in FIG. 8-10A. Provided that the phase angle, ϕ, is small (FIG. 8-10B), its value is directly proportional to the amplitude of the tone. At the peak, X, of the tone cycle, the phase angle has its maximum value; therefore, the rate of change of phase is zero. It follows that the instantaneous RF shift is also zero and that the instantaneous frequency is equal to the unmodulated value, f_c. Consequently, the output signal, e_o, is phase modulated and not frequency modulated. Conversion from PM to FM is achieved by an RC correction network (FIG. 8-11); this circuit also provides a 90° shift for all the components in the audio signal and has an output voltage that is inversely proportional to the modulating frequency.

Notice that the output from the phase modulator fluctuates in amplitude. These amplitudes variations are removed by a following limiter stage.

* **Question 8-37** The emission designation of a phase-modulated telephony signal is:

A. G3E B. F3E C. A3E D. J3E E. R3E

Answer Choice A.

* **Question 8-38** The type of transmitter that contains a crystal oscillator, a varactor diode and an audio correction network is:

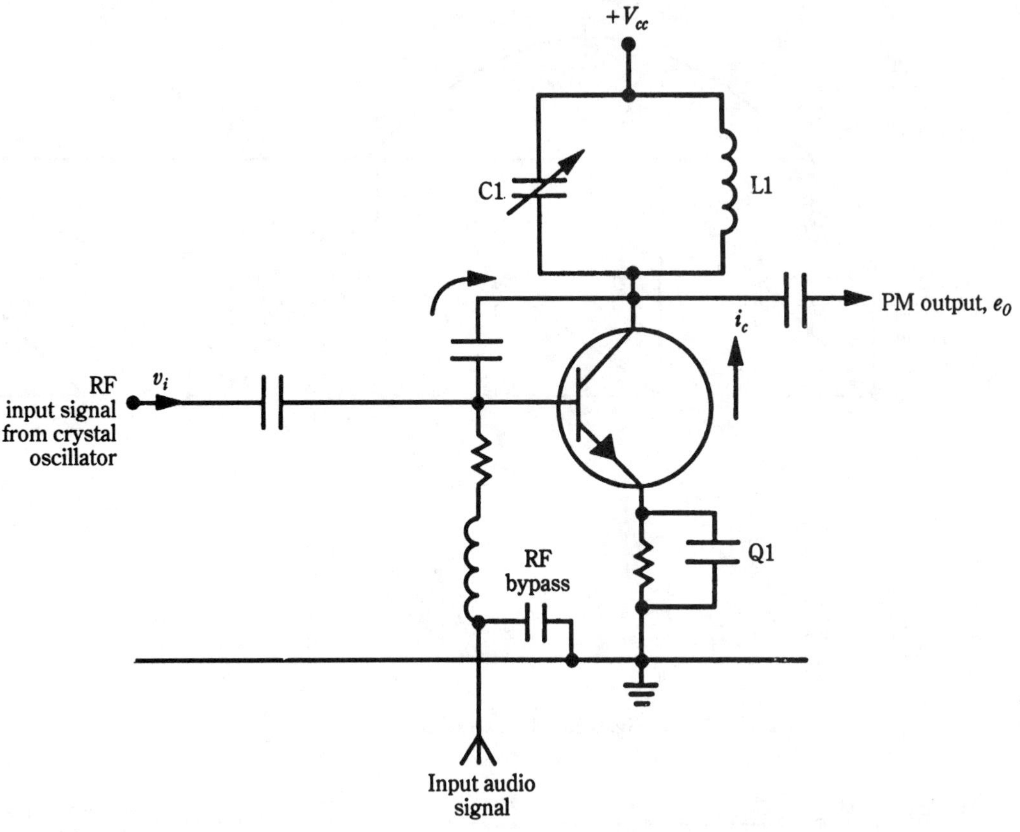

Fig. 8-9 An example of a phase-modulator circuit.

A. AM B. SSB C. direct FM D. indirect FM E. PM

Answer Choice C.

Question 8-39 In a phase-modulated signal, the frequency deviation is directly proportional to the:

A. amplitude of the modulating tone
B. frequency of the modulating tone
C. carrier amplitude
D. carrier frequency
E. product of choices A and B

Answer Choice E.

* **Question 8-40** In a PM transmitter, the amplitude of the audio tone is doubled and the modulating frequency is also doubled. The frequency deviation is:

A. unchanged B. doubled C. multiplied by 4 D. divided by 4 E. halved

Answer Choice C.

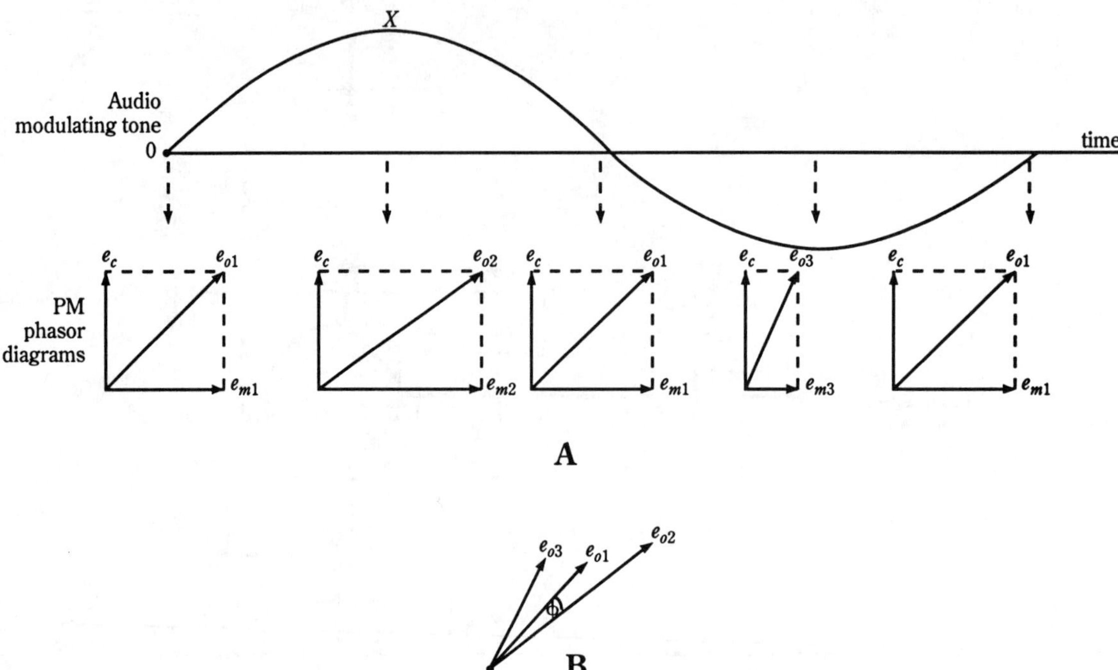

Fig. 8-10 A phasor diagram of the phase modulator.

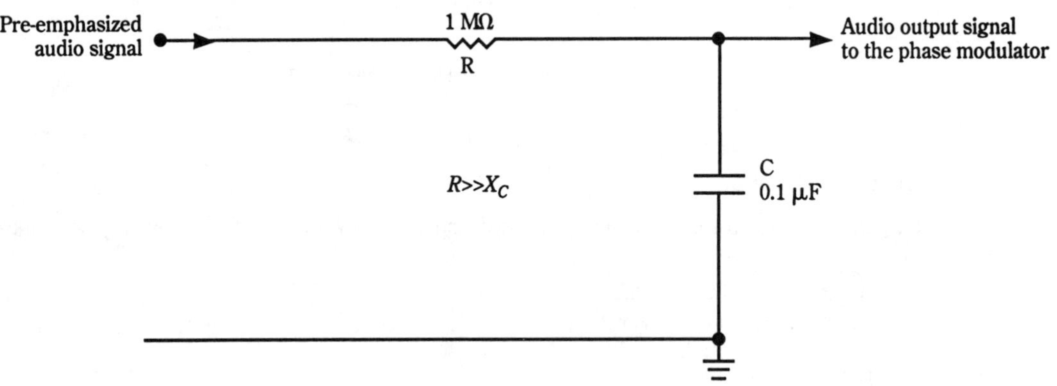

Fig. 8-11 The audio-correction network.

8-5. Frequency-shift keying (FSK) and facsimile

In chapter 5, the keying of a CW transmitter was used to produce an A1A emission, which represented telegraphy (as opposed to telephony). However, the "mark" and "space" intervals present some difficulties to the AM superhet, which must contain a BFO for CW reception. The problem is twofold:

- During the "mark" interval, the AGC bias level is high, but during the "space" interval, the AGC level drops to zero. Unless the AGC filter contains special time-constant circuits, the AGC bias cannot follow the rapid changes between "mark" and "space."
- If a strong code signal is being received, the receiver is quiet during "mark," but during "space," there is no AGC bias and there will be a considerable amount of amplified noise. Consequently, if the code signal is weak and only slightly exceeds the noise level, reception will be extremely difficult.

These problems are overcome if you use a form of frequency modulation known as *Frequency Shift Keying (FSK)*, whose emission designation is F1B. As the name suggests, the carrier is "on" continuously, but its frequency is shifted up and down in accordance with the "mark" and "space" conditions. As shown in FIG. 8-12, the frequency increases during "mark" and falls during "space." FSK is commonly used in teletype systems in which the "mark" frequency is $f_c + 425$ Hz and the "space" frequency is $f_c - 425$ Hz, where f_c is the unmodulated carrier frequency. The difference between the two frequencies is only 850 Hz; both frequencies can be received by tuning the receiver to f_c. Because the amplitude of the FSK signal is constant, the receiver stays in the quieted condition; this is the main advantage of the FSK operation. Its main disadvantage is the greater power requirement for the continuous signal, as opposed to the interrupted signal with ON/OFF keying.

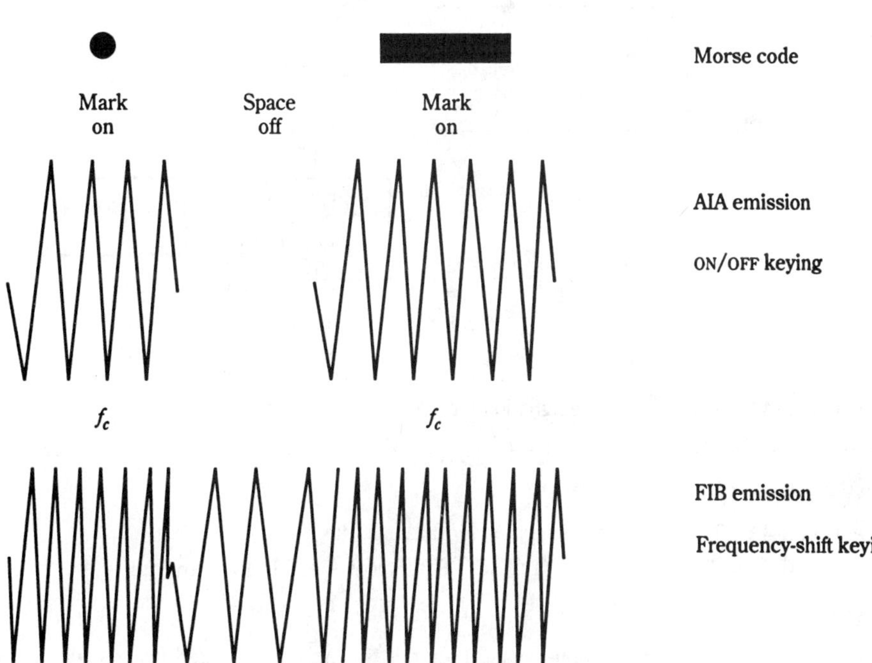

Fig. 8-12 A comparison between ON/OFF keying and frequency-shift keying.

Figure 8-13 illustrates the various types of modulation and their associated designations. Notice the inclusions of the A3C and F3C emissions for facsimile. Over the last decade, there has been a commercial boom in the use of facsimile (fax), which is used to transmit fixed images (such as documents, photographs, and weather maps). The information is conveyed over a line or by means of a radio wave; in the case of a radio wave, the fax system can employ either AM or FM.

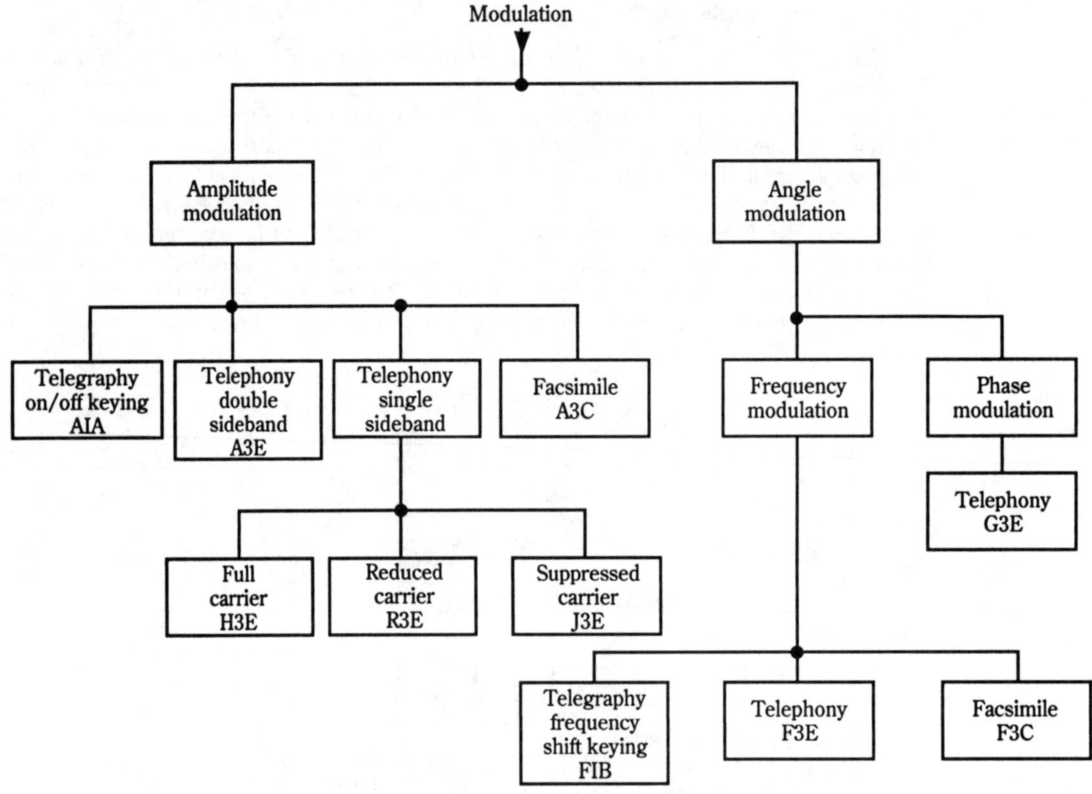

Fig. 8-13 Types of modulation.

Question 8-41 The emission designation for frequency shift keying (FSK) is:

A. A1A B. A1B C. F1A D. F1B E. F2C

Answer Choice D.

Question 8-42 The emission designation for facsimile (fax) is:

A. A3E B. F4E C. A4E D. F3C E. choices A and D are both true

Answer Choice E.

* **Question 8-43** A communications system for the transmission of fixed images that are recorded in a permanent form is called:

A. teletype B. telegraphy C. facsimile D. image projection E. radio photography

Answer Choice C.

* **Question 8-44** The main advantage of Frequency Shift Keying over ON/OFF keying is:

A. its narrower bandwidth
B. the improvement in the receiver's quieting
C. the receiver's AGC bias is maintained at a less constant level
D. its greater power requirement
E. choices B and C are true

Answer Choice B.

9
The FM receiver

In this chapter you will learn:

- about the block diagram of a single conversion FM receiver and how it differs from that of a comparable AM receiver.
- about the purpose and operation of the limiter stage.
- about the purpose and operation of a Foster-Seeley discriminator.
- how a de-emphasis circuit is used to compensate for the pre-emphasis in the FM transmitter.

9-1. Introduction to the FM receiver

Figure 9-1 shows a block diagram of an FM superheterodyne receiver. Although the principle of frequency conversion is the same as that in the AM receiver, the two types of receivers have a number of significant differences:

- The FM signal occupies a wide bandwidth, which must be accommodated by the IF stages. The value of the IF itself must be much higher and is 10.7 MHz in the commercial FM broadcast band (88 to 108 MHz). Because the image channel is separated from the wanted signal by $2 \times 10.7 = 21.4$ MHz, no FM station is the image of another FM station. However, a commonly used aeronautical frequency is 121.5 MHz and this can cause image interference to FM reception.
- A high IF value reduces the amount of freedom from adjacent-channel interference, while a low IF value increases the possibility of image-channel problems. A double-conversion system attempts to have "the best of both worlds." Following the antenna, the first frequency-conversion circuit typically uses a high IF of several MHz to further reduce the possibility of image-channel interference. This is then followed by a second conversion circuit with a low IF of 200 kHz or less in order to achieve a high degree of freedom from adjacent-channel interference.

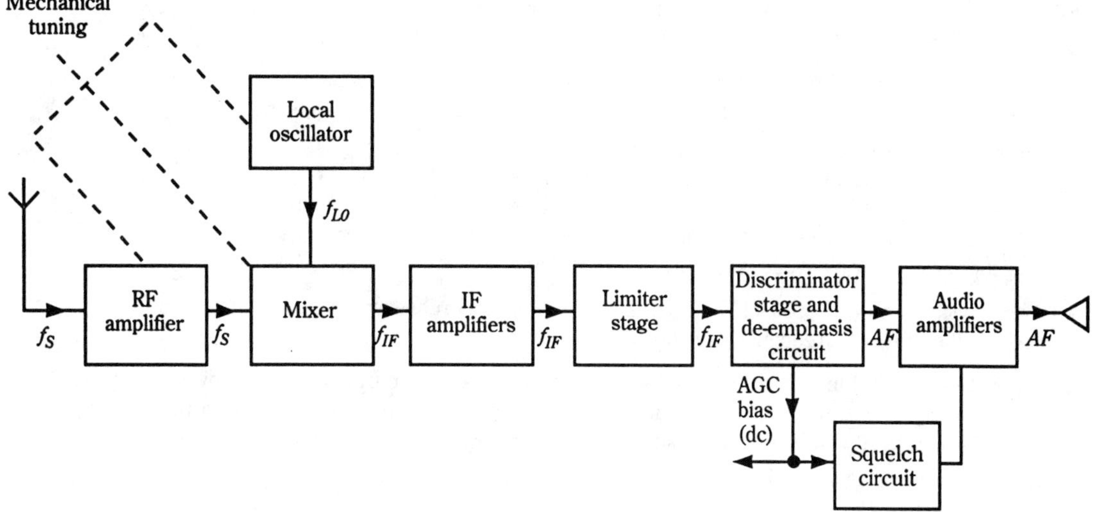

Fig. 9-1 The FM superheterodyne receiver.

- The final IF amplifier is a limiter stage, which removes all amplitude variations from the FM signal before the signal is passed to the discriminator.
- The AM detector is replaced by the combination of an FM discriminator and a de-emphasis circuit.

* **Question 9-1** An FM broadcast receiver is tuned to 98.9 MHz and is experiencing interference from an aircraft that is transmitting on 121.3 MHz. The most probable cause of this difficulty is:

A. crossmodulation B. intermodulation C. adjacent-channel interference D. image-channel interference E. propagation fading

Answer Choice D. The difference frequency between 98.9 MHz and 121.3 MHz is $121.3 - 98.9 = 21.4$ MHz, which is equal to 2×10.7 MHz or twice the value of the receiver's IF. Consequently, the problem is caused by image-channel interference.

* **Question 9-2** An FM receiver is tuned to a carrier frequency of 157.0 MHz. If its local oscillator is generating an output whose frequency is 167.7 MHz, the frequency of the image channel is:

A. 21.4 MHz B. 146.3 MHz C. 135.6 MHz D. 190.1 MHz E. 178.4 MHz

Answer Choice E. The value of the IF is $167.7 - 157.0 = 10.7$ MHz. The image-channel frequency is $167.7 + 10.7$ (or $157 + 2 \times 10.7$) $= 178.4$ MHz.

* **Question 9-3** An FM receiver whose IF is 10.7 MHz, is experiencing image-channel interference from a station transmitting on 121.1 MHz. If the local oscillator is tracking above, the receiver is tuned to:

A. 131.8 MHz B. 142.5 MHz C. 110.4 MHz D. 21.4 MHz E. 99.7 MHz

Answer Choice E. The receiver is tuned to $121.1 - 2 \times 10.7 = 99.7$ MHz.

* **Question 9-4** In QUES. 9-3, the receiver's local oscillator is generating a frequency of:

A. 110.4 MHz B. 10.7 MHz C. 99.7 MHz D. 131.8 MHz E. 142.5 MHz

Answer Choice A. The receiver's local oscillator is generating a frequency of 121.1 − 10.7 = 110.4 MHz.

* **Question 9-5** If an FM transmitter is producing strong harmonics, how would its signal be heard on an FM receiver that is tuned to the second harmonic of the carrier frequency?

A. only odd harmonics are generated by an FM transmitter
B. the audio signal on the loudspeaker would be unintelligible
C. the signal is received and is intelligible, but the modulation index is halved
D. the signal is received and is intelligible, but the frequency deviation is doubled
E. the signal is received and is intelligible, but its bandwidth is reduced

Answer Choice D. The product factor of the transmitter's frequency multiplier stages is doubled and therefore the frequency deviation is doubled.

* **Question 9-6** An FM broadcast receiver is experiencing interference from an airport tower's transmitter, which is operating on 121.4 MHz. If the receiver is tuned to a station whose carrier frequency is close to 100 MHz, the most likely reason for the problem is:

A. mistuning of the transmitter's wave traps
B. intermodulation
C. misalignment of the receiver's IF amplifiers
D. image-channel interference
E. harmonic interference.

Answer Choice D.

* **Question 9-7** An FM broadcast receiver intercepts a 120-MHz transmission from an aircraft in the vicinity. The most probable cause for this interference is:

A. an inadequate ground connection at the input to the receiver
B. a harmonic of the IF (10.7 MHz), which is close to 120 MHz
C. intermodulation between the aircraft's transmitter and a powerful transmitter in the vicinity
D. crossmodulation in the IF stages of the receiver
E. poor image-channel rejection by the receiver

Answer Choice E.

* **Question 9-8** The frequency of the input signal to a double-conversion superhet receiver is 156.7 MHz. If the frequency of the second oscillator is 10.114 MHz, the frequency of the first local oscillator is:

A. 146 MHz B. 146.664 MHz C. 20.814 MHz D. 135.98 MHz E. 21.4 MHz

Answer Choice B. The frequency of the second IF must be 200 kHz or less. For Choice A, the first IF is 156.7 − 146 = 10.7 MHz and the second IF is 10.7 − 10.114 MHz = 586 kHz, which is too high. With Choice B, the first IF is 156.7 − 146.664 = 10.036 MHz, and the second IF is 10.144 − 10.036 MHz = 108 kHz.

9-2. The FM limiter stage

External noise, such as static, primarily amplitude modulates the FM signal. By contrast, internal receiver noise from the active devices and the circuitry creates both amplitude and phase modulation. Virtually all of the AM noise is removed by the limiter stage, and the PM noise can be reduced by using a wide-band, as opposed to a narrow-band system.

The schematic of a typical limiter stage is shown in FIG. 9-2A. The dropper resistor, R, ensures that the JFET is operated with a low drain supply voltage and is therefore easily saturated by weak FM signals of the order of 0.5 V. In addition, the flow of the gate current charges the capacitor, C_g, which subsequently discharges through R_g. The time constant, R_gC_g, is sufficiently short to allow the signal bias to follow rapid fluctuations in the FM signal's amplitude; as a result, there is a limiting effect on the positive peaks of the input signal (FIG. 9-2B). Amplitude variations on the negative peaks are limited by the cut-off action of the JFET. To summarize, the limiter stage has a low, but constant, gain and is operated from a reduced dc supply voltage. Notice that the JFET in FIG. 9-2A is neutralized by the capacitor, C_N.

The presence of the limiter appears to eliminate the necessity for an AGC system. However, such a system might be needed to avoid overdriving the limiter stage. Any strong input signal to the limiter might reduce the angle of the drain current flow to the point where the output to the discriminator starts to fall off. In addition, the AGC bias voltage can be used to operate a squelch circuit.

* **Question 9-9** The stage that feeds into the discriminator of an FM receiver is the:

A. local oscillator
B. first IF amplifier
C. mixer stage
D. RF amplifier
E. final IF amplifier, which also acts as a limiter stage

Answer Choice E.

* **Question 9-10** The purpose of the limiter stage in an FM receiver, is to:

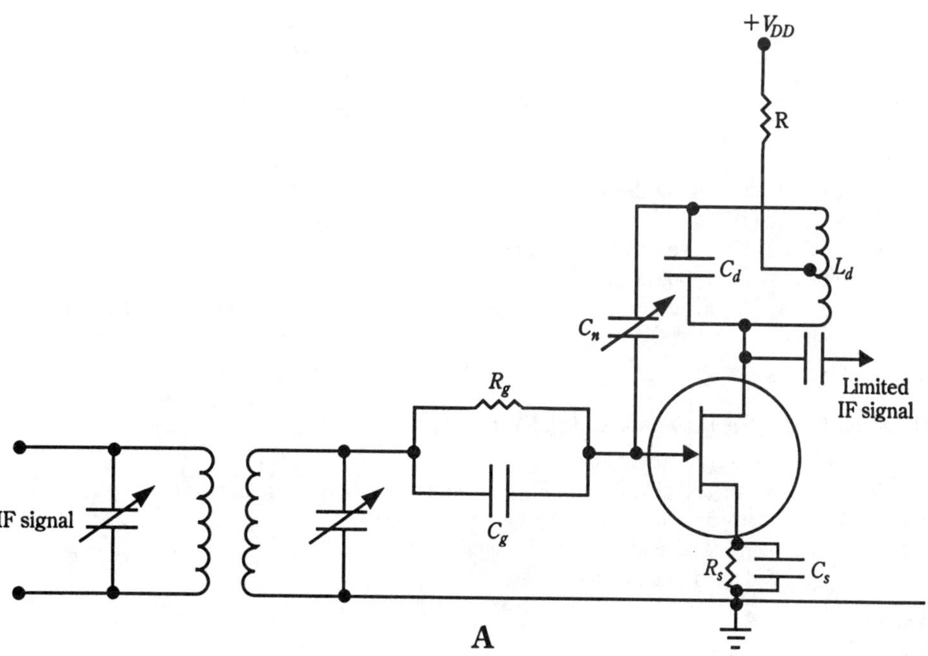

Fig. 9-2 The limiter stage.

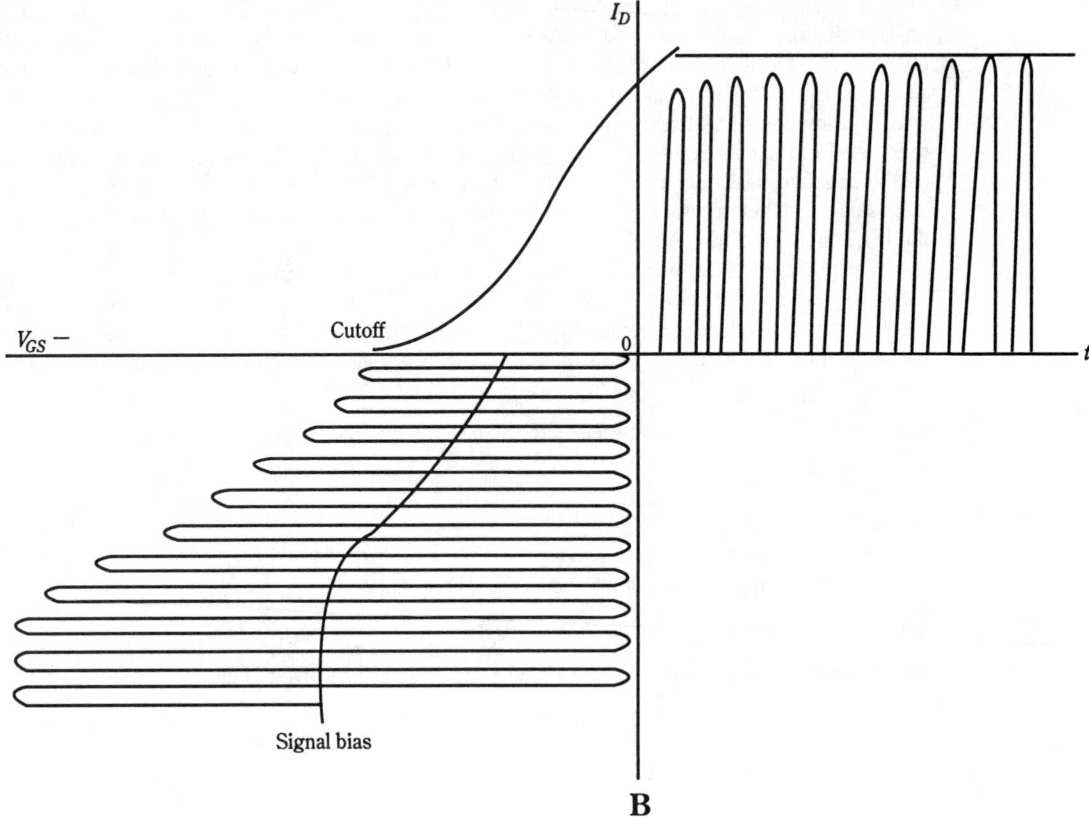

Fig. 9-2 Continued

A. prevent "blasting" of the loudspeaker
B. detect the IF signal
C. provide the required level of AGC bias
D. substitute for a squelch circuit
E. stop any amplitude modulation of the IF signal from being applied to the discriminator stage

Answer Choice E.

* **Question 9-11** The limiter stage of an FM receiver:

A. follows the discriminator stage
B. has a low gain and provides an IF signal with a relatively constant amplitude
C. feeds directly into the de-emphasis circuit
D. provide considerable gain for the IF signal
E. is operated from a high-voltage source

Answer Choice B.

* **Question 9-12** The limiter stage of an FM receiver:

A. feeds directly into the discriminator circuit
B. is an IF amplifier with a low gain

C. operates from a low dc voltage supply
D. is used to improve the signal-to-noise ratio in the output from the final audio stage
E. all of the above choices are true

Answer Choice E.

* **Question 9-13** The limiter stage of an FM receiver:

A. prevents any amplitude modulation of the IF signal, because of noise, from being passed through the discriminator
B. prevents any frequency- or phase-modulated noise from affecting the discriminator
C. limits the amount of frequency deviation in the IF signal
D. limits the overall bandwidth of the IF stages
E. both choices A and B are true

Answer Choice A.

* **Question 9-14** The limiter stage in an FM receiver is located:

A. immediately before the discriminator and has a low gain with a relatively constant output
B. between the mixer stage and the first IF amplifier
C. located immediately after the de-emphasis circuit and has a high gain with a relatively constant output
D. immediately before the mixer stage and has a low gain with a relatively constant output
E. immediately after the discriminator stage and has a high gain with a relatively constant output

Answer Choice A.

* **Question 9-15** The limiter stage of an FM receiver:

A. limits the amplitude of the IF signal to the required level
B. removes all AM noise from the IF signal
C. behaves as a low-pass filter
D. behaves as a high-pass filter
E. choices A and B are true

Answer Choice E.

* **Question 9-16** Which of the following stages in an FM receiver is responsible for drastically reducing the effect of static noise during the reception of a signal?

A. de-emphasis circuit
B. limiter stage
C. Foster-Seeley discriminator
D. mixer stage
E. squelch circuit

Answer Choice B.

9-3. The discriminator stage

One of the most common types of FM detector is the *Foster-Seeley discriminator* (FIG. 9-3). The function of this circuit is to provide an instantaneous audio voltage, which is directly proportional to the amount of instantaneous frequency deviation from the value of the IF (10.7 MHz).

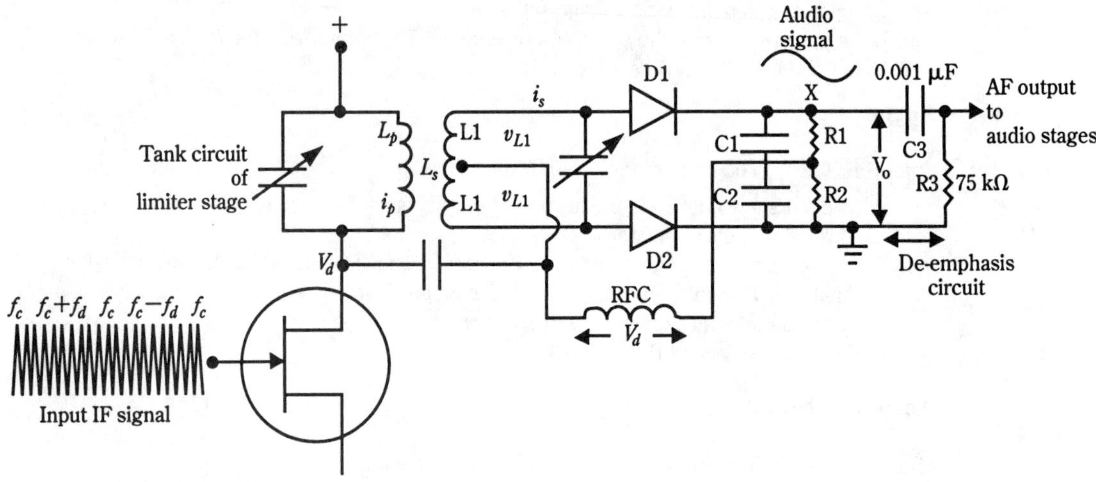

Fig. 9-3 The Foster-Seeley discriminator and the deemphasis circuit.

The operation of the Foster-Seeley discriminator is best explained in terms of phasor diagrams. Assume that the IF signal has been frequency modulated by an audio test tone and that the instantaneous frequency of the input signal is equal to the value of the IF; it is therefore required that the output voltage, v_o, must be instantaneously zero.

The horizontal reference phasor (FIG. 9-4) is the IF voltage, v_d, at the drain of the limiter's JFET. The primary current, i_p, lags v_d by 90° while the secondary voltage, v_s, (mutually induced in the coil, L_s) lags i_p by a further 90° so that v_p and v_s are 180° out of phase (assuming that the primary and secondary coils are wound in the same sense). Because the secondary circuit is resonant at the incoming frequency, the secondary current, i_s, will be in phase with v_s and the voltage, v_L, across L_s will lead i_s by 90°. With respect to the secondary's center-tap, v_{L1} and v_{L2} are 180° out of phase and the voltage across the RF choke is virtually equal to v_d. The IF voltage, v_{D1}, is applied to diode D1 and is the phasor sum of v_{L1} and v_d. Similarly, the voltage v_{D2}, is applied to the diode D2 and is the phasor sum of v_{L2} and v_d. Because v_{D1} and v_{D2} have the same magnitude, the two diodes conduct equally and charge capacitors C_1 and C_2 to the same voltage. However, the voltages across these capacitors are series-opposing, so the output voltage, v_o, is instantaneously zero.

When the instantaneous input frequency rises to the value of $f_{IF} + f_d$, the directions of the v_d, i_p, and v_s phasors remain unchanged (FIG. 9-4). However, the secondary circuit of L_s and C_s now behaves inductively, with respect to the input frequency; consequently, i_s lags v_s by the phase angle, ϕ. The voltage, v_{D1}, is now larger than v_{D2} so that diode D1 conducts more than diode D2. The capacitor, C_1, is charged to a higher voltage than C_2 and the instantaneous output voltage, v_o, is at its maximum possible value.

Now let the instantaneous input frequency fall to $f_{IF} - f_d$ (FIG. 9-4). The secondary circuit becomes capacitive so that i_s leads v_s by the angle, ϕ. Diode D2 carries the larger current so that V_{C2} is greater than V_{C1} and the instantaneous output voltage, V_o, is at its maximum negative value. It follows that one complete sequence of the input signal's frequency variations will result in one cycle of the audio voltage at the discriminator's output point, X.

As described in chapter 8, the modulating signal at the transmitter is pre-emphasized in order to accentuate the higher audio frequencies, and thereby improve their signal-to-noise ra-

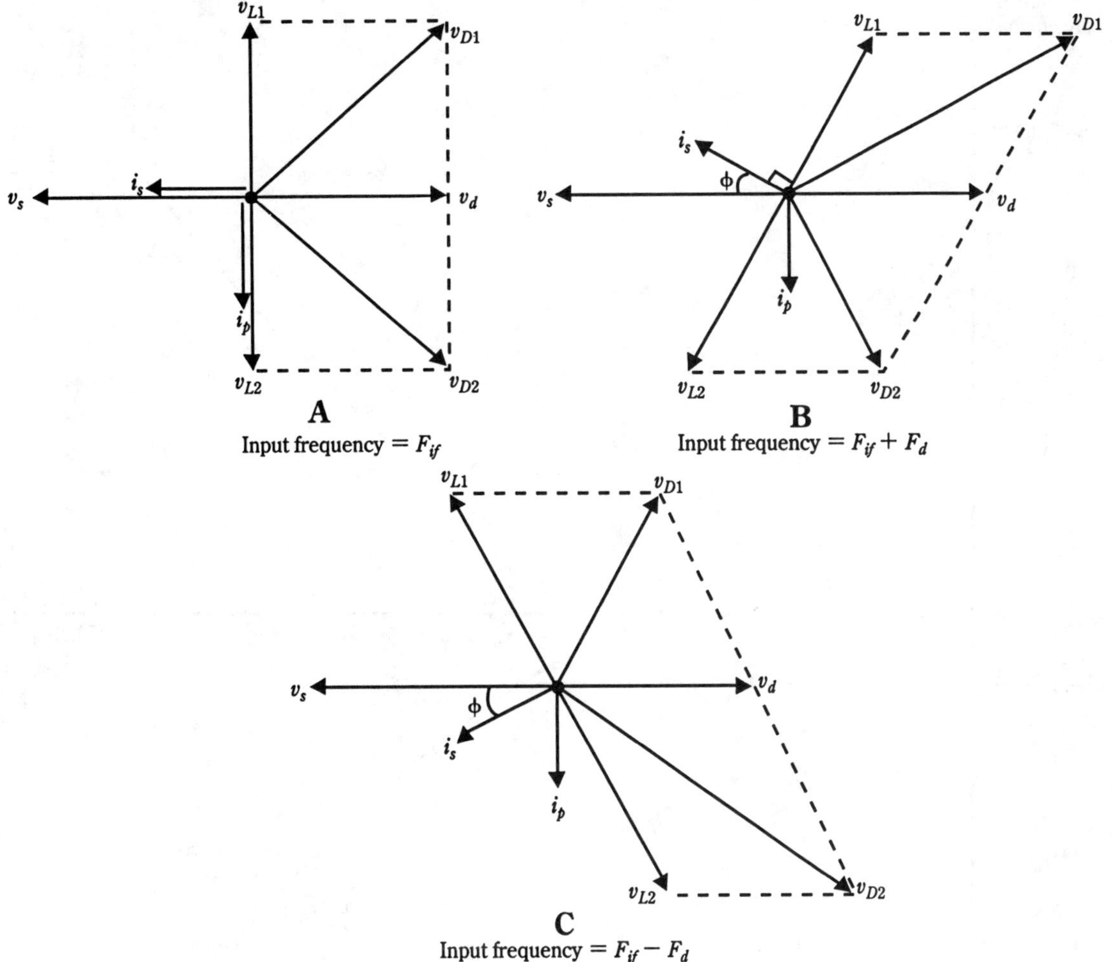

Fig. 9-4 Phasor analysis of the Foster-Seeley discriminator.

tios. It is necessary to restore the tonal balance in the receiver by applying the discriminator output voltage, V_o, to the de-emphasis circuit, C_3R_3, with its time constant of 75 kΩ × 0.001 μF = 75 μs. If the audio frequency increases, the reactance of the capacitor, C_3, decreases, and the output to the audio amplifiers is reduced. The graph of the attenuation versus frequency for the de-emphasis circuit is illustrated in FIG. 9-5; as required, the pre-emphasis and de-emphasis curves are "mirror" images.

Notice that in aligning an FM receiver, you are required to work backward from the discriminator to the antenna. The first stage to be aligned is the discriminator, in which the input tuned circuits are adjusted to resonance. The test FM signal is therefore applied to the base of the limiter circuit.

After the IF stages have all been aligned, the next stage to align is the local oscillator and the RF amplifier.

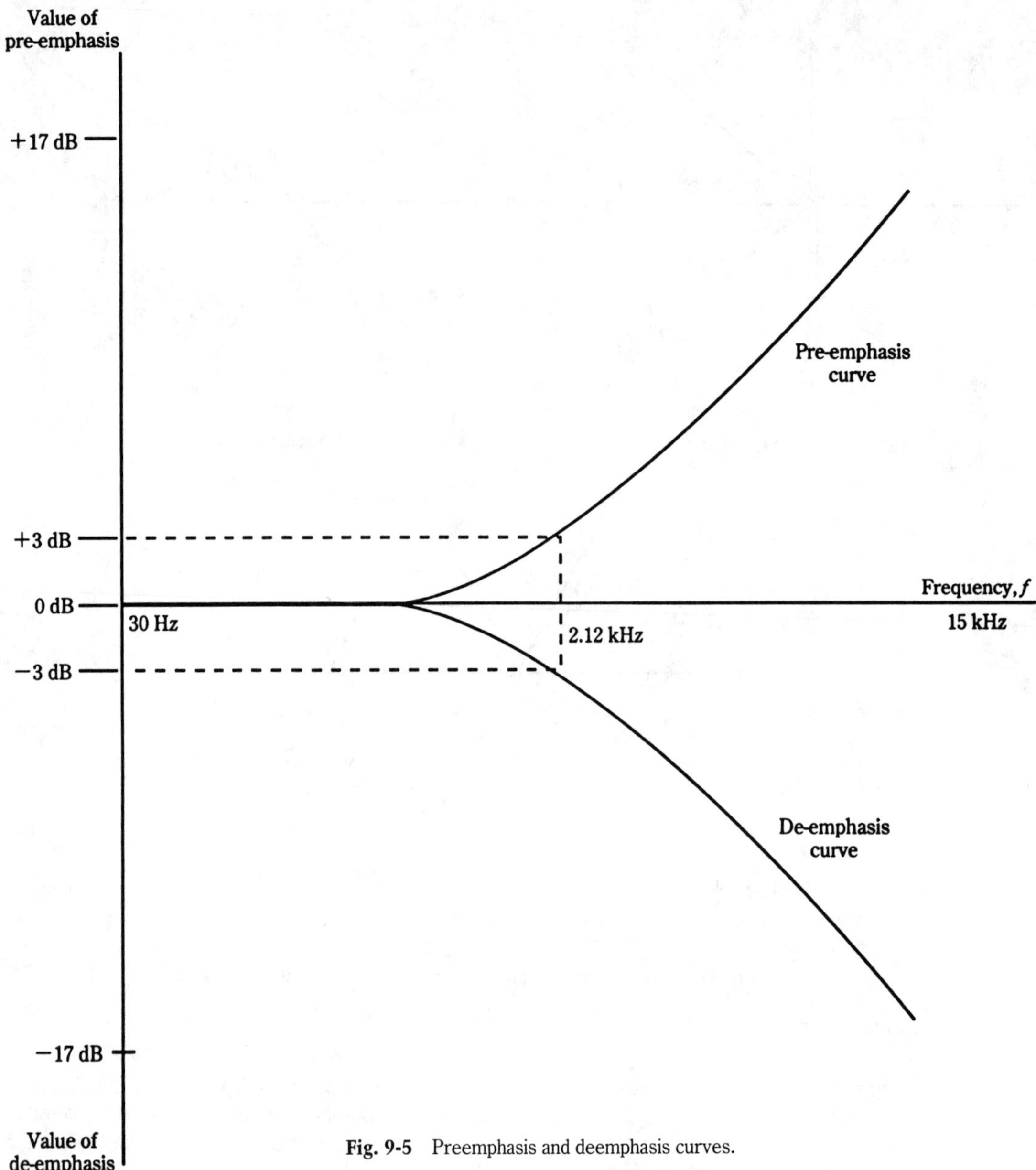

Fig. 9-5 Preemphasis and deemphasis curves.

* **Question 9-17** What defect, if any, exists in the circuit of FIG. 9-6?

A. the RFC choke is not required
B. the diode (D1) must be reversed
C. the diode (D2) must be reversed
D. C1 should be removed
E. the circuit is grounded at the wrong point

Answer Choice E. Refer to FIG. 9-3.

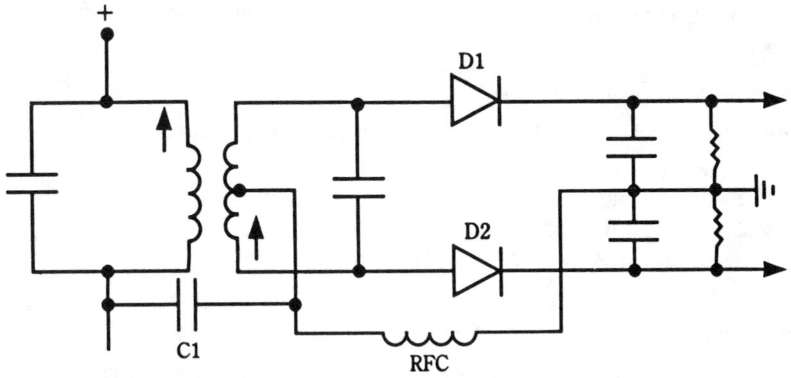

Fig. 9-6 The circuit for question 9-17.

Question 9-18 The diagram of FIG. 9-7 is a:

A. pre-emphasis circuit
B. de-emphasis circuit
C. limiter
D. low-pass filter
E. band-pass filter

Answer Choice B. Refer to FIG. 9-3. The diagram is that of a de-emphasis circuit, with a time constant of 75 μs.

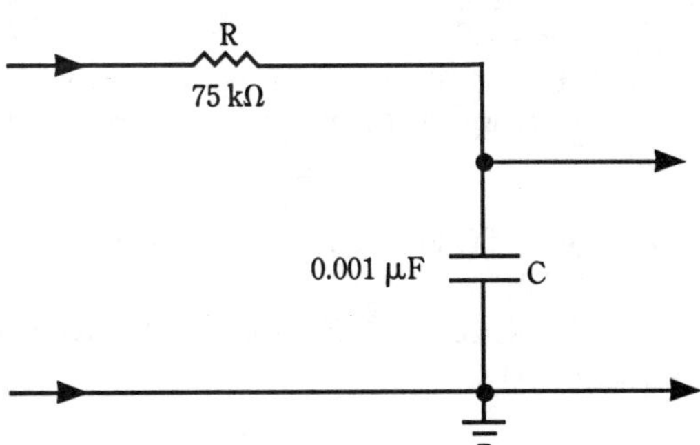

Fig. 9-7 The circuit for question 9-18.

Question 9-19 The de-emphasis circuit in an FM receiver is used to:

A. attenuate low-frequency components in order to restore the tonal balance of the audio signal
B. accentuate high-frequency components in order to restore the tonal balance of the audio signal
C. accentuate low-frequency components in order to restore the tonal balance of the audio signal
D. attenuate high-frequency components in order to restore the tonal balance of the audio signal

E. attenuate low audio-frequency components and accentuate high audio-frequency components

Answer Choice D. Refer to FIG. 9-5.

Question 9-20 Which of the following may contain a de-emphasis circuit?

A. FM receiver
B. VHF AM transmitter
C. double-sideband AM receiver
D. single-sideband AM receiver
E. FM transmitter

Answer Choice A.

* **Question 9-21** Which of the following systems contains a limiter stage, a discriminator, and a de-emphasis circuit?

A. a direct FM transmitter
B. an indirect FM transmitter
C. a single-sideband AM receiver
D. a double-sideband AM receiver
E. an FM receiver

Answer Choice E.

Question 9-22 De-emphasis in an FM receiver means that:

A. the higher audio frequencies, above about 2000 Hz, are progressively attenuated as the audio frequency is increased
B. audio frequencies in the vicinity of 2000 Hz are attenuated
C. the higher audio frequencies, above about 2000 Hz, are progressively accentuated as the audio frequency is increased
D. the frequency band between 2000 and 15,000 Hz is uniformly attenuated
E. frequencies up to 2000 Hz are attenuated, but higher frequencies are accentuated

Answer Choice A.

* **Question 9-23** The IF stages of an FM receiver have been aligned. The next stage to align is the:

A. RF amplifier B. limiter stage C. local oscillator D. mixer stage
E. antenna-coupling circuit

Answer Choice C.

* **Question 9-24** The purpose of an FM discriminator stage is to:

A. convert amplitude variations of the IF signal into audio information
B. improve the signal-to-noise ratio of the audio signal
C. convert frequency variations of the IF signal into audio information
D. de-emphasize the FM signal before its detection
E. reverse the pre-emphasis process, which occurred in the FM transmitter

Answer Choice C.

Question 9-25 When aligning an FM receiver, the first step is to introduce the test signal at the:

A. base of the first stage
B. antenna circuit

C. gate of the limiter stage
D. base of the RF stage
E. output point of the discriminator circuit

Answer Choice C.

* **Question 9-26** A high signal-to-noise ratio is achieved in an FM receiver by:

A. the use of pre-emphasis in the transmitter and de-emphasis in the receiver
B. using a wide band system, as opposed to a narrow-band system
C. the presence of the limiter stage in the receiver
D. designing the RF amplifier to provide high gain with the minimum introduction of internal receiver noise
E. all of the above choices are true

Answer Choice E.

Question 9-27 In an FM receiver, which stage has the IF signal as its input and the audio signal as its output?

A. limiter B. discriminator C. de-emphasis circuit D. mixer E. IF amplifier

Answer Choice B.

* **Question 9-28** Which of the following is an advantage of an FM receiver over an AM receiver?

A. simpler alignment procedure
B. better signal-to-noise ratio
C. smaller audio range
D. lower bandwidth
E. operation at low carrier frequencies

Answer Choice B.

10 Transmission lines, antennas, and propagation

In this chapter you will learn:

- about the distributed electrical properties of transmission lines and the meaning of the surge impedance.
- how a transmission line can be matched to its load termination and about the desirable properties of such a line.
- about the production of standing waves on open-circuited and short-circuited lines.
- how the voltage standing-wave ratio is used to measure the degree of mismatch between a transmission line and its load.
- about the properties of the Hertz dipole.
- how to produce a directional antenna with the aid of parasitic elements.
- how stacked antennas are used to produce a directional antenna array.
- how to calculate the power gain of a complex antenna system.
- about the properties of a Marconi antenna.
- about the factors that control the value of the field strength at a position in the vicinity of a transmitting antenna.
- about the properties of the parabolic dish and its use in a microwave antenna system.
- about the various ways in which a radio wave can travel from a transmitter to a receiver.

10-1. Introduction to transmission lines

Types of transmission lines

Practical considerations require an antenna to be located some distance from its associated transmitter or receiver. A means must, therefore, be provided to transfer the RF power between the equipment and the antenna. Basically, an RF transmission line electrically connects an antenna and a transmitter or a receiver. It must do so efficiently with a minimum loss of power or signal strength.

The four general types of transmission line are: the parallel two-wire line, the twisted pair, the shielded pair, and the concentric (coaxial) line. The use of a particular type of line depends, among other things, on the frequency, the power to be transmitted, and the type of insulation. However, at microwave frequencies, specialized transmission lines are normally used, such as waveguides.

The *two-wire line* (FIG. 10-1A) consists of two parallel conductors that are maintained at a fixed distance apart by means of insulating spacers or spreaders that are placed at suitable intervals. The line has the assets of ease of construction, economy, and efficiency. In practice, such lines used in radio work are generally spaced from 5 to 15 cm apart at frequencies of 14 MHz and below. The maximum spacing for frequencies of 18 MHz and above is 10 cm. In order to keep the radiation from the line at a minimum, it is necessary that the wires be separated by only a small fraction of a wavelength. For best results, the separation should be less than one hundredth of a wavelength.

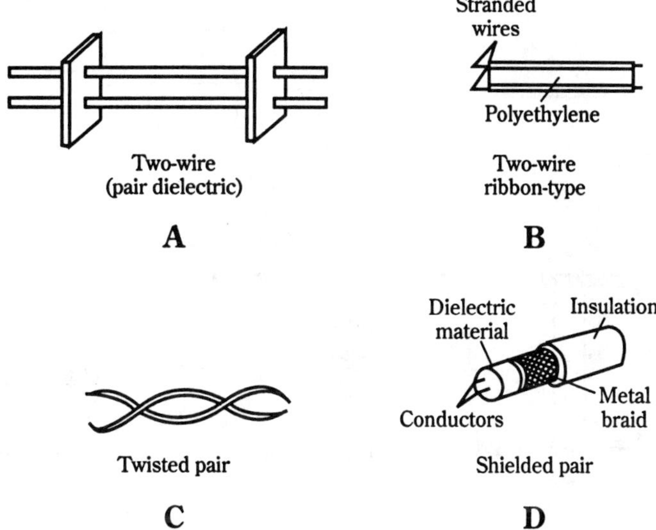

Fig. 10-1 Examples of transmission lines.

At very high frequencies, this criterion will limit the amount of the RF power that can be conveyed by a line. Consequently, the principal disadvantage of the parallel two-wire line is its relatively high radiation loss.

Uniform spacing of a two-wire transmission line can be assured if the wires are embedded in a solid low-loss dielectric, such as polyethylene (FIG. 10-1B). This so-called ribbon type of line is widely used to connect television receivers to their antennas.

The *twisted pair transmission line* is shown in FIG. 10-1C. As the name implies, it consists of two insulated wires that are twisted to form a flexible line without the use of spacers. It is typically used for low-frequency transmission because at the higher frequencies, there is excessive loss occurring in the insulation.

The *shielded pair* (FIG. 10-1D) consists of two parallel conductors that are separated from each other and surrounded by a solid dielectric. The conductors are contained within a copper-braid tubing that acts as a shield. This assembly is covered with a rubber or flexible composition coating to protect the line against moisture.

The principal advantage of the shielded pair is that the two conductors are balanced, with respect to ground, that is, the capacitance between each conductor and the ground is uniform along the entire length of the line, and the wires are shielded against any pickup from stray fields. This balance is achieved by the grounded shield that surrounds the conductors with a uniform spacing through their length.

Coaxial cables are the most widely used type of RF transmission line. They consist of a outer conductor and an inner conductor that is held in place exactly at the center of the outer conductor.

Several types of coaxial cable has come into wide use for feeding RF power to an antenna system. Figure 10-2A illustrates the construction of flexible and rigid coaxial cables. In both cases, one of the conductors is placed inside the other. Because the outer conductor completely shields the inner one, no radiation loss occurs. This is the main advantage of the coaxial line.

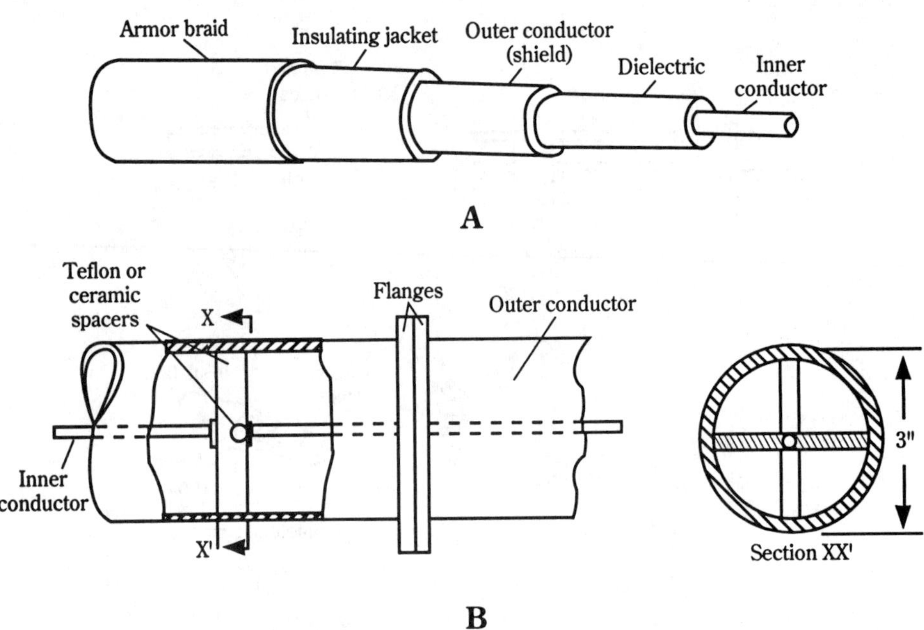

Fig. 10-2 Flexible and rigid coaxial cables.

Distributed electrical constants and the surge impedance

In previous chapters, you were concerned with so-called *lumped circuitry,* where the three electrical properties (resistance, inductance, and capacitance) were related to specific components. For example, a resistor was regarded as being a "lump" of resistance, and all connecting wires were considered to be perfect conductors. By contrast, the resistance, R, associated with a two-wire transmission line is not concentrated into a lump, but is distributed along the entire length of the line. The distributed constant of resistance is therefore measured in the basic unit of *ohms per meter,* rather than ohms.

Because the straight wires of the parallel line are conducting surfaces separated by an insulator or dielectric, the line will possess the distributed constants of self-inductance, L (henrys per meter), and capacitance, C (farads per meter). In addition, no insulator is perfect. Consequently, there is another distributed constant, G (siemens per meter), which is the leakage conductance between the wires. These four distributed constants are illustrated in FIG. 10-3; their order of values in a practical line are *R*: mΩ/m; *L*: μH/m, *C*: pF/m, and *G*: nS/m.

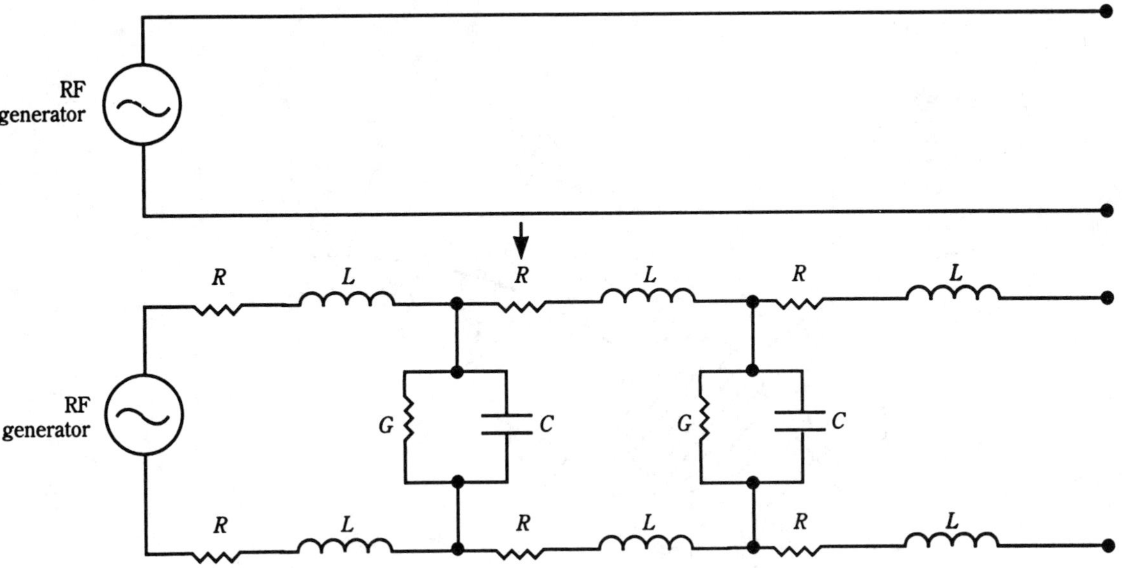

Fig. 10-3 Distributed electrical constants of a two-wire line.

In physical terms, the properties of resistance and leakage conductance will relate to the line's power loss in the form of the heat dissipated and will therefore govern the degree of attenuation, which is measured in decibels per meter (dB/m). The self-inductance results in a magnetic field surrounding the wires, while the capacitance means that an electric field exists between the wires (FIG. 10-4); these L and C properties determine the line's behavior in relation to the frequency.

The two-wire ribbon line that connects an antenna to its TV receiver is often referred to as a *300-Ω line*. But what is the meaning of the 300 Ω? Certainly you cannot find this value with an ohmmeter so you are led to the conclusion that it only appears under working conditions when the line is being used to convey RF power. In fact, the 300-Ω value refers to the line's *surge* or *characteristic impedance* whose letter symbol is Z_o. The surge impedance is theoretically defined as the input impedance at the RF generator to an infinite length of the line (FIGS. 10-5A, and B). In the equivalent circuit of FIG. 10-5B, the *C* and *G* line constants will complete the path for current to flow so that an effective current, *I*, will be drawn from the RF generator whose effective output voltage is *E*. Then the input impedance is:

$$Z_i = Z_o = \frac{E}{I} \text{ ohms } (\Omega) \qquad (10\text{-}1)$$

For a low line that is operating at radio frequencies, $\omega L >> R$ and $\omega C >> G$.

Then:

$$Z_o \approx \sqrt{\frac{L}{C}} \angle 0° \text{ ohms } (\Omega) \qquad (10\text{-}2)$$

where: ω = *angular frequency* (rad./s)

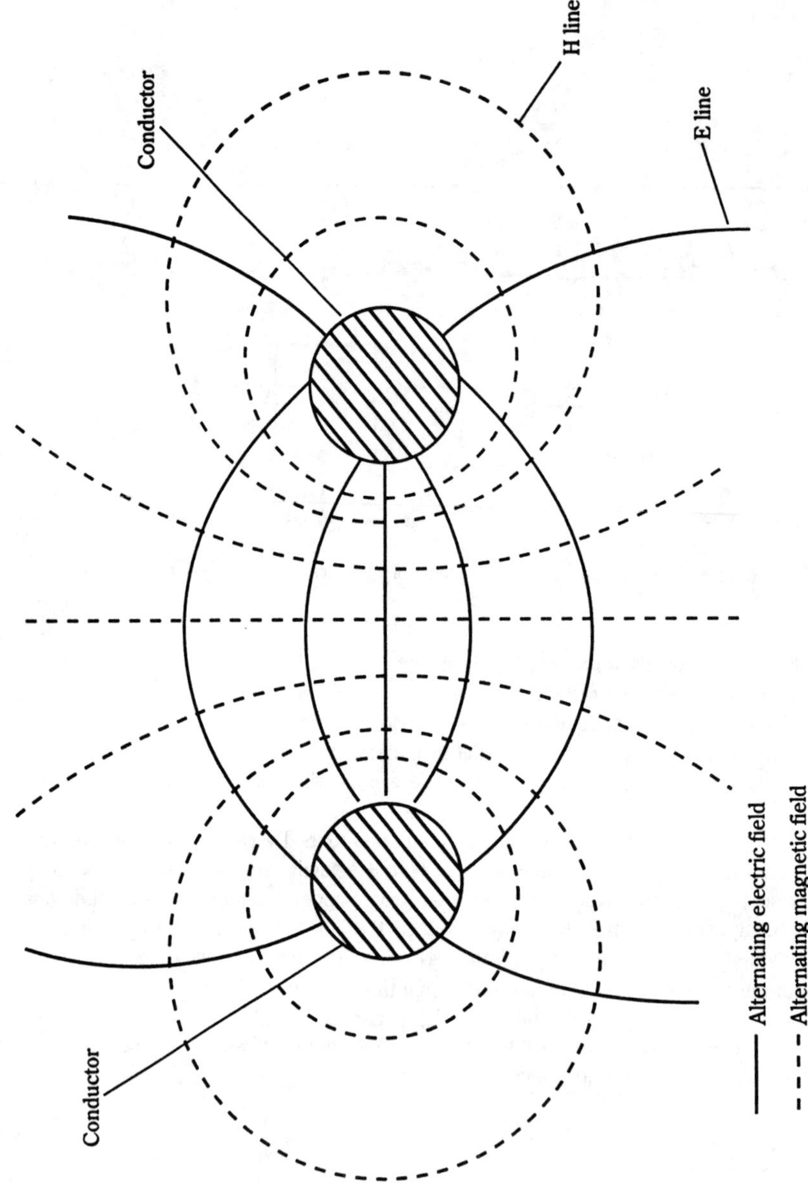

Fig. 10-4 Alternating electric and magnetic fields surrounding a two-wire line.

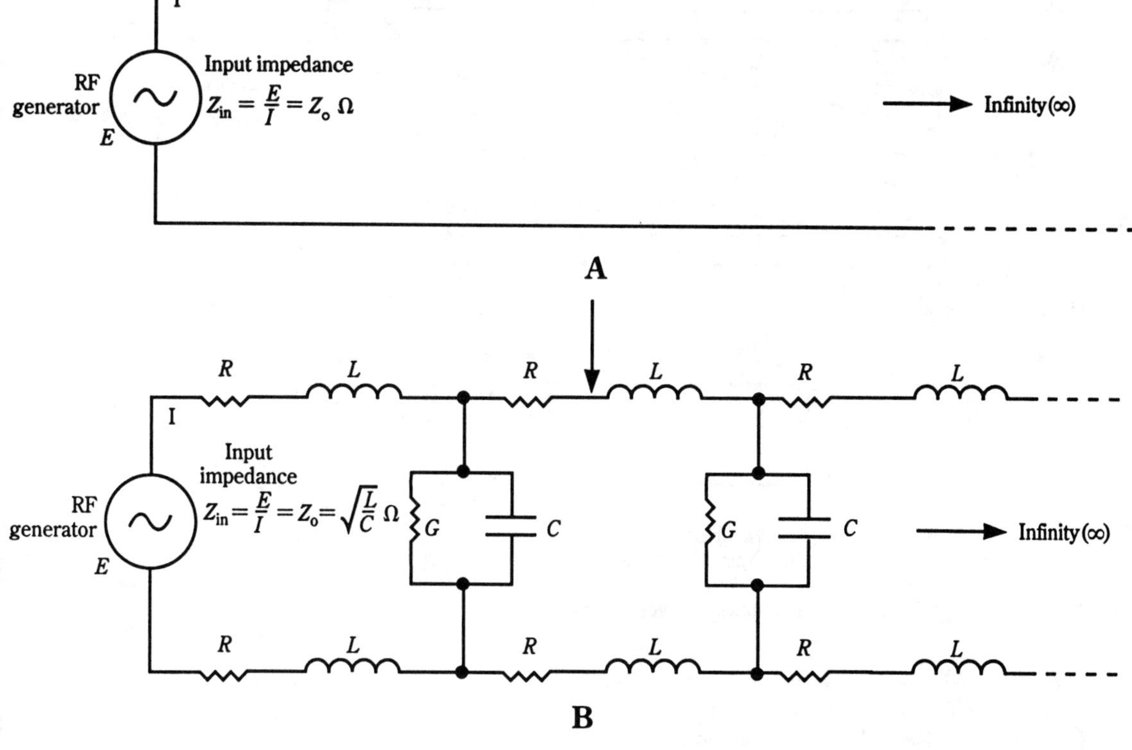

Fig. 10-5 The concept of surge impedance.

An RF line therefore behaves resistively and has a surge impedance of $\sqrt{L/C}\ \Omega$. However, the value of Z_o must also depend on the line's physical construction; the formulas are:

Two-wire line (FIG. 10-6):

$$Z_o = \frac{276}{\sqrt{\varepsilon_r}} \log_{10}\left(\frac{2S}{d}\right) \text{ ohms } (\Omega) \tag{10-3}$$

where: S = spacing between the conductors (m)
d = diameter of each conductor (m)
ε_r = relative permittivity of the insulation

Coaxial cable (FIG. 10-7):

$$Z_o = \frac{138}{\sqrt{\varepsilon_r}} \log_{10}\left(\frac{D}{d}\right) \text{ ohms } (\Omega) \tag{10-4}$$

where: D = diameter of the outer conductor (m)
d = diameter of the inner conductor (m)
ε_r = relative permittivity of the insulation

Many rigid coaxial lines (FIG. 10-2B) are filled with nitrogen gas in order to avoid oxidation and keep out moisture that would otherwise cause fluctuations in the value of the surge impedance.

Question 10-1 Nitrogen gas is used in rigid coaxial cables in order to:

A. increase the value of the surge impedance
B. decrease the value of the surge impedance

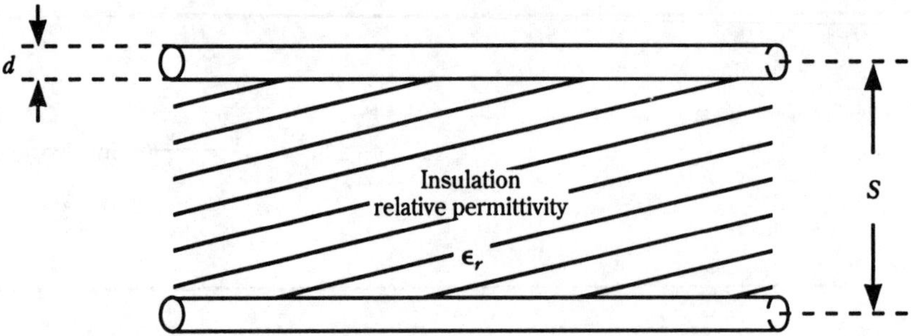

Fig. 10-6 Physical factors that determine the value of the surge impedance of a two-wire line.

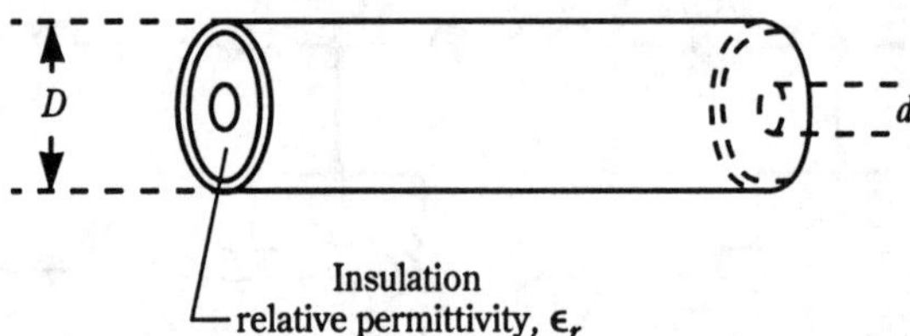

Fig. 10-7 Physical factors that determine the value of the surge impedance of a coaxial cable.

C. increase the dielectric strength of the insulator
D. exclude moisture and avoid oxidation
E. reduce the value of the relative permittivity

Answer Choice D.

* **Question 10-2** The input impedance to an infinite length of RF transmission line:
A. has a phase angle of $+90°$
B. has a phase angle of $-90°$
C. is equal to $\sqrt{C/L}\ \Omega$
D. is equal to the surge impedance
E. choices C and D are true

Answer Choice D. The RF value of the surge impedance is equal to: $\sqrt{\frac{L}{C}}\angle 0°\ \Omega$

10-2. The matched line

Refer to FIG. 10-8; consider the conditions that exist at the position, X Y, on the infinite line. Because there is still an infinite length to the right of X Y, the input impedance at this position looking down the line will be equal to the value of Z_o. Consequently, if the section of the line to the right of X Y, is removed and replaced by a resistive load whose value in ohms is the same as that of the surge impedance, it will still appear to the generator as if it is connected to an infinite line and the input impedance at the generator will remain equal to Z_o.

When a line is terminated by a resistive load of value Z_o, the line is said to be matched to the load. Under matched conditions, the line is most efficient in conveying RF power from the generator (for example, a transmitter) to the load, such as an antenna.

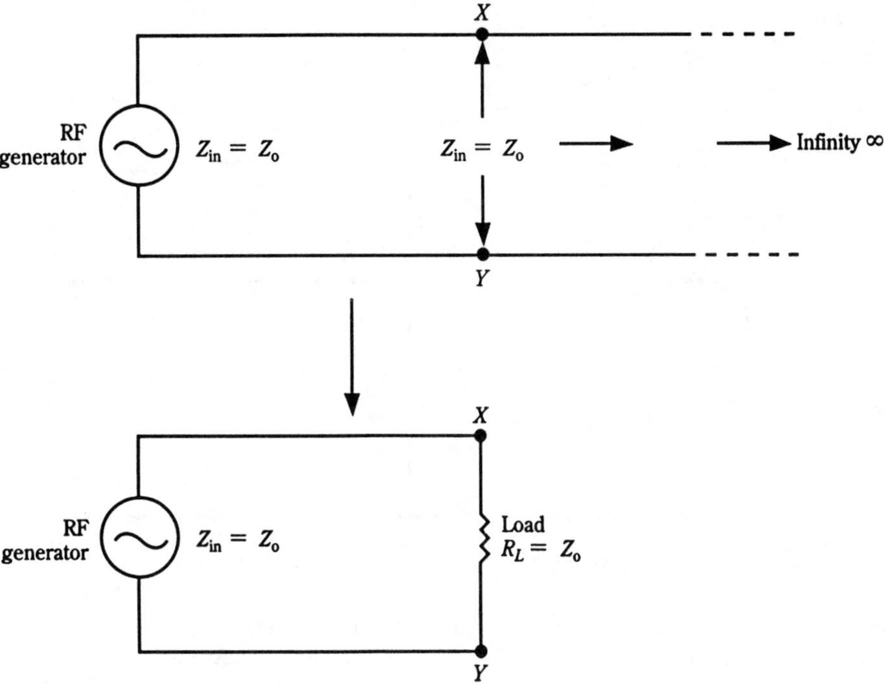

Fig. 10-8 The matched line.

Examine in detail what happens to a matched line. Traveling sine waves of voltage and current start out from the RF generator and move down the line in phase. Because of the small amount of attenuation present in the line, the effective (RMS) values of the voltage and current decay slightly, but at all positions, $V_{rms}/I_{rms} = Z_o$ (FIG. 10-9). Every transmission line therefore introduces a power loss, which is normally measured in decibels (dB).

On arrival at the termination, the power contained in the voltage and current waves is completely absorbed by the load. Neglecting the losses on the line, the RF power, P, conveyed down the line is given by:

$$\begin{aligned} P &= V_{rms} \times I_{rms} \\ &= (I_{rms} \times Z_o) \times I_{rms} \\ &= I^2_{rms} \times Z_o \\ &= \frac{V^2_{rms}}{Z_o} \text{ watts (W)} \end{aligned} \qquad (10\text{-}4)$$

These relationships are comparable with those for a resistor; however, it is important to realize that power is being conveyed down the line and is not being dissipated and lost as heat in the surge impedance.

In earlier chapters, it was assumed that in a series circuit consisting of a source, a two-wire line, and a load, the current was instantaneously the same throughout the circuit. This can only be regarded as true provided that the distances involved in the circuit are small compared with the wavelength of the output from the source. The wavelength (whose letter symbol is the Greek, λ), is defined as the distance between two consecutive identical states in the path of the wave.

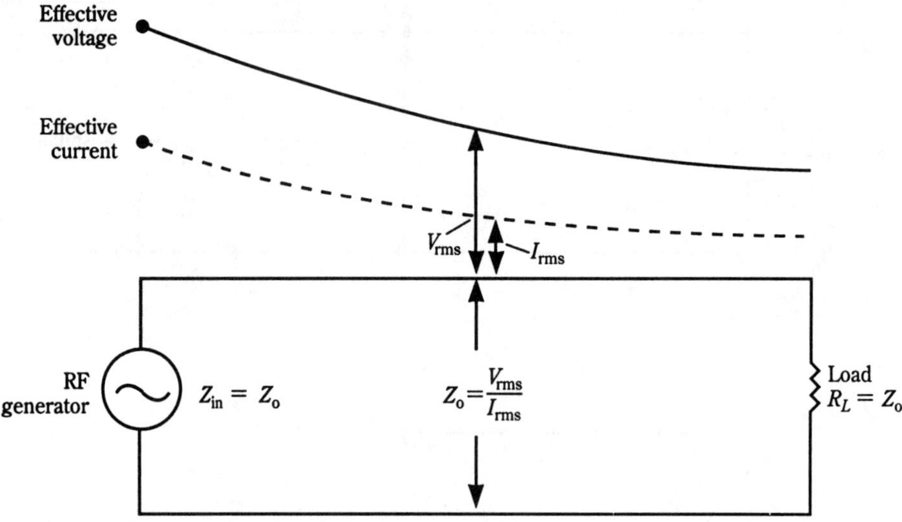

Fig. 10-9 Effective voltage and current distribution on a matched transmission line.

For example, the wavelength of a wave in water is the distance between two neighboring crests (or troughs). On a matched transmission line, the wavelength is the distance between two adjacent positions, where identical voltage (and current) conditions occur instantaneously. Traveling or progressive waves exist on the line because time is involved in propagating RF energy from the source to the load. The waves travel through a distance of one wavelength in a time equal to one period. Because velocity equals distance/time:

$$\begin{aligned} v &= \frac{\lambda}{T} \\ &= \lambda \times \frac{1}{T} \qquad (10\text{–}5) \\ &= f \times \lambda \end{aligned}$$

This yields:

$$\lambda = \frac{v}{f}$$

and:

$$f = \frac{v}{\lambda} \qquad (10\text{-}6)$$

where: v = the velocity in meters per second (m/s)
f = frequency in hertz (Hz)
λ = wavelength in meters (m)
T = period (s)

In free space, the velocity of an electromagnetic wave (radio wave) is a constant, approximately equal to 3×10^8 m/s (the speed of light whose letter symbol is c). For example, a 100-MHz radio wave within the FM broadcast band has a wavelength of:

$$\lambda = \frac{3 \times 10^8 \text{ m/s}}{100 \times 10^6 \text{ Hz}} = 3 \text{ m}$$

In other units, the velocity of a radio wave is 186,000 land or statute miles per second, where 1 statute mile = 5280 feet. Alternatively, the same velocity is equal to 161,700 nautical miles per second, where 1 nautical mile is the distance (at the equator), which subtends an angle of one minute ($1' = 1/60°$) at the center of the earth.

Because 1 nautical mile ≈ 6080 feet ≈ 2027 yards:

$$1 \text{ nautical mile} \approx \frac{6080}{5280} \approx 1.15 \text{ statute miles} \tag{10-7}$$

and:

$$1 \text{ statute mile} \approx \frac{1}{1.15} \approx 0.87 \text{ nautical miles} \tag{10-8}$$

At sea, the speed of a ship is measured in knots, where:

$$1 \text{ knot} = 1 \text{ nautical mile per hour} \tag{10-9}$$

A marine radar set transmits an RF pulse that covers a distance of one nautical mile in a time of 1/161,700 s = 6.184 μs. Therefore, the total time interval for a target of 1 nautical mile (approximately 2000 yards) is the total time for the pulse to reach the target and its echo to return to the receiver; this total time will be: 2 × 6.184 = 12.386 μs.

$$\textit{Radar range in nautical miles} = \frac{\textit{total round-trip interval } (\mu s)}{12.368} \tag{10-10}$$

The speed with which the voltage and current waves move down a transmission line is always less than the velocity of light, c. It follows that the wavelength on the line is shorter than the wavelength in free space.

The features of a matched line are:

- Traveling waves of voltage and current move down the line in phase and their power is completely absorbed by the load.
- The ratio of the effective voltage to the effective current is constant over the entire line and is equal to the surge impedance, Z_o.
- The input impedance at the generator is equal to the surge impedance and is independent of the line's length.
- The power losses on the line are subdivided into:
  - ~ radiation and induction losses which are a problem with parallel-wire lines.
  - ~ the dielectric hysteresis loss, which increases with frequency and depends on the type of insulator used. At microwave frequencies of a few GHz, the dielectric loss is the ultimate reason for abandoning coaxial lines and using waveguides instead.
  - ~ the copper loss, which is associated with the conductor's resistance. At high frequencies, this loss is increased by the skin effect, which confines most of the electron flow to the surface (skin) of a conductor, and therefore reduces the available cross-sectional area. The larger the surface area of the conductors, the lower the loss.

* **Question 10-3** An RF transmission line is used to connect a transmitter to its antenna. If the power output of the transmitter to the line is 1000 W and the line introduces an attenuation of 20 dB, the amount of power reaching the antenna is:

A. 10 W B. 50 W C. 1 W D. 500 E. 100 W

Answer Choice A. Refer to TABLE 2-2. A 20-dB loss is equivalent to a power ratio of 0.01 or 1/100. The power reaching the antenna is 0.01 × 1000 = 10 W.

* **Question 10-4** The wavelength of a 500-MHz signal in free space is:

A. 60 m B. 15 m C. 60 cm D. 0.006 m E. 6 m

Answer Choice C.

Wavelength:

$$\lambda = \frac{c}{f}$$

$$= \frac{3 \times 10^8 \text{ m/s}}{500 \times 10^6 \text{ Hz}} \quad (10\text{-}6)$$

$$= 0.6 \text{ m}$$

$$= 60 \text{ cm}$$

* **Question 10-5** Express a distance of 2.3 statute or land miles in terms of nautical miles:

A. 2.65 B. 1.83 C. 2.37 D. 1.91 E. 2.00

Answer Choice E.

$$\text{Because 1 statute mile} = 0.87 \text{ nautical mile}$$

$$\text{2.3 statute miles} = 2.3 \times 0.87 \quad (10\text{-}8)$$

$$= 2.0 \text{ nautical miles, rounded off}$$

* **Question 10-6** Express a speed of 10 statute miles per hour in terms of knots:

A. 1.5 B. 11.5 C. 15.0 D. 8.7 E. 1.15

Answer Choice D. Since 1 statute mile = 0.87 nautical mile (EQ. 10-8) and 1 knot = 1 nautical mile per hour (EQ. 10-9),

$$\text{10 statute miles per hour} = 10 \times 0.87 \text{ nautical miles per hour}$$

$$= 8.7 \text{ knots}$$

* **Question 10-7** Express a distance of 1.74 nautical miles in terms of land or statute miles:

A. 2.00 B. 2.15 C. 1.50 D. 1.62 E. 1.13

Answer Choice A.

$$\text{Because 1 nautical mile} = 1.15 \text{ statute miles}$$

$$\text{1.74 nautical miles} = 1.74 \times 1.15 \quad (10\text{-}7)$$

$$= 2.00 \text{ statute miles, rounded off}$$

* **Question 10-8** The total time taken for a radio pulse to travel to the target and back to the receiver, is 62 μs. The range of the target in nautical miles is:

A. 4.4 B. 5.0 C. 5.8 D. 10.0 E. 2.5

Answer Choice B.

$$Range = \frac{62 \ \mu\text{s}}{12.368 \ \mu\text{s/n.m}} \quad (10\text{-}10)$$

$$= 5.0 \text{ nautical miles, rounded off}$$

* **Question 10-9** The RF power input to a transmission line is 100 W. If the length of the transmission line is 200 feet and its attenuation is 6 dB/100 ft, calculate the line's output power:

A. 6.25 W B. 25 W C. 3.125 W D. 12.5 W E. 50 W

Answer Choice A.

$$\textit{Total attenuation of the transmission line} = \frac{200 \text{ ft} \times 6 \text{ dB}}{100 \text{ ft.}}$$

$$= 12 \text{ dB}$$

Refer to TABLE 2-3. Because a loss of 3 dB (−3 dB) is equal to a power ratio of 1/2, an attenuation of 12 dB = 4 × 3 dB is the same as a power ratio of $(1/2)^4$ = 1/16. Therefore, the output power is 100 × (1/16) = 6.25 W.

Alternatively:

$$\textit{Output power} = 100\text{ W} \times \text{Antilog}\left(\frac{-12}{10}\right)$$
$$= 6.31\text{ W}$$

* **Question 10-10** On a matched transmission line, the voltage between the conductors at any position is equal to the:

A. product of the line current and the surge impedance
B. square root of the power divided by the surge impedance
C. power divided by the square of the surge impedance
D. result of dividing the line current by the surge impedance
E. square of the power divided by the square of the surge impedance

Answer Choice A. Because $V = I \times Z_o$ (EQ. 10-1), the voltage is equal to the product of the line current and the surge impedance.

* **Question 10-11** A 70-Ω line is matched to a 70-Ω resistive load. The length of the line must be any:

A. odd multiple of one quarter wavelength
B. even multiple of one quarter wavelength
C. even multiple of one half wavelength
D. multiple of one wavelength
E. desired length

Answer Choice E. For a matched line, the length is not critical.

* **Question 10-12** An RF transmission line whose surge impedance is 100 Ω conveys a power of 200 W. Assuming that the line is loss-free and is matched to a resistive load, the value of the line current is:

A. 2 A B. 4 A C. 1 A D. 1.4 A E. 0.71 A

Answer Choice D.

$$\text{Line current, } I = \sqrt{\frac{P}{Z_o}}$$
$$= \sqrt{\frac{200\text{ W}}{100\ \Omega}} \qquad (10\text{-}4)$$
$$= \sqrt{2} = 1.4\text{ A, rounded off}$$

* **Question 10-13** A radar set measures the total time interval for a transmitted pulse to reach the target and its echo to return to the receiver. To determine the radar range in nautical miles, this total time interval in microseconds is divided by:

A. 6.184 B. 12.368 C. 1.15 D. 0.87 E. 24.74

Answer Choice B. Refer to EQ. 10-10.

10-3. The mismatched line

Open- and short-circuited lines

If an RF line is terminated by a resistive load that is not equal to the surge impedance, the generator will still send voltage and current waves down the line in phase, but their power will be only partially absorbed by the load. A certain fraction of the voltage and current waves that arrive (are incident) at the load will be reflected back toward the generator. At any position on the line, the instantaneous voltage (or current) will be the resultant of the incident and reflected voltage (or current) waves; these combine to produce so-called "standing waves." In the extreme cases of open- and short-circuited lines, no power can be absorbed by the load and total reflection will occur.

At the termination of an open-circuited loss-free line, there must be a maximum voltage variation whose peak value is twice that of the incident voltage wave. However, because of the interaction of the incident and reflected waves, there are other fixed positions of maximum voltage variation at distances of λ/2, λ, 3λ/2, etc., from the open-circuit termination (λ = wavelength on the line). At such positions, the incident and reflected waves reinforce one another; the resultant maximum variations are called the voltage *antinode* or *loop*. However, at distances of λ/4, 3λ/4, 5λ/4, etc., there are other stationary positions where the incident and reflected waves totally cancel and the voltage is zero at all times; these are called the voltage *nulls* or *nodes*. The stationary points that occur with a standing wave are in contrast with the traveling or progressive waves, which exist on the matched line. On a traveling wave, for example, a zero-voltage condition moves down the line at a speed that is less than the velocity of light. The distribution of the effective voltage standing wave on a open-circuited loss-less line is shown in FIG. 10-10; this should be compared with the voltage distribution on a matched line (FIG. 10-9).

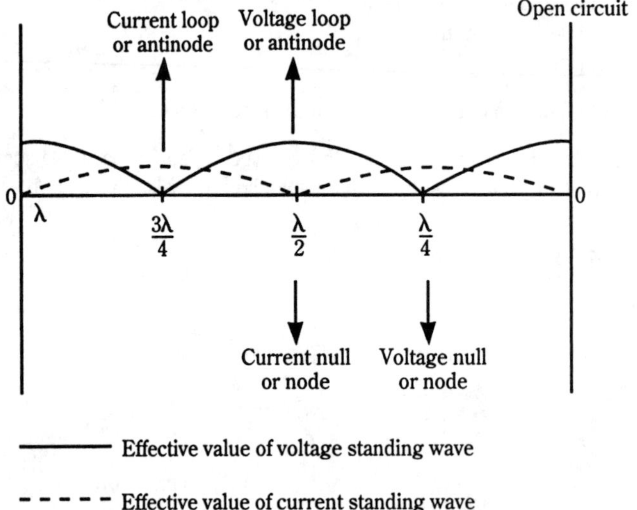

Fig. 10-10 Effective voltage and current distribution on an open-circuited line.

Now, examine the current standing-wave distribution on the open-circuited line. At the termination, there must be a zero current variation so that other current nodes will occur at the λ/2, λ, 3λ/2, etc., positions. Consequently, the current antinodes will exist at distances of λ/4, 3λ/4, 5λ/4, etc., from the open-circuited end. There is a λ/4 separation between a voltage null and its neighboring current nulls and also between a voltage antinode and an adjacent current antinode (FIG. 10-10). The peak of a current antinode is twice the peak value of the incident current wave. Notice that a voltage antinode occurs at the same position as a current node; similarly, a voltage null coincides with a current antinode.

Because a standing-wave voltage and current distribution exists on an open-circuited line, there must also be an impedance distribution. At the λ/4 position, there is a zero-voltage node and a current antinode so that the corresponding impedance is theoretically zero; however, on a practical line, the impedance would be equivalent to a low value of resistance. The conditions are reversed for the $\lambda/2$ position, where there is a zero current node and a voltage antinode. The impedance is theoretically infinite, but (in practice) it is equivalent to a high value of resistance.

The variation of impedance along the open-circuited line is shown in FIG. 10-11. It is striking to find the similarity to the behavior of series and parallel LC circuits. Remember that the impedance response of the series circuit changes from capacitive through resistive (low value) to inductive; by contrast, the parallel circuit has an impedance response that varies from inductive through resistive (high value) to capacitive. These equivalent LC circuits have been included in FIG. 10-11. Because the line exhibits resonant properties, it can be referred to as being *tuned;* by contrast, the matched line is called *flat,* untuned, or nonresonant.

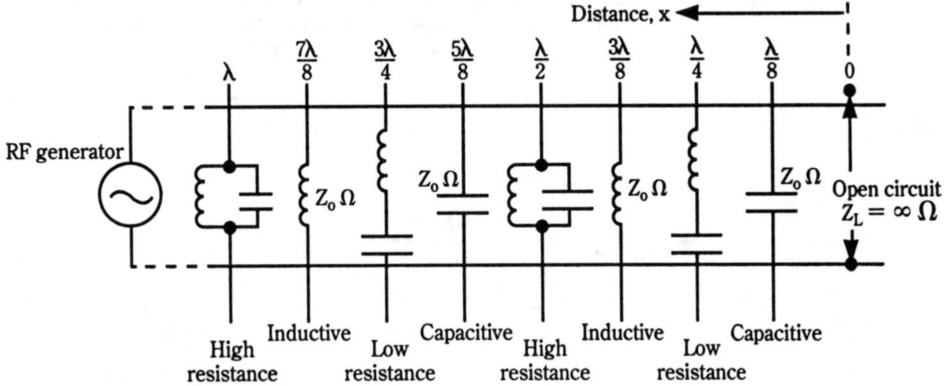

Fig. 10-11 Impedance distribution on an open-circuited line.

Between the open-circuit termination and the $\lambda/8$ position, there is a large voltage distribution and a small current distribution. Therefore, the electric field associated with the distributed capacitance is greater than the magnetic field of the distributed inductance. Consequently, this short length of line behaves capacitively and the input impedance at the $\lambda/8$ position is a capacitive reactance with a value equal to Z_o.

A short-circuited line (FIG. 10-12) also represents a complete mismatch, so total reflection will occur at the termination. At the terminating short, there will be a zero-voltage null and a current antinode. Because the voltage and current conditions are interchanged when compared with the open-circuited line, the impedance at the $\lambda/8$ position is an inductive reactance of value Z_o. At the $\lambda/4$ position, there is a voltage antinode and a current node, so the impedance is equivalent to that of a parallel LC circuit. The impedance will be a capacitive reactance that is equal in value to Z_o at the $3\lambda/8$ position; at the $\lambda/2$ position, the impedance is the same as that of a series LC circuit. Summarizing, there is a $\lambda/4$ shift between the impedance conditions on the open- and short-circuited lines.

Of particular importance is the section of line that is a $\lambda/4$ long (or any odd multiple of $\lambda/4$) and is terminated by a short circuit (FIG. 10-13). Referring to FIG. 10-12, the input impedance is a high value of resistance, which corresponds to a parallel LC circuit. At frequencies in the ultra high frequency (UHF) band, "lumped circuitry" is not practical and the shorted $\lambda/4$ line can then be used to replace a tank circuit. For tuning purposes, the position of the short can be adjusted to resonance.

The resistive termination

Now examine the effect of terminating a loss less line with a resistive load that is not equal to the surge impedance. The amount of reflection will be reduced so that the nodes and antinodes will

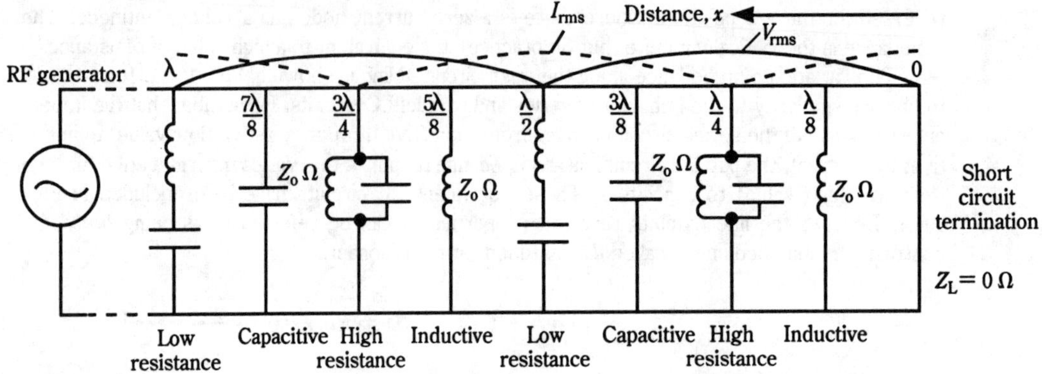

Fig. 10-12 Impedance distribution on a short-circuited line.

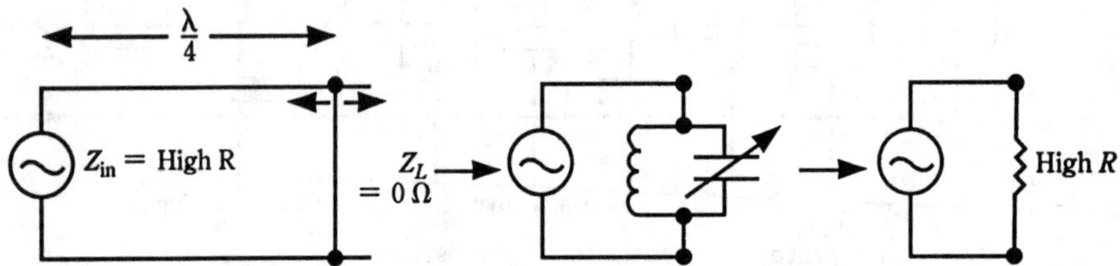

Fig. 10-13 The quarter-wave line with a short-circuit termination.

be less pronounced. Neglecting any losses on the line, the effective voltage and current distribution for the three possible cases of a resistive load, namely $R_L < Z_o$, $R_L = Z_o$, and $R_L > Z_o$, are shown in FIG. 10-14.

The fraction of the incident voltage and current reflected at the load is called the *reflection coefficient,* whose letter symbol is the Greek, rho, P.

Reflected voltage: $$V_r = P \times V_i \text{ volts (V)} \tag{10-11}$$

Reflected current: $$I_r = P \times I_i \text{ amperes (A)} \tag{10-12}$$

Reflected power:
$$\begin{aligned} P_r &= V_r \times I_r \\ &= P^2 \times V_i \times I_i \\ &= P^2 \times \textit{incident power} \end{aligned} \tag{10-13}$$

Load power:
$$\begin{aligned} P_L &= P_i - P_r \\ &= (1 - P^2)P_i \text{ watts (W)} \end{aligned} \tag{10-14}$$

where: V_i = effective incident voltage (V)
I_i = effective incident current (A)
P_i = incident power (W)

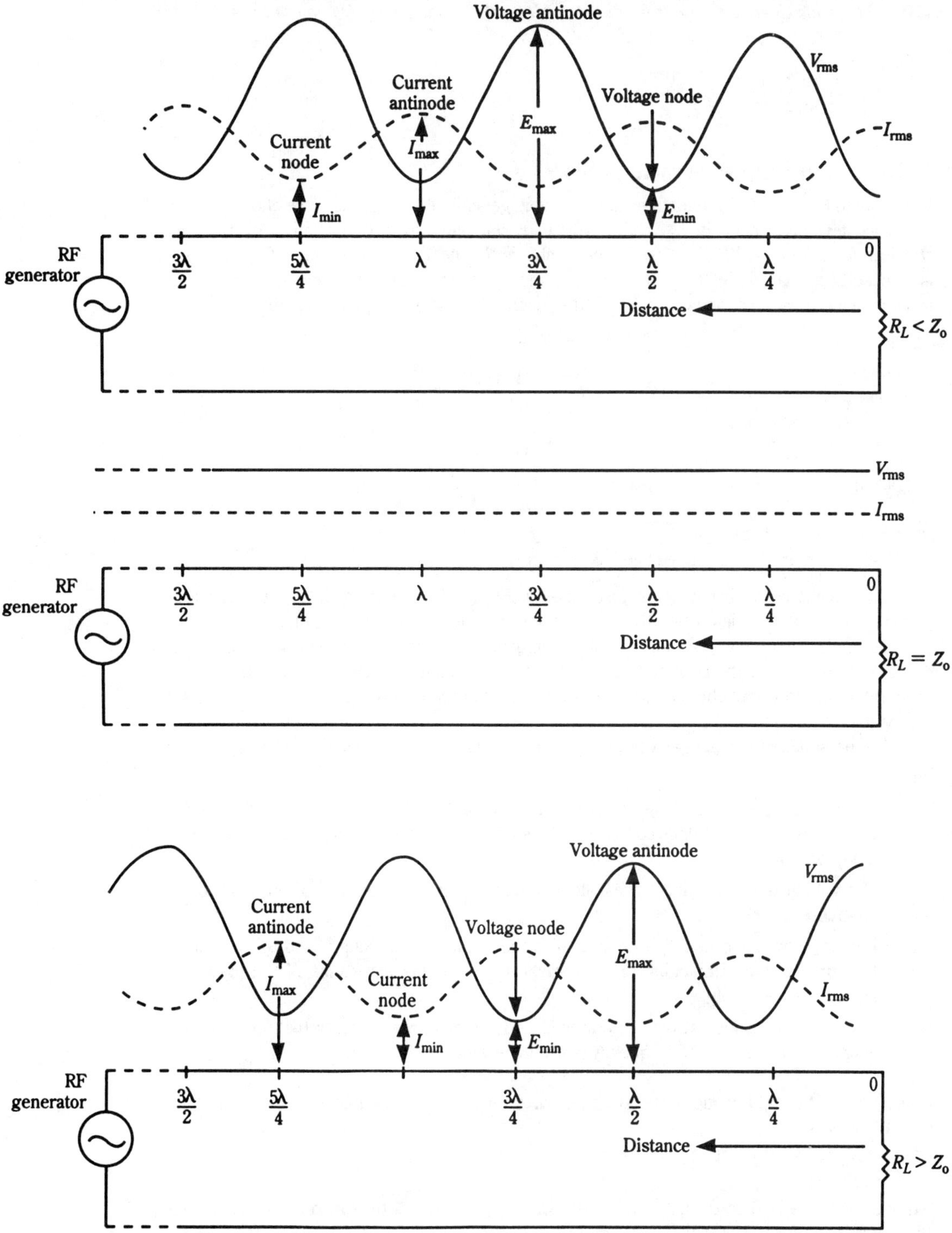

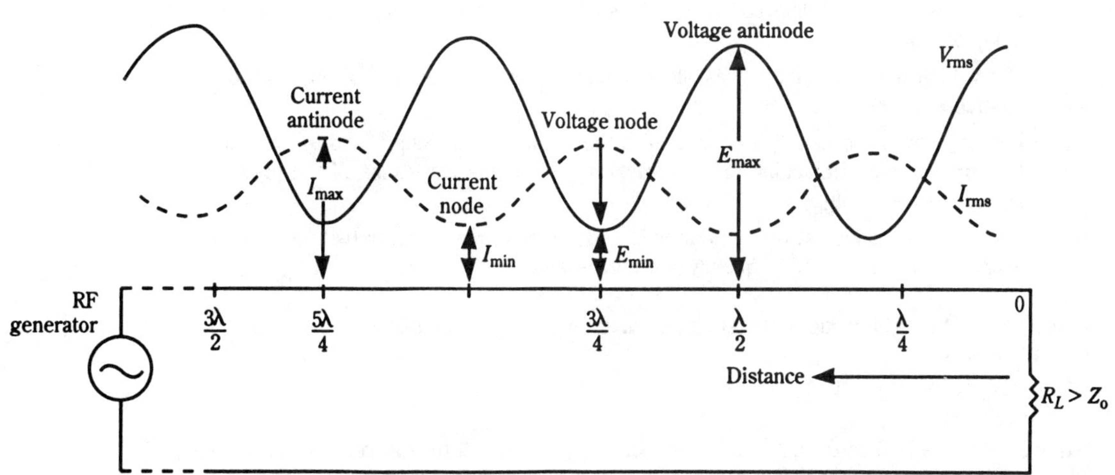

Fig. 10-14 Effective voltage and current distribution on matched and unmatched lines with resistive terminations.

P_r = reflected power (W)
P_L = load power (W)

Voltage standing-wave ratio (VSWR)

Referring to FIG. 10-14, the effective value of a voltage antinode is E_{max}, and the effective value of an adjacent voltage mode is E_{min}. The degree of standing waves is measured by the *voltage standing-wave ratio (VSWR),* whose letter symbol is S. The VSWR is the ratio $E_{max}:E_{min}$, which is also equal in magnitude to $I_{max}:I_{min}$. E_{max} is the result of an in-phase condition between the incident and reflected voltages, and E_{min} is the result of a 180° out-of-phase situation.

Then:

$$E_{max} = V_i + V_r = V_i(1 + P)$$

$$E_{min} = V_i - V_r = V_r(1 - P) \qquad (10\text{-}15)$$

This yields:

$$\text{VSWR, } S = \frac{E_{max}}{E_{min}} = \frac{1 + P}{1 - P}$$

If: $P = 0$ (matched line), $S = 1$
$P = 1$ (open or short-circuited line), $S = \infty$

The VSWR is just a number whose value will range from 1 to ∞. In a practical matched system, a value of S (which is less than 1.2), is normally regarded as acceptable.

The reflectometer is the item of test equipment that is capable of measuring the forward or incident power (P_i), the reflected power (P_r), the reflection coefficient (P), and the standing-wave ratio (S). However, the operator enters the value of the load power ($P_L = P_i - P_r$) in the station log.

The presence of standing waves on a practical transmission line has the following disadvantages:

- The incident power reaching the termination is not fully absorbed by the load. The difference between the incident power and the load power is the power reflected back toward the generator.
- The voltage antinodes might break down the insulation between the conductors and cause arc-over.
- Because power losses are proportional to the square of the voltage and to the square of the current, the attenuation on the practical line increases because of the presence of standing waves.
- The input impedance at the generator is a totally unknown quantity that varies with the length of the line and the frequency of the generator.

* **Question 10-14** The value of the standing-wave ratio (SWR) on a matched line with zero reflected power, is:

A. ∞ B. 1.2 C. 0 D. 1 E. 0.5

Answer Choice D. The theoretically "best" value of the SWR with zero reflection is 1. In EQ. 10-15, if $P = 0$, $S = (1 + 0)/(1 - 0) = 1$.

* **Question 10-15** The RF power output of a transmitter is 25 W, but as a result of an impedance mismatch, the reflected power is 5 W. What value of power is entered in the transmitter's log?

A. 25 W B. 5 W C. 20 W D. 30 W E. 15 W

Answer Choice C. The value of the load power, $P_L = P_i - P_r = 25 - 5 = 20$ W (EQ. 10-14). Therefore, a value of 20 W is entered in the transmitter's log.

* **Question 10-16** The presence of standing waves on a transmission line is the result of:

A. a high level of attenuation on the line
B. terminating the line by a resistive load that is equal in value to the surge impedance
C. reducing the input power to below its critical level
D. an impedance mismatch between the load and the line
E. a reflection coefficient of zero at the terminating load.

Answer Choice D. Standing waves are the result of a mismatch between the line and the load.

* **Question 10-17** A $\lambda/4$ section of line is shorted at one end and connected to an RF generator at the other end. The input impedance at the generator is:

A. theoretically infinite
B. in practice, a high value of resistance
C. equivalent to a parallel resonant LC circuit
D. the result of dividing the value of a voltage antinode by the value of a current node
E. all of the above choices are true

Answer Choice E.

* **Question 10-18** The input power to a loss-free coaxial cable is 5 W. If the reflected power is 7 dB down on the incident power, the output power to the load is:

A. 4 W B. 1 W C. 5 W D. 3 W E. 2 W

Answer Choice A. Refer to TABLE 2-3. The power ratio corresponding to -7 dB is 1/5. Therefore, the reflected power is: $(1/5) \times 5 = 1$ W and the load power is $5 - 1 = 4$ W (EQ. 10-14).

* **Question 10-19** A $\lambda/4$ section of line is terminated by a short circuit and is connected to an RF source at the other end. The input impedance to the line at the source is:

A. inductive B. capacitive C. a low resistance
D. equivalent to a parallel resonant LC circuit
E. theoretically zero

Answer Choice D. The combination of the $\lambda/4$ line and its terminating short is equivalent to a tank circuit.

* **Question 10-20** The outer conductor of a coaxial cable is only grounded at:

A. the input end B. the output end C. its middle
D. the input end and the output end
E. the outer conductor is never grounded

Answer Choice D. To prevent the production of standing waves on the outer conductor, it is normally grounded at the input end and the output end. Sometimes the outer conductor is also grounded at certain intervals along the length.

10-4. The Hertz antenna

An *antenna* is an efficient radiator of electromagnetic energy (radio waves) into free space. The same principles apply to both transmitting and receiving antennas, although the RF power levels for the two antennas are completely different. The purpose of a transmitting antenna is to radiate as much RF power as possible either in all directions (*omnidirectional antenna*) or in a specified direction (*directional antenna*). By contrast, the receiving antenna is used to intercept an RF signal voltage, which is sufficiently large, compared to the noise existing within the receiver's bandwidth.

You already know that the main disadvantage to a twin-wire transmission line is its radiation loss. However, provided that the separation between the leads is short compared with the wavelength, the radiation loss is small because the fields associated with the two conductors will tend to cancel out. Refer to FIG. 10-15A; the equal currents, i, which exist over the last resonant $\lambda/4$ of an open-circuited transmission line, will instantaneously flow in opposite directions so that their resultant magnetic field is weak. However, if each $\lambda/4$ conductor is bent back through 90° (FIG. 10-15B), the currents, i, are now instantaneously in the same direction, so the surrounding magnetic field is strong. In addition, the conductors carry a standing-wave voltage distribution with its associated electric field. The standing-wave voltage and current distributions occur over the complete half-wavelength (FIG. 10-15C); at the center feedpoint, the effective voltage is at its minimum level, while the effective current has its maximum level. The effective voltage distribution is drawn on opposite sides of the two sections to indicate that these sections instantaneously carry opposite polarities. In other words, when a particular point in the top section carries a positive voltage, with respect to ground, the corresponding point in the bottom section has a negative voltage. The distributed inductance and capacitance (FIG. 10-15D) together form the equivalent of a series resonant LC circuit. Notice, however, that the distributed capacitance exists between the two $\lambda/4$ sections and that the ground is not involved in the distribution.

By bending the two $\lambda/4$ sections outward by 90°, you form the $\lambda/2$ dipole or Hertz (Heinrich Hertz, 1857–1894) antenna. This antenna will be resonant at the frequency to which it is cut. You already know that the electrical wavelength in free space is given by:

$$\textit{Electrical wavelength} = \frac{300}{f}\ \text{(m)} = \frac{984}{f}\ \text{feet (ft)} \qquad (10\text{-}16)$$

This leads to:

$$\textit{Electrical half wavelength} = \frac{492}{f}\ \text{feet (ft)} \qquad (10\text{-}17)$$

where: f = frequency in megahertz (MHz)

The voltage and current waves on an antenna travel at a speed that is typically 5% slower than the velocity of light. Therefore, the physical half-wavelength to which the Hertz antenna should be cut, is shorter than the electrical $\lambda/2$.

$$\textit{Physical half wavelength} = \frac{468}{f\ \text{(MHz)}}\ \text{feet (ft)} \qquad (10\text{-}18)$$

For example, at a frequency of 100 MHz (which lies within the FM commercial broadcast band of 88 to 108 MHz), the length required for the Hertz antenna is: 468/100 = 4.68 feet. Such an antenna would be made from two thin conducting rods, each 2.34 ft. long, and positioned remote from ground. At 100 MHz, the antenna behaves as a series resonant circuit with a Q of approximately 10. Therefore, the thin dipole is capable of operating effectively within a narrow range that is centered on the resonant frequency. However, if the operating frequency is below the resonant frequency, the antenna will appear to be too short and will behave capacitively. Likewise, at frequencies above resonance, the antenna will be too long and will be inductive.

When the Hertz dipole is resonant and the RF power is applied at the center of the antenna,

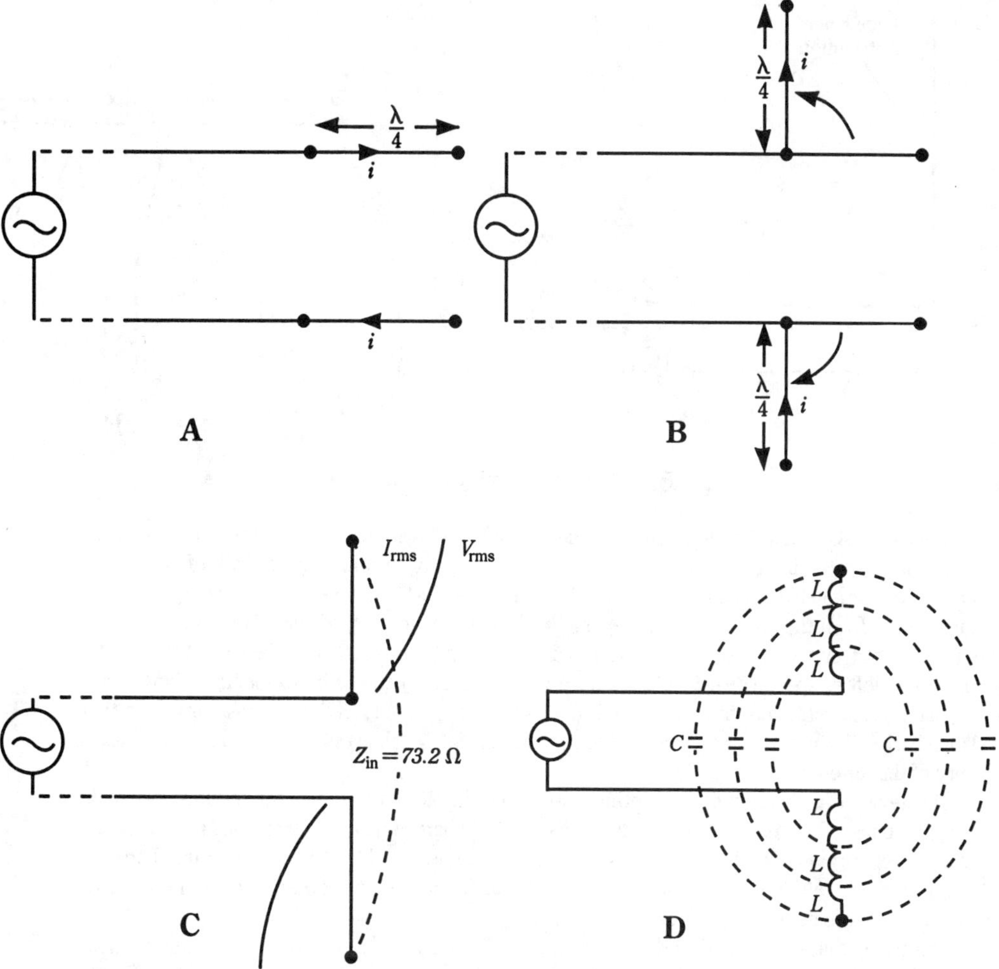

Fig. 10-15 Principles of the Hertz half-wavelength dipole antenna.

the input impedance at the feedpoint is a low resistance, which mathematically can be shown to have a value of 73.2 Ω (for this reason, the antenna is often spoken of as a "70-Ω dipole"). This is referred to as the *radiation resistance* of the dipole and is the ohmic load that the λ/2 antenna represents at resonance; to achieve a matched condition, the dipole should be fed with a 70-Ω line. The RF power, P, at the feedpoint is:

$$P = I_A^2 \times R_A \tag{10-19}$$

where: I_A = effective RF current at the center of the antenna (A)
R_A = radiation resistance (Ω)

As you move from the center of the antenna toward the ends (FIG. 10-16A), the impedance increases from approximately 35 Ω (balanced either side, with respect to ground) to about 2500 Ω (not infinity because of the "end" capacitance effects). Therefore, it is possible to select points on the antenna where the impedance can be matched by a gradual taper to a line whose Z_o is not 70 Ω; such an arrangement is known as a *delta feed* (FIG. 10-16B).

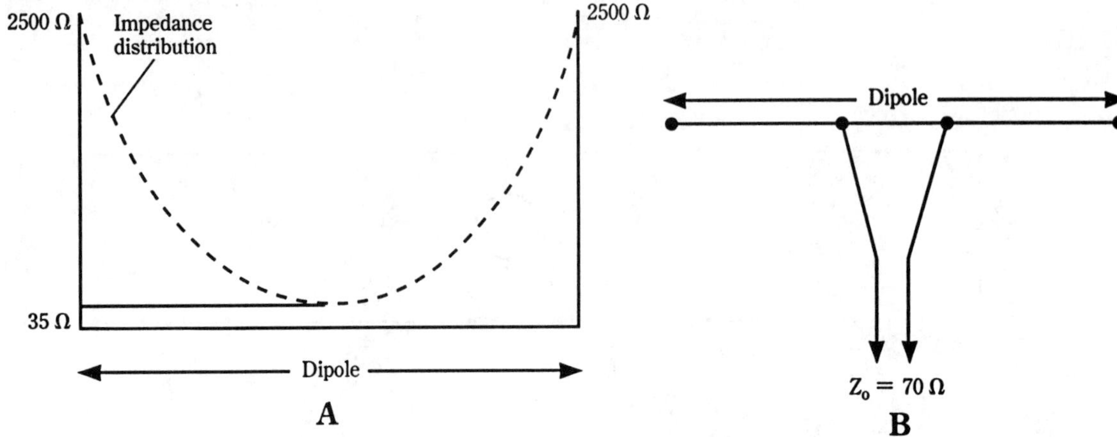

Fig. 10-16 Distribution of impedance along the dipole.

It is established that there are electric and magnetic fields in the vicinity of the antenna (FIG. 10-17A). Because the instantaneous voltage and current on the antenna are 90° out of phase, the same phase relationship applies to the E and H fields (FIG. 10-17B). These fields are continuously expanding out from the antenna and collapsing back with the velocity of light. However, because the action is not instantaneous, the collapse will only be partial, so closed electric and magnetic loops will be left in space (FIG. 10-17C). These loops represent the *radiated* electromagnetic energy that is propagated into free space and travels with the velocity of light. Those flux lines that collapse back into the antenna represent the *induction field,* which is only strong in the immediate vicinity of the antenna.

The fields in space around a $\lambda/2$ antenna are shown in FIG. 10-18. The radiated E and H fields are in time phase, but the two sets of flux lines are 90° apart in space. A vertical Hertz antenna radiates an electric field with vertical flux lines and a magnetic field with horizontal flux lines. In addition, the two sets of flux lines are each at right angles to the direction, in which the electromagnetic energy is being propagated.

The plane that contains E and the direction of propagation is referred to as the *plane of polarization.* A vertical Hertz antenna will radiate a vertically polarized wave with a vertical E field and a horizontal H field. Similarly, a horizontally polarized wave has a horizontal E field, a vertical H field, and is associated with a horizontal antenna. As practical examples, AM broadcast systems have antenna systems that radiate vertically polarized waves, and TV broadcast stations use horizontal polarization.

Radiation patterns

The *radiation pattern* that surrounds an antenna can either represent the field intensity, $\mathcal{E}$, (volts per meter) or the power density (watts per square meter) distribution. The two patterns are similar in appearance. This section is mainly confined to the field intensity, which directly measures the strength of the electric field component in the radio wave. Theoretically, the value of the $\mathcal{E}$ is equal to the voltage induced in a conductor that is 1 meter long and is positioned parallel to the electric flux lines. Although the basic unit of the electric field intensity is the *volt per meter,* more practical units are *millivolts per meter* and *microvolts per meter.*

The *radiation pattern* is a plot of the electric field intensity at a fixed distance from the (transmitting) antenna versus an angle measured in the particular plane for which the pattern applies. In the case of the $\lambda/2$ dipole, it is customary to consider two planes. The $\mathcal{E}$ plane contains

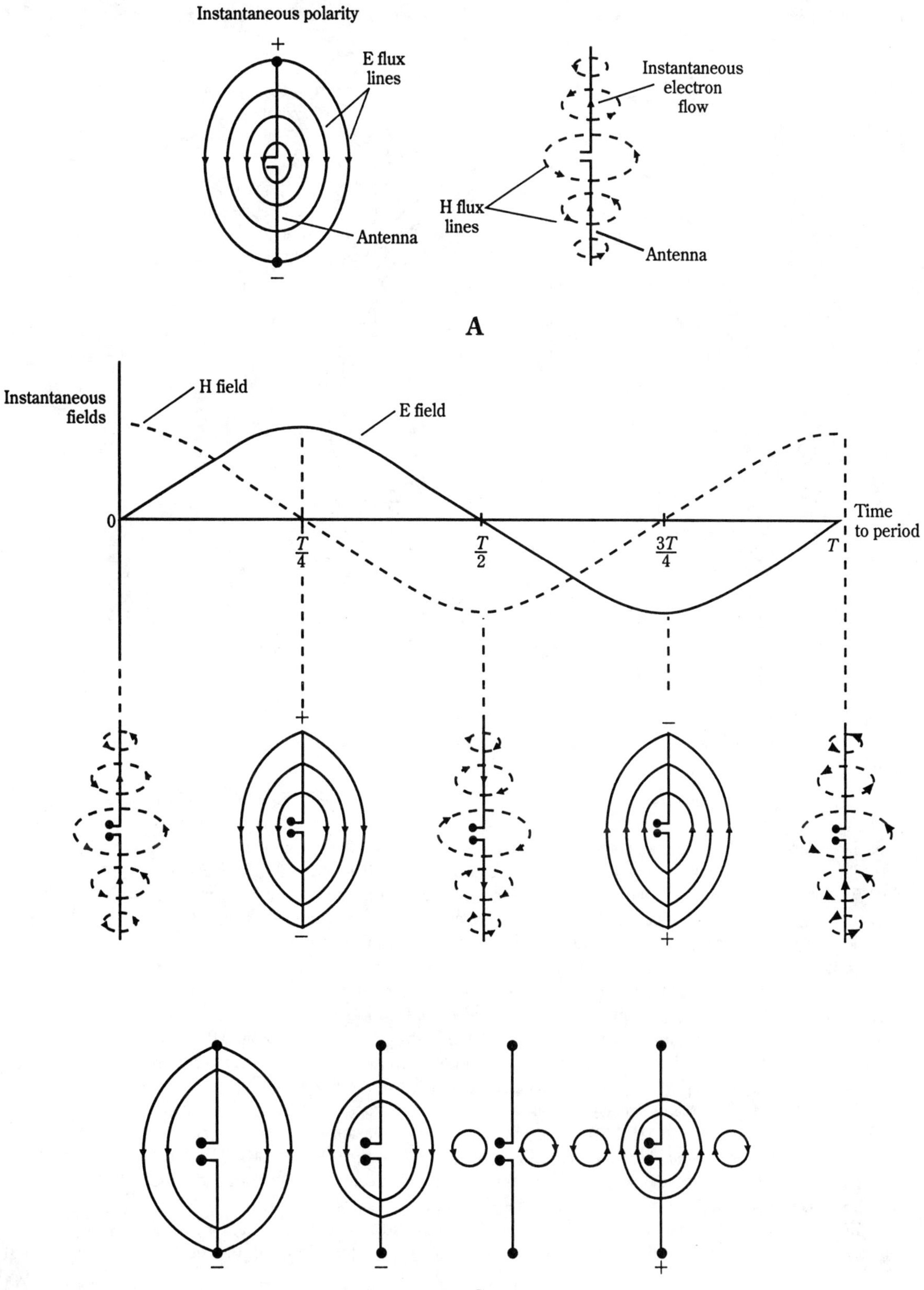

Instantaneous polarity

E flux lines

Antenna

Instantaneous electron flow

H flux lines

Antenna

A

Instantaneous fields

H field

E field

0

$\frac{T}{4}$ $\frac{T}{2}$ $\frac{3T}{4}$ T

Time to period

C

Fig. 10-17 Radiated electric and magnetic fields surrounding the Hertz antenna.

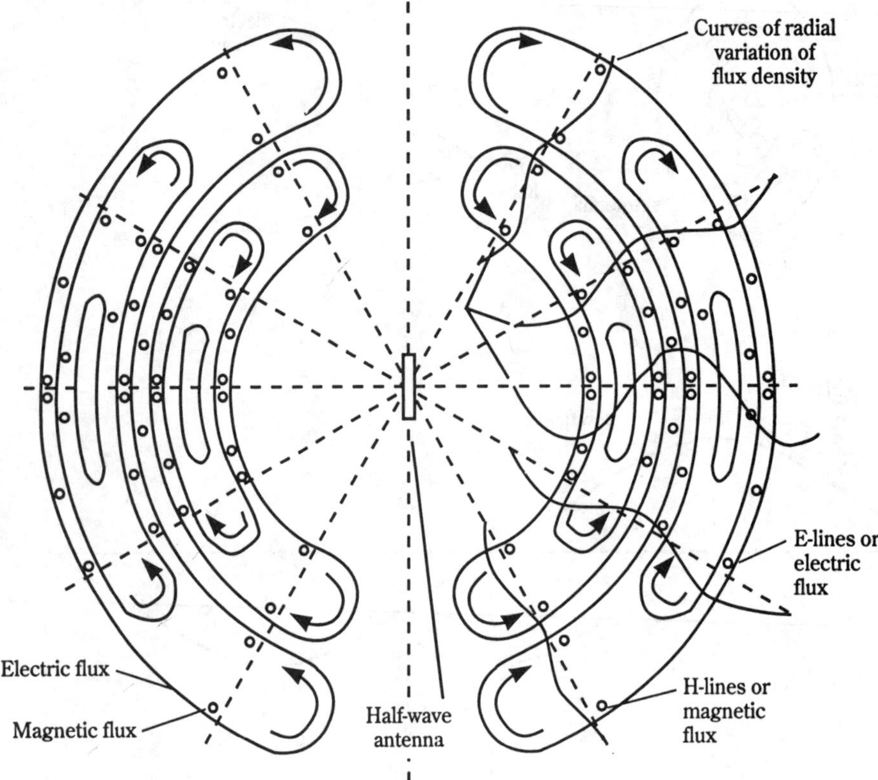

Fig. 10-18 Electric and magnetic fields radiated from the vertical Hertz antenna.

the antenna itself and the electric flux lines, while the magnetic flux lines lie in the H plane, which is at right angles to the antenna at its center point. Combining the results for the two perpendicular planes produces the antenna's complete three-dimensional radiation pattern.

The radiation patterns for a *vertical* dipole are shown in FIGS. 10-19A and B. The maximum field strength will be associated with the center of the antenna, where the highest current distribution exists; practically no radiation will occur from the ends, where the current is minimal.

The vertical radiation pattern that is associated with the $\mathcal{E}$ plane consists of two "oval" shapes (not circles) and is shown in FIG. 10-19A. In direction OP, the strength of the electric field intensity is at its maximum and is represented by the length of OP′, while OQ′ (which is shorter than OP′) is a measure of the field intensity in the direction of OQ. For the direction of OT, the length intercepted by the radiation plot is zero. Consequently, the $\mathcal{E}$ value is zero. Points P_1 and P_2 are those where the electric field intensity is 0.707 of its maximum value (OP′); the beam width is then angle P_1OP_2 between the half-power points and is about 50° for the $\lambda/2$ dipole.

The vertical dipole radiates equally well in all horizontal directions so that its pattern in the magnetic plane is a circle (FIG. 10-19B). The complete three-dimensional pattern will then resemble a *toroidal shape* or *doughnut surface* with no hole in the center (FIG. 10-19C). The same pattern will apply to a vertical dipole used for reception purposes; in any particular direction, the length intercepted by the pattern will be a measure of the received signal strength.

In the vicinity of a single vertical antenna, the horizontal radiation can be found by joining together all positions of equal field strength; with a flat, perfectly conducting ground, the result is

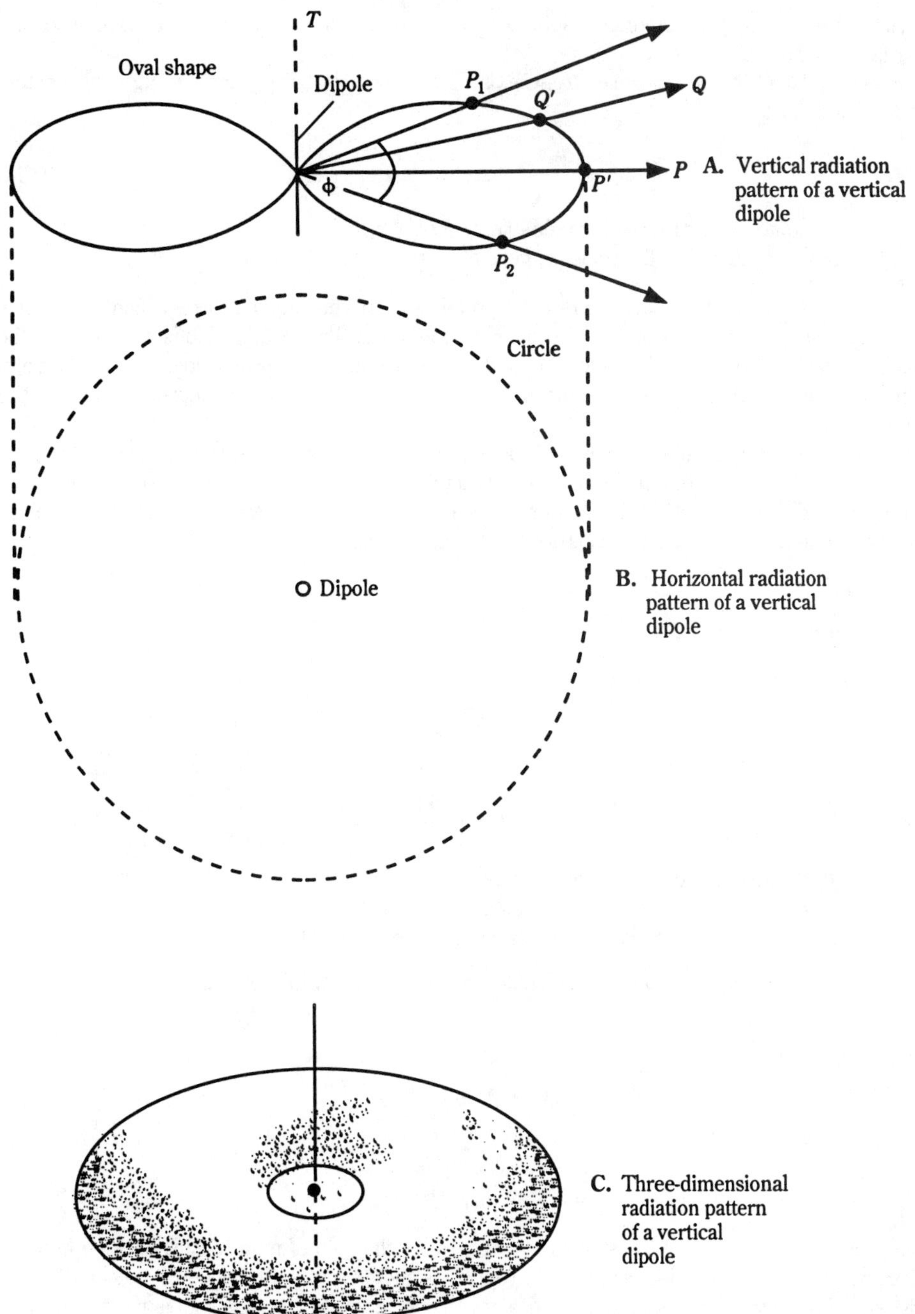

Fig. 10-19 The radiation pattern surrounding a vertical dipole.

a circular field strength contour. In practice, such a contour is distorted, which is caused by irregularities in the terrain.

The value of the vertical field strength, $\mathcal{E}$, in the horizontal plane surrounding a thin center-fed vertical dipole, is:

$$\mathcal{E} = \frac{60\, I_A}{d} \text{ volts per meter (v/m)} \tag{10-20}$$

where: I_A = antenna current at the feedpoint (A)
d = distance from the transmitting dipole (m)

The field strength is therefore directly proportional to the antenna current, and is inversely proportional to the distance from the transmitting antenna. This relationship is only true for the radiated field; for the induction field, the field strength is inversely proportional to the square of the distance. Therefore, the induction field is only important in the immediate vicinity of the antenna.

Because the transmitter's operating power is directly proportional to the square of the antenna current, the radiated field strength is directly proportional to the square root of the transmitter power. For example, a thin center-fed dipole has a radiated resistance of 73.2 Ω, so if the RF power delivered to the antenna is 1 kW, the antenna current is:

$$I_A = \sqrt{\frac{P}{R_A}}$$

$$= \sqrt{\frac{1000 \text{ W}}{73.2\ \Omega}}$$

$$= 3.696 \text{ A}$$

Therefore:

$$P = I_A^2\, R_A$$

and:

$$R_A = \frac{P}{I_A^2} \tag{10-21}$$

where: P = the operating power by the direct method (W)
I_A = the antenna current at the antenna feedpoint (A)
R_A = the antenna resistance at the antenna feedpoint (Ω)

The field strength at a position one mile (= 1609.3 m) from the antenna is:

$$\mathcal{E} = \frac{60\, I_A}{d}$$

$$= \frac{60 \times 3.696}{1609.3}$$

$$= 0.1378 \text{ volts per meter}$$

$$= 137.8 \text{ millivolts per meter}$$

This value is used as the FCC standard to determine the gain of more sophisticated antennas. For example, when parasitic elements as reflectors and directors are added to a dipole, the radiated RF power is concentrated in particular directions, so the antenna gain is increased. This gain can either be considered in terms of field strength or power.

From measurements taken at a distance of 1 mile from the antenna, the *field gain* is the ratio of the field strength produced by the complex antenna system to the field strength (137.8 mV/m) that is created by a simple ideal dipole (assuming that this dipole is capable of directly replacing the complex antenna); in both cases, the antenna power is 1 kW. Because the square of the field intensity is directly proportional to the radiated power, the *power gain* of the antenna is equal to (field gain)^2 and is either expressed as a ratio or in dB. Sometimes the term *antenna system power gain* is used; this generally takes into account the transmission-line loss.

The *effective radiated power (ERP)* is the power propagated along the axis of the principal radiation lobe associated with a directional antenna.

The equations are:

$$ERP = \textit{rf carrier power input to the transmission line} \times \textit{antenna system power gain ratio} \quad (10\text{-}22)$$

$$= \textit{RF carrier power delivered to the antenna} \times \textit{antenna power gain ratio} \quad (10\text{-}23)$$

$$= \textit{RF carrier power delivered to the antenna} \times \textit{antenna field gain}^2 \quad (10\text{-}24)$$

In addition:

Antenna power gain in dB:

$$= 10 \log_{10} \textit{antenna power gain ratio} \quad (10\text{-}25)$$

$$= 20 \log_{10} \textit{antenna field gain ratio} \quad (10\text{-}26)$$

$$= \textit{power gain of antenna system in dB} + \textit{transmission line loss in dB} \quad (10\text{-}27)$$

Before attempting some of the following questions, you should refer to chapter 2, which covers the topic of decibels.

* **Question 10-21** The rods of a vertical Hertz antenna are shortened in length. As a result, the:

A. antenna behaves as an inductive load
B. impedance of the antenna decreases
C. resonant frequency of the antenna increases
D. radiated power from the antenna increases
E. directivity of the antenna in the horizontal plane increases

Answer Choice C. From EQ. 10-18, the resonant frequency,

$$f = \frac{468}{\textit{length of Hertz antenna} \text{ (ft)}} \text{ MHz}$$

If the length is shortened, the resonant frequency increases.

* **Question 10-22** If the Hertz antenna is too short, this dipole can be brought to resonance by:

A. adding a capacitor in series with the antenna
B. lowering the frequency of the transmitter
C. adding an inductor in series with the antenna
D. adding a capacitor in parallel with the antenna
E. using a short length of transmission line

Answer Choice C. If the antenna is too short, it behaves as a capacitive load and can therefore be brought to resonance by adding an inductor in series.

* **Question 10-23** At a distance of 0.25 mile from a transmitting antenna, the field strength is found to 560 μV/m. The field strength at a distance of one mile is:

A. 35 μV/m B. 140 μV/m C. 70 μV/m D. 2240 μV/m E. 1120 μV/m

Answer Choice B. From EQ. 10-20, the value of the field strength is inversely proportional to the distance from the antenna. Therefore, if the distance is quadrupled, the field strength will be quartered so that its new value is: (1/4) × 560 = 140 μV/m.

* **Question 10-24** The RF power to a transmitter's antenna is 12.5 kW. If the antenna's power gain is 3 dB, the effective radiated power is:

A. 37.5 kW B. 25 kW C. 12.5 kW D. 6.25 kW E. 50 kW

Answer Choice B. Refer to TABLE 2-3. A +3-dB gain is equivalent to a power ratio of 2 so that the effective radiated power is: 2 × 12.5 = 25 kW.

* **Question 10-25** A transmission line is 200 ft long and its input RF power is 500 W. The line has an attenuation of 3 dB/100 ft and feeds an antenna whose power gain is 9 dB. The effective radiated power is:

A. 125 W B. 250 W C. 750 W D. 1000 W E. 1500 W

Answer Choice D. Overall dB gain = (−3 dB × 200 ft/100ft) +9 dB = +3 dB. Because a +3-dB gain is equivalent to a power ratio of 2, the effective radiated power is: 2 × 500 W = 1000 W.

* **Question 10-26** The total length of a Hertz dipole is increased from 2.5 to 2.8 feet. As a result, the antenna's:

A. input impedance is capacitive
B. radiated power increases
C. resonant frequency decreases
D. power gain increases
E. input impedance falls

Answer Choice C. The resonant frequency is inversely proportional to the antenna's length (EQ. 10-18). Consequently, if the length is increased, the resonant frequency decreases.

* **Question 10-27** A transmission line introduces a loss of 7 dB and is used to feed an antenna array, whose power gain is 3 dB. If the input RF power to the transmission line is 1000 W, the effective radiated power is:

A. 800 W B. 2000 W C. 200 W D. 300 W E. 400 W

Answer Choice E. Refer to TABLE 2-3. A loss of 7 dB is equivalent to a power ratio of 1/5, whereas a gain of 3 dB is the same as a power ratio of 2. Therefore, the effective radiated power is 1000 × 2 × 1/5 = 400 W.

* **Question 10-28** A Hertz antenna is operating on a frequency of 2182 kHz and consists of a horizontal wire that is slung between two towers. The frequency of its third harmonic is:

A. 6546 kHz B. 727 kHz C. 4364 kHz D. 6.55 MHz E. choices A and D are true

Answer Choice E. Frequency of the third harmonic = 3 × 2182 = 6546 kHz = 6.546 MHz, rounded off. Choices A and D are true.

* **Question 10-29** A vertical Hertz dipole:

A. is omnidirectional in the horizontal plane
B. is omnidirectional in the vertical plane
C. is unidirectional in a vertical plane
D. receives equally well from all horizontal directions
E. choices A and D are true

Answer Choice E. Refer to FIG. 10-19. Choices A and D are both true.

* **Question 10-30** Where are the positions of maximum and minimum values of effective voltage and current on a resonant Hertz dipole?

A. maximum voltage and current exist at the center of the antenna
B. maximum voltage and current exist at the ends of the antenna
C. maximum voltage and minimum current exist at the center of the antenna
D. minimum voltage and maximum current exist at the center of the antenna
E. minimum voltage and minimum current exist at the ends of the antenna

Answer Choice D. Refer to FIG. 10-15C.

10-5. Parasitic elements

A vertical Hertz dipole has a circular (omnidirectional) radiation pattern in the horizontal plane. The directional properties can be modified by adding parasitic elements to the antenna system. These parasitic elements are metal structures (for example, rods) that are not electrically connected (nondriven) and are placed in the vicinity of the driven dipole. The radiated field from the dipole induces a voltage and current distribution on the parasitic element, which then reradiates the signal. At any position in space, the total field strength will be the phasor resultant of the field radiated from the dipole and the reradiated field from the parasitic element.

Let the parasitic element be in the form of a rod that is more than $\lambda/2$ long (FIG. 10-20). This rod therefore behaves inductively and, as a result of various phase relationships, its reradiated field reinforces the dipole field in the X direction, but the two fields tend to cancel in the Y direction. The parasitic element therefore behaves as a reflector because its effect is to increase the radiation in the forward direction (from the parasitic rod toward the dipole) at the expense of the radiation in the backward direction. By comparing the field strengths along the axes of the two lobes, you can calculate the *front-to-back* ratio, as defined by the ratio of the forward field strength to the backward field strength. For a single reflector rod, the front-to-back ratio can be adjusted up to a value of 3.1; to take into account the reduction in field strength between the dipole and the parasitic elements, the separation and the length of the reflector rod are typically optimized to 0.1λ and 0.55λ, respectively.

If the length of the parasitic rod is reduced to less than half of the physical wavelength (FIG. 10-21), the rod behaves capacitively. This parasitic element now behaves as a director, because it directs the radiation toward the major lobe. Typically, the length of the director rod is 0.45 of the physical wavelength and its separation from the driven dipole is 0.1λ.

A combination of driven dipole, a reflector rod, and a director rod forms a Yagi array (FIG. 10-22), which has a power gain of 5 to 7 dB. The power gain can be further increased by adding additional director rods. With the major lobe further increased at the expense of the minor lobe, the Yagi system is a unidirectional antenna.

* **Question 10-31** The effect of adding parasitic elements to a Hertz dipole, is to:

A. increase the antenna's power gain
B. make the antenna more omnidirectional
C. make the antenna more unidirectional
D. reduce its resonant frequency
E. choices A and C are true

Answer Choices A and C are both true. Choice E. The addition of parasitic elements to a dipole increases its directional characteristics and raises its power gain.

* **Question 10-32** The reason for adding parasitic elements to a $\lambda/2$ antenna is to:

A. reduce the antenna's *Q* value
B. reduce the antenna's resonant frequency
C. increase the antenna's directivity

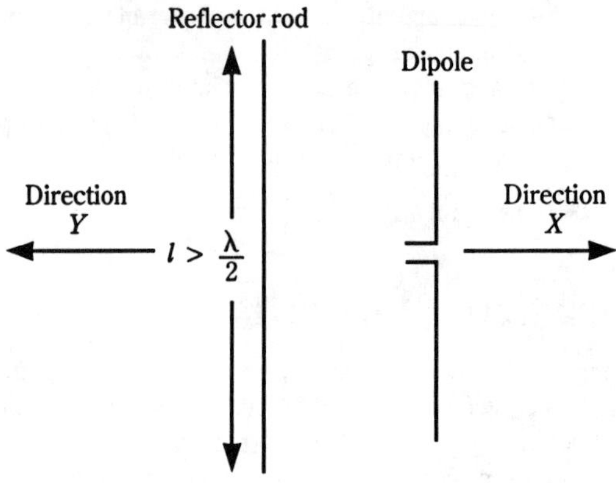

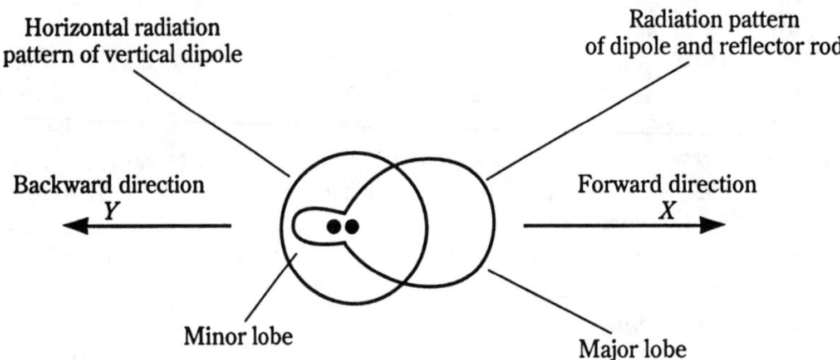

Fig. 10-20 The principle of the reflector parasitic element.

D. lower the antenna's power gain
E. increase the power in the backward direction

Answer Choice C.

* **Question 10-32** It is required to increase the directional properties of a Hertz dipole, which is used for reception purposes. This can be done by:

A. increasing the dipole's length
B. adding an inductor in series with the dipole
C. adding a capacitor in series with the dipole
D. reducing the dipole's length
E. adding parasitic elements

Answer Choice E.

10-6. Stacking antennas (driven arrays)

The unidirectional antenna system can be formed by using a driven dipole together with one or more parasitic elements. Even greater directivity and power gain can be obtained from an array

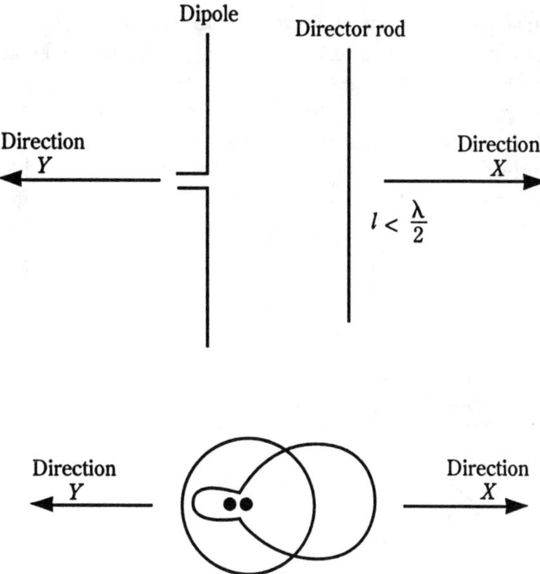

Fig. 10-21 The principle of the director parasitic element.

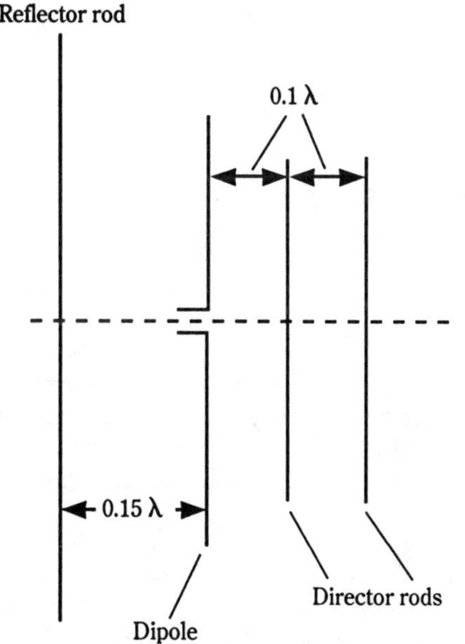

Fig. 10-22 The unidirectional Yagi antenna.

of driven antennas whose fields tend to reinforce in the required direction and to cancel in other directions. This effect is achieved by optimizing the spacing of the antennas and the phase relationships between their currents.

The two basic arrangements of stacked antennas are called *broadside* and *collinear.* In the simplest broadside example, two vertical dipoles are spaced $\lambda/2$ apart horizontally and are then fed in phase. Maximum radiation will then occur in the two horizontal directions, X, and Y (FIG. 10-23A), where the distances to the centers of the dipoles are equal. By contrast, there would ideally be no resultant radiation in the horizontal directions, *P* and *Q*, because the two distances would differ by a $\lambda/2$. This would introduce a 180° phase difference between the two dipole fields at any position along the *P* and *Q* directions so that the fields would tend to cancel; this is illustrated in the horizontal radiation pattern of FIG. 10-23B. Relative to the antennas, the horizontal-radiation pattern is rotated through a right-angle if the dipoles are fed 180° out of phase.

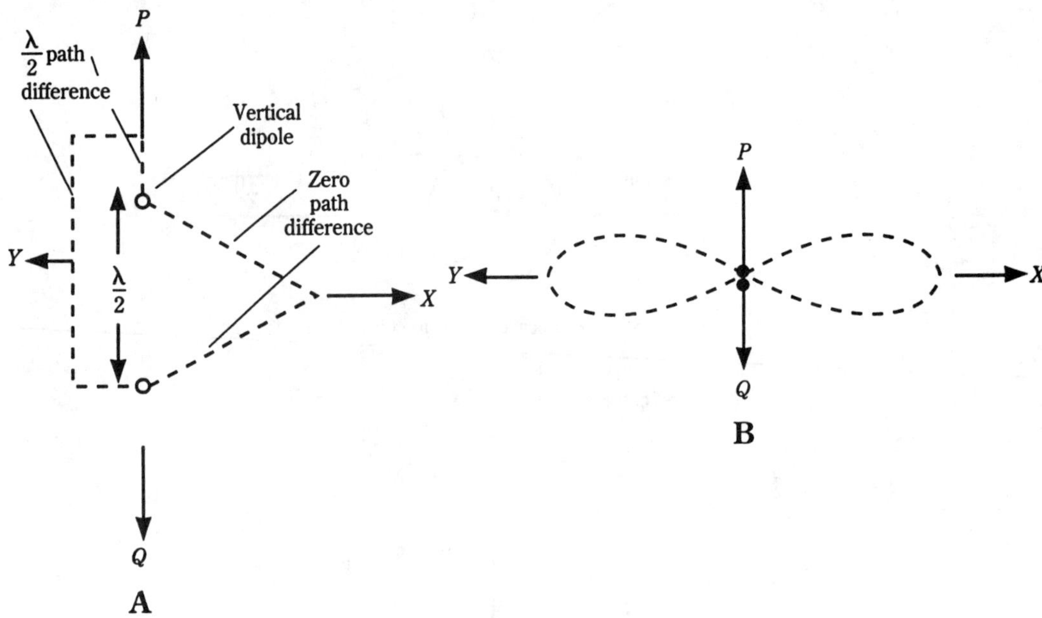

Fig. 10-23 Two dipoles in a broadside array.

Increased directivity is obtained by using a greater number of broadside antennas. For example, if five vertical dipoles are arranged along a line with $\lambda/2$ spacing between adjacent dipoles (FIG. 10-24A), the total length of the array is 2λ, and its radiation pattern is illustrated in FIG. 10-24B. Although the major lobes are more pronounced, there are also a number of parasitic or minor lobes.

In a simple collinear arrangement, two horizontal dipoles are placed side by side, with their centers separated by about a wavelength. Along certain directions in the horizontal plane, the distances to the centers of the dipoles will differ by $\lambda/2$ so that cancellation will occur. If the collinear array is increased to four dipoles, which are spaced $\lambda/2$ apart, the horizontal pattern consists of two major and four parasitic lobes (FIG. 10-25).

* **Question 10-33** A receiver is connected to a number of stacked antennas which are positioned at various angles to each other. The purpose of this antenna array is to:

A. provide an omnidirectional reception pattern
B. increase the magnitude of the received signal
C. provide a unidirectional reception pattern

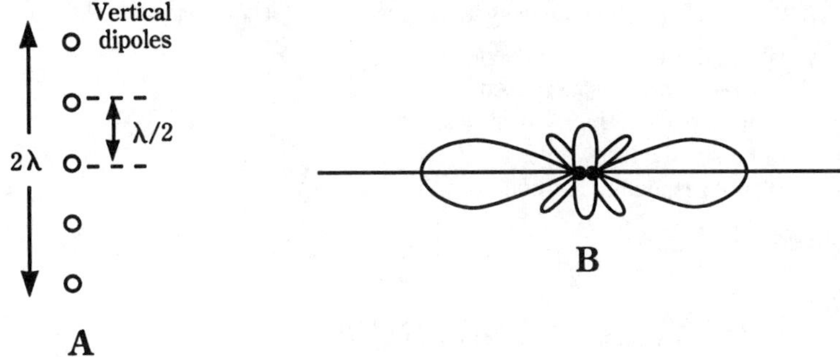

Fig. 10-24 Four dipoles in a broadside array.

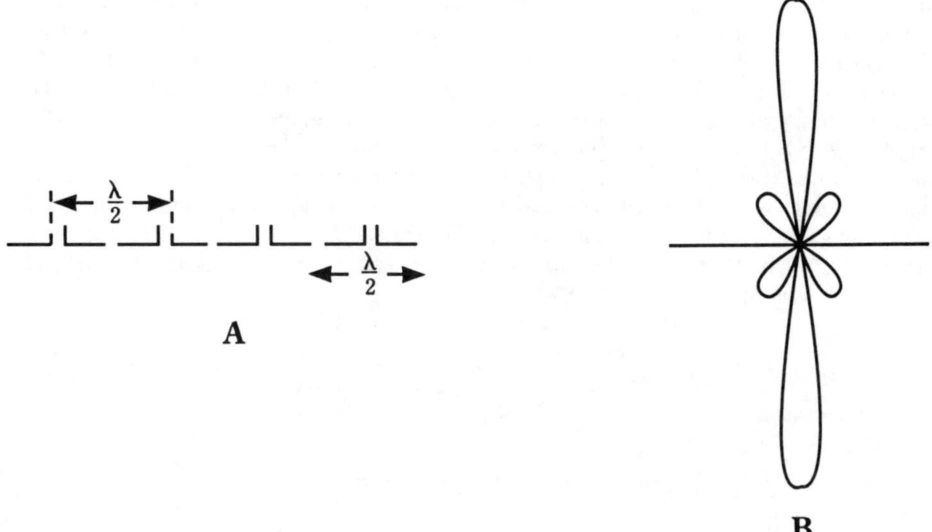

Fig. 10-25 Four dipoles in a collinear array.

D. increase the size of the major lobe at the expense of the side lobes
E. choices B, C, and D are true

Answer Choice E.

* **Question 10-34** A driven array of stacked antennas is connected to a transmitter. The reason for this array is to:

A. provide a decrease in the antenna's power gain
B. provide a more unidirectional radiation pattern in the forward direction
C. increase the amount of radiation in the backward direction
D. raise the resonant frequency of the antenna system
E. reduce the antenna's bandwidth

Answer Choice B.

* **Question 10-35** A receiver's antenna system consists of stacked elements. As a result the:

A. selectivity of the array is increased
B. sensitivity of the array is increased
C. resonant frequency of the array is reduced
D. signal-to-noise ratio is lowered
E. array will not respond to harmonics

Answer Choice B.

10-7. The Marconi antenna

At an operating frequency of 2 MHz, the required physical length of a resonant Hertz dipole is 468/2 (MHZ) = 234 feet. It is difficult to position a vertical antenna of this size so that it is remote from ground. However, the dipole could be in the form of a longwire antenna, slung horizontally between two towers, from which the antenna is insulated (FIG. 10-26). Clearly, the vertical Hertz antenna is not a practical proposition at low frequencies and is replaced by the $\lambda/4$ unipole or *Marconi antenna.* The Marconi antenna can be regarded as a Hertz dipole, in which the lower half is replaced by a nonradiating ground-image antenna (FIG. 10-27A). Unlike the Hertz antenna, ground is an integral part of the Marconi antenna system; this also means that the Hertz dipole is balanced with both $\lambda/4$ sections mounted remote from ground. The Marconi unipole is unbalanced, because part of the antenna is ground itself. In the same way, the twin line with neither conductor grounded is a balanced transmission line, and a coaxial cable is unbalanced with its outer conductor grounded at intervals along its length. For the $\lambda/4$ Marconi antenna, the vertical radiation pattern will be the same as the pattern for the top half of the vertical dipole; the horizontal pattern will again be a circle (FIG. 10-27B).

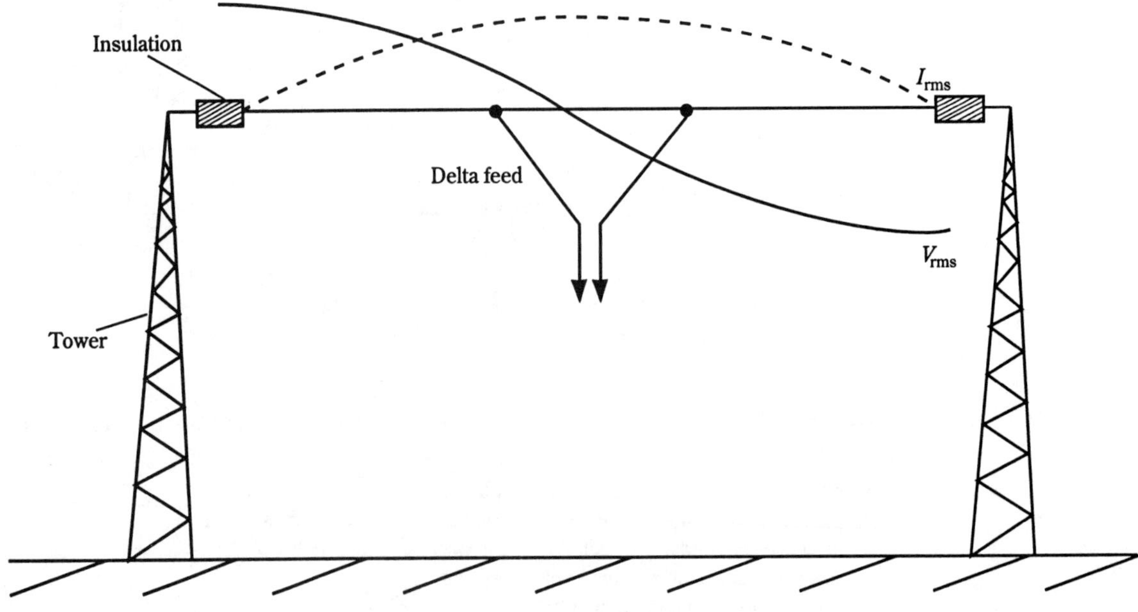

Fig. 10-26 The horizontal Hertz wire antenna.

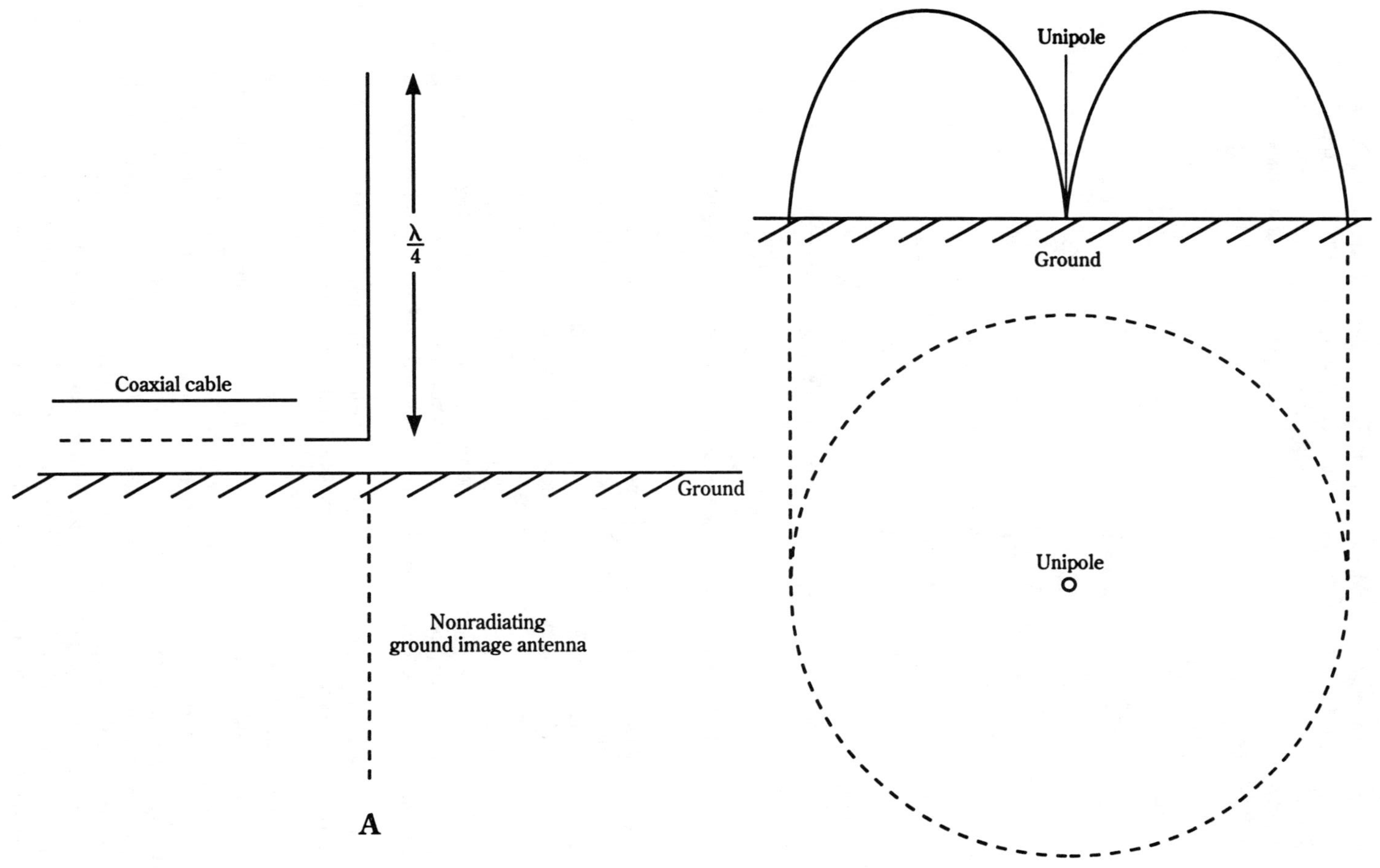

Fig. 10-27 The quarter-wave Marconi unipole antenna.

The distributed inductance of the Marconi antenna is associated with the vertical $\lambda/4$ rod, and the distributed capacitive exists between the rod and ground (FIG. 10-28). It is therefore impossible to operate with a horizontal Marconi antenna; this compares with the Hertz dipole, which can be mounted either vertically or horizontally. Consequently, all Marconi antennas radiate only vertically polarized waves.

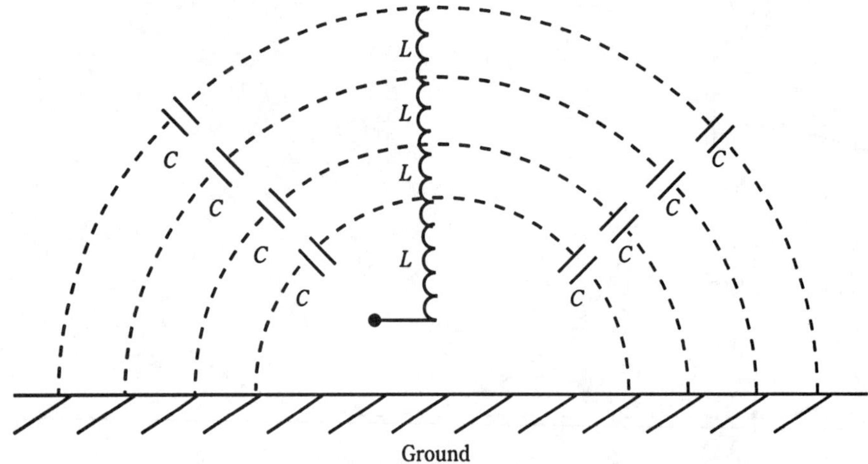

Fig. 10-28 Distributed inductance and capacitance of the Marconi antenna.

The effective voltage and current distribution on the resonant Marconi antenna is comparable with the distribution on the upper half of the Hertz dipole (FIG. 10-29). If the $\lambda/4$ antenna is end-fed by an unbalanced coaxial cable, the radiation resistance is $73.2/2 = 36.6\ \Omega$, which is the effective resistive load of a resonant Marconi antenna. The electrical $\lambda/4$ is given by the expression $246/f$ feet, and the Marconi antenna's physical length is $234/f$ feet, where f is the frequency in MHz. If the operating frequency is below the resonant value, the unipole is too short and behaves capacitively; however, the antenna can be tuned to resonance by adding an inductor in series (FIG. 10-30A). When operating above the resonant frequency, the antenna is too long, behaves inductively, and can be tuned to resonance with the aid of a series capacitor (FIG. 10-30B).

One type of practical Marconi antenna is the vertical whip (a rod that is flexible to a limited extent); an end-fed whip antenna is commonly mounted on the top of an automobile so that the roof can act as the required ground plane. If the antenna is positioned in the vicinity of the rear bumper, most of the ground plane will be provided by the road surface. If it is required to operate a whip antenna at the top of a building, it is necessary to provide the antenna with an apparent ground or *counterpoise*. This normally consists of a wire structure that is mounted just beneath the feedpoint of the antenna and is connected to the outer conductor of the coaxial cable. The main distributed capacitance then exists between the whip and the counterpoise, which itself acts as a large capacitance in relation to ground. For this reason, the counterpoise should be normally larger in size than the antenna, and must be well insulated from ground.

Another type of vertical radiator is a *steel tower*, which can be tapered to optimize the current distribution. Such towers can either be end-fed or shunt-fed (FIG. 10-31). With shunt feeding, the bottom of the tower is connected directly to ground, and the center conductor of the coaxial cable is joined to a point, P, on the tower, where the resistive component of the antenna's impedance

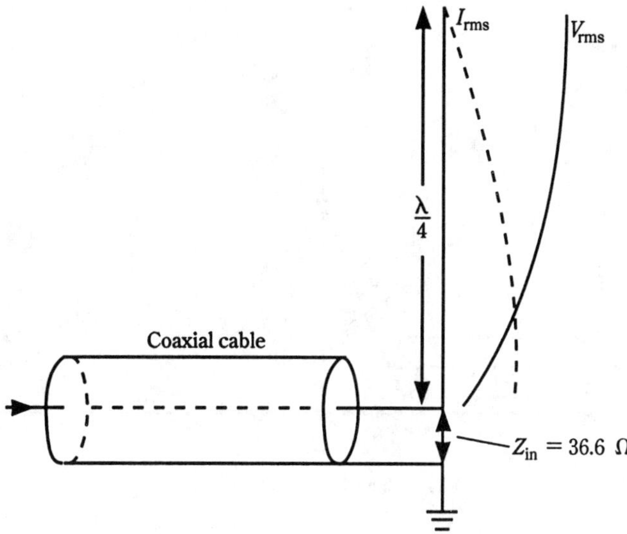

Fig. 10-29 Effective voltage and current distribution on a Marconi antenna.

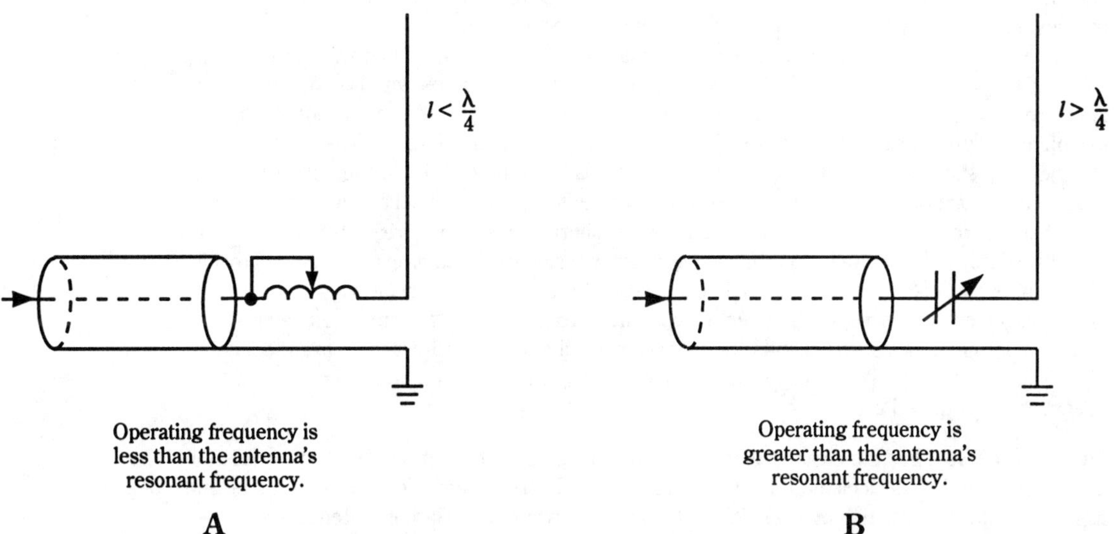

Fig. 10-30 Tuning a Marconi antenna to resonance.

can be matched to the surge impedance of a coaxial cable. With the grounded end behaving as a short circuit, the impedance at point P, is inductive and this reactance is canceled by the capacitor, C. It is worth mentioning that the dc resistance between P and ground is virtually zero.

To improve the quality of the ground and therefore reduce ground losses, it is common practice to add a ground system, which consists of a number of bare copper conductors, arranged radially and connected to a center point beneath the antenna. The center point is then joined to the outer conductor of the coaxial cable. These ground radials are from $\lambda/10$ to $\lambda/2$ in length and

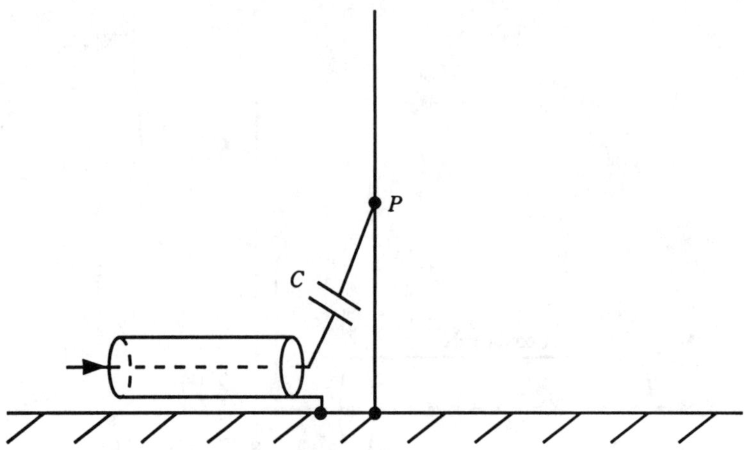

Fig. 10-31 Shunt-feeding a vertical antenna.

are buried a short distance down; in addition, the ground can be further improved by laying copper mats beneath the surface. The ultimate purpose of the radial ground system is to improve the antenna efficiency, defined as the ratio of the RF power radiated from the antenna as useful electromagnetic energy to the RF power applied to the antenna feedpoint.

A tower can either be self-supporting or supported by guy wires. Such wires can pick up some of the live transmitted radiation; reradiation from the guy wires will then occur and will interfere with the EM wave transmitted from the antenna. To keep the reradiation effect to a minimum, an insulator is connected to each end of the guy wire, and intermediate insulators are attached at a spacing of about $\lambda/10$ apart. These insulators are normally of the porcelain "egg" type so that if one of the insulators breaks, the guy wire still provides mechanical support.

If at low frequencies, the vertical antenna is too short for mechanical reasons, the amount of useful vertically polarized radiation can be increased by using *top loading;* examples are shown in FIGS. 10-32A and 10-32B. Because the current is zero at the open end of the antenna, the inverted "L" arrangement will increase the effective current distribution over the antenna's vertical section. A more practical construction is the metallic spoked wheel, which will increase the amount of the distributed capacitance to ground, and will therefore lower the antenna's resonant frequency to the required value.

* **Question 10-36** From measurements, it is determined that the input power to a transmission line is 100 W and the associated reflected power is 1 W. If the transmission line is 50 ft long and has a distributed attenuation of 6 dB/100 ft, the output power to the Marconi antenna is:

A. 49.5 W B. 50 W C. 99 W D. 47 W E. 48.5 W

Answer Choice A.

$$\textit{Effective power input} = 100 - 1 = 99 \text{ W}$$

$$\textit{Total attenuation of line} = \frac{6 \text{ dB} \times 50 \text{ ft}}{100 \text{ ft}} = 3 \text{ dB}$$

Refer to TABLE 2-3. An attenuation of 3 dB corresponds to a power ratio of 0.5.

$$\textit{Output power to the antenna} = 0.5 \times 99 = 49.5 \text{ W}$$

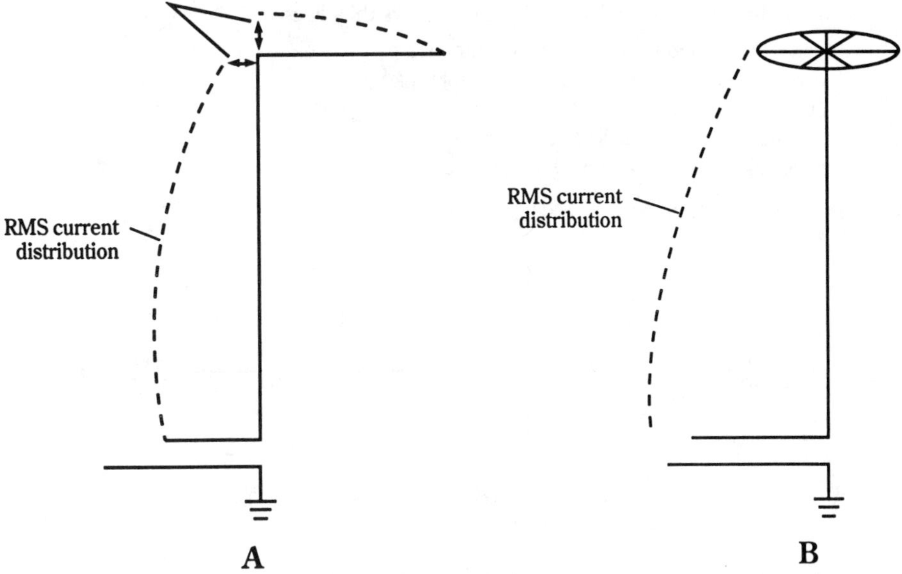

Fig. 10-32 Examples of "top-loading" an antenna.

* **Question 10-37** The electrical length of a Marconi antenna can be increased by adding a (an):

A. inductor in series
B. capacitor in series
C. capacitor in parallel
D. resistor in parallel
E. inductor in parallel

Answer Choice A. Refer to FIG. 10-30A.

* **Question 10-38** If a capacitor is added in series with a Marconi antenna:

A. the length of the antenna will be electrically shorter
B. the input impedance will be unchanged
C. its resonant frequency will increase
D. the radiation pattern will become more unidirectional
E. choices A and C are true

Answer Choice E. Refer to FIG. 10-30B.

* **Question 10-39** A Marconi antenna radiates a fundamental power output of 500 W. If the power output at the second harmonic is 0.5 W, the attenuation of the second-harmonic component, when compared with the fundamental component, is:

A. 1000 dB B. 5 dB C. 20 dB D. 30 dB E. 10 dB

Answer Choice D.

$$N = 10 \log \frac{0.5 \text{ W}}{500 \text{ W}}$$

$$= 10 \log 0.001 \qquad (2\text{-}26)$$

$$= 10 \times (-3) = -30 \text{ dB}$$

Attenuation of the second harmonic component is 30 dB.

* **Question 10-40** The broken line in FIG. 10-33 shows the effective:

A. voltage distribution on a λ/2 Hertz antenna
B. current distribution on a λ/4 Marconi antenna
C. current distribution on a λ/2 Hertz antenna
D. voltage distribution on a λ/4 Marconi antenna
E. impedance distribution on a λ/4 Marconi antenna

Answer Choice A. Refer to FIG. 10-26.

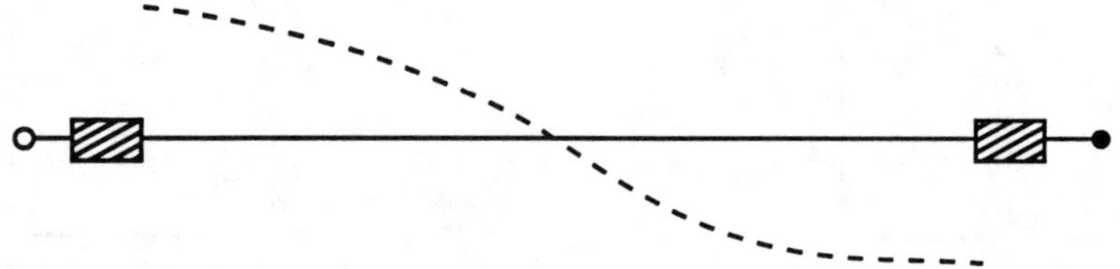

Fig. 10-33 The illustration for question 10-40.

* **Question 10-41** The electrical length of a Marconi antenna may be shortened by adding a (an):

A. parallel LC resonant circuit in series
B. series LC resonant circuit
C. capacitor in series
D. inductor in series
E. inductor in parallel

Answer Choice C. Refer to FIG. 10-30B.

* **Question 10-42** The broken line in FIG. 10-34 shows the effective:

A. voltage distribution on a λ/4 Marconi antenna
B. current distribution on a λ/2 Hertz antenna
C. current distribution on a λ/4 Marconi antenna
D. voltage distribution on a λ/2 Hertz antenna
E. radiated power distribution on a λ/4 Marconi antenna

Answer Choice B. Refer to FIG. 10-26.

* **Question 10-43** When a vertical antenna is shunt-fed, the:

A. the impedance at the feed point is capacitive
B. impedance at the feedpoint is inductive
C. RF impedance between the feedpoint and ground is zero
D. dc resistance between the feedpoint and ground is zero
E. choices B and D are true

Answer Choice E. Refer to FIG. 10-31.

* **Question 10-44** A λ/4 Marconi antenna radiates a signal whose frequency is 520 kHz. The frequency of the fifth harmonic is:

A. 2600 MHz B. 104 kHz C. 2.6 MHz D. 2600 kHz E. choices C and D are true

Answer Choices C and D are true. Choice E.

Fig. 10-34 The illustration for question 10-42.

Frequency of the fifth harmonic:

$$\begin{aligned} f &= 5 \times 520 \text{ kHz} \\ &= 2600 \text{ kHz} \\ &= 2.6 \text{ MHz} \end{aligned}$$

* **Question 10-45** If an inductor is added in series with a vertical Marconi antenna:

A. the antenna will be electrically longer
B. resonant frequency will decrease
C. the antenna will be electrically shorter
D. the horizontal radiation pattern will no longer be omnidirectional
E. choices A and B are correct

Answer Choices A and B are true. Choice E.

* **Question 10-46** A vertical steel tower radiates a signal whose fundamental frequency is 450 kHz. The frequency of its seventh harmonic is:

A. 3150 kHz B. 3.15 MHz C. 3150 Hz D. 3150 MHz E. choices A and B are true

Answer Choices A and B are both true. Choice E.

Frequency of the seventh harmonic:

$$\begin{aligned} f &= 7 \times 450 \\ &= 3150 \text{ kHz} \\ &= 3.15 \text{ MHz} \end{aligned}$$

* **Question 10-47** It is required to increase the resonant frequency of an end-fed Marconi antenna. This can be achieved by:

A. adding a capacitor in series
B. adding an inductor in series
C. adding an inductor in parallel
D. reducing the physical length of the antenna
E. choices A and D are true

Answer Choice E. The shorter is the antenna, the higher is its resonant frequency (choice D). By adding a capacitor in series, the electrical length of the antenna is lowered (choice A).

* **Question 10-48** A transmitter is connected to a vertical Marconi antenna, which:

A. radiates equally well in all horizontal directions
B. radiates equally well in all vertical directions
C. has a unidirectional radiation pattern in the horizontal plane
D. requires a vertical antenna for the reception of the radiated signal
E. choices A and D are true

Answer Choices A and D are true. Choice E. The Marconi antenna has an omnidirectional radiation pattern in the horizontal plane (choice A). The radiated signal is vertically polarized and requires a vertical antenna for its reception (choice D).

10-8. The dummy antenna

The tuning and testing procedures for a transmitter must be carried out in radio silence and reduced power so that there is no radiation to cause interference problems. The antenna is therefore disconnected from its transmitter, which is then coupled to a dummy antenna whose circuitry is shown in FIG. 10-35. The electrical properties of the dummy antenna are a non-inductive resistance, R, (for low-power transmitters a light bulb can be used) in series with a capacitance, C. The purpose of the capacitor is to cancel the reactance of the coupling network, L, to the transmitter.

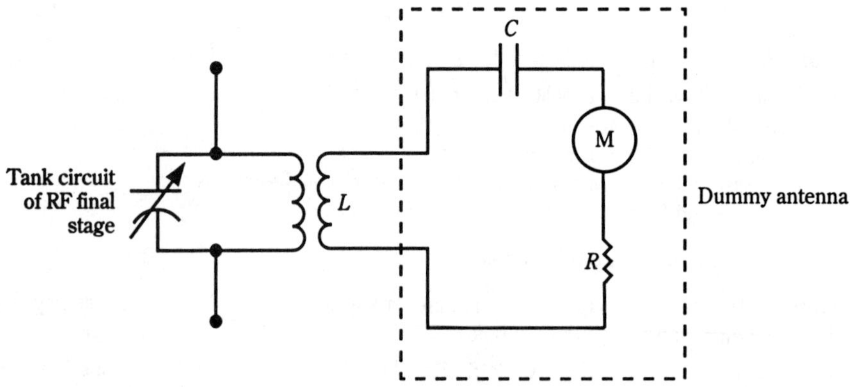

Fig. 10-35 The dummy antenna.

The meter, M, measures the RF current flowing through the dummy antenna so that the RF power, P, absorbed by the dummy antenna is:

$$P = I^2 R \text{ watts} \tag{10-28}$$

where: I = the RF current in the dummy antenna (A)
R = the resistance of the dummy antenna (Ω)

At full power, the value of P should be comparable with the normal operating power delivered to the antenna.

* **Question 10-49** During tuning and testing procedures, which must be carried with minimum radiation (radio silence), the transmitter is coupled to a (an):

A. λ/4 antenna
B. loop antenna
C. shortened Hertz antenna
D. array of parasitic elements
E. dummy antenna

Answer Choice E.

10-9. Microwave antenna with the parabolic reflector

At microwave frequencies of 1 GHz to 30 GHz, it is possible to design highly directive antenna systems of reasonable size. One of the most common systems uses a paraboloid as a "dish" reflector with a flared wave guide termination placed at the focus (FIG. 10-30A). If a paraboloid was infinitely large, the result of the reflection would be to produce a unidirectional beam with no spreading. However, with a paraboloid of practical dimensions, there is some degree of spreading and the radiation pattern then contains a major lobe (and a number of minor lobes), as illustrated in FIG. 10-36B. The full lobe is, of course, three dimensional. The pattern is only shown in one plane.

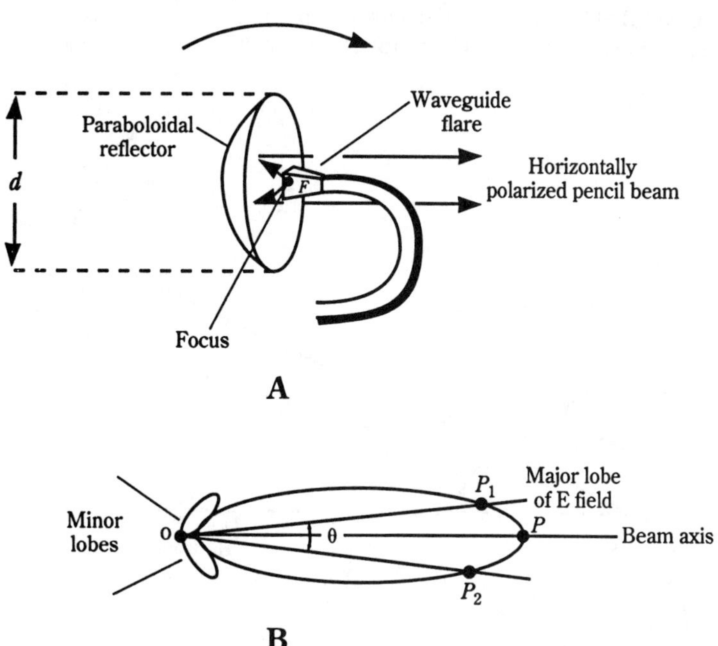

Fig. 10-36 A microwave antenna with a parabolic reflector.

Referring to the narrow major lobe that is produced by the antenna with the paraboloid reflector, the beamwidth in the horizontal plane is measured by the angle, P_1OP_2, where P_1 and P_2 are the half-power points. In radar systems, typical beamwidths are of the order of 1° to 5°. Because of the construction of the paraboloid, the horizontal and vertical beamwidths are not necessarily the same. For a microwave link, the normal beamwidth is 2°; with such narrow beamwidths, the power gains of the antenna systems are extremely high.

For a paraboloid reflector to be effective, the value of d must be greater than 10 wavelengths. Consequently, such reflectors would not be practical in the VHF band because of their excessive size.

The beamwidth is given by:

Beamwidth angle: $$\theta = \frac{70\lambda}{d} \text{ degrees} \quad (10\text{-}29)$$

With respect to the $\lambda/2$ dipole standard, the power gain, G_p, is given by:

$$G_p = 6\left(\frac{d}{\lambda}\right)^2 \quad (10\text{-}30)$$

where: λ = wavelength (m)
d = diameter of paraboloid (m)

Microwave antennas with parabolic dishes are also used to establish satellite communications either in the 6-GHz (uplink)/4-GHz (downlink) band or in the 14-GHz/11-GHz band. When aiming the microwave antenna at a geostationary satellite, there are two angles (FIG. 10-37) to consider:

- The angle (α) of elevation in the vertical plane
- The angle (β) of the bearing in the horizontal plane. The value of β is normally called the angle of *azimuth,* as measured from true North. In FIG. 10-37, the azimuth is 200°.

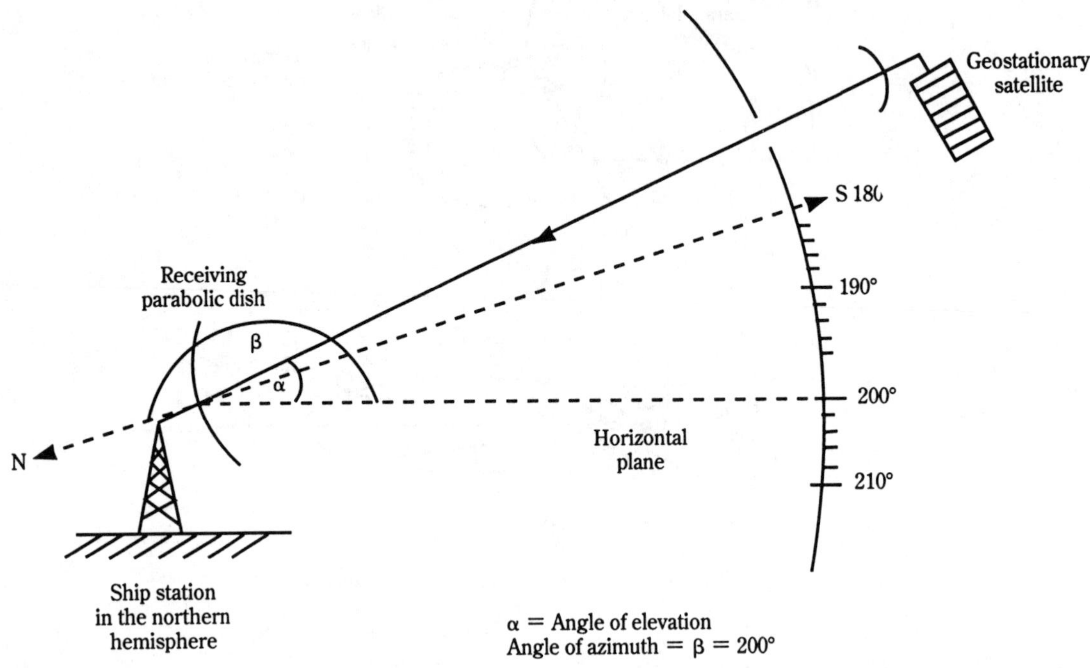

Fig. 10-37 Aiming a microwave antenna at a satellite.

* **Question 10-50** When aiming a ship-borne microwave antenna at a geostationary satellite, the azimuth is:

A. the angle of aim in the vertical plane
B. the angle of aim in the horizontal plane
C. normally measured from magnetic North
D. the angle between the vertical and the line of aim
E. an angle that can never exceed 90°

Answer Choice B.

* **Question 10-51** A marine radar set has a microwave antenna system whose azimuth is:

A. the angle of elevation measured in degrees
B. the angle of bearing in the horizontal plane and is measured in degrees

C. measured in degrees from true North
D. the angle that the diameter of the paraboloid subtends at the focus
E. choices B and C are true

Answer Choice E.

10-10. Propagation

The word *propagation* is derived from the Latin verb *propagare*—to travel, and describes the various ways by which a radio wave travels from the transmitting antenna to the receiving antenna. Start by considering a long $\lambda/2$ antenna, which is fed at one end by a coaxial cable with its outer conductor grounded. The 3-D radiation pattern of the wave resembles a large "doughnut" that is laying on the ground with the antenna as its center (FIG. 10-38A). Part of the radiated wave moves downward and outward in contact with the ground and is affected by the conditions at and below the surface of the earth. This component of the radiation is referred to as the *ground* or *surface wave.*

Higher up the antenna, the radiation is little affected by the ground conditions. This portion is called the *space* or *direct wave,* which travels in a practically straight line from the transmitting antenna to the receiving antenna (direct-line propagation). Operating in conjunction with the space wave is the ground *reflected wave* (FIG. 10-38B), by which the signal arrives at the receiving antenna through two different paths.

Toward the top of the antenna, the radiation moves outward and upward to the ionosphere, which is an ionized layer of gas (primarily hydrogen) that extends from about 35 to 250 miles above the earth's surface. This portion of the radiation is referred to as the *sky* or *indirect wave,* which is refracted by the ionosphere back to earth.

The ground, space, and sky waves are illustrated in FIG. 10-39. Primarily, the ground wave is used for long-distance communication by high-power transmitters at relatively low frequencies; as an example, the signals from commercial AM stations are carried by the ground wave. The space wave mainly operates at very high frequencies for both short-distance and long-distance communications; practical examples are TV and FM broadcasts, as well as communication systems that use satellites. The sky wave, which travels through the ionosphere, is used for long-distance fixed-service communications and operates in the shortwave band.

Ground wave

The ground wave can only be used with vertically polarized signals, which are radiated from a vertical antenna system. As the wave passes over and through the ground, there is a velocity difference between the portions that travel through the air and through the earth. As a result, the wave front leans forward and there is an electric field component, which is parallel to the earth's surface. This creates a voltage stress so that ground currents flow and energy is absorbed from the wave. At the same time, the magnetic field component of the radio wave cuts the earth and induces eddy currents, so further energy is absorbed. With a horizontally polarized wave, the losses would be enormous and the wave could be completely wiped out at a short distance from the transmitting antenna.

For a vertically polarized wave, the range (because of ground losses) depends on the conductivity of the ground and the frequency used. The attenuation rises rapidly as the frequency is increased so that the ground-wave transmission is limited to frequencies between 5 kHz and 2 MHz. The lower end of this spectrum is used for long-distance submarine transmissions with extremely high-power transmitters. The wavelengths of these broadcasts are of the order of miles so that the ground wave can be *diffracted* or bent around the earth's surface, and the signal can be received well beyond the horizon by a submarine operating at periscope depth. In fact,

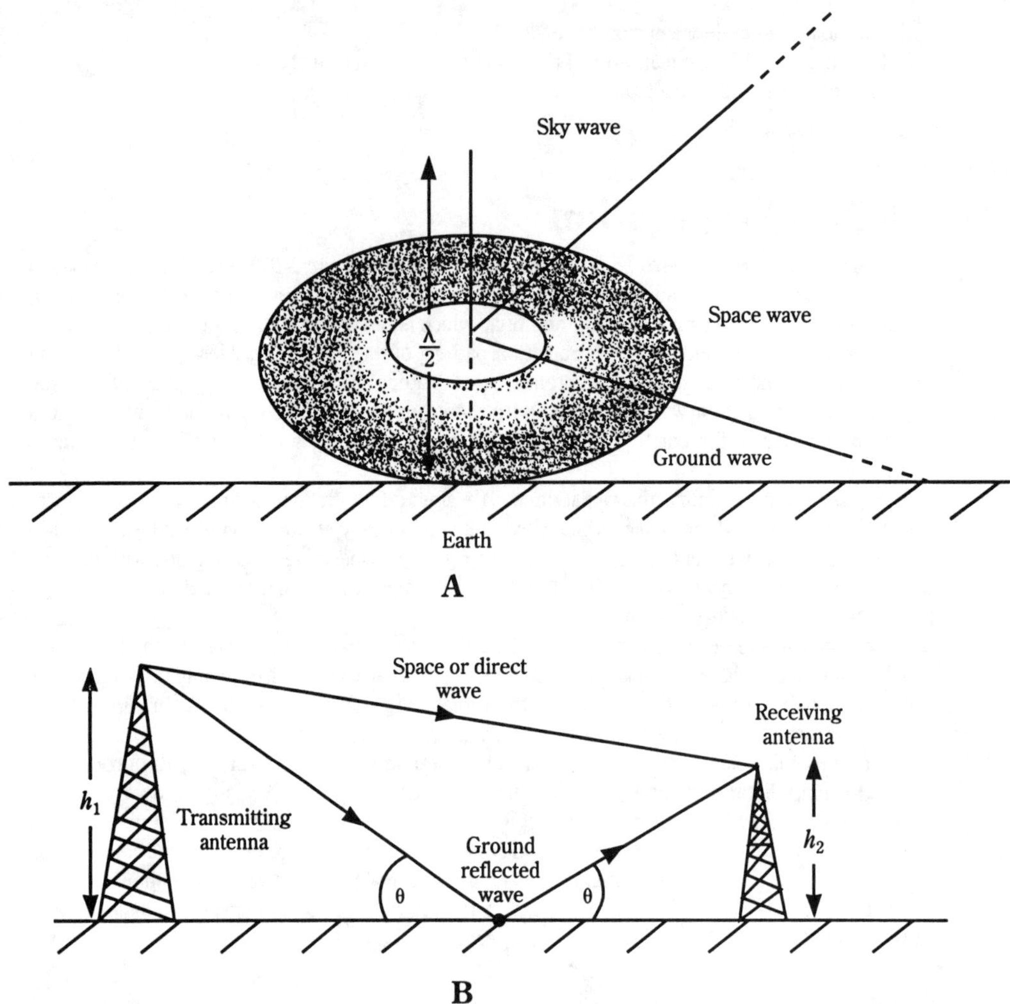

Fig. 10-38 Components of radiation from the half-wave antenna.

providing that the transmitter power is sufficient (up to 1 MW), the ground-wave coverage could be worldwide. The disadvantage of using the ground wave under these conditions is the need for enormous antenna systems that are relatively inefficient; as an example, one such system is slung between two mountains that are 20 miles apart. This antenna has an efficiency of about 15%.

Because the electrical properties of the earth, along which the ground wave travels, are relatively constant, the signal strength from a particular station does not vary greatly at any given point. This is essentially true in most localities, and is the main advantage of using ground wave, as opposed to sky wave for long-distance communications. Exceptions would be those areas with distinct rainy and dry seasons; in these cases, the difference in the amount of moisture causes the soil's conductivity to change. The conductivity of salt water is approximately 5000 times greater than that of dry soil. Transmitters for submarine communications are therefore built as close to the ocean's edge as possible to take advantage of the superior ground wave propagation over salt water.

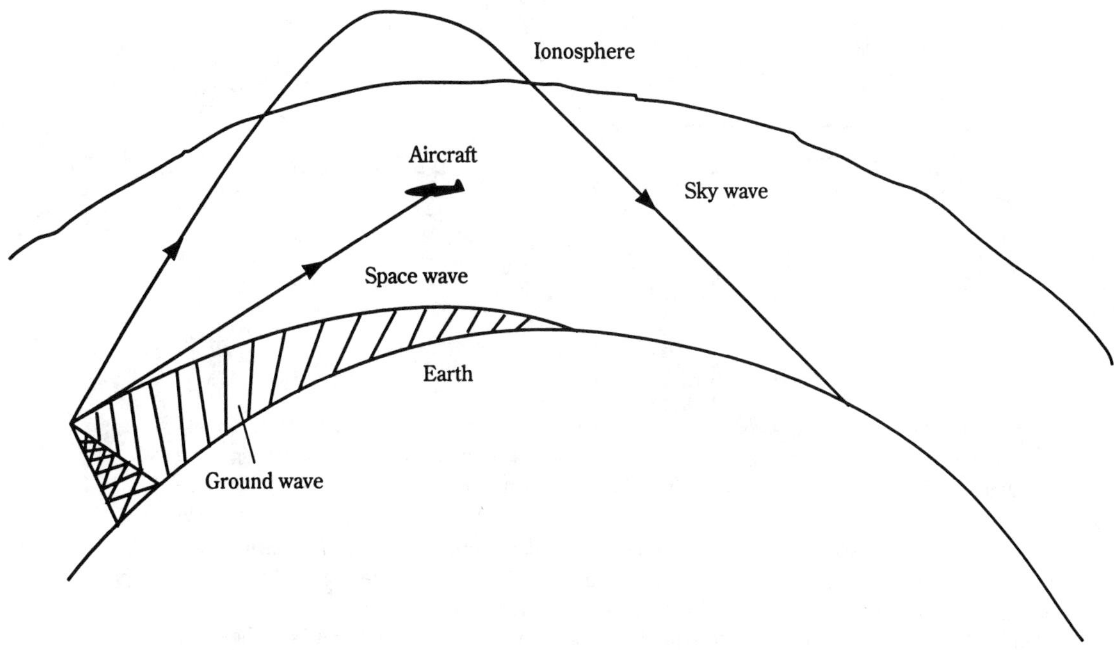

Fig. 10-39 Ground, space, and sky waves.

Another use of ground wave occurs in the *Long Range Navigation System (Loran C),* which uses a frequency of 100 kHz in the low frequency (LF) band. Earlier systems of the same type included Loran A and Loran B, but these are no longer operational. For still greater distances, there is the Omega navigational system, which uses a frequency of 10.2 kHz in the *very low frequency (VLF)* band.

Space wave

The *space wave* is the radiation component that travels in a practically straight line from the transmitting antenna to the receiving antenna. This method of propagation is the one most commonly used in modern communications; everyday examples are TV and FM broadcasts, as well as radar and microwave links. The frequencies used in these systems extend above 30 MHz. At these high frequencies, the ground-wave range is negligible. Radio waves in this part of the frequency spectrum cannot normally be refracted back to earth by the ionosphere, so sky-wave propagation is impossible.

If the transmitting and receiving antennas are both located on the ground, the range of the space wave is limited by the curvature of the earth (FIG. 10-40A). For example, the "hump" of the Atlantic Ocean between England and America is approximately 200 miles high and therefore communication by space wave between these two countries can only occur via satellite. Figure 10-40B shows the limiting line-of-sight condition, in which the line joining the tops of the antennas just grazes the earth's surface. The optical range is then given by:

$$\begin{aligned} D &= 1.23\,(\sqrt{h_1} + \sqrt{h_2}) \text{ land miles} \\ &= 1.06\,(\sqrt{h_1} + \sqrt{h_2}) \text{ nautical miles} \end{aligned} \qquad (10\text{-}31)$$

where: h_1, h_2 = antenna heights (feet)

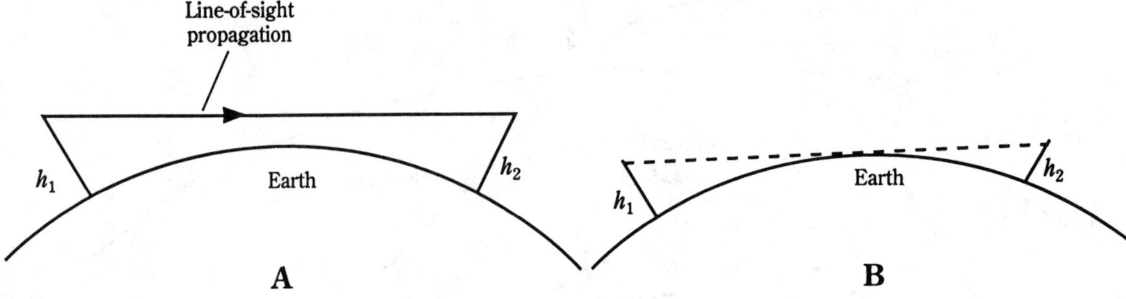

Fig. 10-40 Space-wave propagation.

In practice, the space wave is refracted by the earth's atmosphere so that 10% to 15% must be added to the optical range. As an example, calculate the maximum range when the transmitting and receiving dipoles are mounted on board two ships and each dipole is 64 feet above the surface of the sea. The optical range is $1.23 (\sqrt{64} + \sqrt{64}) = 1.23 \times 16 = 19.7$ land miles. After allowing an additional 10 to 15% for atmospheric refraction, the maximum radio range for marine communications is approximately 22 land miles or 20 sea miles. However, if one of these ships was communicating with an aircraft flying at 10,000 feet, the optical range increases to $1.23 (\sqrt{64} + \sqrt{10{,}000}) = 1.23 \times 108 = 133$ land miles and the maximum radio range is about 145 miles. For the same reason, it is customary to increase the possible range and service area by locating TV and FM antenna systems on mountain tops. In addition to the line-of-sight transmission and the atmosphere refraction, a further small increase in the range is caused by the diffraction around the earth's surface. This is particularly true when there is a sharp discontinuity (such as the top of a mountain). For a signal in the UHF band, the majority of the radiated power continues on in a straight line, but an appreciable amount is diffracted down the far side of the mountain (FIG. 10-41). This phenomenon is known as ***knife-edge diffraction*** (or refraction).

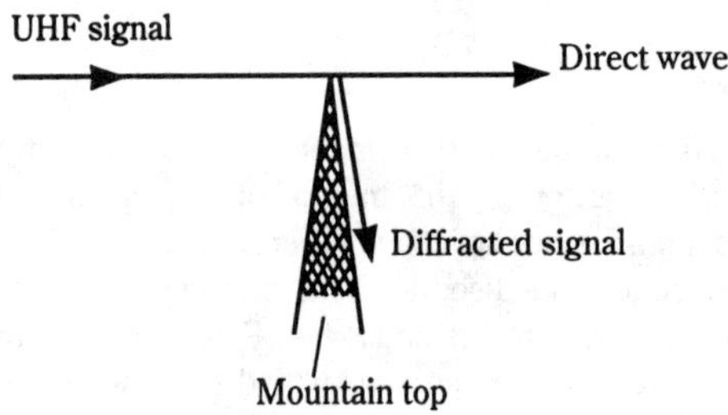

Fig. 10-41 Knife-edge diffraction.

Sky wave

The existence of the ionosphere is caused by the sun's ultraviolet radiation, which divides the neutral atoms of gas into positive ions and negative electrons. Such a medium is capable of refracting (bending) a radio wave. Provided that the amount of refraction is sufficient, some of the radiation from the transmitting antenna will be returned to the earth.

Figure 10-42A shows some sample rays emanating from an antenna system that is operating in the shortwave band. Provided that the frequency is sufficiently high, the ray (1), which is perpendicular to the edge of the ionosphere, passes through into outer space with no refraction.

As the angle of incidence (i) is increased, more refraction occurs until at a certain angle, the first sky wave (4) is returned to the earth. For angles of incidence greater than the critical value, the sample rays penetrate the ionosphere to a lesser depth, but their refraction occurs over a longer distance so that they suffer a greater degree of attenuation. Consequently, the extent of the reception zone is limited (FIG. 10-42B).

The *skip distance* (FIG. 10-42A) is the separation between the transmitting antenna and the point where the first sky wave is returned to the earth's surface. If the frequency is increased, the refraction in the ionosphere decreases, and the skip distance increases. Between all the

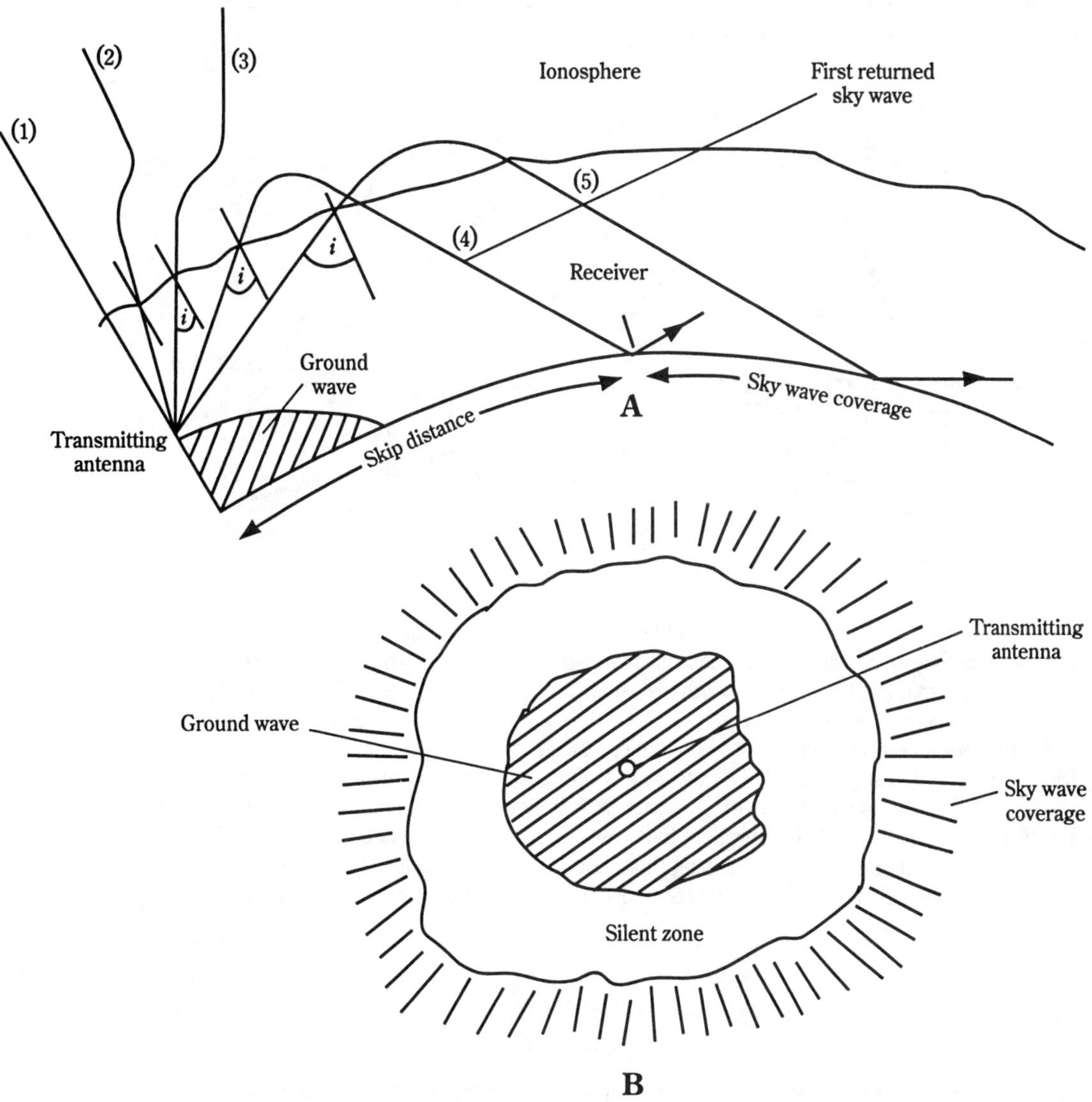

Fig. 10-42 Refraction of sky waves. skip distance and silent zone.

positions where the intensity of the ground wave has fallen below the noise level and the places where the sky waves are first returned, there is a skip or silent zone in which no reception is possible (FIG. 10-42B). The amount of the silent zone can be reduced by lowering the frequency. However, if the ground and sky-wave coverages overlap, the two received signals will have taken different paths and the result will be a form of interference fading.

The sky waves described so far have been single-hop transmissions, where the wave has been refracted only once in the ionosphere before being picked up by the receiver. However, it is possible for the wave to be refracted by the earth back into the ionosphere so that refraction occurs for a second time (FIG. 10-43). This process might be repeated for a number of times, and is referred to as *multihop transmission,* which can be used to transmit over long distances within the frequency range of 9 to 30 MHz. However, in general, single-hop transmissions result in greater field intensities than the multihop type.

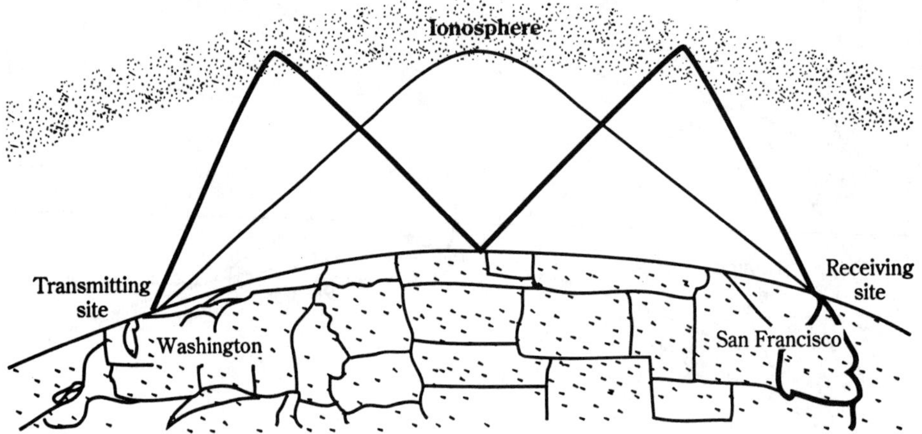

Fig. 10-43 Multihop transmission.

As illustrated in FIG. 10-43, it is possible for a receiver to pick up the signal by both single-hop and multihop transmission. Because the two paths are different, there will be interference fading. Notice that the transmitter and the receiver are located in different time zones. All time zones use *Universal Time Coordinated (UTC)* as a reference. This reference uses a 24-hour clock (military time) and is the time at 000° Longitude, which passes through the Greenwich Observatory in England. Consequently, UTC is the same as Greenwich Mean Time (GMT). For example, the time on the Pacific Coast of North America is eight hours behind GMT; consequently, 3 PM Pacific Standard Time (PST) is equivalent to 3 + 8 = 11 PM at Greenwich or 2300 hrs UTC.

Other USA time zones are Mountain Standard Time (MST) Central Standard Time (CST) and Eastern Standard Time (EST). The relationships between these times zones and UTC are:

$$\text{PST} + 8 \text{ hrs} = \text{UTC} \qquad (10\text{-}32)$$

$$\text{MST} + 7 \text{ hrs} = \text{UTC} \qquad (10\text{-}33)$$

$$\text{CST} + 6 \text{ hrs} = \text{UTC} \qquad (10\text{-}34)$$

$$\text{EST} + 5 \text{ hrs} = \text{UTC} \qquad (10\text{-}35)$$

At the equator, the center of each time zone is separated from the centers of its neighboring time zones by slightly more than 1000 miles.

Propagation under the various frequency bands

The following frequency bands were named at the result of the Atlantic City Conference (1947).

very low frequency (VLF)	3 to 30 kHz
low frequency (LF)	30 to 300 kHz
medium frequency (MF)	300 kHz to 3 MHz
high frequency (HF)	3 to 30 MHz
very high frequency (VHF)	30 to 300 MHz
ultra high frequency (UHF)	300 MHz to 3 GHz
super high frequency (SHF)	3 to 30 GHz
extremely high frequency (EHF)	30 to 300 GHz

Since 1947, the extremely low frequency (ELF) band of 300 Hz – 3 kHz has been added.

VLF and LF bands Propagation in the VLF and LF bands mainly depends on the use of the ground wave. Vertically polarized radiation is invariably used, and the coverage can be worldwide provided the transmitter's power is sufficient. Sky waves are refracted back by the lowest portion of the ionosphere between 35 and 50 miles above the earth's surface. On their return to earth, the sky waves will establish further ground waves.

MF band The range of the ground wave can extend to several hundred miles. For frequencies up to 2 MHz, the sky waves are returned by the middle of the ionosphere between 90 and 120 miles. During day conditions, the absorption is high, but at night the sky wave can be received well beyond the ground-wave range. However, if the sky waves are returned within the ground-wave coverage, severe interference fading can result.

HF band The ground-wave range is of the order of 100 miles or less. Sky waves are normally refracted back by the top of the ionosphere between 150 and 250 miles. Single-hop transmissions can cover distances of 2000 to 2500 miles with frequencies up to 20 MHz. Multihop transmission can cover any distance in the frequency range of 10 to 30 MHz.

VHF (and higher) bands The ground-wave coverage can virtually be ignored. Communication is by space wave with its range primarily limited by "line-of-sight" conditions. Above 30 MHz, atmospheric noise is less than in the lower frequency bands. Within this frequency range, the radio waves normally pass straight through the ionosphere.

* **Question 10-52** The operating frequency of the Loran C navigational system is:

A. 10.2 kHz B. 100 MHz C. 100 kHz D. 102 kHz E. 2182 kHz

Answer Choice C.

* **Question 10-53** The operating frequency of the Omega navigational system is:

A. 100 kHz B. 102 kHz C. 2182 kHz D. 10.2 kHz E. 1.02 kHz

Answer Choice D.

* **Question 10-54** The operating frequency of Loran C lies within the:

A. LF band B. VLF band C. ELF band D. MF band E. HF band

Answer Choice A. The operating frequency of Loran C is 100 kHz, which lies within the LF band of 30 to 300 kHz.

* **Question 10-55** The operating frequency of the Omega navigational system lies within the:

A. LF band B. VLF band C. ELF band D. MF band E. HF band

Answer Choice B. The operating frequency of the Omega navigation system is 10.2 kHz, which lies within the VLF band of 3 to 30 kHz.

* **Question 10-56** Which of the following operating frequencies is used for the modern Loran navigational system?

A. Loran A: 1950 kHz
B. Loran B: 900 kHz
C. Loran C: 100 kHz
D. Loran D: 10.2 kHz
E. Loran E: 3.7 kHz

Answer Choice C.

* **Question 10-57** The maximum range in nautical miles of marine VHF transmissions, is normally:

A. 15 B. 20 C. 30 D. 40 E. 50

Answer Choice B.

* **Question 10-58** The frequency range of the VLF band is:

A. 3 to 30 MHz B. 30 to 300 kHz C. 3 to 30 kHz D. 3 to 30 Hz E. 300 to 3000 Hz

Answer Choice C. The VLF band covers the range of frequency from 3 to 30 kHz.

* **Question 10-59** The frequency range of the MF band is:

A. 300 to 3000 Hz B. 3 to 30 MHz C. 300 kHz to 3 MHz
D. 300 to 3000 kHz E. choices C and D are true

Answer Both choices C and D are true. Choice E. The MF band covers the frequency range of 300 to 3000 kHz (choice D). This range can also be expressed as 300 kHz to 3 MHz (choice C).

* **Question 10-60** The frequency range of the LF band is:

A. 3 to 300 kHz B. 30 to 300 Hz C. 30 to 3000 kHz D. 30 to 300 kHz
E. 300 to 3000 kHz.

Answer Choice D. The LF band covers the frequency range of 30 to 300 kHz.

* **Question 10-61** The VHF band covers the frequency range of:

A. 30,000 to 300,000 kHz B. 3 to 30 MHz C. 300 MHz to 3 GHz D. 30 to 300 MHz E. choices A and D are true

Answer Choices A and D are both true. Choice E. The VHF band covers the frequency range of 30 to 300 MHz (choice D). This range may also be expressed as 30,000 to 300,000 kHz (choice A).

* **Question 10-62** The SHF band covers the frequency range of:

A. 3 to 30 MHz B. 30 to 300 MHz C. 3 to 30 GHz D. 300 to 3000 MHz
E. 30 to 300 GHz

Answer Choice C.

* **Question 10-63** The UHF band covers the frequency range of:

A. 30 to 300 GHz B. 3 to 30 MHz C. 300 to 3000 MHz D. 30 to 300 MHz
E. 3 to 30 GHz

Answer Choice C.

* **Question 10-64** The EHF band covers the frequency range of:

A. 3 to 30 MHz B. 30 to 300 MHz C. 300 to 3000 MHz D. 3 to 30 GHz
E. 30 to 300 GHz

Answer Choice E.

* **Question 10-65** Express 3:00 PM Pacific Standard Time (PST) in terms of Universal Time Coordinated (UTC):

A. 0700 B. 1100 C. 1500 D. 0300 E. 2300

Answer Choice E.
From EQ. 10-32:

$$\begin{aligned} \text{UTC} &= \text{PST} + 8 \text{ hours} \\ &= 1500 + 0800 \\ &= 2300 \text{ hours} \end{aligned}$$

* **Question 10-66** Express 3:00 PM Central Standard Time (CST) in terms of Universal Time Coordinated (UTC):

A. 0900 B. 1900 C. 1500 D. 2100 E. 2000

Answer Choice D.

From EQ. 10-34:

$$\begin{aligned} \text{UTC} &= \text{CST} + 6 \text{ hours} \\ &= 1500 + 0600 \\ &= 2100 \text{ hours} \end{aligned}$$

* **Question 10-67** Express 6:00 PM Pacific Standard Time (PST) in terms of Universal Time Coordinated (UTC):

A. 1000 B. 0200 C. 0600 D. 1400 E. 2200

Answer Choice B.

From EQ. 10-32:

$$\begin{aligned} \text{UTC} &= \text{PST} + 8 \text{ hours} \\ &= 1800 + 0800 \\ &= 2600 (-\ 2400) \\ &= 0200 \text{ hours} \end{aligned}$$

* **Question 10-68** Express 3:00 PM Eastern Standard Time (EST) in terms of Universal Time Coordinated (UTC):

A. 2000 B. 1000 C. 0300 D. 2300 E. 1800

Answer Choice A.

From EQ. 10-35:

$$\begin{aligned} \text{UTC} &= \text{EST} + 5 \text{ hours} \\ &= 1500 + 0500 \\ &= 2000 \text{ hours} \end{aligned}$$

* **Question 10-69** Express 9:00 AM Mountain Standard Time (MST) in terms of Universal Time Coordinated (UTC):

A. 0200 B. 1600 C. 0900 D. 1700 E. 1500

Answer Choice B.

From EQ. 10-33:

$$\begin{aligned} \text{UTC} &= \text{MST} + 7 \text{ hours} \\ &= 0900 + 0700 \\ &= 1600 \text{ hours} \end{aligned}$$

* **Question 10-70** The time of 2300 Universal Time Coordinated (UTC) is equivalent to:

A. 3:00 PM PST B. 11:00 PM PST C. 5:00 PM MST D. 5:00 PM EST
E. 4:00 PM CST

Answer Choice A.

From EQ. 10-32:

$$\begin{aligned} \text{PST} &= \text{UTC} - 8 \text{ hours} \\ &= 2300 \text{ hours} - 8 \text{ hours} \\ &= 11 \text{ PM} - 8 \text{ hours} \\ &= 3{:}00 \text{ PM} \end{aligned}$$

Notice that this time is the same as 4:00 PM MST, 5:00 PM CST, and 6:00 PM EST.

* **Question 10-71** Which of the following bands is least affected by static interference?

A. 300 to 3000 kHz B. 3 to 30 MHz C. 30 to 300 kHz D. 300 MHz to 3 GHz
E. 30 to 300 MHz

Answer Choice D. The higher the radio frequency, the less is the amount of static interference.

* **Question 10-72** Which of the following frequencies are most affected by the phenomenon of knife-edge diffraction?

A. the VLF and LF bands B. 300 to 3000 kHz C. 3 to 30 MHz
D. the UHF band E. 30 to 300 MHz

Answer Choice D.

* **Question 10-73** The phenomenon of knife-edge diffraction refers to:

A. total refraction in the ionosphere
B. total refraction caused by a temperature inversion
C. the bending around a mountain ridge by a UHF signal
D. the bending around the earth by a ground-wave signal
E. the scattering of a VHF signal from the troposphere

Answer Choice C.

* **Question 10-74** When a space-wave signal passes over a mountain ridge, a small part of the signal is diffracted down the far side of the mountain. This phenomenon is called:

A. discontinuity scattering
B. tropospheric ducting
C. knife-edge diffraction
D. space-wave refraction
E. refraction in the atmosphere

Answer Choice C.

* **Question 10-75** The signal radiated from the antenna of a marine MF transmitter is:

A. horizontally polarized
B. elliptically polarized
C. vertically polarized
D. circularly polarized
E. either choice A or C is true

Answer Choice C. A transmitter in the MF band must radiate a vertically polarized radio wave.

Question 10-76 An antenna system is operating in the HF band and is radiating a signal toward the ionosphere. If the frequency is increased and the antenna system is still resonant, the:

A. skip distance increases
B. amount of bending in the ionosphere is increased
C. skip distance decreases
D. skip distance remains the same
E. choices A and B are true

Answer Choice A. If the frequency is increased, the amount of bending in the ionosphere is less and the skip distance increases.

Question 10-77 For a radio wave traveling in free space, its velocity:

A. is constant
B. increases in the microwave region
C. is equal to the velocity of light
D. is constant only for frequencies above the VHF band
E. choices A and C are true

Answer Choice E. In a vacuum (free space), the velocity of a radio wave is constant and equal to the velocity of light.

Question 10-78 A mobile receiver experiences "dead" areas of reception as the result of:

A. atmospheric absorption
B. tropospheric scatter
C. shading of the RF signal by hills and trees
D. knife-edge refraction
E. sporadic E

Answer Choice C.

Question 10-79 The ELF band covers the frequency range of:

A. 3 to 30 kHz B. 300 to 3000 Hz C. 3 to 30 Hz D. 30 to 300 Hz E. 30 to 300 kHz

Answer Choice B. The ELF band covers the frequency range of 300 Hz to 3 kHz or 300 to 3000 Hz.

11
Microwave techniques

In this chapter you will learn:

- about the features which distinguish microwave operation from the techniques of the lower RF bands.
- about the various types of resonant cavity which simulate the behavior of LC circuits.
- hcw the properties of waveguides differ from those of conventional transmission lines.
- how waveguides are joined together with minimum reflection effects.
- about microwave tubes including the magnetron, the klystron, the reflex klystron and the traveling wave tube.
- the principle of the Faraday rotation and its application to the isolator and the circulator.

11-1. Introduction to microwave

The primary purpose of this chapter is to provide you with an introduction to various aspects of microwave techniques. The frequency range of the microwave region is open to debate. Some textbooks state that the range commences where the UHF TV band finishes (890 MHz), and others contend that the start of the microwave band coincides with the beginning (300 MHz) of the UHF band. The most popular view is that microwave extends from 1 GHz (10^9 Hz) to 1 THz (10^{12} Hz); this corresponds to a range of wavelengths from 30 cm to 0.3 mm. However, the majority of microwave equipment operates between 1 and 100 GHz, which includes the *super high frequency (SHF)* band of 3 to 30 GHz. As already discussed, all microwave frequencies will be propagated by the space or direct wave, which travels in a practically straight line from the transmitter.

Within the microwave region, there are a number of designated bands; the most common are shown in TABLE 11-1.

The top limit of the microwave frequencies is the beginning of the *infrared* or heat region, which ranges from 1 to 375 THz. Next comes the narrow visible light spectrum which extends

Table 11-1. Microwave bands and their frequency ranges.

Band	Frequency range (GHz)
L	1.2 – 2.7
S	2.6 – 3.95
C	3.95 – 5.85
X	8.2 – 12.4
K	18.0 – 26.5

from red, 375 THz (wavelength: 0.8 micron = 8×10^{-7}m), to violet, 750 THz (wavelength:0.4 micron = 4×10^{-7}m). Rounding off the electromagnetic (EM) wave spectrum, there are ultraviolet (UV), X-rays, gamma (γ) rays, and cosmic rays.

Before covering microwave techniques in depth, here are some of the features that distinguish microwave from the lower RF bands. These are:

- **The tuned circuits** Knowing that the resonant frequency is:

$$f_r = \frac{1}{2\pi\sqrt{LC}} \text{ hertz (Hz)}$$

  you will find that the values of L and C required for a resonant frequency of 10 GHz (X-band) are respectively much less than 1 μH and 1 pF. With these small values, it is impossible to use "lumped" circuits because the leads that connect the inductor and the capacitor would probably have much more inductance and capacitance than the total values required. Therefore, use distributed circuits that are in the form of cavities.

- **The insulators** All insulators suffer to some degree from dielectric hysteresis loss, which increases as the frequency is raised. In the microwave region, this type of loss is too severe to permit you to use such insulators as porcelain, lucite, bakelite, waxed paper, etc. You are therefore required to introduce special insulators, examples of which are polyethylene, polystyrene, and teflon.
- **The transmission lines** At microwave frequencies it is impossible to use a conventional coaxial cable, except for very short lengths. The principal reason is the severe dielectric loss, which results in a high degree of attenuation. The main type of practical microwave line is the waveguide, which is basically a hollow metal pipe with a rectangular or circular cross-section.
- **The active devices** Conventional tubes are limited to below 2 GHz, as a result of the transit time effect. At higher frequencies, you must use active devices which actually use transit time to achieve amplification or oscillation. Such tubes include magnetrons, klystrons, and *traveling waves tubes* (TWTs).

* **Question 11-1** The frequency range of the microwave region is generally regarded as extending from:

A. 1 to 500 MHz
B. 1000 to 10,000 GHz
C. 1 to 1000 GHz

D. 10 to 100 GHz
E. 300 to 3000 MHz

Answer Choice C.

11-2. Resonant cavities

In chapter 10, the equivalence between the quarter-wave line and the parallel LC tank circuit was discussed (FIG. 11-1A). At the X-band frequency of 10 GHz, the wavelength is 3 cm, and therefore the quarter-wave line would appear to be 0.75 cm long before being terminated by a short circuit; in practice the phase velocity on the line is lower than the free space velocity so that the actual length is somewhat less. Irrespective of the length considerations, the skin effect loss on such a line is severe and its Q is correspondingly low. However, if a second identical quarter-wave line were paralleled with the first at the open end (FIG. 11-1B), the total inductance, L_T is theoretically halved, while the total capacitance, C_T, is doubled. This means that the resonant frequency of the parallel combination:

$$f_r = \frac{1}{2\pi\sqrt{L_T C_T}} \text{ hertz (Hz)}$$

is unchanged, and:

$$Q = R \times \sqrt{\frac{C_T}{L_T}}$$

is increased.

It follows that more and more parallel quarter-wave lines can be added until you finally create a solid cylindrical "can" (FIG. 11-1C). Such a structure has no radiation loss and its RF resistance is extremely low; the result is a high Q value of several thousand. The larger the diameter of the can, the lower is its resonant frequency.

The cylinder is only one of a variety of possible cavity shapes. Instead of a shorted quarter-wave twin lead, you can start with a curved piece of wire (fraction of a turn), which will mainly represent the required inductance. The ends of the wire can run geometrically in parallel to provide most of the capacitance (FIG. 11-2A). This shape can then be revolved to form a surface of revolution; the result is the *rhumbatron* or *reentrant cavity,* whose electric and magnetic fields are indicated in FIG. 11-2B. Figure 11-2C illustrates another version of the reentrant cavity.

If the shape of FIG. 11-2A is extended into the paper, the result is a *hole and slot cavity* (FIG. 11-3), which is cut from a block of solid copper, and it is commonly used in magnetrons.

Question 11-2 The cavity resonator:

A. is equivalent to an LC resonant circuit
B. produces a frequency which is independent of the cavity size
C. is confined to frequencies below 100 MHz
D. has a low Q factor for narrow-band operation
E. is confined to operation in the VHF band

Answer Choice A.

11-3. Waveguides

Chapter 10 covered the theory of the twin-lead transmission line, which is operated successfully at frequencies well below the microwave region. Such a line suffers from the following losses:

- **The copper loss** This loss is associated with the resistance of the conductors, which will dissipate energy in the form of heat. At microwave frequencies, the copper loss is

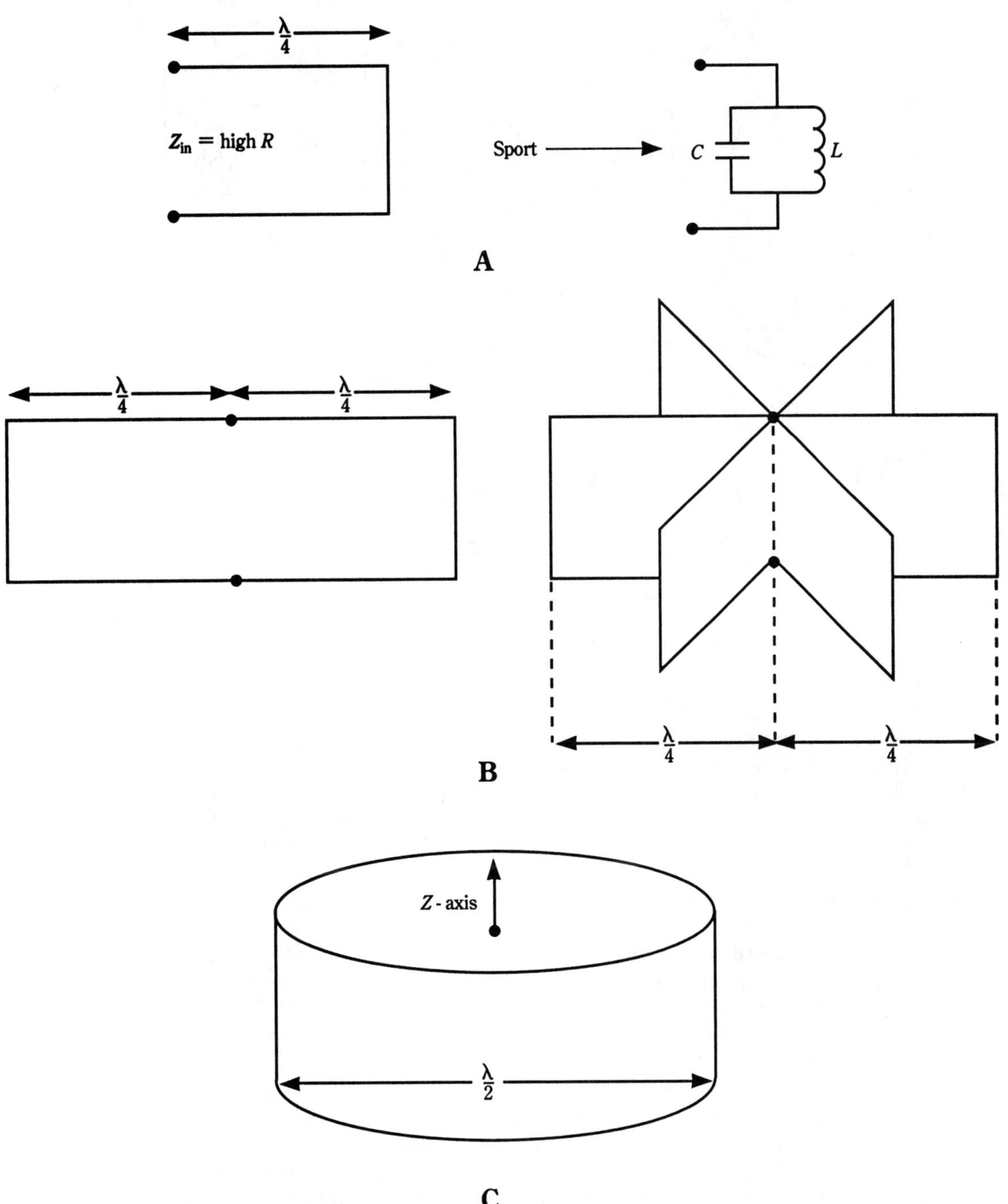

Fig. 11-1 The cylindrical "can" as a resonant cavity.

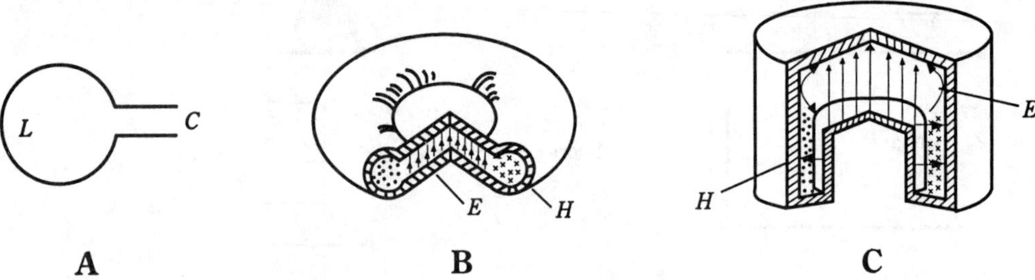

Fig. 11-2 The reentrant cavity.

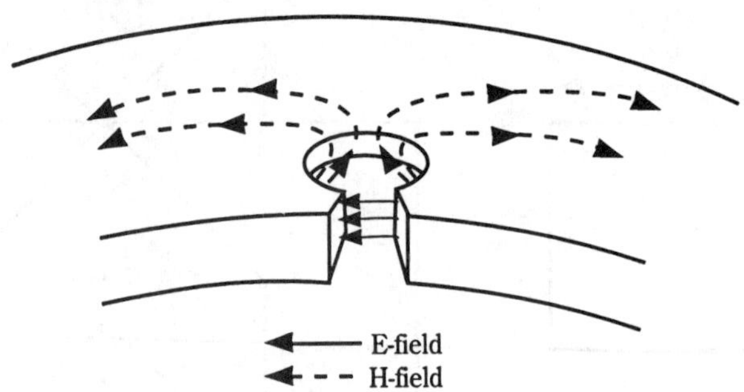

Fig. 11-3 The "hole and slot" cavity.

primarily the result of "skin effect," which restricts the flow of the current to a very small layer at the conductor's surface. The greater is the surface area of the conductor, the less are its skin effect and its consequent copper loss. A twin-lead line uses a pair of conductors with a small surface area so that the copper loss is severe. By contrast, the waveguide is a hollow metal pipe with a cross-section that is rectangular, circular, or elliptical. In any case, the surface area involved is much larger so that the copper loss is limited to a low value. In addition, the loss can be further reduced by plating the inside surfaces of the guide with gold or silver.

- **The dielectric loss** This loss is related to the type of insulator between the conductors. All insulating materials suffer to some degree from dielectric hysteresis loss, which causes the insulator to dissipate energy in the form of heat. This effect increases with the frequency, and in the microwave region, the hysteresis loss for most insulators is extremely severe. However, a waveguide uses a dielectric of dry air or inert gas, such as nitrogen; for these dielectrics, their hysteresis losses are relatively low and they are able to exclude moisture.
- **The radiation loss** The twin-lead line does not confine the electric and magnetic fields in a direction that is perpendicular to the plane, which contains the conductors. As previously discussed in chapter 10, the electric and magnetic fields are respectively associated with the voltage and the current on the line. When the separation between the conductors becomes an appreciable fraction of a wavelength, energy will escape from the line by radiation. The higher the frequency, the shorter the wavelength and the greater the radiation loss. By contrast, a waveguide represents a closed metallic surface; the electric and magnetic fields are therefore confined and any radiation loss is negligible.

The coaxial cable is an improvement over the two-wire line. Because the outer conductor is extended around the inner conductor, the electric and magnetic fields are contained, so there is virtually no radiation loss. The copper loss is reduced because of the outer conductor's larger surface area. However, there remains the dielectric loss, which cannot be eliminated; even if an air dielectric was used, the inner conductor would have to be supported at intervals by insulating spacers. Dielectric hysteresis is the ultimate reason why you must finally turn to waveguides and abandon coaxial cables. At 3 GHz, the typical attenuation for a coaxial cable is 0.6 dB per meter, but with a waveguide it is only 0.02 dB per meter. To look at this situation in practical terms, a 5-meter length of coaxial cable would have an attenuation of $5 \times 0.6 = 3$ dB, which is equivalent to a half-power loss. In other words, if 100 W of RF power was introduced into a 5-meter length of coaxial cable, only 50 W would emerge. By contrast, the waveguide would have to be $3/0.02 = 150$ meters long to produce a half-power loss. At 10 GHz, the figures are even more dramatic; 3 dB per meter for the coaxial cable, but only 0.03 dB per meter for the waveguide.

There is a further advantage for the waveguide, in terms of power capacity. With a coaxial cable, the power capability is primarily determined by the spacing between the conductors. If the power being conveyed is excessive, large voltages are established between the conductors and arcing might occur across the dielectric. A circular waveguide is regarded as a coaxial cable with the inner conductor removed. Consequently, the spacing and the power capacility of a circular waveguide are greater than those of a coaxial cable with the same external dimensions (FIG. 11-4).

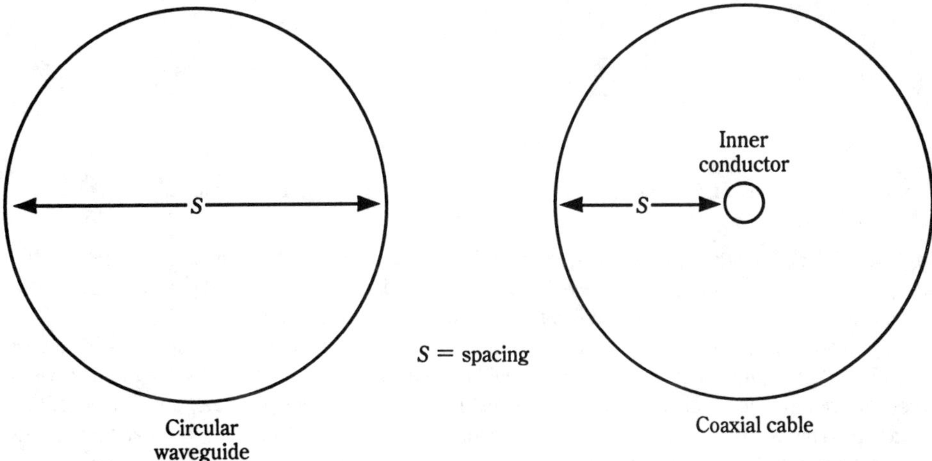

Fig. 11-4 A comparison between the circular waveguide and the coaxial cable.

By now, you must be thinking "waveguides have all the advantages with regards to attenuation and power capacility, so why ever bother with coaxial cables?" The answer, in one word, is *size*. In order for an electromagnetic wave to propagate successfully down a rectangular guide (FIG. 11-5), the wide dimension, *a*, must exceed one-half-wavelength, corresponding to the frequency of the wave. Consequently, at a frequency of 100 MHz, the wavelength is 3 meters; therefore, *a* must exceed 1.5 meters (roughly 5 feet!). Such a waveguide would be extremely cumbersome and expensive.

If the wide dimension must be greater than half a wavelength long, it follows that for a particular waveguide there must be a lower frequency limit, which is known as the *cut-off value*, f_c; at this frequency, the wide dimension is exactly one-half wavelength long. For example, an S-band rectangular guide that operates over 2.6 to 3.95 GHz, has an inner wide dimension of 7.214 cm, which corresponds to a cut-off frequency of $300/(2 \times 7.214 \times 10^{-2} \times 10^{3}) = 2.078$ GHz. In the X-band of 8.2 to 12.4 GHz, the waveguide's inner wide dimension is 2.286 cm and

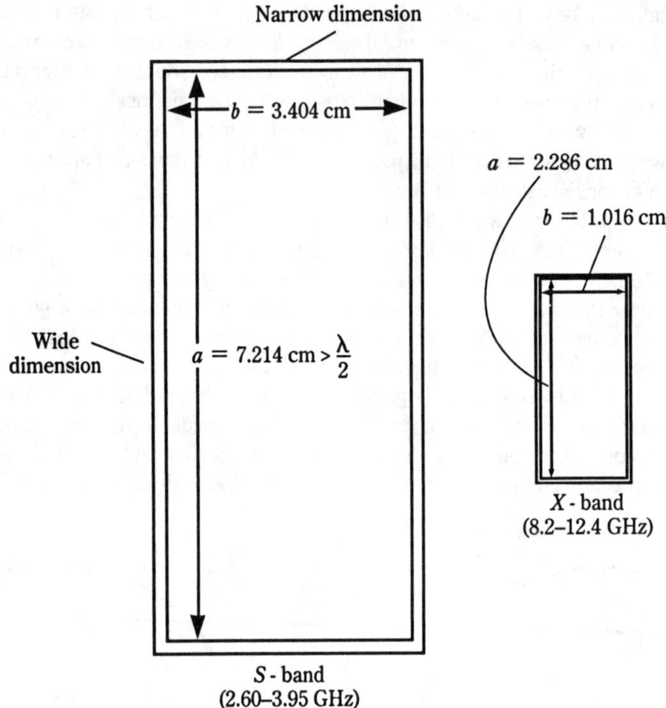

Fig. 11-5 A comparison between the sizes of rectangular waveguides.

the cut-off frequency is 150/22.86 = 6.557 GHz. For a number of reasons, the operating frequency range of a rectangular guide is limited between 1.25 f_c and 1.9 f_c. By contrast, a coaxial cable can be used from dc up to and including the lower part of the microwave region.

Apart from considerations of size and frequency range, a waveguide system is expensive and mechanically rigid. The ideal solution would be one continuous section of waveguide between the transmitting and receiving points. However, this is normally not practical, and it is necessary to join various sections together to form a complete line. At the joins, care must be taken to prevent discontinuities inside the waveguide, and to avoid any leakage of the RF energy.

* **Question 11-3** Why is it impossible to use a waveguide at low radio frequencies?

A. high dielectric loss
B. severe attenuation
C. excessive skin effect
D. excessive radiation
E. the size of the waveguide

Answer Choice E.

* **Question 11-4** Why is nitrogen gas sometimes used in waveguides?

A. to increase the distributed capacitance
B. to keep the waveguide dry
C. to reduce the skin effect at the walls of the guide
D. to lower the voltage rating
E. to raise the guide's wave impedance

Answer Choice B.

* **Question 11-5** Waveguides are:

A. hollow, metal, rectangular, or circular tubes that are used to convey RF power in the SHF band
B. used as low-pass filters in the HF band
C. more economical than coaxial cables when operated at low frequencies
D. more effective over long distances
E. designed with no joins

Answer Choice A.

* **Question 11-6** Waveguides are manufactured:

A. to exclude moisture as much as possible
B. with no long horizontal runs
C. from copper or brass
D. with internal silver plating to reduce the loss from skin effect
E. all of the above choices are true

Answer Choice E.

* **Question 11-7** At frequencies in the VHF band and the lower part of the UHF band, waveguides are not practical owing to excessive:

A. copper loss B. dielectric loss C. radiation loss D. standing waves E. size

Answer Choice E.

11-4. Waveguide joints

Because it is practically impossible to build a waveguide system in one piece, it is normally constructed in sections that must be connected by joints. Any irregularities in the joints cause reflection effects, create standing waves, and increase the attenuation. A proper permanent joint affords a good connection between the two sections of the waveguide and has very little effect on the E- and H-field patterns. During manufacture, the waveguide sections are machined to within a few mils (0.001") and then welded together. The result is a hermetically sealed and mirror-smooth joint.

In locations where sections of a waveguide system must be taken apart for normal maintenance and for repair, you obviously cannot use a permanent joint. In order to allow portions of the waveguide to be separated, the sections are connected by semipermanent joints, of which the simplest is the *bolted flange* (FIG. 11-6A). Here, the two sections are merely bolted together with a gasket to exclude moisture. However, a superior solution is the *choke joint* (FIGs. 11-6B and C), which is the one most commonly used. This consists of flanges that are connected to the waveguide at its center. In FIG. 11-6C, the right-hand flange is flat and the one on the left is slotted one-quarter wavelength, $\lambda/4$, deep from the inner surface of the waveguide. This slot is positioned at a distance of one-quarter wavelength from the point where the flanges are joined. Because the quarter-wavelength slot is terminated by a short circuit, the two quarter-wavelengths together form a half-wavelength section, which presents a short circuit at the place where the walls are joined together. The result is an *electrical* short circuit at the junction of the two waveguides. The two sections might actually be separated by as much as a tenth of a wavelength, which is 3 mm at 10 GHz in the X-band. This operation allows you to seal the interior of the waveguide with a rubber gasket to exclude moisture. Any moisture introduces a discontinuity, creates standing waves, alters the guide's impedance, increases the attenuation and causes cor-

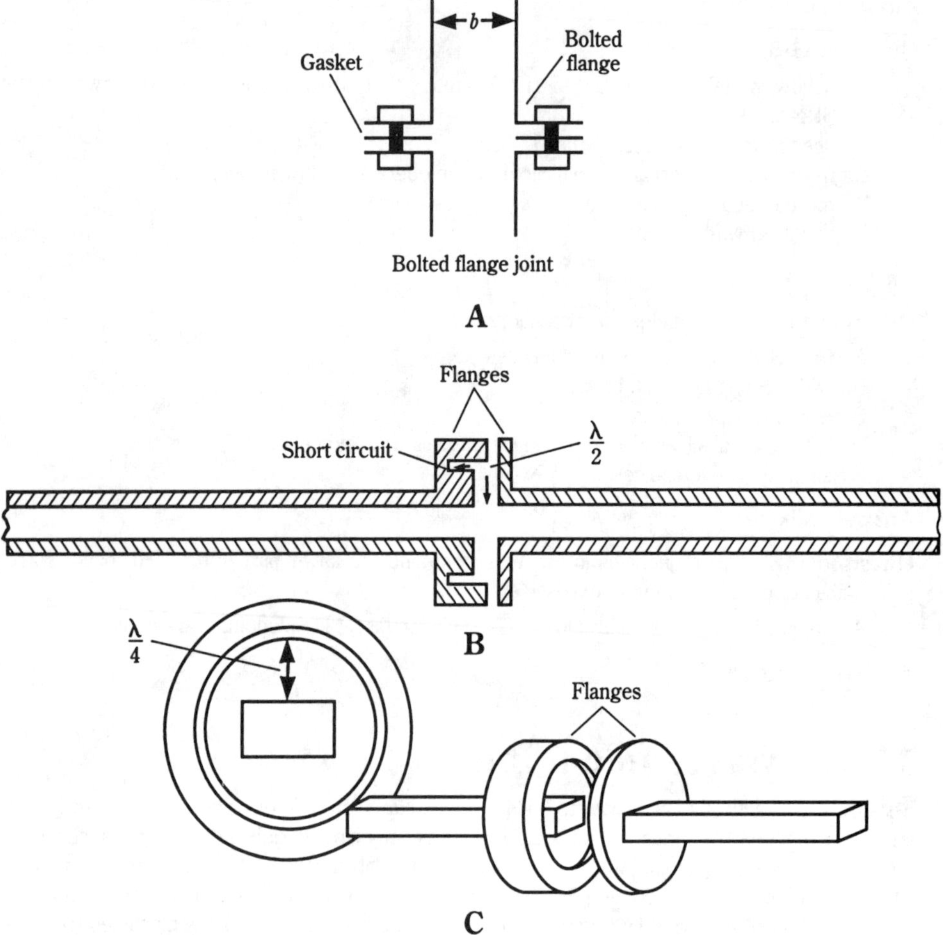

Fig. 11-6 Waveguide joints.

rosion. For these reasons, level runs of a waveguide should be avoided; in addition, a small hole is sometimes drilled at a waveguide's lowest point so that any accumulation of moisture can be drained out. As an example, the waveguide run from a radar transmitter to its antenna should be kept to a minimum length.

The quarter-wavelength distance from the walls to the slot is modified slightly to compensate for the small reactance that is introduced by the short circuit and the open circuit from the slot to the periphery of the flange. The loss introduced by a well-designed choke joint is less than 0.03 dB, while a flange joint has a loss of 0.05 dB or more.

Rotating joints are usually required in a radar set where the transmitter and the receiver are stationary, but the antenna system is revolving. A choke joint is used to separate the sections mechanically, but to join them electrically. Because radar systems mainly use rectangular waveguides, the circular rotating joint must be inserted between two rectangular sections. The joint then consists of two sections of circular guide; one section is rotating while the other is stationary. At the end of each of the sections there is a transition between the circular guide and the rectangular guide.

* **Question 11-8** A choke joint:

A. has two flanges that are mechanically separated by a half-wavelength
B. provides a loss of 0.3 dB
C. is used with rotating waveguide sections
D. is used when two waveguide sections are joined in parallel
E. presents an inductive reactance to the waveguide

Answer Choice C

11-5. Microwave tubes

The ultimate limitation on conventional tubes is the transit time taken by an electron to cross from the heated cathode to the plate. The electron's terminal velocity depends on the accelerating voltage and not on the distance through which the acceleration occurs. If the accelerating voltage is 100 V, the terminal velocity is 5.933×10^6 m/s (approximately 2% of the velocity of light) and the average velocity is $5.933 \times 10^6/2 = 2.9665 \times 10^6$ m/s. The time taken for an electron to cross a distance of 1 mm is $10^{-3}/(2.9665 \times 10^6) = 10^{-9}/2.9665$ s, which is the period that corresponds to the frequency of nearly 3 GHz. Consequently, conventional UHF tubes are limited to about 2 GHz and below. Because the transit time is the limiting factor for conventional tubes, it follows that an active microwave tube must actually use the transit time in order to achieve amplification and/or oscillation.

Examples of microwave tubes:

- The *magnetron tube* is normally the heart of a pulsed radar system. The *magnetron* is an oscillator that is capable of generating a short-duration RF pulse with a peak power output of the order of megawatts. However, there is a long time interval between pulses, so the duty cycle is low. For example, a magnetron generates 500 pulses per second, but the time interval for each pulse is only 1 μs. The period between pulses is 1/500 s = 2000 μs; therefore the duty cycle is only:

$$\begin{aligned} \textit{Duty cycle} &= \frac{\textit{Active interval}}{\textit{Total period}} \\ &= \frac{\textit{Active interval}}{\textit{Sum of active and inactive intervals}} \\ &= \frac{1\ \mu\text{s}}{2000\ \mu\text{s}} = 0.0005 \end{aligned}$$

If the peak power is 1 MW:

$$\begin{aligned} \textit{Average power} &= \textit{Peak power} \times \textit{Duty cycle} \\ &= 1{,}000{,}000 \times 0.0005 = 500\ \text{W} \end{aligned}$$

The magnetron is also the active device in the microwave oven, which operates at a frequency of 2.45 GHz. The space where the food is placed is coupled to the magnetron's resonant cavity.

The frequency range of magnetrons, as a whole, covers 0.6 to 30 GHz. For a particular magnetron, the frequency is normally fixed, but there are methods of obtaining a limited tuning range as high as 10% of the center frequency.

- The *multicavity klystron tube* is a stable microwave power amplifier that provides high gain (3 to 90 dB) at medium efficiency (30 to 50%). The frequency range of multicavity klystrons extends from 3 to 30 GHz.

- The *reflex klystron tube* is a microwave oscillator with a power output of only a few milliwatts, and a very low efficiency of 5% or less. Its frequency can be tuned mechanically over a 30% range, and electronically over a range of 2% or less. Its main use is in test equipment, and as the local oscillator in a radar receiver.
- The *traveling wave tube (TWT)* is a high-gain, low-noise, wide-band microwave amplifier. Because no resonant cavities are used, the upper frequency limit of a TWT can be twice its lower limit.

The primary use of the TWT is voltage amplification (although power TWTs with characteristics similar to those of a power klystron have been developed). The wide bandwidth and low-noise characteristic have made the TWT ideal for use as RF amplifiers in microwave and electronic countermeasures equipment. For these purposes, TWTs have been designed for frequencies as low as 300 MHz, but as high as 50 GHz.

The magnetron

Basically, the magnetron is a diode and has no grid. A magnetic field in the space between the plate (anode) and the cathode serves as the controlling mechanism. The plate of a magnetron does not have the same physical appearance as the plate of an ordinary electron tube. Because conventional LC networks became impractical at microwave frequencies, the plate is fabricated into a cylindrical copper block that contains resonant cavities that serve as tuned circuits. The magnetron's base differs greatly from the conventional base. It has short, large-diameter leads that are carefully sealed into the tube and shielded (FIG. 11-7).

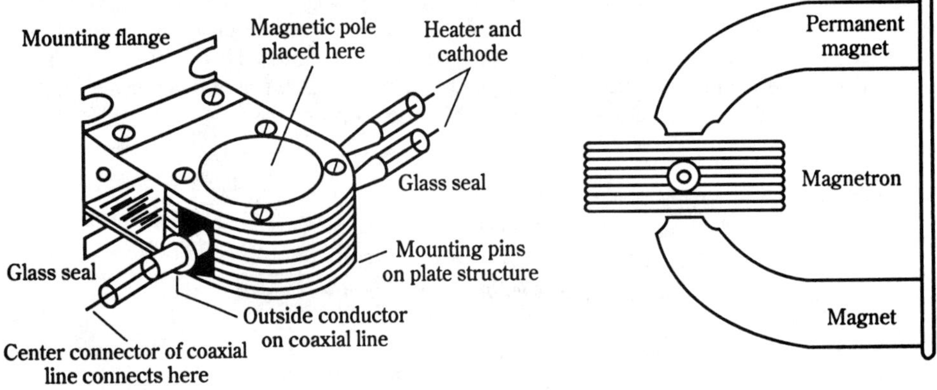

Fig. 11-7 The construction of the magnetron.

The cathode and the filament are at the center of the tube and are supported by the filament leads, which are large and rigid enough to keep the cathode and the filament fixed in position. The output lead is usually a probe or loop that extends into one of the tuned cavities and is coupled into the waveguide. The plate structure (FIG. 11-8) is a solid block of copper. The cylindrical holes around its circumference are the resonant cavities. A narrow slot runs from each cavity into the central portion of the tube, and divides the inner structure into as many segments as there are cavities. Alternate segments are strapped together to put the cavities in parallel, with regard to the output. These cavities then control the output frequency in the π mode. The straps are circular metal bands that are placed across the top of the block at the entrance slots to the cavities. Because the cathode current is of the order of several amperes, the cathode must be large and must be able to withstand high operating temperatures. Such a cathode must also have good emission characteristics, particularly under back bombardment because much of the output power is derived from the large number of electrons that are emitted when high-velocity electrons return to strike the cathode.

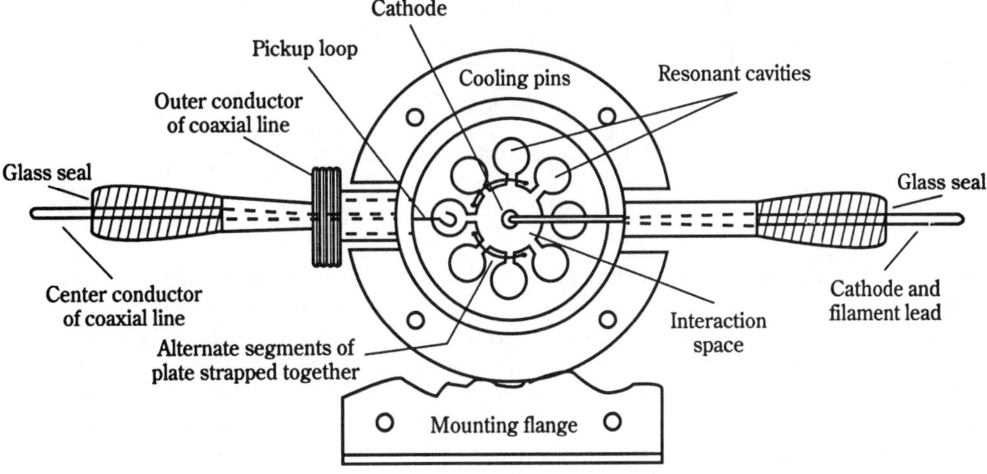

Fig. 11-8 A cutaway view of the magnetron.

The cathode is directly heated, and is constructed of a high-emitting material. The open space between the anode and the cathode is called the *interaction space* because it is in this space that the electric and magnetic fields interact to exert a force on the electrons. The magnetic field is normally provided by a strong magnet, mounted around the magnetron so that the direction of the magnetic field is parallel with the axis of the cathode. The cathode is mounted in the center of the interaction space.

Because the anode is exposed while the cathode leads are carefully sealed, the anode is grounded and a large negative voltage of several kV is applied to the cathode during the time of the magnetron's oscillation.

Operation of the magnetron.

The resultant electric field in the electron resonant magnetron is a combination of the ac fields and the dc field. The dc field extends radially between the anode and the cathode and the ac fields are caused by the RF oscillations, which are induced in the resonant cavities of the anode block.

Figure 11-9 shows the ac fields between adjacent segments at the instant of the peak value of one alternation in the RF oscillations that occur in the cavities.

A strong dc field extends from the anode to the cathode, and is caused by a large negative dc voltage pulse that is applied to the cathode. This strong dc field causes electrons to accelerate toward the anode after they have been emitted from the cathode. These accelerated electrons take energy from the dc electric field. Oscillations are sustained in a magnetron because the electrons gain energy from the dc field, and give up this energy to the ac fields as they pass through these fields.

In FIG. 11-9, consider an electron, e_1, which is shown entering the field around the slot entrance to cavity X. The clockwise rotation of the electron path is caused by the interaction of the magnetic field around the moving electron with the permanent magnetic field, which is

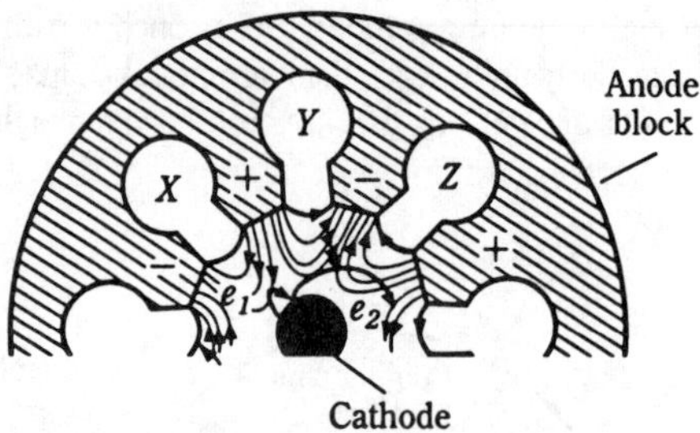

Fig. 11-9 The motion of the electrons in the presence of the magnetron's electric and magnetic fields.

assumed to be entering the paper in FIG. 11-9. Notice that the electron, e_1, which has entered the ac field around cavity X, is going against the direction of the ac field. This electron will therefore take energy from the ac field and will be accelerated so that it turns more sharply as its velocity increases. Electron e_1 will therefore turn away from the anode, and when it strikes the cathode, it will give up the energy it received from the ac field in the form of heat. This will force more electrons to leave the cathode and accelerate toward the anode. By contrast, electron e_2 is slowed down by the ac field and therefore gives up some of its energy to that field. Because electron e_2 loses some of its velocity, the deflection force that is exerted by the H-field is reduced and the electron path deviates to the left (in the direction of the anode), and not in the direction of the cathode (as was the case with electron e_1).

The cathode to anode potential and the magnetic field strength (E-field to H-field relationship) determines the time that is taken by electron e_2 to travel from a position in front of cavity Y to a position in front of cavity Z. This time is equal to approximately one-half period of the RF oscillation of the cavities. When electron e_2 reaches a position in front of cavity Z, the ac field of that cavity will be reversed from that shown in FIG. 11-9. As a result, electron e_2 will give up energy to the ac field of cavity Z and will slow down still further. Electron e_2 will actually give up energy to each cavity as it passes, and will eventually reach the anode when its energy is expended. Therefore, electron e_2 will have helped to sustain the oscillation because it has taken energy from the dc field and given it to the ac fields. Electron e_1, which took energy from the ac field around cavity X, did little harm because it immediately returned to the cathode.

Electrons, such as e_2, that give energy to the ac field as they rotate clockwise from one ac field to the next, stay in the interaction space for a considerable time before striking the anode. The commulative action of so many electrons with some being returned to the cathode while others are directed toward the anode, forms a pattern that resembles the spokes of a wheel (FIG. 11-10).

This overall space charge "wheel" rotates about the cathode at an angular velocity of two anode segments for each cycle of the ac field, and it also has a phase relationship that enables the electron concentration to deliver energy continuously, and therefore sustain the RF oscillations. Electrons emitted from the area of the cathode between the spokes are, as previously covered, quickly returned to the cathode.

A magnetron's RF energy can be removed by means of a coupling loop. At frequencies lower than 10 GHz, the coupling loop is made by bending the inner conductor of a coaxial cable into a loop and soldering the end to the outer conductor so that the loop projects into the cavity (FIG. 11-11A). To obtain sufficient pickup at higher frequencies, the loop is located at the end of the cavity (FIG. 11-11B).

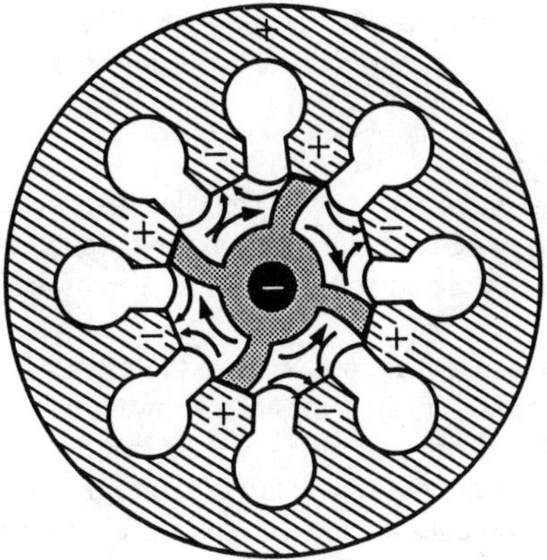

Fig. 11-10 Concentrations of the electrons in the interaction space.

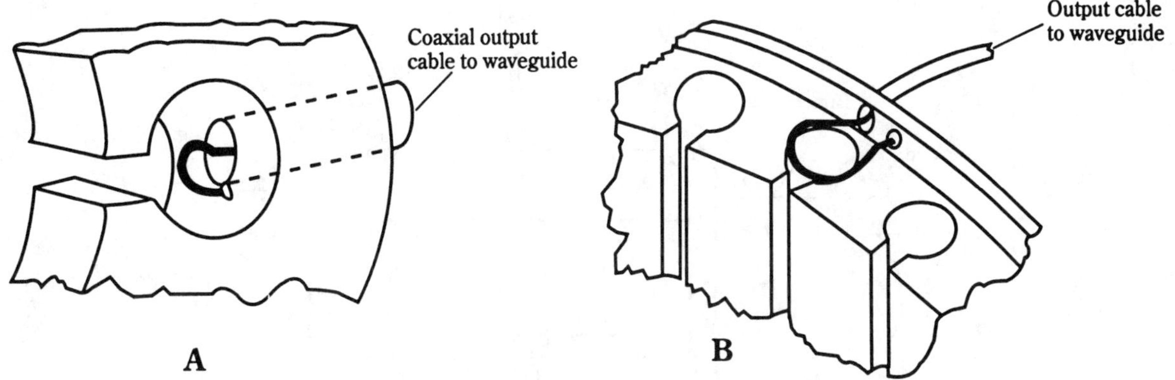

Fig. 11-11 Methods of coupling from the "hole and slot" magnetron.

Defects in the magnetron

The main indication of a defective magnetron is a low reading of the magnetron current so that the undercurrent relay drops out. The CRT will then show noise and the sweep, but the radar echoes will be unusually weak and fuzzy or will not be seen at all. In addition, the automatic frequency control (AFC) system will be ineffective.

If the magnetron itself is within its operating limits, but the external magnet is too weak, the magnetron current will increase, but the frequency of the oscillation will drift, and the AFC system will not be effective. Under extreme conditions, the oscillation might entirely cease. To avoid such weakening, the technician should not subject the magnet to extreme heat or any physical shocks. Furthermore, all metal tools should be kept away from the magnet's presence.

In terms of general precautions, the technician, when servicing or maintaining a radar set on board a ship, should make certain that all power is shut off, and that all capacitors are fully discharged. In particular, CRTs must be handled with great care. One further point, arcing might occur in the modulator unit, the magnetron, the waveguide assembly, and other parts of the radar system. Such arcing can present a hazard if the ship is handling explosive or inflammable material.

The klystron amplifier

The *klystron tube* is a stable microwave power amplifier that provides high gain at medium efficiency. Depending on the type of tube, klystron power outputs range from a few milliwatts to several megawatts peak power, and over 100 kW, average power. The power gains vary from 3 to 90 dB.

Klystron amplifiers are somewhat noisy and are therefore used mainly as power amplifiers. However, they have applications in many facets of microwave technology.

The klystron tube makes a virtue of the very thing that defeats the triode—the transit time of the electrons as they cross from the cathode to the plate. By contrast, the klystron modulates the velocity of the electrons so that as the electrons travel through the tube, electron bunches are formed (density modulation). These bunches deliver a positive feedback voltage to the output resonant circuit of the klystron.

Figure 11-12 shows a cutaway representation of the basic klystron amplifier. The klystron amplifier consists of three separate sections: the electron gun, the RF section, and the collector.

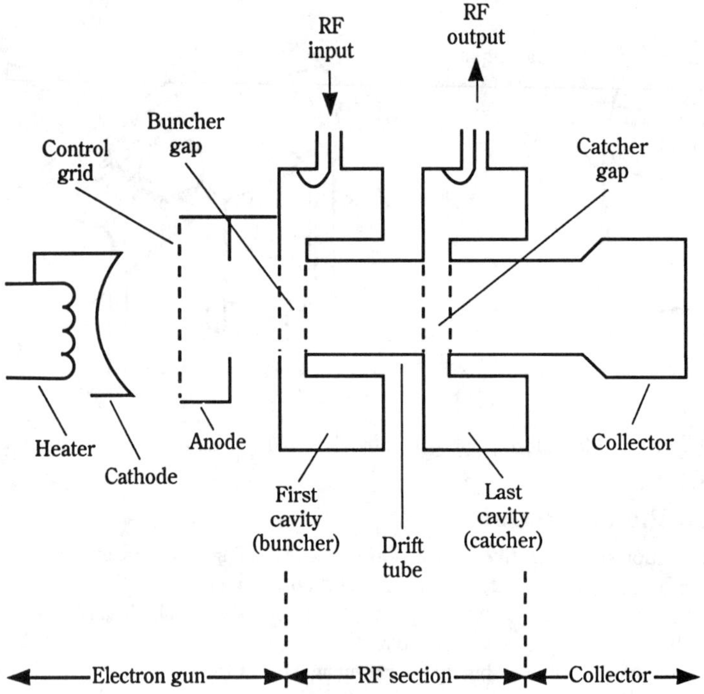

Fig. 11-12 The klystron amplifier.

First, consider the electron gun structure. It consists of a heater, cathode, control grid, and anode. Electrons are emitted by the cathode and are drawn toward the anode, which is operated at a positive potential with respect to the cathode. The electrons are formed into a narrow beam by either electrostatic or magnetic focusing techniques; this ensures that the electron beam does not spread out. The control grid is used to govern the number of electrons that reach the anode region. It can also be used to turn the tube completely on or off in certain pulsed amplifier applications.

The electron beam is well formed by the time it reaches the anode. The beam passes through a hole in the anode and on to the RF section of the tube, and eventually strikes the collector. The electrons are then returned to the cathode through an external power supply. It is evident that the collector of the klystron acts much like the plate of a triode insofar as the collection of electrons is concerned. However, there is one important difference. The plate of the triode is normally connected, in some fashion, to the output RF circuit, but in a klystron amplifier, the collector has no connection to the RF circuitry.

Look at the RF section of the basic klystron amplifier. This part of the tube is quite different from a conventional triode circuit because the resonant circuits used in a klystron amplifier are reentrant cavities.

Referring to FIG. 11-12, the electrons pass through the cavity gaps in each of the resonators, as well as through the cylindrical metal tube between the gaps. This metal tube forms the so-called *drift space*. In a klystron amplifier, the low-level RF input signal is coupled to the first resonator, which is called the *buncher cavity*. The signal can be coupled through either a waveguide or a coaxial connection. If the cavity is tuned to the frequency of the RF input, it will be excited into oscillation. An electric field will exist across the buncher gap, alternating at the input frequency. For half of a cycle, the electric field will be in a direction that will cause the field to increase the velocity of electrons flowing through the gap. On the other half-cycle, the field will be in a direction that will cause the field to produce a decrease in electron velocity. This effect is called *velocity modulation* (FIG. 11-13A). Notice that when the voltage across the cavity gap is negative, the electrons will decelerate; when the voltage is zero, the electrons will be unaffected, and when the voltage is positive, the electrons will accelerate.

After leaving the buncher gap (FIG. 11-13B) the electrons proceed through the tube's drift region, then on to the collector. In the drift region, the electrons that have been speeded up by the electric field in the buncher gap, will tend to overtake electrons that have been slowed down. Because of this action, bunches of electrons will begin to form in the drift region, and will be completely formed by the time they reach the gap of the last cavity, which is called the *catcher cavity*. Bunches of electrons periodically flow through the gap of this catcher cavity, and during the time between bunches, relatively few electrons flow through the gap. The time between the arrival of the electron bunches is equal to the period of the cycle of the RF input signal.

The initial bunch of electrons flowing through the catcher cavity will cause the cavity to oscillate at its resonant frequency. This sets up an alternating electric field across the catcher cavity gap (FIG. 11-13C). With the right design and operating potentials, a bunch of electrons will arrive in the catcher cavity gap at the proper time to be retarded by the RF field, and therefore energy will be given to the catcher cavity.

The RF power in the catcher cavity will be much greater than that applied in the buncher cavity. This is because of the ability of the concentrated bunches of electrons to deliver large amounts of energy to the catcher cavity. Because the electron beam delivers some of the energy to the output cavity, it arrives at the collector with less total energy than it had when it passed through the input cavity. This difference in beam energy is approximately equal to the energy that is delivered to the output cavity.

It is appropriate to mention here that velocity modulation does not form perfect bunches of electrons. There are some electrons that come through the input cavity with the wrong phase relationship, and show up in the output cavity gap between the bunches. The electric field across the gap at the time these "out-of-phase" electrons come through, is in a direction to accelerate them. This causes some energy to be taken from the cavity. However, much more energy will be

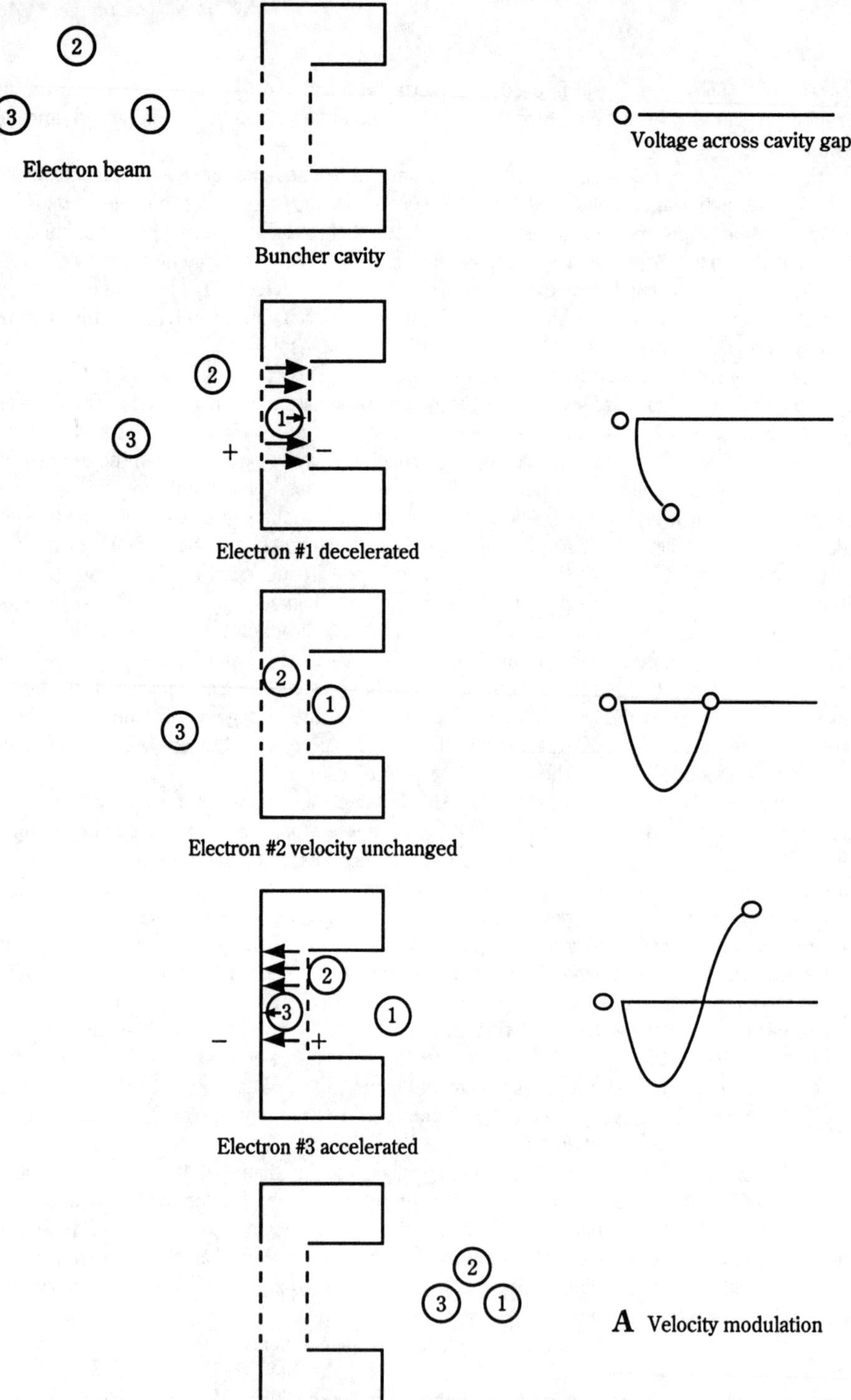

Fig. 11-13 The amplifying action of the klystron.

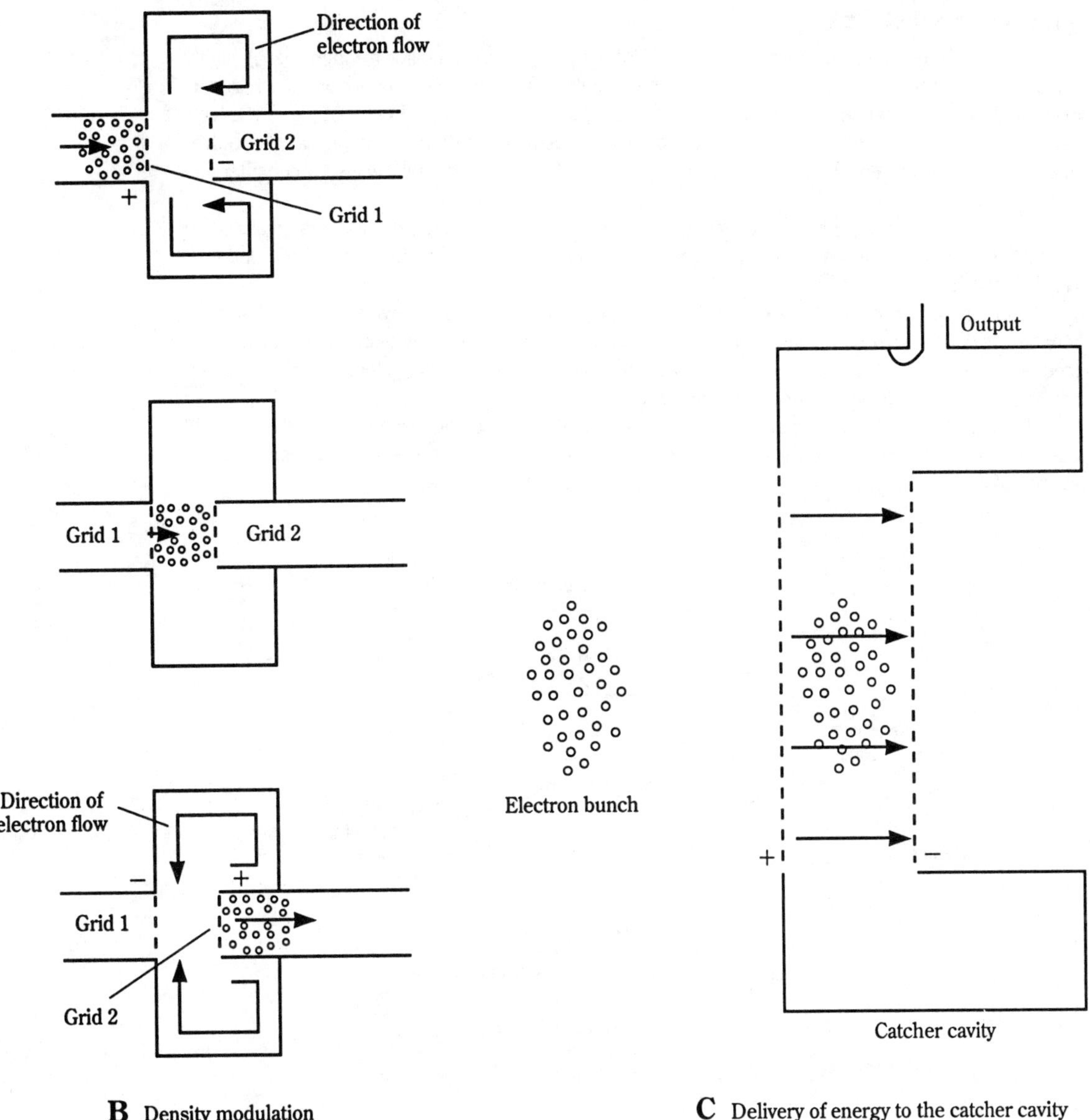

B Density modulation

C Delivery of energy to the catcher cavity

Fig. 11-13 Continued

contributed to the output cavity by the concentrated bunches of electrons than will be withdrawn from it by the relatively small number of "out-of-phase" electrons.

Notice that if the output from the catcher cavity is coupled back to the input circuit of the buncher cavity, the klystron stage will behave as an oscillator and not as an amplifier.

The reflex klystron

In a radar system, most receivers use 30 or 60 MHz as their intermediate frequencies. A highly important factor in receiver operation is the tracking stability of the local oscillator, which generates the frequency that beats with the incoming signal to produce the IF. For example, if the local oscillator frequency is 3000 MHz, a frequency shift of as much as 0.1% would be a 3-MHz frequency shift. This is equal to the bandwidth of most receivers, and would cause a considerable loss in gain.

In receivers that use crystal mixers, the power required of the local oscillator is small, being only 20 to 50 mW in the 4-GHz region. Because of the very loose coupling, only about one mW reaches the crystal.

Another requirement of a local oscillator is that it must be tunable over a range of several megahertz. This is to compensate for changes in the transmitted frequencies, and in its own frequency. It is desirable that the local oscillator has the capability of being electronically tuned by varying the voltage applied to one of its electrodes.

Because the reflex klystron (FIG. 11-14) meets all of these requirements, it is commonly used as the local oscillator in microwave receivers. Basically, this type of klystron consists of a source of electrons, a reentrant cavity, and a repeller or reflector plate.

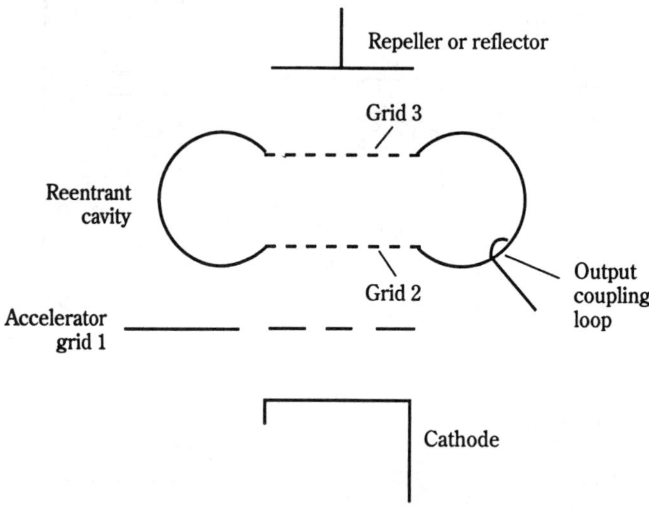

Fig. 11-14 The principle of the reflex klystron.

The electrons that are accelerated by grid 1 will be velocity modulated as they pass through the cavity grids (grids 2 and 3). After moving through the cavity grids, the electrons will be traveling at different velocities. Because the reflector plate is made highly negative, with respect to the cathode, these electrons will be repelled from the reflector and will reverse their direction. The high-velocity electrons will come physically closer to the reflector plate than either the medium- or low-velocity electrons. After repulsion, all electrons will be directed back toward the cavity grids. A bunching action then occurs on the return trip of the electrons. The distance that the electrons move before they are repelled by the negative reflector is a function of the voltage on the accelerating grid, the dc value of the negative cathode voltage, the negative dc voltage applied to the reflector, and the magnitude of the RF voltage existing on the cavity grids because of the oscillation in the cavity resonator. These applied voltages and the physical construction of the klystron should be such that the electrons will return to the cavity grids in bunches.

When the bunch of electrons return, the potential of the cavity grids is important. At the time of return, the potential applied to the cavity grids must be such that some of the energy of the bunch is absorbed. The maximum absorption of energy will occur when the bunched electrons reach the midpoint between the cavity grids as the RF voltage between these grids reaches its peak value. This provides the necessary level of positive feedback to sustain a continuous oscillation.

The operating frequency of the tube can be varied over a small range by changing the voltage on the reflector plate. This potential determines the transit time of the electrons between their first and second passages through the resonator. However, the output power of the oscillator is affected considerably more than the frequency by changes in the magnitude of the reflector voltage. This is because the output power depends on the fact that the electrons are bunched at exactly the time of the deceleration half-cycle of the oscillating voltage. The volume of the resonant cavity is mechanically altered to change the oscillator's frequency. The reflector voltage can be varied over a narrow range to provide minor frequency adjustments. For example, if the reflector voltage is made more negative, the bunching will occur earlier in time so that the period of the oscillation is reduced and the frequency is slightly increased; however, the power output is less. The range of frequencies that can be obtained by varying the reflector voltage is about 1% of the cavity frequency.

In practice, the reflex klystron is operated in conjunction with an AFC circuit. Because the reflector voltage is effective in making small changes in frequency, the AFC circuit is used to control the reflector voltage to maintain the correct intermediate frequency. Notice that the coarse frequency of oscillation is determined by the dimensions of the cavity and there is, on most reflex klystrons, a mechanical adjustment that varies the cavity size. For example, a 10-GHz X-band klystron can be mechanically tuned between 8.5 and 11.5 GHz.

The traveling wave tube

The *traveling wave tube (TWT)* is a high-gain, low-noise, wide-bandwidth microwave amplifier. The TWTs are capable of gains of 40 dB or more, with bandwidths in which the upper frequency is twice the lower frequency. TWTs have been designed for frequencies as low as 300 MHz, and as high as 50 GHz.

The primary use for the TWT is broadband voltage amplification (although high-power TWTs, with characteristics that are similar to those of a power klystron, have been developed). Their wide bandwidth and low noise characteristics make them ideal for use as RF amplifiers in microwave equipment.

Figure 11-15 is a pictorial diagram of a TWT. Notice that there are no resonant cavities; this accounts for the wide bandwidth available. The electron gun produces a stream of electrons, which are focused into a narrow beam by an axial magnetic field, much the same as in a klystron tube. This field is produced by a permanent magnet or an electromagnet that surrounds the helix portion of the tube. The narrow beam is accelerated, as it passes through the helix, by a high potential on the helix and the collector.

The electron beam in a klystron travels, for the most part, in regions that are free from RF electric fields; the beam in a TWT is continually interacting with an RF electric field that propagates along an external circuit that surrounds the beam.

To achieve amplification, the TWT must propagate a wave whose phase velocity is nearly synchronized with the velocity of the electron beam. It is difficult to accelerate the beam to more than about one-fifth the velocity of light. Therefore, the forward velocity of the RF field propagating along the helix must be reduced to nearly that of the beam.

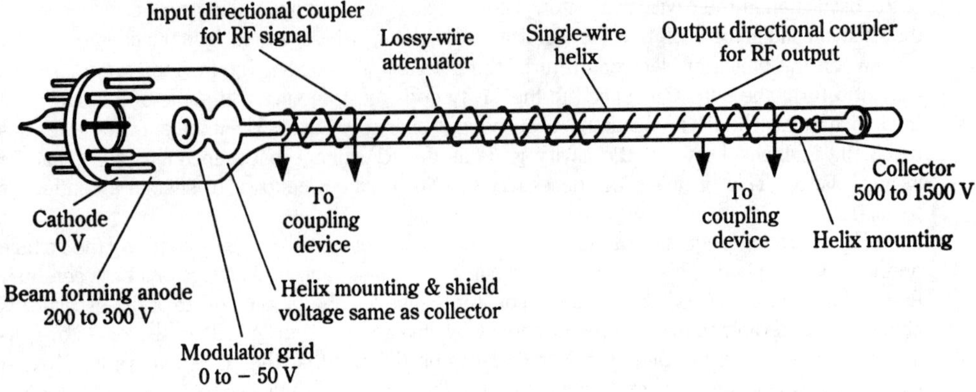

Fig. 11-15 The traveling-wave tube.

The phase velocity in a waveguide that is uniform in the direction of propagation is always greater than the velocity of light. However, this velocity can be reduced below the velocity of light by introducing a periodic variation of the circuit in the direction of propagation. The simplest form of variation is obtained by wrapping the circuit in the form of a helix, which acts as a *slow wave* structure.

As previously explained, the electronic beam is focused and constrained to flow along the axis of the helix. The longitudinal components of the input signal's RF electric field, along the axis of the helix or slow wave structure, continually interact with the electron beam to provide the amplification of the TWT. This interaction is pictured in FIG. 11-16, which illustrates the RF electric field of the input signal, as it propagates along the helix, and penetrates into the region occupied by the electron beam.

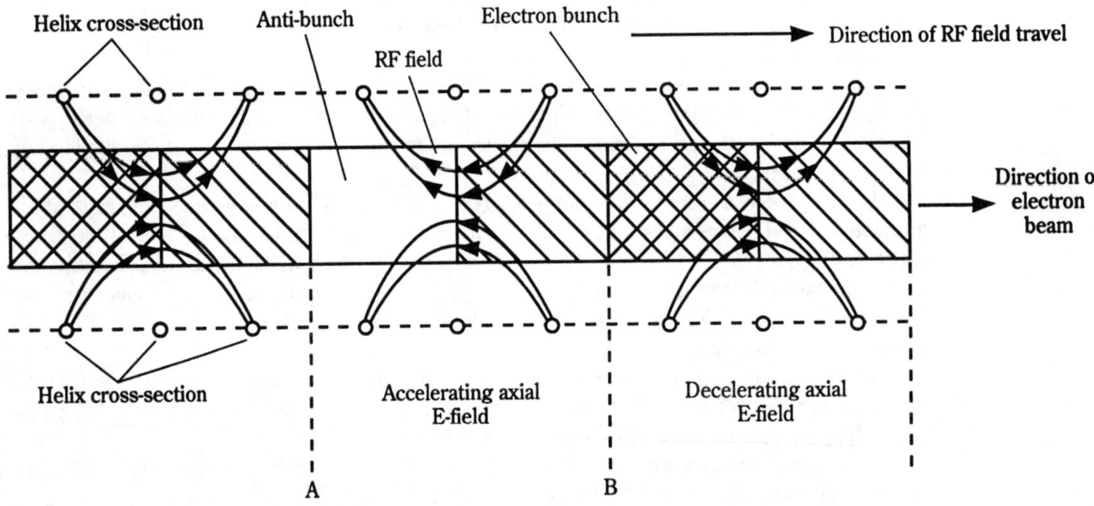

Fig. 11-16 Interaction between the RF signal and the electron beam in a traveling-wave tube.

First, consider the case where the electron beam velocity is exactly synchronized with the circuit's phase velocity. The electrons then experience a steady dc electric force, which tends to bunch them around position A, and debunch them around position B. This action is caused by the accelerating and decelerating electric fields, and is similar to velocity and density modulation, which was previously covered. In this case, as many electrons are accelerated as are decelerated; hence, there is no net energy transfer between the beam and the RF electric field. To achieve amplification, the electric beam is adjusted to travel slightly faster than the RF electric field propagating along the helix. The bunching and debunching mechanisms just covered are still at work, but the bunches now move slightly ahead of the fields on the helix. Under these conditions, more electrons are in the decelerating field to the right of A than are in the accelerating field to the right of B. Because more electrons are decelerated than are accelerated, the energy balance is no longer maintained. Therefore, energy is transferred from the beam to the RF field, and the signal is magnified.

The fields can propagate in either direction along the helix. This leads to the possibility of oscillation as a result of the reflections back along the helix. This tendency is minimized by placing some resistive material near the input end of the slow wave structure. This resistance might take the form of a lossy attenuator (FIG. 11-15) or a graphite coating placed on insulators that are adjacent to the helix. Such lossy sections completely absorb any backward traveling wave. The forward wave is also absorbed to a great extent, but the signal is carried past the attenuator by the bunches of electrons. Because these bunches are not affected as they pass by the attenuator, they are capable of reinstituting the signal on the helix.

* **Question 11-9** The input signal is introduced into the traveling-wave tube at the:

A. cathode
B. anode
C. control grid of the electron gun
D. cathode end of the helix
E. collector end of the helix

Answer Choice D.

* **Question 11-10** Which of the following is used as a high-power microwave oscillator?

A. reflex klystron B. traveling wave tube C. thyraton D. magnetron E. klystron

Answer Choice D.

* **Question 11-11** A reflex klystron is oscillating at the frequency of its resonant cavity. If the reflector voltage is made slightly less negative, the:

A. output power would increase
B. bunching would occur earlier in time
C. oscillation will cease
D. positive feedback will increase
E. the frequency will decrease

Answer Choice E.

* **Question 11-12** What is the purpose of the electromagnets surrounding the traveling wave tube?

A. to slow down the signal on the helix
B. to accelerate the electron beam
C. to focus the electron beam and prevent the electrons from spreading out

D. to attenuate the signal on the helix
E. to couple the signal on the helix to the output waveguide

Answer Choice C.

11-6. The isolator and the circulator

The ferrite isolator

The *isolator* is a device that has a low forward loss, but a high reverse loss. This effect is the result of the nonreciprocal phase shift created by a ferrite material that is the heart of the isolator circuit. In 1845, Michael Faraday demonstrated that the plane of polarization of a linearly polarized light wave rotated when the light was passed through certain materials in a direction parallel to the flux lines of an external magnetic field. The same effect is produced in the microwave region when operating with ferrite materials. Such materials are transparent to electromagnetic waves, have excellent magnetic properties, and have very high values of specific resistance.

The basic principle of a microwave isolator is illustrated in FIG. 11-17A. At the input end, there is a rectangular waveguide, which (relative to the plane of the paper) is fed by an EM-wave with vertical electric flux lines. A transition is now made to a circular waveguide, and a resistive attenuator vane is inserted parallel to the original rectangular guide's wide dimension. Because the E-lines are perpendicular to the plane of the vane, no attenuation occurs.

The next step is to pass the wave through the ferrite specimen that is situated in the presence of the external magnetic field. The result is to twist the plane of polarization through 45° in the clockwise direction. The emerging electric field is also at right-angles to the second resistive vane, so the attenuation of the isolator in the forward direction has been kept to a minimum. Finally, there is another conversion from a circular to a rectangular waveguide, whose orientation corresponds to the emerging wave's plane of polarization.

If you now attempt to send the same signal as a reverse wave back through the isolator, the plane of polarization will be twisted 45° in the same direction as the shift of the forward wave (FIG. 11-17B). Consequently, when the reverse wave emerges from the ferrite specimen, the E-lines will be parallel to the first attenuator vane, and severe attenuation is the result. Typically, the low forward loss is about 1 dB or less, whereas the high reverse loss is 20 dB or more. If the external magnetic field is supplied by an electromagnet, whose current can be varied, the characteristic of the isolator can be changed. One of the main uses of such an isolator is to buffer a microwave source from the varying load.

The circulator

The properties of the ferrite specimen used in the isolator can be adapted to the *circulator.* There are many applications of circulators, but the principle is to establish various entry-exit points or *ports* where the RF power can either be fed or extracted. Figure 11-18 shows a circulator that uses the principle of the 45° Faraday rotation. The results of the circulator are:

- When a vertically polarized wave enters port 1, its plane of polarization is rotated through 45° by the ferrite specimen and the wave then leaves through port 2. Port 3 and port 4 represent incompatible junctions.
- A 45° polarized wave entering port 2 is horizontally polarized after passing through the ferrite specimen and will therefore exit from port 3. Likewise, a wave entering port 3 has its plane of polarization rotated through 45° and only leaves through port 4.
- A wave entering port 4 will be vertically polarized after leaving the ferrite specimen and will emerge from port 1.

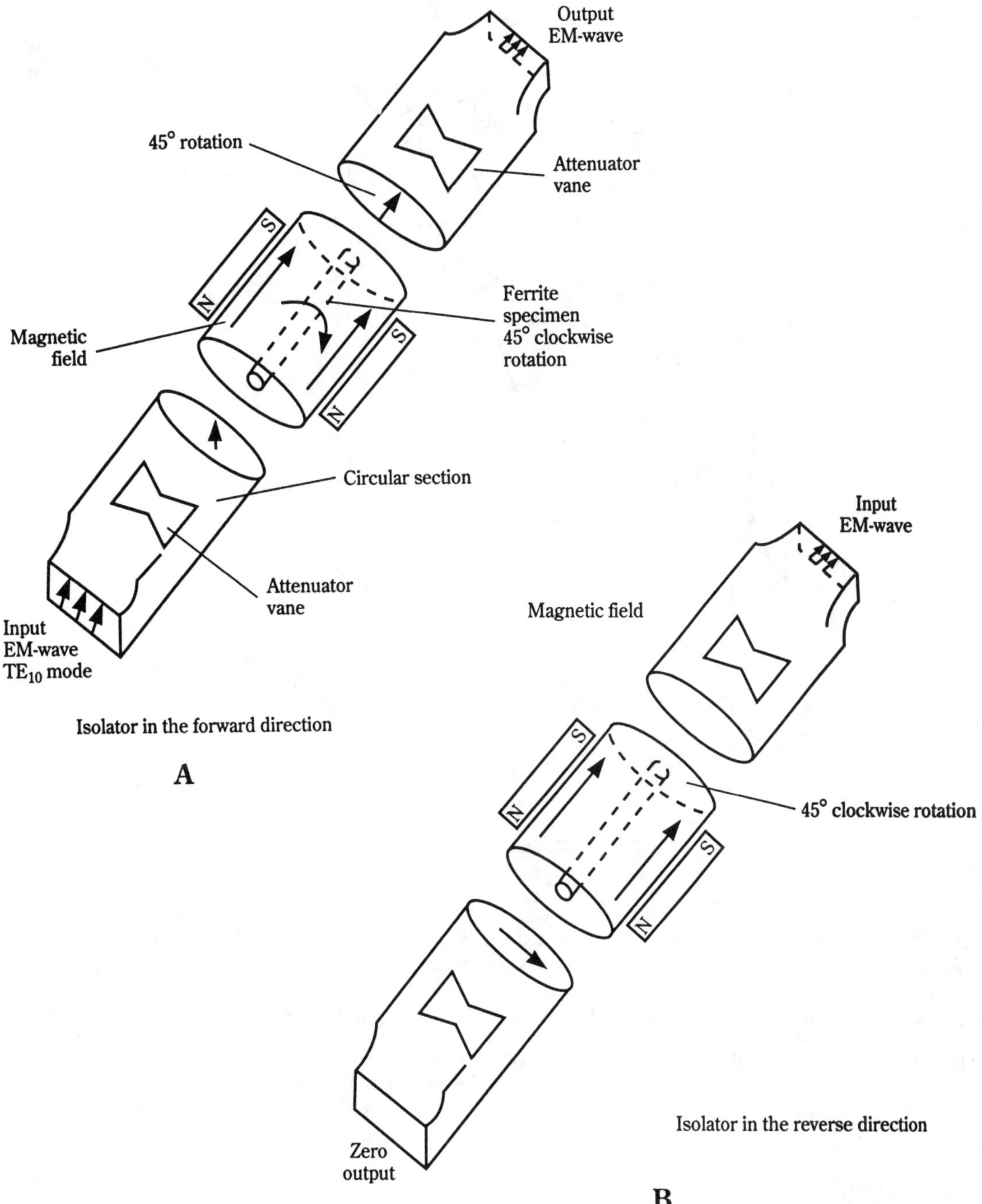

Fig. 11-17 The rotation ferrite isolator.

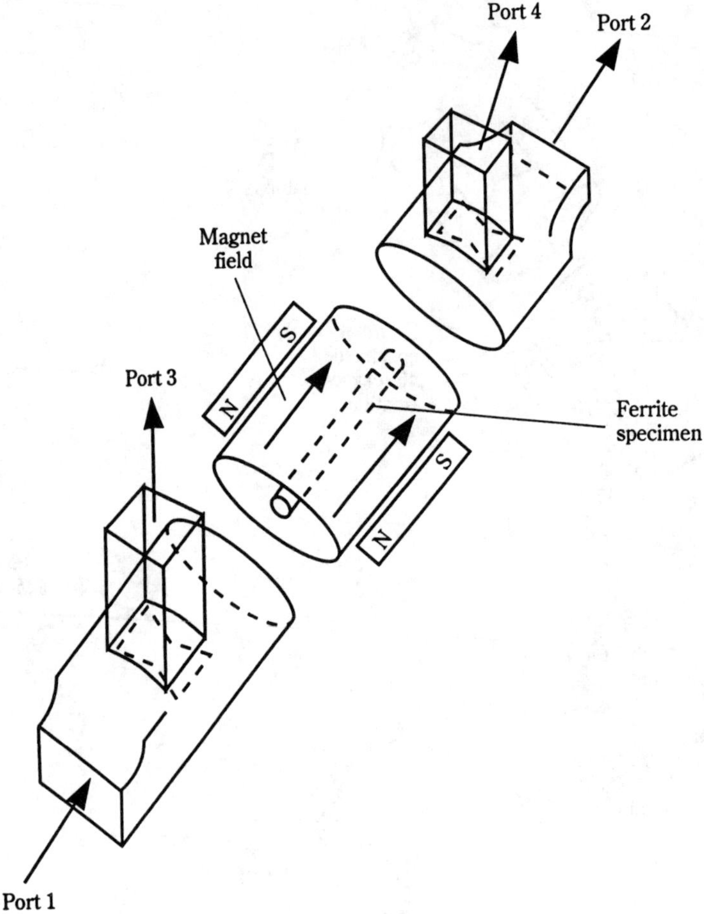

Fig. 11-18 The principle of the circulator.

These results are summarized in the circular network diagram of FIG. 11-19. As a simple rule, a 90° rotation from the entrance port in the clockwise direction of the circular arrow will automatically locate the single exit port. Such an arrangement could be used as the duplexer of a radar system, which uses the same antenna for both the transmitter and the receiver.

* **Question 11-13** Which of the following is the ferrite device that buffers a microwave source from the effects of a varying load, and thereby prevents the formation of standing waves on the connecting waveguide?

A. circulator B. isolator C. diplexer D. duplexer E. inhibitor

Answer Choice B.

* **Question 11-14** An isolator is a:

A. ferrite device that operates on the principle of the Faraday rotation
B. four-port circulator with one port blocked
C. device that operates on the principle of ferromagnetic resonance

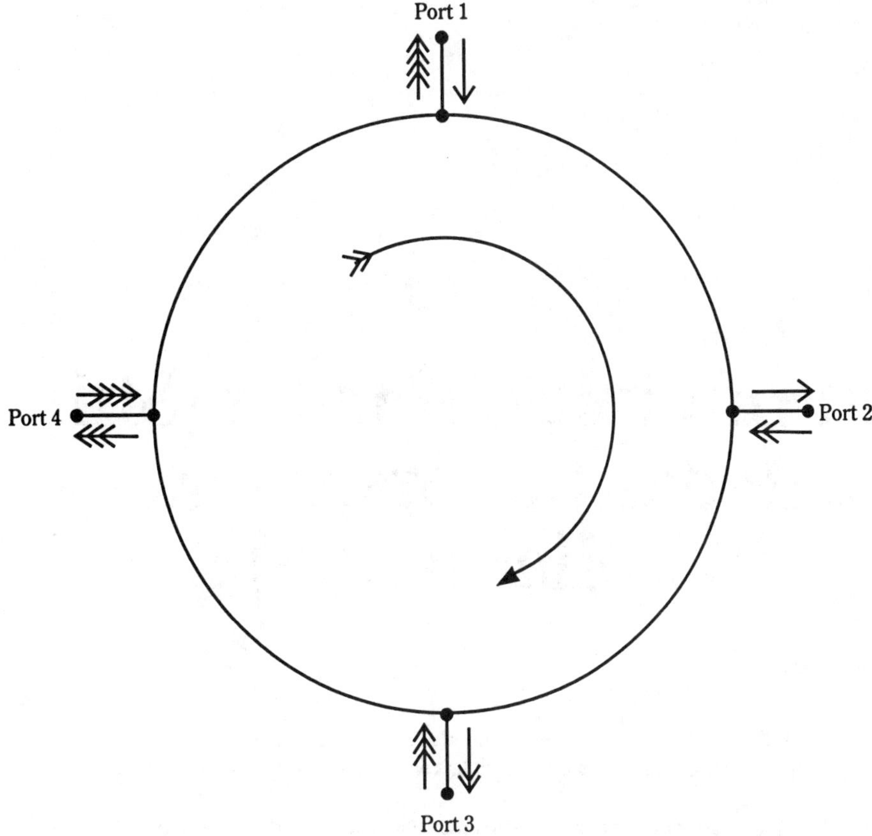

Fig. 11-19 The four-port circulator.

D. duplexer that connects two transmitters to a single antenna
E. diplexer that connects a transmitter and a receiver to a single antenna.

Answer Choice A.

* **Question 11-15** Which of the following devices permits a microwave signal to travel in one direction with virtually no loss, but severely attenuates any signal attempting to travel in the reverse direction?

A. wave trap B. isolator C. tunnel diode D. circulator E. diplexer

Answer Choice B.

* **Question 11-16** A duplexer circuit allows a transmitter and a receiver to operate from the same antenna with virtually no interaction. This circuit can be replaced by a (an):

A. circulator B. lossy waveguide C. isolator D. gyrator E. bidirectional coupler

Answer Choice A.

12

Principles of radar (Ship Radar Endorsement—Element 8)

In this chapter you will learn:

- about the basic blocks that are contained in a marine radar set.
- about the radar equation and the various relationships between the parameters of a pulsed radar set.
- how the radar range of a target is related to its corresponding time interval.
- about the features of a radar receiver and the factors that control its intermediate frequency and bandwidth.
- how a crystal diode fulfills the requirements of the receiver's mixer stage.
- how the echo box is used to provide an artificial target for test purposes.
- about the properties of various radar antennas.
- how a duplexer circuit enables the radar transmitter and receiver to use a common antenna circuit.
- the principles behind the operation of the Plan-Position Indicator (PPI) display.
- about the various forms of radar interference and its effect on communications receivers and other equipment.
- the meaning of the Doppler effect and its application to continuous-wave (CW) radar systems.
- about the principles of certain navigational radar systems.
- about the FCC Rules and Regulations pertaining to ship radar stations.

12-1. Introduction to radar

RADAR (Radio Aid to Direction-finding And Ranging) uses radio signals that are reflected or re-radiated from such objects as ships and aircraft in order to obtain their ranges and bearings (FIG. 12-1). In some cases, the height or elevation of aircraft is also determined. The signals used take the form of very short bursts or pulses of VHF or a much higher radio frequency that uses line-of-sight propagation (space or direct wave).

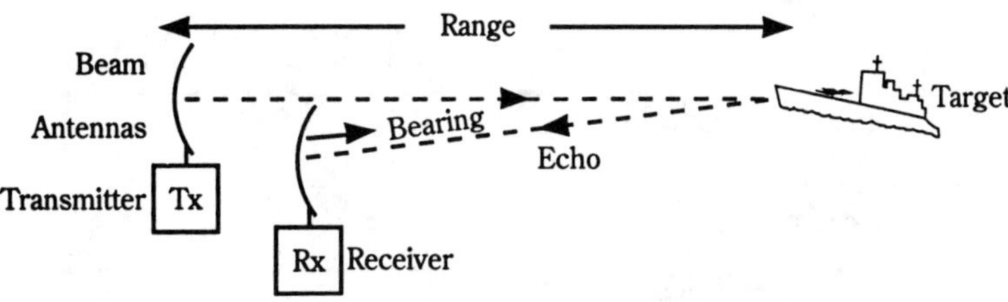

Fig. 12-1 The principles of radar.

The range is found by:

- Measuring the very short time interval between the start of the transmitted pulse and the start of the reflected signal pulse or echo.
- Using the speed of radio waves in the atmosphere, which is about 162,000 sea miles/s or 1 sea mile in 6.1 μs.

Because the radar signal covers twice the target range, it follows that the time for a radar range of 0.5 sea mile (or 1000 yards approx.) is 6.1 μs. Consequently, the signal pulse must be of very short duration, sometimes less than 1 μs if echoes from nearby targets are not to overlap. These very short time intervals are measured by the time base of a cathode ray tube. One of the most common and simplest forms of CRT time base is one in which the spot is made to move or sweep uniformly from left to right, obeying the range scale by moving 1000 yards every 6.1 μs. The start of this sweep from zero range is synchronized with the transmission of the pulse. At the same time, the echo pulses from the receiver are applied to one of the Y plates, which causes sharp vertical deflections or "pips" on the trace (FIG. 12-2). The leading edge of the initial pip appears at the start of the trace or zero range because this part of the signal comes directly from the transmitter. The target range can then be read off opposite the leading edge of the echo "pip." By high-speed reception of this procedure, the moving spot gives the impression of a steady trace or line. In order to do this, the spot flies back or retraces rapidly to the start of the scale and awaits the next transmission and the accompanying sweep. At the same time, it is arranged that the spot is seen or "brightened" during the sweep only; the beam is cut off and the spot "blacked out" for the remaining time.

The *Pulse Repetition Frequency (PRF)* or *repetition rate* varies in different equipment. If a certain radar set has a PRF of 500 Hz (FIG. 12-3A), the transmitter and the sweep are triggered 500 times every second. The bearing of the target is obtained by using directional or beam antennas for transmission and reception.

The target bearing can then be given by training the antenna for the maximum echo amplitude on the CRT display. The stages of the radar system's block diagram (FIG. 12-3A) are found in many radar sets; the functions of these various stages are:

- The *transmitter* is normally in three main units:
  - ~ The trigger unit, which produces short pulses at the same repetition rate as the frequency of the ac supply, or the natural frequency of an astable multivibrator. A blocking oscillator can also be used in a Trigger Unit.
  - ~ The modulator unit, which is controlled by the trigger pulses and provides very short pulses of several kV, to the oscillator, which is usually a magnetron (chapter 11).
  - ~ The oscillator, which is normally the power-output stage of the transmitter and passes RF pulses to the antenna system.

Echo
Echo
Y_1
Video signals
Flyback
Sweep
X_1
Echo
X_2
Time-base voltage
0
Range scale
in 1000 yd or
6-μs divisions
Range
Y_2
9
k
Brightening pulses
Repetition
period
1/500 sec or 2000 μs

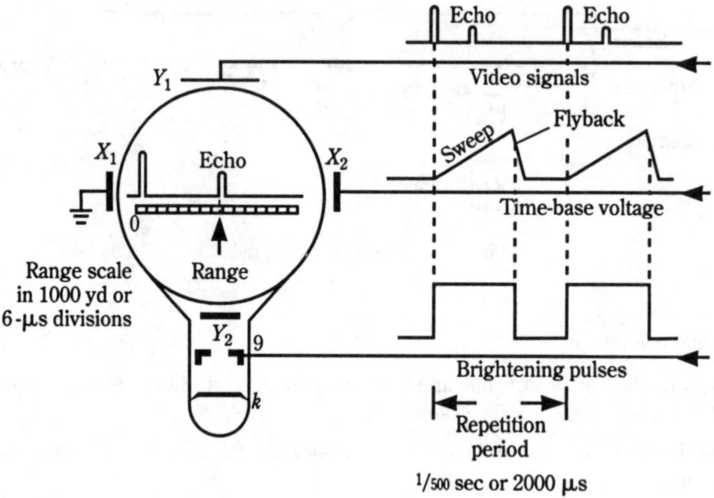

Fig. 12-2 The measurement of range.

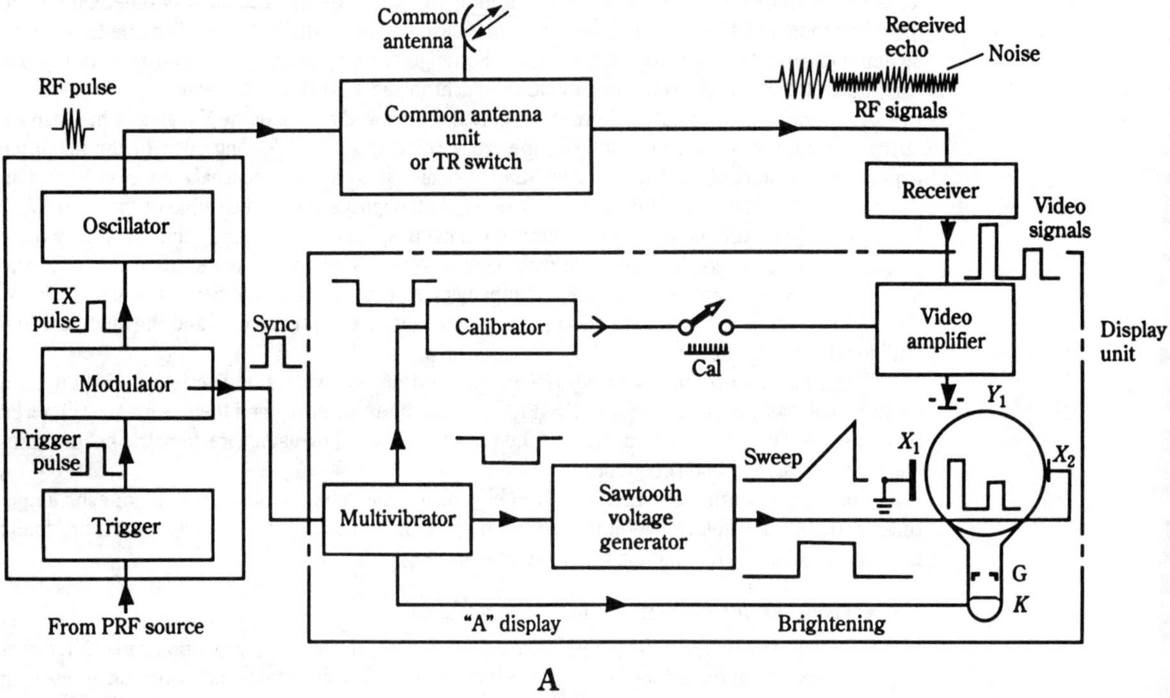

Common
antenna
Received
echo
Noise
RF pulse
Common antenna
unit
or TR switch
RF signals
Receiver
Video
signals
Oscillator
TX
pulse
Sync
Calibrator
Cal
Video
amplifier
Display
unit
Modulator
Y_1
Trigger
pulse
Sweep
X_1
X_2
Multivibrator
Sawtooth
voltage
generator
Trigger
G
K
From PRF source
"A" display
Brightening
A

Fig. 12-3 The basic pulsed radar set.

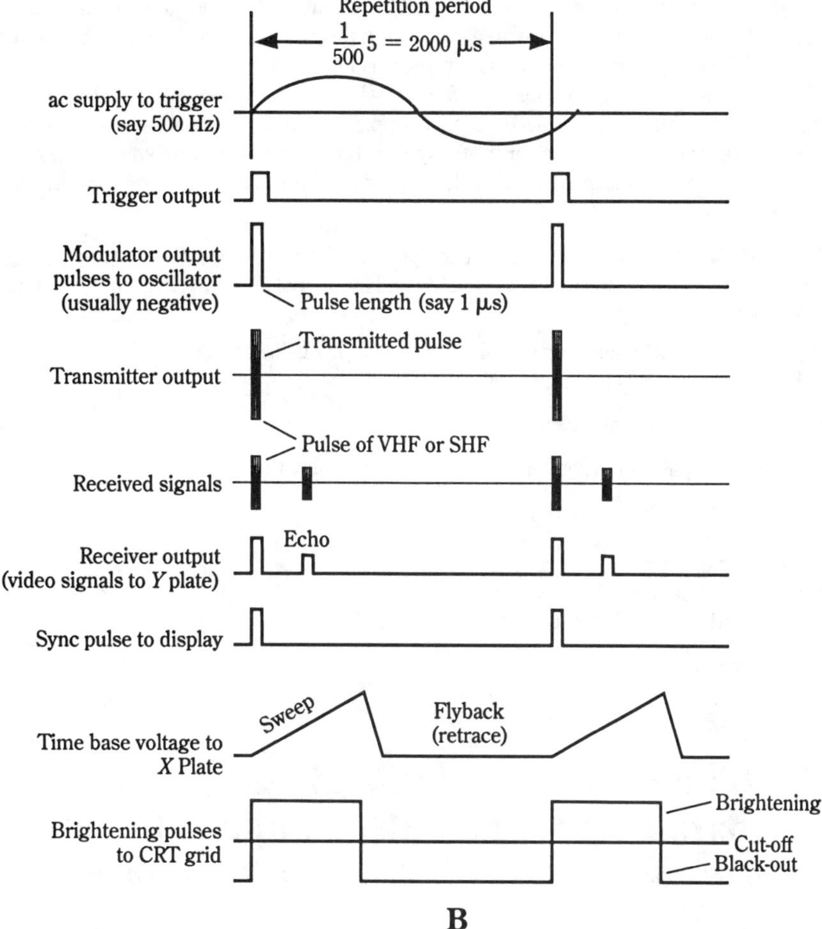

Fig. 12-3 Continued

- The *antenna.* In a few sets, separate antennas can be used for the transmitter and the receiver, but most sets use a duplexing system so that the same antenna is used for transmission and reception in order to reduce topweight and space. The common transmit/receive (T/R) switch effectively connects the antenna to the transmitter during the pulse interval and then to the receiver for the remaining time.
- The *receiver* is a sensitive, wideband superhet. The detected output signals take the form of voltage pulses, called *video signals,* which, when applied to one Y plate of the CRT, are seen as "pips" on the display.

  Noise, developed in the initial stages of the receiver, takes the form of "grass" on the display. The weakest detectable signal should be of greater amplitude than the grass; the minimum readable signal/noise ratio should therefore be greater than 1:1 (0 dB).
- The *display* (FIG. 12-3B). A synchronizing (sync) pulse from the modulator triggers the multivibrator, which produces square waves, whose periods approximate to the time for the maximum range or sweep length. One such square wave switches a time-base stage

to generate a simultaneous sawtooth voltage, which can be amplified and applied to the CRT's X plates to provide the sweep and flyback (retrace). Another square wave is applied to the CRT so that only the sweep movement is brightened.

Some displays also include: a *calibrator,* which provides a check that the sweep rate conforms with the range scale by producing pips or spots at suitable range intervals. A *range marker* or *strobe* in the form of a spot can be adjusted for any known range on the trace. The strobe is aligned with the leading edge of the target echo when measuring its range.

* **Question 12-1** A marine radar set detects the presence of a target on the surface of the ocean. Which of the following is the form of propagation used by the pulse in traveling from the transmitter to the target?

A. ground wave B. space wave C. sky wave D. indirect wave
E. choices B and D are true

Answer Choice B. Space or direct wave.

* **Question 12-2** A pulsed radar set is used to determine only the:

A. range of a target
B. bearing of a target
C. elevation of a target
D. range and bearing of a surface target
E. range and elevation of an aircraft

Answer Choice D.

12-2. The radar equation and parameters of a pulsed radar set

The sensitivity or the maximum detection range of a pulsed radar set is proportional to:

$$\sqrt[4]{\frac{P_t \times G_t \times A_r \times \delta}{P_r}} \qquad (12\text{-}1)$$

where: P_t = transmitter peak power output (W)
G_t = gain or directivity of the transmitting antenna
A_r = effective area of receiving antenna (m^2)
δ = a factor governed by the reflecting properties of the target—size, conductivity, inclination, etc.
P_r = the minimum detectable received signal power (W); this must exceed the receiver noise

Hence, the maximum range of a system can be increased by:

- Increasing the transmitter power output and bearing in mind that the range is proportional to the fourth root of the peak power, it would be necessary to increase the transmitted power sixteen times in order to double the range.
- Reducing the beam width.
- Reducing the receiver noise, primarily in the design of the initial stages.

The main parameters that are associated with the pulsed radar set are:

Pulse shape

Pulses of various shapes can be used in radar systems, but for various practical reasons, the rectangular shape is usually chosen.

Pulse duration (width or length)

The pulse duration is the duration of the rectangular pulse and is normally measured in microseconds. For most radar sets, the duration lies between 0.1 and 10 μs. It is a factor in determining the minimum obtainable range because the echo pulse and the transmitted pulse must not overlap.

Increasing the pulse duration will increase the energy content of the pulse and will increase the minimum range. However, those targets whose difference in range corresponds to the pulse duration, cannot be distinguished on the display; for example, a pulse duration of 0.1 μs will cover approximately 160 yards of range on the display.

The duration of the pulse is determined in the modulator unit which contains an artificial discharge line of N sections. The expression for the pulse duration is $2N\sqrt{LC}$ seconds, where L and C are the inductance and the capacitance of each section. The discharge occurs through a thyratron or a rotary spark gap.

Pulse repetition time (or period)

The *pulse repetition time* is the time interval between the leading edges of successive rectangular pulses. It is a factor in obtaining the maximum range obtainable because the echoes from a particular pulse must be received before the next pulse is transmitted. However, for range reliability, the pulse repetition time must be kept sufficiently short to allow a number of pulses to be received from a particular target.

Pulse repetition frequency (or rate)

The *pulse repetition frequency* is also known as the *pulse frequency* and is the reciprocal of the pulse repetition time. The values of pulse frequency generally lie between 250 and 5000 Hz. The higher the pulse frequency, the greater is the intensity of the echoes on the display; the result is an improvement in the target's definition.

Peak power

The *peak power* is the average power transmitted during the duration of the pulse. This can vary from several kW to a few MW. It has been shown that the maximum range available is directly proportional to the fourth root of the peak power; in order to triple the range, it would require the transmitter power to be increased 81 times.

Average power

This is the *average power* taken over the pulse repetition period. It follows that:

$$\frac{\textit{The average power}}{\textit{The peak power}} = \frac{\textit{The pulse duration}}{\textit{The pulse repetition time}} \tag{12-2}$$

Both of these ratios are equal to the duty cycle, which has no units. The value of the duty cycle typically ranges from 0.01 to 0.0001.

Power gain (*G*) of the antenna

The maximum range is proportional to the square root of the antenna gain. Increasing the range by increasing the gain reduces the beam width and improves the *bearing resolution,* which is the ability to distinguish between targets at the same range, but on different bearings.

Antenna rotation rate

The *antenna rotation rate* rate is limited by the number of the received pulses that are required for each target. The higher the antenna rotation rate, the lower will be the intensity of the echoes on the display.

Radio frequency

The efficiency of surface detection increases with the value of the radio frequency. Moreover, as the radio frequency is increased, the size of the antenna and the waveguide elements decreases. The parabolic reflectors used with centimeter wavelengths can provide very narrow pencil beams, which are especially suitable for accurate bearing measurements. The practical beam width or beam angle in degrees is given by:

$$\textit{Beam width} = \frac{61\lambda}{d} \qquad (12\text{-}3)$$

where: λ = wavelength (m)
d = width of parabolic reflector (m)

The *beam width* is the angle between those two directions in which the received signal power falls to half of the maximum value, which is obtained along the beam axis.

The radio bands that are allocated to marine radar sets are 2.9 to 3.1 GHz, 5.46 to 5.65 GHz, and 9.3 to 9.5 GHz. All of these are in the GHz range, which corresponds to wavelengths of the order of centimeters. The relationship between the frequency, f, and the wavelength, λ, in free space is:

$$f = \frac{30}{\lambda} \qquad (12\text{-}4)$$

and:

$$\lambda = \frac{30}{f} \qquad (12\text{-}5)$$

where: f = frequency (GHz)
λ = wavelength (cm)

The following relationships exist between the various parameters:

$$\begin{aligned} \textit{Pulse duration} &= \frac{\textit{average power} \times \textit{pulse repetition time}}{\textit{peak power}} \\ &= \frac{\textit{average power}}{\textit{peak power} \times \textit{pulse frequency}} \\ &= \frac{\textit{duty cycle}}{\textit{pulse frequency}} \end{aligned} \qquad (12\text{-}6)$$

$$\begin{aligned} \textit{Pulse repetition time} &= \frac{\textit{pulse duration} \times \textit{peak power}}{\textit{average power}} \\ &= \frac{\textit{pulse duration}}{\textit{duty cycle}} \end{aligned} \qquad (12\text{-}7)$$

$$\textit{Pulse repetition frequency} = \frac{\textit{average power}}{\textit{pulse duration} \times \textit{peak power}}$$

$$= \frac{\textit{duty cycle}}{\textit{pulse duration}} \quad (12\text{-}8)$$

$$\textit{Average power} = \frac{\textit{peak power} \times \textit{pulse duration}}{\textit{peak repetition time}}$$

$$= \textit{peak power} \times \textit{duty cycle} \quad (12\text{-}9)$$

$$\textit{Peak power} = \frac{\textit{average power} \times \textit{pulse repetition time}}{\textit{pulse duration}}$$

$$= \frac{\textit{average power}}{\textit{pulse duration} \times \textit{pulse frequency}}$$

$$= \frac{\textit{average power}}{\textit{duty cycle}} \quad (12\text{-}10)$$

$$\textit{Duty cycle} = \textit{pulse duration} \times \textit{pulse frequency}. \quad (12\text{-}11)$$

* **Question 12-3** A radar set with a peak pulsed power output of 500 kW, has a pulse repetition rate (frequency) of 400 per second. What is the value of the pulse repetition time?

A. 25 ms B. 4.0 ms C. 400 μs D. 2500 μs E. 0.0004 s

Answer Choice D.

$$\text{The } \textit{pulse repetition time} = \frac{1}{\textit{pulse frequency}}$$

$$= \frac{1}{400} \text{ second}$$

$$= 2500 \ \mu\text{s}$$

* **Question 12-4** If in QUES. 12-3, the pulse width is 0.5 μs, what is the average pulse power?

A. 100 W B. 250 W C. 400 W D. 500 W E. 800 W

Answer Choice A.

$$\text{The } \textit{duty cycle} = \frac{\textit{pulse width}}{\textit{pulse repetition time}}$$

$$= \frac{0.5}{2500} = \frac{1}{5000}$$

$$\text{The } \textit{average power} = \textit{peak power} \times \textit{duty cycle}$$

$$= 500 \text{ kW} \times \frac{1}{5000} = 100 \text{ W}$$

* **Question 12-5** Pulsed radar sets are primarily used to find the:

A. size and speed of a target
B. speed and course of a target
C. target's range and bearing
D. target's range and speed
E. direction and size of a target

Answer Choice C.

* **Question 12-6** Marine radar transmitters are allowed to operate on:

A. 2460 to 2650 MHz B. 6900 to 7100 MHz C. 7300 to 7500 MHz
D. 8900 to 9100 MHz E. 9300 to 9500 MHz

Answer Choice E. The frequency bands allocated to marine radar sets are 2.9 to 3.1 GHz, 5.46 to 5.65 GHz and 9.3 to 9.5 GHz.

* **Question 12-7** In a pulsed radar set, the duty cycle is equal to:

A. $\frac{1}{\textit{pulse frequency} \times \textit{pulse width}}$

B. $\frac{\textit{peak power}}{\textit{average power}}$

C. $\frac{\textit{pulse repetition time}}{\textit{pulse duration}}$

D. $\frac{\textit{pulse width}}{\textit{pulse frequency}}$

E. the reciprocal of A

Answer Choice E.

* **Question 12-8** In a marine radar set, the pulse duration is 0.5 μs. What is the maximum range separation (in yards) between two targets that cannot be distinguished on the display?

A. 246 B. 328 C. 164 D. 82 E. 41

Answer Choice D. The maximum range separation is $(1/2) \times 0.5 \times 328 = 82$ yards.

* **Question 12-9** The peak power output of a pulsed radar set is multiplied by a factor of 16. Assuming that all other parameters remain the same, the maximum range obtainable will be multiplied by:

A. 2 B. 4 C. 8 D. 16 E. 32

Answer Choice A. The maximum range obtainable is proportional to the fourth root of the transmitter's peak power output. The maximum range is therefore multiplied by $\sqrt[4]{16} = 2$.

* **Question 12-10** The pulse frequency of a radar set is 400. If the value of the duty cycle is 2×10^{-4} and the average power of the transmitted pulse is 200 W, what is the pulse width in microseconds?

A. 0.1 B. 0.2 C. 0.25 D. 0.5 E. 1.0

Answer Choice D.

$$\begin{aligned}\textit{Pulse width} &= \frac{\textit{duty cycle}}{\textit{pulse frequency}} \\ &= \frac{2 \times 10^{-4}}{400} \text{ second} \\ &= 0.5 \times 10^{-6} \text{ second} \\ &= 0.5\ \mu\text{s}\end{aligned}$$

* **Question 12-11** In QUES. 12-10, what is the peak power of the transmitted pulse?

A. 1.0 MW B. 500 kW C. 250 kW D. 200 kW E. 100 kW

Answer Choice A.

$$\begin{aligned} \textit{Peak power} &= \frac{\textit{average power}}{\textit{duty cycle}} \\ &= \frac{200}{2 \times 10^{-4}} \\ &= 10^{6}\text{ W} \\ &= 1\text{ MW} \end{aligned}$$

* **Question 12-12** The pulse frequency of a radar set is reduced but the peak power, the pulse duration, and the radio frequency remain the same. As a result:

A. the definition of the targets on the P.P.I. display will be improved
B. the average power will be increased
C. the value of the duty cycle will increase
D. the maximum range available may be increased
E. the bandwidth of the signal in the IF stages will be increased

Answer Choice D.

12-3. Radar ranges and their corresponding time intervals

A radar pulse is an electromagnetic wave that travels with the velocity of light in air. At standard temperature and pressure, this velocity is 2.997×10^{8} meters per second or 161,700 nautical miles per second, where 1 nautical mile ≈ 6080 feet ≈ 2027 yards.

The time taken for a radar pulse to travel 1 nautical mile is 6.184 μs. Therefore, the total time interval for a target range of 1 nautical mile is the total time for the pulse to reach the target and the echo to return to the receiver; this will be $2 \times 6.184 = 12.368$ μs.

The distance traveled by a radar pulse in 1 μs = 0.161711 nautical miles, which is approximately 328 yards. Therefore, a pulse duration of 1 μs will cover a range interval of 328/2 = 164 yards.

Summarizing:

$$\begin{array}{l}\textit{Radar range in}\\ \textit{nautical miles}\end{array} = \frac{\textit{total round-trip time interval (in } \mu s\textit{)}}{12.37} \qquad (12\text{-}12)$$

and therefore, the total time interval in microseconds for the pulse to travel to the target and back is $12.37 \times$ the radar range in nautical miles.

$$\begin{array}{l}\textit{Distance to the}\\ \textit{target in nautical miles}\end{array} = \frac{\begin{array}{c}\textit{time taken by the transmitted pulse}\\ \textit{to reach the target in microseconds}\end{array}}{6.18} \qquad (12\text{-}13)$$

so that the time in microseconds taken by the transmitted pulse to reach the target is $6.18 \times$ the distance to the target in nautical miles. The total distance traveled by the pulse to the target and back to the receiver is 2 times the radar range.

* **Question 12-13** If the range of a target is 7.5 nautical miles, what is the time interval (in μs) between the radar pulse being transmitted and the target echo being received?

A. 46.3 B. 93 C. 186 D. 162 E. 81

Answer Choice B. The total time interval is $7.5 \times 12.37 = 93$ μs.

* **Question 12-14** If the time interval between a radar pulse being transmitted and the echo being received, is 105 μs, what is the range of the target in nautical miles?

A. 16.98 B. 8.49 C. 19.56 D. 9.78 E. 4.89

Answer Choice B. The range in nautical miles is 105/12.37 = 8.49.

* **Question 12-15** If the time interval between a radar pulse being transmitted and the echo being received is 87 μs, what is the total distance in nautical miles from the radar set to the target and back again?

A. 16.20 B. 8.10 C. 14.07 D. 32.40 E. 7.03

Answer Choice C. The total distance in nautical miles is: 2 × 87/12.37 = 14.07.

12-4. The radar receiver

The RF echo pulses reflected by a distant object are similar in shape to the transmitted pulse that was covered earlier, but are considerably diminished in amplitude. These minute signals are amplified and converted into video signals by the receiver. A voltage amplification of the order of 10^{10} is required to produce a video pulse of sufficient amplitude to control the beam of a CRT. The receiver must accomplish this amplification with a minimum introduction of noise.

In addition to having high gain and a low noise figure, the receiver must provide a sufficient bandwidth to pass the many harmonics that are contained in the video pulses. This is to minimize distortion of the pulse shape. The receiver must also accurately track, or follow, the transmitter in frequency because any amount of drift will diminish the reception of the echo signal. The receiver tuning range only needs to be equal to that of the transmitter.

The superheterodyne receiver is exclusively used in pulsed microwave systems. A simplified block diagram of a radar receiver, based on the superheterodyne principle, is shown in FIG. 12-4. The echo signal enters the system by the antenna shown in the upper left-hand corner of FIG. 12-4. It passes through the duplexer (covered later in this chapter) and is amplified by the low-noise RF amplifier (such as a TWT). When external noise is negligible, the noise generated by the input stage of the receiver largely determines the receiver's sensitivity. In early radar receivers and in many present-day receivers, an RF amplifier is not used and the mixer is the first stage (as indicated by the broken line in FIG. 12-4). The function of the mixer stage, or first detector, is to translate the RF to a lower intermediate frequency.

Mixing is accomplished by heterodyning the returned RF signal signal echo with a local oscillator signal in a nonlinear device (crystal mixer) and extracting the signal component at the difference frequency (IF), which is normally of the order of 30 to 60 MHz. By converting the RF carrier frequency to the lower intermediate frequency, it is easier to obtain the necessary gain and the required bandwidth characteristic of the receiver. The second detector, which is most often a crystal rectifier, extracts the video modulation from the carrier. This modulation is amplified in the video stages to a level that is high enough to operate the indicator or display devices.

One of the requirements of the radar receiver is that its internal noise is kept to a minimum. It is important, therefore, that the input stages of the receiver are designed with low noise figures. If the mixer is the first stage, its crystal characteristics will include low conversion loss and a low noise-to-temperature change ratio. Any noise generated by the local oscillator must be kept out of the mixer stage, either by inserting a narrowband filter between the local oscillator and the crystal or by the using a balanced mixer.

As the bandwidth of the RF portion of the receiver is relatively wide, the frequency-response characteristic of the IF amplifier determines the overall response characteristic of the receiver. It is in the design of the IF portion of the receiver that the response characteristics are accomplished in conjunction with the necessary signal-to-noise ratio.

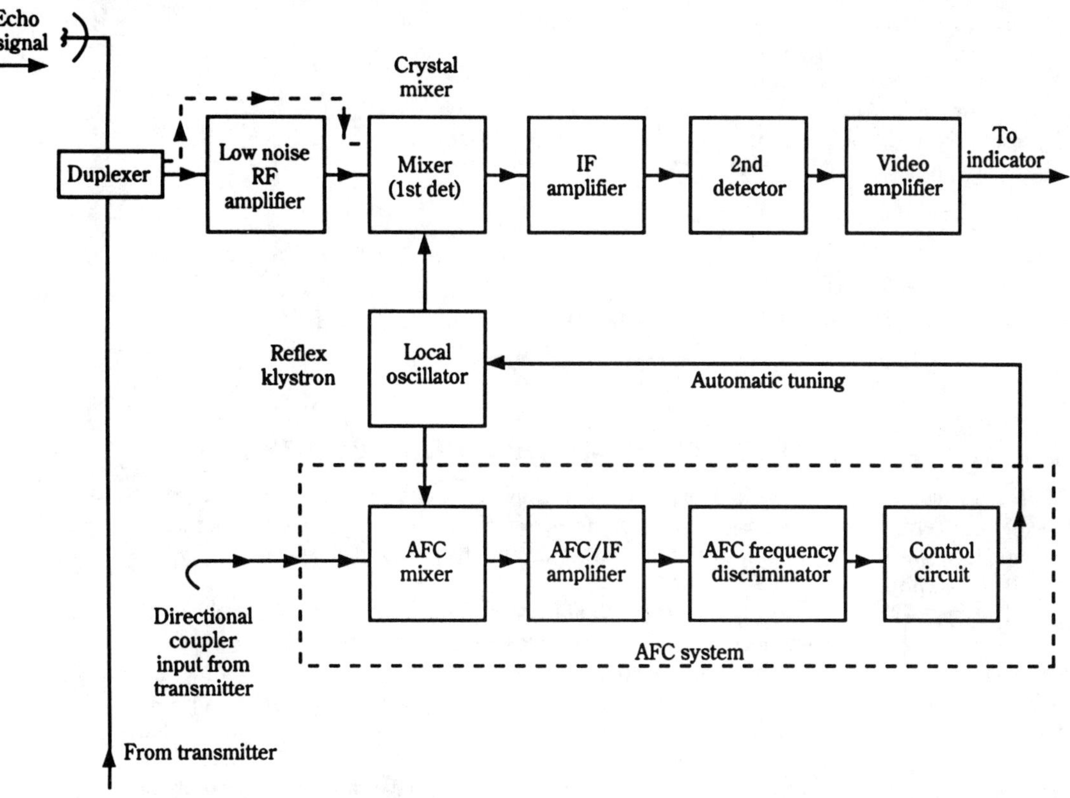

Fig. 12-4 A block diagram of a radar receiver.

Automatic frequency control

The *automatic frequency control* (*AFC*) stages, which are normally used to keep the receiver in tune with the transmitter are known as a *difference-frequency system.* In this system, a portion of the signal is coupled into the AFC mixer and is heterodyned with the local oscillator signal. If the transmitter and the receiver are correctly tuned, the resultant difference frequency will be at the required IF. If the receiver is not in tune with the transmitter, the difference frequency will be incorrect. Any deviation is then detected by the AFC discriminator (ratio detector), which, in turn, generates an error voltage, whose magnitude is proportional to the deviation from the correct IF, and whose polarity determines the direction of the error. This error voltage corrects the frequency of the local oscillator (reflex klystron), which is connected to both the receiver mixer and the AFC mixer.

* **Question 12-16** Which of the following tubes would normally be used in the local oscillator section of a SHF radar receiver?

A. thyratron B. magnetron C. multicavity klystron D. reflex klystron
E. carcinotron

Answer Choice D.

* **Question 12-17** In the receiver of a marine SHF radar set, a ratio detector might be used as:

A. the first detector stage and as an alternative to the crystal mixer
B. the second detector stage
C. part of the STC system
D. part of the AFC system
E. none of the above is true. A ratio detector could serve no useful purpose in a radar receiver

Answer Choice D.

* **Question 12-18** The operating frequency of a marine radar set is 3 GHz. The value of the receiver's IF would typically be:

A. 455 kHz B. 10.7 MHz C. 4.5 MHz D. 12.75 MHz E. 30 MHz

Answer Choice E.

12-5. The mixer stage of the radar receiver

Many radar receivers do not use RF amplifiers. They simply use a crystal mixer stage at the front end of the receiver. A crystal is used instead of an electron diode because at microwave frequencies the tube would generate excessive noise. Most electron tubes would also be limited by the effects of transit time.

The type of crystal commonly used is the *point-contact silicon crystal diode.* Unlike the junction diode, the point-contact diode depends on the pressure of contact between a point and a semiconductor crystal for its operation. Figures 12-5A and 12-5B illustrate a cut-away view of a point-contact diode. One section of the diode consists of a small rectangular crystal, which is formed from n-type silicon. A fine beryllium-copper, bronze-phosphor, or tungsten wire, called the *catwhisker* presses against the crystal and forms the other part of the diode. During the manufacture of the point-contact diode, a large current is passed from the catwhisker to the silicon crystal. The result of this large current is the formation of a small region of p-type material around the crystal in the vicinity of the point contact so that the pn junction is produced.

The reason for using the pointed wire instead of a flat metal plate is to produce a high-intensity electric field at the point contact without using a large external source voltage. It is not possible to apply large voltages across the average semiconductor diode because of excessive heating.

The end of the catwhisker is one of the terminals of the diode. It has a low-resistance contact to the external circuit. A flat metal plate, on which the crystal is mounted, forms the lower contact of the diode with the external circuit. Both contacts with the external circuit have low resistances.

The characteristics of the point-contact diode (FIG. 12-5C) under forward and reverse bias are somewhat different from those of the normal junction diode. With a forward bias, the resistance of the point-contact diode is higher than that of the junction diode. With reverse bias, the current flow through a point-contact diode is not as independent of the voltage applied to the crystal as it is in the junction diode. The point-contact diode has an advantage over the junction diode in that the capacitance between the catwhisker and the crystal is less than the capacitance between the two regions of the junction diode. As such, the capacitive reactance existing across the point-contact diode is higher and the capacitive current that will flow in the circuit at high frequencies is smaller. A cut-away view of the entire point-contact diode is shown in FIG. 12-5D.

The simplest type of radar mixer stage is the *single-ended* or *unbalanced crystal mixer.* This type of mixer is ilustrated in FIG. 12-6 and uses a tuned section of coaxial transmission line, $\lambda/2$ long, which matches the crystal to the signal echo and the local oscillator (LO) input. The injection from the local oscillator is accomplished by means of a probe, while the signal is fed in by means of a slot in the coaxial assembly. This slot would normally be inserted in the duplexer waveguide assembly and is properly oriented to provide coupling of the returned echo signal. In this appli-

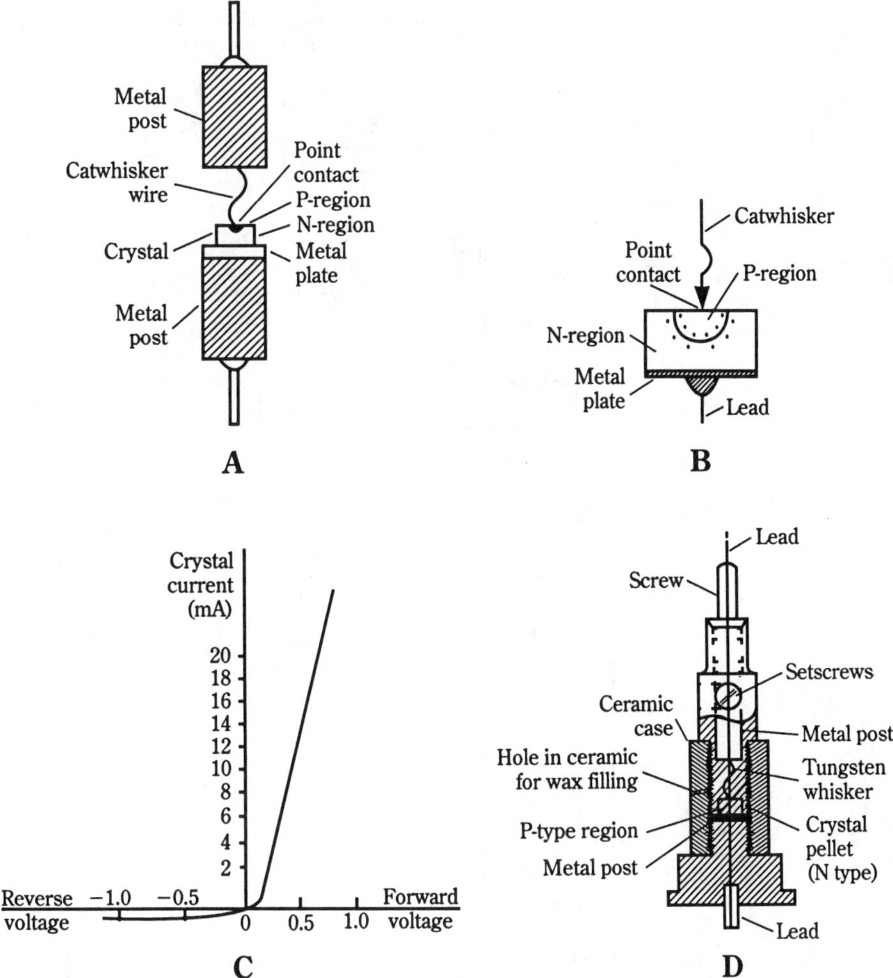

Fig. 12-5 The silicon-tungsten crystal mixer.

cation, the unwanted signals at the output of the mixer (the carrier, the local oscillator frequency, and the sum of these two signals) are effectively eliminated by the resonant circuit, which is tuned to the intermediate, or difference, frequency. One advantage of the unbalanced crystal mixer is its simplicity. It has, however, one major disadvantage, which is its inability to cancel the local-oscillator noise. You will recall that a reflex klystron (chapter 11) generates a high degree of noise, and it will be difficult to detect weak signals if the noise is allowed to pass through the mixer along with the signal. One type of mixer that cancels local-oscillator noise is the balanced or hybrid mixer, sometimes called the *magic tee* (FIG. 12-7).

If the meter, M, in FIG. 12-6 reads zero or a low value, it is possible that the mixer crystal is defective. Other indications of a defective crystal are unusually weak echoes on the display or no echoes seen at all. In addition, the CRT might show an excessive level of grass (noise). The crystal can be checked by measuring its front- (250 to 500 Ω) to-back (10,000 Ω) resistance ratio, which should be about 1 to 20 or more. However, you should take great care in testing or

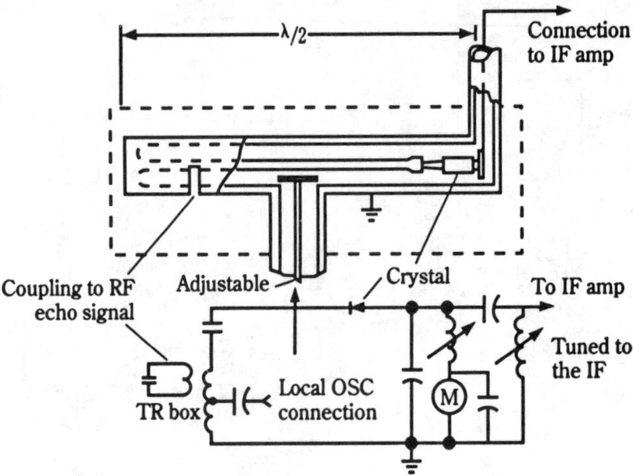

Fig. 12-6 The single-ended crystal mixer.

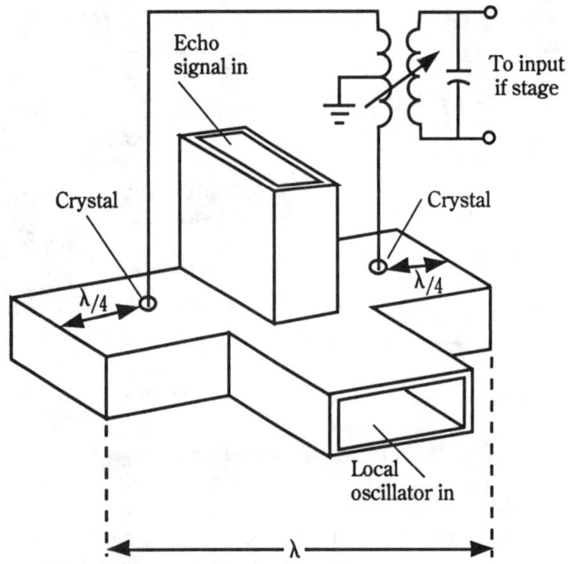

Fig. 12-7 The magic tee crystal mixer.

replacing crystals, which can easily be ruined by excessive static charges. You should first discharge yourself by touching a grounded point, and the crystal itself must be wrapped in lead foil when in storage.

* **Question 12-19** Which of the following might not cause damage to a silicon crystal diode?

A. the application of very frequency voltages in the SHF band
B. excessive current
C. mechanical pressure

D. static charges
E. a defective duplexer

Answer Choice A.

* **Question 12-20** In an SHF-pulsed radar set, the mixer (1st detector) stage of the receiver normally uses a:

A. pn-junction diode
B. low transit time triode
C. silicon crystal diode
D. npn transistor
E. thermionic diode

Answer Choice C.

12-6. The IF amplifier stages

The IF section of a radar receiver determines the receiver's gain, signal-to-noise ratio, and effective bandwidth. These stages must have sufficient gain and dynamic range to accommodate the expected variations in the echo-signal power. They must also have a low noise figure and a band-pass that is wide enough to accommodate the range of frequencies that are associated with an echo pulse.

To achieve accurate ranging, it is necessary to preserve the shape of the rectangular pulse and, in particular, its leading edge. This requires a wide bandwidth for the radar receiver's intermediate- and video-amplifier stages in order to pass the numerous harmonics that are associated with a short-duration pulse (chapter 2). The bandwidth and the pulse duration are related by:

$$\textit{Bandwidth in MHz} = \frac{2}{\textit{pulse duration} \text{ (in } \mu\text{s)}}$$

or:

$$\textit{Pulse duration} \text{ (in } \mu\text{s)} = \frac{2}{\textit{bandwidth} \text{ (MHz)}} \qquad (12\text{-}14)$$

Because a wide bandwidth is required, the gain of each IF amplifier stage is low and, therefore, the number of such stages in a radar receiver can be five or more.

* **Question 12-21** In a SHF pulsed radar set, the circuit of FIG. 12-8 could represent a (an):

A. compensated video amplifier
B. pulse limiter stage
C. IF amplifier
D. modulator stage
E. second detector stage

Answer Choice C.

* **Question 12-22** In an SHF marine radar set, the pulse frequency is 500 per second and the pulse duration is 0.5 μs. What is the bandwidth required by the IF stages of the receiver?

A. 10 MHz B. 5 MHz C. 4 MHz D. 2 MHz E. 1 MHz

Answer Choice C. The bandwidth required by the IF stages $= \frac{2}{t}$ MHz, where t = the pulse duration (in μs). The bandwidth is therefore $\frac{2}{0.5} = 4$ MHz.

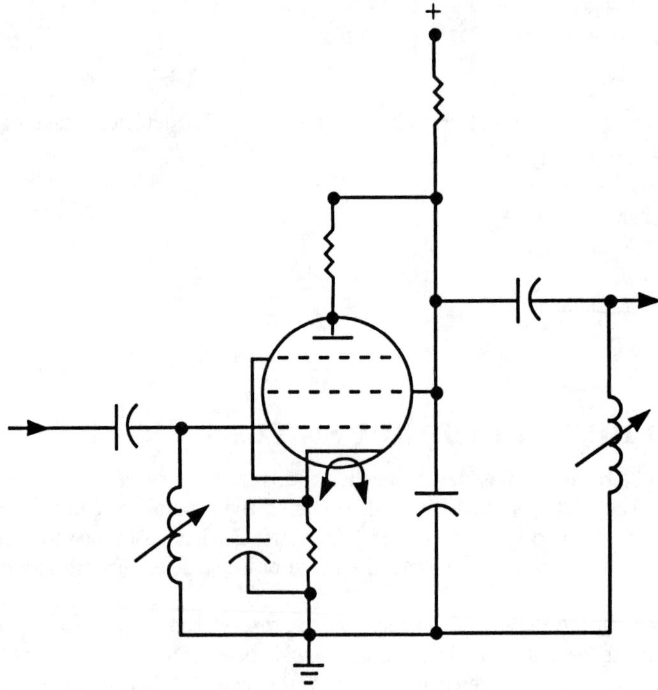

Fig. 12-8 The circuit diagram for question 12-21.

* **Question 12-23** The common number of IF stages in the superheterodyne receiver of a marine radar set, is:

A. 1 B. 2 C. 3 D. 4 E. more than 5

Answer Choice E.

* **Question 12-24** The diagram of FIG. 12-9 is that of a pulsed radar receiver. Block A represents the:

A. signal discriminator
B. local oscillator
C. signal crystal mixer
D. microwave preamplifier
E. AFC crystal detector stage

Answer Choice C.

* **Question 12-25** In the diagram of QUES. 12-24, Block B represents the:

A. signal crystal mixer
B. detector stage
C. signal discriminator
D. reflex klystron stage
E. AFC crystal detector stage

Answer Choice D.

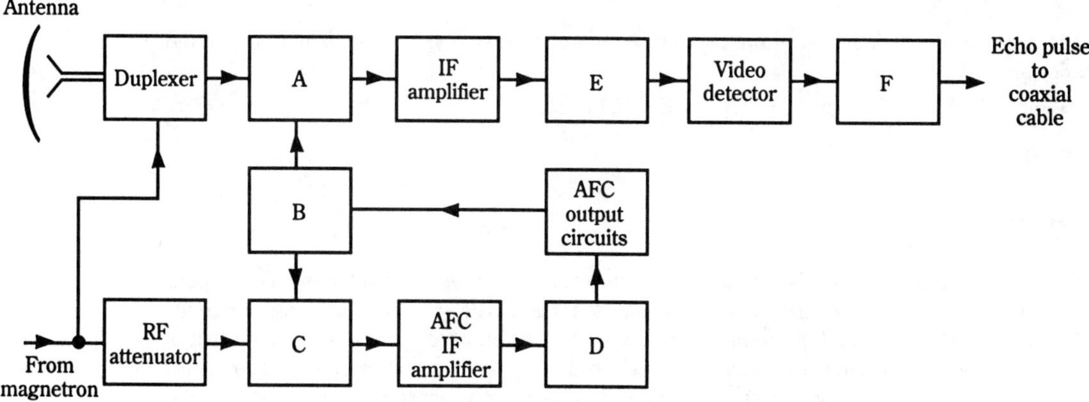

Fig. 12-9 The block diagram for questions 12-24 through 12-29.

* **Question 12-26** In the diagram of QUES. 12-24, Block C represents the:

A. signal crystal mixer
B. AFC crystal detector stage
C. AFC discriminator
D. second detector stage
E. local oscillator

Answer Choice B.

* **Question 12-27** In the diagram of QUES. 12-24, Block D represents the:

A. local oscillator
B. AFC discriminator
C. signal's second detector stage
D. AFC crystal detector stage
E. reflex klystron stage

Answer Choice B.

* **Question 12-28** In the diagram of QUES. 12-24, Block E represents the:

A. signal discriminator stage
B. crystal mixer stage
C. second detector stage
D. signal limiter stage
E. AFC crystal detector stage

Answer Choice C.

* **Question 12-29** In the diagram of QUES. 12-24, Block F represents a (an):

A. high-gain video amplifier
B. compensated video power amplifier
C. pulse-shaping amplifier
D. emitter follower
E. noise limiter

Answer Choice D.

* **Question 12-30** The back-to-front resistance ratio of a mixer crystal diode is normally of the order of:

A. 1:1 B. 2:1 C. 5:1 D. 10:1 E. 20:1 or more

Answer Choice E.

12-7. The echo box

It is often necessary to check the overall performance of a microwave radar set in situations where it is difficult to obtain echoes from objects at suitable ranges. The *echo box* is a simple device for checking roughly the overall performance of the system. It is merely a resonant cavity that is designed to possess a high Q. The cavity is shock-excited by the transmitter pulse and continues to ring and emit a signal that is spread along the time base for an appreciable distance after the cessation of the transmitter pulse. A possible arrangement is shown in FIG. 12-10. The echo box is fed through a screened low-loss cable from a pick-up probe that is fixed near the edge of the reflector. The energy abstracted from the transmitted pulse is stored as a resonant mode in the box and is re-radiated to the receiver as an exponentially decaying signal. For the greater part of its duration, the signal saturates the receiver, but finally drops to a level, at which this is no longer so. The appearance on the display is illustrated in FIG. 12-10. The range at which the echo box response disappears into the noise level gives an indication of the overall performance of the system.

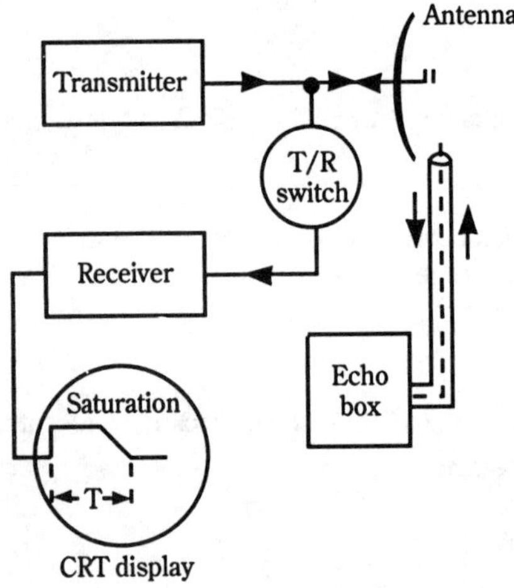

Fig. 12-10 The principle of the echo box.

Echo boxes are of two types, tuned and untuned. *Tuned echo boxes* require tuning to the frequency of the transmitter, which shock-excites the box into oscillation. *Untuned echo boxes* are very large cavity resonators, whose dimensions are much greater than the wavelength of the radar set. They are usually hollow cubes with copper walls.

* **Question 12-31** The echo box in a radar set is used:

A. as a dummy antenna, which can be matched to the magnetron
B. to provide an artificial target for test purposes
C. as a low Q resonant cavity for measuring the receiver's bandwidth

D. as a preamplifier for the received target echoes
E. as part of the AFC system

Answer Choice B.

12-8. Radar antennas

At microwave frequencies, it is possible to devise compact beam antennas, which use parabolic sheets or "mesh" reflectors; the radiator, such as a waveguide flare or dipole, is then placed at the focus of the parabola. Such reflectors usually take the forms that are illustrated in FIG. 12-11 and are either:

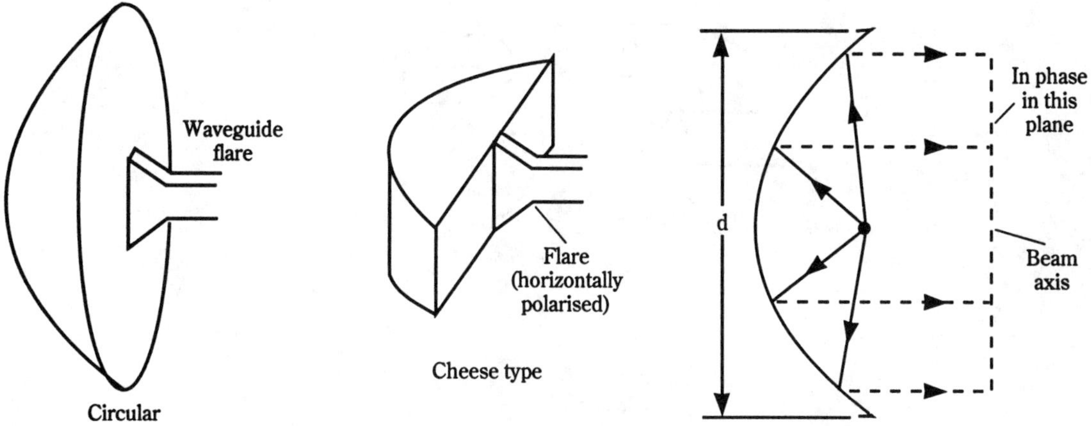

Fig. 12-11 A microwave beam antenna.

- a circular paraboloid that produces a "pencil" beam, which is relatively narrow in all planes.
- a "cheese-type" reflector, from which the beam is relatively narrow in the plane of the parabola only.

Because the path lengths from the focus of the plane shown are the same, the system resembles a stacked array so giving a beam width in the plane of the parabola of roughly 61 λ/d degrees, where λ is the wavelength of the radar signal. For example, if $d \approx 3$ m and $\lambda = 10$ cm, (S band), the beamwidth is approximately 2°, but if $d \approx 1.5$ m, $\lambda = 3$ cm, (X band), the beamwidth is only 1.2°.

Although most radar antennas employ the circular or "cheese-type" parabolic reflectors, some of the modifications and alternative systems in use are:

- **The hoghorn** (FIG. 12-12A) uses a modified flare in which a small parabolic reflector is built into the flare and directs energy horizontally into the cheese-type parabolic reflector; this has the effect of reducing the vertical beamwidth.
- **The quarter cheese** (FIG. 12-12B) This antenna is basically half of a normal cheese type and provides a more efficient feed from the flare.
- **The cutler feed** (FIG. 12-12C) This is the method of feeding a circular paraboloid and reduces reflector obstruction by the guide.

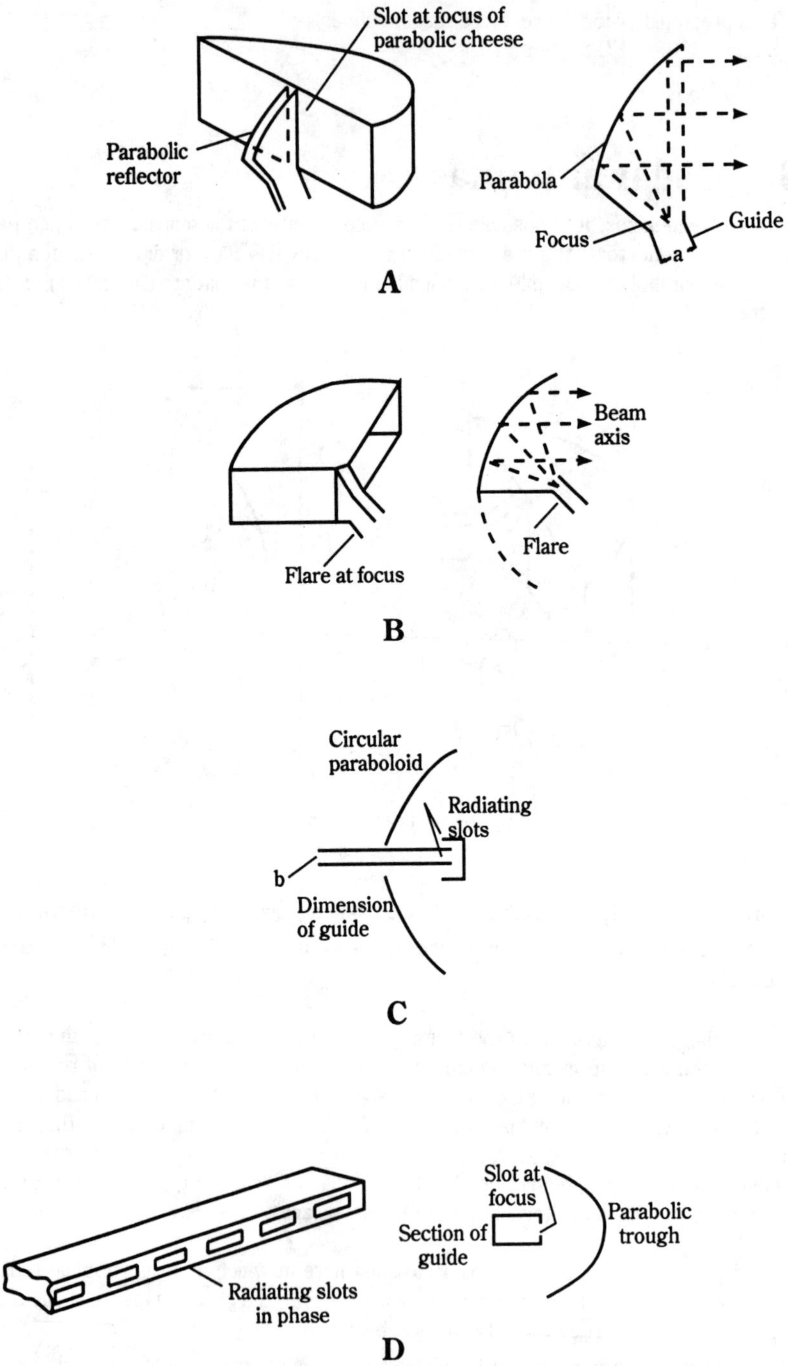

Fig. 12-12 Examples of microwave antennas.

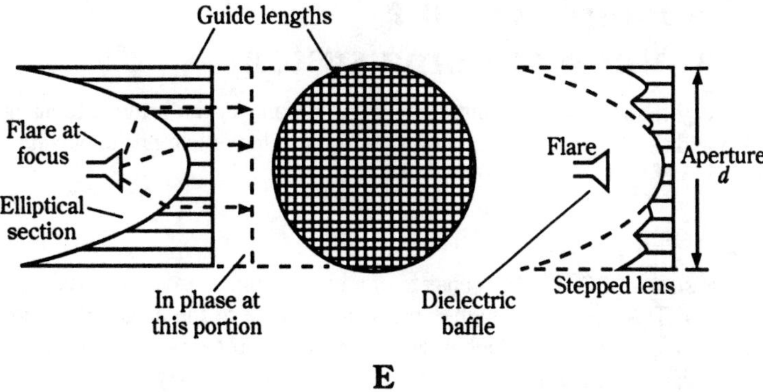

E

Fig. 12-12 Continued

- **The slot antenna** uses a number of in-phase radiating slots (FIG. 12-12D). These behave as a stacked array and give a narrow horizontal beamwidth. The vertical beamwidth can be reduced by adding a "pig-trough" parabolic reflector (as shown).
- **The lens antenna** has the advantage of removing the waveguide obstruction in front of the antenna. The lens comprises a honeycomb of short "waveguide" lengths that have an elliptical cross-section (FIG. 12-12E). With the flare in focus, the higher phase velocity in the lens makes for effectively equal path lengths to the outside of the lens, and so provides a pencil beam of approximately 61 λ/d degrees, where λ is the wavelength of the radar signal.

The bulk of the lens is usually reduced by cutting away elliptical sections, as in the "stepped" lens. In this case, the various path distances from the flare to the outer surface of the lens can differ by multiples of the wavelength.

Whatever type of microwave antenna is used, it is important to choose its location so that the minimum number of obstructions are encountered while the antenna is screening the area in the vicinity of the ship. This is most important for the directions dead ahead and on either bow.

Some loss in the echo signal strength might occur if excessive dirt is allowed to accumulate on the reflector. It is also important for the dielectric baffle at the end of the waveguide flare to be cleaned periodically.

* **Question 12-32** The antenna system of a marine radar set uses a parabolic reflector in order to:

A. widen the beam and increase the surface coverage
B. match the impedance of the waveguide horn and free space
C. eliminate the requirement for separate transmitter and receiver antenna systems
D. lower the field gain and thereby broaden the antenna system's response
E. provide a unidirectional narrow beam

Answer Choice E.

* **Question 12-33** In a SHF radar system, the end of the waveguide horn is positioned at the parabolic reflector's:

A. centroid B. center C. focus D. apex E. vertex

Answer Choice C.

12-9. The duplexer of a common antenna system

To reduce top-weight, space, and the antenna drive mechanism, the same antenna is often used for transmission and reception. Such common antenna working or antenna duplexing usually uses gas switches.

Gas switch

A basic tuned *gas switch* (FIG. 12-13A) consists of a high-Q tuned circuit shunted by a small sensitive gas-filled gap. This presents a high dynamic impedance to the signal, if not ionized, but if the gap breaks down as a result of a higher signal voltage, it presents a very low impedance, and thereby prevents signals from exceeding that level.

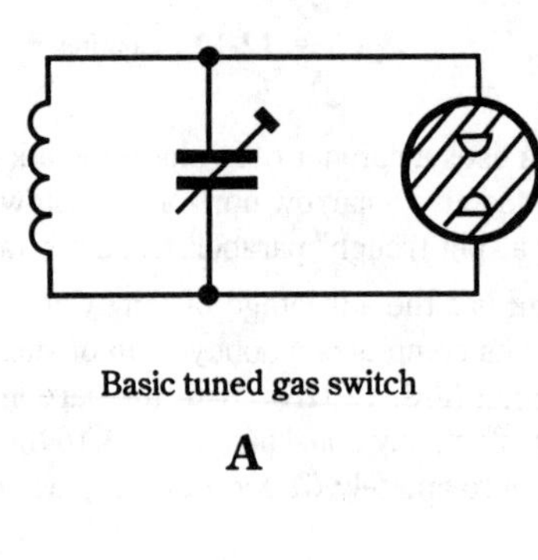

Basic tuned gas switch

A

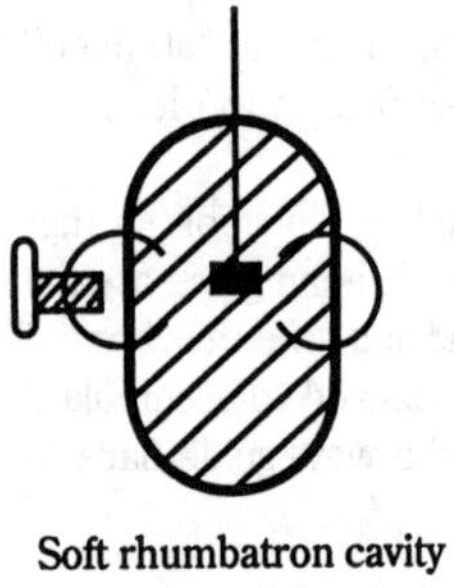

Soft rhumbatron cavity

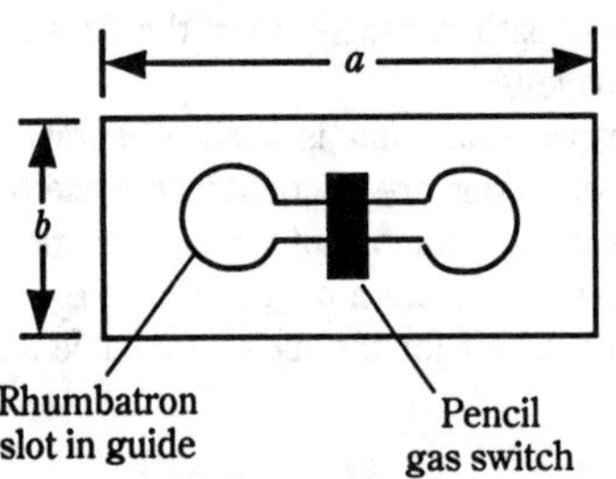

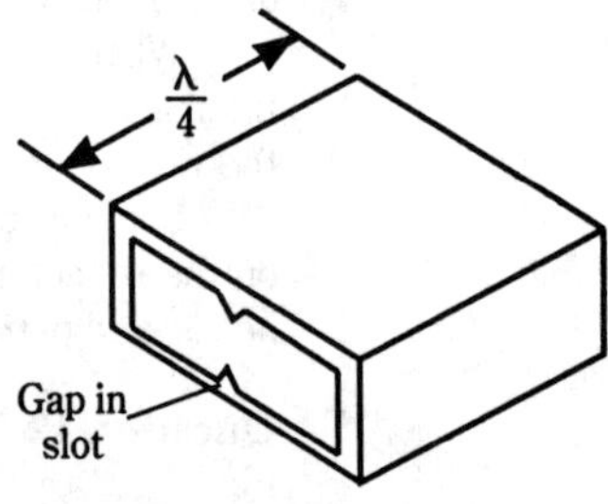

Gas-filled resonant cavity

B

Fig. 12-13 Various types of gas switches.

Microwave gas switches usually use a tuned cavity, often in the form of a gas-filled rhumbatron, the lips of which serve as the gap (FIG. 12-13B), which also shows other variations. An additional priming electrode, to which a dc "keep-alive" voltage or pulse is applied, can be used to ionize part of the gap so that it breaks down for still lower signal voltages.

These centimetric gas switches can be used in various ways (FIG. 12-14). In FIG. 12-14A, the gas switch is inserted, with slot coupling, in the waveguide; this is effectively in parallel with the equivalent lines. If the gas switch breaks down, it tends to "short-circuit" the line; otherwise the line is unaffected.

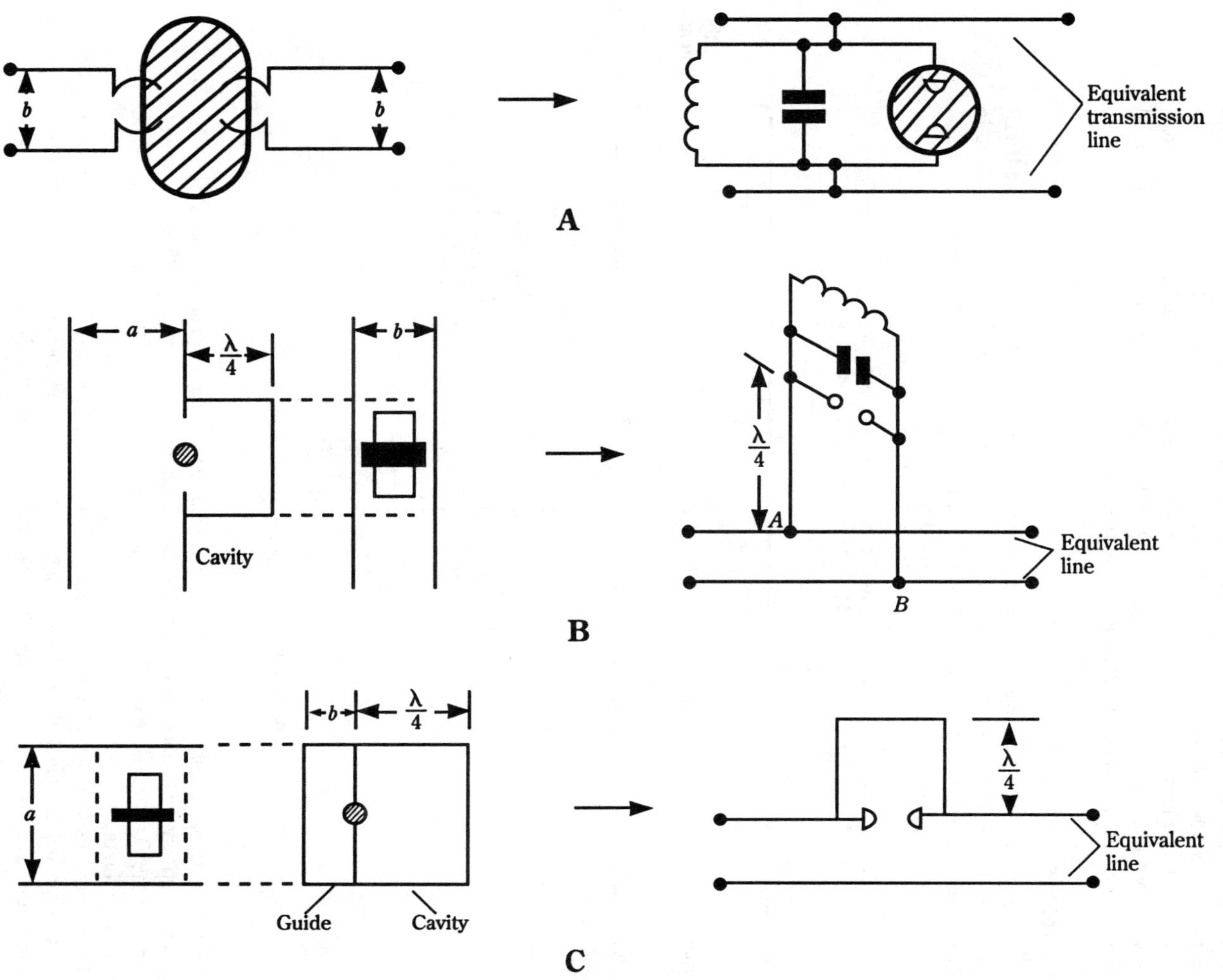

Fig. 12-14 An example of gas-switch connections.

In FIG. 12-14B, the gas switch is slot-coupled to the narrow wall of the guide. In this case, if the gas switch is ionized, it presents an "open-circuit" between the points A and B for the equivalent lines, which are therefore unaffected. If, however, the gap is not ionized, the open circuit that was caused by the gas switch causes a short-circuit across points A and B.

In FIG. 12-14C, the gas switch is slot-coupled to the wide wall of the guide; this is effectively in series with one of the equivalent lines. If this gap breaks down, the line is continuous, but if the switch is not ionized, a net open-circuit appears across the line.

The duplexer

The purpose of a *duplexer* is to connect the transmitter effectively to the antenna during transmission and the antenna to the receiver for the remaining time. The system shown in FIG. 12-15 uses two tuned gas switches, which are slot-coupled to the narrow wall of the guide.

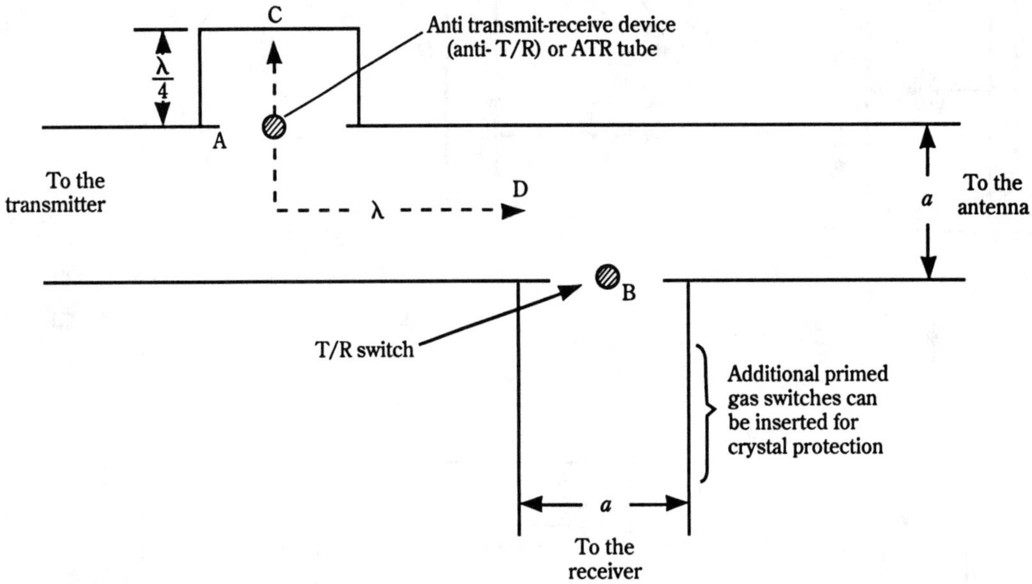

Fig. 12-15 A microwave antenna duplexer system.

During the transmission, both gas switches are ionized and short circuit the associated slots so that an effectively continuous guide connects the transmitter to the antenna. The small break-through from the Transmit/Receive (T/R) switch to the receiver gives rise to the signal shown at the zero range on the display.

During the reception period, the gas switches do not normally ionize. The open circuit at the Anti-T/R switch and the effect of the short circuit, C, give rise to a short circuit, D, which blocks the path to the transmitter and reduces the loss in the received signals. Hence, an effectively continuous waveguide path is provided from the antenna through the T/R switch to the receiver.

Crystal protection

The point-contact silicon crystal mixer that is used as initial stage of a radar receiver, may be damaged by currents in excess of about 1 mA. Such damage by strong-received signals can be reduced by the T/R switch. Further protection is usually provided by one or two additional primed gas switches that are inserted in the guide that leads to the receiver. Because of the time lag in the ionization, an early dc priming pulse from the transmitter can be used to cause ionization before any appreciable portion of the transmitter pulse breaks through to the receiver.

* **Question 12-34** The purpose of the Anti-T/R switch is to:

A. protect the T/R switch from being overloaded by the transmitted pulse
B. prevent the transmitted pulse from breaking through to the receiver
C. allow the received echo pulse to activate the echo box
D. prevent the receiver from being affected by interference from another radar set in the vicinity
E. provide the received echo pulse with a high impedance path in the direction of the transmitter

Answer Choice E.

* **Question 12-35** The circuit of FIG. 12-16 represents a (an):

A. echo box
B. directional coupler for measuring the reflected power
C. VSWR indicator
D. duplexer
E. dual-stub matching device

Answer Choice D.

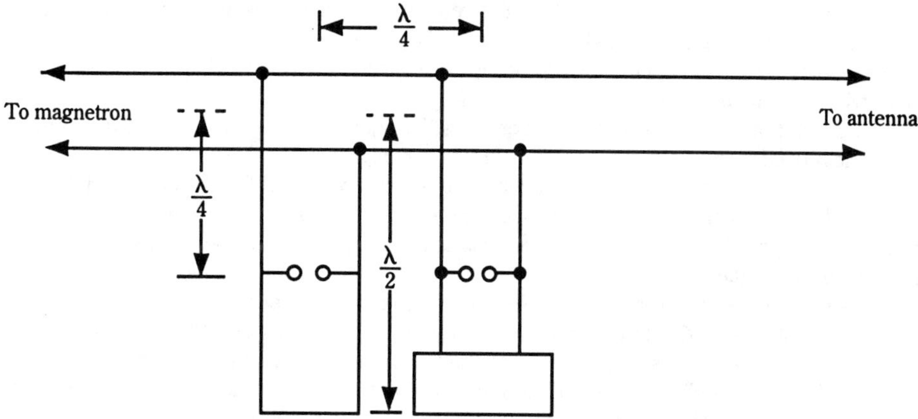

Fig. 12-16 The circuit diagram for question 12-35.

12-10. The plan-position indicator (PPI)

The *plan-position indicator* (*PPI*) display is normally used for warning and navigational purposes (FIG. 12-17). Your own ship appears as a bright spot or "paint" at the center of the CRT screen, which uses a high-persistance phospher and an internal aquadag coating as the final anode. Other ships or aircraft appear as bright spots in their correct relative positions, and provide an all-round warning display from which the range and bearing of any target can be read.

The display is given by a semi-bright radial trace, which revolves in step with a continuously

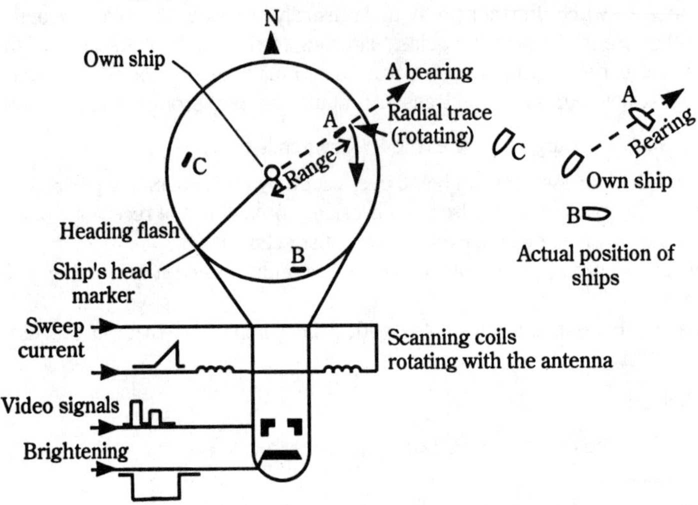

Fig. 12-17 The P.P.I. display.

rotating antenna. The PPI time-base unit applies a suitable sawtooth current pulse to a pair of deflecting or scanning coils that are fitted around the neck of the CRT and rotated in step with the antenna. Alternatively, some PPI displays use fixed-coil scanning in which linear sawtooth pulses are applied simultaneously at the pulse-repetition frequency to two fixed scanning coils, which are external to the CRT and are 90° apart. These pulses are amplitude modulated at the antenna-rotation frequency and produce a linear trace of constant length, which rotates synchronously with the antenna.

The brightening pulse takes the form of a negative square wave applied to the CRT cathode; this pulse is used to bring the sweep to the threshold of brightness.

Video signals are applied as positive pulses to the grid of the CRT and therefore give bright spots on the trace. Calibrator and range-maker pulses can be applied in the same way, producing rings as the trace rotates. Because the CRT has an afterglow property, the "paints" are retained to some extent as the trace rotates.

When the radar beam instantaneously points dead ahead, a switch closes in the antenna system and a short-duration brightening pulse is applied to the grid of the PPI tube. This momentarily intensifies the radar sweep and the operator can then accurately determine the relative bearings of all targets. This indication that the radar beam is dead ahead is called *heading flash.* However, if a bright flashing condition is observed in general on the PPI display, it might be caused by a defective crystal in the receiver's AFC system.

One form of interference that appears on a PPI display is called *sea return.* This is caused by the reception of radar pulses, which are reflected off the top of waves and are returned to the antenna system. The appearance on the display is a solid interference pattern, which is similar to that of noise; the effect obscures targets (such as ships), whose range is a few miles from the moving radar set. The problem is reduced by including a *sensitivity time control* (*STC*), which lowers the receiver's gain for short-range targets. The result weakens the interference pattern of the sea return so that the operator can more easily discern the stronger echoes that are reflected from the ships.

* **Question 12-36** Which of the waveforms shown is associated with the current that flows through the deflection coils of a PPI display?

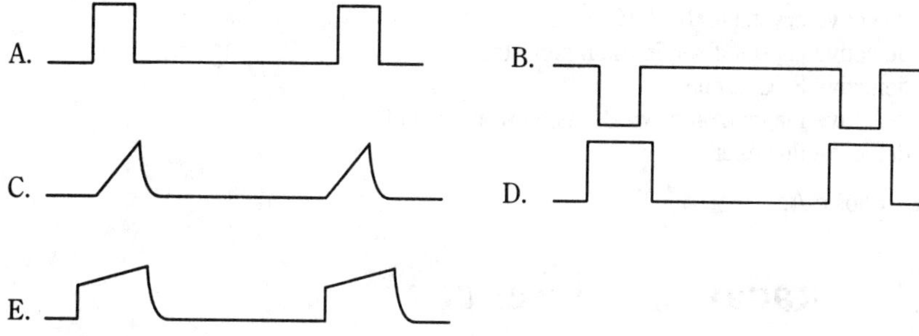

Answer Choice C.

* **Question 12-37** On a PPI display, heading flash is achieved by use of a (an):

A. electronic synchronizer that is included in the sweep generator circuit
B. electronic generator, which feeds a negative pulse to the PPI grid
C. mechanical switch that is associated with the rotating antenna
D. electronic timer that is calibrated to synchronize with the rotating antenna
E. crystal oscillator, followed by the shaping circuit for the intensifier pulse

Answer Choice C.

* **Question 12-38** It is required to produce range-marker circles on a PPI display with a separation of ½ nautical miles in range between adjacent circles. The frequency of the range-marker oscillator is:

A. 186.2 kHz B. 161.7 kHz C. 93.1 kHz D. 323.4 kHz E. 213.8 kHz

Answer Choice B. The time interval corresponding to a range of ½ nautical mile $= \frac{12.3678}{2} =$ 6.1839 μs. The frequency of the range-marker oscillator $= \frac{10^6}{6.1839}$ Hz $= 161.7$ kHz.

* **Question 12-39** The bright circle of light at the center of a PPI display is caused by:

A. a defective TR box
B. a defective STC control
C. the normal "sea return"
D. interference from other radar sets
E. the transmitted pulse and is a normal condition

Answer Choice E.

* **Question 12-40** In a pulsed radar set, the STC circuit is used to:

A. counteract the effects of frequency drift in either the magnetron or the reflex klystron
B. reduce interference from the effects of sea return
C. improve the target bearing resolution
D. increase the receiver sensitivity for the echoes from targets at maximum range
E. vary the pulse frequency in order to control the maximum target range

Answer Choice B.

* **Question 12-41** Which of the following might be the cause of the appearance of bright flashing pie sections on the PPI display?

A. defective crystal in the AFC circuit
B. defective crystal diode in the mixer stage
C. defective STC circuit
D. defective magnetron or weak magnetron magnet
E. defective duplexer

Answer Choice A.

12-11. Radar interference

In a microwave radar set, the carrier frequency is of the order of a few GHz. This carrier is amplitude modulated by a short-duration pulse (between 0.1 and 10 μs), whose repetition frequency generally extends from 250 to 5000 Hz. The pulse itself is extremely rich in harmonics. Therefore, there is a wide range of sideband frequencies. The mixing or heterodyning that occurs between these sidebands results in the production of further frequencies. Consequently, there is an extremely wide range of interference from a radar set.

If this form of radar interference is intercepted by a communications receiver, the audio result is a rough note whose fundamental frequency is equal to the pulse repetition rate. The harshness of the tone is caused by the many harmonics that are associated with the pulse. When the interference is radiated from the antenna, the tone will wax and wane as the antenna rotates; if the interference comes directly from the transmitter, the strength of the tone will remain constant. Because the range of interference is so wide, the communications receiver cannot tune out the unwanted frequencies; furthermore, the radar pulse might break through to the receiver's second detector stage and then any subsequent elimination of the interference is impossible. Because the spectrum of unwanted frequencies is so broad, radar interference is possible on virtually any communications frequency.

Another form of radar interference is the type of noise known as "hash," whose audio effect is a continuous scratching sound. Hash can be caused by:

1. Improper grounding, shielding, and bonding of waveguides, connecting cables and various items of radar equipment. It is particularly important to avoid long lines between the modulator and the oscillator units since radiation will readily occur unless the lines are properly terminated and shielded.
2. Sparking occurs in any motor-generator set that is used in the radar system. This effect can be minimized by checking the condition of the commutator's brushes, slip rings, filters, and power connections.

As well as communications receivers, radar interference will also affect the performance of the radio direction-finding (DF) equipment. If the cause of the problem is the radar transmitter on another ship, the DF loop can be rotated for a while so that the source of the interference can be located. However, if the radar set and the DF receiver are on the same ship, it is possible that no nulls will occur as the loop is rotated—especially if the interference comes directly from the transmitter or exists on a power line. This can be checked by temporarily shutting down the radar set and finding whether the interference still persists.

Loran (Long-Range Navigation) is a method of radio navigation, which is also affected by radar interference. The radar pulses produce narrow vertical pulses or "spikes," which move across the Loran display while hash appears as "grass" on the scanning lines. It is virtually impossible to eliminate the spikes, but the effect of hash can be reduced by installing low-pass filters on all power lines and by improving the standards of all shielding, grounding, and bonding. Grounding is particularly important because if all external metal parts are effectively grounded, we can avoid the possibility of electrical shock to the ship's personnel.

Radar interference can also be responsible for activating the ship's auto-alarm system. This problem is normally investigated by plugging a set of earphones into the jack provided and listening for the hash or the harsh tone. Again, you can temporarily shut down the radar set and see if the problem remains.

Summarizing, the radar interference appears aurally as a harsh tone accompanied by hash and it affects the performances of the auto alarm, the Loran navigation, and the public-address system, as well as communication receivers and the direction-finding equipment.

* **Question 12-42** A marine radar set might cause interference problems in:

A. Loran
B. communications receivers
C. the auto-alarm system
D. the direction-finding equipment
E. all of the above

Answer Choice E.

12-12. The Doppler effect and the CW radar system

Apart from the use of short-duration RF pulses, there are two other possible radar systems. In FM radar, the RF wave is modulated by a sawtooth; the difference between the instantaneous frequencies being transmitted and received will then be a direct measure of the reflecting object's range. The most common use of this system is in the radio altimeter, in which the reflecting object is the earth as seen from the aircraft. The instantaneous frequency difference will be an accurate measurement of the vertical distance between the ground and the aircraft.

In a *CW radar system,* the velocity of a target, but not its range, can be determined. The principle is based on the *Doppler effect,* in which the frequency of the signal radiated from the reflecting object is shifted when the object is moving relative to the receiver; an example of such a system is a police speed trap.

Let the reflecting object be moving with a component of velocity $+V_s$ in the direction of propagation; the result will be to produce a change in the wavelength, and hence a shift in the frequency at the receiver. If f_s is the wavelength and T is the period ($= 1/f_s$) of the radiation from the source when stationary:

$$\text{New wavelength, } \lambda_r = \lambda_s - V_s \times T \tag{12-15}$$

$$\textit{Velocity of propagation} = c = f_s \lambda_s = f_r (\lambda_s - V_s \times T) \tag{12-16}$$

where f_r is the received frequency and c is the velocity of an electromagnetic wave (300,000,000 meters per second or 984,000,000 feet per second).

Then:

$$f_r = \frac{c}{\lambda_s - V_s \times T}$$

$$= \frac{c}{\lambda_s - \dfrac{V_s}{f_s}}$$

$$= f_s \times \left(\frac{c}{c - V_s}\right) \tag{12-17}$$

If the source is stationary, but the receiver is moving with a component of velocity $+V_r$ in the direction propagation, there is, as regards the receiver, an apparent change in the velocity of propagation.

$$\text{Apparent velocity of propagation} = c - V_r$$
$$= \lambda_s \times f_r$$

Therefore:

$$f_r = \frac{c - V_r}{\lambda_s} = f_s \times \frac{(c - V_r)}{c} \qquad (12\text{-}18)$$

If the source and the receiver are both moving:

$$f_r = f_s \times \frac{c - V_r}{c - V_s} \qquad (12\text{-}19)$$

$$\text{The Doppler frequency shift} = f_r - f_s$$
$$= f_s \times \left(\frac{c - V_r}{c - V_s} - 1\right)$$
$$= f_s \times \frac{(V_s - V_r)}{(c - V_s)} \qquad (12\text{-}20)$$
$$\approx f_s \times \frac{(V_s - V_r)}{c}$$

because c is much greater than V_s. The shift therefore depends on the frequency of the source and the velocities of the source and the receiver in the direction of propagation. If the relative velocity is 1 mile per hour and $f_s = 1$ GHz:

$$\textit{Doppler frequency shift} = \frac{10^9 \times 5280}{9.84 \times 10^8 \times 3600}\ \text{Hz}$$
$$= 1.5\ \text{Hz per mph per GHz} \qquad (12\text{-}21)$$

For a CW radar set, the two-way propagation shift is $2 \times 1.5 = 3.0$ Hz per mph per GHz.

* **Question 12-43** The Doppler effect is used in CW radar to determine the:

A. target range
B. bearing of the target
C. target size
D. target speed
E. target's elevation

Answer Choice D.

Note: When answering QUES. 12-43 thru 12-53, you might need to refer to chapters 10 and 11.

Question 12-44 If the interior dimensions of a rectangular waveguide are 1.25×3 inches, the guide's cut-off wavelength in inches, is:

A. 6.0 B. 2.5 C. 1.5 D. 3.0 E. 1.25

Answer Choice A. The cut-off wavelength $= 2 \times$ the wide dimension of the waveguide $= 2 \times 3.0 = 6.0$ inches.

Question 12-45 As a result of measurements taken with the aid of a directional coupler, it is discovered that the power reflected from the end of the waveguide is 5% of the incident power. The VSWR in the waveguide is:

A. 1.05 B. 1.58 C. 1.29 D. 1.25 E. 1.15

Answer Choice B. The reflection coefficient, $\rho = \sqrt{\frac{5}{100}} = \sqrt{0.05} = 0.2236$. The VSWR,

$$S = \frac{1 + \rho}{1 - \rho} = \frac{1.2236}{0.7764} = 1.58.$$

* **Question 12-46** Which of the following frequency ranges is generally regarded as applicable to the operation of klystrons?

A. 600 MHz to 3 GHz
B. 3000 MHz to 60 GHz
C. 3 to 30 GHz
D. 300 MHz to 60 GHz
E. 600 MHz to 30 GHz

Answer Choice E.

* **Question 12-47** The circuit of FIG. 12-18 represents a:

A. modulator unit
B. complete synchronizer unit
C. tuned-line oscillator
D. blocking oscillator
E. duplexer unit

Answer Choice A.

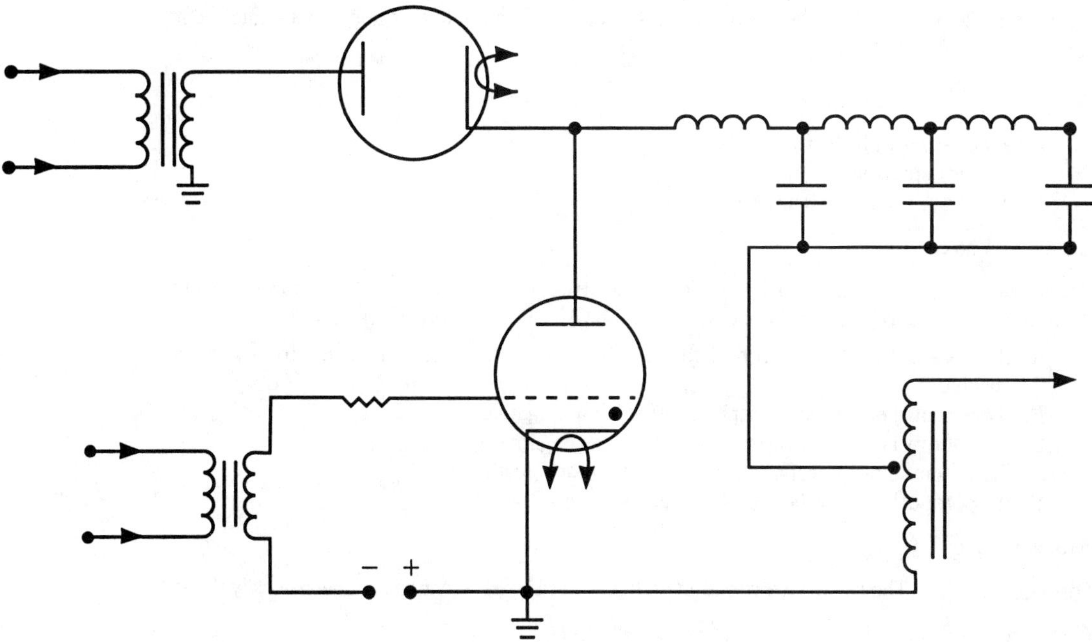

Fig. 12-18 The circuit diagram for question 12-47.

* **Question 12-48** The purpose of the polystyrene window placed across the end of the waveguide, is:

A. as an alternative to the horn radiator
B. to match the waveguide impedance to the impedance of free space
C. to form the E-M energy into a narrow beam
D. to act as a resonant iris and lower the value of the VSWR
E. choices A and B are true

Answer Choice E.

* **Question 12-49** Which of the following can occur if a magnetron's magnet becomes too weak?

A. the magnetron current meter will indicate an increase
B. internal arcing in the tube of the modulator unit
C. the magnetron's undercurrent relay will drop out
D. internal arcing in the magnetron
E. the curvature of the paths taken by the electrons will increase

Answer Choice A.

* **Question 12-50** In the modulator unit of the pulsed radar set, the artificial-discharge transmission line is used to:

A. provide the calibrated pulses, which create the range-marker circles
B. determine the duration of the transmitted pulse
C. determine the duty cycle
D. determine the pulse repetition rate
E. match the load of the magnetron to the load that is required by the thyratron

Answer Choice B.

* **Question 12-51** Which of the following can be found in the modulator unit of a marine radar set?

A. a thyratron
B. a magnetron
C. a multi-cavity klystron
D. a rotary spark gap
E. choices A and D are true

Answer Choice E.

* **Question 12-52** In a marine radar set, the magnetron frequency starts to drift upwards from 3003 MHz when the reflex klystron's output is 2973 MHz. If the receiver's IF is 30 MHz:

A. the potential of the klystron of the klystron's reflector plate will change from zero to positive
B. the potential of the reflector piate will be more negative
C. the potential of the reflector plate will be less negative
D. the potential of the reflector plate will be more positive
E. the potential of the reflector plate will be less positive

Answer Choice C.

* **Question 12-53** The reflex klystron of an SHF pulsed radar receiver can be mechanically tuned by:

A. screwing a brass plug into the wall of the cavity
B. changing the pressure on the cavity's flexible wall

C. varying the depth to which an iron-dust slug is inserted into the cavity wall
D. adjusting the capacitance between the reflector and the cavity
E. choices A and B are true

Answer Choice E.

* **Question 12-54** A modulator's artificial discharge line consists of three LC sections, each of inductance $L = 6.5\ \mu$H and capacitance $C = 4000$ pF. The pulse duration is equal to:

A. 5 μs B. 4 μs C. 2 μs D. 1 μs E. 0.5 μs

Answer Choice D.

$$\begin{aligned}\text{Pulse duration} &= 2N\sqrt{LC}\\ &= 2 \times 3 \times \sqrt{6.5 \times 10^{-6} \times 4000 \times 10^{-12}}\text{s}\\ &\approx 1.0 \times 10^{-6}\text{s}\\ &= 1\ \mu\text{s}\end{aligned}$$

* **Question 12-55** Which of the following waveforms best represents a magnetron's output to the waveguide?

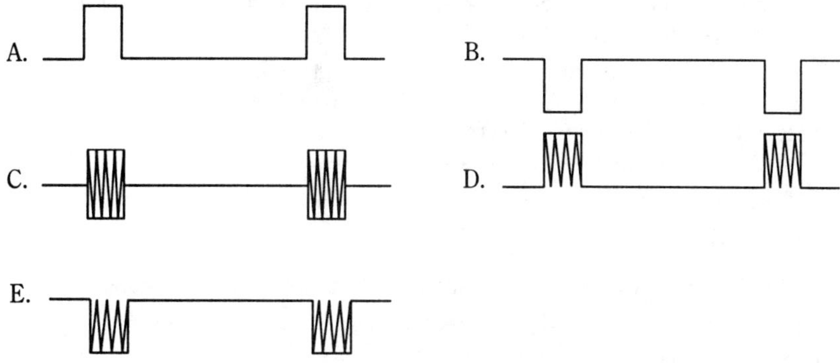

Answer Choice C.

12-13. FCC rules and regulations pertaining to ship radar stations

The following are extracts from the rules and regulations that apply to ship radar stations:

1. The operator who is responsible for the installation, servicing, and maintenance of ship radar equipment must possess:

   either (a) a ship radar endorsement to a First-Class Radiotelephone License
   or (b) a ship radar endorsement to a Second-Class Radiotelephone License
   or (c) a ship radar endorsement to a General Radiotelephone License

Exception: Unlicensed personnel are allowed replace receiver tubes and fuses (under the supervision of the licensed operator).

2. Ship radar equipment is operated by the master of the ship or his designee.
3. A person without a radio operator's license is allowed to operate a ship radar station provided that:

(a) the radar equipment uses a nontunable, pulsed-type magnetron or other fixed tuned device.
(b) the radar equipment is entirely operated by external controls.

4. The station licensee and the responsible installation, service and maintenance operator are jointly responsible for supervising all entries in the station record. Entries in this record include:
   (a) date and place of initial installation
   (b) all necessary steps that are taken to remedy any inference found to exist at the time of such installation.
   (c) the nature and date of any complaint (including interference to radio communication) arising subsequent to the initial installation.
   (d) the reason for the trouble leading to the complaint, including the name of any component or conponent part that failed or was not properly adjusted.
   (e) the date and nature of the remedial measures taken.
   (f) name, license number, and date of the ship radar endorsement for the responsible installation, service and maintenance operator.

* **Question 12-56** In order to be responsible for installation, maintenance and servicing of a ship radar station, the operator must possess a:

A. ship radar endorsement to a First-Class Radiotelegraph License
B. ship radar endorsement to a General Radiotelephone License
C. Second-Class Radiotelegraph License
D. First-Class Radiotelegraph License
E. choices A and B are true

Answer Choice E.

* **Question 12-57** Who of the following are allowed to operate a ship radar station?

A. those who possess a First-Class or Second-Class Radiotelegraph License
B. those possessing a General Radiotelephone License
C. those possessing a Ship Radar Endorsement
D. the Master of the ship or his designee
E. the station licensee or his designee

Answer Choice D.

* **Question 12-58** The tubes of a radar receiver as well as fuses can be replaced:

A. only by the holder of a ship radar endorsement
B. only by the holder of a First-Class Radiotelegraph License
C. only by the Master or his designee
D. only by the holder of a General Radiotelephone License
E. by an unlicensed person under the supervision of the responsible licensed operator

Answer Choice E.

* **Question 12-59** Under what conditions can a Ship Radar station be operated by unlicensed personnel?

A. the radar equipment is entirely operated by external controls
B. whenever the holder of a Ship Radar Endorsement is on board
C. whenever the holder of a General Radiotelephone License is on board

D. the radar equipment uses a nontunable pulsed magnetron
E. choices B and D are true

Answer Choice E.

* **Question 12-60** When carrying out maintenance on ship radar equipment, which of the following entries must be made in the station record?

A. date and place of initial installation
B. nature and date of any complaint
D. details of all component failures
D. responsible operator's name and the date of his Ship Radar Endorsement
E. all of the above choices are true

Answer Choice E.

* **Question 12-61** Entries are made in the maintenance log of a Ship Radar station, by:

A. an operator with a First-Class Radiotelegraph License
B. an operator with a General Radiotelephone License
C. an operator with a Ship Radar Endorsement to a Second-Class Radiotelegraph License
D. the Master or his designee
E. an unlicensed person under the supervision of the operator responsible for service and maintenance

Answer Choice C.

* **Question 12-62** Which of the following maintenance procedures may be carried out by unlicensed personnel?

A. fine tuning of the magnetron frequency
B. replacement of receiver tubes and fuses
C. adjusting the resonant frequency of the reflex klystron
D. optimizing the value of the waveguide system's SWR
E. optimizing the performance of the duplexer

Answer Choice B.

12-14. Navigational radar systems

Radar is used extensively as a navigational aid for ships and aircraft; examples include altimeters and beacons. In its simplest form, an aircraft's altimeter is a small, low-power, downward-looking system that is capable of providing a continuous reading of the aircraft's height, relative to the ground, which returns a very strong echo.

The beacon transponder contains a receiver, a low-power transmitter, and an omnidirectional antenna. When such a beacon receives the pulses from an aircraft's search radar system, it automatically transmits its reply in the form of pulses, which use a different radio frequency. It follows that the aircraft's radar system must have a separate receiving channel to detect the presence of the beacon.

A more sophisticated form of beacon is a complete radar system with both an interrogator and a transponder (FIG. 12-19). As an example, the Distance Measuring Equipment (DME) radar beacon system operates with the FAA's VHF Omni-Range (VOR) stations, whose positions are shown on the flight chart. At each of these stations, a DME transponder is installed. When the aircraft's interrogator transmits pulses to a particular transponder, the replies are intercepted by a receiver. By measuring the time interval between the transmission of an interrogating pulse and

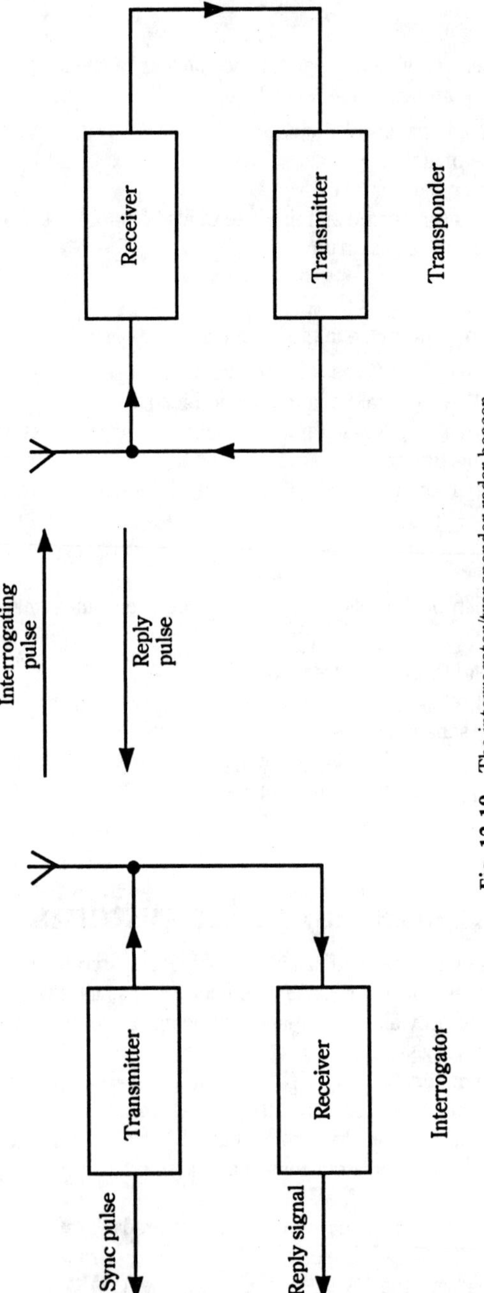

Fig. 12-19 The interrogator/transponder radar beacon.

the reception of the reply, the aircraft can obtain its exact range from the VOR station. This range and the rate of change of range are then displayed on the aircraft's instrument panel.

* **Question 12-63** An aircraft's navigational aid measures the time interval between an interrogatory pulse and the reply from a radar beacon. The system is called:

A. search radar
B. transponder time-interval measurement
C. interrogatory friend or foe
D. distance-measuring equipment
E. interrogator transponder range

Answer Choice D.

13

Number systems and digital principles

In this chapter you will learn:

- about modern number systems and the concepts of "zero" and "positional notation."
- about the binary number system and how to convert binary numbers into decimal numbers and vice-versa.
- to relate the octal number system to the binary and decimal number systems.
- to relate hexadecimal numbers to binary, octal, and decimal numbers.
- about Venn diagrams and how they relate to the fundamental concepts of Boolean algebra.
- about the OR, AND, NOT, NOR, NAND, EX-OR, EX-NOR logic circuits, and their associated truth diagrams.
- how a number of these gates are used to produce combinatorial logic circuits.

13-1. Modern number systems

A number system is any set of symbols or characters used to enumerate objects and perform mathematical computations (such as addition, subtraction, multiplication, and division). All number systems are related to each other by symbols or characters commonly referred to as *digits*. Modern number systems have certain digits in common; however, these systems do not all use the same number of digits, as shown in TABLE 13-1.

The most commonly used system is the Hindu-Arabic system, which uses the digits, 0, 1, 2, 3, 4, 5, 6, 7, 8, and 9. There a total of 10 digits, so you have a decimal or base-10 system. Because most measurements are made with this system, it will be used as the basis for a discussion of other number systems.

Number systems in ancient times were used primarily to take measurements and keep records because mathematical computations using the Greek, Roman, and Egyptian number systems were extremely difficult. The lack of an adequate number system was probably a major factor in hampering scientific development in these early civilizations. Obviously, mathematical computations were difficult with Roman numerals, where, for example, MCMLXXXIX is equivalent to 1989 in the decimal system.

The acceptance of two basic concepts has greatly simplified mathematical computations and has led to the development of modern number systems. These two concepts are: the use of zero to signify the absence of a unit, and the principle of positional value.

The principle of positional value consists of assigning to a digit a value that depends on its position within a given number. For example, the digit 6 has a different value in each of the decimal numbers 876, 867, and 687. In the first number, 876, the digit 6 has its base value of 6. In the second number, 867, the digit 6 has a value of 60 (6×10 or 6×10^1). In the third number, 687, the value of the digit 6 is 600 (6×100, or 6×10^2).

Sometimes a position within a given number does not have a value. However, if this position is totally disregarded, there is no way to distinguish between two different numbers, such as 706 and 76. The 0 is therefore used to signify that a particular position within a certain number has no value assigned.

The use of 0 and positional value has greatly simplified counting and mathematical computations. Consequently, these concepts are used in all modern number systems.

Positional notation

The standard form of writing numbers is known as *positional notation.* The value of a particular digit depends not only on its basic value, but also on its position within a number. For example, the decimal number 2365.74 is the standard shorthand form of the quantity two thousand three hundred sixty five, seven-tenths, four-hundredths. Expressing this number in its general form:

$$2365.74 = (2 \times 10^3) + (3 \times 10^2) + (6 \times 10^1) + (5 \times 10^0) + (7 \times 10^{-1}) + (4 \times 10^{-2})$$

In this number, the 2 carries the most weight of all the digits and is called the most significant digit (MSD). By contrast, the 4 carries the least weight and is referred to as the least significant digit (LSD).

A number can be expressed with positional notation in any system. The general form for expressing a number is:

$$N = (d_n \times r^n) + \ldots + (d_2 \times r^2) + (d_1 \times r^1) + (d_0 \times r^0) + (d_{-1} \times r^{-1}) + (d_{-2} \times r^{-2}) + \ldots + (d_{-n} \times r^n) \qquad (13\text{-}1)$$

where: N = the number expressed in a positional notation form
r = the base which is raised in turn to a series of exponents
d = the digits of the number system

A base point, such as a decimal point, is not required in the general form because at the position of the point, the exponent changes from positive to negative. In the shorthand form, the base point is between the $d_0 \times r^0$ and $d_{-1} \times r^{-1}$ values.

Every number system has a base with a certain value. The hexadecimal, decimal, octal, and binary systems have bases whose values are respectively 16, 10, 8, and 2. The division between integers (whole numbers) and fractions is recognized by the position of the base point. In addition:

- The base of a number system is equal to the number of the different characters used to indicate all the various magnitudes that a digit might represent. For example, the decimal system, with its base of 10, has 10 digits whose magnitudes are 0 through 9.
- The value of the base is always one unit greater than the largest-value characters in the system. This follows from the fact that the base is equal to the number of the characters, and the characters themselves start from zero. As an example, the highest value digit in the decimal system is 9; therefore, the base is $9 + 1 = 10$.

- The positional notation does not, by itself, indicate the value of the base. The symbol "123.41" could represent a number written in a system that has a base value of five (4 + 1) or more. To avoid confusion, numbers written in systems other than the decimal system, have the base denoted by a subscript, such as 123.41_8. The base subscript is always written as a decimal number.
- Any number can easily be multiplied or divided by the base of its number system. When multiplying a number by its base, move the base point one digit to the right of its former position. For example, $123.41_8 \times 8 = 1234.1_8$. To divide a number by its base, move the base point one digit to the left of its former position so that $123.41_8 \div 8 = 12.341_8$.
- In any number system, the symbol "10" always equals the value of the base. This follows from the fact that the value of the base is one unit greater than the highest-value character.

Counting

In any system using positional notation, the rules for counting are the same, and are independent of the base. With the octal system as an example, the rules are:

- Start from zero and then add 1 to the least significant digit until the series of all the basic characters in sequence is complete. Such a series is known as a *cycle,* which, for the octal system, would be 0, 1, 2, 3, 4, 5, 6, 7.
- Because 7 is the highest-value character in the octal system, the next number requires two digits. Begin the start of the two-digit numbers with 0 as the least significant digit and place a 1 to the left of the 0. Therefore, the series becomes 0, 1, 2, 3, 4, 5, 6, 7, 10, 11, 12, 13, 14, 15, 16, 17, 20, 21, and so on.
- When a digit reaches its maximum value, replace it with a 0 and then add 1 to the next more significant digit. Consequently, the series is:
  . . . 16, 17, 20, 21 . . . 26, 27, 30, 31 . . . 36, 37, 40, 41
  . . . 46, 47, 50, 51 . . . 56, 57, 60, 61 . . . 66, 67, 70, 71
  . . . 76, 77
- When two or more consecutive digits reach the maximum value, replace them with 0s and add 1 to the next more significant digit. The series continues as:
  . . . 76, 77, 100, 101 . . . 176, 177, 200, 201 . . . 276, 277, 300, 301
  . . . 376, 377, 400, 401 . . . 476, 477, 500, 501 . . . 576, 577, 600, 601
  . . . 676, 677, 700, 701 . . . 767, 777, 1000, 1001 . . .
- Notice that, in any number system, the maximum whole number to be expressed by N digits is given by,
  Maximum number $= r^N\text{-}1$
  where r = base value. For example, $777_8 = 8^3\text{-}1 = 511_{10}$. (13-2)

* **Question 13-1** Express 11010_2 as a number to the base 10:

A. 25_{10} B. 24_{10} C. 11_{10} D. 13_{10} E. 19_{10}

Answer Choice A. From EQ. 13-1.

$$11010_2 = (1 \times 2^4) + (1 \times 2^3) + (0 \times 2^2) + (1 \times 2^1) + (0 \times 2^0)$$
$$= 16 + 8 + 0 + 2 + 0$$
$$= 26_{10}$$

13-2. The binary number system

The *binary number system* has a base of 2 and is used in virtually all digital circuits, as well as in computers. Because the base is 2, there will only be two digits: 0 and 1. This is an enormous advantage because it is relatively easy to design electronic circuits that have only two possible states. For example, a bipolar transistor can either be in the saturation mode or in the cutoff mode, and these two states can then correspond to two different output voltages from the circuit containing the transistor. Owing, for example, to temperature variations, such voltages are bound to fluctuate to a certain extent, so the two states will each correspond to a limited voltage range. This is illustrated in FIG. 13-1, where the 0 state is from 0 V to 1 V, and the 1 state exists between 9 V and 12 V; this means that the range between 1 and 9 V is not used. The situation, as described, is sometimes referred to as *positive logic*. By contrast, *negative logic* means that the voltage levels are interchanged so that the range of 9 V to 12 V represents the 0 state, and the 0 V to 1 V range indicates the 1 state. This chapter only covers positive logic.

The simplicity of the binary system is its advantage over other systems. For example, with a decimal system, it would be necessary to design circuits capable of working with 10 different voltage ranges, each of which would correspond to a digit between 0 and 9.

Binary numbers use positional notation, so that the value of a particular digit depends not only on the digit's value but also on its position within the number.

Using EQ. 13-1:

Binary Number:

$$\underbrace{11010}_{\text{whole number}} \cdot \underbrace{011}_{\text{fraction}} \quad (\cdot = \text{base point})$$

$$\begin{aligned} 11010 \cdot 011 &= (1 \times 2^4) + (1 \times 2^3) + (0 \times 2^2) \\ &+ (1 \times 2^1) + (0 \times 2^0) + (0 \times 2^{-1}) \\ &+ (1 \times 2^{-2}) + (1 \times 2^{-3}) \\ &= 16 + 8 + 2 + 0.25 + 0.125 \\ &= 26.375_{10} \end{aligned}$$

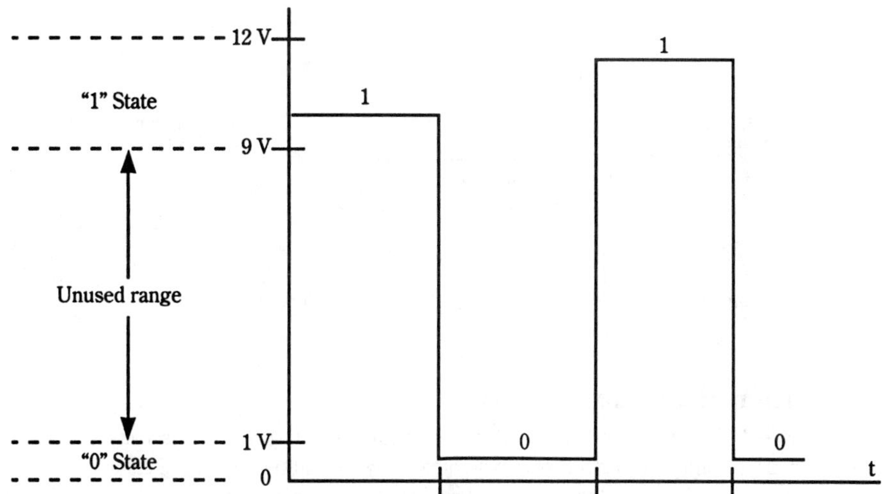

Fig. 13-1 The binary voltage levels.

As an abbreviation, binary digits are referred to as *bits*. In our example, the most significant bit (MSB) is the leftmost 1, which has a value of $(1 \times 2^4) = 16$, whereas the least significant bit (LSB) is the rightmost 1, which has a value of only $(1 \times 2^{-3}) = 0.125$.

In a binary number, the leftmost 1 (FIG. 13-2) is referred to as the *MSB* because it is multiplied by the highest coefficient. Once the MSB has been determined, all positions to the left of the MSB have no significance even though they might be occupied by zeros; this must be true because in a given number, any position unoccupied or occupied by a zero does not have a value assigned.

Whether or not a value is assigned, all bit positions to the right of the MSB must be occupied by a 1 or a 0 (so that one number can be distinguished from another). The bit position at the extreme right of a given number is always considered to be occupied by the LSB, even though it might contain a zero to indicate that no value has been assigned to this position.

The value of the number shown in FIG. 13-2 is 32768 + 8192 + 2048 + 64 + 16 + 8 = 43096. This illustrates the disadvantage of the binary system, namely the large number (16) of bits required to be equivalent to a decimal number having only 5 significant digits. The maximum decimal number to be represented by N bits is $2^N - 1$ (EQ. 13-2). For example, $1111_2 = 2^4 - 1 = 15_{10}$.

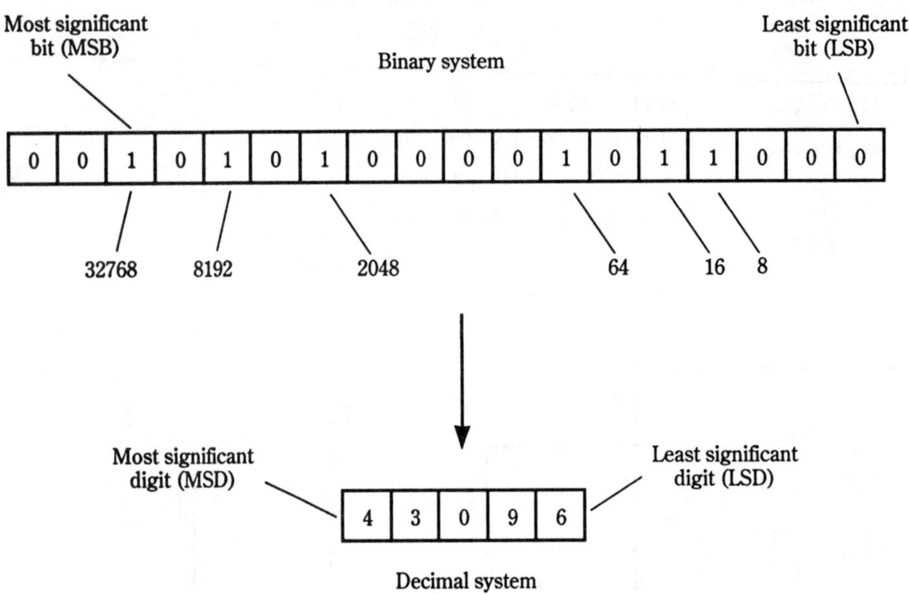

Fig. 13-2 Positional notation in the binary and decimal systems.

Representation of a binary number

If a device has only two possible operating states, a number of such devices can be used to represent a binary quantity. A single-throw switch has only two states: open and closed.

If an open switch is in the 0 state, while a closed switch is in the 1 state, the switches shown in FIG. 13-3 indicate the binary number $11001_2 = 25_{10}$.

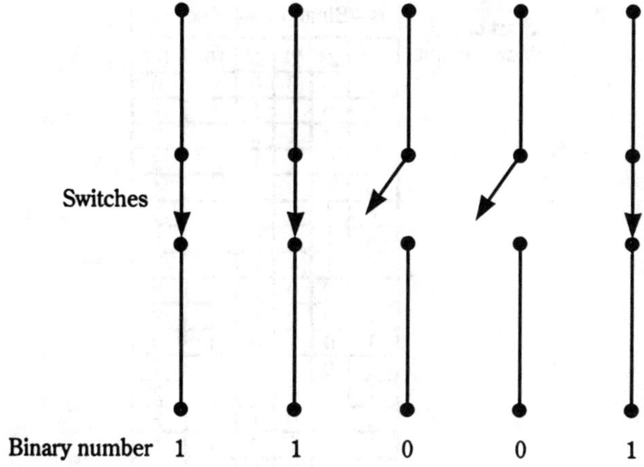

Fig. 13-3 Representation of a binary number with the aid of switches.

Binary counting

Beginning with zero count, all bits in FIG. 13-4 are in the 0 state. First count: The 2^0 position changes from 0 to 1. Second count: the 2^0 position reverts back to 0, and the 2^1 position changes from 0 to 1. Third count: the 2^0 position changes to 1, and the 2^1 position remains at 1. Fourth count: the 2^0 and 2^1 positions are 0, and the 2^2 position changes from 0 to 1. Observing the pattern, the 2^0 position changes from 0 to 1 or 1 to 0 with every count. In the general 2^N position, the bit will stay at 0 for 2^N counts and then change to 1 for the next 2^N counts.

Binary-to-decimal conversion

The binary-to-decimal conversion can be achieved by using EQ. 13-1. For example:

$$\begin{aligned} 10011_2 &= (1 \times 2^4) + (0 \times 2^3) + (0 \times 2^2) + (1 \times 2^1) + (1 \times 2^0) \\ &= 16 + 2 + 1 \\ &= 19_{10} \end{aligned}$$

Alternatively, the conversion can be carried out using a calculator. First locate the MSB and then proceed as follows:

Entry, Key				Display
1	[×]	2	[+]	2
0	[×]	2	[+]	4
0	[×]	2	[+]	8
1	[×]	2	[+]	18
1			[=]	19

This method is sometimes referred to as the *double-dabble*.

Start of binary count

2^3	2^2	2^1	2^0	10^1	10^0
0	0	0	0		0
0	0	0	1		1
0	0	1	0		2
0	0	1	1		3
0	1	0	0		4
0	1	0	1		5
0	1	1	0		6
0	1	1	1		7
1	0	0	0		8
1	0	0	1		9
1	0	1	0	1	0
1	0	1	1	1	1
1	1	0	0	1	2
1	1	0	1	1	3
1	1	1	0	1	4
1	1	1	1	1	5

(Columns 2^3–2^0: Binary; columns 10^1–10^0: Decimal)

Fig. 13-4 Binary counting.

Decimal-to-binary conversion

One method of decimal-to-binary conversion is to reverse the procedure described for binary-to-decimal conversion. For example, the nearest power of two to 119_{10} is 64 (2^6). The remainder is 119 − 64 = 55, for which the nearest power of two is 32. This leaves a new remainder of 55 − 32 = 23. Repeating the process, 23 − 16 = 7, 7 − 4 = 3, 3 − 2 = 1. Then:

$$\begin{aligned} 119_{10} &= 2^6 + 2^5 + 2^4 + 0 + 2^2 + 2^1 + 2^0 \\ &= 1 \quad 1 \quad 1 \quad 0 \quad 1 \quad 1 \quad 1 \\ &= 1110111_2 \end{aligned}$$

A second method uses repeated division by 2. Using the same decimal number 119_{10}:

$$\frac{119}{2} = 59 \quad \text{remainder 1 (LSB)}$$

$$\frac{59}{2} = 29 \quad \text{remainder 1}$$

$$\frac{29}{2} = 14 \quad \text{remainder 1}$$

$$\frac{14}{2} = 7 \quad \text{remainder 0}$$

$$\frac{7}{2} = 3 \quad \text{remainder 1}$$

$$\frac{3}{2} = 1 \quad \text{remainder 0}$$

$$\frac{1}{2} = 0 \quad \text{remainder 1 (MSB)}$$

Then, 119_{10} is equal to 1110111_2.

* **Question 13-2** Express the decimal number 11_{10} as a binary number to the base 2.

A. 1101_2 B. 1100_2 C. 1110_2 D. 1011_2 E. 1101_2

Answer Choice D.

$$\begin{aligned} 11_{10} &= 8_{10} + 2_{10} + 1_{10} \\ &= 1 \times 2^3 + 0 \times 2^2 + 1 \times 2^1 + 1 \times 2^0 \\ &= 1011_2 \end{aligned}$$

Alternatively, by the repeated division method:

$$\frac{11}{2} = 5 \quad \text{remainder } 1$$

$$\frac{5}{2} = 2 \quad \text{remainder } 1$$

$$\frac{2}{2} = 1 \quad \text{remainder } 0$$

$$\frac{1}{2} = 0 \quad \text{remainder } 1$$

Therefore, $11_{10} = 1011_2$.

* **Question 13-3** Express the binary number 1101_2 as a decimal number to the base 10.

A. 12_{10} B. 13_{10} C. 8_{10} D. 11_{10} E. 14_{10}

Answer Choice B. From EQ. 13-1:

$$\begin{aligned} 1101_2 &= (1 \times 2^3) + (1 \times 2^2) + (0 \times 2^1) + (1 \times 2^0) \\ &= 8 + 4 + 0 + 1 \\ &= 13_{10} \end{aligned}$$

* **Question 13-4** Express the hexadecimal number D_{16} or the binary number 1101_2 as a decimal number to the base 10:

A. 11_{10} B. 12_{10} C. 14_{10} D. 8_{10} E. 13_{10}

Answer Choice E. Refer to TABLE 13-1. Hexadecimal number D_{16}, is equivalent to the decimal number, 13_{10}. Alternatively, from EQ. 13-1:

$$\begin{aligned} 1101_2 &= (1 \times 2^3) + (1 \times 2^2) + (0 \times 2^1) + (1 \times 2^0) \\ &= 8 + 4 + 0 + 1 \\ &= 13_{10} \end{aligned}$$

13-3. The octal number system

It is very simple to convert between octal (base 8) and binary (base 2) numbers. Consequently, when such a computer is involved with large quantities of binary numbers, each consisting of many bits, it is more convenient for the operators to program the information using octal numbers. However, remember that the computer's digital circuits operate only with the binary system.

Although you can convert between octal and decimal numbers directly, it is preferable to use the binary system as an intermediate step (FIG. 13-5). The same principle applies to hexadecimal-to-decimal conversions.

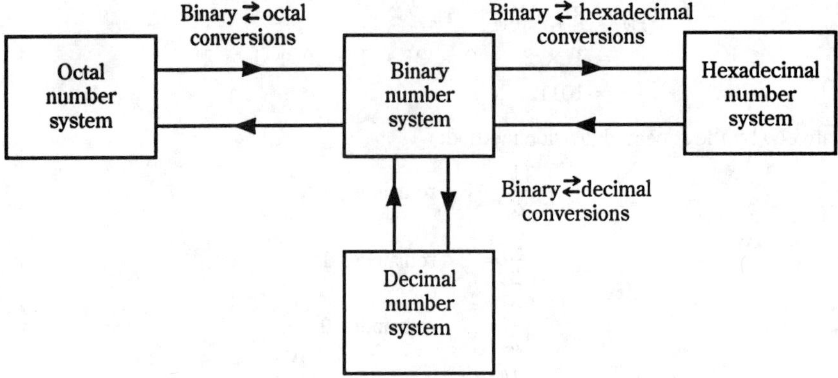

Fig. 13-5 Preferred conversions between the various number systems.

Direct octal-to-decimal conversion

To achieve this conversion, use EQ. 13-1. For example:

$$235.7_8 = (2 \times 8^2) + (3 \times 8^1) + (5 \times 8^0) + (7 \times 8^{-1})$$
$$= 157.875_{10}$$

Direct decimal-to-octal conversion

To convert a decimal whole number into its equivalent octal number, use the repeated division method with 8 as the division factor. For example, 437_{10} is equivalent to:

$$\frac{437}{8} = 54 \quad \text{remainder 5 (LSD)}$$
$$\frac{54}{8} = 6 \quad \text{remainder 6}$$
$$\frac{6}{8} = 0 \quad \text{remainder 6 (MSD)}$$

Therefore, $437_{10} = 665_8$.

Octal-binary conversion

Because the base of the binary system is 2 and the base of the octal system is $8 = 2^3$, you can convert from octal whole numbers to binary whole numbers by changing each octal digit into its three-bit binary equivalent. As an example:

$$1426 = \underbrace{1}_{001}\ \underbrace{4}_{100}\ \underbrace{2}_{010}\ \underbrace{6}_{110}$$
$$= 1100010110_2$$

Notice that the two 0s to the left of the MSB are discarded.

Binary-octal conversion

To convert from binary whole numbers to octal whole numbers, reverse the octal-to-binary procedure. Starting at the binary point and moving to the left, mark off the bits in groups of 3, then express each group in its octal equivalent. If the number of bits is not exactly divisible by 3, complete the last group by adding one or two 0s to the left of the MSB. For example:

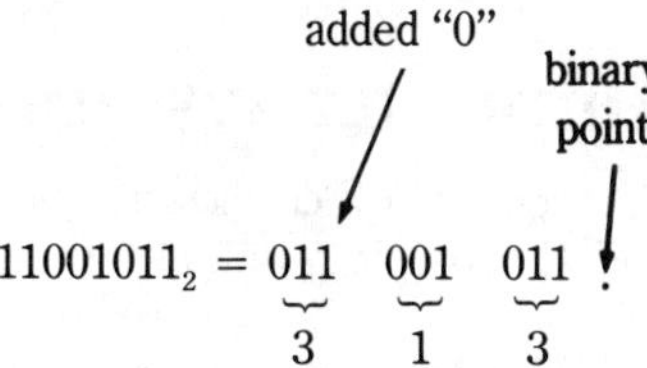

$$11001011_2 = \underbrace{011}_{3}\ \underbrace{001}_{1}\ \underbrace{011}_{3}.$$

Therefore, $11001011_2 = 313_8$.

* **Question 13-5** Convert the octal number, 673_8 into its equivalent decimal number.

A. 443_{10} B. 453_{10} C. 513_{10} D. 429_{10} E. 449_{10}

Answer Choice A. From EQ. 13-1:

$$673_8 = (6 \times 8^2) + (7 \times 8^1) + (3 \times 8^0) = 443_{10}$$

* **Question 13-6** Convert the decimal number, 5693_{10}, into its equivalent octal number.

A. 12674_8 B. 13075_8 C. 12973_8 D. 12563_8 E. 12773_8

Answer Choice B. Using the repeated division method:

$$\frac{5693}{8} = 711 \quad \text{remainder } 5$$

$$\frac{711}{8} = 88 \quad \text{remainder } 7$$

$$\frac{88}{8} = 11 \quad \text{remainder } 0$$

$$\frac{11}{8} = 1 \quad \text{remainder } 3$$

$$\frac{1}{8} = 0 \quad \text{remainder } 1$$

Therefore, $5693_{10} = 13075_8$.

* **Question 13-7** Convert to binary number, 11011001_2, to its equivalent octal number:

A. 661_8 B. 662_8 C. 321_8 D. 631_8 E. 331_8

Answer Choice E. Binary number, $11011001_2 = \underbrace{011}_{3}\ \underbrace{011}_{3}\ \underbrace{001}_{1}$

$$= 331_8$$

* **Question 13-8** Convert the octal number, 673_3, into its equivalent binary number:

A. 101111101_2 B. 110101011_2 C. 110111011_2 D. 110110101_2 E. 110111111_2

Answer Choice C. Octal number, $673_8 = \underbrace{110}_{6}\ \underbrace{111}_{7}\ \underbrace{011}_{3} = 110111011_2$

13-4. The hexadecimal number system

The hexadecimal number system (Base 16) requires 16 characters: the digits 0,1,2,3, 4,5,6,7,8,9, followed by the letters A,B,C,D,E,F. As shown in TABLE 13-1, the letters A through F are equivalent to the decimal values 10 through 15.

Although you can convert between hexadecimal and decimal numbers directly, it is possible to use the binary system as an intermediate step (see FIG. 13-5). Hexadecimal numbers are frequently used in conjunction with computer memories and with various forms of programming.

Direct hexadecimal-to-decimal conversion

To obtain a hexadecimal-to-decimal conversion, use EQ. 13-1. For example:

$$\begin{aligned} 1B6_{16} &= (1 \times 16^2) + (11 \times 16^1) + (6 \times 16^0) \\ &= 256 + 176 + 6 \\ &= 438_{10} \end{aligned}$$

Direct decimal-to-hexadecimal conversion

A decimal whole number is converted into its equivalent hexadecimal number using the repeated division method with 16 as the division factor. For example, 5831_{10} is equivalent to:

Table 13-1. A comparison of number systems.

Decimal	Binary	Octal	Hexadecimal
0	00000	0	0
1	00001	1	1
2	00010	2	2
3	00011	3	3
4	00100	4	4
5	00101	5	5
6	00110	6	6
7	00111	7	7
8	01000	10	8
9	01001	11	9
10	01010	12	A
11	01011	13	B
12	01100	14	C
13	01101	15	D
14	01110	16	E
15	01111	17	F
16	10000	20	10
17	10001	21	11
18	10010	22	12

$$\frac{5831}{16} = 364 \quad \text{remainder } 7$$
$$\frac{364}{16} = 22 \quad \text{remainder } 12 \text{ (C)}$$
$$\frac{22}{16} = 1 \quad \text{remainder } 6$$
$$\frac{1}{16} = 0 \quad \text{remainder } 1$$

Therefore, $5831_{10} = 16C7_{16}$.

Hexadecimal-to-binary conversion

Because the base of the binary system is 2 and the base of the hexadecimal system is $16 = 2^4$, you can convert from hexadecimal whole numbers to binary whole numbers by changing each hexadecimal digit into its four-bit binary equivalent. As an example:

$$3B7D_{16} = \underbrace{3}_{0011} \quad \underbrace{B}_{1011} \quad \underbrace{7}_{0111} \quad \underbrace{D}_{1101}$$
$$= 11101101111101_2$$
$$= 15229_{10} \text{ by the "double-dabble" method}$$

It is clear that the hexadecimal system can represent large numbers more efficiently than the binary system can.

Binary-to-hexadecimal conversion

To convert from binary whole numbers to hexadecimal whole numbers, reverse the hexadecimal-to-binary procedure. Starting at the binary point and moving to the left, mark off the bits in groups of four, then express each group in its hexadecimal equivalent. If the number of bits is not exactly divisible by 4, the last group can be completed by adding one, two, or three 0s to the left of the MSB. For example:

$$11010111010011_2 = \underbrace{0011}_{3} \quad \underbrace{0101}_{5} \quad \underbrace{1101}_{D} \quad \underbrace{0011}_{3} \; . \leftarrow \text{binary point}$$

Therefore: $11010111010011_2 = 35D3_{16}$
$= 13779_{10}$

* **Question 13-9** Convert the hexadecimal number, $A6B_{16}$, into its equivalent binary number:
A. 110110010110_2 B. 1010111001001_2 C. 101001101001_2 D. 101001101011_2
E. 101011011001_2

Answer Choice D.

$$\text{Hexadecimal number, } A6B_{16} = \underbrace{A(10)}_{1010} \quad \underbrace{6}_{0110} \quad \underbrace{B(11)}_{1011}$$
$$= 101001101011_2$$
$$(= 2667_{10})$$

Question 13-10 Convert the binary number, 11100101111_2, into its equivalent hexademical number.

A. $82E_{16}$ B. $72E_{16}$ C. $82F_{16}$ D. $73F_{16}$ E. $72F_{16}$

Answer Choice E.

$$\text{Binary number, } 11100101111_2 = \underbrace{0111}_{7}\ \underbrace{0010}_{2}\ \underbrace{1111}_{F(15)}$$

$$= 72F_{16}$$

Question 13-11 Convert the decimal number, 4376_{10}, into its equivalent hexadecimal number.

A. 1117_{16} B. 1118_{16} C. 1018_{16} D. 1108_{16} E. 1008_{16}

Answer Choice B. By the repeated division method:

$$\frac{4376}{16} = 273 \quad \text{remainder } 8$$

$$\frac{273}{16} = 17 \quad \text{remainder } 1$$

$$\frac{17}{16} = 1 \quad \text{remainder } 1$$

$$\frac{1}{16} = 0 \quad \text{remainder } 1$$

Therefore, $4376_{10} = 1118_{16}$.

13-5. Introduction to Boolean algebra: the "OR" operation

Boolean algebra was developed by the English logician and mathematician George Boole (1815–1864). In the spring of 1847, Boole wrote a pamphlet entitled *A Mathematical Analysis of Logic.* This was followed in 1854 by his more exhaustive treatise, *An Investigation of the Laws of Thought.* It is this later work that forms the basis for our present-day mathematical theories used for the analysis of logical processes.

Although conceived in the nineteenth century, little practical application was found for Boole's work until 1938, when it was discovered that his algebra could be adapted to the analysis of switching circuits. With the advent of modern computers, Boolean algebra has become an important subject in the understanding of complex digital circuitry.

Classes and elements

In our world, it is logical to visualize two divisions: all things of interest are in one division, and all things not of interest are in the other division. These two divisions make up a set or a class that is designated as the *universal class.* All things contained in the universal class are referred to as *elements* or *variables.* You can also visualize another class, which contains no elements; such a set is designated as the *null class.*

In a particular discussion, certain elements of the universal class can be grouped together to form combinations, which are known as *subclasses.* Each subclass of the universal class is dependent on its elements and the possible states (stable, unstable, or both) that these elements might have.

Boolean algebra is limited to the use of elements that only possess two possible logic states, both of which are stable. If you have two elements A and B, their possible states can be designated in a number of ways, as shown in TABLE 13-2.

Table 13-2. Possible states for *A* and *B*.

Logic 1	Logic 0
True	False
Yes	No
High	Low
+10 V	0 V
ON	OFF
Closed switch	Open switch

Notice that in Boolean algebra there are only two numbers: 0 and 1. Moreover, this form of algebra does not contain such concepts as squares, square roots, reciprocals, and logarithms.

If you have two elements, each of which has two states, there are $2^2 = 4$ possible subclasses. If the states of A and B are true or false and you use the connective word AND, the four subclasses are:

- A true AND B false
- A true AND B true
- A false AND B true
- A false AND B false

However, if the connective word OR is used, there are four additional subclasses:

- A true OR B false
- A true OR B true
- A false OR B true
- A false OR B false

Venn diagrams

A *Venn diagram* is a topographical picture of logic. Such a diagram is composed of the universal class, which is divided into subclasses. The number of these subclasses depends on the number of elements.

As an example, let A equal cars and B equal the color red. With the connective word AND, the four subclasses are:

- Cars AND Not red
- Cars AND Red
- Red AND Not Cars
- Not Cars AND Not Red

With the connective word OR, the four additional subclasses are:

- Red OR Not Cars
- Not Cars OR Not Red

- Cars OR Not Red
- Cars OR Red

All these subclasses are shown in FIG. 13-6. The shaded area in each diagram represents the particular subclass.

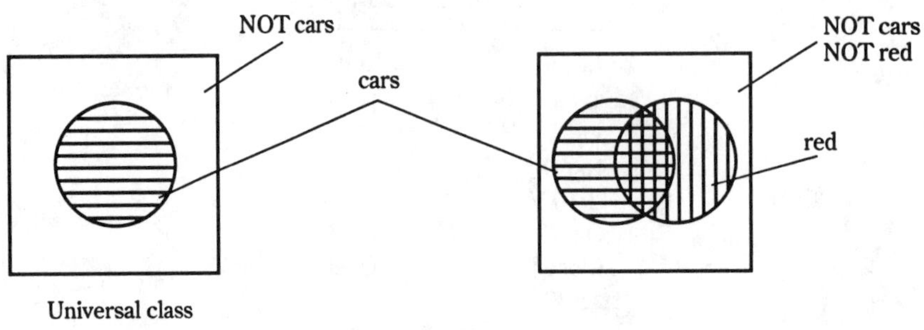

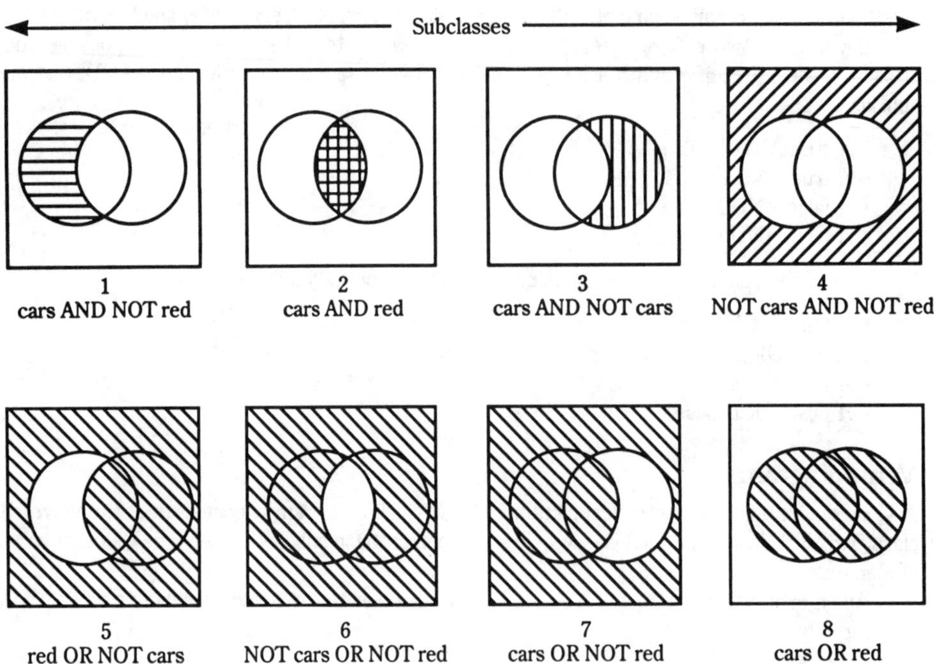

Fig. 13-6 Examples of Venn diagrams.

Symbols in Boolean algebra

The symbols used in Boolean algebra are common in other branches of mathematics, but in certain cases their meaning is slightly different. The principal symbols are explained in TABLE 13-3. From this table it follows that logic circuits have only three basic operations: AND, OR, and NOT.

Table 13-3. Boolean algebra symbols.

Symbol	Meaning
=	As in conventional mathematics the equal sign represents the relationship of equivalence between the expressions which are so connected.
· or ×	These symbols indicate the logic product which is also known as the AND operation. Frequently this operation is indicated without the use of a symbol so that $AB = A \times B = A \cdot B$
+	The plus sign indicates the logic sum which is also known as the OR operation.
–	The overbar signifies logical complementation or inversion which is known as the NOT operation.
( ), [ ], { }	The grouping symbols mean that all the contained terms must be treated as a unit.

Truth tables

For any Boolean operation, there is a corresponding truth table that shows the various outputs of the operation for each possible way the states of the input elements can be assigned. In a truth table, the states are designated as 0 and 1; if there are only two input elements, the corresponding truth table is as shown in TABLE 13-4.

The operation's output will be a function of A and B and is therefore designated as $f(A,B)$. Notice that the top to bottom sequence of the input elements is the same as that of binary counting.

Table 13-4. The truth table for A and B.

Input	Elements	Output
A	B	$f(A, B)$
0	0	?
0	1	?
1	0	?
1	1	?

The OR operation

The Venn diagram in FIG. 13-7A, has two elements (variables), which are designated A and B. The shaded area represents the subclass, which is $A + B$ in Boolean notation. The corresponding equation in Boolean algebra is expressed as:

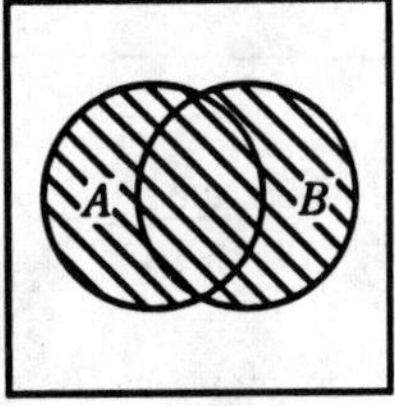

Venn diagram for *A* OR *B*

A

Input elements		OR output
A	*B*	$f(A,B) = A + B$
0	0	0
0	1	1
1	0	1
1	1	1

Truth table for OR operation

B

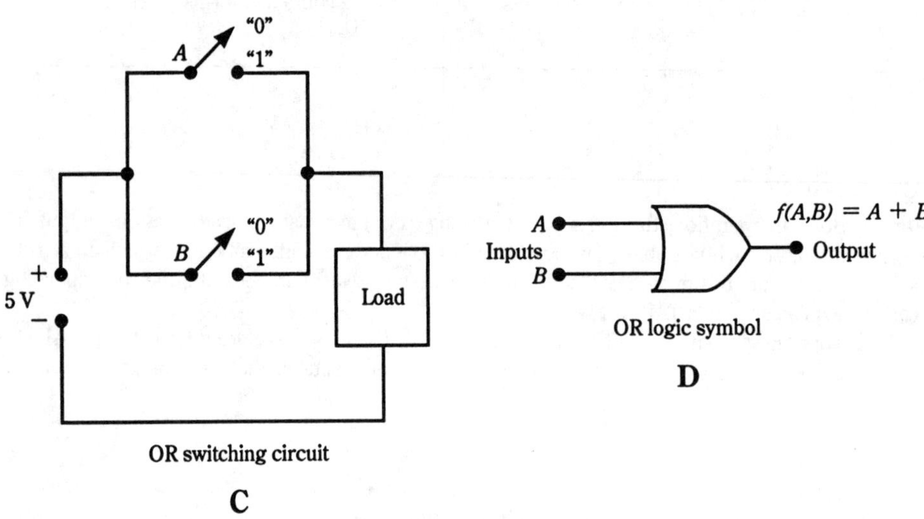

OR switching circuit

C

OR logic symbol

D

Fig. 13-7 The OR operation.

$$f(A,B) = A + B \qquad (13\text{-}2)$$

This expression is called an *OR operation* because it represents the last of the four OR subclasses illustrated in the Venn diagrams of FIG. 13-6. The equation "$f(A,B)$ equals $A + B$" is read as either "$f(A,B)$ equals *A* plus *B*" or "$f(A,B)$ equals *A* OR *B*."

Figure 13-7B illustrates the truth table of the OR operation. When *A* and *B* are each 0, the output is also 0. If either *A* or *B* takes the value of 1, the output $f(A,B)$, equals 1. However, if both *A* and *B* are equal to 1, $f(A,B)$ is 1, not 10 as in binary addition, because $A + B$ represents the logic sum and in Boolean algebra, only two numbers exist: 0 and 1.

Figure 13-7C shows the switching circuit that represents the OR operation. It consists of two switches in parallel. The circuit is ON (1) if either switch *A* or switch *B* is in the CLOSED (1) state. The circuit is also ON (1) if both switch *A* and switch *B* are CLOSED (1), but it is OFF (0) if, and only if, both switch *A* and switch B, are OPEN (0). Notice that the high and low values applied to the load are 5 and 0 V, respectively.

The "OR" gate

The *OR gate* is a digital circuit that has two or more inputs, represented by the logic voltage levels 0 and 1. For example, the logic 1 level (high) might be + 5 V, and the logic 0 level (low) is only + 0.5 V. The output of the gate is the logic sum of the inputs and has a voltage level (either 1 or 0), that is the result of carrying out the OR operation on the inputs. The logic symbol for the OR gate is shown in FIG. 13-7D.

If there are only two inputs, A and B, the OR gate operates in such a way that its output, A or B, is low (0) if, and only if, both A and B are in the 0 state. By contrast, if either A or B or both are in the 1 state, the gate's output is high and in the 1 state.

With more than two inputs, the same principles apply. In all cases, when one or more of the inputs is in the 1 state, the output is high. The outputs will be low only when all of the inputs are in the 0 state.

To summarize the results of the OR operation:

1. For the OR operation, the output is in the 0 state if, and only if, all of the inputs are in the 0 state. Therefore:

$$f(A,B,C\ldots) = A + B + C + \cdots = 0 \quad \text{if } A = B = C = \cdots = 0 \tag{13-3}$$

2. For the OR operation, the output is in the 1 state when any one of the inputs is in the 1 state. Therefore:

$$f(\mathrm{A,B,C}\ldots) = A + B + C + \cdots = 1 \quad \text{if } A \text{ or } B \text{ or } C \text{ or } \cdots = 1 \tag{13-4}$$

3. For the OR operation, the output is in the 1 state if more than one of the inputs is in the 1 state. For example:

$$f(A,B,C\ldots) = 1 + 0 + 1 + 1 + 0 + 0 + 1 \cdots = 1$$

* **Question 13-12** Which of the following logic gates corresponds to the truth table of FIG. 13-8?

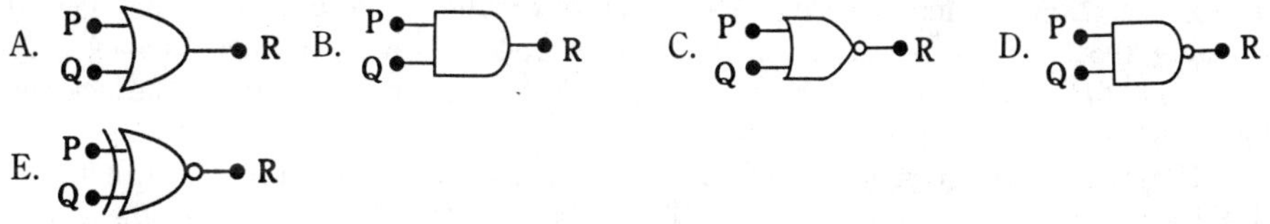

A. P, Q → R (OR gate) B. P, Q → R (AND gate) C. P, Q → R (NAND gate) D. P, Q → R (NAND gate)

E. P, Q → R (EX-NOR gate)

Answer Choice A. Refer to FIG. 13-7B.

* **Question 13-13** Which of the following logic circuits has an operation that corresponds to two or more switches (or relays) in parallel?

A. AND gate B. NAND gate C. OR gate D. NOR gate E. EX-OR gate

Answer Choice C. Refer to FIG. 13-7.

13-6. The AND operation

The Venn diagram in FIG. 13-9A has two elements (variables, which are designated A and B. The shaded area represents the subclass, which is AB or $A \cdot B$ or $A \times B$ in Boolean notation. The corresponding equation in Boolean algebra is expressed as:

$$f(A,B) = AB = A \cdot B = A \times B \tag{13-5}$$

P	Q	R
False	False	False
False	True	True
True	False	True
True	True	True

Fig. 13-8 Truth table for question 13-12.

This expression is called an *AND operation* because it represents the second of the four AND subclasses illustrated in the Venn diagrams of FIG. 13-6. The equation $f(A,B) = AB$ is read as "$f(A,B)$ equals A AND B," which is the logic product of A and B.

Figure 13-9B depicts the truth table for the AND operation. When A and B are each 0, the output is also 0. If either A or B takes the value of 0, $f(A,B)$ is 0. However, if both A and B are in the 1 state, $f(A,B)$ is 1. The rules for the AND operation are the same as those for binary multiplication.

Figure 13-9C shows the switching circuit that represents the AND operation. It consists of two switches in series so that the circuit is off (0) if either switch A or switch B is open (0). The circuit is also off (0) if both switch A and switch B are open (0). The circuit is on (1) if, and only if, both switches A and B are closed (1). Notice that the high and low logic values applied to the load are 5 V and 0 V, respectively.

The AND gate

The AND gate is a digital circuit that has two or more inputs, represented by the logic voltage levels, 0 and 1. For example, the logic 1 level (high) might be + 5 V, while the logic 0 level (low) is only + 0.5 V. The output of the gate is the logic product of the inputs and has a voltage level (either 1 or 0) that is the result of carrying out the AND operation on the inputs. The logic symbol for the AND gate is shown in FIG. 13-9D.

If there are only two inputs, A AND B, the AND gate operates in such a way that its output, A AND B., is high (1) if, and only if, A AND B are in the 1 state. By contrast, if either A or B or both are in the 0 state, the gate's output is low and in the 0 state.

With more than two inputs, the same principles apply. In all cases, when one or more of the inputs is in the 0 state, the output is low. The output will be high only when all the inputs are in the 1 state.

To summarize the results of the AND operation:

1. For the AND operation, the output is in the 1 state if, and only if, all inputs are in the 1 state. Therefore,

$$f(A,B,C \cdots) = ABC \cdots = 1 \text{ if } A = B = C \cdots = 1 \qquad (13\text{-}6)$$

2. For the AND operation, the output is in the 0 state when any one or more of the inputs is in the 0 state. Therefore:

$$f(A,B,C...) = ABC \cdots = 0 \text{ if } A \text{ or } B \text{ or } C \text{ or} \cdots = 0 \qquad (13\text{-}7)$$

* **Question 13-14** Which of the following logic gates corresponds to the truth table of FIG. 13-10?

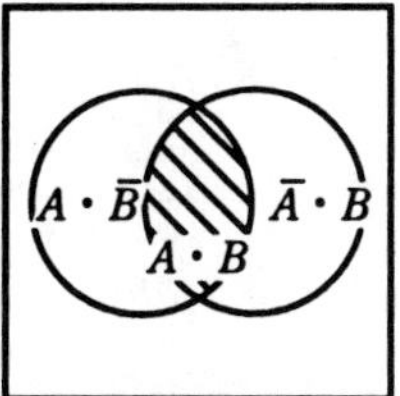

Venn diagram for *A* AND *B*

A

Input elements		AND output
A	*B*	$f(A,B) = A \cdot B$
0	0	0
0	1	0
1	0	0
1	1	1

Truth table for AND operation

B

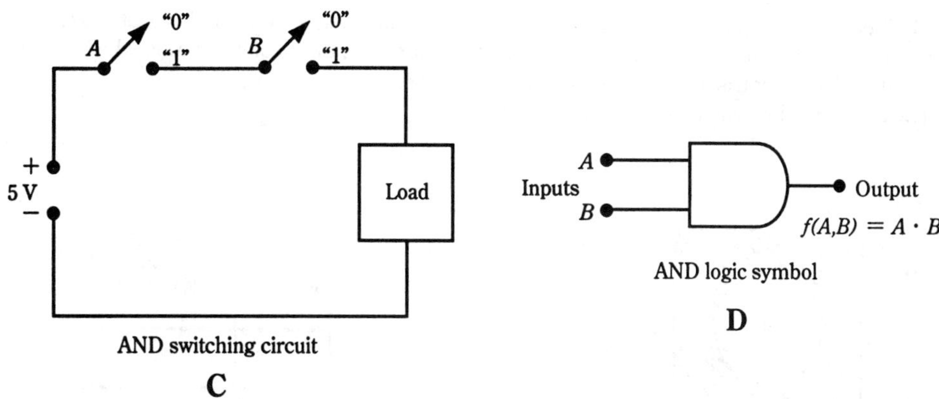

AND switching circuit

C

AND logic symbol

D

Fig. 13-9 The AND operation.

A. P Q R B. P Q R C. P Q R D. P Q R

E. P Q R

Answer Choice B. Refer to FIG. 13-9B.

* **Question 13-15** Which of the following logic circuits has an operation that corresponds to two or more switches (or relays) in series?

A. AND gate B. NAND gate C. OR gate D. NOR gate E. EX-OR gate

Answer Choice A. Refer to FIG. 13-9C.

P	Q	R
Low	Low	Low
Low	High	Low
High	Low	Low
High	High	High

Fig. 13-10 Truth table for question 13-14.

13-7. The NOT operation

The Venn diagram in FIG. 13-11A has one input element, or variable, which is designated as A and is represented by the clear area. The shaded area represents the Boolean output, which is indicated by $\bar{A}$ or A', and is the complement, or inverse, of A.
The corresponding equation is: $F(A) = \bar{A} = A'$

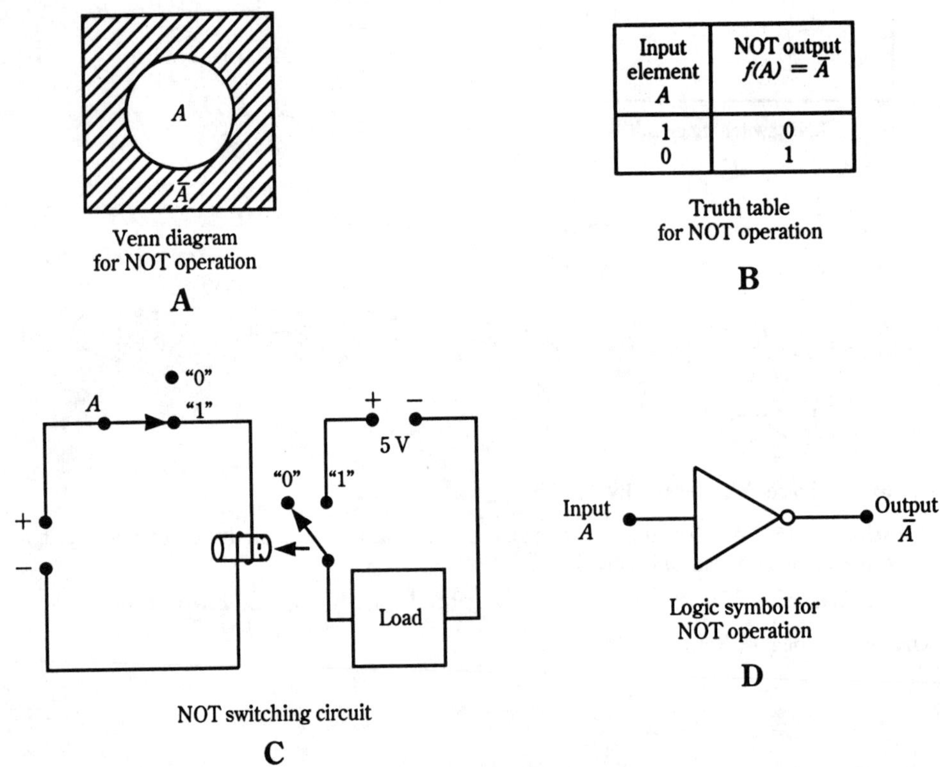

Fig. 13-11 The NOT operation.

The equation is read as "Output, $f(A)$ is NOT A." Notice that, unlike the AND and OR operations, the NOT operation can only be performed on a single input element.

Because the logic value of $\bar{A}$ is opposite to the logic value of A, it follows that: (a) if $A = 0$, $\bar{A} = 1$ because NOT 0 is 1; and (b) if $A = 1$, $\bar{A} = 0$ because NOT 1 is 0. The results of this reasoning are shown in the truth table of FIG. 13-11B.

The NOT switching circuit is shown in FIG. 13-11C. The requirement of a NOT circuit is that a signal injected at the input produces the complement, or inversion, of this signal at the output. When switch A is closed and is in state 1, the relay opens the circuit to the load and the load circuit is, therefore, off (0). However, when switch A is open and is in state 0, the relay closes the load circuit, which is then in the on (1) condition. Notice that the high and low logic values applied to the load are 5 and 0 V, respectively.

The logic symbol for the NOT circuit is shown in FIG. 13-11D. The presence of the small circle, or *bubble,* on a logic symbol is always an indication of inversion. The input and output logic levels are interchanged: consequently, an input level of 1 corresponds to an output level of 0 and vice-versa.

The NOT operation is summarized as follows:

$$f(A) = \bar{A} = 1 \text{ when } A = 0$$
$$f(A) = \bar{A} = 0 \text{ when } A = 1$$

The OR, AND, and NOT circuits provide the three basic Boolean operations. Comparing the rules for these operations:

OR	AND	NOT
$0 + 0 = 0$	$0 \cdot 0 = 0$	$\bar{0} = 1$
$0 + 1 = 1$	$0 \cdot 1 = 0$	$\bar{1} = 0$
$1 + 0 = 1$	$1 \cdot 0 = 0$	
$1 + 1 = 1$	$1 \cdot 1 = 1$	

* **Question 13-16** Which of the following logic circuits corresponds to the truth table of FIG. 13-12?

A. NAND operation B. NOR operation C. OR operation D. AND operation E. NOT operation

Answer Choice E. Refer to FIG. 13-11B.

Input	Output
High	Low
Low	High

Fig. 13-12 The truth diagram for question 13-16.

13-8. The NOR operation

If there are two input elements, A and B, each of which has two alternative stable states, 0 and 1, there will be a total of 16 possible truth tables. Assuming that the 0, 0, 0, 0 and 1, 1, 1, 1 outputs have no use, there are 14 remaining tables that can be arranged in 7 pairs. In each pair, the outputs of one table will be the complements of the outputs from the other table. It follows that there must exist a truth table that is the complement or inversion of the table for the OR operation. This new truth table will refer to the NOR operation, which is a combination of the OR and NOT operations.

In FIG. 13-13A, the unshaded area of the Venn diagram represents the subclass *A* OR *B;* the shaded area is the subclass *A* OR *B,* when negated of complemented. The Boolean expression for *A* OR *B,* when negated or inverted is: $f(A,B) = \overline{A\ OR\ B} = \overline{A + B}$.

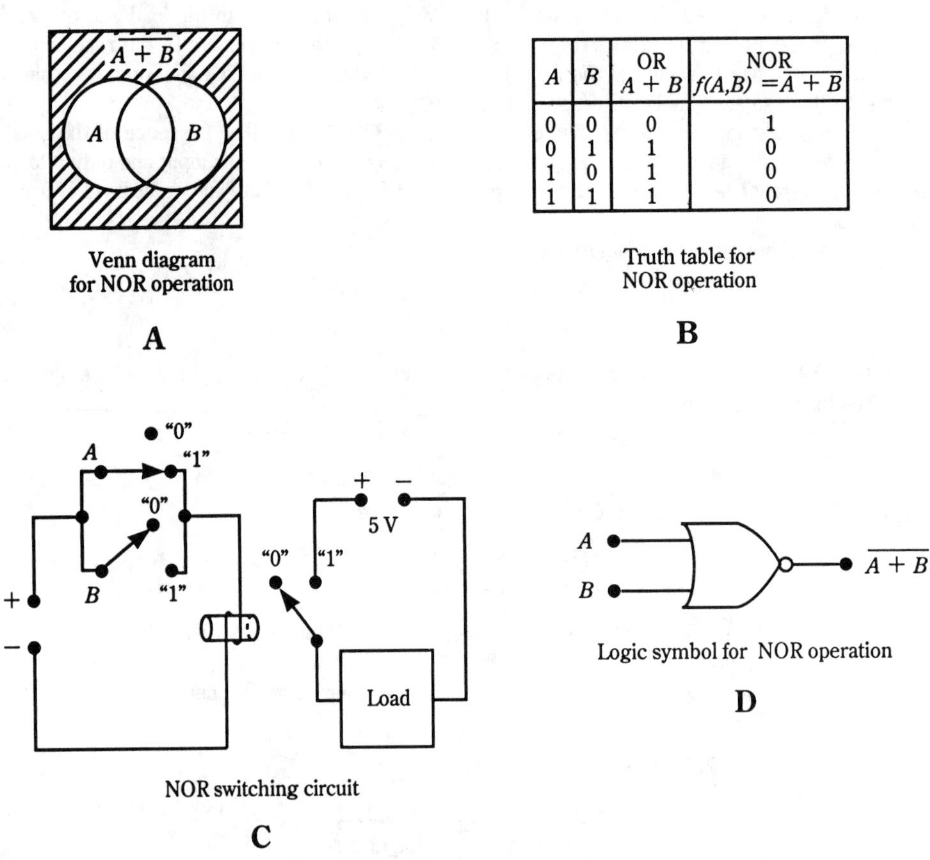

A	B	OR $A + B$	NOR $f(A,B) = \overline{A + B}$
0	0	0	1
0	1	1	0
1	0	1	0
1	1	1	0

Fig. 13-13 The NOR operation.

The truth table for the NOR operation is shown in FIG. 13-13B. This table shows that if either *A* or *B* or both *A* and *B* is in the 1 state, then the output $f(A,B)$ is in the 1 state.

The NOR equivalent switching arrangement is the result of combining the OR switching circuit and the NOT switching circuit (FIG. 13-13C). If either switch *A* or switch *B,* or both, is in the closed (1) position, the load circuit is inactive or off (0). However, if both of the switches *A* and *B* are open (0), the load circuit is active or on (1).

The logic symbol for the NOR gate is shown in FIG. 13-13D. It is a combination of the OR gate and bubble, which indicates inversion. The NOR gate is commonly used in digital circuitry and is equivalent to an OR gate followed by an inverter. For the NOR operation, the Boolean equation is:

$$\text{Output, } f(A,B) = \overline{A + B} \tag{13-9}$$

Notice that $\overline{A + B}$ is not the same as $\bar{A} + \bar{B}$. For example, if $A = 1$ and $B = 0$, $\overline{A + B} = \overline{1 + 0} = \bar{1} = 0$, but $\bar{A} + B = \bar{1} + \bar{0} = 0 + 1 = 1$.

* **Question 13-17** Which of the following logic gates corresponds to the truth table of FIG. 13-14?

A. NOR gate B. NAND gate C. AND gate D. EX-NOR gate E. OR gate

Answer Choice A. Refer to FIG. 13-13B.

P	Q	R
False	False	True
False	True	False
True	False	False
True	True	False

Fig. 13-14 The truth table for question 13-17.

13-9. The NAND operation

In FIG. 13-15A, the unshaded area of the Venn diagram represents the subclass *A AND B*. The shaded area is the subclass *A* AND *B* when negated or complemented; this subclass, $\overline{A \text{ AND } B}$, is shown in the Venn diagrams of FIG. 13-6. The Boolean equation of *A* AND *B*, when negated or inverted, is: $f(A,B) = \overline{A \cdot B}$.

The truth table for the NAND operation is shown in FIG. 13-15B. The table shows that if both *A* and *B* are in the 1 state, the output is in the 0 state. For all other possible combinations of the *A* and *B* states, the output is in the 1 state.

The equivalent NAND switching arrangement (FIG. 13-15C) is a combination of AND and NOT circuits. If either or both of the switches *A* and *B* are open (0), the load circuit is on (1). However, if both of the switches *A* and *B* are closed (1), the load circuit is off (0).

The logic symbol for the NAND gate is shown in FIG. 13-15D. There are two input elements, *A* and *B*, into an AND gate, whose output, $A \cdot B$ is fed into a NOT circuit; the final output, $f(A,B)$, is then $\overline{A \cdot B}$.

For the NAND operation, the Boolean equation is:

$$\text{Output, } f(A,B) = \overline{A \cdot B}. \tag{13-11}$$

Notice that the entire group, $A \cdot B$, is complemented, and this is not the same as the logic product of the two elements when they are complemented separately $(\bar{A} \cdot \bar{B})$. For example, if $A = 1$ and $B = 0$, $\overline{A \cdot B} = \bar{0} = 1$, but $\bar{A} \cdot \bar{B} = 0 \cdot 1 = 0$.

* **Question 13-18** Which of the following logic gates corresponds to the truth table of FIG. 13-16?

A. P Q R B. P Q R C. P Q R D. P Q R

E. P Q R

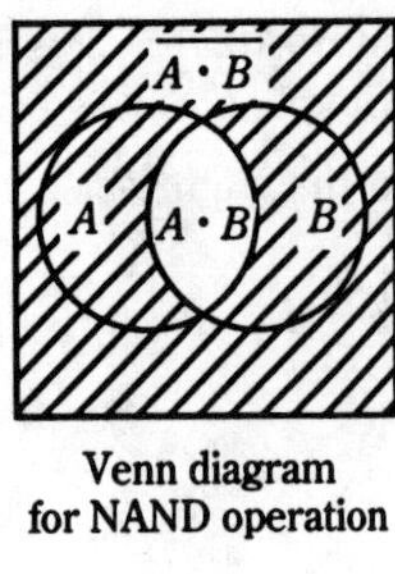

Venn diagram for NAND operation

A

A	B	AND $A \cdot B$	NAND $f(A,B) = \overline{A \cdot B}$
0	0	0	1
0	1	0	1
1	0	0	1
1	1	1	0

Truth table for NAND operation

B

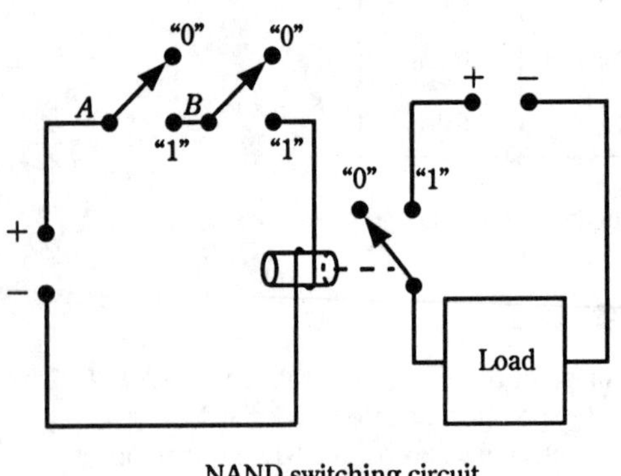

NAND switching circuit

C

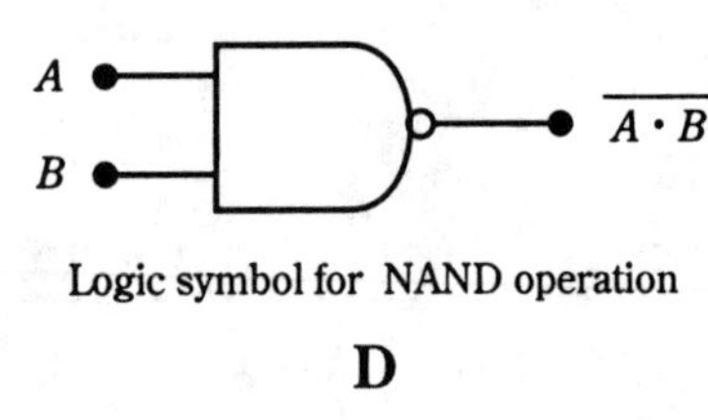

Logic symbol for NAND operation

D

Fig. 13-15 The NAND operation.

P	Q	R
Low	Low	High
Low	High	High
High	Low	High
High	High	Low

Fig. 13-16 Truth table for question 13-18.

Answer Choice E. Refer to FIG. 13-15B.

13-10. The exclusive-OR operation

The exclusive-OR (abbreviated *EX-OR*) operation is actually a special application of the OR operation and appears quite frequently in digital circuitry. In the EX-OR operation, either inputs *A* or B must be in the 1 state in order for the output, $f(A,B)$, to be in the 1 state; however, if both A and B are in the 1 state or in the 0 state at the same time, the output is in the 0 state.

The Venn diagram for the EX-OR operation is shown in FIG. 13-17A. This diagram does not appear in any of those shown in FIG. 13-6 and is therefore, a new subclass. The Boolean equation for the EX-OR operation is:

$$f(A,B) = \overline{A} \cdot B + A \cdot \overline{B} \tag{13-12}$$

If:

$$A = 0,\ B = 0,\ f(A,B) = 1 \cdot 0 + 0 \cdot 1 = 0$$
$$A = 0,\ B = 1,\ f(A,B) = 1 \cdot 1 + 0 \cdot 0 = 1$$
$$A = 1,\ B = 0,\ f(A,B) = 0 \cdot 0 + 1 \cdot 1 = 1$$
$$A = 1,\ B = 1,\ f(A,B) = 0 \cdot 1 + 1 \cdot 0 = 0$$

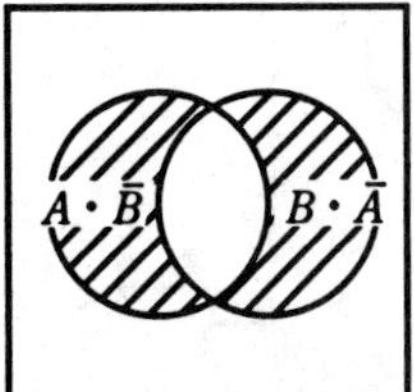

Venn diagram for EX-OR operation

A

Input elements		EX-OR output
A	B	$f(A,B) = A \cdot \overline{B} + B \cdot \overline{A}$
0	0	0
0	1	1
1	0	1
1	1	0

Truth table for EX-OR operation

B

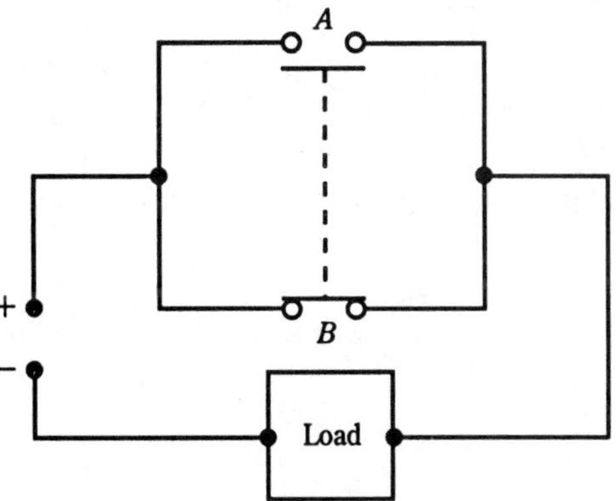

EX-OR switching circuit

C

Logic symbol for EX-OR operation

D

Fig. 13-17 The EX-OR operation.

These results are shown in the truth table of FIG. 13-17B. Notice that the EX-OR gate always has only two inputs. There are no EX-OR gates with three or more inputs.

In the equivalent switching circuit (FIG. 13-17C) for an EX-OR gate, the two switches are mechanically linked together so that one or the other, but not both, can be closed at any particular time.

The EX-OR gate actually consists of inverters, AND gates, and an OR gate. The required combination of these logic circuits is shown in FIG. 13-18. However, the EX-OR gate is used sufficiently often to be given its own symbol (FIG. 13-17D). For the EX-OR operation:

$$f(A,B) = \overline{A} \cdot B + A \cdot \overline{B} = A \oplus B \qquad (13\text{-}13)$$

The $\oplus$ symbol is used to represent the EX-OR gate operation.

To summarize the EX-OR gate operation:

1. The output is only in the 1 state when the two input elements are in different states.
2. If the two input elements are in the same state, the output is in the 0 state.

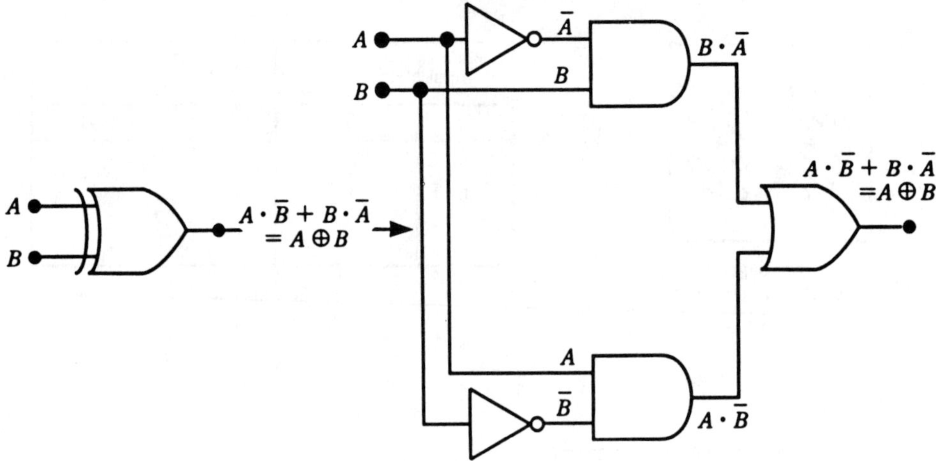

Fig. 13-18 An equivalent logic circuit of the EX-OR gate.

Question 13-19 Which of the following logic gates corresponds to the truth table of FIG. 13-19?

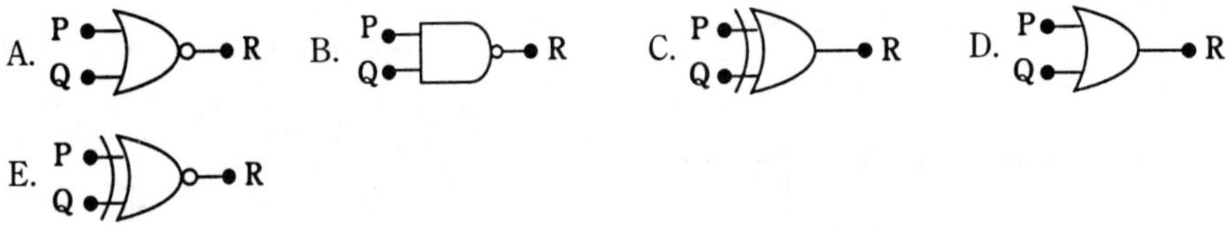

A. P, Q — R

B. P, Q — R

C. P, Q — R

D. P, Q — R

E. P, Q — R

Answer Choice C. Refer to FIG. 13-17B.

P	Q	R
False	False	False
False	True	True
True	False	True
True	True	False

Fig. 13-19 The truth table for question 13-19.

13-11. The exclusive-NOR operation

The exclusive-NOR (abbreviated EX-NOR) operation is the least common of all the operations discussed. It is merely the inverse of the EX-OR operation. Consequently, an EX-NOR circuit can be formed by following an EX-OR gate with an inverter.

In the EX-NOR operation, both of the input elements, A and B, must be in the same state (either 0 or 1) in order for the output, $f(A,B)$, to be in the 1 state; however, if A and B are in opposite states at the same time, the output is in the 0 state.

The Venn diagram for the EX-NOR operation is shown in FIG. 13-20A. This diagram does not appear in any of those shown in FIG. 13-6, and is therefore a new subclass.

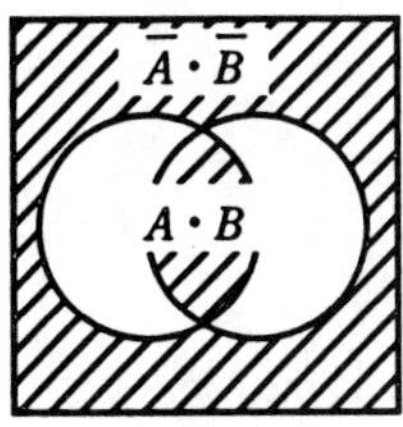

Venn diagram
for EX-NOR operation

A

Input elements		EX-NOR output
A	B	$f(A,B) = A \cdot B + \bar{A} \cdot \bar{B}$
0	0	1
0	1	0
1	0	0
1	1	1

Truth table for
EX-NOR operation

B

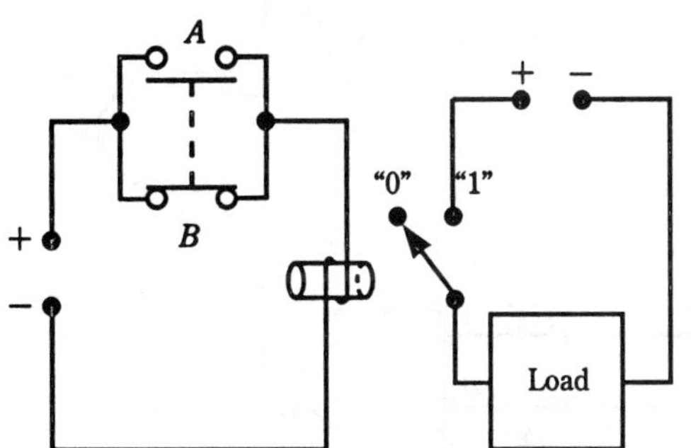

EX-NOR switching circuit

C

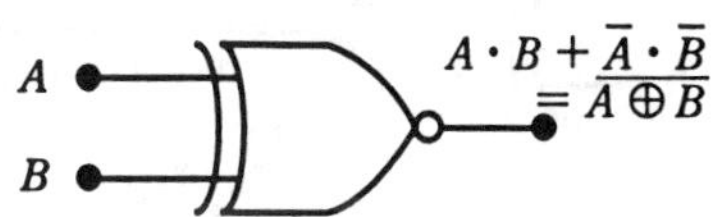

Logic symbol for EX-NOR operation

D

Fig. 13-20 The EX-OR operation.

The Boolean equation for the EX-NOR operation is:

$$f(A,B) = A \cdot B + \bar{A} \cdot \bar{B} \qquad (13\text{-}14)$$

Notice that this logic expression is not the same as $A - B + \overline{A - B}$, which must always equal 1.

If

$$A = 0,\ B = 0,\ f(A,B) = 0 \cdot 0 + 1 \cdot 1 = 1$$
$$A = 0,\ B = 1,\ f(A,B) = 0 \cdot 1 + 1 \cdot 0 = 0$$

$$A = 1,\ B = 0,\ f(A,B) = 1 \cdot 0 + 0 \cdot 1 = 0$$
$$A = 1,\ B = 1,\ f(A,B) = 1 \cdot 1 + 0 \cdot 0 = 1$$

These results are shown in the truth table of FIG. 13-20B. Notice that, like the EX-OR gate, the EX-NOR gate always has only two inputs. There are no EX-NOR gates with three or more inputs.

The equivalent switching circuit (FIG. 13-20C) for the EX-NOR gate is a combination of the switching circuit for the EX-OR gate and the inverter. The two switches, A and B, are mechanically linked so that one or the other, but not both, can be closed. If either A or B is closed (1), the switch in the load circuit is open so that the load circuit is off (0).

The EX-NOR gate is actually composed of inverters, AND gates, and an OR gate. The required combination of these logic circuits is shown in FIG. 13-21. The corresponding symbol for the EX-NOR gate appears in FIG. 13-20D. For the EX-NOR operation:

$$f(A,B) = A \cdot B + \bar{A} \cdot \bar{B}$$

This can be abbreviated to: $$f(A,B) = \overline{A \oplus B} \qquad (13\text{-}15)$$

To summarize the EX-NOR operation:

1. The output is only in the 1 state when the two input elements are in the same state.
2. If the two input elements are in opposite states, the output is in the 0 state.

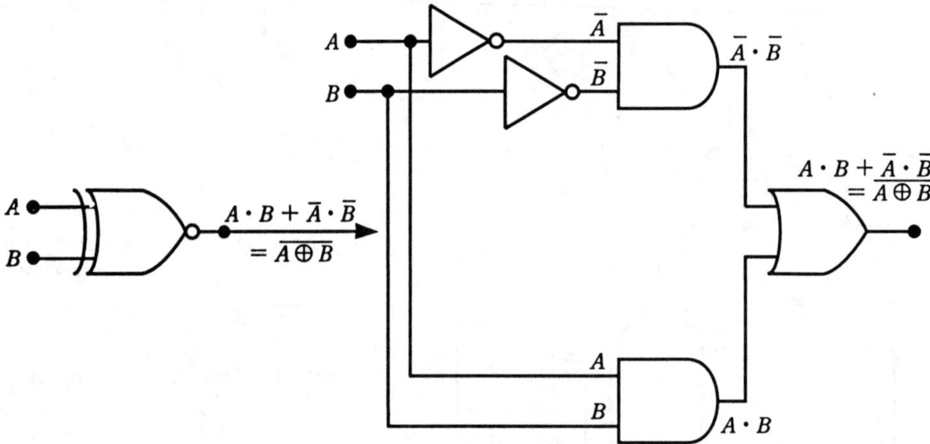

Fig. 13-21 The equivalent logic circuit of the EX-NOR gate.

* **Question 13-20** Which of the following logic gates corresponds to the truth table of FIG. 13-22?

A. P Q R B. P Q R C. P Q R D. P Q R

E. P Q R

Answer Choice E. Refer to FIG. 13-20B.

P	Q	R
Low	Low	High
Low	High	Low
High	Low	Low
High	High	High

Fig. 13-22 The truth table for question 13-20.

* **Question 13-21** Which of the following logic gates corresponds to the waveforms of FIG. 13-23?

A. OR gate B. AND gate C. NAND gate D. NOR gate E. EX-NOR gate

Answer Choice B. Assign 0 and 1 logic states to the waveforms of the input and output elements. The following truth table emerges:

Inputs		Outputs
A	*B*	*f(A,B)*
0	0	0
0	1	0
1	0	0
1	1	1

Refer to FIG. 13-9. The truth table corresponds to that of an AND gate.

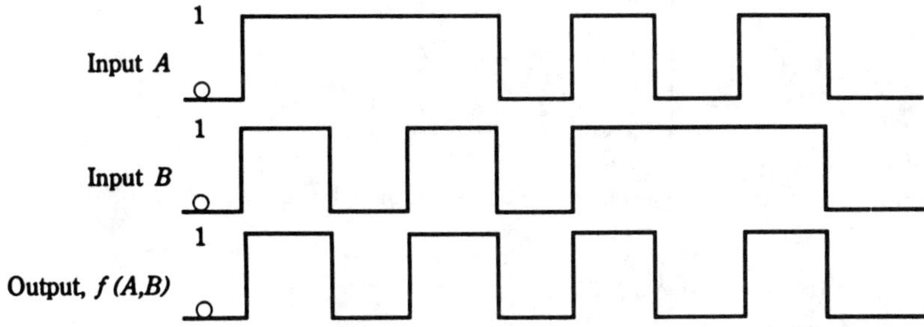

Fig. 13-23 Waveforms for question 13-21.

* **Question 13-22** Where of the following waveforms represents the output from the logic circuit shown in FIG. 13-24?

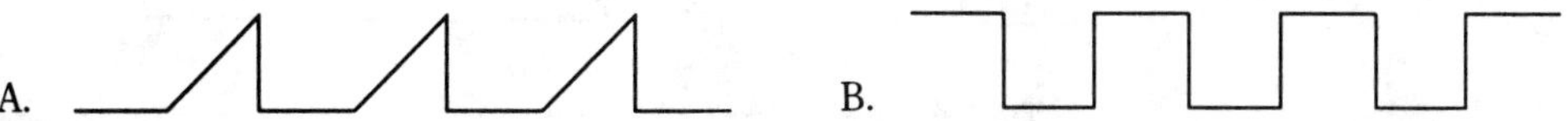

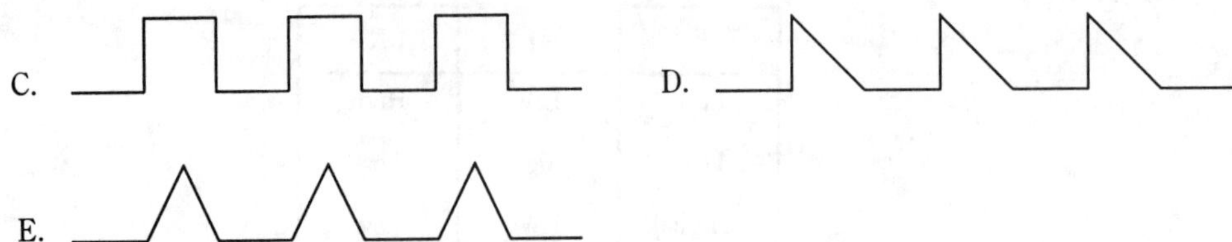

Answer Choice B. Figure 13-24 illustrates a NOR gate. When the input waveform is in its 0 state, the output is 1. However, when the input waveform is in its 1 state, the output is 0. Consequently, the output waveform is inverted, when compared with the input waveform.

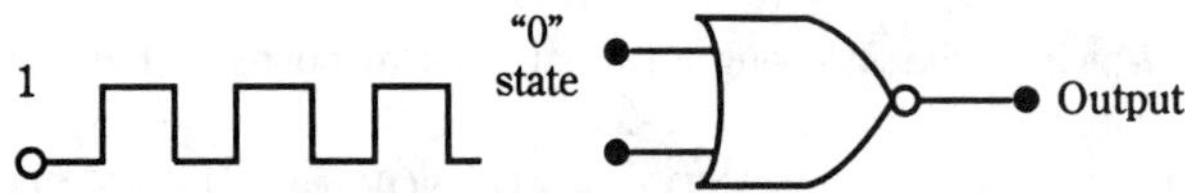

Fig. 13-24 The logic circuit for question 13-22.

* **Question 13-23** Which of the following logic gates corresponds to the waveforms of FIG. 13-25?

A. NOR B. NAND C. OR D. NAND E. EX-NOR

Answer Choice C. Assign 0 and 1 logic states to the waveforms of the input and output elements. The following truth table emerges:

Inputs		Outputs
A	*B*	*f(A,B)*
0	0	0
0	1	1
1	0	1
1	1	1

Refer to FIG. 13-7. The truth table corresponds to that of an OR gate.

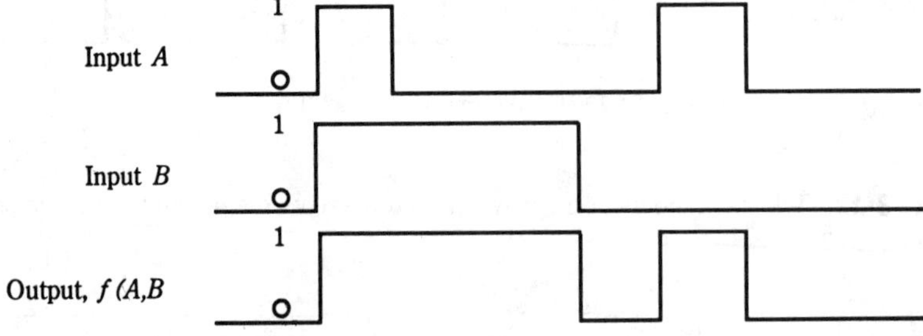

Fig. 13-25 Waveforms for question 13-23.

13-12. Combinatorial logic circuits

In the previous few sections, you have looked at individual logic operations, each with its own Venn diagram, Boolean equation, and truth table. You will now investigate the results of combining inverters with the various gates to produce combinatorial logic circuits. In each such circuit, you can assign 0 and 1 states to the various inputs and then obtain the circuit's truth table.

As an example, consider the combinatorial logic equivalent of FIG. 13-26A. The truth table (FIG. 13-26B) is derived by applying each sequence of the three input elements to the logic circuit. Figure 13-26A shows the logic states at the various points for $A = 0$, $B = 0$, $C = 1$.

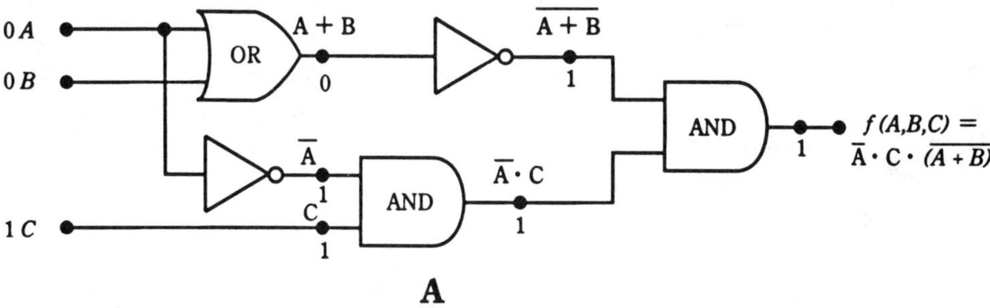

Inputs			Output
A	*B*	*C*	*f(A,B,C)*
0	0	0	0
0	0	1	1
0	1	0	0
0	1	1	0
1	0	0	0
1	0	1	0
1	1	0	0
1	1	1	0

B

Fig. 13-26 An example of a combinatorial logic circuit.

The logic state at any point in a combinatorial circuit can be determined from measurements taken by a voltmeter. However, a logic probe performs the same function and has the advantages of a smaller size and a direct readout.

* **Question 13-24** In the combinatorial logic circuit of FIG. 13-27, all of the inputs are in the low state so that the output is also low. Which single input can be changed from low to high in order to produce a high output?

A. A B. B C. C D. D E. E

Answer Choice E. To produce a high output, both inputs to the right-hand AND gate must be high so that the elements *A* and *B* must not be changed. Changing either *C* or *D* will still result in a low input to the OR gate. However, if *E* is changed from low to high, the output from the OR gate is high and the output is also high.

* **Question 13-25** Which of the following provides a high output from the logic circuit of FIG. 13-28?

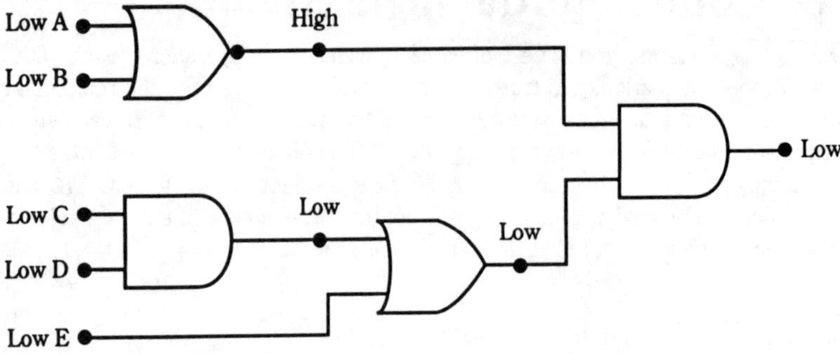

Fig. 13-27 The logic circuit for question 13-24.

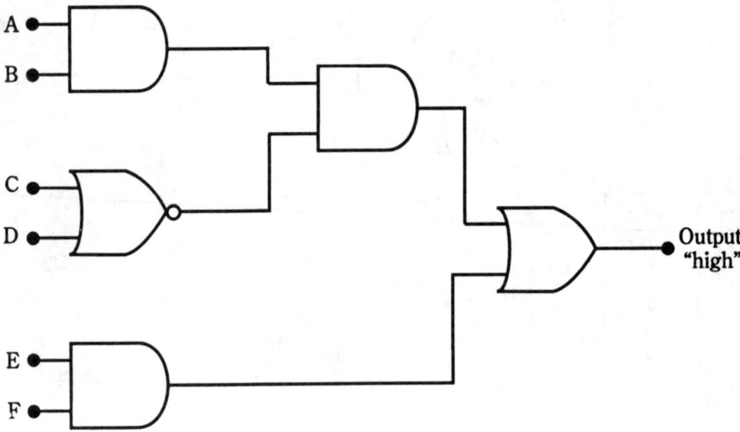

Fig. 13-28 The logic circuit for question 13-25.

A. A high, B high, C low, D low, E high, F high
B. A high, B low, C high, D low, E high, F low
C. A high, B high, C low, D high, E high, F low
D. A high, B low, C low, D low, E high, F low
E. A high, B low, C low, D low, E high, F low

Answer Choice A. One method of obtaining the answer is to try out each choice in turn and find out which one works! Alternatively, you can observe that for the output to be high, one of the OR gate inputs must be "high." For the lower input to be high, both *E* and *F* must be high (choice A). For the upper input to be high, both *A* and *B* must be high (choice C), and, in addition, both *C* and *D* must be low (which is not satisfied by choice C). Consequently, the only possible answer is choice A.

* **Question 13-26** Which of the following statements is true for the combinatorial logic circuit of FIG. 13-29?

A. Point *A* is low, but points *B* and *C* are both high
B. Point *A* is high, but points *B* and *C* are both low
C. Points *A* and *B* are both high, but point *C* is low

D. Points *A* and *B* are both low, but point *C* is high
E. Points *A* and *C* are both high, but point *B* is low

Answer Choice C. The two highs applied to the NAND gate cause point *A* to be low. The high and low inputs to the first OR gate cause point *B* to be high. Point *C* is also high because of the low and high inputs to the second OR gate.

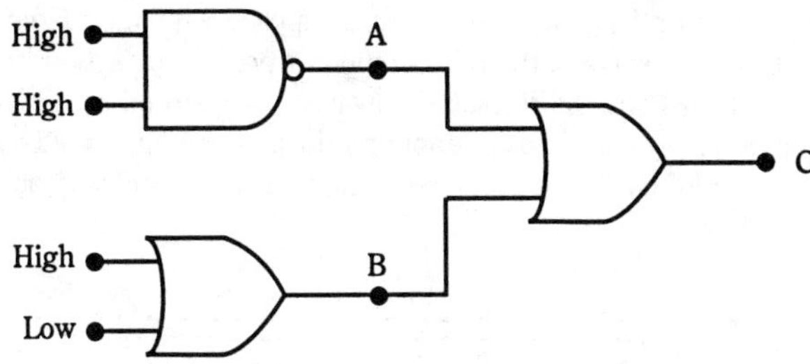

Fig. 13-29 The logic circuit for question 13-26.

* **Question 13-27** Which of the following statements are true for the combinatorial logic circuit of FIG. 13-30?

A. Points *A* and *B* are both low, but point *C* is high
B. Point *A* is high, but points *B* and *C* are both low
C. Points *A* and *C* are low, but point *B* is high
D. Points *A, B,* and *C* are all high
E. Points *A* and *B* are both high, but point *C* is low

Answer Choice C. The high and low inputs to the top AND gate cause point *A* to be "low." The two high inputs to the bottom AND gate cause point *B* to be "high." Point *C* is "low" due to the low and high inputs to the NOR gate.

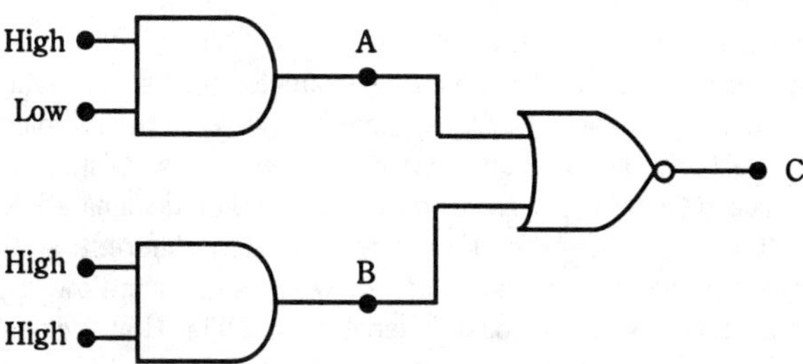

Fig. 13-30 The logic circuit for question 13-27.

* **Question 13-28** When compared with a voltmeter, a logic probe:

A. has less loading up effect B. has a direct readout C. is smaller in size
D. is less accurate E. choices B and C are true

Answer Choice E.

13-13. Basic microcomputer system

A microcomputer system is configured to include a microprocessor and the other hardware elements necessary for the particular application. You will be concerned with a basic microcomputer intended for direct use by a human operator. The differences between this basic microcomputer and one serving to automate some process, for example, will largely exist in the nature of the devices providing data to the computer, and those that must accept processed data, control signals, etc., from the computer. The basic computer is supplied with information from a keyboard, as shown in FIG. 13-31. The results of the microcomputer processing actions are displayed to the operator. Both the keyboard and the display hardware are regarded as peripheral devices, not part of the microcomputer proper. These peripheral devices are interfaced with the rest of the microcomputer by means of hardware elements, referred to respectively as the *input port* and the *output port.*

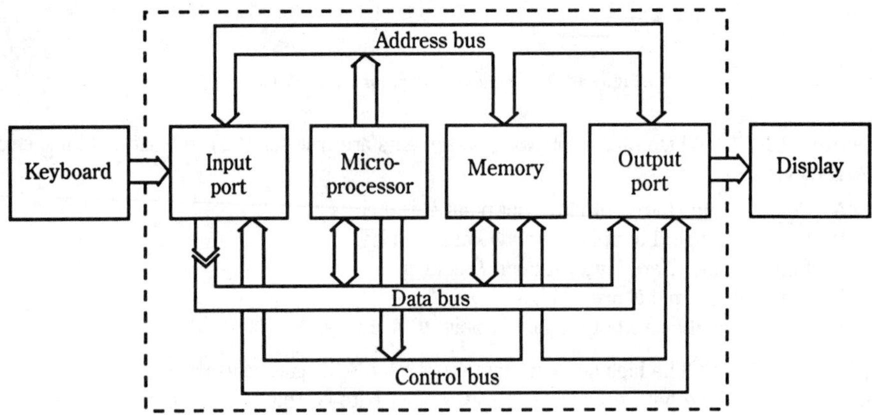

Fig. 13-31 The basic microcomputer system.

Perhaps the most prominent features shown in FIG. 13-31 are the buses labeled Address Bus, Data bus, and Control bus. The Data bus, for example, consists of eight parallel leads permanently connected to the ports and the other, main hardware elements, namely, the *Microprocessor* and the *memory.* At any one time, an electronic pathway is established so that one, and only one, of these can place data on the bus in order that another designated element can be the receiver. At another time the sender and the receiver might be different, so the bus is a general communications system between those elements for which data must flow. Eight bits, constituting one word, are transferred simultaneously over the Data bus. However, 16 or more bits can be included in a word for other microprocessors so that the bus must be correspondingly wide in the microcomputer.

This microcomputer has a total memory capacity of $2^{16} = 65,536$ words. This means that a 16-bit address bus is needed. Addresses are transferred from the microprocessor to the memory for the purpose of designating the particular memory location from which a data word (8 bits) is to be extracted (read) or stored (written). The microprocessor can also designate the input port or the output port as participants in data transfer by specifying those unique addresses assigned to each by the microcomputer designer. The address bus functions essentially the same way as the Data bus in that one sender, always the microprocessor, controls the signal levels on the bus so that the designated receiver can obtain the 16-bit address.

The microcomputer is required to perform a number of specific actions in achieving an overall objective. These actions are prearranged through the preparation of a computer program which is stored in memory. The instructions in this program are interpreted by the microprocessor, which directs these actions by means of pulsed signals placed on one or more electrical leads known collectively as the *control bus*. The program can also provide addresses and data that are necessary in the execution of the program.

* **Question 13-29** A microcomputer has a total memory capacity of 4096 words. If there are 8-bits for each word, the required minimum number of address lines is?

A. 16 B. 8 C. 12 D. 14 E. 11

Answer Choice C. If N is the required minimum number of address lines, $2^N = 4096$. Because $\sqrt{4096} = 64$ and $2^6 = 64$, $(2^6)^2 = 2^{12} = 4096$. Therefore, $N = 12$.

* **Question 13-30** A microcomputer has a 12-bit address bus with 8-bits to each word. The total memory capacity of words in the microcomputer is:

A. 24 B. 8192 C. 2048 D. 4096 E. 16384

Answer Choice D. The total memory capacity is $2^{12} = 4096$ words.

14

FCC rules and regulations

This chapter has only one objective—to present to you all the essential Rules and Regulations (R & R) required to pass the FCC Commercial General Radio-Telephone Examination. These R & Rs have been condensed and extracted from the Code of Federal Regulations (CFR) Title 47, Part 80 to end; this CFR contains 690 pages, so considerable care had to be exercised in selecting the required material.

As far as the FCC examinations are concerned, this is probably the most important chapter in the book. The examination contains 100 multiple choice questions with a passing grade of 75 or more correct. Between 20 and 30 questions are directly related to the R & Rs, so it is very difficult to pass the examination without an adequate knowledge of these regulations. Moreover, the regulations involve facts (much like a driving test), and these facts must be memorized.

Chapter 14 has been placed at the end of the book because the regulations contain technical terms (decibels, bandwidth, power, voltage, hertz, and so on) that have appeared in the earlier chapters.

Finally, I express considerable gratitude to Mr. Thomas Le Blanc, who has granted me permission to use the following material from his book *General Radiotelephone Operator's License Study Guide, Second Edition,* TAB Books #3318.

Although the main purpose of this summary of Rules and Regulations is a preparation for the FCC exam, the importance of this information should not be underestimated. The bulk of the rules and regulations address the subjects of general operating procedures, and technical standards of equipment. The knowledge of general operating procedures enables the radio operator to be effective and professional in his manner. Good operating procedure leads to an efficient and noninterfering use of the shared radio spectrum. Knowledge of, and adherence to, the technical standards leads to the efficient transmission and reception of radio signals. Above all, a thorough understanding of emergency procedures can be a life and death matter. A radio operator that is involved in emergency communications told me "There is no greater satisfaction than a person you helped, later coming to you and telling you 'thanks.'"

Glossary

The following is a summary of Federal Communications Commission (FCC) Rules and Regulations. They are covered in detail in the Code of Federal Regulations, Title 47, Parts 1, 2, 13, 17, 23, 80 and 87, which relates to the subject of telecommunications. This glossary is not intended to be a substitute for the complete Code of Federal Regulations. It is intended to serve as a quick reference to the more commonly used sections, and to summarize the important sections that are covered on the FCC exam.

Annual inspection (R & R 80.59) Compulsory ship stations must be inspected and certified annually. FCC Form 801 must be submitted to the Engineer in Charge of the FCC District Office that is nearest to the proposed place of inspection. It must be sent at least three days before the proposed inspection date. The same form may be used to apply for inspection of bridge-to-bridge radio installations. FCC Form 808 must be used if the inspection is to be on a holiday or after normal working hours. A temporary waiver of annual inspection may be granted for a period not to exceed 30 days. Detailed inspection of compulsory radiotelephone installations of small passenger boats is required every five years (R & R 80.903).

* **Question 14-1** How often are compulsory ship stations inspected and certified?

A. annually
B. every six months
C. every three years
D. every five years
E. inspection is only carried out when requested

Answer Choice A.

* **Question 14-2** When requesting an inspection of a Compulsory Ship Station, how long before the proposed inspection date must FCC Form 801 be submitted?

A. at least 3 days
B. at least 5 days
C. at least 10 days
D. at least 15 days
E. at least 30 days

Answer Choice A.

Applications (R & R 80.23, 1.921)

1. A new ship station license must be applied for at least 60 days before it will be needed. FCC Form 506 shall be used. It must be signed by:

   a. vessel owner, or
   b. vessel's operating agency, or
   c. ship station licensee, or
   d. master of the vessel.

2. Ship-station license-renewal applications must be made during the license term and should be filed within 90 days, but not later than 30 days prior to the end of the license term (R & R 1.926). The normal term of the station license is five years from the date of original issuance, major modification, or renewal. FCC Form 405-B shall be used. If modification is used, FCC Form 506 shall be used.

3. Application for FCC ship-radio inspection must be submitted to nearest field office at least 3 days before desired inspection by one of the following (see annual inspections):

a. vessel owner, or
b. vessel's operating agency, or
c. ship station licensee, or
d. master of the vessel

* **Question 14-3** Who of the following submits an application for the inspection of a compulsory ship station?

A. vessel owner
B. vessel's operating agency
C. ship station's licensee
D. master of the vessel
E. any of the above choices may submit the application

Answer Choice E.

* **Question 14-4** When applying for a new ship station license, how many days before the license is needed, must the application be submitted?

A. at least 3 days
B. at least 10 days
C. at least 15 days
D. at least 30 days
E. at least 60 days

Answer Choice E.

* **Question 14-5** The application for a ship's station license renewal must be signed by the:

A. ship's master
B. ship's owner
C. ship's radio officer
D. general radiotelephone operator
E. applicant

Answer Choice E.

* **Question 14-6** The circuitry of a marine transmitter is modified so that the operating frequency is changed. The correct procedure is to:

A. immediately inform the regional office of the FCC
B. measure the transmitter's frequency against an accepted standard and enter the results in the station log
C. apply for a new callsign
D. submit a station modification request on FCC Form 506
E. there is no correct procedure because the operating frequency must never be changed

Answer Choice D.

* **Question 14-7** An application for a ship's station license renewal must be filed within ____ days, but not later than ____ days prior to the end of the license term.

A. 60, 15 B. 90, 30 C. 30, 10 D. 60, 10 E. 30, 15

Answer Choice B.

Associated ship unit (R & R 80.5) A portable VHF transmitter for use in the vicinity of the ship station with which it is associated. For more information, see the section on "Portable Ship Units."

Authority of the master (R & R 80-114) The service of each ship station must at all times be under the ultimate control of the master, who must require that each operator or such station comply with radio regulations that are in force. These rules are varied when the vessel is under control of the U.S. Government.

Authorization of power (R & R 80.63) In the interest of avoiding interference to other operations, all stations shall radiate only as much power as is necessary to ensure a satisfactory service. Designation of effective radiated power may appear on the station license. Except for transmitters that use single sideband or independent sideband emissions, each radio transmitter rated for carrier power in excess of 100 watts must contain instruments that are necessary to determine the transmitter power during operation.

Auto alarms (R & R 80.259, 80.261, 80.269, 80.317, 80.318, 80.811, 80.817)

Purpose: To attract attention of persons on watch or to activate automatic alarm devices. An auto-alarm signal announces one of the following:

1. That a distress call is about to follow.
2. That a transmission of an urgent cyclone warning is about to follow. This shall be used by coast stations.
3. The loss of a person or persons overboard. The message must be preceded by the urgency signal.

Signal generator: Produces two sinusoidal audio tones (2200 and 1300 Hz) with a duration of 250 milliseconds. This international radiotelephone alarm signal operates on 2182 kHz and can be transmitted from 30 to 60 seconds at a time. The international radiotelegraph alarm signal is transmitted on 500 kHz and consists of a series of 12 dashes that are sent in one minute; the duration of each dash is four seconds and the duration of the interval between consecutive dashes is one second.

Testing requirements (keying device) (R & R 80.811) The automatic-alarm-signal keying device must be tested for correct timing adjustment of the keying mechanism. Do not transmit when making the test. Tests shall be made as follows:

1. Prior to the vessel's departure from each port.
2. On each day that the vessel is outside of a harbor or port.
3. If the vessel is in two or more ports within one day, the required test need be made only once.
4. If the vessel is in port for less than one day, the required test for that day may be made before arrival or after departure.

The radiotelephone auto alarm signal is tested by feeding the alarm signal to a dummy antenna on a frequency other than 2182 kHz.

Testing requirements (receiving unit) (R & R 80.817) No reference to the testing of radiotelephone auto-alarm receiving equipment was found in the CFR. However, the radiotelegraph auto alarm testing was as follows: The radio officer must test the radiotelegraph auto alarm at least every 24 hours while the ship is in the open sea, as follows:

1. Test the auto alarm by using a testing device to determine whether it will respond to the proper tone sequence.
2. Determine the proper function of the auto-alarm receiver by comparison of received signals on 500 kHz by the main receiver.

* **Question 14-8** The international radiotelephone auto-alarm signal consists of:

A. two sinusoidal audio tones with frequencies of 2300 and 1200 Hz
B. two sinusoidal audio tones, which are transmitted alternately, each with a duration of 200 ms

C. a combination of two tones, which must be transmitted continuously for at least 20 seconds
D. two sinusoidal audio tones with frequencies of 2200 and 1300 Hz
E. two sinusoidal audio tones, which are transmitted alternately, each with a duration of 300 ms

Answer Choice D.

* **Question 14-9** The test of the keying device for the automatic alarm system is conducted:

A. prior to the vessel's departure from each port
B. on each day that the vessel is outside a harbor or port
C. only once if the vessel is in two or more ports within one day
D. either before arrival or after departure if the vessel is in port for less than one day
E. all of the above choices are true

Answer Choice E.

* **Question 14-10** A vessel with a compulsory ship station is at sea. Which of the following systems must be active when no radio operator is on watch?

A. emergency Position-Indicating Radio Beacon
B. the auto-alarm system
C. emergency transmitter
D. bridge-to-bridge transmitter
E. portable ship units

Answer Choice B.

* **Question 14-11** The signal generator of the auto-alarm signal produces:

A. a continuous 1000-Hz tone
B. a continuous 2182-Hz tone
C. two audio tones of frequencies 2300 and 1200 Hz, transmitted alternately
D. two audio tones, each with a duration of 250 ms, with the combination transmitted continuously for at least 20 seconds, but not more than one minute
E. choices C and D are true

Answer Choice D.

* **Question 14-12** When testing the radiotelephone auto-alarm transmission:

A. feed the main antenna with the 2182-kHz signal
B. feed the 2182-kHz signal to a dummy antenna
C. feed the dummy antenna with a signal whose frequency is not 2182 kHz
D. feed the main antenna with a signal whose frequency is not 2182 kHz
E. only the FCC can conduct tests on the radiotelephone auto-alarm system

Answer Choice C.

* **Question 14-13** The purpose of the radiotelephone auto-alarm system is to provide an alert that:

A. a distress signal is about to follow
B. a transmission of an urgent cyclone warning is about to follow
C. there is information about the loss of a person or persons overboard
D. an important safety message is about to follow
E. all of the above choices are true

Answer Choice E.

* **Question 14-14** The radiotelephone auto alarm receiver is used to:

A. activate automatic alarms in the radio room, bridge, and radio operator's quarters
B. alert the radio operator on watch that a distress signal or other important safety information is about to be transmitted
C. test the auto-alarm system
D. receive signals on 500 kHz
E. choices A and B are true

Answer Choice E.

* **Question 14-15** The transmission of the radiotelephone auto-alarm signal is tested:

A. daily
B. prior to leaving port
C. by feeding the alarm signal to a dummy antenna
D. by operating on a frequency other than 2182 kHz
E. all of the above choices are true

Answer Choice E.

* **Question 14-16** The transmission of the radiotelephone auto-alarm signal is tested on a frequency of:

A. 2182 kHz
B. 121.5 MHz
C. 500 MHz
D. not a distress frequency
E. either choice A, B, or C is correct

Answer Choice D.

Bandwidth (R & R 80.205) *Authorized bandwidth* is the maximum occupied bandwidth authorized to be used by a station. Authorized bandwidths for various types of emissions are summarized in TABLE 14-1.

Table 14-1. Bandwidths for various emission types.

A1A	0.4 kHz	
A3E	8 kHz	
F3C	3 kHz	
F3C	20 kHz	(Applicable only to facsimile in the 156–162 MHz and 216–220 MHz bands)
F3E	20 kHz	(Applicable only when maximum frequency deviation is 5 kHz)
G3E	20 kHz	(Applicable only when maximum frequency deviation is 5 kHz)
H3E	3 kHz	
J3E	3 kHz	
R3E	3 kHz	

Bandwidth of emission (R & R 2.202) Occupied or necessary bandwidth is the frequency bandwidth, where, below its lower and its upper frequency limits, the mean powers radiated are equal to 0.5 percent of the total mean power radiated by a given emission. This bandwidth:

1. Contains 99 percent of the total radiated power.
2. Contains carrier, sidebands and harmonics.
3. Includes any frequency that contains 0.25 percent of the total radiated power.

* **Question 14-17** The bandwidth, which is occupied by the carrier, both sidebands and harmonics, is called the:

A. bandwidth of emission
B. authorized bandwidth
C. occupied bandwidth
D. operating bandwidth
E. choices A and C are true

Answer Choice E.

* **Question 14-18** The maximum occupied bandwidth, which can be used by a marine radio station is called the:

A. authorized bandwidth
B. bandwidth of emission
C. operating bandwidth
D. necessary bandwidth
E. occupied bandwidth

Answer Choice A.

* **Question 14-19** The frequency bandwidth, where, below its lower and above its upper frequency limits, the mean power radiated is equal to 0.5% of the total mean power radiated by a given emission, is called the:

A. bandwidth of emission
B. occupied bandwidth
C. authorized bandwidth
D. operating bandwidth
E. choices A and B are true

Answer Choice E.

* **Question 14-20** The bandwidth that is occupied by a marine transmission contains:

A. 99% of the total radiated power
B. carrier and sidebands
C. harmonics
D. any frequency component whose power is at least 0.25% of the total radiated power
E. all of the above choices are true

Answer Choice E.

Bridge-to-bridge communications (R & R 80.161, 80.309, 80.331, 80.1001–1023)

Purpose: Navigational only.

License requirement: The operator must have a restricted radiotelephone operator permit or higher class license.

Power:

- Must be capable of 8 to 25 W.
- Each transmitter (portable and nonportable) shall have the capacity of reducing its power

to a value of not less than 0.70 W and not more than 1 W. Generally, the power is limited to 1 W with a G3E emission on the navigational frequency of 156.65 MHz (channel 13).

- High power (more than 1 W) may be used only under the following conditions:
  1. In an emergency station.
  2. When rounding a bend in a river or navigating through a blind spot.
  3. When a ship fails to respond to a call on low power.

Frequency: Channel 13 (156.65 MHz) is the international bridge-to-bridge frequency.

Who may operate bridge-to-bridge transmitters:

1. Master of the vessel.
2. The person in charge of navigation of the vessel.

A continuous watch on channel 13 must be maintained:

1. By the master of the vessel or person in charge of navigation.
2. When the vessel is within 100 miles of U.S. shores.

Station identification requirements:

1. Name of vessel may be used, in lieu of the station call sign.
2. ID at start and end of transmission and every 15 minutes during a long transmission.

Bridge-to-bridge station (R & R 80.5) A bridge-to-bridge station is a radio station that is located on a ship's navigational bridge or main control station operating on a specified frequency (channel 13), which is used only for navigational communications, in the 156- to 162-MHz band.

* **Question 14-21** What is the international bridge-to-bridge frequency?

A. channel 13 B. channel 16 C. 156.65 MHz D. 156.8 MHz
E. choices A and C are true

Answer Choice E.

* **Question 14-22** What is the normal power output of a bridge-to-bridge transmitter?

A. 0.5 W B. 1 W C. 5 W D. 8 W E. 25 W

Answer Choice B.

* **Question 14-23** A bridge-to-bridge transmitter is operating on channel 13 with a power output of 15 W. This is legal if:

A. the ship being called on low power fails to respond
B. the ship is rounding a bend in a river
C. there is an emergency situation
D. the ship is navigating through a blind spot
E. all of the above choices are true

Answer Choice E.

* **Question 14-24** What is the minimum power capability of a bridge-to-bridge transmitter?

A. 500 mW B. 400 mW C. 0.7 W D. 1 W E. 3 W

Answer Choice C.

* **Question 14-25** Who of the following is allowed to operate bridge-to-bridge transmitters? Only:

A. the holder of a Marine Operator Permit
B. the holder of a General Radiotelephone License
C. the Master of the vessel
D. the person in charge of navigation
E. choices C and D are true

Answer Choice E.

* **Question 14-26** What are the station identification requirements for bridge-to-bridge communications?

A. the station callsign is mandatory
B. identification is only required at the end of a transmission
C. identification is only required at the start of a transmission
D. the name of the vessel is used in lieu of the station callsign
E. identification is required every 30 minutes during a long transmission

Answer Choice D.

* **Question 14-27** The bridge-to-bridge radiotelephone transmitter:

A. must be capable of 8 to 25 W
B. is normally limited to a power output of 1 W
C. has a minimum power capability of 0.7 W
D. uses a G3E emission on the navigational frequency of 156.65 MHz
E. all of the above choices are true

Answer Choice E.

* **Question 14-28** A continuous watch on channel 13 must be maintained:

A. by the Master of the vessel
B. by the person in charge of navigation
C. when the vessel is within 100 miles of U.S. shores
D. by the vessel's radio operator
E. choices A, B, and C are true

Answer Choice E.

* **Question 14-29** What is the minimum license requirement for the operator of a bridge-to-bridge transmitter?

A. none
B. Marine Operator Permit
C. General Radiotelephone License
D. Second-Class Radiotelegraph License
E. Restricted Radiotelephone Operator Permit

Answer Choice E.

* **Question 14-30** Bridge-to-bridge communications on channel 13 are identified by:

A. name of the vessel in lieu of the callsign
B. callsign and country of registration
C. callsign, name of vessel, and country of registration
D. name of vessel and port of origin
E. name of vessel and port of destination

Answer Choice A.

* **Question 14-31** The purpose of bridge-to-bridge transmitters is:

A. general ship-to-shore communications
B. on-board communications
C. for communicating only outside 100 miles of U.S. shores
D. navigational only
E. restricted to communications with foreign ships

Answer Choice D.

* **Question 14-32** Those vessels that are subject to the Bridge-to-Bridge Act, must:

A. have a transmitter with a maximum power capability of 1 W
B. be capable of operating on channel 16
C. maintain a constant watch on 156.65 MHz when the vessel is within 100 miles of U.S. shores
D. be capable of an emission on 156.8 MHz
E. choices B and C are true

Answer Choice C.

* **Question 14-33** Under which of the following conditions may the output power of a bridge-to-bridge transmitter exceed 1 W?

A. when communicating with a coastal station and the vessel is more than 100 miles away from U.S. shores
B. when transmitting on a frequency other than the international bridge-to-bridge frequency
C. when rounding a bend in a river
D. when the transmitter is not being used for a navigational purpose
E. the output power of a bridge-to-bridge transmitter must never exceed 1 W

Answer Choice C.

* **Question 14-34** In bridge-to-bridge communications, the power output of the transmitter is limited to 1 W:

A. when there is an emergency
B. when rounding a bend in a river
C. when a ship fails to respond to a call
D. under normal navigational conditions
E. when the vessel is navigating through a blind spot

Answer Choice D.

* **Question 14-35** At sea, the best frequency to use for bridge-to-bridge communications is:

A. 2450 kHz B. 121.5 MHz C. 243 MHz D. 156.65 MHz E. 157.75 MHz

Answer Choice D.

Calling frequency (R & R 80.111) Initial contact may be made on a calling frequency. Calling a particular station must not continue for more than 30 seconds in each instance. If there is no reply, the call may be sent three more times at intervals of two minutes. If there is still no reply, the station may be called again in fifteen minutes. When contact is made, the two stations must move to a "working frequency" for normal communications. To facilitate reception of distress calls, all transmissions on 2182 kHz and 156.8 MHz must not exceed one minute. Thus, the calling frequency is left clear for possible distress calls.

* **Question 14-36** When initiating a radiotelephone call:

A. never use the distress frequency of 2182 kHz
B. never use the distress frequency of 156.8 MHz
C. the call signal must not continue for more than 30 seconds in each instance
D. do not repeat the call if there is no reply until 10 minutes have elapsed
E. always use the working frequency

Answer Choice C.

* **Question 14-37** When establishing the initial contact between two marine stations, the call signal is limited to:

A. 15 seconds and then not repeated for 1 minute if there is no reply
B. 30 seconds and then not repeated for 2 minutes if there is no reply
C. 45 seconds and then not repeated for 3 seconds if there is no reply
D. 1 minute and then not repeated for 5 minutes if there is no reply
E. 90 seconds and then not repeated for 5 minutes if there is no reply

Answer Choice B.

* **Question 14-38** A calling frequency is:

A. not assigned to a particular radiotelephone station
B. for example, 2182 kHz
C. one on which all stations generally listen
D. not used for the main bulk of the message traffic
E. all of the above choices are true

Answer Choice E.

* **Question 14-39** The international radiotelephone calling frequency in the marine service is:

A. 2182 kHz B. 2282 kHz C. 2128 kHz D. 2281 kHz E. 500 kHz

Answer Choice A.

* **Question 14-40** A marine radiotelephone station has been called three times at intervals of two minutes, but there is no reply. The calling must not be renewed until after:

A. 3 minutes B. 5 minutes C. 10 minutes D. 15 minutes E. 30 minutes

Answer Choice D.

* **Question 14-41** A working frequency:

A. is used to establish the initial radio contact between two marine stations
B. is used for test purposes only
C. is the frequency to which all stations generally listen
D. may have an assigned value of 2182 kHz
E. none of the above choices is true

Answer Choice E.

Call signs (R & R 2.302) Callsigns are assigned by the Commission to various classes of stations. The callsign consists of letters only or a combination of letters and digits. For example, a ship radiotelephone callsign may consist of:

1. Two letters followed by four digits, as WA2000, or
2. Three letters followed by four digits, as WZZ9999.

When stations operating on two or more classes are authorized to the same licensee for the same location, the Commission may elect to assign a separate callsign to each station in a different class.

When calling another station, the correct procedure is represented by:

"WA2000 . . . WA2000 . . . WA2000. This is WZZ9999 . . .
WZZ9999 . . . WZZ9999. Over"

Callsigns must be sent in English at the beginning and end of each communication with any other station. The callsign must also be transmitted at 15-minute intervals during a lengthy communication.

Calls to establish communication must be initiated on an available common working frequency if such a frequency exists and if it is known that the called ship maintains a simultaneous watch on the common working frequency and the appropriate calling frequency.

* **Question 14-42** A callsign:

A. is a marine station's name and identification
B. is transmitted by a station so that other monitoring stations may easily identify the station of origin
C. must be sent clearly and distinctly so that unnecessary repetition of the call letters is avoided
D. consists of letters or a combination of letters and digits
E. all of the above choices are true

Answer Choice E.

* **Question 14-43** When operating with a J3E transmitter on 2182 kHz or a VHF G3E transmitter on 156.8 MHz:

A. the initial calling signal must not last longer than 30 seconds
B. a call must not be repeated until a 2-minute interval has elapsed
C. there must be a 15-minute waiting period after three attempts at calling have been made
D. the transmitter is switched from the calling frequency to the working frequency as soon as contact is made
E. all of the above choices are true

Answer Choice E.

* **Question 14-44** Which of the following represents the correct procedure for calling another station?

A. KXYZ . . . KXYZ . . . KXYZ. This is KABC . . . KABC . . . KABC. Over.
B. KXYZ . . . KXYZ . . . KXYZ. This is KABC. Over.
C. KXYZ. This is KABC. Over.
D. KXYZ . . . KXYZ . . . KXYZ. This is KABC . . . KABC . . . KABC. Out.
E. KXYZ . . . KXYZ . . . KXYZ. This is KABC. Out.

Answer Choice A.

* **Question 14-45** A marine station's callsign is transmitted:

A. at the beginning of a communication
B. at the end of a communication
C. at 15-minute intervals during a lengthy communication
D. in the English language
E. all of the above choices are true

Answer Choice E.

* **Question 14-46** A vessel maintains a simultaneous watch on both calling and common working frequencies. When communicating with this vessel, the initial call is made on:

A. 2128 kHz B. 156.8 MHz C. the calling frequency
D. the common working frequency E. channel 13

Answer Choice D.

* **Question 14-47** When calling another ship, a radio operator must identify his/her own ship's radio station by means of its:

A. assigned callsign only
B. callsign and port of origin
C. callsign and port of destination
D. callsign and name of ship
E. callsign, name of ship, and country of registration

Answer Choice A.

* **Question 14-48** The FCC requires that all radiotelephone transmissions from a ship's station are identified by the:

A. name of the ship
B. callsign
C. working frequency
D. name of the operator
E. home port

Answer Choice B.

Carrier suppression (See *Emission types*)

Changes during license term (R & R 80.29) When changes are made during the license term, the Commission may have to be notified. Table 1-2 summarizes the types of changes and the required action.

Table 14-2. Changes during the license term.

Type of change	Required action
Mailing address	Written notice to the Commission.
Name of licensee	Written notice to the Commission.
Name of vessel	Written notice to the Commission.
Addition of new transmitting equipment that operates on frequencies not authorized by present license	Application for modification.
Addition of transmitting equipment that operates on frequencies authorized by present license	None, provided the new equipment is type accepted and the emission characteristics remain the same.
Transfer of control of a corporation	Comply with Section 1.924 of this chapter (CFR Title 47)
Assignment of a radio station license	Comply with Section 1.924 of this chapter (CFR Title 47)

It is important to know that only certain types of station licenses may be assigned. Section 1.924 of Title 47 contains the necessary information regarding this. This section states that licenses for stations in the Amateur, Aviation (aircraft), Personal, and Maritime (ship) Radio Services cannot be assigned. Whenever there is a change of ownership of one of these stations, the new owner must apply for a new license. Upon receipt of the new license, the former license must be surrendered for cancellation. The following may be assigned:

1. Coast stations in the Maritime Services and Alaska Public-Fixed Stations may apply for assignment with FCC Form 503.

2. Ground stations in the Aviation Services may apply for assignment with FCC Form 406.

* **Question 14-49** If the ownership of a vessel changes, what is the correct procedure regarding the license for the ship's main transmitter?

A. the present license may be assigned to the new owner
B. when the present license expires, the new owner must submit an application for its renewal
C. an FCC representative must conduct an inspection of the transmitter before assigning the present license to the new owner
D. the new owner must submit an application for a new license
E. the present license must be destroyed and the transmitter must be recertified by the FCC

Answer Choice D.

* **Question 14-50** Upon the sale of a vessel, the correct procedure regarding the radio transmitter's license, involves:

A. renewing the existing license when it expires
B. the new owner submitting an application for a new license
C. surrendering the existing license for cancellation upon receipt of the new license
D. an inspection of the transmitter within 30 days by the FCC
E. choices B and C are true

Answer Choice E.

Changes in authorized stations (R & R 87.35) An application for a modification of license shall be filed when any change is to be made that would result in deviation from the terms of the authorization. For example, anything that will affect the following:

1. frequency tolerance
2. modulation
3. emission
4. power
5. bandwidth

No application for modification of radio station license is required for the following:

1. To add a survival craft station, using type-accepted transmitters.
2. For the addition or subtraction of new transmitters, as long as they perform the same functions and operate on the same frequencies as the transmitters specified on the license.

* **Question 14-51** The circuitry of a marine transmitter is modified so that its operating power is changed. The correct procedure is to:

A. immediately inform the regional office of the FCC
B. measure the new value of the operating power and enter the result in the station log
C. apply for a new callsign
D. submit a station modification request on FCC Form 506
E. there is no correct procedure because the operating power must never be changed

Answer Choice D.

Class of emissions (See *Emission types*)

Classification of operator licenses (R & R 13.2) Commercial radio operator licenses and endorsements issued by the Commission are classified in accordance with the Radio Regulations of the International Telecommunications Union as follows:

1. First-Class Radiotelegraph Operator's Certificate
2. Second-Class Radiotelegraph Operator's Certificate
3. Third-Class Radiotelegraph Operator's Certificate
4. General Radiotelephone License
5. Marine Radio Operator Permit
6. Restricted Radiotelephone Operator Permit
7. Ship Radar Endorsement
8. Six-Months'-Service endorsement (for First- and Second-Class Radiotelegraph Licenses)

Notice that the General Radiotelephone Operator's License is only required for the following services: Marine, Aviation, and International Fixed. Once issued, the General Radiotelephone Operator's License is valid for the lifetime of the operator.

* **Question 14-52** Which of the following services requires that maintenance work on the transmitters be carried out by the holder of a General Radiotelephone License?

A. CB radios
B. AM broadcast
C. FM broadcast
D. two-way police communications
E. marine

Answer Choice E.

* **Question 14-53** For how long is an FCC General Radiotelephone License valid?

A. 3 years B. 5 years C. 4 years D. 10 years E. for the lifetime of the licensee

Answer Choice E.

* **Question 14-54** Who of the following is eligible to apply for a General Radiotelephone License?

A. a United States citizen who cannot speak English
B. an alien who is eligible for employment in the United States
C. a mute person
D. a deaf person
E. a nonresident alien who is under age

Answer Choice B.

Compulsory ship (R & R 80.901) Any ship that is required to be equipped with radiotelecommunications equipment in order to comply with the radio-navigation provisions of a treaty to which the vessel is subject. There are compulsory radiotelegraph installations for cargo vessels of 1600 gross tons and upward, and for all passenger ships, irrespective of size. Compulsory radiotelephone installations are required in cargo ships of 300 gross tons and upward, but less than 1600 gross tons on international voyages. Radiotelephone installations are also required for small passenger boats that transport six or more passengers. By contrast, a "voluntary ship" is not required to be equipped with radiocommunications equipment.

* **Question 14-55** On a compulsory ship radiotelegraph, installations are required for cargo vessels of:

A. 300 gross tons and upward
B. 500 gross tons and upward
C. 800 gross tons and upward
D. 1000 gross tons and upward
E. 1600 gross tons and upward

Answer Choice E.

* **Question 14-56** Which of the following vessels are required to install compulsory radiotelephone communications equipment?

A. cargo ships of 300 gross tons and upward, but less than 1600 tons on international voyages
B. all passenger ships of 100 gross tons and upwards
C. all voluntary ships
D. small passenger boats that transport six or more passengers
E. choices A and D are true

Answer Choice E.

* **Question 14-57** Which of the following vessels are required to install compulsory radiotelegraph communications equipment?

A. cargo ships of 1600 gross tons and upward
B. all large passenger ships
C. cargo ships of 300 gross tons and upward, but less than 1600 tons on international voyages
D. small passenger boats that transport six or more passengers
E. choices A and B are true

Answer Choice E.

* **Question 14-58** On a compulsory ship, a radiotelephone communications system may be installed in lieu of a radiotelegraph system provided the ship's tonnage does not equal or exceed:

A. 300 B. 600 C. 900 D. 1200 E. 1600

Answer Choice E.

Contents of radio communications (R & R 80.88) It is unlawful to disclose the content of any radio communication to anyone, except that the party to whom the communication is addressed. The only exception is if you hear the message of a ship or aircraft in distress. An operator may not use any information heard, for his own benefit, or for the benefit of anyone else who is not entitled to receive it.

* **Question 14-59** Licensed Radio operators are prohibited from:

A. disclosing the content of an intercepted distress message
B. communicating directly with a foreign country
C. divulging for his/her own personal gain the content of an intercepted message
D. disclosing the content of an intercepted message transmitted by an amateur station for the benefit of the general public
E. disclosing the content of an intercepted message to the addressee

Answer Choice C.

Contents of station records (R & R 23.48, 80.409) Voluntary ships are not required to have a station log. The licensee of a compulsory ship shall maintain a technical log of the station operation showing:

1. Signature of each licensed operator responsible for the operation of the transmitting equipment and an indication of his/her hours of duty.
2. Listing of the frequencies used, including:
   a. Type of emission. Information regarding the type of emission is shown on the back of the license of the radio station.
   b. Starting and ending times of each period of communications.
   c. Points of communications used.

3. Power input to the final stage of each transmitter.
4. Dates and results of frequency measurements.

For stations in the *international fixed public control service,* the licensee shall maintain a technical log of the station operation showing:

1. Normal hours of operation and dates and times of interruptions to service.
2. Dates and results of each frequency measurement.
3. When service of maintenance duties are performed, the responsible operator shall sign and date the station record giving details of all duties that are performed by him/her or under his/her supervision. He/she must also include his/her name and the class, serial number, and date of expiration of his/her license.

* **Question 14-60** What details are contained in the station (technical) log of a compulsory ship?

A. signature of each licensed operator responsible for the operation of the transmitting equipment
B. hours of duty for each licensed operator responsible for the operation of the transmitting equipment
C. listing of the frequencies used
D. power input to the transmitter's final stage
E. all of the above choices are true

Answer Choice E.

* **Question 14-61** For a particular transmitter, the details of its type of emission are shown:

A. on the durable nameplate, which is attached to the transmitter
B. on the front page of the station log
C. in CFR Title 47 of the FCC Rules and Regulations
D. on the back of the radio station's license
E. details on the type of emission are provided by the FCC upon application

Answer Choice D.

Control point (aviation stations) (R & R 87.75, 87.95) The control point is the operating position of the station. Each station shall be provided with a "control point" at the location of the transmitting equipment. The control point must meet the following requirements:

1. Such position must be under the control and supervision of the licensee.
2. It is the position where monitoring facilities are located.
3. It is the position where the transmitter can, without delay, be rendered inoperative.
4. It is the position at which the required licensed radio operator, responsible for the actual operation of the transmitter, is stationed.
5. The four previous requirements do not apply to aeronautical enroute stations.

Note: The current authorization, or photocopy, for each station at a fixed location shall be prominently displayed at the principal control point of the transmitter(s).

The airport control tower uses the following frequency bands for communicating with aircraft during landing:

118.000 to 121.400 MHz
121.600 to 121.925 MHz
123.600 to 128.800 MHz
132.025 to 135.975 MHz

There is a 25-kHz spacing between adjacent channels.

* **Question 14-62** Which of the following frequency bands does an aircraft control tower use to communicate with aircraft during their landing?

A. 118.000 to 121.400 MHz
B. 121.600 to 121.925 MHz
C. 123.600 to 128.800 MHz
D. 132.025 to 135.975 MHz
E. all of the above choices are true

Answer Choice E.

Control point (ship stations) (R & R 80.80) The *control point* is the operating position of the station. Each ship station control point must be capable of:

1. Starting and discontinuing operation of the station.
2. Changing frequencies.
3. Changing from transmission to reception and vice-versa.
4. Reducing transmitter power when necessary.

Note: The current authorization, or a photocopy, for each station at a fixed location shall be prominently displayed at the principal control point of the transmitter(s).

* **Question 14-63** The operating position of a radio station is:

A. at the location of the transmitter
B. at the location of the receiver
C. either at the location of the transmitter or at the location of the receiver
D. at the control point
E. on the bridge

Answer Choice D.

Cooperative use of frequency assignments (R & R 80.87, 80.89, 80.92) Each radio channel is available for use on a shared basis only and is not available for the exclusive use of any one station licensee. Cooperation is important in order to minimize interference. For example, in regions of heavy traffic, intervals must be left between radiotelephone calls so that other stations sharing the same channel, can have the opportunity to make their calls.

Station operators should:

1. Listen to the frequency before starting the transmission. Make sure the frequency is not in use.
2. Keep transmissions as short as possible.
3. Turn off the transmitter when not in use.

Station operators should not:

1. Engage in superfluous communications.
2. Use selective calling on 2182 kHz or 156.8 MHz (*selective calling* is a method of transmission that allows reception only by specific stations. Tone-coded signals are used).
3. Transmit a general call or signals not addressed to a particular station.
4. Transfer while on land.

* **Question 14-64** Radiotelephone stations that use a shared channel:

A. should listen in on the channel first to avoid disrupting any communication that is already in progress
B. must decrease their operating powers by 20% to reduce the possibility of harmful interference
C. must limit each transmission to a period that does not exceed five minutes

D. must leave an interval between calls
E. choices A and D are true

Answer Choice E.

* **Question 14-65** Radio operators who transmit in the marine bands must:

A. listen in on the frequency before starting transmission
B. leave intervals between radiotelephone calls in regions of heavy traffic
C. keep transmissions as short as possible
D. not engage in superfluous communications
E. all of the above choices are true

Answer Choice E.

* **Question 14-66** In order to prevent interference in the marine mobile service, a radio operator must:

A. not transmit a general call or signals that are not addressed to a particular station
B. not engage in superfluous communications
C. turn off the transmitter when it is not in use
D. before initiating a transmission, make sure that another station is not transmitting on the same frequency
E. all of the above choices are true

Answer Choice E.

* **Question 14-67** In the marine mobile services a radio operator must prevent interference with other channels by:

A. using the highest level of power to ensure good communications
B. using the highest level of modulation required for good communications
C. using selective calling on 2182 kHz
D. turning off the transmitter when not in use
E. allowing no communication to exceed 30 minutes in duration

Answer Choice D.

Definitions (stations and services) (R & R 2.1, 80.5, 87.5)

Aeronautical mobile service A mobile service between aeronautical stations and aircraft stations, or between aircraft stations, that survival craft stations may participate in.

Aeronautical station A land station in the aeronautical mobile service. In certain cases, the station may be located on board ship or on a platform at sea.

Aircraft station A mobile station in the aeronautical mobile service, other than a survival craft station, that is located on board an aircraft.

Base station A land station in the land mobile service that carries on a service with land mobile stations.

Coast station A land station in the marine mobile service.

Coordinated universal time (UTC) UTC is equivalent to mean solar time at the prime meridian (0 degrees longitude), formerly called *GMT*.

Duplex operation A mode of two-way communications, where both persons may talk at the same time, like on the telephone. This requires the use of two frequencies: one for receiving and one for transmitting (see *simplex*).

Effective radiated power Effective radiated power (ERP) in a given direction is the product of the power supplied to the antenna and its gain relative to a $\lambda/2$ dipole.

Emergency position-indicating radiobeacon station A station in the mobile service, the emissions of which are intended to facilitate search and rescue operations.

Facsimile A form of telegraphy for the transmission of fixed images. The images are reproduced in permanent form at the receiver.

Fixed public service A radiocommunications service that is carried on between fixed stations open to public correspondence.

Fixed service A service of radiocommunications between specified fixed points.

Fixed station A station in the fixed service.

Frequency tolerance The maximum permissible departure by the center frequency of the frequency band occupied by an emission from the assigned frequency.

International fixed public radiocommunication service A fixed service, the stations of which are open to public correspondence and, which in general, is intended to provide radio communication between any one of the states or U.S. possessions or any foreign point, or between U.S. possessions and any other point. This service also involves the relaying of international traffic between stations that provide this service.

Land mobile service A mobile service between base stations and land mobile stations, or between land mobile stations.

Land mobile station A mobile station in the land mobile service that is capable of surface movement within the geographical limits of a country or continent.

Land station A station in the mobile service that is not intended to be used while in motion.

Maritime mobile service A mobile service between coast stations and ship stations, between ship stations, or between assorted on-board communication stations. Survival craft and EPIRB stations also participate in this service.

Mobile station A station in the mobile service that is intended to be used while in motion or during halts at unspecified points.

Navigational communications Safety communications that pertain to the maneuvering of vessels or the directing of vessel movements. Such communications are primarily for the exchange of information between stations and, secondarily, between ship stations and coast stations.

Operational fixed station A station that provides control, repeater, or relay functions for its associated coast station.

Point of communication *Point of communication* is a specific location that is designated in the license that a station is authorized to communicate for the transmission of public correspondence.

Racon Radionavigation system.

Radionavigation A system of determining the position of a vessel by the use of radio waves.

Survival craft station A mobile station in the maritime or aeronautical mobile service that is intended solely for survival purposes.

Distortion (R & R 80.213) Distortion of a transmitter's signal can be caused by several internal malfunctions. However, one external way to distort a signal is by shouting into the microphone. Another way is by turning up the microphone gain control. Modulation beyond 100 percent can occur. This makes the signal less understandable as well as louder.

* **Question 14-68** Shouting into a microphone might cause:

A. possible interference with the transmissions of other stations on adjacent frequencies
B. overloading of the microphone
C. overmodulation of the transmitted signal
D. severe distortion of the voice signal so that the message is unintelligible
E. all of the above choices are true

Answer Choice E.

* **Question 14-69** Overmodulation of a transmitted signal might:

A. be caused by the transmitter's circuitry
B. be caused by the operator shouting into the microphone
C. cause severe distortion of the audio signal at the receiver
D. cause interference with other stations operating on nearby frequencies
E. all of the above choices are true

Answer Choice E.

Distress call (R & R 80.311–80.322) Distress calls can be made only under the authority of the master of the vessel. The distress call has absolute priority over all other transmissions.

Radiotelegraph distress procedure is sent in International Morse Code at a speed of 8 to 16 words per minute. The procedure consists of the following:

1. Radiotelegraph alarm signal.
2. The distress call, consisting of:
   a. The distress signal, SOS, sent three times.
   b. The word DE (meaning "this is").
   c. The callsign of the station in distress, sent three times.
3. The distress message, consisting of:
   a. The distress signal SOS.
   b. The name of the station in distress.
   c. Particulars of its position.
   d. The nature of the distress.
   e. The kind of assistance desired.
   f. Any other information that might facilitate rescue.
4. Two dashes of 10 to 15 seconds each.
5. The callsign of the station in distress.

Radiotelephone distress procedure:

1. Radiotelephone alarm signal (whenever possible).
2. Distress call, consisting of:
   a. The distress signal, mayday, spoken three times.
   b. The words "this is."
   c. The callsign of the station in distress, spoken three times.
3. The distress message, consisting of:
   a. The distress signal, mayday.
   b. The name of the station in distress.
   c. Particulars of the vessel's position.
   d. The nature of the distress.
   e. The kind of assistance required.
   f. Any other information that may facilitate rescue (for example, the length, color, and type of vessel, number of persons on board, position of ship, etc.).
4. The distress transmission shall be made slowly and distinctly.

* **Question 14-70** Which of the following must be included in the transmission of a distress message?

A. ship's name, port of origin, port of destination, nature of distress
B. ship's name, Master's name, port of destination, nature of help requested
C. ship's name, position, nature of distress, nature of help requested

D. ship's name, owner's name, position, nature of help requested
E. ship's name, course and speed (if any), nature of distress, nature of help requested

Answer Choice C.

* **Question 14-71** The correct procedure for a distress call is:

A. the word "mayday" (spoken three times), the words "this is," followed by the callsign of the station in distress (spoken three times)
B. the words "this is" (spoken three times) and the word "mayday" (spoken three times)
C. the letters SOS (spoken three times), the letters DE, followed by the callsign of the station in distress (spoken three times)
D. the word "mayday," the words "this is," followed by the callsign, and name of ship (spoken three times)
E. the word "mayday" (spoken three times), the words "this is," followed by the callsign (spoken three times), and name of the ship in distress

Answer Choice A.

* **Question 14-72** A radiotelephone distress message from a ship's station, shall contain the following:

A. the word "mayday," spoken three times, followed by the words "this is"
B. the callsign of the station in distress, spoken three times
C. the name of the ship in distress and ship's position
D. the nature of distress and kind of assistance required. Details of any other information that might facilitate rescue
E. all of the above choices are true

Answer Choice E.

* **Question 14-73** The international marine radiotelephone distress signal is the:

A. letters SOS, spoken three times
B. word "mayday," spoken three times
C. word "pan," spoken three times
D. word "security," spoken three times
E. auto-alarm signal

Answer Choice B.

* **Question 14-74** If a ship has foundered and is sinking, the radiotelephone operator would send the distress signal of:

A. "pan," spoken three times
B. SOS, spoken three times
C. "security," spoken three times
D. "mayday," spoken three times
E. "disaster," spoken three times

Answer Choice D.

* **Question 14-75** Under which of the following conditions must a radiotelephone transmission contain the callsign and the name of the ship?

A. bridge-to-bridge communications
B. all communications should contain this information
C. when calling on 2182 kHz

D. when the transmission is a distress call
E. for on-board communications

Answer Choice D.

* **Question 14-76** Which of the following signals has the highest priority?

A. distress B. urgency C. safety D. security E. emergency

Answer Choice A.

* **Question 14-77** Who of the following has the authority to order the transmission of a distress call?

A. the ship's radio operator
B. the holder of a General Radiotelephone License
C. the ship's Master
D. the ship's owner, if on board
E. choices C and D are true

Answer Choice C.

Distress frequencies (R & R 80.313)

Radiotelephone Distress Frequencies

- 2182 kHz (in the Medium Frequency Range). J3E emission is used.
- 156.8 MHz (channel 16, international distress and calling frequency) in the VHF range. G3E emission is used.
- 121.5 MHz (universal Simplex clear channel for aircraft in distress). A3E emission is generally used.

Note: Except when making a distress call, it is illegal to transmit a general call on these frequencies, that is, a communication that is not addressed to a particular station. In addition, the testing of a distress signal must be carried out with the aid of a dummy antenna.

Radiotelegraph Distress Frequency

- 500 kHz. A2B emission is used.

* **Question 14-78** Which of the following frequencies is used for the distress carrier in the 100- to 137-MHz band?

A. 121.5 MHz B. 124.5 MHz C. 111.5 MHz D. 123.5 MHz E. 112.5 MHz

Answer Choice A.

* **Question 14-79** In the MF band of 1605 to 3500 kHz, the radiotelephone distress frequency and the type of emission are:

A. 2128 kHz, A3E B. 2812 kHz, R3E C. 2182 kHz, J3E D. 2.182 MHz, R3E
E. 2.218 MHz, J3E

Answer Choice C.

* **Question 14-80** During landing an aircraft is communicating with the control tower. Which of the following frequencies would not be used for this procedure?

A. 121.5 MHz B. 121.6 MHz C. 121.9 MHz D. 123.6 MHz E. 132.0 MHz

Answer Choice A. The aircraft would not use the distress frequency of 121.5 MHz.

* **Question 14-81** In the VHF band of 156 to 162 MHz, the radiotelephone distress frequency and the type of emission are:

A. 156.65 MHz, G3E B. 156.8 MHz, J3E C. 158.6 MHz, F3E
D. 156.8 MHz, G3E E. 156.6 MHz, J3E

Answer Choice D.

* **Question 14-82** The radiotelephone distress and calling frequency in the MF band, is:

A. 2182 kHz B. 500 kHz C. 2128 kHz D. 2812 kHz E. 2218 kHz

Answer Choice A.

* **Question 14-83** The testing of the radiotelephone distress signal must be carried out:

A. on the authority of the ship's Master
B. by sending the transmission to the main antenna
C. only when in port
D. with the aid of a dummy antenna
E. only when beyond 100 miles from U.S. shores

Answer Choice D.

* **Question 14-84** What is the carrier frequency and purpose of channel 16?

A. 156.65 MHz. Bridge-to-bridge communications
B. 457.525 MHz. Survival craft station
C. 156.8 MHz. Distress and calling frequency
D. 2182 kHz. Distress and calling frequency
E. 121.5 MHz. Distress and calling frequency

Answer Choice C.

* **Question 14-85** Which of the distress frequencies lies within the band of 1605 kHz to 27500 kHz?

A. 2182 kHz B. 2182 MHz C. 2.182 MHz D. 218.2 kHz
E. choices A and C are true

Answer Choice E.

Eligibility for new license (R & R 13.5, 80.15, 87.3)

You are eligible for a commercial license if:

1. You are a U.S. citizen or an alien who is eligible for employment in the U.S.
2. You hold a valid United States pilot certificate.
3. You hold a foreign aircraft pilot certificate valid in the United States, provided there is a reciprocal agreement between the countries.

You are not eligible for a license if:

1. You are afflicted with complete deafness or complete muteness, or a complete inability for any other reason to transmit correctly and to receive correctly by telephone, spoken messages in English.
2. Your license is under suspension or is involved in suspension proceedings.
3. You are involved in any pending litigation based on alleged violation of the Communications Act of 1934, as amended.

Note: No applicant who is eligible to apply for any commercial radio operator license shall, by reason of any physical handicap, other than those mentioned above, be denied the privilege of applying and being permitted to attempt to prove his qualifications (by examination if examination is required) for such operator license.

* **Question 14-86** Who of the following is not eligible to apply for a new General Radiotelephone License?

A. an alien who is ineligible for employment in the U.S.
B. a person who is unable to communicate in the English language
C. a person who is afflicted with complete deafness
D. a person who is afflicted with complete muteness
E. all of the above choices are true

Answer Choice E.

Emergency locator transmitter (ELT) (R & R 87.5, 87.193, 87.195, 87.197) A transmitter intended to be actuated manually or automatically, and operated automatically as part of an aircraft or survival craft station, as a locating aid for survival purposes. ELTs can be tested as follows:

1. Operator uses the manually activated test switch, that switches the transmitter's output to a dummy load.
2. If the unit is not fitted with a manual test switch.
   a. Testing can be done in coordination with, or under the control of, a Federal Aviation Administration representative to ensure that no transmission of radiated energy occurs that will result in a false distress signal.
   b. If testing with FAA involvement is not feasible, brief operational tests are authorized. The tests are to be conducted within the 5 minutes of any hour and must not be longer than three audio sweeps. A dummy antenna must be inserted if possible.

Frequencies

- 121.5 MHz. Type of emission A3E, A3N, or NON.
- 243.0 MHz. Emergency and distress only.

* **Question 14-87** The battery of an Emergency Locator Transmitter must be changed after:

A. one year
B. the transmitter has been used in an emergency situation
C. six months
D. the date specified by the manufacturer when 50% of its useful life has expired
E. choices B and D are true

Answer Choice E.

* **Question 14-88** The frequency used by the Emergency Locator Transmitter is:

A. 156.8 MHz
B. 156.65 MHz
C. 121.5 MHz
D. 243 MHz
E. choices C and D are true

Answer Choice E.

* **Question 14-89** When testing the Emergency Locator Transmitter (ELT):

A. the operator uses a manually activated test switch that switches the transmitter's output to a dummy load
B. the test can be done in coordination with an FCC representative
C. an operational test is conducted within the first 10 minutes of any hour
D. the test must not be longer than five audio sweeps
E. no test can be carried out in the absence of a manually activated test switch

Answer Choice A.

* **Question 14-90** The Emergency Locator Transmitter (ELT) may be tested:

A. in coordination with, or under the control of an FAA representative
B. within the first five minutes of any hour
C. by using a manually activated test switch which switches the transmitter's output to a dummy load
D. by conducting no more than three audio sweeps
E. all of the above choices are true

Answer Choice E.

Emergency position indicating radiobeacons (EPIRBs) (R & R 80.1051–80.1057)

Purpose: The EPIRB station is an Emergency Locating Transmitter (ELT) that is used to facilitate search and rescue operations. It is authorized on vessels that travel more than 32 kilometers (20 miles) from shore.

Requirements:

1. Must be battery operated.
2. Must be waterproof and weather resistant.
3. Must have operating instructions understandable to untrained persons.
4. Exterior must have no sharp edges.
5. Must activate automatically when it floats free of a sinking vessel (class A).
6. Must have a manually activated test switch that must be held in position for testing. When released, the EPIRB returns to its normal state.

Power: 8 to 25 W

Frequencies: 1. 121.5 MHz 2. 243.0 MHz

Battery replacement:

1. To be replaced following use in an emergency situation.
2. To be replaced before the expiration date, established by the manufacturer (when 50 percent of its useful life has expired).
3. Expiration date (month and year) shall be marked on the battery and on the outside of the transmitter.

Operational tests:

1. Manual test switch is used.
2. Antenna should be replaced with a dummy load to prevent radiation of a false distress signal. The dummy load shall reduce radiation to a level not to exceed 25 μV/m at a distance of 150 feet.
3. Can be tested in coordination with the U.S. Coast Guard.
4. When Coast Guard involvement is not possible, brief tests are authorized, provided that they are conducted during the first 5 minutes of any hour. The test shall not last longer than three audio sweeps or one second, whichever is longer.

Special requirements for EPIRB stations

Class A A class A EPIRB station must:

1. Have the ability to float free of a sinking ship.
2. Activate automatically when it floats free of a sinking ship.
3. Have an antenna that deploys automatically when the EPIRB is activated.
4. Use A3N emission on a mandatory basis and A3E and NON emissions on an optional basis with the frequencies of 121.5 and 243.0 MHz.
5. Not exceed 90 seconds during transmission of A3E or NON emission and must then be followed by a transmission of at least 3 minutes of A3N emission.

6. Have an Effective Radiated Power (ERP) of less than 75 mW after 48 hours of continuous operation.
7. Be switched to a dummy antenna whose load is equivalent to that of the EPIRB antenna during testing the transmitter's output. The radiation must not exceed 25 μV/m at a distance of 150 feet, irrespective of the direction from the EPIRB.

Class B The class-B EPIRB differs from the class-A type in the following respects:

1. The class-B EPIRB may be turned on automatically or manually by an on/off switch.
2. The equipment of the class-B EPIRB must be designed to be deployed, its controls activated or its antenna erected by a single action task, which can be performed by either hand.
3. If a U.S. Coast Guard coordination is not possible, brief operational tests may be conducted for the first five minutes of any hour. Each test is not allowed to last more than three audio sweeps or one second, whichever is longer.

Class C The class-C EPIRB must meet the following requirements:

1. Operate on frequencies of 156.75 and 156.8 MHz with a G3N emission.
2. Use the International Radiotelephone Auto-Alarm signal.
3. Effective Radiated Power (ERP) must not be less than 1 W.
4. Test are conducted within the first five minutes of any hour for not more than 10 seconds.
5. The EPIRB must turn off automatically after 24 hours $\pm 5\%$. It is possible to restart the transmission sequence by placing the on/off switch momentarily in the Off position and then returning it to the On position.

Class S The class-S EPIRB differs from the class-A type in the following respects:

1. The class-S EPIRB must be able to float or be permanently secured to a survival craft.
2. Class-S EPIRBs may provide either continuous or intermittent operation.

Note: The requirements for battery replacement and testing of class-S EPIRBs are the same as that of class-A EPIRBs.

* **Question 14-91** The battery of the Emergency Position Indicating Radio Beacon (E.P.I.R.B) must be changed:

A. when 60% of its useful life remains
B. after its use in an emergency situation
C. before the expiration date established by the manufacturer
D. after its tenth test has been carried out
E. choices B and C are true

Answer Choice E.

* **Question 14-92** The Emergency Position Indicating Radio Beacon (E.P.I.R.B) should be checked to ensure proper operation:

A. prior to leaving port
B. daily
C. only after its use in an emergency situation
D. once a month
E. once a year

Answer Choice E.

* **Question 14-93** The Emergency Position Indicating Radio Beacon (E.P.I.R.B) must have its battery replaced:

A. when 50% of its useful life has expired
B. before the expiration date established by the manufacturer
C. once a year
D. after carrying out an operational test
E. choices A or B, whichever is earlier

Answer Choice E.

* **Question 14-94** If U.S. Coast Guard involvement is not possible, the test of the Emergency Position Indicating Radio Beacon (E.P.I.R.B) is carried out:

A. prior to leaving port
B. monthly during an international voyage
C. once a year
D. during the first five minutes of any hour and must last no longer than three audio sweeps
E. for a period of 15 seconds

Answer Choice D.

* **Question 14-95** A class-S Emergency Position Indicating Radio Beacon (E.P.I.R.B):

A. must be capable of floating or being secured to a survival craft
B. must have its battery replaced after emergency use
C. must have its battery replaced before the expiration date established by the manufacturer
D. may be tested during the first five minutes of any hour
E. all of the above choices are true

Answer Choice E.

* **Question 14-96** On which of the following frequencies do class-A and class-B EPIRBs operate?

A. 156.8 MHz B. 156.75 MHz C. 121.5 MHz D. 243 MHz
E. choices C and D are true

Answer Choice E.

* **Question 14-97** A class-S Emergency Position Indicating Radio Beacon (E.P.I.R.B) is tested:

A. with the aid of a dummy antenna whose load is the same as that of the EPIRB's antenna
B. by using a manually activated test switch
C. without the radiation exceeding 25 μV/m at a distance of 150 feet
D. during the first five minutes of any hour
E. choices A, B, and C are true

Answer Choice E.

* **Question 14-98** A class-C Emergency Position Indicating Radio Beacon (E.P.I.R.B) can be tested:

A. in coordination with the U.S. Coast Guard
B. by switching to a dummy antenna
C. without the radiation exceeding 25 μV/m at a distance of 150 feet
D. during the first five minutes of each hour with the testing not lasting more than ten seconds
E. choices A and D are true

Answer Choice E.

* **Question 14-99** A class-B Emergency Position Indicating Radio Beacon (E.P.I.R.B) is tested:

A. by switching to a dummy antenna
B. in coordination with the U.S. Coast Guard
C. during the first five minutes of each hour with the test not lasting more than one second
D. without the radiation exceeding 25 μV/m at a distance of 150 feet
E. all of the above choices are true

Answer Choice E.

* **Question 14-100** Which of the following frequencies are used by a class-C Emergency Position Indicating Radio Beacon (E.P.I.R.B)?

A. 156.75 MHz B. 156.8 MHz C. 156.65 MHz D. 121.5 MHz
E. choices A and B are true

Answer Choice E.

* **Question 14-101** Without the coordination of the U.S. Coast Guard, the class-B Emergency Position Indicating Radio Beacon (E.P.I.R.B) may be tested:

A. in complete radio silence
B. with G3E emission
C. on the frequency of 156.8 MHz
D. with an output power of less than 1 mW
E. during the first five minutes of each hour for a period that is not to exceed one second or three audio sweeps

Answer Choice E.

Emission types (R & R 2.201, 80.207) Authorized classes of emission have been given standard designations. For example, A3E refers to double-sideband full-carrier amplitude-modulated telephony, and J3E refers to single-sideband suppressed-carrier amplitude-modulated telephony. A full explanation of how these designations can be determined is found in chapter 6.

Equipment and service tests (R & R 23.32)

1. *Equipment tests:* Upon completion of construction of a radio station in exact accordance with the terms of the construction permit, the permittee is authorized to test the equipment for a period not to exceed 10 days, provided that:
   a. The engineer in charge of the district in which the station is located is notified two days in advance of the beginning of tests.
   b. The Commission reserves the right to cancel or suspend such tests, or change the date of the tests if such action appears to be in the public interest, convenience, and necessity, by notifying the permittee.
2. *Service tests:* When construction and equipment tests are completed in exact accordance with the terms of the construction permit, and after an application for the station license has been filed with the Commission showing the transmitter to be in satisfactory operating condition, the permittee is authorized to conduct service tests for a period not to exceed 30 days, provided that:
   a. The engineer in charge of the district in which the station is located is notified 2 days in advance of the beginning of tests.
   b. The Commission reserves the right to cancel such tests, or suspend, or change the date of the tests if such action appears to be in the public interest, convenience, and necessity, by notifying the permittee.
   c. Service tests will not be authorized after the expiration date of the construction permit.

Note: The authorization of these tests shall not be construed as constituting a license to operate but as a necessary part of the construction.

* **Question 14-102** Upon completion of construction of a radio station, equipment tests may be carried out during a period not to exceed:

A. 5 days B. 10 days C. 15 days D. 20 days E. 30 days

Answer Choice B.

* **Question 14-103** After construction of a radio station and the completion of the equipment tests, service tests may be carried out for a period not to exceed:

A. 5 days B. 10 days C. 15 days D. 20 days E. 30 days

Answer Choice E.

Frequency deviation (R & R 80.213) Transmitters using F3E or G3E emission in the band of 156 to 162 MHz or G3E in the band 216 to 220 MHz shall be capable of proper technical operation with a frequency deviation of ± 5 kHz, which is defined as 100 percent modulation.

* **Question 14-104** For 100% modulation the frequency deviation of Marine transmitters which operate in the 156- to 162-MHz band and use F3E or G3E emission, is:

A. 3 kHz B. 8 kHz C. 20 kHz D. 5 kHz E. 6 kHz

Answer Choice D.

Frequency measurements (Aviation) (R & R 87111) Measurements of the operating frequencies of airborne transmitters may be required by the Commission in individual circumstances. The operating frequencies of all non-airborne transmitters authorized for operation in the Aviation Service shall be measured at the following times to ensure compliance with the tolerance specified in these rules:

1. When a transmitter is originally installed.
2. When any change or adjustment is made in a transmitter that might affect an operating frequency
3. Whenever there is reason to believe that an operating frequency has shifted beyond the applicable tolerance.
4. Upon receipt of an official notice of off-frequency operation.

Frequency measurements (Marine) (R & R 83.111 from CFR, October 1985 edition) A determination shall be made that the carrier frequencies of each transmitter are within prescribed tolerances as follows:

1. When a transmitter is originally installed.
2. When any change or adjustment is made in the transmitter that might affect the carrier frequency or stability thereof.
3. Upon receipt of an official notice of off-frequency operation.

* **Question 14-105** The operating carrier frequencies of marine transmitters shall be determined:

A. when a transmitter is originally installed
B. when any change or adjustment is made that might affect a transmitter's operating frequency or its stability
C. upon receipt of an official notice of off-frequency operation
D. before the transmitter is removed prior to replacement
E. choices A, B, and C are true

Answer Choice E.

* **Question 14-106** The carrier frequency of a ship-borne transmitter must be measured:

A. on a daily basis with the aid of a dummy antenna
B. on a weekly basis with reduced carrier power
C. on a monthly basis in conjunction with the U.S. Coast Guard
D. prior to leaving port
E. frequency measurements are not carried out, unless some change is made to the transmitter that affects its operating frequency

Answer Choice E.

* **Question 14-107** The frequency of an airport's aviation transmitter is determined:

A. when the transmitter is originally installed
B. when any change or adjustment is made in the transmitter that might affect its operating frequency
C. upon receipt of an FCC notice of off-frequency operation
D. when there is reason to believe that the operating frequency has shifted beyond its tolerance
E. all of the above choices are true

Answer Choice E.

Frequency stability (Aviation) (R & R 87.133) The carrier frequency of each station in the Aviation Services must be maintained within acceptable tolerances. Table 14-3 lists these tolerances in parts per million (p.p.m) for various types of stations. These figures pertain to the maximum tolerance permitted after January 1, 1985 for new and replacement transmitters.

Table 14-3. Frequency stability, in parts per million.

Aeronautical stations	(100 to 2450 MHz)	20 ppm
Aircraft stations	(9 to 535 kHz)	100 ppm
	(1605 to 4000 kHz)	100 ppm
	(4 to 29.7 MHz)	100 ppm
	(100 to 137 MHz)	30 ppm
	(136 to 470 MHz)	30 ppm
	(470 to 2450 MHz)	20 ppm
Survival craft stations	(500 kHz)	20 ppm
	(2182 kHz)	20 ppm
	(836 kHz)	50 ppm
	(121.5 MHz)	50 ppm
	(243 MHz)	50 ppm

When transmitting single-sideband emissions, the carrier frequency shall be maintained within a certain number of hertz of the specified carrier frequency. Table 14-4 lists these frequency tolerance values for various stations in the Aviation Services.

Table 14-4. Frequency stability, in Hertz.

1. For other than Civil Air Patrol Sations:	
a. All ground stations	10 Hz
b. All aircraft stations	20 Hz
2. For Civil Air Patrol Sations:	
a. All land stations	50 Hz
b. All mobile stations	50 Hz

Frequency tolerance (Marine) (R & R 80.209) Authorized frequency tolerance for transmitters aboard ships, type accepted or type approved after November 1977, is generally 20 Hz. For example, a J3E (single sideband) transmitter on 2182 kHz is allowed to deviate a maximum of 20 Hz. This rule of thumb holds true up to 156 MHz, where the tolerance deviation changes to 10 p.p.m. It drops to 5 p.p.m. at 216 MHz. Tolerance for narrow-band direct printing is 15 Hz. Digital selective calling emissions are limited to a deviation of 10 Hz.

Frequency tolerance (International Fixed Public Radio Communications Services) (R & R 23.16) Frequency tolerances shall be maintained as prescribed in Table 14-5. The tolerances are applicable to new transmitters installed after September 19, 1973, and to all transmitters after September 19, 1975.

Table 14-5. Frequency tolerances for international fixed services.

Frequency range	Percent	Parts per million
10 to 50 kHz	0.1	1000
50 to 535 kHz	0.02	200
1605 to 30,000 kHz	0.0015	15
30 to 50 MHz	0.002	20
50 to 1000 MHz	0.0005	5
1000 to 1850 MHz	0.001	10

To determine parts per million (ppm), simply move the present decimal point six places to the right. For example, 0.02% is 0.0002. When the point is moved six places to the right, you have 20 ppm. If a transmitter operates on 121 MHz, TABLE 14-5 shows that its tolerance is 0.0005 percent, or 5 ppm. Therefore, 121,000,000 × 0.000005 = 605 Hz. Thus, the transmitter must operate no more than 605 Hz above or below 121 MHz. If you know that the ppm is 5, simply multiply 121 × 5 and arrive at the same 605 Hz. If you are given a parts-per-million figure and want to convert it to a percentage, simply move the decimal four places to the left. The accuracy of the frequency-measuring device must be taken into account when determining if the transmitter is within its required frequency tolerance.

* **Question 14-108** For an aircraft station operating with F3E emission in the frequency range of 100 to 137 MHz, the frequency tolerance is:

A. 20 ppm B. 30 ppm C. 50 ppm D. 20 Hz E. 100 ppm

Answer Choice B. Refer to TABLE 14-3.

* **Question 14-109** For aircraft stations employing single-sideband transmissions, the frequency tolerance is:

A. 20 ppm B. 30 ppm C. 50 ppm D. 20 Hz E. 30 Hz

Answer Choice D. Refer to TABLE 14-4.

* **Question 14-110** A survival craft station is operating on a frequency of 121.5 MHz. The frequency tolerance of this station is:

A. 30 ppm B. 20 ppm C. 20 Hz D. 30z Hz E. 50 ppm

Answer Choice E. Refer to TABLE 14-3.

* **Question 14-111** A marine transmitter is operating on a frequency of 2182 kHz with J3E emission. The frequency tolerance of this transmitter is:

A. 20 ppm B. 20 Hz C. 30 Hz D. 30 ppm E. 50 Hz

Answer Choice B.

* **Question 14-112** A marine transmitter is operating on a frequency of 156.8 MHz. The frequency tolerance of this transmitter is:

A. 10 Hz B. 20 Hz C. 30 Hz D. 50 Hz E. 10 ppm

Answer Choice E.

* **Question 14-113** Marine radiotelephone transmitters with single sideband emissions have a frequency tolerance of:

A. 20 Hz B. 20 ppm C. 30 Hz D. 50 Hz E. 10 ppm

Answer Choice A.

* **Question 14-114** A marine transmitter is operating on a frequency of 216 MHz. The frequency tolerance of this transmitter is:

A. 5 ppm B. 10 ppm C. 10 Hz D. 20 Hz E. 100 Hz

Answer Choice A.

* **Question 14-115** The frequency tolerance of aeronautical stations operating in the band of 100 to 2450 MHz is:

A. 20 ppm B. 20 Hz C. 10 ppm D. 5 ppm E. 30 ppm

Answer Choice A. Refer to TABLE 14-3.

* **Question 14-116** A marine transmitter is operating on a frequency of 156.8 MHz. Express the tolerance of this transmitter in hertz:

A. 3136 Hz B. 1568 Hz C. 6272 Hz D. 784.5 Hz E. 4704 Hz

Answer Choice B. The tolerance is 10 ppm, which is equivalent to $10 \times 156.8 = 1568$ Hz.

* **Question 14-117** A station in the International Fixed Services is operating within the 1605- to 30,000-kHz band. The frequency tolerance of this station is:

A. 0.02% B. 15 ppm C. 0.0015% D. 20 ppm E. choices B and C are true

Answer Choice E. 15 ppm $= 15 \times 10^{-4}\% = 0.0015\%$.

General Radiotelephone Operator License (R & R 13.2, 80.155, 80.159, 80.169, 87.133, 87.135) This license conveys all the operating authority of the Marine Radio Operator Permit.

No person may therefore hold both at the same time. All adjustments of radiotelephone transmitting equipment in any maritime, coast, or ship station, made during installation, servicing, or maintenance of that equipment, which might affect its proper operation, may be made only by, or under the immediate supervision of, a person who holds a General Radiotelephone Operator License, or a First- or Second-Class Radiotelephone Operator's Certificate.

Adjustments or tests relating to the installation, servicing, or maintenance of an aviation radio station, which might affect its proper operation, may be made only by, or under, the immediate supervision of a person who holds a General Radiotelephone Operator License, or a First- or Second-Class Radiotelephone Operator's Certificate.

* **Question 14-118** An Emergency Locator Transmitter is operating on a frequency of 243 MHz with a tolerance of 50 parts per million (ppm). Which of the following frequencies lies within the quoted tolerance?

A. 243.012 MHz B. 242.968 MHz C. 243.013 MHz D. 242.987 MHz
E. all of the above choices are true

Answer Choice A. The tolerance (in hertz) is $\pm 243 \times 50 = \pm 12150$ Hz $= \pm 0.01215$ MHz. The upper frequency limit is 243.01215 MHz and the lower frequency limit is 242.98785 MHz.

* **Question 14-119** The holder of a General Radiotelephone Operator's License, is not required to be on board a ship in order to:

A. operate a ship's radar system provided that the system can be operated by using external controls only and contains a fixed frequency-pulsed magnetron
B. operate a bridge-to-bridge communications system
C. operate on-board communications
D. operate a mobile station which is intended solely for survival purposes
E. all of the above choices are true

Answer Choice E.

* **Question 14-120** The holder of a General Radiotelephone License is required:

A. when a cargo ship's station power exceeds 1500 W of peak envelope power
B. when a passenger ship carries more than six passengers and its station power exceeds a carrier of 250 W or a peak envelope power of 1500 W
C. to maintain FCC-approved transmitters in the marine, aviation, and international fixed services
D. to operate a voluntary ship station that is sailing on a domestic voyage and is operating in the VHF band only
E. choices A, B, and C are true

Answer Choice E.

* **Question 14-121** What class of license is required to operate the marine station on a large passenger ship if the station power exceeds 250 W carrier power and 1500 W peak envelope power?

A. Marine Radiotelephone Operator Permit
B. Restricted Radiotelephone Permit
C. General Radiotelephone License
D. Second-Class Radiotelephone License
E. choices C and D are true

Answer Choice E.

* **Question 14-122** For which of the following services does a operator require a General Radiotelephone Operator's License?

A. police two-way radio
B. ambulance two-way radio
C. railroad two-way radio
D. citizen's band radio
E. none of the above choices is true

Answer Choice E.

Inspection by foreign governments (R & R 80.79) The radio operator on board a ship must allow officials of foreign governments to examine the radio station license if they so request. The radio operator must facilitate the examination in order that the officials can be satisfied that the station complies with international radio regulations.

* **Question 14-123** If a mobile station on a U.S. ship visits a foreign country, the government of that country may, under the 1959 Geneva Treaty:

A. inspect the station logs
B. request full details of the radio installations
C. require that the transmitter is kept "off the air" for the duration of the visit
D. require that the station license be produced for inspection
E. demand a list of the frequencies that the station will be using during the visit

Answer Choice D.

Instrument landing system (ILS) (R & R 87.5) This is a radionavigational system that provides aircraft with horizontal and vertical guidance just before and during landing and, at certain fixed points, indicates the distance to the reference point of landing. The total system contains two parts:

1. The *Instrument Landing System Glide Path* is a system of vertical guidance, which indicates the vertical deviation of the aircraft from its optimum path of descent.
2. The *Instrument Landing System Localizer* is a system of horizontal guidance, which indicates the horizontal deviation of the aircraft from its optimum path of descent along the axis of the runway or along some other path when used as an offset.

* **Question 14-124** When an aircraft is descending towards a runway, the ILS Localizer unit indicates the:

A. vertical deviation from the optimum path of descent
B. deviation from the optimum speed of descent
C. azimuth of the aircraft in relation to the axis of the runway
D. horizontal deviation from the optimum path of descent along the axis of the runway
E. vertical angle between the axis of the aircraft and the axis of the runway

Answer Choice D.

* **Question 14-125** What part of the Instrument Landing System (ILS) is used to indicate the horizontal deviation of an aircraft from its optimum path of descent along the axis of the runway?

A. distance-measuring equipment (DME) B. VOR system C. glide path
D. localizer E. racon station

Answer Choice D.

* **Question 14-126** What part of the Instrument Landing System (ILS) is used to indicate the vertical deviation of an aircraft from its optimum path of descent?

A. distance-measuring equipment (DME) B. ELT C. localizer D. glide path
E. altimeter

Answer Choice D.

* **Question 14-127** When an aircraft is descending toward a runway, the ILS glide path unit indicates the:

A. vertical deviation from the optimum path of descent
B. deviation from the optimum speed of descent
C. azimuth of the aircraft in relation to the axis of the runway
D. horizontal deviation from the optimum path of descent along the axis of the runway
E. vertical angle between the axis of the aircraft and the axis of the runway

Answer Choice A.

* **Question 14-128** Which of the following is part of the Instrument Landing System (ILS)?

A. altimeter
B. glide path
C. distance-measuring equipment (DME)
D. localizer
E. choices B and D are true

Answer Choice E.

* **Question 14-129** Which of the following best describes the ILS instrument system? It is:

A. an aircraft's cockpit instrument that provides three separate items of information in relation to the runway
B. a system of vertical guidance only
C. a system of horizontal guidance only
D. an aircraft cockpit instrument that provides three separate items (height, horizontal deviation, and bearing) of information in relation to the runway
E. part of the DME system

Answer Choice A.

License term (R & R 80.25, 87.51) Ship stations are licensed for a period of five years. Licenses for stations in the Aviation Services will normally be issued for a term of five years from the date of original issuance, major modification, or renewal. First- and Second-Class Licenses were formerly issued for five years. The General Radiotelephone Operator License is now issued for life.

* **Question 14-130** The radio license of a compulsory ship is valid for:

A. 3 years B. 5 years C. 10 years D. 15 years E. the lifetime of the transmitter

Answer Choice B.

Listening watch (R & R 80.146–80.148, 80.304–80.310) All ship and coast stations that are licensed to transmit radiotelephony are required to maintain an efficient and continuous watch on the radiotelephone distress frequency (2182 kHz) whenever such a station is not being used for communication. The watch may be conducted from:

1. The principal operating position, or
2. The room from which the vessel is normally steered.
3. The listening watch must be maintained for at least three minutes two times each hour, beginning on the hour and on the half hour. All stations must refrain from transmitting on that frequency at those times (silent period, except for distress, urgency, or safety messages).

Coast stations operating in the 156- to 162-MHz band and serving in rivers and inland lakes (except for the Great Lakes) must maintain a safety watch on 156.8 MHz.

Telegraphy stations must maintain a listening watch on 500 kHz of three minutes twice each hour, beginning at 15 minutes and 45 minutes after each hour. Do not confuse this with the radiotelephone watch that is outlined above.

* **Question 14-131** When a radio operator is required to "stand watch" on the International Radiotelephone Distress frequency, under which of the following circumstances may the operator cease to listen?

A. when the station is being used for transmission on 2182 kHz
B. when poor reception is caused by severe conditions of static and fading
C. when all received signals are badly distorted and are barely intelligible
D. when the station is being used for communication on other channels
E. choices A and D are true

Answer Choice E.

* **Question 14-132** All ships that are licensed to transmit telephony on one or more frequencies in the band 1605 to 3500 kHz are required to maintain a listening watch on 2182 kHz for:

A. at least three minutes, two times each hour, beginning on the hour and the half hour
B. three minutes, twice each hour, beginning at 15 and 45 minutes past each hour
C. at least three minutes, once each hour, beginning on the hour
D. at least two minutes, two times each hour, beginning on the hour and the half hour
E. at least two minutes, two times each hour, beginning at 15 and 45 minutes past each hour

Answer Choice A.

* **Question 14-133** Each ship station on board a ship that is navigating the Great Lakes and is licensed to transmit by telephony within the band of 1605 to 3500 kHz, shall during the hours of service, maintain an efficient watch on:

A. 2182 kHz B. 2282 kHz C. 2128 kHz D. 2281 kHz E. 2218 kHz

Answer Choice A.

* **Question 14-134** A compulsory ship is assigned a working frequency of 1980 kHz. On which frequency must an efficient listening watch be maintained?

A. 1960 kHz B. 2000 kHz C. 3960 kHz D. 2182 kHz E. 2128 kHz

Answer Choice D.

* **Question 14-135** A compulsory ship is assigned working frequencies of 2550 and 7350 kHz. On which frequency must an efficient listening watch be maintained?

A. 2550 kHz B. 3750 kHz C. 2530 kHz D. 7370 kHz E. 2182 kHz

Answer Choice E.

* **Question 14-136** Except for distress, urgency, or safety messages, marine stations licensed to transmit radiotelephony must observe a silent period:

A. for three minutes after 15 minutes past the hour
B. for three minutes after 45 minutes past the hour
C. for three minutes after the hour
D. for three minutes after the half hour
E. choices C and D are true

Answer Choice E.

* **Question 14-137** All ships that are licensed to transmit telephony in the band of 1605 to 3500 kHz, must monitor the International Radiotelephone Distress frequency:

A. continuously
B. only during distress, urgency, and safety signals
C. only during the silent periods
D. from 9 PM to 9 AM
E. once every hour

Answer Choice A.

* **Question 14-138** Each U.S. cargo ship that is equipped with a radiotelephone station for compliance with Chapter 1V of the Safety Convention, shall, while on watch, maintain a continuous watch on:

A. 2182 kHz B. 500 kHz C. 156.65 MHz D. 156.8 MHz
E. choices A and D are true

Answer Choice E.

* **Question 14-139** While at sea, each U.S. cargo ship that is equipped with a radiotelephone station for compliance with Part 11 of Title 111 of the Communications Act, shall:

A. maintain a continuous watch on 2182 kHz in the radio operator's room
B. maintain a continuous watch on 156.8 MHz in the room from which the vessel is steered
C. use a watch receiver with a loudspeaker and a radiotelephone auto alarm to maintain a continuous watch on 2182 kHz
D. use the radiotelephone auto alarm to maintain a continuous watch on 156.8 MHz
E. choices B and D are true

Answer Choice E.

* **Question 14-140** A compulsory ship is assigned working frequencies in the 1605- to 3500-kHz band and is also equipped with VHF communications equipment. On which of the following frequencies shall a continuous watch be maintained?

A. 2128 kHz B. 2182 MHz C. 156.65 MHz D. 156.8 MHz E. 121.5 MHz

Answer Choice D.

Logs (R & R 23.48) For stations in the international fixed public control service, the licensee shall maintain a technical log of the operating station showing:

1. Normal hours of operation and times of interruptions to service.
2. Dates and results of each frequency measurement.
3. When service or maintenance duties are performed, the responsible operator shall sign and date the station record and give pertinent details of all duties performed by him/her or under his/her supervision.

Logs (R & R 23.47, 23.48, 80.409, 80.413, 80.1153) *Ship radiotelephone stations* shall maintain a log. Pages of the log shall be numbered in sequence and each page shall include the name of the vessel, the callsign of the station, country of registry, and the official number of the vessel. The station licensee and the radio operator in charge of the station are responsible for the maintenance of the station log. The following entries are required:

1. A summary of all distress, urgency and safety traffic.
2. A summary of communications conducted on other than VHF frequencies.

3. A reference to important service incidents.
4. The position of the ship at least once per day.
5. The name of the operator at the beginning and end of the watch period.
6. The time that the watch begins when the vessel leaves port and the time it ends when the vessel reaches port.
7. The time that the watch is discontinued and the reason.
8. The time when storage batteries are charged.
9. The results of required equipment tests.
10. The results of inspections and tests of compulsorily fitted lifeboat radio equipment.
11. A daily statement about the condition of the required radiotelephone equipment, as determined by communications tests.
12. When the master is notified about improperly operating radiotelephone equipment.
13. Pertinent details of all installation, service, or maintenance work done. The technician shall log in all the pertinent work he/she himself/herself has done and must sign his/her name.

Retention of logs: Station logs shall be retained by the licensee as follows:

1. Routine logs must be maintained for a period of one year from the date of entry.
2. Logs involving distress communications shall be retained for a period of three years from the date of entry.
3. Logs that include communications that are under FCC investigation shall be retained until such time as the Commission specifically authorizes them to be destroyed.

* **Question 14-141** Which of the following details are contained in the log of a ship's radiotelephone station?

A. summary of all distress, urgency, and safety traffic
B. details of all installation, service, and maintenance work carried out
C. signature of the operator at the beginning and end of a watch period
D. name of the vessel and its callsign
E. all of the above choices are true

Answer Choice E.

* **Question 14-142** Routine station logs are normally required to be retained for a period of:

A. 1 year B. 2 years C. 3 years D. 5 years
E. these logs must be retained until the FCC authorizes their destruction

Answer Choice A.

* **Question 14-143** Station logs that contain information about certain distress communications must be retained for a period of:

A. 1 year B. 2 years C. 3 years D. 5 years
E. these logs must be retained until the FCC authorize their destruction

Answer Choice C.

* **Question 14-144** Station logs that contain information about communications under FCC investigation, must be retained for a period of:

A. 1 year B. 2 years C. 3 years D. 5 years
E. these logs must be retained until the FCC authorize their destruction

Answer Choice E.

Lost license (R & R 13.71) If your license is lost or destroyed, you must apply for a new one. The application must be made with an explanation of how it was lost. If the lost license is later found, it (or the duplicate) must be returned to the FCC for cancellation.

* **Question 14-145** If an operator's license is lost, the operator:

A. must immediately notify the Commission
B. can obtain a duplicate until the time of renewal
C. may apply for a duplicate to the FCC office that issued the original license
D. must, within 15 days, notify the FCC office in Washington, DC, of the loss
E. choices A and C are true

Answer Choice C.

* **Question 14-146** If an operator's license or permit has been lost or destroyed, the:

A. operator can request a duplicate license by filing an application with the FCC field office that issued the original license
B. operator may continue to operate the station at which he/she is employed
C. operator shall cease to operate the station at which he/she is employed until he/she obtains a duplicate of the license
D. operator may post a signed copy of his/her application for a duplicate license in lieu of the license document
E. choices A, B, and D are true

Answer Choice E.

* **Question 14-147** An operator who lost his/her license, has now obtained a duplicate, if the operator finds the original license at a later date, he/she must:

A. destroy the original license immediately
B. destroy the duplicate immediately
C. return the duplicate to the FCC for cancellation
D. return the original to the FCC for cancellation
E. either choice C or D

Answer Choice E.

Main transmitter (R & R 80.253) The main transmitter of a compulsory ship must be equipped to measure:

1. Antenna current.
2. Transmitter power supply voltages.
3. Plate or collector currents.

Antenna power must be determined at the operating carrier frequency by the product of the antenna resistance and the square of the effective antenna current ($P = I^2R$), both measured at the same point in the antenna circuit.

The main transmitter operates on a frequency of 500 kHz with a tolerance of ± 20 Hz. If the transmitter's operating power is more than 250 W, the power must be reduced to 150 W when used for telegraphy.

* **Question 14-148** Which of the following is the operating frequency of the main transmitter on a compulsory ship?

A. 500 kHz B. 2182 kHz C. 156.8 MHz D. 156.65 MHz E. 121.5 MHz

Answer Choice A.

* **Question 14-149** The operating power of a compulsory ship's main transmitter is determined by:

A. the product of the plate voltage and the dc level of the plate current
B. the product of the plate voltage and the antenna current
C. the product of the antenna current an the associated antenna resistance
D. the product of the (*antenna current*)^2 and the antenna resistance
E. none of the above choices is true

Answer Choice D.

Maintenance tests of licensed station R & R 23.43, 80.96, 87.93) Licensed stations are authorized to carry out routine tests, as is required for proper maintenance of the stations. The tests must not cause interference with the service of other stations.

Marine radio operator permit (R & R 13.4, 13.28, 80.167) A permit issued by the FCC for a period of five years. The holder of this permit is allowed to operate only those transmitters that:

1. Have simple, external switching devices.
2. Do not require manual adjustment of frequency-determining elements.

Modulation requirements (R & R 80.213)

1. When double-sideband emission is used, the peak modulation must be maintained between 75 and 100%.
2. When frequency or phase modulation is used (in the 156- to 162-MHz and 216- to 220-MHz bands), the peak modulation must be maintained between 75 and 100%.
3. Transmitters using A3E, F3E, and G3E emission must have a modulation limiter to prevent any modulation over 100%.
4. Ship stations using G3D or G3E emission (in the 156- to 162-MHz and 216- to 220-MHz bands) must be capable of maintaining the proper frequency deviation of ±5 kHz.
5. Coast station transmitters operating in the 156- to 162-MHz band must be equipped with an audio low-pass filter. This filter must be installed between the modulation limiter and the modulated RF stage. At frequencies above 20 kHz, the attenuation must be at least 50 dB greater than that at 1 kHz.

* **Question 14-150** When a marine transmitter uses double-sideband emission, the peak modulation must be maintained between:

A. 50 to 90% B. 60 to 95% C. 70 to 100% D. 75 to 100% E. 80 to 100%

Answer Choice D.

* **Question 14-151** When a marine transmitter uses frequency or phase modulation, the peak modulation must be maintained between:

A. 60 to 90% B. 65 to 100% C. 70 to 100% D. 75 to 100% E. 80 to 100%

Answer Choice D.

* **Question 14-152** For a ship station using G3D or G3E emission in the 156- to 162-MHz band, the frequency deviation corresponding to 100% modulation is:

A. 10 kHz B. 5 kHz C. 20 kHz D. 25 kHz E. 75 kHz

Answer Choice B.

* **Question 14-153** Certain marine transmitters operating in the 156- to 162-MHz band must be equipped with an audio low-pass filter, which is installed between the modulation limiter and the modulated RF stage. This filter must:

A. attenuate audio frequencies above 3 kHz. The degree of attenuation must be at least 10 dB greater than at 1 kHz
B. attenuate audio frequencies above 5 kHz. The degree of attenuation must be at least 15 dB greater than that at 1 kHz
C. attenuate audio frequencies above 20 kHz. The degree of attenuation must be at least 50 dB greater than that at 1 kHz
D. attenuate audio frequencies above 15 kHz. The degree of attenuation must be at least 25 dB greater than that at 5 kHz
E. attenuate audio frequencies above 10 kHz. The degree of attenuation must be at least 20 dB greater than that at 3 kHz

Answer Choice C.

* **Question 14-154** For ship station that uses G3D or G3E emission in the 216- to 220-MHz band, the frequency deviation corresponding to 100% modulation is:

A. 5 kHz B. 10 kHz C. 20 kHz D. 25 kHz E. 75 kHz

Answer Choice A.

Nameplate (R & R 80.1021) A durable nameplate shall be mounted on the required radiotelephone transmitting and receiving equipment. The nameplate shall show at least the name of the manufacturer and the type of model number.

* **Question 14-155** The durable nameplate mounted on a marine transmitter indicates:

A. name of the manufacturer
B. assigned frequency
C. type of emission
D. assigned power
E. date on which the transmitter was placed into service

Answer Choice A.

* **Question 14-156** The durable nameplate mounted on a marine transmitter indicates:

A. assigned frequency
B. operating power
C. frequency tolerance
D. model number
E. type of emission

Answer Choice D.

* **Question 14-157** The durable nameplate mounted on a marine transmitter indicates the:

A. date on which the transmitter was placed into service
B. dates on which the transmitter was inspected
C. assigned frequency
D. assigned power
E. name of manufacturer and model number

Answer Choice E.

Navigational communications (R & R 80.5, 80.1007) Safety communications that pertain to the maneuvering of vessels or the directing of vessel movements. Such communications are primarily for the exchange of information between ship stations or between ship stations and coast stations (see *bridge-to-bridge communications*).

Need for licensed commercial radio operators See *General Radiotelephone Operator License* and *Marine Radio Operator Permit.*

Nomenclature of frequencies (R & R 2.101) This is the classification of frequency ranges. For example, VHF (very high frequency) is the band of frequencies from 30 to 300 MHz. This is covered in detail in chapter 10.

On-board communications (R & R 80.1175) A low-powered mobile station in the maritime mobile service. On-board stations communicate with:

1. Other units of the same station for operational communications.
2. On-board stations of another ship or shore facility to aid in oil-pollution prevention during transfer of 250 or more barrels of oil.
3. Other units of the same station in the immediate vicinity of the ship for operational communications related to docking, life-boat emergency drills or in the maneuvering of cargo barges and lighters.
4. The assigned carrier frequencies for on-board communications are 467.750, 467.775, 467.800, and 467.825 MHz. For on-board repeater stations the corresponding assigned carrier frequencies are, respectively, 457.525, 457.550, 457.575, and 457.600 MHz.

* **Question 14-158** For an on-board communications transmitter, the operator must possess a:

A. Marine Operator Permit
B. Restricted Radiotelephone Permit
C. General Radiotelephone License
C. Second-Class Radiotelephone License
E. no license is required by the operator assigned to the control point

Answer Choice E.

* **Question 14-159** Which of the following carrier frequencies is assigned to an on-board mobile communications unit?

A. 2182 kHz
B. 243 MHz
C. 156.8 MHz
D. 156.65 MHz
E. 467.75 MHz

Answer Choice E.

* **Question 14-160** An on-board mobile unit is used to establish communications with:

A. other units of the same station for operational communications
B. on-board stations of another ship during the transfer of 250 or more barrels of oil
C. other units of the same station in the immediate vicinity of the ship while the ship is docking
D. on-board units of other ships owned by the same licensee
E. choices A, B, and C are true

Answer Choice E.

* **Question 14-161** Which of the following frequencies is assigned to UHF transmitters used for on-board communications?

A. 647.750 MHz B. 467.775 MHz C. 567.800 MHz D. 477.825 MHz
E. 667.875 MHz

Answer Choice B.

* **Question 14-162** A UHF transmitter is used for on-board communications, and is operating on a frequency of 467.825 MHz. Its corresponding repeater station frequency is:

A. 457.525 MHz B. 457.550 MHz C. 457.575 MHz D. 457.600 MHz
E. 457.625 MHz

Answer Choice D.

* **Question 14-163** An on-board mobile unit is used to communicate with:

A. all on-board units of another ship with which the mother ship is already communicating
B. all ships that are assisting in the docking of the mother ship
C. the emergency equipment of any survival craft
D. on-board units of all other ships which are within 5 miles of the mother ship
E. none of the above choices is true

Answer Choice E.

Operation of ship transmitter (R & R 80.89) The ship station may not be operated from any location except the ship. It is illegal to operate it while the ship is being transported, stored, or parked on land.

Operating procedure (FCC Bulletin FO-32)

To initiate a call to another ship:

1. Monitor the frequency before transmitting. Make sure it is clear. This is one of the most important things for a radio operator to learn.
2. Initiate the call on the calling frequency. This is used only for making initial contact. Transmission should not exceed one minute on 2182 kHz or 156.8 MHz (these frequencies should be left clear for possible emergency use).
3. Move to a working frequency for the communication.

Procedure words:

1. "Over" means you expect a reply from the station you are talking with.
2. "Clear" or "out" means your communication is complete and you do not expect a reply.
3. "Roger" means that you received the transmission correctly.
4. "Words twice" can either signify: "Because communications are difficult, every phrase in this message will be sent twice" or this phrase can be used to make the following request "Communication is difficult. Please send every phrase twice."
5. "Say again" means "repeat."
6. "Break" signifies a separation between parts of a single message and therefore means "This is the end of the first part of the message. The second part of the message now follows."
7. "Wilco" means "Your last message received, understood and will be complied with."
8. "Standby" signifies that "you are asked to wait for another call or for additional instructions."

Restrictions: You may not engage in any of the following:

1. Unnecessary transmissions.
2. Unidentified transmissions.
3. Superfluous communications.
4. Idle "chit-chat."
5. Communications containing obscene, indecent, or profane words or meaning.
6. Transmission of false callsigns.
7. Willful or malicious interference.
8. Signals not addressed to a particular station.

* **Question 14-164** When initiating a call to another ship, the first step is:

A. transmit on the working frequency
B. transmit on the calling frequency
C. switch to maximum power
D. monitor the working frequency before transmitting
E. test the transmitter for correct operation

Answer Choice D.

* **Question 14-165** To call another ship when the working frequency lies in the 1605- to 3500-kHz band:

A. the first step is to monitor the working frequency
B. if the working frequency is clear, initiate the call on the frequency of 2182 kHz
C. the call signal should not continue for more than 30 seconds
D. if there is no reply to the call, the call signal shall not be repeated until after an interval of two minutes
E. all of the above choices are true

Answer Choice E.

* **Question 14-166** In regions of heavy traffic, to avoid interference with communication already in progress and prior to making a call, an operator must:

A. switch to minimum power
B. test the transmitter for proper operation
C. listen in on the working frequency and wait before making a call if communications are already in progress
D. listen in one the calling frequency to establish whether a lengthy communication is in progress
E. decide to limit the initial call to less than one minute

Answer Choice C.

* **Question 14-167** A radio operator may signify "This conversation is ended and no response is expected" by using the word:

A. clear B. roger C. over D. out E. either choice A or C is true

Answer Choice E.

* **Question 14-168** A radio operator may request "Communication is difficult. Please send every phrase twice" by using the word(s):

A. repeat B. words twice C. say again D. retransmit E. message twice

Answer Choice B.

* **Question 14-169** Which of the following word(s) is used to signify "You are requested to wait for another call (or for additional information)?"

A. standby B. stay on watch C. continue to listen D. break E. stay alert

Answer Choice A.

* **Question 14-170** An operator may signify "My transmission is ended and I expect a response from you" by using the word:

A. over B. out C. roger D. wilco E. clear

Answer Choice A.

* **Question 14-171** An operator may signify a separation between portions of a message by using the word:

A. break B. separate C. pause D. split E. divide

Answer Choice A.

* **Question 14-172** A radiotelephone operator may signify "Your last message was received, understood, and will be complied with" by the use of the word:

A. wilco B. confirmed C. roger D. clear E. out

Answer Choice A.

* **Question 14-173** The word "Roger" is used by an operator to signify that:

A. "I have received all of your last transmission"
B. "your last message was received, understood, and will be complied with"
C. "my transmission is ended and I expect a response from you"
D. "the transmission is ended and no response is expected"
E. "part of the transmission has been sent and there will be a pause before sending the remainder of the message"

Answer Choice A.

* **Question 14-174** If an operator wishes the whole or part of the communication to be repeated, he/she uses the word(s)

A. repeat B. words twice C. say again D. retransmit E. message twice

Answer Choice C.

* **Question 14-175** In which of the following may a radio operator not engage?

A. unnecessary transmissions
B. unidentified transmissions
C. superfluous communications
D. personal communications
E. all of the above choices are true

Answer Choice E.

* **Question 14-176** In which of the following may a radio operator not engage?

A. communications containing obscene or profane words
B. transmission of false callsigns
C. willful or malicious interference
D. signals not addressed to a particular station
E. all of the above choices are true

Answer Choice E.

Operator's responsibility (R & R 13.63) The licensed operator responsible for the maintenance of a transmitter may permit other persons to adjust a transmitter in his/her presence for the purpose of carrying out tests or making adjustments that require specialized knowledge or skill, provided that he/she shall not be relieved thereby from responsibility for the proper operation of the equipment.

Other forms of station identification (R & R 2.303) The following indicates forms of identification that may be used in lieu of callsigns by the specified classes of stations:

1. *Aircraft (U.S. registry) telephone:* Registration number preceded by the type of the aircraft, or the radiotelephony designator of the aircraft operating agency followed by the flight identification number.
2. *Aircraft (foreign registry) telephone:* Foreign registry identification that consists of five characters. This may be preceded by the radiotelephony designator of the aircraft operating agency or it may be preceded by the type of the aircraft.
3. *Aeronautical:* Name of the city, area, or airdrome served, together with such additional identification as may be required.
4. *Aircraft survival craft:* Appropriate reference to parent aircraft (e.g., the air carrier, parent aircraft flight number or identification, the aircraft registration number, the name of the aircraft, the name of the aircraft owner, or any other pertinent information).
5. *Public Coast (radiotelephone) and Limited Coast (radiotelegraph):* The approximate geographic location in a format that is approved by the Commission.
6. *Fixed:* Geographic location.
7. *Land mobile (public safety, forestry conservation, highway maintenance, local government, shipyard, land transportation, and aviation services):* Name of station license (in abbreviated form, if practical), or the location of station, or name of city, area, or facility served. Individual stations may be identified by additional digits following the more general identification.
8. *Land mobile (railroad radio service):* Name of railroad, train number, caboose number, engine number, or name of fixed wayside station. A railroad's abbreviated name or initial letters may be used. Unit designations may be used in addition to the station identification to identify an individual unit or transmitter of a base station.

Passing score (R & R 13.24) To pass a written examination, an applicant must answer at least 75% of the questions correctly.

Percent modulation (R & R 80.213, 87.73) In general, marine transmitters shall be adjusted so that transmission of speech produces peak modulation between 75 and 100%. Aviation regulations state between 70 and 100%.

* **Question 14-177** On peaks of voice modulation, aviation transmitters must maintain a percentage modulation value that lies between:

A. 60 to 90% B. 70 to 95% C. 70 to 100% D. 75 to 100% E. 80 to 100%

Answer Choice C.

* **Question 14-178** On peaks of voice modulation, marine transmitters must maintain a percentage modulation value that lies between:

A. 60 to 90% B. 70 to 95% C. 70 to 100% D. 75 to 100% E. 80 to 100%

Answer Choice D.

Phonetic alphabet (FCC Bulletin FO-32) An internationally recognized alphabet. It may be used when communications are difficult or when signals are weak. Words are simply spelled out using the standard phonetic alphabet (chapter 8). For example, "radio" would be spelled: "romeo, alpha, delta, india, oscar."

* **Question 14-179** The standard phonetic alphabet words that correspond to the letters G, H, I, are:

A. Gold, Harry, Ink
B. Golf, Hotel, India
C. Good, Hotel, India
D. Golf, Hat, Ink
E. Good, Harry, India

Answer Choice B.

* **Question 14-180** A word list that is useful in identifying letters or words that sound like other letters or words of different meaning, is known as the:

A. Morse alphabet
B. radio alphabet
C. phonetic alphabet
D. telephonic vocabulary
E. word alphabet

Answer Choice C.

* **Question 14-181** A: Alpha, B: Bravo, and C: Charlie are part of the:

A. semantic system of communications
B. phonetic alphabet
C. Morse vocabulary
D. telephonic dictionary
E. symbolic code

Answer Choice B.

* **Question 14-182** When communications are weak or difficult, the radio operator should:

A. overmodulate the transmission
B. turn off the transmitter
C. shout into the microphone
D. switch from the working frequency to the calling frequency
E. use the phonetic alphabet

Answer Choice E.

Plurality of stations (R & R 80.37, 80.115) One station license may be issued to authorize a designated maximum number of marine utility stations operating at temporary unspecified locations.

* **Question 14-183** A licensee operates 10 marine utility stations in the same area. The number of licenses required is:

A. 10 B. 5 C. 2 D. 1 E. marine utility stations do not require a license

Answer Choice D.

Points of communication (R & R 80.505) Private coast stations and marine utility stations are authorized to communicate:

1. With any mobile station for the exchange of communications.
2. With any land station for the purpose of aiding the exchange of safety communications.
3. With ship stations.

A private coast station and associated marine utility stations serving and located on a shipyard regularly engaged in construction or repair, are authorized to communicate between stations when they are licensed to the same entity and communications are limited to serving the needs of ships on a noninterference basis.

Portable ship units (Also called handhelds, walkie-talkies, and associated ship units) (R & R 80.115)

License: When at sea, they are under the authorization of the ship station license.

Power: Limited to 1 W.

Frequency: Must be equipped to transmit on:

1. Channel 16 (156.8 MHz) (safety and calling frequency).
2. At least one appropriate intership frequency.

May be used:

1. Only to communicate with the ship station with which it is associated or with associated ship units of the same ship.
2. For operational communications aboard a ship.

May not be used:

1. From shore.
2. To communicate with other vessels not associated with their vessel.

Station identification requirements:

1. Operator must give the callsign of vessel with which it is associated, followed by an appropriate unit designator.
2. Must be done at least every 15 minutes.
3. Testing. No specific testing procedures are required.

Note: These must not be confused with portable units that are licensed as marine utility stations. These may be operated either on a ship or on shore.

* **Question 14-184** On which of the following frequencies are handheld portable transmitters authorized to transmit?

A. 156.8 MHz
B. 2182 kHz
C. 156.65 MHz
D. one appropriate intership frequency
E. choices A and D are true

Answer Choice E.

* **Question 14-185** What is the maximum authorized power for handheld portable units on board ship?

A. 1 W B. 3 W C. 5 W D. 8 W E. 25 W

Answer Choice A.

* **Question 14-186** Handheld portable units are used to communicate:

A. from shore
B. with all ships within the transmitter's range

C. with the ship station with which the portable unit is associated
D. with associated ship units of the mother ship
E. choices C and D are true.

Answer Choice E.

* **Question 14-187** Handheld portable ship units are identified by:

A. callsign only
B. callsign and name of mothership
C. name of ship only
D. callsign and appropriate unit designator
E. appropriate unit designator only

Answer Choice D.

* **Question 14-188** How often must handheld portable ship transmitters be tested?

A. prior to leaving port
B. once a day
C. once a week
D. once a month
E. no specific testing procedures are stated in the FCC Rules and Regulations

Answer Choice E.

* **Question 14-189** Portable handheld ship transmitters when at sea:

A. require their own individual licenses
B. are operated under the authorization of the ship station license
C. must each be operated by a General Radiotelephone licensee
D. must each be operated by the holder of a Marine Operator Permit
E. must each be operated by the holder of a Restricted Radiotelephone Permit

Answer Choice B.

* **Question 14-190** Handheld portable ship transmitters may:

A. be used to communicate from the shore
B. only be used for bridge-to-bridge communications
C. increase their power outputs to over 8 W under emergency conditions
D. communicate with other ships not associated with their own ship
E. none of the above choices is true

Answer Choice E.

* **Question 14-191** Handheld portable ship transmitters must not:

A. communicate with other ships that are not associated with their own ship
B. communicate from shore
C. transmit with an operating power greater than 1 W
D. transmit on channel 13
E. all of the above choices are true

Answer Choice E.

* **Question 14-192** Handheld portable transmitters are identified:

A. by the callsign of the vessel followed by the appropriate unit designator
B. every 10 minutes
C. every 15 minutes

D. the name of the vessel followed by the appropriate unit designator
E. choices A and C are true

Answer Choice E.

* **Question 14-193** A compulsory ship has one main transmitter and eight handheld portable transmitters. The number of radio station licenses required is:

A. 9 B. 1 C. 2 D. 3 E. 5

Answer Choice B.

* **Question 14-194** Handheld portable ship units:

A. have an operating power which is limited to 1 W
B. must transmit on channel 16, which corresponds to a frequency of 156.8 MHz
C. operate under the authorization of the ship's radio station license
D. are used for communications on board the mother ship
E. all of the above choices are true

Answer Choice E.

* **Question 14-195** An auxiliary ship unit that is associated with a mother ship may communicate with:

A. other auxiliary ship units of the same mother ship
B. the mother ship
C. all ships within the range of the auxiliary ship's transmitter
D. any auxiliary unit operating on channel 16
E. choices A and B are true

Answer Choice E.

Posting of operator licenses (R & R 13.74, 87.97)

1. Must be conspicuously posted at the place where operator is on duty (the principal control point of the station). It must be available for inspection upon request.
2. If several work stations are used, the original license must be posted at one location and a photocopy must be carried to the other work stations.

* **Question 14-196** An operator normally exhibits his/her authority to operate a marine station by:

A. posting a valid operator license or permit in the Master's cabin
B. posting a valid operator license or permit at the control point of the transmitter
C. keeping the original license or permit in his/her possession and posting a photostat copy at his/her place of duty
D. depositing the original license or permit in the ship's safe
E. keeping the original license on his/her person and exhibiting a "posting statement" at his/her place of work

Answer Choice B.

* **Question 14-197** The licensed operator of a marine utility station must:

A. carry his/her license on his/her person while on duty
B. post a photocopy of his/her license at the location from which the station is operated
C. post a "posting statement" at the transmitter's control point
D. carry a photocopy of his/her license while on duty
E. either choice A or D is true

Answer Choice E.

* **Question 14-198** If a radio operator services and maintains more than one radio station:

A. the operator's license is posted at the primary control point and a photocopy of the license is carried on his/her person
B. the operator must obtain a verification card from the regional FCC office
C. a photocopy of his/her license must be posted at the control point of each transmitter
D. the operator's license must be enclosed with the details of all the transmitters that the operator is servicing
E. the operator does not post his/her license but carries it on his/her person at all times.

Answer Choice E.

* **Question 14-199** A radio operator may carry a photocopy of his/her General Radiotelephone License on his/her person when:

A. the license is posted at the control point of the primary transmitter
B. when the operator is employed at a number of work stations
C. the original license has been lost
D. the original license has been forwarded for renewal
E. choices A and B are true

Answer Choice E.

* **Question 14-200** If a radio operator services a number of marine transmitters at different locations, where is the operator's license held?

A. in the Master's safe
B. on the operator's person
C. the license is posted at the control point of the primary transmitter
D. the license is deposited with the ship's license
E. none of the above choices is true

Answer Choice B.

Power (R & R 80.215) The power that may be authorized in the Aviation Services shall not be greater than the minimum required for satisfactory technical operation. It shall be specified in the following terms:

1. *Amplitude modulation transmitters:* For stations using amplitude modulation with both sidebands and full carrier, authorized power shall be specified in terms of unmodulated radio frequency carrier power at the transmitter output terminals.
2. *Other transmitters:* For stations using other types of modulation, the power authorized shall be specified in terms of peak envelope power at the transmitter output terminals. Peak envelope power (PEP) is defined as the mean power during one radio frequency cycle at the highest crest of the modulated envelope.

Power can be determined either by direct measurement or by multiplying the plate input power to the final amplifier by an appropriate factor.

Priority of communications (R & R 80.91) The various categories of communications have been arranged in order of priority as follows:

1. Distress calls:
   a. Indicate that a mobile station is threatened by grave and imminent danger and requests immediate assistance.
   b. Mayday is the radiotelephone distress signal.
   c. SOS is the radiotelegraphy distress signal.

2. Urgency signals:
   a. Indicate that the calling station has a very urgent message concerning the safety of the ship, aircraft, or vessel, or the safety of a person.
   b. In radiotelephony, the signal consists of the word "pan," spoken three times.
   c. Shall be sent only on the authority of the master of the ship or person who is responsible for the mobile station.
   d. Mobile stations that hear the urgency signal shall continue to listen for at least three minutes. At the end of this period, if no urgency message has been heard, they may resume their normal service.
3. Safety signals:
   a. Indicate that the station is about to transmit a message concerning the safety of navigation or give important meteorological warnings.
   b. In radiotelephony, the signal consists of the word "security," spoken three times.
   c. All stations hearing the safety signal shall listen to the safety message until they are satisfied that the message is of no concern to them. They shall not make any transmission likely to interfere with the message.
4. Radio direction-finding communications
5. Navigation communications (aircraft): Communications relating to the navigation and safe movement of aircraft engaged in search and rescue operations.
6. Navigation communications (ships): Communications relating to the navigation, movements and needs of ships, and weather observation messages destined for an official meteorological service.
7. Government communications
8. Service communications
9. All other communications

* **Question 14-201** In the marine service, the term "safety communications" includes:

A. distress signals only
B. urgency signals only
C. safety signals only
D. urgency and safety signals only
E. distress, urgency and safety signals.

Answer Choice E.

* **Question 14-202** A message that gives an important meteorological warning is preceded by the word(s):

A. weather alert
B. security
C. danger
D. met warning
E. met alert

Answer Choice B.

* **Question 14-203** A radiotelephone transmission that is preceded by the word "security" is:

A. concerned with the safety of navigation
B. concerned with important meteorological warnings
C. sent by a ship or aircraft that is threatened by serious or imminent danger

D. concerned with the safety of some person on board a ship or aircraft
E. either choice A or B is true

Answer Choice E.

* **Question 14-204** When a calling station has a vital message to send concerning the safety of a passenger or crew member, its transmission is preceded by the word:

A. pan B. security C. safety D. emergency E. mayday

Answer Choice A.

* **Question 14-205** The urgency signal:

A. is preceded by the word pan spoken three times
B. may be transmitted only on the authority of the Master of the ship carrying the marine station
C. has priority over all other communications except distress
D. is intercepted by mobile stations which must continue to listen for at least three minutes
E. all of the above choices are true

Answer Choice E.

* **Question 14-206** When transmitted by radiotelephony, the Safety signal is indicated by the word:

A. safety B. mayday C. security D. pan E. SOS

Answer Choice C.

* **Question 14-207** A message concerning the safety of navigation is preceded by the word:

A. warning B. care C. safety D. security E. pan

Answer Choice D.

* **Question 14-208** The signal sent by an aircraft that is threatened by serious and imminent danger is preceded by the word:

A. mayday B. danger C. pan D. security E. emergency

Answer Choice A.

* **Question 14-209** When transmitted by radiotelephony, the distress signal is indicated by the word:

A. SOS B. mayday C. distress D. security E. pan

Answer Choice B.

* **Question 14-210** A radiotelephone transmission that is preceded by the word *Pan,* is:

A. sent by a ship or aircraft that is threatened by serious or imminent danger
B. concerned with the safety of navigation
C. concerned with important meteorological warnings
D. concerned with the safety of some person on board a ship or aircraft
E. none of the above choices is true

Answer Choice D.

* **Question 14-211** In the marine service, which of the following has a higher priority than communications preceded by the urgency signal?

A. communications preceded by the safety signal
B. distress calls, distress messages and distress traffic
C. government radio telegrams
D. communications relating to the navigation and safe movement of aircraft
E. communications relating to radio-direction finding

Answer Choice B.

* **Question 14-212** Which of the following is arranged in the correct order of communications priority for the marine mobile service?

A. distress, urgency, safety signals
B. distress, safety, urgency signals
C. urgency, safety, distress signals
D. safety, distress, urgency signals
E. safety, urgency, distress signals

Answer Choice A.

* **Question 14-213** A marine station which hears an emergency signal, must:

A. immediately alert all ships in the vicinity
B. immediately inform the Master of the vessel
C. continue to listen for a period of not less than three minutes
D. cease all transmissions for at least 30 minutes
E. ignore the signal if it is not addressed to the ship on which the marine station is located

Answer Choice C.

* **Question 14-214** If an operator hears an urgency signal, he/she must continue to listen for a minimum period of:

A. 3 minutes B. 5 minutes C. 6 minutes D. 10 minutes E. 15 minutes

Answer Choice A.

* **Question 14-215** The Urgency signal must only be sent from a mobile station on the authority of:

A. General Radiotelephone Licensee
B. senior radio operator
C. Master of the vessel
D. person in charge of the mobile station
E. choice C and D are true

Answer Choice E.

* **Question 14-216** When an Urgency signal is transmitted by a mobile station, it indicates that:

A. the mobile station is threatened by grave and imminent danger
B. there is a message concerning the safety of navigation or important meteorological warnings
C. there is a message relating to the navigation and safe movement of aircraft engaged in search and rescue operations
D. there is a very important message concerning the safety of the ship, aircraft or other vessel, or the safety of a person
E. there is a message relating to the weather observation information destined for an official meteorological service

Answer Choice D.

* **Question 14-217** The radiotelephone Urgency signal con... of the ...rd:

A. pan, spoken three times
B. mayday, spoken three times
C. urgent, spoken three times
D. safety, spoken three times
E. security, spoken three times

Answer Choice A.

* **Question 14-218** Which of the following has the second priority of communications?

A. distress signals
B. safety signals
C. urgency signals
D. navigational signals
E. radio direction-finding communications

Answer Choice C.

* **Question 14-219** Which of the following has the first priority of communications?

A. safety signals
B. urgency signals
C. weather warnings
D. distress signals
E. navigational warnings

Answer Choice D.

* **Question 14-220** Which of the following is arranged in the correct priority of communications in the marine mobile service?

A. distress calls, safety signals, urgency signals and radio direction-finding communications
B. distress calls, radio direction-finding communications, urgency signals and safety signals
C. distress calls, urgency signals, radio direction-finding communications, safety signals
D. distress calls, urgency signals, safety signals, radio direction-finding communications
E. distress calls, safety signals, urgency signals, radio direction-finding communications

Answer Choice D.

Profanity: If a radiotelephone operator on duty hears profanity being used at his/her marine station, the operator must make every effort to prevent the profanity from being transmitted over the air and should warn the offender against the use of profanity. The operator must also take steps to end the transmission and must enter all the relevant details in the station log. Finally, a report must be submitted to the Federal Communications Commission.

* **Question 14-221** If a radiotelephone operator on duty hears profanity being transmitted over the air, the operator must:

A. take steps to end the transmission
B. enter all relevant details in the station log
C. warn the offender against the use of profanity
D. submit a report of the incident to the FCC
E. all of the above choices are true

Answer Choice E.

Security of communication (R & R 80.88) Secrecy must be observed with all radio communications transmitted or rec... The content must not be given to anyone or used for personal profit (see "Violation... Secrecy provisions do not apply to intercepted:

* **Question 14-222** ...arding the safe movement of aircraft

A. messa... regarding the scheduling of ships
B. m...ess messages from ships or aircraft
C. messages regarding the navigation of ships
E. all of the above choices are true

Answer Choice C.

* **Question 14-223** Under which of the following circumstances may an operator use the information in an intercepted communication for his personal benefit?

A. when the communication has been transmitted by a government agency
B. when the communication has been transmitted by an amateur
C. when the communication has been transmitted for the use of the general public
D. when a communication relates to a ship in distress
E. all of the above choices are true

Answer Choice E.

* **Question 14-224** An operator is permitted to divulge the contents of an intercepted message when:

A. authorized to do so by the Master of the ship
B. the message is specifically a Police communication
C. the message is specifically a Government communication
D. the message relates to an aircraft in distress
E. an operator is never permitted to divulge the contents of an intercepted message

Answer Choice D.

Shipboard antennas (R & R 80.863, 80.876) Marine antennas within the VHF band shall be vertically polarized. These antennas must be as nondirectional as possible.

* **Question 14-225** Marine VHF transmitters use antennas that are:

A. vertically polarized
B. horizontally polarized
C. circularly polarized
D. omnidirectional
E. choices A and D are true

Answer Choice E.

Silent period (R & R 80.301, 80.304)

1. Shall be observed at each hour and each half hour for a period of 3 minutes. For example, from 10:00 to 10:03 and 10:30 to 10:33.
2. Except for messages of distress, urgency, and vital navigational warnings, ship stations shall not transmit on 2182 kHz during the silent period.

Note: There is a similar silent period on 500 kHz for radiotelegraph stations. It occurs 15 minutes later than the radiotelephone silent period (see *listening watch*).

* **Question 14-226** During the silent period, a radiotelephone ship station may not transmit on 2182 kHz, except for:

A. distress calls
B. urgency signals
C. safety signals
D. government communications
E. choices A, B, and C are true

Answer Choice E.

* **Question 14-227** On the frequency of 2182 kHz, a radiotelephone silent period shall be observed for:

A. three minutes commencing at the hour and the half hour
B. three minutes commencing at the hour only
C. three minutes commencing at 15 minutes and at 45 minutes past the hour
D. three minutes commencing at the half hour only
E. five minutes commencing at 15 minutes and at 45 minutes past the hour

Answer Choice A.

* **Question 14-228** For a marine station, one receiver must be tuned to the international radiotelephone distress frequency:

A. only during the silent period
B. from 0900 to 2100 UTC
C. only when the ship is in international waters
D. only when initiating a call on 2182 kHz
E. on a continuous basis

Answer Choice E.

Simplex: Two-way communications where both stations operate on the same frequency. When operating in the simplex mode, you must wait until the other station stops transmitting before you start transmitting. When using simplex operation, the operator should pause for a moment before transmitting, in case someone needs to "break in" with an emergency, or to make contact with another station (see *duplex*).

* **Question 14-229** With the simplex mode:

A. the two stations operate on different frequencies
B. simultaneous communication in both directions is possible
C. the two stations operate on the same frequency
D. only telegraphy can be used
E. it is only possible to operate a one-way communications system

Answer Choice C.

Single sideband: A type of emission, where the one sideband is filtered out. The carrier can be reduced or suppressed. When single sideband is used, the upper sideband (higher frequency) is selected (see *emission types*).

In an SSSC system (J3E emission), the carrier must be suppressed to a power level that is at least 40 dB below the peak envelope power. For both marine and aircraft stations, the bandwidth for a J3E emission is 3 kHz.

* **Question 14-230** For a marine station that produces a J3E emission, the carrier must be suppressed below the peak envelope power by at least:

A. 3 dB B. 10 dB C. 20 dB D. 30 dB E. 40 dB

Answer Choice E.

* **Question 14-231** When compared with the peak envelope power, the carrier of an aeronautical J3E emission must be suppressed by at least:

A. 10 dB B. 20 dB C. 30 dB D. 40 dB E. 50 dB

Answer Choice D.

* **Question 14-232** For an aeronautical SSSC transmitter, the carrier of its J3E emission must be suppressed below the peak envelope power by at least:

A. 20 dB B. 30 dB C. 40 dB D. 50 dB E. 60 dB

Answer Choice C.

* **Question 14-233** The authorized bandwidth for aviation SSSC transmitters operating below 50 MHz, is:

A. 2.8 kHz B. 3 kHz C. 5 kHz D. 4 kHz E. 8 kHz

Answer Choice C.

Squelch control: A control on the radio receiver that tunes out the background noise when the receiver is not receiving communications (chapter 8). Set the control just beyond the point where the background noise is cut off. When received signals are very weak, they might not be much stronger than the background noise level. If this is the case, it might be necessary to "open up" the squelch control so that the station can be heard.

Standard forms: (R & R 1.922, 80.19, 87.29) Forms can be obtained from the Federal Communications Commission at Gettysburg, Pennsylvania 17325; Washington, DC 20554, or any District Office. Table 14-6 lists many of the more commonly used FCC forms.

Table 14-6. FCC forms.

FCC FORM	TITLE
404	Application for new or modified aircraft radio station license.
404-A	Application for temporary Aircraft Radio Station Operating Authority.
405-A	Application for renewal of radio license without modification.
405-B	Application for license renewal without modification.
406	Application for Ground Station Authorization in the aviation services.
480	Application for Civil Air Patrol Radio Station Authorization.
503	Application for Land Radio Station License (or modification) in the maritime services.
506	Application for renewal of Ship Radio Station License. Also used in application for modification of license.
506-A	Temporary operating authority, Ship Radio Station License and Restricted Radiotelephone Operator Permit.
525	Application for Disaster Communications Radio Station Construction Permit and License.
801	Application for radio inspection and certification.

Station identification: (R & R 2.303, 80.102, 80.104, 80.231, 87.115)

Aircraft stations:

1. Aircraft radio station callsign, or
2. Abbreviated callsign consisting of:
   a. Type of aircraft, followed by:
   b. The last three characters of the registration marking, or:
3. Assigned FCC Control Number (for ultralight aircraft), or:
4. The radiotelephony designator of the aircraft operating agency (assigned by the FAA) followed by the flight identification number (assigned by the company).

Bridge-to-bridge stations:

1. Name of vessel may be used in lieu of the station callsign.
2. Identification shall be made at the beginning, and upon completion of each transmission. The intervals shall not exceed 15 minutes.

Land station in the aviation service:

1. Station call letters, or:
2. Its location, or:
3. Assigned FAA identifier, or:
4. Name of city

Portable ship units:

1. The operator must give name of vessel with which he/she is associated, followed by a unit number, designating which mobile unit he/she is using.
2. Identification shall be made at the beginning, and upon completion of each transmission. The intervals shall not exceed 15 minutes.

Private coast stations: Stations located at drawbridges and transmitting on channel 13 may identify by use of the name of the bridge in lieu of the callsign.

Radar transmitters: Must not transmit station identification.

Ship station:

1. Ship stations using radiotelephony shall identify by announcing in the English language the station-assigned callsign.
2. An exception to the above is where bridge-to-bridge channel 13 (156.65 MHz) is used. In this case, identification may be made with the name of the ship in lieu of the callsign.
3. When the official callsign is not assigned by the Commission, the name of the ship on which the station is located or the name of the licensee may be used.
4. Identification shall be made at the beginning and upon completion of each transmission. The intervals shall not exceed 15 minutes.

Survival craft stations:

1. The callsign of parent aircraft, or:
2. Official aircraft registration of parent aircraft, followed by a single digit other than 0 or 1.
3. No identification is required when distress signals are transmitted automatically.

Station license: (R & R 80.13, 80.56) It is not legal to operate a radio station within the United States or its territories unless it is properly licensed in accordance with the Communications Act of 1934. Willful or repeated operation of an unlicensed radio station is punishable by fines or imprisonment (see *violations*). Licenses may not be assigned or transferred when ownership of the vessel is transferred. The new owner must file for a new authorization.

Survival craft station: (R & R 80.5, 80.829–835) A mobile station is the maritime or aeronautical mobile service is intended solely for survival purposes, and is located on any lifeboat, life raft, or other survival equipment. General requirements for survival-craft radio equipment are as follows:

1. Must be buoyant.
2. Equipment must be operated without tools.
3. Must have instruction manual for maintenance.
4. Simple instructions must be prominently attached.
5. The transmitter must be pretuned to the required frequencies.
6. It must be able to transmit the international radiotelegraph distress signal, alternately on 500 and 8364 kHz.
7. Radiotelephone transceivers must be able to transmit and receive on either 457.525 or 156.8 MHz. Power must be at least 0.1 W.

* **Question 14-234** Tests of survival-craft emergency-radio equipment must be conducted:

A. within 24 hours prior to the ship's departure from a port
B. by connecting the transmitter to a dummy antenna
C. at weekly intervals
D. to include the determination of the specific gravity or voltage of any batteries
E. all of the above choices are true

Answer Choice E.

* **Question 14-235** Marine emergency-radio equipment on a survival craft must be tested:

A. on full power with the transmitter connected to its normal antenna
B. only when the ship is more than 100 miles from U.S. shores
C. prior to departure
D. at weekly intervals while at sea
E. choices C and D are true

Answer Choice E.

Suspension of license: (R & R 1.85) When grounds exist for suspension of an operator license, the suspension shall not take place until 15 days after the notification of the operator. The operator must make written application to the Commission (for a hearing) within that 15-day period. The license must be sent to the Commission in Washington.

* **Question 14-236** If a licensee receives a Notification of Suspension and does not apply for a hearing, the suspension order becomes effective within:

A. 3 days B. 7 days C. 10 days D. 15 days E. 30 days

Answer Choice D.

* **Question 14-237** Which of the following is not grounds for suspension of operator licenses?

A. malicious interference with other radio communications
B. violation of any provision of any act or treaty binding on the United States
C. willful damage to radio equipment
D. knowingly transmitting false or deceptive signals
E. transmission of superfluous radio communications

Answer Choice B. In order to be grounds for suspension, the act or treaty must be one which the FCC is authorized to administer.

* **Question 14-238** Upon receipt of a Notice of Suspension of his/her license, the licensee must normally mail his/her application for a hearing within:

A. 5 days B. 10 days C. 15 days D. 30 days E. 60 days

Answer Choice C.

Suspension of transmission: (R & R 5.153, 80.90) If any deviation from the technical requirements is detected, transmission shall be immediately suspended until such malfunction is corrected. Examples of such deviations are:

1. If the transmitter is off frequency.
2. If the transmission becomes distorted.
3. If the modulation exceeds 100 percent.
4. If the transmitter's output contains strong harmonics.

The only exception shall be in the event of an emergency, where temporary communications can be resumed until the emergency condition is over. At that time, transmission shall again be terminated for necessary repair work.

* **Question 14-239** Measurements have shown that a marine transmitter is off frequency. The operator must immediately:

A. notify the ship's Master of the transmitter's malfunction
B. enter the details of the malfunction in the station log
C. inform the FCC of the malfunction within 15 days
D. turn off the transmitter and carry out the necessary repair
E. all of the above choices are true

Answer Choice D.

* **Question 14-240** It is discovered that the signal from a marine transmitter is severely distorted. The operator must immediately:

A. lower the percentage of modulation
B. suspend transmission
C. lower the value of the operating power
D. commence to use the phonetic alphabet
E. speak more softly into the microphone

Answer Choice B.

* **Question 14-241** Measurements have shown that the signal from a marine transmitter contains strong harmonics that exceed their authorized limits. The operator must immediately:

A. measure the operating carrier power
B. add low-pass filters to the antenna's circuitry
C. suspend transmission
D. measure the bias level on the final stage
E. adjust the position of the Faraday screen

Answer Choice C.

* **Question 14-242** When a compulsory ship has left her port of departure, the operating power of the 2182-kHz transmitter suddenly falls to zero. The operator must immediately:

A. contact the ship's Master
B. switch to channel 13 and operate with another transmitter
C. switch to channel 16 and use the VHF transmitter
D. shut down the transmitter and carry out the necessary repairs
E. contact the communications repair installation at the port of destination

Answer Choice D.

* **Question 14-243** The transmitter of a marine station is deviating from its technical requirements. The operator must immediately:

A. switch to the dummy antenna
B. suspend transmission
C. inform the ship's Master, who alone can authorize the transmission to be resumed
D. reduce the percentage of modulation
E. lower the level of the operating power

Answer Choice B.

Temporary operating authority: (R & R 1.925, 88.41) An application for a new aircraft radio-station license may operate the aircraft radio station pending issuance of a station license for a period of 90 days under a temporary operating authority. This is evidenced by a properly executed certification made on FCC Form 404-A. The applicant shall use the aircraft FAA registration number as a temporary callsign.

Test of radiotelephone installation: (R & R 80.1023) Unless normal use of the required radiotelephone installation demonstrates that the equipment is in proper operating condition, a test communication for this purpose must be made by a qualified operator each day the vessel is navigated. If the equipment is not in proper operating condition, the Master must be notified promptly. The Master must have it restored to effective operating condition as soon as possible.

Testing procedure: (R & R 80.101) Station licensees must not cause harmful interference. When radiation is necessary and unavoidable, the following testing procedure must be followed:

1. The operator must not interfere with transmissions in progress.
2. The testing station's call sign, followed by the word "test" must be announced.
3. If any station responds "wait," the test must be suspended for a minimum of 30 seconds.
4. Tests must not exceed 10 seconds, and must not be repeated until at least one minute has elapsed. On 2182 kHz or 156.8 MHz, the time between tests must be a minimum of five minutes.
5. Operator must end the test with the station's callsign.

* **Question 14-244** A radiotelephone ship station should send a test transmission:

A. every day if the station is sharing a channel
B. provided the authorized power is less than 1 kW
C. every day, provided that the station is not sharing a channel
D. unless normal use is sufficient to indicate that the radio equipment is operating correctly
E. under no circumstances may test transmissions be sent more than once a week

Answer Choice D.

* **Question 14-245** On the frequency of 2182 kHz or 156.8 MHz in a region of heavy traffic, what is the minimum period of time that must elapse before a test transmission is repeated?

A. 1 minute B. 2 minutes C. 3 minutes D. 4 minutes E. 10 minutes

Answer Choice A.

* **Question 14-246** Immediately prior to sending a test signal, a marine radiotelephone operator hears the word "wait." The operator should:

A. cancel the test completely
B. send his test message as rapidly and as briefly as possible
C. after waiting an appropriate interval of time, repeat his callsign, followed by the word "test" and then see if there is a further response
D. switch to the nearest channel on which no communication is occurring
E. the situation as described is impossible because a test transmission would never be interrupted by the word "wait"

Answer Choice C.

* **Question 14-247** Which of the following shall be included in the voice announcement at the conclusion of a test transmission?

A. the operating power of the testing station
B. the official callsign of the testing station
C. the frequency on which the test was conducted
D. the name of the ship on which the marine testing station is located
E. choices B and D are true

Answer Choice B.

* **Question 14-248** Test transmissions of a marine radiotelephone installation are sent:

A. in order to find out whether other stations are maintaining their required testing watch
B. to ensure that the radio equipment is functioning normally
C. in order to assess the FCC's monitoring capabilities
D. with the use of an unmodulated carrier
E. choices A, B, and C are true

Answer Choice B.

* **Question 14-249** A marine radiotelephone transmitter operating on 2182 kHz is to be tested while the ship is at sea. The procedure involves:

A. listening to make sure the channel is not being used
B. changing to a working frequency before initiating the test
C. transmitting the station's callsign (normally given three times), followed by the word "test"
D. a test on the international radiotelephone distress frequency is never allowed
E. choices A and C are true

Answer Choice E.

* **Question 14-250** A marine radiotelephone transmitter may be tested:

A. during the experimental period between 12 midnight local time and local sunrise
B. after receiving official authorization from the regional FCC office
C. as required, in order to ensure proper operation of the equipment
D. only on low power
E. under the authority of the ship's Master

Answer Choice C.

* **Question 14-251** What is the maximum duration of the test signal that is transmitted from a marine radiotelephone station?

A. 10 seconds B. 20 seconds C. 30 seconds D. 1 minute E. 5 minutes

Answer Choice A.

* **Question 14-252** During the testing period for a marine radiotelephone station, the operator must first listen to make sure that the channel is not being used. Then the operator's voice announcement consists of:

A. the official callsign (normally given three times), followed by the word "test"
B. the word "test" (normally given three times), followed by the name of the vessel
C. the official callsign (normally given three times), followed by the test signal whose duration is not to exceed 10 minutes
D. the name of the vessel (normally given three times) followed by the word "test"
E. the official callsign (normally given three times), followed by the reasons for carrying out the test

Answer Choice A.

Tone (one way) paging operations These services operate in the 806 to 824 MHz, 851- to 859-MHz, 896- to 901-MHz, and the 935- to 940-MHz bands. The authorized emissions for non-voice paging operations are A1A, A1D, A2B, A2D, F1B, F1D, F2B, F2D, G1B, G1D, G2B, and G2D.

* **Question 14-253** Which of the following is an authorized emission for tone paging communications?

A. A2E B. R2D C. J3E D. F2B E. A1C

Answer Choice D.

Tower lights: (R & R 23.39, 87.113) If antenna and aviation tower lights are not monitored by automatic means, they must be inspected every 24 hours. Appropriate entries shall be made in the station's technical log. The lights must operate from sunset to sunrise, and must be checked daily. Any observed or known failure of a top light or rotating beacon light not corrected within 30 minutes shall be reported immediately to the nearest Flight Service Station or office of the Federal Aviation Administration. Part 17 of the FCC Rules and Regulations covers this in more detail. All flashing or rotating beacons and automatic lighting-control devices must be inspected at least once every three months to ensure that such apparatus is functioning properly.

* **Question 14-254** The lights of an antenna tower must be displayed:

A. from 9 PM to 9 AM, local time
B. on a continuous basis
C. from 12 midnight to local sunrise
D. from sunset to sunrise
E. from 6 PM to 6 AM, local time

Answer Choice D.

* **Question 14-255** The lights of an antenna tower are not monitored by automatic means. These lights must be visually inspected:

A. whenever the manual control is used
B. once every two days
C. on a weekly basis
D. once every 24 hours
E. between sunset and sunrise, local time

Answer Choice D.

* **Question 14-256** All flashing or rotating beacons and automatic lighting control devices must be inspected:

A. every 24 hours
B. once every week
C. once every month
D. once every 3 months
E. once every 6 months

Answer Choice D.

* **Question 14-257** If any top light or any flashing beacon of an antenna tower is extinguished or malfunctioning:

A. the transmitter must be shut down
B. the FCC regional office must be immediately informed
C. the nearest Flight Service station must be informed if the problem cannot be corrected within 30 minutes
D. the office of the Federal Aviation Administration must be informed if the problem cannot be corrected within 30 minutes
E. either choice C or D is true

Answer Choice E.

* **Question 14-258** If an intermediate light of an antenna tower is extinguished or malfunctioning, the:

A. fact must be entered in the station log
B. FCC regional office must be immediately informed
C. nearest Flight Service station must be informed if the problem cannot be corrected within 30 minutes
D. the office of the Federal Aviation Administration must be informed if the problem cannot be corrected within 30 minutes
E. the transmitter must be shut down

Answer Choice A.

* **Question 14-259** If the lights of an aviation tower are not monitored by automatic means, such lights must be checked:

A. at 9 AM and at 9 PM
B. between sunset and sunrise, local time
C. at the beginning of each hour
D. once every 24 hours
E. once every three months

Answer Choice D.

* **Question 14-260** The regulations regarding the required daily observations of antenna tower lights are to be found:

A. in FAA Rules and Regulations
B. on the back of the station license
C. in Part 13 of the FCC Rules and Regulations
D. in Part 17 of the FCC Rules and Regulations
E. in Part 80 of the FCC Rules and Regulations

Answer Choice D.

* **Question 14-261** If there is a malfunction in the automatic actuation switch controlled by the photocell, the antenna tower lights must burn:

A. continuously
B. from 6 PM to 6 AM
C. from local sunset to 8:30 AM
D. from local sunset to local sunrise
E. from 6 PM to local sunrise

Answer Choice A.

* **Question 14-262** In the event of an antenna tower's light failure, which of the following details must be entered in the station log?

A. nature of failure
B. date and time that the failure was observed
C. date, time, and nature of the adjustments, repairs, or replacements made
D. identification of the air-traffic communications stations notified of the failure, together with the date and time of the notification
E. all of the above must be entered

Answer Choice E.

* **Question 14-263** If the top light of an antenna tower fails, the time allowed for correction of the fault before reporting the failure is:

A. 15 minutes B. 30 minutes C. 60 minutes D. 90 minutes
E. the fault must be reported immediately

Answer Choice B.

* **Question 14-264** Which of the following provisions apply to the lighting of an antenna tower whose height exceeds 150 feet?

A. the tower lights must be visually checked once every 24 hours, if they are not monitored by automatic means
B. the details of any failure or malfunction of a tower light must be entered in the station log
C. the failure of a top light must be reported immediately unless the problem is corrected within 30 minutes
D. the lights and automatic lighting control devices must be inspected every three months
E. all of the above choices are true

Answer Choice E.

Transmitter adjustments and tests by operator: (R & R 87.135) All transmitter adjustments or tests during or coincident with the installation, servicing, or maintenance of a radio station, that may affect the proper operation of such station, shall be made by or under the immediate supervision and responsibility of a person holding a General Radiotelephone or First Class or Second Class Radiotelegraph Operator Licensee who shall be responsible for the proper functioning of the station equipment.

Transmitter measurements: (R & R 87.63, 87.73, 87.111)

1. *Carrier frequency* shall be checked as follows:
   a. During the initial installation.
   b. When any change is made in the transmitter that may influence the operating frequency.
   c. Upon receipt of an official notice of off-frequency operation.

Note: The output of the transmitter shall be checked against a suitable frequency standard. The National Bureau of Standards sets the frequency standard. A transmitter using crystal control shall have its frequency checked at least once per year.

2. *Modulation percent:* the transmitter modulation shall be properly adjusted to produce peak modulation between 75 and 100 percent.
3. *Power measurements:* when the manufacturer's rated power of a transmitter is greater than 120 percent of the authorized power, the actual power output of the transmitter shall be determined as follows:
   a. During the initial installation.
   b. When any change is made in the transmitter that may influence the power output.

Note: The carrier power of a ship station radiotelephone transmitter must be at least 8, but not more than 25 W. All marine transmitters must be capable of reducing their carrier power to 1 W or less. The maximum operating power of aeronautical Multicom stations is 10 W.

* **Question 14-265** A crystal-controlled marine transmitter must have its output carrier frequency checked at least once every:

A. day B. week C. month D. three months E. year

Answer Choice E.

* **Question 14-266** The carrier power of a ship station's radiotelephone transmitter must:

A. not exceed 25 W
B. not exceed 100 W
C. be at least 10 W
D. be at least 8 W
E. choices A and D are true

Answer Choice E.

* **Question 14-267** The carrier frequency of an aviation transmitter must be checked:

A. during the initial installation
B. when any change is made in the transmitter that might influence the operating frequency
C. upon receipt of an official notice of off-frequency operation
D. before the transmitter is removed or replaced
E. choices A, B, and C are true

Answer Choice E.

* **Question 14-268** The operating power output of a ship station's radiotelephone transmitter must be determined if the authorized power is less than the manufacturer's rated power output by:

A. 5% B. 10% C. 15% D. 20% E. 25%

Answer Choice D.

* **Question 14-269** All ship station's radiotelephone transmitters must be capable of reducing the operating carrier power to:

A. 1 W or less B. 2 W or less C. 3 W or less D. 5 W or less E. 8 W or less

Answer Choice A.

* **Question 14-270** A marine VHF transmitter must be capable of:

A. producing a carrier power of at least 8 W
B. producing a carrier power that does not exceed 25 W

C. reducing its carrier power to 1 W or less
D. producing a modulation percentage between 75% and 100% on modulation peaks of frequent recurrence
E. all of the above choices are true

Answer Choice E.

* **Question 14-271** An aviation transmitter must have its output operating frequency checked:

A. during the initial installation
B. when any change in the transmitter is made that might affect the operating frequency
C. upon receipt of an official notice of off-frequency operation
D. on a monthly basis
E. choices A, B, and C are true

Answer Choice E.

* **Question 14-272** The maximum operating power of an aeronautical multicom station is:

A. 50 W B. 25 W C. 8 W D. 10 W E. 5 W

Answer Choice D.

* **Question 14-273** The operating carrier power of marine transmitters with G3E or F3E emission in the 156- to 162-MHz frequency band, must not exceed:

A. 1 W B. 3 W C. 5 W D. 10 W E. 25 W

Answer Choice E.

* **Question 14-274** A marine VHF transmitter with F3E emission must be capable of reducing its operating power to:

A. 0.1 W or less B. 1 W or less C. 5 W or less D. 8 W or less E. 25 W or less

Answer Choice B.

Transmitter 150-mile range requirement: (R & R 80.807) The radiotelephone transmitter, in all radiotelegraph equipped vessels, must be capable of transmission of A3E or H3E emission on 2182 kHz, clearly perceptible signals from ship to ship during daytime under normal conditions and circumstances over a minimum range of 150 nautical miles. The output power is not less than 25 W of carrier power (A3E) or 60 W of peak envelope power (H3E) on the frequency of 2182 kHz.

* **Question 14-275** A compulsory ship of 300 gross tons and upward, but less than 1000 gross tons, has a radiotelephone transmitter that must be capable of a daytime minimum range of:

A. 25 nautical miles
B. 50 nautical miles
C. 100 nautical miles
D. 150 nautical miles
E. 200 nautical miles

Answer Choice D.

* **Question 14-276** A compulsory cargo ship of 300 gross tons and upward, but less than 1600 gross tons, has a radiotelephone installation, which on A3E or H3E emission must be capable of a daytime minimum range of:

A. 25 nautical miles
B. 50 nautical miles

C. 100 nautical miles
D. 150 nautical miles
E. 200 nautical miles

Answer Choice D.

* **Question 14-277** A cargo ship of 100 gross tons is sailing on an international voyage. Her compulsory radiotelephone installation must be capable of a daytime minimum range of:

A. 250 nautical miles
B. 200 nautical miles
C. 150 nautical miles
D. 100 nautical miles
E. 50 nautical miles

Answer Choice C.

* **Question 14-278** A compulsory ship is equipped with a radiotelegraph installation. Its associated radiotelephone installation must be capable of not less than:

A. 25 W carrier power (A3E) or 60 W peak envelope power (H3E)
B. 20 W carrier power (A3E) or 50 W peak envelope power (H3E)
C. 60 W peak envelope power for A3E and H3E emissions
D. 50 W peak envelope power for J3E emissions on 1282 kHz
E. 50 W peak envelope power for H3E and J3E emissions

Answer Choice A.

Type acceptance: (R & R 2.901–908, 2.961–969, 2.981–1003) Equipment that meets FCC specifications is "type accepted." The "Radio Equipment List, Equipment Acceptable for Licensing" is available from any FCC District Office.

1. Transmitters may not be modified in either basic design in any way that would affect their output power, operating frequency, frequency stability, or modulation percentage.
2. Type-accepted transmitters will have the following on the transmitter name plate.
   a. Name of Manufacturer
   b. FCC ID number

Type approval: The FCC conducts tests on the equipment to ensure that it meets specifications.

Type acceptance: The manufacturer tests the equipment to ensure that it meets specifications.

Note: Before a newly installed transmitter can be put into normal service, it must be inspected and certified by the FCC.

* **Question 14-279** The following information appears on the name plates of type-accepted transmitters:

A. name of the manufacturer
B. operating frequency
C. type of emission
D. FCC ID number
E. choices A and D are true

Answer Choice E.

* **Question 14-280** If a transmitter has received "type approval:"

A. the manufacturer has tested the transmitter to ensure that the specifications have been met
B. a General Radiotelephone licensee on board the ship has tested the transmitter to ensure that the specifications have been met
C. the transmitter was built by a manufacturer who is licensed by the U.S. Government
D. the FCC has conducted tests on the transmitter to ensure that the specifications have been met
E. "type approval" is the preliminary step toward "type acceptance"

Answer Choice D.

* **Question 14-281** Before a newly installed transmitter can be put into normal service, it must:

A. receive type-approval
B. receive type-acceptance
C. either choice A or B
D. be inspected and certified by the FCC
E. be tested by the Senior General Radiotelephone Operator on board the ship

Answer Choice D.

* **Question 14-282** If a transmitter has received "type acceptance:"

A. the manufacturer has tested the transmitter to ensure that the specifications have been met
B. a General Radiotelephone licensee on board ship has tested the transmitter to ensure that the specifications have been met
C. the transmitter was built by a manufacturer who is licensed by the U.S. government
D. the FCC has conducted tests on the transmitter to ensure that the specifications have been met
E. "type acceptance" is the step that follows "type approval"

Answer Choice A.

Unattended operation When a transmitter is left unattended by a radio operator, precautions must be taken to make certain that the equipment is inaccessible to all unauthorized persons and cannot be operated by them in any way. Preferably, the transmitter should be shut down; in any case, it must be secured by locking or other means.

* **Question 14-283** If a radio operator leaves a transmitter unattended:

A. the transmitter can be left, but it must be operated in the unattended automatic mode
B. a note of the operator's whereabouts must be included in the station log
C. the transmitter must be inaccessible to unauthorized persons
D. all power must be removed from the transmitter
E. either choice A or C is true

Answer Choice C.

* **Question 14-284** If a marine transmitter is left unattended by a radio operator:

A. all power must be removed from the transmitter
B. the microphone must be removed
C. the antenna must be disconnected from the transmitter
D. the transmitter must be rendered inaccessible to all unauthorized personnel
E. choices A and D are true

Answer Choice D.

Violations: (R & R 5.162, 13.62, 80.149, FCC Bulletin FO-32) No licensed commercial-radio operator shall violate or cause, aid, or abet the violation of any Act, treaty, or convention binding on the United States, which the Commission is authorized to administer, or any regulation made by the Commission under such Act, treaty or convention.

1. If a person receives a notice of violation, a written response must be made within 10 days. It shall contain a full explanation of the incident and shall set forth the steps taken to correct the deficiency and prevent its recurrence.
2. Fines and penalties for violations are summarized in TABLE 14-7.

Table 14-7. Violations and penalties.

Violation	Not More Than	or	Not More Than	or	Both
Failure to comply with any Rule, Regulation, Restriction or Condition of the Communications Act or FCC Rules and Regulations.	$500.00 for each violation for each and every day of the offense				
Willfull violation of a provision of the Communications Act.	$10,000.00		One year imprisonment (First offense). Two years imprisonment (Second Offense)		X
Willful violation of the Communications Act for commercial advantage or private financial gain.	$25,000.00		One year imprisonment		X

* **Question 14-285** When an operator receives a notice of violation, he/she must forward a written response within:

A. 3 days B. 5 days C. 10 days D. 15 days E. 30 days

Answer Choice C.

* **Question 14-286** For a first offense, the penalty for willfully violating a provision of the Communication Act of 1934, is:

A. cancellation of the operator's license
B. a fine of not more than $500.00 for each provision violated
C. a fine of not more than $10,000.00, or imprisonment for a term not exceeding two years, or both
D. a fine of not more than $10,000.00, or imprisonment for a term not exceeding one year, or both
E. a fine of not more than $25,000.00

Answer Choice D.

* **Question 14-287** For a first offense, the penalty for willfully violating a Rule, Regulation, Restriction or Condition of the Communications Act of 1934, is a:

A. fine of not more than $500.00 for each and every day of the offense
B. fine of not more than $10,000.00 or imprisonment for a term not exceeding one year, or both
C. fine of not more than $10,000.00 or imprisonment for a term not exceeding two years, or both

D. fine of not more than $25,000.00
E. fine of not less than $500.00 for the offense, regardless of its duration

Answer Choice A.

* **Question 14-288** For a second offense, the penalty for willfully violating a provision of the Commissions Act of 1934, is a fine of not more than:

A. $20,000.00, or imprisonment for a term not exceeding two years, or both
B. $10,000.00, or imprisonment for a term not exceeding two years, or both
C. $20,000.00, or imprisonment for a term not exceeding one year, or both
D. $10,000.00, or imprisonment for a term not exceeding one year, or both
E. $25,000.00

Answer Choice B.

* **Question 14-289** For willfully violating a provision of the Communications Act of 1934 for commercial advantage or private financial gain, the penalty is a fine of not more than:

A. $25,000.00 or imprisonment for a term not exceeding one year, or both
B. $20,000.00 or imprisonment for a term not exceeding one year, or both
C. $20,000.00 or imprisonment for a term not exceeding two years or both
D. $10,000.00 or imprisonment for a term not exceeding one year, or both
E. $25,000.00 or imprisonment for a term not exceeding two years, or both

Answer Choice A.

VHF omni-range (VOR) stations These are FAA stations, whose positions are shown on every flight chart and are used in conjunction with the Distance-Measuring Equipment (DME) radar-beacon system. At each of the VOR stations, a DME transponder is installed. When the aircraft's interrogator transmits a pulse to a particular transponder, the replies are intercepted by a receiver, which is part of the interrogator system. By measuring the time interval between the transmission of the interrogating pulse and the reception of the reply, the aircraft can obtain its exact range from the VOR station. This range and the rate of change of range are then displayed on the aircraft's instrument panel.

VOR stations are assigned frequencies in the 112.050- to 117.950-MHz band with a 50-kHz spacing between adjacent channels.

* **Question 14-290** Which of the following frequencies can be assigned to a VOR station?

A. 111.05 MHz B. 115.05 MHz C. 118.10 MHz D. 121.50 MHz E. 119.05 MHz

Answer Choice B.

* **Question 14-291** The system that measures the range from an aircraft's interrogator to the transponder of a radio beacon, is called:

A. Interrogatory Friend or Foe (IFF)
B. Omega (Ω)
C. Long-range navigation (LORAN)
D. Interrogator-Transponder Transit (ITT)
E. Distance-Measuring Equipment (DME)

Answer Choice E.

Watch (see *Listening Watch*)

Appendix
New FCC questions

The following "new" questions have appeared in the August 1991 and February 1992 Element 3 examinations. The answer to each question contains a corresponding page reference to the text.

* **Question A-1** A capacitor is charged to 100 V and is then switched across a resistor. When the voltage across the capacitor has fallen to 14 V, the duration of the discharge as measured in time constants, is approximately:

A. 0.3 B. 1.0 C. 2.0 D. 2.5 E. 3.0

Answer Choice C. The capacitor has lost 100 − 14 = 86% of its initial voltage. This corresponds approximately to two time constants (86.5%).

* **Question A-2** In the logic circuit of FIG. A-1, five entire sequences of the clock input to the flip-flop circuit have been completed. The output of the circuit is:

A. Q B. $\bar{Q}$ C. 1 D. 0 E. $Q + \bar{Q}$

Answer Choice D. The complementary inputs to the AND gate are Q and $\bar{Q}$. The output is $Q.\bar{Q} = 0$, irrespective of whether $Q = 0$ or $Q = 1$.

* **Question A-3** Four complete sequences of a square wave take place in 100 ms. How many complete cycles of the square wave occur in 790°?

A. 1 B. 2 C. 3 D. 4 E. 5

Answer Choice B. The number of cycles in 790° is 790°/360° = 2.19.

* **Question A-4** In the circuit of FIG. A-2, the voltage across the resistor, R3, is:

A. 2.5 V B. 0.7 V C. 1.8 V D. 0.23 V E. 3.33 V

Answer Choice D. The diode D1 is conducting and its voltage drop is assumed to be 0.7 V. By the voltage division rule, the voltage drop across R1 is 0.7 V × 5 Ω/(5 Ω + 10 Ω) = 0.23 V.

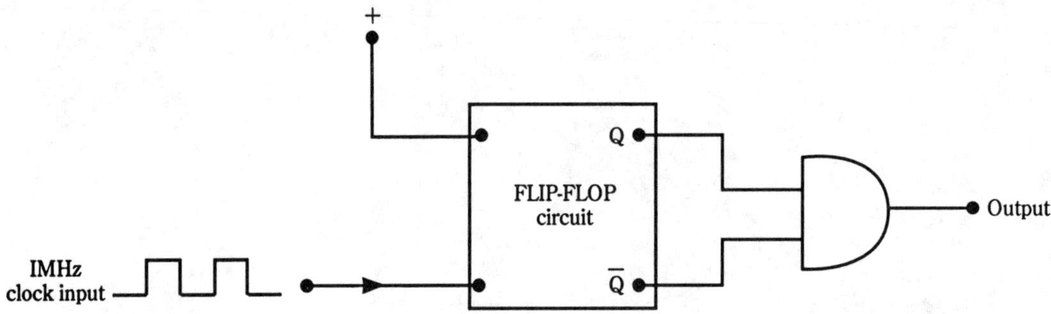

Fig. A-1 The circuit for question A-2.

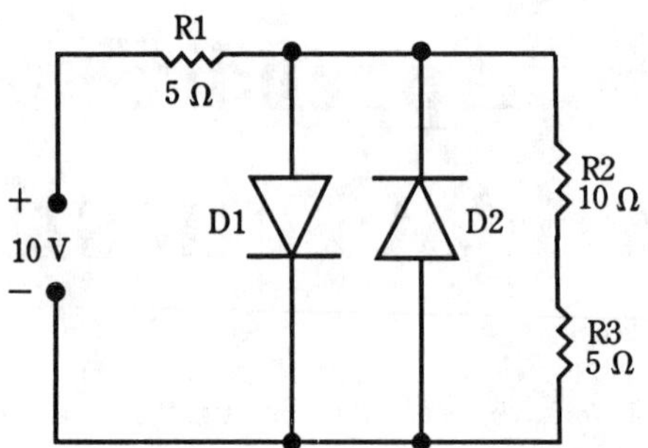

Fig. A-2 The circuit for question A-4.

* **Question A-5** At microwave frequencies, waveguides are preferred over coaxial cables because of their:

A. lower attenuation
B. lower cost
C. greater flexibility
D. smaller size
E. greater frequency range

Answer Choice A. Because of their lower dielectric hysteresis loss, waveguides are preferred over coaxial cables at microwave frequencies.

Question A-6 In the month of December, 3 PM Eastern Standard Time is equivalent to:

A. 1900 UTC B. 2000 UTC C. 2100 UTC D. 1800 UTC E. 2200 UTC

Answer Choice B. Standard Time and Universal Time Coordinated are independent of daylight savings time and therefore the answer is the same for either June or December. 3 PM EST = 1500 + 0500 = 2000 UTC (EQ. 10-35).

* **Question A-7** Three land or statute miles is equivalent to:

A. 3.45 nautical miles
B. 2.61 nautical miles
C. 2.45 nautical miles

D. 2.52 nautical miles
E. 3.61 nautical miles

Answer Choice B. Three land miles is equivalent to $3 \times 0.87 = 2.61$ nautical miles.

* **Question A-8** A temperature of 40° C (Celsius or Centigrade) is equivalent to:

A. 92° F B. 104° F C. −11° F D. 72° F E. 8° F

Answer Choice B. A temperature of 0° C (pure melting ice) is equivalent to 32° F (Fahrenheit). Moreover, a temperature of 100° C (pure boiling water) is the same as 212° F. It follows that a temperature difference of $212 - 32 = 180°$ F must be equal to $100 - 0 = 100°$ C. Therefore, $100/20 = 5°$ C is the same as $180/20 = 9°$ F. The conversion equations between the two temperature scales are:

$$T° \text{ F} = 32 + \frac{9\, T° \text{ C}}{5}$$

and:

$$T° \text{ C} = \frac{5}{9}(T° \text{ F} - 32)$$

Consequently, if $T = 40°$ C, the corresponding Fahrenheit temperature is $32 + 9 \times 40/5 = 104°$ F.

* **Question A-9** Which of the following frequency bands are assigned to VOR stations?

A. 112.050 to 117.950 MHz
B. 118.050 to 122.950 MHz
C. 108.050 to 111.850 MHz
D. 112.200 to 117.850 MHz
E. 110 to 115 MHz

Answer Choice A. VOR stations operate in the band of 112.050 to 117.950 MHz with a channel spacing of 50 kHz. These stations can also be assigned frequencies in the 108 to 112 MHz band.

* **Question A-10** At midnight two ships at sea are 135 miles apart. On which of the following frequencies can communication be established between the two ships?

A. 1.535 MHz B. 3.548 MHz C. 2182 kHz D. 2460 kHz E. 156.65 MHz

Answer Choice D. The maximum range for VHF communications is normally 20 miles, so choice E is eliminated. Midnight is the start of a silent period, so communication on 2182 kHz is not permitted. The marine band lies between 1605 kHz and 3500 kHz; consequently, choices A and B are not possible.

* **Question A-11** In the circuit of FIG. A-3, calculate the value of the voltage at the point F, with respect to ground:

A. + 5.35 V B. + 2.5 V C. + 6.5 V D. − 5.35 V E. − 7.9 V

Answer Choice B. The resistors are connected in series. By using the voltage division rule, the voltage, at F is: $+9 \text{ V} \times 220\ \Omega/(220\ \Omega + 470\ \Omega + 100\ \Omega) = +9 \times 220/790 = +2.5$ V.

* **Question A-12** A resistor in a radio transmitter has been found to be defective. The factory's recommended rating is 150 ohms, 5%, ½ watt. In the event that an exact replacement cannot be found, which of the following resistors will provide safe operation without degrading the transmitter's performance?

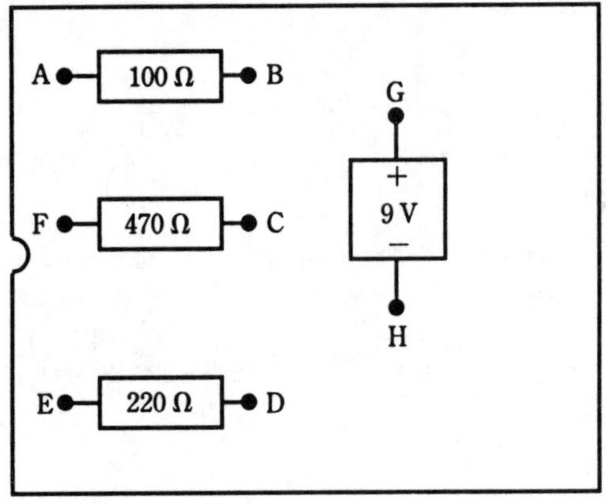

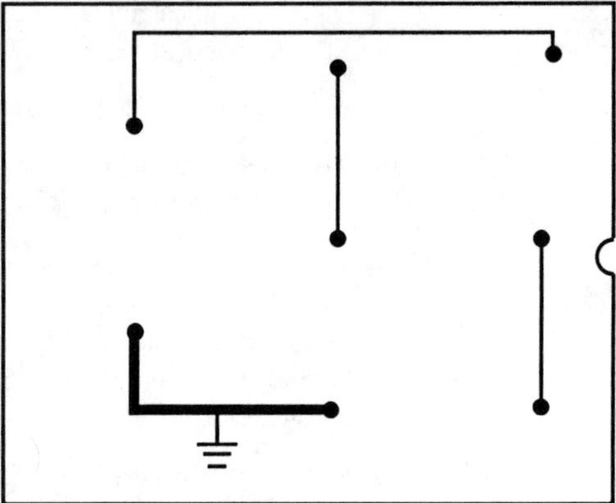

Fig. A-3 The circuit for question A-11.

A. 150 ohms, 5%, ¼ watt
B. 180 ohms, 5%, ½ watt
C. 150 ohms, 10%, ½ watt
D. 147 ohms, 1%, ½ watt
E. 140 ohms, 5%, ½ watt

Answer Choice D. The 147-Ω resistor has the correct power rating and its tolerance lies entirely within the resistance range of the defective resistor.

* **Question A-13** The amount of inductive coupling between the two tuned circuits of an amplifier can greatly affect its gain and frequency response. Doubled-tuned circuits that are very tightly coupled, result in:

A. optimum frequency response but relatively poor gain
B. overloading of the following stages by the excessively high gain of the circuit
C. interaction between the two tuned circuits so that the tuning of one circuit will cause detuning of the other circuit
D. poor gain and a broad frequency response
E. very sharp selectivity with good adjacent-channel rejection

Answer Choice D.

Question A-14 A current surge has blown the fuse of a radio transmitter. The fuse's recommended ratings are 4 amps, 120 volts, fast-acting. In the event that an exact replacement cannot be found, which of the following fuses will provide safe operation without degrading the transmitter's performance?

A. 2 amps, 120 volts, fast-acting
B. 4 amps, 100 volts, fast-acting
C. 4 amps, 140 volts, fast-acting
D. 3 amps, 110 volts, fast-acting
E. 5 amps, 110 volts, fast-acting

Answer Choice C. The 4-A current rating is the same as that of the blown fuse. The voltage rating is a measure of the circuit's protection *after* the fuse has blown (the higher is the voltage rating, the greater is the fuse's physical length). Consequently, the 140-V rating is more likely to prevent an arc from occurring across the blown fuse.

Question A-15 Which of the following provides the best results when shrinking heat-shrinkable tubing?

A. match
B. soldering iron
C. light bulb
D. heat gun or similar hot air source
E. cigar

Answer Choice D.

Question A-16 In a superheterodyne receiver, the received frequency is 156.0 MHz, the first IF frequency is 10.7 MHz and the second local oscillator frequency is 10.245 MHz. What is the frequency of the first local oscillator?

A. 455.000 kHz
B. 20.945 MHz
C. 135.035 MHz
D. 145.300 MHz
E. 145.755 MHz

Answer Choice D. The first local oscillator frequency is 156.0 $\pm$ 10.7 MHz = 166.7 MHz or 145.3 MHz.

Index

B

C

T

U

V

W